Standard Normal Distribution

Numerical entries represent the probability that a standard normal random variable is between $-\infty$ and z where $z = \dfrac{x - \mu}{\sigma}$.

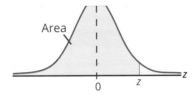

z	0.00	0.01	0.02	0.03	0.04	0.05	0.06	0.07	0.08	0.09
0.0	0.5000	0.5040	0.5080	0.5120	0.5160	0.5199	0.5239	0.5279	0.5319	0.5359
0.1	0.5398	0.5438	0.5478	0.5517	0.5557	0.5596	0.5636	0.5675	0.5714	0.5753
0.2	0.5793	0.5832	0.5871	0.5910	0.5948	0.5987	0.6026	0.6064	0.6103	0.6141
0.3	0.6179	0.6217	0.6255	0.6293	0.6331	0.6368	0.6406	0.6443	0.6480	0.6517
0.4	0.6554	0.6591	0.6628	0.6664	0.6700	0.6736	0.6772	0.6808	0.6844	0.6879
0.5	0.6915	0.6950	0.6985	0.7019	0.7054	0.7088	0.7123	0.7157	0.7190	0.7224
0.6	0.7257	0.7291	0.7324	0.7357	0.7389	0.7422	0.7454	0.7486	0.7517	0.7549
0.7	0.7580	0.7611	0.7642	0.7673	0.7704	0.7734	0.7764	0.7794	0.7823	0.7852
0.8	0.7881	0.7910	0.7939	0.7967	0.7995	0.8023	0.8051	0.8078	0.8106	0.8133
0.9	0.8159	0.8186	0.8212	0.8238	0.8264	0.8289	0.8315	0.8340	0.8365	0.8389
1.0	0.8413	0.8438	0.8461	0.8485	0.8508	0.8531	0.8554	0.8577	0.8599	0.8621
1.1	0.8643	0.8665	0.8686	0.8708	0.8729	0.8749	0.8770	0.8790	0.8810	0.8830
1.2	0.8849	0.8869	0.8888	0.8907	0.8925	0.8944	0.8962	0.8980	0.8997	0.9015
1.3	0.9032	0.9049	0.9066	0.9082	0.9099	0.9115	0.9131	0.9147	0.9162	0.9177
1.4	0.9192	0.9207	0.9222	0.9236	0.9251	0.9265	0.9279	0.9292	0.9306	0.9319
1.5	0.9332	0.9345	0.9357	0.9370	0.9382	0.9394	0.9406	0.9418	0.9429	0.9441
1.6	0.9452	0.9463	0.9474	0.9484	0.9495	0.9505	0.9515	0.9525	0.9535	0.9545
1.7	0.9554	0.9564	0.9573	0.9582	0.9591	0.9599	0.9608	0.9616	0.9625	0.9633
1.8	0.9641	0.9649	0.9656	0.9664	0.9671	0.9678	0.9686	0.9693	0.9699	0.9706
1.9	0.9713	0.9719	0.9726	0.9732	0.9738	0.9744	0.9750	0.9756	0.9761	0.9767
2.0	0.9772	0.9778	0.9783	0.9788	0.9793	0.9798	0.9803	0.9808	0.9812	0.9817
2.1	0.9821	0.9826	0.9830	0.9834	0.9838	0.9842	0.9846	0.9850	0.9854	0.9857
2.2	0.9861	0.9864	0.9868	0.9871	0.9875	0.9878	0.9881	0.9884	0.9887	0.9890
2.3	0.9893	0.9896	0.9898	0.9901	0.9904	0.9906	0.9909	0.9911	0.9913	0.9916
2.4	0.9918	0.9920	0.9922	0.9925	0.9927	0.9929	0.9931	0.9932	0.9934	0.9936
2.5	0.9938	0.9940	0.9941	0.9943	0.9945	0.9946	0.9948	0.9949	0.9951	0.9952
2.6	0.9953	0.9955	0.9956	0.9957	0.9959	0.9960	0.9961	0.9962	0.9963	0.9964
2.7	0.9965	0.9966	0.9967	0.9968	0.9969	0.9970	0.9971	0.9972	0.9973	0.9974
2.8	0.9974	0.9975	0.9976	0.9977	0.9977	0.9978	0.9979	0.9979	0.9980	0.9981
2.9	0.9981	0.9982	0.9982	0.9983	0.9984	0.9984	0.9985	0.9985	0.9986	0.9986
3.0	0.9987	0.9987	0.9987	0.9988	0.9988	0.9989	0.9989	0.9989	0.9990	0.9990
3.1	0.9990	0.9991	0.9991	0.9991	0.9992	0.9992	0.9992	0.9992	0.9993	0.9993
3.2	0.9993	0.9993	0.9994	0.9994	0.9994	0.9994	0.9994	0.9995	0.9995	0.9995
3.3	0.9995	0.9995	0.9995	0.9996	0.9996	0.9996	0.9996	0.9996	0.9996	0.9997
3.4	0.9997	0.9997	0.9997	0.9997	0.9997	0.9997	0.9997	0.9997	0.9997	0.9998

Critical Values

Level of Confidence	$z_{\alpha/2}$
0.80	1.28
0.90	1.645
0.95	1.96
0.98	2.33
0.99	2.575

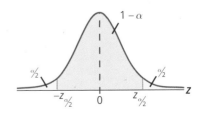

Discovering Statistics and Data

Third Edition

James S. Hawkes

Editors: Robin Hendrix, Amber Widmer

Assistant Editor: Wesley Duckett

Copy Editors: Barbara Miller, Luke Tiscareno

Designers: Trudy Gove, D. Kanthi, E. Jeevan Kumar, U. Nagesh, B. Syam Prasad, James Smalls, Patrick Thompson, Rebekah Wagner, Tee Jay Zajac

VP Research & Development: Marcel Prevuznak

Director of Content: Kara Roché

A division of Quant Systems, Inc.

546 Long Point Road, Mount Pleasant, SC 29464

Printed in the United States of America 🇺🇸

10 9 8 7 6 5 4 3 2 1

ISBN: 978-1-946158-72-7

Contents

Chapter 1
Statistics and Problem Solving

Chapter 2
Data, Reality, and Problem Solving

Chapter 3
Visualizing Data

Chapter 4
Describing and Summarizing Data from One Variable

Chapter 5
Discovering Relationships

Chapter 6
Probability, Randomness, and Uncertainty

Chapter 7
Discrete Probability Distributions

Chapter 8
Continuous Probability Distributions

Chapter 9
Samples and Sampling Distributions

Chapter 10
Estimation: Single Samples

Chapter 11
Hypothesis Testing: Single Samples

Chapter 12
Inferences about Two Samples

Chapter 13
Regression, Inference, and Model Building

Chapter 14
Multiple Regression

Chapter 15
Analysis of Variance (ANOVA)

Chapter 16
Looking for Relationships in Qualitative Data

Chapter 17
Nonparametric Tests

Preface

Letter from the Author

This new edition maintains a relaxed, conversational writing style of previous editions, with new efforts to make the reader smile occasionally. The new edition pays homage to the technology-driven data explosion, and new and larger real data sets have been added. Additionally, we have a strong focus on data visualization.

Further improvements made in this edition include the following:

Technology Integration

- Technology instructions, data sets, and interactive activities now reside on the companion website stat.hawkeslearning.com for easier access and the ability to stay current as updated versions of technologies become available. Other technologies requested by users will be added.

- The technology images and output have been updated to reflect the latest versions of Excel, Minitab®, and the TI-83/84 Plus calculators. Geospatial data visualization examples using the R Statistical Programming Language are incorporated, with support for R available at stat.hawkeslearning.com.

Modernized Pedagogy

- The recommendations included in the Guidelines for Assessment and Instruction in Statistics Education (GAISE), published by the American Statistical Association, were carefully considered and incorporated whenever possible.

- One of the key feature requests from users was a modernization of our hypothesis testing procedures. To accomplish this, we streamlined our hypothesis testing steps from ten steps to six, incorporated both critical values and P-values for all tests, and established stricter checking of assumptions prior to conducting a hypothesis test. The new ASA guidelines on hypothesis testing were also incorporated in the text.

Expansion and Presentation of Content

- Numerous vignettes have been integrated to demonstrate the uses of statistics in technology and science.

- Over 60 new examples and over 200 new exercises have been added.

- Historical and modern multivariable visualizations and techniques have been included.

- The Table of Contents has been streamlined to contain fewer individual sections in a chapter, while at the same time expanding the content to make each section more robust and complete.

- Basic concept questions have been added to help students understand and reflect on what they have learned in each section (a GAISE guideline).

- The solution content in our examples has been expanded to better model the statistical thinking process for students and aid them in making valid conclusions from data (also a GAISE guideline).

- Simple Linear Regression and Multiple Regression are now discussed separately.

- Important content has been summarized in procedure, formula, or definition boxes to enhance student learning and to aid students in reviewing the content for assessments.

Games and Simulations

- New web-based games and simulations within the courseware have been developed to illustrate and provide interaction with significant statistical concepts often misunderstood by students:

  The Central Limit Theorem and sampling distributions

  Recognition of different distribution types

  Understanding the relationship between Type I and Type II errors in hypothesis testing

  Predictive Analytics – The Direct Mail Game

- The Direct Mail Game is featured in the text to encourage more students to use it in the courseware. This role-playing game is one of the best platforms for integrating statistical ideas into decision making and makes a great bridge from the study of probability to statistical inference.

Being able to think statistically is an important lifelong asset for decision making. This book will help develop students' intuition about statistical concepts and their potential applications. Given the data-rich world students will be entering, there will undoubtedly be many opportunities for exploration and analysis of data during their careers. This text will be a useful beginning in that process.

Sincerely,

James S. Hawkes

Companion Site

Overview

Our companion site contains data sets, technology instructions, and other resources that may be of interest or assistance to the student. Please visit

stat.hawkeslearning.com

and navigate to *Discovering Statistics and Data, 3rd Edition* from the homepage.

Data Sets

Throughout the book you will find marginal annotations that direct the reader to the companion site to access a full data set.

You will find all these data sets on the companion site available to download in various file formats.

You will also find these annotations in the Exercise sections. We have incorporated data exercises to allow the student to practice the concepts learned in the section on real-world data. To obtain the data to complete the problem, you will visit the companion site and download the required data set.

Here are a couple of examples of what you will see.

Data

stat.hawkeslearning.com
Data > California DDS Expenditures

Data

The full Amazon stock price data set can be found on stat.hawkeslearning.com under **Data Sets > Amazon Stock Price.**

Technology Instructions

Beside many of our examples you will find technology explanations depicting a result found using technology. To get full, step-by-step instructions on how to obtain that result using the technology shown, or many others, navigate to the technology area of the companion site and locate the topic indicated in the textbook's margin. We provide directions for many technologies including calculators, Microsoft Excel, Minitab® Statistical Software, R, and more. As technology changes and grows, so will our resources!

Here are a couple of examples of what you will see.

Technology

Standard normal probabilities can be found using the pnorm function in R. For instructions, visit stat.hawkeslearning.com and navigate to **Technology Instructions > Normal Distribution > Normal Probability (cdf)**.

```
> pnorm(1.37,
lower.tail = FALSE)
[1] 0.08534345
>
```

Technology

A two-sample hypothesis test between two means when the population standard deviations are known can be calculated on the TI-83/84 Plus calculator using the 2-SampZTest function. For instructions please visit stat.hawkeslearning.com and navigate to **Technology Instructions > Hypothesis Testing > Two-Sample z-Test.**

```
2-SampZTest
 μ₁>μ₂
 z=1.754116039
 p=.0397052687
 x̄₁=11
 x̄₂=10
↓n₁=40
```

Other Resources

Other resources available on the companion site include downloadable formula pages and statistical tables, as well as a curated collection of websites and tools that may be of interest or aid to someone who is learning statistics.

Getting Started

Below are two scenarios from the textbook where a student would utilize **stat.hawkeslearning.com**.

Accessing Data Sets Use Case

Description: A student is completing exercises for an assignment and needs access to the "San Francisco Salaries 2014" Data Set in Excel to complete a problem.

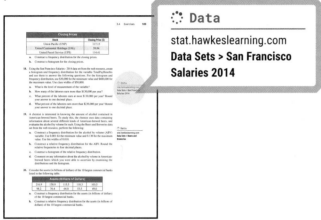

He/she navigates to the companion site using the following steps.

1. Go to stat.hawkeslearning.com

2. Navigate to *Discovering Statistics and Data, 3rd Edition*.

3. Select Data Sets.

4. Click on "Excel" next to "San Francisco Salaries 2014."

5. Open the **San_Francisco_Salaries_2014** spreadsheet in Microsoft Excel.

Accessing Calculator Instructions Use Case

Description: A student is reading through Chapter 12 for an assignment and needs help calculating the *P*-value on his/her TI-84 calculator.

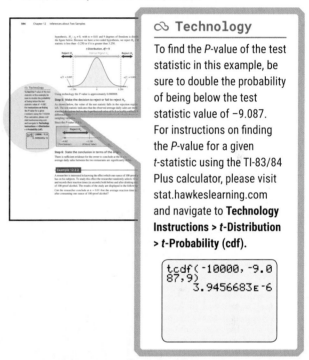

He/she navigates to the companion site using the following steps.

1. Go to stat.hawkeslearning.com

2. Navigate to *Discovering Statistics and Data, 3rd Edition*.

3. Select Technology Instructions.

4. Click on the Topic tab.

5. Type "t-Distribution" within the search bar.

6. Select the button under **TI Calculator** next to ***t*-Distribution > *t*-Probability (cdf)**.

Acknowledgments

Thank you to all who were involved in the first and second editions of this text as this laid the groundwork for this new edition.

For the third edition, I would like to thank Robin Hendrix, Amber Widmer, and Wesley Duckett for their work editing this edition. Also, thanks to Steven Steinbacher for his help in finding data resources to use in the book.

I am deeply appreciative of the efforts of our reviewers, Sangit Chatterjee, Leslie Jones, Martin Jones, Kevin Hastings, Hasan Hamdan, and Chelsie Messenger for their invaluable editorial and proofreading comments.

Support ⊕

If you have questions or comments concerning *Discovering Statistics and Data* we can be contacted as follows:

Phone: (843) 571-2825

E-mail: support@hawkeslearning.com

Web: hawkeslearning.com

Our support hours are 8:00 A.M. to 10:00 P.M. (ET), Monday through Friday.

Discovering Statistics and Data

Third Edition

James S. Hawkes

"The most beautiful thing we can experience is the mysterious. It is the source of all true art and science."

— Albert Einstein

1 CHAPTER

Statistics and Problem Solving

An Ocean of Data

Although you usually can't see it, data is pouring out of everything electronic—phones, cars, computers, appliances, cameras, airplanes, medical equipment, telescopes, atom smashers, DNA sequencers, environmental monitors, manufacturing sensors, social media sites, email, text, and a multitude of other places. We live in a world where the amount of data being generated is incomprehensible, and it keeps growing. The phenomenal growth of stored data is one of the significant achievements of modern civilization and can be considered a measure of the technical advancement of any civilization.

Between 1986 and 2020 the data storage capacity worldwide will have increased by a factor of more than 15,000. Large amounts of data are impacting all the natural sciences and leading to new discoveries in physics, biology, astronomy, and cosmology. In addition, new online businesses are changing the way people shop, find jobs, find relationships, get directions, get recommendations, and find the answers to many questions. Our society is in the midst of a data revolution whose eventual impact may be greater than the industrial revolution. New wealth and convenience have already been created on a massive scale, and there is much more to come. One of the companies that has participated in this technological revolution is Amazon.

Amazon has changed the way we shop. The story of Amazon's success is a story in which statistics and data play a very large role. Originally, Amazon just sold books. Because they were born as an internet book store, keeping data about their customers was relatively easy and straightforward. Amazon tracked

- What customers purchased,
- What they looked at and didn't buy,
- How they navigated through the site,
- How they were affected by promotions, reviews, or web design layouts,
- Relationships between individuals and groups.

Amazon saw their data as opportunity to understand the kind of books customers wanted to read. As the Chinese general Sun Tzu said,

> *"Opportunities multiply as they are seized."*

Wow, did the opportunities multiply for Amazon!

Amazon's success is heavily influenced by a connection to their customers through the data they have collected and analyzed. Basically, Amazon set the standard in online retail for the data a company needs to collect to compete. So far, Amazon is at the top of the online retail mountain. The story you will hear about as you read this book is that data represents an opportunity to learn something. Because the amount of data being stored in the world is doubling every two years, it seems like there is going to be a lot of opportunity for individuals willing and able to tangle with it.

1.1   **The Meaning of Data**

Historically we have associated data with measurements and numbers that were purposefully generated to help solve a problem. For example, in 3800 BC the Babylonian empire was interested in things that could be taxed or had some potential military value (especially the availability of adult males for their armies). Trying to solve their taxation and military problems caused Babylonians to perform the first census by counting people, livestock, butter, honey, milk, and other consumables in their territories. Obtaining data in those days must have been a time-consuming and rather expensive task, but the data came from measurements or counts, had a purpose, and there was some expectation the data would be examined later.

What constitutes data is changing. Presently, the average smartphone owner uses about 3,000,000,000 (3 billion) bytes of data per month, and this number is growing rapidly. The word "data" in this context is different from the historical notion of purposeful measurement to solve a problem. When you stream a video on your phone, the data will never be analyzed by anyone. However, anytime you use your web browser, your movements around the web are probably being recorded in a database by your browser provider, who, in turn, will sell that data to a digital marketing group. The marketing group will employ statistical methods to determine what and how they can market to you on behalf of their business clients. At least this data is still a measurement of sorts.

Another category of data comes from the desire to create artificial intelligence. As researchers confront the problem of reproducing human "intelligence," they must solve the same data problems we humans do—comprehending large volumes of visual and audio data. An enormous amount of what is considered data in the quest for artificial intelligence are not even measurements in the traditional sense. For example, recently an artificial intelligence company taught a computer how to play an old Atari video game in the same way humans learn, by looking at the screen using a video camera as "eyes." In other words, the pixels on the screen were the data for the machine-learning model.

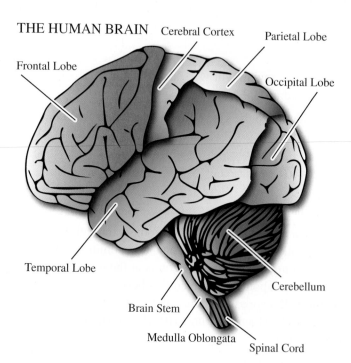

THE HUMAN BRAIN

Fortunately, humans are born with the ability to perform powerful sensory and data-analytic feats. The brain receives the equivalent of 100 million bytes of sensory information (data) for each second of sensory experience. The eyes alone generate the equivalent of about 90 million bytes of information per second. Assuming we are awake 16 hours, then the eyes produce roughly the equivalent to 5.18 trillion (5,180,000,000,000) bytes of data per day. This data plus audio, olfactory, and tactile data are analyzed by the brain's 100 billion neurons. Some neurons in the cerebellum are thought to have 200,000 inputs per neuron. Neurons in the cerebral cortex are thought to have around 10,000 connections per neuron.

At the other end of the connection spectrum are the neurons in the retina which only have a few connections. This means there are hundreds of trillions of neural connections in your brain. Essentially, your brain is a supercomputer that produces your model of physical reality that you call the "now."

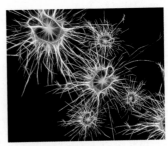

Neurons

In addition to creating the "now," our brains produce data-driven predictive reality models that are extremely useful in making decisions. *Do I have enough time to safely cross the street now, or should I wait until the oncoming car goes by? Should I make a left turn now, or should I wait until the oncoming bus passes?* The brain also designs experiments to gather relevant data for decision making. For example, every morning when you take a shower, most people stick their hand or foot into the shower to sense temperature (gather relevant data) before deciding to jump in.

Statisticians do the same sort of things you do unconsciously as you go about your daily life. They analyze data using pictures and summary measurements to build data-driven predictive models. They develop methods of designing experiments and gathering data that are cost effective and diminish bias. Essentially, statistics is a "formal" way of thinking with data.

1.1   **Exercises**

Basic Concepts

1. Describe 3 types of data discussed in the section.
2. Explain why your brain can be considered a supercomputer.
3. What are some of the "things" that statisticians do?

1.2   **Statistics as a Career**

We live in the information age, an economy and culture based on computers and information. Consequently, there is an overwhelming amount of new data being produced every year, but there have not been large increases in the number of statisticians being produced annually. That is why Hal Varian, Google's chief economist, said,

"I keep saying the sexy job in the next 10 years will be statisticians. People think I'm joking but who would've guessed that computer engineers would've been the sexy job of the 1990s? The ability to take data—to be able to understand it, to process it, to extract value from it, to visualize it, to communicate it—that's going to be a hugely important skill in the next decades."

The chart depicts the number of statistics degrees conferred in the U.S. by year and by degree[1]. It also illustrates the growing interest in the field of statistics. However, notice that the number of PhD statisticians isn't growing nearly as fast as the number with Master's and Bachelor's degrees. Many industry experts are worried

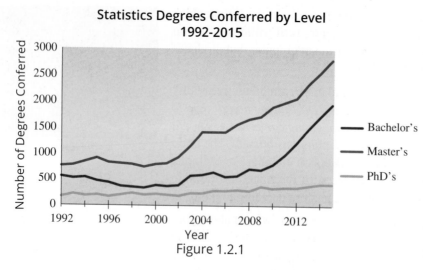

Figure 1.2.1

that the U.S. isn't producing enough highly-trained data scientists. Therefore, companies are providing considerable incentives in the form of lucrative salaries to convince people that careers in statistics and data science are well worth their while.

We will begin our journey into statistics by discussing some of the reasons there is so much data being produced. Then we discuss the influence of computing and data networks on statistics and then move into statistical issues related to data.

1.2   Exercises

Basic Concepts

1. What job is predicted to be the "sexy" job in the next ten years?

2. How does the chart show that there is a growing interest in the field of statistics?

3. Research the salaries of statisticians and data scientists. How do their salaries compare to other professions like engineering and computer science?

1.3   The Data Explosion

To discuss the data explosion, we need to understand numbers of very large magnitudes. It is not uncommon to have a cell phone or computer that has 64 gigabytes (64 billion) bytes of memory. However, data is accumulating in databases so fast we need much larger numbers to describe the sizes of modern databases.

Table 1.3.1 - Quantifying Bytes		
	Data Storage Quantities	
1,000,000,000	10^9	1 gigabyte (1 billion bytes)
1,000,000,000,000	10^{12}	1 terabyte (1 trillion bytes)
1,000,000,000,000,000	10^{15}	1 petabyte (1 quadrillion bytes)
1,000,000,000,000,000,000	10^{18}	1 exabyte (1 quintillion bytes)
1,000,000,000,000,000,000,000	10^{21}	1 zettabyte (1 sextillion bytes)

As was mentioned earlier, the eyes produce the equivalent of 5,180,000,000,000 bytes of data per day. Using data storage language, this would be 5.18 terabytes. In April 2011, the Library of Congress claimed it had 235 terabytes of data storage. Data files containing multiple terabytes of data are fairly common, but are still considered large files from an information processing perspective.

A petabyte is 1,000 terabytes. One petabyte of data is equivalent to the data required to generate high-definition video 24 hours a day for 13.3 years. Examples of data on the petabytes scale include the following:

- AT&T is thought to transfer more than 30 petabytes of data through its networks every day.

- YouTube currently generates in the neighborhood of 80–100 petabytes of new data annually.

- In 2014 Facebook's data warehouse had upwards of 300 petabytes of data storage capacity.

- The Internet Archive collects digitized materials, including websites, software applications/games, music, movies/videos, moving images, and nearly three million public-domain books. Its collection is currently approaching 20 petabytes.

- New optical telescopes are coming online that will produce 15 terabytes of new data for astronomers every day. The total amount of data collected over the life of the project will be roughly 60 petabytes.

From an information technology perspective, a database that contains several petabytes of data would be considered an extraordinarily large database and very challenging to process. It is unknown what the world's largest database is, but in 2017 the Large Hadron Collider in the CERN Laboratory near Geneva, Switzerland had about 600 petabytes of data available for analysis. Analyzing data on the petabyte scale usually requires large clusters of computing power with tens of thousands of processors.

An exabyte is 1,000,000 terabytes or one quintillion bytes. One exabyte would be the data required to watch high definition video 24 hours a day for 13,300 years. One exabyte could hold one hundred thousand times the printed material stored at the Library of Congress. Exabytes is the unit of data storage that historically has been used to express the world's technical capacity to store data.[2]

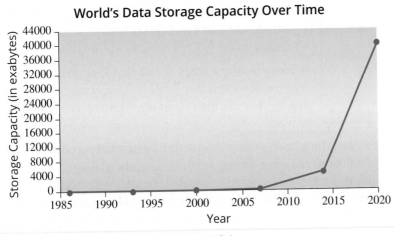

World's Data Storage Capacity Over Time

Figure 1.3.1

Table 1.3.2 - World's Data Storage Capacity	
Year	Storage Capacity (exabytes)
1986	2.6
1993	15.8
2000	54.5
2007	295
2014	5000
2020	40000

According to IBM, 2.5 exabytes of data are created every day, worldwide. More recent estimates have been as large as 5 exabytes per day. Thankfully, most of this data is not committed to long-term storage. In 2016, Google's data storage capacity was estimated to be about 10–15 exabytes of data. It has been estimated that the storage requirement to store every word ever spoken by human beings in all history recorded in 16-bit audio would be about 42 exabytes.

A zettabyte is 1,000,000,000 terabytes (one billion terabytes). In 2016 global internet traffic exceeded one zettabyte annually. In 2014 the world's capacity to store data had reached 5 zettabytes. If we added every single grain of sand on the earth and multiplied that number by 75, that would roughly equal 40 zettabytes, which is the expected worldwide volume of stored data in 2020.

Why is So Much Data Being Created Now?

New Sources of Data

The internet and World Wide Web have created enormous opportunity to generate and collect data. Every time we go online, carry our GPS-equipped smartphones, use social media and chat applications, post photos or videos or audio files, and send email, we are leaving our digital "footprints" in databases all over the internet.

Essentially, there are two ways in which data is stored, structured and unstructured. Relational databases store data in structured form. That is, data is stored in row/column format plus some other sophisticated data structures. Unstructured data is data that doesn't reside in a relational database, in other words, everything else. Things like email, videos, web pages, texts, and audio files are all examples of unstructured data.

Unstructured data is growing exponentially, particularly in social media and communication applications. For example,

- Facebook has 1.15 billion mobile daily active users.
- In 2015, 205 billion email messages were sent per day.
- In 2017, 8.6 trillion text messages are sent annually worldwide, and 4 million text messages are sent each minute in the US.

A cross-industry study found that less than half of an organization's structured data is actively used in decision-making. Far less than 1% of unstructured data is analyzed or used.

Table 1.3.3 - Example of Structured Data			
FIPS Code	State	Area name	% of adults with less than a high school diploma, 1970
1001	AL	Autauga County	54.8
1003	AL	Baldwin County	59.4
1005	AL	Barbour County	68.8
1007	AL	Bibb County	73.1
1009	AL	Blount County	70.5
1011	AL	Bullock County	72.9
1013	AL	Butler County	70.5
1015	AL	Calhoun County	58.6
1017	AL	Chambers County	67.4
1019	AL	Cherokee County	69.8
1021	AL	Chilton County	73.2
1023	AL	Choctaw County	68.2
1025	AL	Clarke County	62.7
1027	AL	Clay County	66.8
1029	AL	Cleburne County	73.1
1031	AL	Coffee County	59.9

One of the more interesting studies using unstructured data used tweets to forecast the spread of an influenza epidemic through real-time tweets relating to symptoms and treatments of the disease. A similar study was done on the spread of chikungunya in Puerto Rico. In infectious disease control, the faster a model can predict where an epidemic has spread, the more influence organizations like the Center for Disease Control (CDC) can have on the propagation of the disease. Although the influenza "Twitter" model has been criticized, it was two weeks ahead of the CDC models in forecasting the spread of the disease.

Surge in Sensors

The poet William Butler Yeats wrote a poem called "Under Ben Bulben" that contained the line "measurement began our might." Yates died in 1939 and probably could never have imagined how prophetic he was. Even an older iPhone like the 6S Plus has the following sensors: proximity sensor, ambient light sensor, 12MP camera (photon sensor), accelerometer, gyroscope, compass, barometer, near field communication (NFC) technology (a relative of RFID), touch ID fingerprint scanner, and a pressure sensitive display.

An estimated 10 billion sensors were sold in 2011. Since 2011 there has been a rapid increase in sensor use. Each sensor can generate large volumes of data. For example, one sensor at the Large Hadron Collider can generate 14,000,000 measurements per second.

Sensors are low-cost ways of collecting measurements and provide data critical to automating any machine or process. Modern factories will have thousands of sensors that feed data into their process control system. Sensors are also used in environmental monitoring systems, machine optimization and control, games, phones, security systems, computers, and appliances. They are even used in trash cans.

Sensors have enabled manufacturers to capture and harness extraordinary levels of data. In industrial settings, they are used to detect position, speed, proximity, pressure, temperature, humidity, level, viscosity, flow, current and voltage, vibration, weight, and almost anything you can imagine. A chemical plant making ink or paint or lubricants or hydraulic fluids or fuels might use sensors to measure flow, pressure, level, temperature, and viscosity to feed their process control system. The process control system monitors, stores, and analyzes sensor data for irregularities and either takes automated action or informs maintenance personnel to act.

Sensors are also used to gather data in an environmental setting. For example, diamond mines in Canada have heavy metal sensors to detect any chemical leakage from the mine. These sensors are monitored 24 hours per day. Superfund sites (land identified by the EPA containing extremely hazardous waste) are similarly monitored to detect movement in the contaminates. Earthen dams are monitored for changes in soil viscosity which may endanger the structural integrity of the dam. If you are interested in designing control systems using computers and sensor data, there is an engineering major you might wish to consider called control engineering.

Another enormous source of data that is facilitated by the internet is remote sensing. Remote sensing means acquiring information about an object or phenomenon without making physical contact with the object. Remote sensing is used in medicine, particularly X-rays, CT scans, ultrasounds, and MRIs. It is also used in numerous fields including geography, hydrology, ecology, oceanography, forestry, economics, the military, intelligence, geology, and even archeology. In the nonmedical fields, a considerable amount of remotely sensed data comes from satellites.

There are over 4300 satellites orbiting the earth, but only about one third of them are operational. One satellite, however, can produce enormous quantities of data For example, the Sentinel-1 (launched in 2014) is a European satellite that collects imagery using radar 24 hours a day and in all weather conditions. This satellite generated 5 petabytes of data in its first two years of operation. Sentinel 1B was launched in 2016, and two other Sentinel satellites are planned. In addition, there are lots of tiny satellites being launched. In 2017, a company called Planet Labs launched over 100 shoe box size satellites for imaging the earth. Their flock of

Examples of Remote Sensing Technologies

Satellite: There are hundreds of remote sensors used in different types of satellites and other space born systems. These sensors collect massive amounts of data about the earth, the solar system, and even collision detection to avoid other space born objects.

Conventional radar: A system for detecting the presence, direction, distance, and speed of aircraft, ships, and other objects, by sending out pulses of high-frequency electromagnetic waves that are reflected off the object back to the source.

Doppler radar: A radar tracking system using the Doppler effect to determine the location and velocity of a storm, clouds, precipitation, etc.

Seismograph: An instrument used to detect and measure earthquakes.

Sonar: A system for the detection of objects under water and for measuring the water's depth by emitting sound pulses and detecting or measuring their return after being reflected.

The Host with the Most

South Korea is the world's most connected nation, with broadband connections reaching 98% of homes. However, only about 85% are thought to use the Internet regularly.

satellites can completely image the earth every 24 hours and can produce very large image datasets.

Virtually every machine we use has integrated sensors. For example, automobiles have 60–100 sensors on board. Since reliable self-driving cars and trucks seem to be the future of the automobile industry, it is not surprising that by 2020 the number of sensors on a vehicle is expected to reach 200. In 2020 the automobile industry is forecasted to produce 107 million vehicles worldwide. These vehicles will use over 20 billion sensors. Imagine the data output of 20 billion sensors. However, 20 billion is nothing compared to the estimated one trillion sensors that may be deployed and connected to the internet by 2020 as part of the creation of the "Internet of Things" (IoT). The IoT is creating huge volumes of structured and unstructured data. Assume each sensor on the IoT can produce 10 measurements per second, and the 2020 sensor estimate is cut in half. Even if only 500 billion sensors are connected to the internet, sensor data alone could generate 5 trillion pieces of data per second. If this happens, in one year these sensors would generate an incomprehensible 157 exabytes of data (157,000,000,000,000,000,000 bytes).

1.3   Exercises

Basic Concepts

1. What is an exabyte?

2. What are the two ways to store data?

3. What is a sensor?

4. List 3 examples of remote sensing technology.

5. Name two things that you use everyday that contain sensors.

1.4   The Fusion of Data, Computing, and Statistics

Modern Computing: Alan Turing

There have been many contributors to modern computing, but a few contributors deserve special mention. Early electronic computers had to be physically rewired to change their "program". Alan Turing was the first person to come up with the notion of a "stored program" in which the program was stored in memory rather than literally "hard wired." He presented this idea in a 1936 paper. While this was a fundamental idea, before modern computers were created, the building blocks needed to be invented.

The Apollo moon landing was an epic event in American history. Without digital computers, it probably wouldn't have happened. The Apollo Guidance Computer (AGC) provided computation guidance, navigation, and control of the Command module and the Lunar Module. It was the first computer to use integrated circuits. Additionally, NASA used IBM System/360 Model 75 mainframes on the ground to perform independent computations and communication to the spacecraft, as well as monitor the astronauts' health and environmental data.

The iPhone 6 is a relatively old version of the iPhone. It uses an Apple-designed processor that can execute 3.36 billion instructions per second. Its processor can perform instructions 120,000,000 times faster than the AGC. If you had given an iPhone 6 to NASA engineers in 1969, it would have appeared to be alien technology.

The iPhone 6 is at least 1000 times more powerful—some have estimated over 1,000,000 times—than all the NASA combined computer resources in 1969.

Why is this important to statisticians? When you apply statistical methods to increasingly larger data sets, there are very few data sets you are likely to encounter that could challenge modern computers. Using current computing technologies, data sets that are feasible to process simple statistical models in a reasonable amount of time are on the order of terabytes. We will discuss some exceptions in the section on Big Data. This leads us to data networks.

Data Networks

All the personal computers and sensors available today would not be very useful if they could not easily share data over a private or public network. Private computer networks exist in almost every company, educational institution, and business that uses computers. You even have a private network in your home if you have Wi-Fi there. In the 1980s private networks ran on proprietary software, and one network vendor's software did not easily communicate with other network vendor systems.

For large organization like the US Department of Defense, which had many different networks, this was a problem. A group within the defense department, the Advanced Research Projects Agency Network (ARPANET), took the first steps to "connect" private networks. In 1983 a standard communication protocol TCP/IP (Transmission Control Protocol/Internet Protocol) was adopted by ARPANET. This was the beginning of the internet. Now, TCP/IP is used by virtually every private network in the world and almost all private networks are connected (the internet) to one another and can share data. In the early days of the internet, private networks were connected, but there was not a great "system" for sharing data. In 1990 an English computer scientist, Tim Berners-Lee, working at the Large Hadron Collider (LHC) in the CERN Laboratory near Geneva, Switzerland, proposed a global hyperlinked information system for sharing information between computer systems. His memo to CERN management proposed a "hypertext project" named World Wide Web as a "web" of "hypertext documents" to be viewed by "browsers" using client-server architecture. Berners-Lee built the first web server in 1991. Now, there are over 80 million web servers and 1.2 billion web sites worldwide.

1.4   **Exercises**

Basic Concepts

1. What invention made the Apollo moon landing possible?

2. How is data typically shared?

3. What does ARPANET stand for?

4. What does TCP/IP stand for and why is it important?

5. Who built the first web server?

The First Analog Computer

Mechanical aids to computation have been around for a long time. The Sumerian abacus appeared somewhere between 2700-2300 BC. The Greeks invented what is considered the first analog computer called the Antikythera mechanism; it was used for astronomical calculations in 150-100 BC. It took one thousand years for another computing device to attain the complexity of the Antikythera.

The Prototype

The prototype of what we call a computer today (digital computers) was created in the late 1940s. However, until about 1978, digital computers were only affordable by business and government entities. The first tidal wave of new data was generated by personal computers. But the data generated by personal computers really wasn't an important contributor to global data until data networks evolved.

Flash Boys: Data Velocity

Flash Boys is a book written by Michael Lewis about high frequency stock trading. Part of the book describes the great lengths a firm went to reduce the time it takes to send a buy or sell order between New York and Chicago. The best available time in 2008 was 14.65 milliseconds (14.65 thousands of a second). But theoretically it should be possible to communicate between the two cities over a fiber line in 12 milliseconds. The book tells the story of what it took to build and market a "direct" fiber run between New York and Chicago at a cost of 300 million dollars. Note, that is 300 million dollars spent to improve data velocity by slightly more than 2 milliseconds.

1.5   **Big Data**

Big Data is a loosely defined concept used to describe data sets produced by our globally networked, internet-driven, sensor-laden world. Interest in Big Data has been steadily increasing as evidenced below by the number of Google searches of the term.[3]

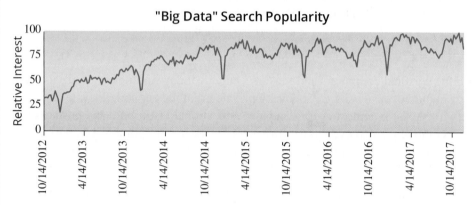

While there isn't broad agreement on exactly what Big Data is, there is broad agreement that Big Data will accelerate the pace of discovery in science, as well as innovation in commerce. In fact, that has already happened.

There have been numerous ideas about what makes data "Big Data." Most experts would agree that it is a large volume of data, structured or unstructured. Beyond that, opinions differ. One criteria that is appealing is any data set that is too large to process on commonly available computer systems. More recently the term has been used to refer to a set of analytical models that are used on data sets, regardless of their size. At the moment, the most common meaning of Big Data is a set of data sufficiently large to be challenging to analyze at a typical data center. As a frame of reference, the minimum for a large data center would be on the order of tens of thousands of servers and thousands of data storage arrays.

Another characteristic of Big Data is that it requires teams of programmers, database programmers, statisticians, and machine-learning experts to analyze the data. The Big Data team will usually be using highly scalable cloud computing resources.

Data has many attributes. However, Big Data seems to have four attributes that make it different: volume, variety, velocity, and veracity. These characteristics constitute the four Vs of Big Data.

- **Volume** is the scale of the data, and Big Data implies large volumes of data. According to IBM, most companies in the U.S. have at least 100 terabytes of stored data. But some companies have exabytes of data and are receiving 100's of terabytes of new data every day.

- **Variety** is the different forms data can take—from traditional data elements in a structured database to highly unstructured images, twitter feeds, movies, and audio.

- **Velocity** is how fast data is being sent to the data processing and data management infrastructure. There is a technical term called "streaming data" which is data generated continuously and usually in small amounts by thousands of data sources. Streaming data would be common in e-commerce, gaming, social networks, stock trading, and telemetry data from monitoring systems. One aspect of Big Data is that the data streams have substantial velocity. YouTube, for example, has an amazingly large data stream.

→   300 hours of video uploaded every minute

→   5 billion videos watched every day

→   30 million visitors per day

It is quite a technical challenge to neatly place high velocity data into the appropriate data repository every minute of every hour of every day without fail.

- **Veracity** is the trustworthiness of the data. Data is a major asset of any company, institution, or government agency. Uncertainty, bias, or inaccuracies in the data make the information less valuable for meaningful analysis and decision–making.

Sources of Big Data in Science

Despite the availability of enormous computing power, some areas of science and industry have data sets so large that they overwhelm modern computing systems. In the sciences, particle physics, astronomy, genomics, meteorology, and internet searches have amassed enormous quantities of data.

Science is being profoundly affected by an abundance of measurements. Almost all large natural science data sets grow because their data is being measured and gathered by specially designed automated measurement systems (machines).

- In the case of genomics, the development of very fast and relatively inexpensive DNA sequencers.

- In the case of astronomy and cosmology, it is new telescopes with very large digital camera arrays.

- In the case of meteorology, it is satellite imagery and automated weather sensors.

- In the case of particle physics, it is particle colliders (like the eight-billion-dollar Large Hadron Collider LHC).

These sensing machines are generating enormous quantities of data from their sensor arrays. The data they are providing offer a huge opportunity to advance our understanding of science and medicine.

Medicine

It used to be that doctors recorded everything they did on your chart. Now, it all goes into a database. This happens every day on every patient. For example, your doctor may order a test such as an MRI of your brain or an echocardiogram of your heart. It would not be unusual for an MRI of your brain to be 220+ megabytes of data. An echocardiogram could be as little as 40 megabytes, and an interventional study (a surgical procedure) could be as much as one gigabyte. Even a chest x-ray would be about 20 megabytes. Medical technology generates an enormous amount of data. Figure 1.5.1 shows the number of echocardiograms paid for just by Medicare from 2007 to 2011. Storing just the annual echocardiography data that Medicare pays for would require roughly 280 petabytes uncompressed.[4]

Data Compression and Big Data

The size of medical imaging files can be greatly reduced by data compression. Compression that eliminates statistical redundancy yet enables the complete restoration of the original data is called "lostless." There are many forms of "lostless" data compression. For example, telescope imagery has many images that are nearly the same, it would not be surprising if the images are stored as difference from a previous image. This is called data differencing. The storage size of some forms of Big Data can be dramatically shrank using compression designed for specific data types. In 2012 a special algorithm was developed for compressing genetic data. The algorithm achieved 20-fold compression (shrunk the file by 95%). Newer algorithms for genetic data have compression rates up to 1200-fold enabling an entire 6 billion pair genome to be stored in 2.5 megabytes.

"The Most Important Master's Thesis of the 20th Century"

In 1948, Claude Shannon wrote a paper entitled "A Mathematical Theory of Communication" which was the foundational work for a field now called information theory. The paper introduced the term "bit" and demonstrated that a series of bits "1s and 0s" (eight of them make a byte) could be used to represent all information. The bit/byte would become the standard unit for data storage and network communication of the future. Shannon's foundational work in information theory was not his only contribution. His masters thesis has been called the most important masters thesis of the 20th century. It showed that electrical switches could be configured to perform Boolean logic functions (i.e. digital logic). Shannon's work became the foundation of digital circuit design. Digital circuits are the fundamental component of all digital computers and without them we would not have modern computers, nor modern statistics.

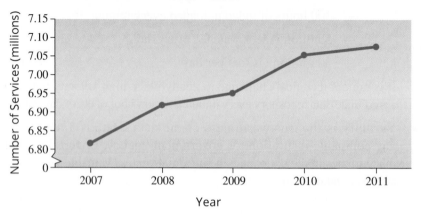

Figure 1.5.1

Once a patient's data is anonymized, it can be combined and aggregated. Looking at disease from a broad perspective of aggregated patient health data can provide new insight in a disease process. It can reveal biomarkers that were unknown, and more easily predict the trajectory of a disease, and perhaps, offer an intervention.

For example, there are two large cancer databases that have followed hundreds of thousands of cancer victims for 15 years or more. Once an oncologist diagnoses the specific cancer, they need to develop a treatment plan. A good oncologist will usually recall 6–8 similar cases to help formulate the plan. Now, the oncologist can call upon a cancer database that will have thousands of similar cases, and the information system attached to the database can make recommendations for the treatment plan.

Also, the oncologist might use the cancer-genome atlas—which classifies cancers by their genome—looking for treatments against a specific cancer genome. The oncologist might utilize the new field of proteomics, which is a study of the proteins in a patient's blood. One drop of blood passed through a superconducting magnet can generate 40+ gigabytes of data on all the proteins in the blood, which is the environment that the cancer cells are growing in.

Genomics

Genomics is a field that maps and studies the DNA (genomes) of biological entities. Every plant, animal, bacteria, and virus has a design that is contained in its genetic material (DNA) stored in each cell. The DNA is a blueprint for the organism. It determines whether an organism will produce leaves or legs, and of course many other things. In 1995 the genomes of two bacteria, homopholus influenza and microplasm genitalia, were sequenced, meaning the letters of their DNA were read and stored. The influenza genome is 2,000,000 base pairs long. Once there were large volumes of data, it wasn't long before computer scientists and statisticians began entering the field of biology.

The DNA strand is made up of four chemical building blocks, called nucleotides [adenine (A), thymine (T), guanine (G) and cytosine (C)]. Essentially, DNA encodes information. Human DNA has about 3 billion base pairs of nucleotides. Sequencing a human genome means to determine the specific base pairs for nearly all 3 billion pairs associated with the individual's genome. So, one entry into a human genomic database contains various combinations of ATGC for the individual's 3 billion base pairs.

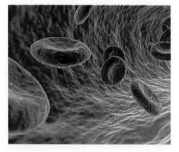

Genomics is around 20 years old. The Human Genome Project originally took 10 years to process one human genome; now this can be achieved in less than a week. As of 2015 all genomic data represented approximately 25 petabytes. The amount of data being produced in genomics daily is currently doubling every seven months. Within the next decade, genomics is looking at generating somewhere between 2 and 40 exabytes a year, depending upon whether the data doubles every seven months or every 18 months as shown in Figure 1.5.2.[5]

It is estimated that 1 billion people will have their DNA sequenced by 2025. If this happens, genomic databases will likely be the largest databases in existence.

There are databases that contain large numbers of completely sequenced human genomes. There are databases with completely sequenced genes for people with autism, cancer, muscular dystrophy, heart disease, and virtually any other disease that might have a genetic component. There are DNA databases that specialize in specific mammals, insects, bacteria, viruses, and plants.

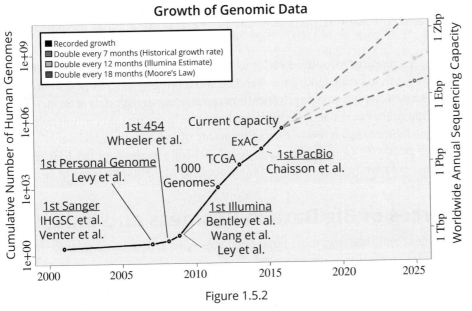

Figure 1.5.2

Astronomy and Cosmology

The Sloan Digital Sky Survey (SDSS) began collecting astronomical data in 2000. The telescope collects data at the rate of about 200 gigabytes per night. In its first few weeks of operation, it collected more data than all the data collected in the history of astronomy.

The Large Synoptic Survey Telescope (LSST) being built in Chile is the successor to SDSS. When it goes fully online in 2018, it will acquire 15 terabytes of data per night or 1.28 petabytes annually. That is, each night it acquires 75 times more data than the SDSS. The data will be images and will be analyzed by computer programs that require massive amounts of computing power.

The James Webb telescope is scheduled to be launched in 2018. It will operate 1,000,000 miles from earth and will be 5 times more powerful than the Hubble telescope. The James Webb telescope will be able to directly image exoplanets of nearby stars. If the downlinks on the satellite work perfectly for 10 years, it will generate 209 terabytes of data over its life.

There are plant and animal species that have genomes that dwarf the human genome in size.

The marbled lungfish genome contains 133 billion base pairs. It is the largest animal genome. The largest plant genome is a rare Japanese flower named Paris japonica. It has 149 billion base pairs, making it 50 times the size of a human genome—and the largest genome ever found.

As of 2017, one of the largest genomes ever sequenced is the loblolly pine. Its genome contains 22 billion base pairs, although much of it is repetitive.

In October of 2017 a group of six scientists sequenced the bread wheat genome. Because the genome contains six copies of each chromosome, the genome has approximately 16 billion base pairs.

https://commons.wikimedia.org

The Square Kilometer Array

The Square Kilometer Array, or SKA, is the name of what will soon be the world's largest radio telescope. It is a global scientific endeavor that will generate a tremendous amount of data. When fully operational in the 2030s, SKA will produce several petabytes of data per second. In terms of annual data production, this is anywhere from 50–100 times the annual global internet traffic in 2016. In order for data of this quantity and magnitude to be collected and processed, the central supercomputer requires the processing power of 100,000,000 average 2017 personal computers. Getting the data to the supercomputer in a timely and efficient manner requires enough fiber optic cable to wrap around the equator twice. You may be asking yourself, "What do we get for all of this effort?" SKA will provide us with the ability to detect electromagnetic output from extreme distances. The telescope will be so sensitive that it will be able to detect an airport's radar system from tens of light years away. This level of detail will help test our understanding of fundamental physics, find other habitable planets, and search for extraterrestrial life. The quest for knowledge, and the desire to drive science ever forward is increasingly being driven by data.

NASA has 100 active missions. In the time it took to read the previous sentence NASA downloaded 1.73 gigabytes of data from its missions. The rate of NASA's data gathering is growing exponentially. NASA has plans for missions that will stream 24 terabytes a day.

But the mother of all telescopes is the forthcoming $2.1 billion Square Kilometre Array (SKA) radio telescope. When it is completed in 2020, its designers believe it could generate more data in one day than the entire internet in one year. Further, it will be 10,000 times more powerful than any other telescope. Given the amount of data it produces, SKA will require three times the computing power of the world's largest supercomputer in 2017.

Physics

The Large Hadron Collider (LHC) is a 17-mile ring filled with superconducting magnets that send protons in opposite directions at nearly the speed of light, only to have them smash into one another. It has an annual budget of over one billion dollars and cost many billions to build. The LHC is regarded as the pinnacle of modern science.

The biggest finding from the LHC thus far has been the discovery of the Higgs Boson, a particle predicted by the standard model of physics but never shown to exist. The LHC has an amazing 150 million sensors that deliver data at an incredible 14 million times per second. Inside the accelerator there are 600 million collisions per second. Since only a few of the collisions are of interest, the LHC "only" stores about 25 petabytes of data per years. As of 2017 the analysis of the LHC data is done on a computing grid with 500,000 processors and 500 petabytes of storage.

Sources of Big Data in Business and Industry

In business and industry, most large machines have sensors that monitor system components many times per second:

- General Electric (GE) manufactures a gas turbine with 200 embedded sensors which generate about 600 gigabytes of data per day. One gas turbine would generate 219 terabytes of data in a year. GE is the largest producer of gas turbines in the world with more than 10,000 gas and steam turbines operating throughout the world. Assuming all these turbines have the same number of embedded sensors, the data generated by all these machines would be on the order of 2 exabytes annually.

- GE also produces aircraft engines that generate 10 data points per second on 1000 parameters (sensors). On a flight from New York to London one of these engines would generate about 8 gigabytes of data. One model of GE aircraft engine is used on approximately 2000 Boeing 737 aircrafts. Most commercial aircraft fly about 3000 hours per year. At two engines per aircraft, the Boeing 737 aircraft fleet generates about 92 petabytes of data per year.

- A modern commuter train's sensors will collect and send 9,000,000 data points per hour.

- A smart energy meter could send 35 gigabytes of data per day.

- Modern buildings are full of sensors that monitor sound, temperature, humidity, and motion.

- Computer logs monitor and diagnose computer system problems. Even a 50 server data center will generate 100 gigabytes of log data per day.

- Worldwide there are about 100 billion credit card transactions per year. Building fraud prevention models for credit cards has become a Big Data problem.

- By the year 2020, 50 billion machines are expected to be connected to the internet.

In industrial applications—like gas turbines, aircraft engines, and train motors—sensor data is used to determine an optimal operations strategy and to detect the root cause of failures and defects in near real-time. Companies also use sensor data to look for correlations among variables that may signal a design improvement in the system.

In 2016, a company developed a model to forecast corn yield per acre. It was an unusual model because the model used one petabyte of satellite imagery data that was run through a cluster of 30,000 computer processors to predict average corn yields per acre for 2016. Interestingly, the satellite image model predicted an average corn yield of 169 bushels per acre yield for 2016. The US Department of Agriculture (USDA) predicted 175.1 bushels per acre and the actual corn yield for 2016 was 178 bushels per acre. This is a case where Big Data modeling is not always good. But the accuracy of this kind of modeling will undoubtedly improve.

Satellite image data is also being used to produce revenue forecasts for large box retailers (e.g., Walmart, Target). Using satellite imagery, computer programs count cars in these retailers' parking lots every day and connect this data with quarterly revenue estimates.

1.5   **Exercises**

Basic Concepts

1. What is Big Data?
2. What are the four attributes of Big Data?
3. List two sources of Big Data in science.
4. List two sources of Big Data in business and industry.

1.6   **Introduction to Statistical Thinking**

What methods do statisticians use to make predictions? The most difficult part of the process is finding a sample that accurately reflects the larger group under study. In statistics the group we wish to study is called the **population**.

A Far-Out Population

The planet Mars contains numerous populations that scientists have wanted to learn about since the planet was first discovered. US scientists have been trying to estimate all sorts of things about the planet, including the planet's climate, geology, and history. NASA has sent 14 successful missions to sample various aspects of this planet: four Mariner missions between 1965-1971, two Viking Landers in 1976, Mars Pathfinder and Mars Surveyor in 1997, the Mars Odyssey in 2001, the Mars Exploration Rovers in 2004, the Mars Reconnaissance Orbiter in 2006, Phoenix in 2008, Curiosity in 2012, and MAVEN in 2014. Three future missions are planned, including the InSight mission, which is set to launch in 2018. If you are interested in seeing some of the images, or looking at some of the sample data collected from these missions, go to the mars.jpl.nasa.gov web site.

Population

A **population** is the total set of subjects or things we are interested in studying.

DEFINITION

Populations are defined by what a researcher is studying and can come in all shapes and sizes. If someone is studying monkeys in Brazil, then all the monkeys in Brazil would constitute the population. If you are studying students at your college, then all the students attending your college represent a population.

Frame

A list containing all members of the population is referred to as a **frame**.

DEFINITION

According to the Census Bureau in 2017 there are about 324 million people in the United States and about 7.6 billion people around the world. The frame for the population of the US would be a rather long list containing about 324 million names. Although a previous census would be a good start in developing a frame for the US population, it is doubtful that an exact frame could ever be developed at a given point in time since there is one new birth every 8 seconds, one death every 12 seconds, and one new immigrant every 39 seconds. There are just too many people being born, dying, and immigrating over a 10-year period to get an exact frame for the US population. But for problems that deal with smaller populations, frames are easily developed. For example, if your statistics class were the population under consideration, the class roll would be the frame for the population.

Census

A strict definition of a **census** is a survey that includes all the elements or units in the frame.

DEFINITION

Population Parameters

Population parameters are facts about the population. Since parameters are descriptions of the population, a population can have many parameters.

DEFINITION

For a presidential election, some population parameters in which candidates and pollsters will be interested are:

- The percentage of eligible voters who will vote on Election Day.
- The percentage of voters who will vote for a specific candidate.
- The percentage of men who favor a candidate.
- The percentage of women who favor a candidate.
- The percentage of people in the 18–25 age group who favor a candidate.
- The average income of voters who favor a candidate.

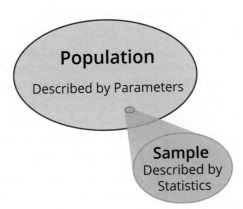

The parameters mentioned in the example are either averages or percentages. However, other measures such as the maximum or minimum value of the population measurement as well as other characteristics would be considered population parameters. For a specific population at a specific point in time, population parameters do not change; they are fixed numbers. But seldom will the value of a population parameter be known since the value involves all the population measurements which are usually too expensive or time consuming to collect. It is the statistician's job to discover these values. This is done by taking a sample and using the sample measurements to estimate the desired population measurement.

Sample

A **sample** is a subset of the population which is used to gain insight about the population. Samples are used to represent a larger group, the population.

DEFINITION

Statistic

A **statistic** is a fact or characteristic about the sample.

DEFINITION

For any given sample a statistic is a fixed number. Because there are lots of different potential samples that could be drawn from a population, statistics will vary depending on the sample selected. Statistics are used as estimates of population parameters. See Figure 1.6.1.

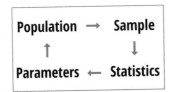

Figure 1.6.1

Studying an entire population can be an expensive proposition. In 2010 the census cost the government $13 billion. Because of the enormous expense, even the United States government with its vast resources does not undertake a census of its citizens but once every ten years. Yet amazingly accurate information about the population, even large populations like the United States, can be found by using a small sample. If the sample is a good representation of the population, then the conclusions reached using sample data will likely be reasonable for the population as a whole. A statistician faces the interesting problem of developing a representative sample, without spending an inordinate amount of time or money.

Political pollsters spend much of their resources developing a representative sample of Americans who will cast their votes on Election Day. After the sample is identified, the problem becomes one of obtaining candidate preferences from the selected voters. Tallying the responses and computing the actual percentages will take a computer at most a few seconds. After the estimates of the population parameters are calculated, one of the interesting statistical questions is, how good are the estimates? If we cannot determine how much faith we should place in our estimates, it will be difficult to use the estimates to make decisions. The process of selecting samples and determining the reliability of our estimates is a large part of what statistics is about.

1.6   Exercises

Basic Concepts

1. What is a population?

2. What is a frame?

3. What is a population parameter?

4. What is a sample?

5. What is a statistic?

6. Describe the relationships between populations, samples, parameters and statistics.

Exercises

7. A heart researcher is interested in studying the relationship between diets which are high in calcium and blood pressure in adult females. The researcher randomly selects 20 female subjects who have high blood pressure. Ten subjects are randomly assigned to try a diet which is high in calcium. The other subjects are assigned to a diet with a standard amount of calcium. After one year the average blood pressures for subjects in both groups will be measured and compared to decide if diets high in calcium decrease the average blood pressure.

   a. Identify the population.

   b. What characteristic of the population is being measured?

c.   Identify the sample.

d.   Is the purpose of the data collection to perform descriptive or inferential statistics?

8.   The National Center for Drug Abuse is conducting a study to determine if heroin usage among teenagers has changed. Historically, about 1.3 percent of teenagers between the ages of 15 and 19 have used heroin one or more times. In a survey of 1824 teenagers, 37 indicated they had used heroin one or more times.

a.   Identify the population.

b.   What characteristic of the population is being measured?

c.   Identify the sample.

d.   Is the purpose of the data collection to perform descriptive or inferential statistics?

9.   Heavy episodic or binge drinking is a serious problem in colleges and universities in the United States. A study reported in *The Journal of the American Medical Association* (JAMA) surveyed a total of 17,592 students selected from 140 US 4-year colleges in order to examine the extent of binge drinking. The study found that 44% of the students surveyed admitted to being binge drinkers. A binge drinker was defined as consuming five or more drinks in a row for men and four or more drinks in a row for women during the two weeks prior to the survey.

a.   Identify the population.

b.   What characteristic of the population is being measured?

c.   Identify the sample.

d.   What are some problems associated with collecting the type of data described in this problem?

10.   A nurse is interested in the growth curve of boys from infancy to the age of 18. One thousand boys are randomly selected, and their heights are measured at various intervals from birth until the age of 18. Based on these measurements, growth curves are constructed based on the percentage of heights observed to be at or below a certain height at each interval (this population characteristic is called a percentile and will be discussed in Chapter 4).

a.   Identify the population.

b.   What characteristic of the population is being measured?

c.   Identify the sample.

d.   Is the purpose of the data collection to perform descriptive or inferential statistics?

11.   A personnel director is interested in determining how effective a new reading course will be in improving the reading comprehension of her company's employees. The director randomly selects twenty employees and determines the average reading comprehension both before and after instruction in the reading course.

a.   Identify the population.

b.   What characteristic of the population is being measured?

c.   Identify the sample.

d.   Is the purpose of the data collection to perform descriptive or inferential statistics?

12. A predominance of body fat, adiposity, can be associated with a myriad of human illnesses including hypertension, diabetes, stroke, heart disease, gallbladder disease, and breast cancer. A standard measure of overall adiposity is the Quetelet index, which is defined as the weight (kg) divided by the square of the height (m). In a study in the *American Journal of Epidemiology*, the Quetelet index was measured on a sample of women between the ages of 35–65 years visiting a breast screening clinic in New York City. The average value of the Quetelet index computed for the women sampled was 25.2. Assume that one of the goals of the study is to estimate the average Quetelet index for all women attending the breast screening clinic.

a.   Identify the population.

b.   What characteristic of the population is being measured?

c.   Identify the sample.

d.   What is the unknown population parameter in this problem?

e.   What is the estimate of this parameter?

1.7   Descriptive vs. Inferential Statistics

The science of statistics is divided into two categories, **descriptive** and **inferential**. Descriptive methods describe and summarize data, while inferential methods aid in making decisions and predictions about populations and processes for which it is impractical to obtain measurements on each member.

Descriptive Statistics

The emphasis in **descriptive statistics** is analyzing observed measurements usually from a sample. With descriptive statistics we try to answer questions such as:

- What is a typical value for the measurements?

- How much variation do the measurements possess?

- What is the shape or distribution of the measurements?

- Are there any extreme values in the measurements and, if so, what does that tell us?

- What is the relative position of a particular measurement in the group of data?

- What kind of relationship exists, if any, when there are two variables and how strong is the relationship?

Descriptive Statistics

Descriptive statistics is the collection, organization, analysis, and presentation of data.

DEFINITION

The application of descriptive statistical tools is usually *ad hoc*, that is, the exact method of analysis changes from one problem to the next. Sometimes the application of descriptive statistics can raise as many questions as it answers. And when that happens, statistics is working at its best as a problem-solving or process-improvement tool.

The importance of descriptive statistics as an information-producing tool relates to the amount of data to be comprehended. If there are only two observations, say 6 and 4, then comprehending the data in its entirety is not difficult and descriptive statistical aids are of little value. However, the 400 observations representing the cost of tuition at 400 colleges and universities in 2016 from Table 1.7.1 suggest a different story. Individually inspecting 400 tuition values would produce very little useful knowledge. To comprehend a large set of data, it must be summarized. That is the function of descriptive statistical techniques. Descriptive techniques are the most common statistical applications.

Examples of Descriptive Statistics

- Frequency Distribution
- Measures of Central Tendency:
  - Mean
  - Median
  - Mode
- Measures of Dispersion:
  - Range
  - Variance
  - Standard Deviation

Inferential Statistics

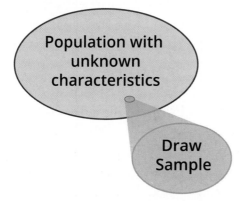

It would be preferable to have measurements of the entire population, but in most cases this data is either not obtainable or would be much too costly to obtain. For example, to be absolutely certain that all car air bags will inflate in head-on collisions would require each new car to be crash tested in a head-on crash. If 100 percent inspection were a requirement, cars would be a scarce commodity. Fortunately for automobile manufacturers, statistical sampling techniques can reliably estimate, with a relatively small sample, the fraction of air bags that will inflate.

Inferential Statistics

The objective of **inferential statistics** is to make reasonable guesses about population characteristics using sample data.

DEFINITION

Table 1.7.1 - The Cost of a Year's Tuition at 400 Colleges and Universities in 2016

10632	27650	34140	17000	22950	24140	21304	13432	23429	8282
41072	14616	10587	27080	25020	13590	19137	10560	4944	16138
31598	49644	11320	26200	10430	26500	12494	6900	3450	31420
10266	12996	11700	24390	13830	19247	17133	12003	4895	22467
25152	15000	21830	24200	23130	27492	17339	25166	18056	17276
17136	29994	6999	12123	28800	10860	24461	16841	24268	18954
17654	34034	21816	10980	14410	31888	23935	6112	25050	28659
20622	26261	10852	27736	35200	10120	12728	20674	20246	21673
15656	11520	15980	37650	12384	16761	19040	20142	20712	32396
25950	49906	35510	24270	14270	19280	6030	5936	25852	16847
19178	46040	16064	20440	6336	8040	18332	2260	18364	23542
17504	12250	29280	33430	35982	24300	26334	17842	21821	29832
21826	5996	22170	9685	17650	11800	8780	10977	18279	16234
11941	15980	25742	16252	21945	17805	30987	8357	16222	19788
4176	20242	22900	10575	13356	40870	27365	22081	30689	31516
25458	30168	45377	15070	31996	12204	32024	23845	29920	7614
7416	32786	49241	10525	21780	14400	8200	20677	31225	7644
30030	45104	32172	31870	22440	23069	24009	22154	22304	7692
10440	20835	28280	48526	4940	13203	5442	18732	9240	27890
6000	22760	26900	35074	13968	33144	22728	33673	19744	20856
9200	49346	10764	36160	16906	45390	12990	24932	18140	18005
17515	39808	19870	23508	17373	38430	20144	17016	7710	4564
17729	29226	16685	22790	15666	18998	10754	8200	7557	5850
18032	23031	18849	42180	28090	47260	9570	8894	6968	20926
38139	45400	15506	14296	31318	14400	31346	6390	31144	8502
38659	24860	7050	35150	32124	15266	28866	18610	19370	20182
37960	23440	12168	42084	11665	22088	31780	22446	28880	21024
12690	46012	27110	47030	25825	48996	32800	10632	25362	19142
23704	24075	36422	46808	18048	17632	5660	30256	18508	7702
17988	34828	27180	47350	28150	29650	30298	21328	22881	11957
34125	37120	38040	15590	11800	6300	16130	21208	8963	18406
9132	30000	15630	14890	43960	19940	4650	15015	27712	5151
11558	10750	49506	24592	37236	11656	16252	14802	17430	27447
21570	23300	33320	29560	22080	30850	10830	15008	45002	33222
9189	25360	9000	18048	19560	49350	4956	10870	36934	28804
34908	30166	23121	41161	21522	15604	5064	14460	5482	25016
22286	21900	19240	12075	13730	48280	21501	6156	8366	7932
11233	22645	27800	18093	27600	48611	4248	20978	6248	19408
8282	33492	31200	35465	26590	23970	34143	30326	14394	16959
8282	50080	31754	24450	37010	22780	20963	10633	22210	24708

1.7   **Exercises**

Basic Concepts

1. Define inferential statistics.

2. What is the difference between descriptive and inferential statistics?

1.8   **The Consequences of Statistical Illiteracy**

Part of being an intelligent human being is the desire to learn the truth about the world we live in. But as Oscar Wilde said in *The Importance of Being Earnest*:

> *"The truth is rarely pure and never simple."*

*Oscar Wilde
(1854 - 1900)*

We rely on our personal experience and the information provided by others to develop our individual versions of the truth. Consequently our personal truth is vulnerable to subjectivity and the quality of the information available. To some extent, life is a struggle over subjectivity and incorrect information. The struggle is further compounded by the fact that we are intentionally provided misleading information, to arrive at conclusions that are not true. Unfortunately, all too often this information is presented in *statistical* form. A cursory look at professional journals or even a newspaper suggests the pervasive use of statistics, often to provide some quantitative basis for a conclusion. All too often there is less than a full explanation of the statistical methods used, and it is left to the reader to evaluate the appropriateness of the author's statistical techniques.

To intelligently appreciate or produce statistical information, you must be statistically literate to defend yourself from a persuasive but fallacious statistical argument, to decrease your vulnerability to pseudo-sciences, and to diminish the chances of making poor and sometimes injurious personal decisions.

A statistically literate person understands the language of statistics and understands statistical concepts and reasoning. To become statistically literate one should be able to think "statistically". This will involve asking questions like:

1. Where did the data come from?

2. How was it sampled and is the sample large enough?

3. How reliable or accurate were the measures used to generate the reported data?

4. Are the reported statistics appropriate for this kind of data?

5. Is a graph drawn appropriately?

6. How was this probabilistic statement calculated?

7. Do the claims make sense?

8. Should there be additional information?

9. Are there alternative interpretations?

1.8   Exercises

Basic Concepts

1. What does it mean to be statistically literate?

2. What types of questions should a statistically literate person ask?

CR   Chapter Review

Key Terms and Ideas

- Big Data
- Volume
- Variety
- Velocity
- Veracity
- Population
- Frame

- Census
- Parameter
- Sample
- Statistic
- Descriptive Statistics
- Inferential Statistics
- Statistical Literacy

Additional Exercises

1. In a study, seat belt users were found to have 20% fewer fatalities than those who do not wear seat belts. Do these results prove that seat belts reduce the chances of a fatality?

2. States having an abundance of coastline have an obvious advantage over landlocked states, or states with little coastline, in that their economies may profit from an extensive fishing industry, tourism, shipping or other water related activities. Alaska, the leader by far in miles of coastline, has a total of 6640 miles, of which 5580 miles border the Pacific Ocean and 1060 miles border the Arctic. Florida, the leader in the continental United States, has a total of 1350 miles with 580 miles on the Atlantic Ocean and 770 miles on the Gulf of Mexico. Of all states with some coastline, New Hampshire, with 13 miles of coastline, is in last place.

    a. Identify the population.

    b.   What characteristic is being measured?

3. A young actuary (statistician usually working in the insurance industry) has been asked to summarize the number of automobile accident claims by region for his company. He randomly selects 50 automobile accident claims which his company has settled in the last year and counts the number of accidents in each region: North, South, East and West. He summarizes the counts by region in a chart and gives the results to his supervisor.

    a.   Identify the population.

    b.   What characteristic of the population is being measured?

    c.   Identify the sample.

    d.   Is the purpose of the data collection to perform descriptive or inferential statistics?

4. In a study in *Psychological Reports*, a sample of 547 nonsmokers was selected from a large Midwestern university. The sample contained 330 women and 217 men. These students were asked to complete a questionnaire concerning students who smoked. Seventy-six percent of those surveyed strongly agreed with the statement, *I am less likely to want a smoker for a roommate.* Sixty-three percent of those surveyed strongly agreed with the statement, *I am less likely to want a smoker for a date.* Sixty-seven percent of those surveyed strongly agreed with the statement, *I am less likely to want a smoker for a husband or wife.*

    a.   Identify the population.

    b.   What characteristics of the population are being measured?

    c.   Identify the sample.

    d.   Give one statistical inference that may be made from the data.

    e.   Why is this called an inference?

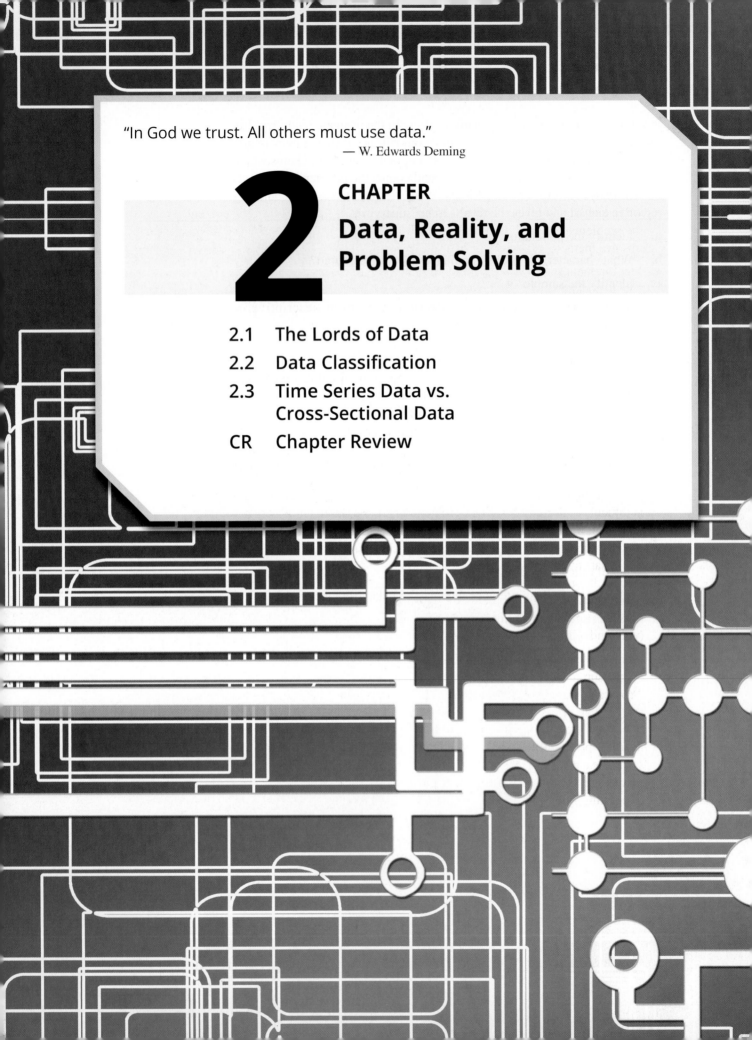

"In God we trust. All others must use data."
— W. Edwards Deming

CHAPTER

2 Data, Reality, and Problem Solving

Introduction

For most people, the words "data" and "measurement" are words that don't spark a lot of enthusiasm. So why should you be interested in measurement and data? Your career will essentially be a choice of the kinds of problems you desire to solve. The more difficult the problems you decide to solve, the more you will depend upon data and measurement to solve them.

Measurement is so pervasive in our culture because long ago our species learned that if you do not know what "reality" is, it is difficult to predictably change it to a more desirable state. That is why we seem to want to measure just about everything in the physical world: temperature, weight, distances, pressures, speed, earthquakes (Richter scale), and many more. We even try to measure feelings and mental states like love, neuroticism, happiness, and depression.

Type "measurement" into an Internet search engine and you will be surprised by the number of organizations that are devoted to measurement. One of those groups, The International Society of Automation (ISA), plays a prominent role in setting worldwide measurement standards. Without complex measurements and standards, just about all the conveniences that we take for granted (telephones, automobiles, refrigerators, televisions, airplanes, and computers) would not exist.

So what makes the data and measurement both personal and interesting? Problems! It is difficult to think of a serious problem where measurement and data would not be an important part of developing solutions. Measurements can also be quite costly. An oil company considering the purchase of an oil lease might spend millions for a seismic survey to evaluate the size of a potential oil reserve. For companies that do oil exploration, seismic data are the company's crown jewels. Data can be just as important on the personal level. If you need an MRI the cost will be substantial. According to the Healthcare Bluebook's national fair price, an abdominal MRI (without contrast) would be $776. For a brain MRI (with and without contrast), it's $1261.

Businesses have the difficult problem of being profitable and consequently depend heavily on measurement, data, and statistical thinking. In fact, there is an old management adage, "You can't manage what you can't measure." Perhaps this adage would be better stated as "you can't manage unless you know what 'reality' is." That is why there are so many important measurement systems in a business. The accounting system is designed to measure profitability and to inform management of potential problems. The inventory system is a measurement tool designed to measure the status of inventory, indicate when reorders should be placed, and spot potential inventory theft. The cash flow system is a forecasting system that measures the company's need for cash.

Web Tracking and the Author

The author of this book was having a conversation with a family member in his home about automatic potato peelers. The family member used his phone to do a search on automatic potato peelers to determine which manufacturers had the highest consumer rating. When the author got on the internet the following morning, guess what ads were appearing on his frequently visited web pages— advertisements for automatic potato peelers. Ultimately, the ads worked, and the potato peeler is fantastic!

2.1   The Lords of Data

Measurement and selling the resulting data is big business. Those advertisements that seem to follow you around on whatever device you are using to access the internet are there because of web tracking. Approximately 75% of the world's 500 most popular websites contain web trackers. About half of these sites use four web tracking systems. These systems collect an enormous amount of data about you and produce a browsing profile. For example, a browsing profile might include data like:

- You frequently visit sites about computers,
- You probably live in Bangor, Maine,
- You have looked at ads for diapers,
- You buy games from a speciality gaming store,
- You play fantasy football.

The web trackers then sell their data to other firms for marketing purposes. Did you know...

- …that most prescriptions are recorded in a database at the local pharmacy and then sold (without names attached) to firms that collect and summarize this information? The data is then resold to pharmaceutical companies, enabling them to measure how often specific doctors prescribe their drugs. As a consequence, they are able to measure the effectiveness of their salespersons.

- …that when you are late on a car payment, house payment, or credit card payment, the information will wind up in a national credit database? This database is used by companies in the credit business to assess credit worthiness. It is also used by many businesses in employment screening.

- …that banks and other institutions that issue credit cards keep data on your spending habits? This data is used to build models to help prevent credit card fraud. If the bank's model determines that you have used your credit card to make "unusual" purchases, it's possible that someone from the credit card company will call and confirm that you did make the purchases. This proactive use of data has prevented an enormous amount of credit card fraud.

- …that when you order something from a mail order company, your name and what you ordered is recorded and frequently sold to other businesses? Even your grocery store gives you a card so it can collect and sell data on what and how often you buy grocery items.

- …that you can log on to the internet and obtain current satellite imagery of virtually any place in the world? You might enjoy typing the words "satellite imagery" into your internet search engine to explore a bit.

Whether you are a business that sells data or a company that collects its own data to improve customer experience, collecting and maintaining large collections of data is costly. Before the advent of the World Wide Web it was uncommon to have really large amounts of data to analyze. Now, large teams of employees are required to acquire and maintain data. Data is captured with programs designed and written by personnel with job titles like:

- Systems architect
- Interface designer

- Application developer
- Web developer
- Mobile applications developer

- Application security specialist
- Project management specialist

Once the data is captured a new group of personnel is needed to preserve the data in a readily accessible form. These individuals have job titles like:

- Database architect
- Database developer

- Database administrator
- Database security specialist

Neither the developers nor the database specialists could survive without network and computer hardware platforms to support them. The networking and hardware platform requires personnel with job titles like:

- Network architect
- Network administrator
- Network technician

- Network security specialist
- Server administrator
- Network and database performance monitor

If you were to search the salaries of any of these job titles, you would find that they are all well-paid positions. Which implies institutions have spent an enormous amount of financial resources on their data.

Measurement

Part of becoming a problem solver and user of statistics is developing an ability to appraise the quality of measurements. For many problems, what you measure and how you measure it is more important than how you analyze the data. Thus, it is not surprising that the science of statistics is just as concerned with producing good data as it is with interpreting it.

When you encounter data, ask yourself: is the data credible? Consider the following questions:

> 1. Is the concept under study adequately reflected by the proposed measurements?
> 2. Is the data measured accurately?
> 3. Is there a sufficient quantity of the data to draw a reasonable conclusion?

If each of these questions can be answered affirmatively, the data is likely credible.

The development of a suitable measurement involves two essential questions: *What should be measured?* and *How should the concept be measured?* Measures (sometimes called metrics) are developed from the field of study, not statistics. Suppose you decide to measure the speed of an object. The concept of speed is well-defined. It is measured in distance per unit of time (for example, 60 miles per hour). Therefore, determining the speed of an object will require two variables to be measured, one distance and the other time. There are well-defined standard measures (such as feet, yards, miles) to use for distance traveled, as well as time, so the measurement is relatively easy to obtain. However, measuring someone's intelligence is another story. How do you define intelligence? Are there standard measures that can be applied? While IQ tests exist, what do they really measure?

Year of 1903

A little more than 100 years ago, our world looked drastically different. Advancements in science and technology have made a massive difference in how we live our lives.

- The average life expectancy in the U.S. was forty-seven.
- Only 14 percent of the homes in the U.S. had a bathtub.
- Only 8 percent of the homes had a telephone.
- A three-minute call from Denver to New York City cost eleven dollars.
- There were only 8,000 cars in the U.S. and only 144 miles of paved road.
- The maximum speed limit in most cities was 10 mph.
- The tallest structure in the world was the Eiffel Tower.
- The average wage in the U.S. was 22 cents per hour.
- More than 95 percent of all births in the U.S. took place at home.
- One in ten US adults was illiterate.
- Only 6 percent of all Americans had graduated from high school.

The more well-defined a concept, the easier it is to develop measurements for it. Our ability to comprehend the world we live in is rooted in good measurement.

Science and Data

Measurement and data are an integral part of science. Methods for exploring research problems have been developed over a long period of time and have become standards in the scientific community. These methods are collectively known as the **scientific method**.

The Scientific Method

1. Gather information about the phenomenon being studied;

2. On the basis of the data, formulate a preliminary generalization or hypothesis;

3. Collect further data to test the hypothesis;

4. If the data and other subsequent experiments support the hypothesis, it becomes a law.

PROCEDURE

Statistics and data are fundamental to the scientific method. Data from carefully designed experiments is the ultimate evidence that supports or discredits new theories. Causation is very hard to prove!

The data collection process in stages one and three of the scientific method can be quite different. The first step of the scientific method is exploratory, finding out the *"reality"* about the subject under consideration. Since the data in this phase need not produce convincing evidence, whatever data is available is used to generate ideas. However, the third step begins the validation of a hypothesis. Scientists are trained to be critical thinkers. If a new idea is to be accepted by the scientific community, convincing evidence must be developed at the third stage. *The manner in which the data is collected is an important part of that evidence.* If the evidence is to be persuasive, a data gathering strategy (an experimental design) that will produce data without the unwelcome influences of *confounding* variables is required.

Because of science's emphasis on data, statistics has become inextricably linked with the scientific method. A branch of statistics focuses on designing experiments that yield data with maximum information. Other branches of statistics focus on exploratory methods for examining data that yield the hypotheses mentioned in step two. Still other branches develop theories to test the hypotheses using data collected from an experiment.

Confounding Variables

Confounding variables arise when a researcher is trying to determine if one variable is related to another. Sometimes, another variable unknowingly influences an experiment, and this is called a **confounding variable**. For example, suppose you were researching whether genetic differences between two species of oaks impacted resistance to insects. You find 30 red oaks and 30 white oaks, and select 50 leaves from each oak. Next, you measure the area of each leaf that was eaten by insects. Suppose you find significantly more insect damage on the white oak leaves. Is this caused by the difference in genetics of the two oak varieties? Maybe, but there are other variables that may be confounding your study. What about the age of the trees, might this have an effect? What about the location of the trees? Were any of the trees treated with a fungicide? All these variables (age, location, and level of fungicide) could be confounding the results.

Confounding Variables

Confounding variables are "extra" variables that are not accounted for during experimentation and can cause results to become skewed.

DEFINITION

Decision-Making and Data

Collecting data is a natural part of our lives. A practical concern such as *What will I have for dinner?* we encounter everyday. Although virtually no one formally applies the scientific method to such a problem, most people perform experiments and collect data (by eating). This leads to generalizations such as *I hate asparagus* or *I like ice cream.* After sufficient experimentation, these generalizations become personal preference laws.

Selecting the evening meal does not have incredible consequences, yet important problems, by definition, do.

Decision-Making Method

1. Clearly define the problem and any influential variables.
2. Decide upon objectives and decision criteria for choosing a solution.
3. Create alternative solutions.
4. Compare alternatives using the criteria established in the second step.
5. Implement the chosen alternative.
6. Check the results to make sure the desired results are achieved.

PROCEDURE

Notice the first step in the Decision-Making Method is to define the problem. This is important because almost *any solution to the right problem is better than the best solution to the wrong problem.*

Measurement, Data, and Problem Definition

When you go to a physician what is the first thing the physician does? Most physicians measure your weight, temperature, and blood pressure before he/she meets with you. During the examination, the doctor will elicit more data. If there is insufficient data to make a diagnosis, more data (perhaps the dreaded blood test) will be ordered. In the medical world it is extremely important to know what reality is, that is why there is so much data gathered. Data is just as important in solving business problems.

Consider a trucking company manager who is beginning to hear a few complaints about freight being delivered late. If the Operations Manager of the trucking company keeps data on the number of shipments delivered late each week, then statistics can be used to help assess the magnitude of the problem. For example, if the number of late deliveries is plotted (see Figure 2.1.1), the data in the graph confirms a disturbing trend. Late deliveries are on the rise. Left unsolved, this problem can jeopardize jobs and the existence of the business.

Late Deliveries Each Week

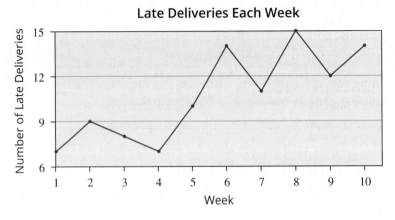

Figure 2.1.1

Suppose a nurse takes a patient's temperature once each hour. After recording the measurements in the patient's chart, the data is plotted (see Figure 2.1.2). The data reveals a potential problem. Undoubtedly, more data will be needed.

Patient's Temperature History

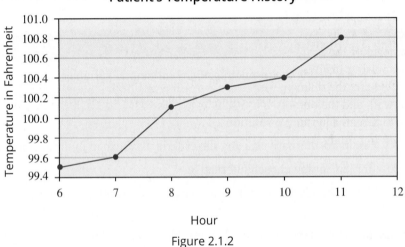

Figure 2.1.2

Graphical and numerical summaries are frequently useful in discovering the existence of a problem as well as in shedding light on what some of the potential causes may be. In many instances, problems are caused by systems that don't operate as they are designed. Collecting data (finding out system "reality") and using simple statistical tools to monitor a system are the most common ways of ensuring a system performs properly.

Problems are not always the result of a diagnosis of some complaint or system malfunction. A problem may well be the result of an inquiry into unexpectedly good system performance. In this context, a problem presents itself as an opportunity for improvement. Suppose, for example, a calculus instructor develops a new method for teaching Introductory Calculus. Measurements are kept on his students as well as students taking subsequent calculus courses. Using statistical methods to compare students using the *new method* to those using the *old method* can be valuable in pointing out potential educational improvements that may be used at other institutions.

Statistics as Criteria for Decision-Making

The second point in the decision-making paradigm suggests defining objectives and developing criteria in order to evaluate various alternative decisions. Not all statistics are simple means, proportions, or standard deviations. Managers and researchers often develop their own statistical measures for summarizing some aspect of a phenomenon. In baseball, for example, teams regularly compute the Earned Run Average (ERA) of each pitcher. This statistic summarizes the average number of earned runs per nine innings pitched. ERA is used as a criterion for comparing and evaluating pitchers as well as for salary negotiations. The Mean Time Before Failure (MTBF) is a statistic that is used to compare the reliability of various equipment or components. The Consumer Price Index (CPI) is a summary statistic that describes the overall price level in the United States. This statistic is an economic measure of inflation and is used in labor contracts to escalate wages as well as to calculate cost of living increases in social security payments.

What Should I Measure, and How Should It Be Measured?

What should be measured depends on the problem to be solved. Sometimes what should be measured is obvious and relatively easy. If the problem is to maintain or improve a system, key variables are monitored and decisions are made on the basis of the level of these variables. For example, if you are responsible for a machine manufacturing pistons, then some of the variables that should be measured and controlled are: the diameter of the piston, the length of the piston, the width of the piston wall, and the number of defects on the piston's surface. However, if you are trying to design a system to perform automated stock trading, deciding what variables are important could take years to discover, if ever.

A precisely defined concept is usually easy to measure. The less precise (the fuzzier) the concept the more difficult the measurement becomes. There is a vast difference in measuring the height of a person and in measuring his/her intelligence. Defining height is relatively simple. It is nothing more than the vertical length of an object. There are standard scales, such as inches and feet, that everyone agrees upon, that can be used to measure height. The National Institute of Standards and Technology maintains rods which define a government standard for distance measures (feet and inches). Because these standards are widely accepted, if ten different people measure the same person's height, there should not be large differences in their measurements. This is not true when measuring intelligence. The National Institute of Standards and Technology does not have a measuring rod for intelligence. It is unlikely that ten randomly selected people could agree on a definition of intelligence, much less on how it should be measured. Intelligence is a fuzzy concept because there is no universally accepted definition and hence there can be no universally accepted standard of measure. If a concept cannot be precisely defined, it cannot be measured precisely. How do you measure fuzzy concepts?

Measuring Fuzzy Concepts

Fuzzy concept definitions produce fuzzy measurements. One could devote an enormous amount of time developing measuring instruments for fuzzy concepts such as love, rivalry, and prejudice, and still have a poor measurement. These concepts

Albert Einstein
1879–1955

Albert Einstein wondered what it would be like to travel on a wave of light. He published his work on the general theory of relativity in 1916, which connected the ideas of space, time, and speed. Isaac Newton's theories had been the accepted *scientific law* describing space, time, and speed for over two hundred years. Einstein's ideas were very controversial, challenging existing beliefs in a fundamental way. Einstein's ideas were not established as conventional wisdom until many experiments yielded data confirming them.

Caution

The conclusions suggested by statistics can be no stronger than the quality of the measurements which produced the statistical evidence. Fuzzy or confounded measurements must produce fragile conclusions.

are fuzzy because they are perceptions. No person can be sure that their perception of love, rivalry, or prejudice is the same as someone else's interpretation. Science that relies on fuzzy measurements usually makes the assumption that everyone's idea of the concept is more or less alike.

Often when measuring fuzzy concepts, the instrument used to measure the concept ends up defining the concept. The Wechsler Adult Intelligence Scale (WAIS) is a test that is often used to measure intelligence—an IQ test. There could be a long debate over what constitutes intelligence. For most researchers studying intelligence, developing a new instrument to measure intelligence, however it is defined, is simply not a practical alternative. If a measuring device is needed for a fuzzy concept, using an established instrument like the WAIS is usually the method of choice. However, the necessity for using a measuring instrument does not validate the instrument.

There has been a great deal of controversy in recent years over whether the SAT or ACT accurately measures scholastic development. Still the SAT and ACT are important parts of the college admission process. Why? Because college admission committees apparently believe there is no better alternative. When measurements purport to represent what you believe is a fuzzy concept, it is important to think critically about the measurements. Are they valid measures of the intended concept? This issue is important and will again be addressed later in the chapter in the levels of measurement section.

Collecting Data

Essentially, there are two ways to obtain data: **observation** and **controlled experiments**. The data collection method is related to the nature of the problem to be solved and the ethical and practical constraints of collecting data in some environment. There are many instances in which controlled experiments that would produce particularly appropriate data are not practical or would be unethical. For example, medical researchers cannot randomly pluck an infant's liver in order to experiment with a new artificial one.

There are many instances in which data that has been collected provides either no information or misleading information about the effect under study.

A high school physics teacher wants to determine if there is any beneficial effect of studying calculus before taking physics. He obtains the records of his physics students and compares the group of students that had calculus or are taking it concurrently with those who have not. The average physics grade for those having had calculus is a great deal higher than those that had not. The conclusion reached from this data is: The study of calculus improves one's understanding of physics. Does the data and the manner in which it was collected support such a conclusion?

Students who elect to take calculus generally have higher than average skills in mathematics. Are the higher physics grades of the calculus students due to their above average mathematical skills or to the content of the calculus course? Because of the data collection method, the data is not of sufficient quality to reach a conclusion as to the benefits of taking calculus prior to taking the physics course. A confounding variable (the exceptional mathematical ability of students electing calculus) makes it impossible to distinguish the effects we wish to study.

Coping with Poorly Measured Concepts

In a statistical analysis, it is usually not possible to recover from poorly measured concepts or badly collected measurements. Unfortunately, during your lifetime you will be bombarded with statistics derived from poorly measured concepts, confounded measurements, and simply fictitious data. When confronted with statistical evidence of any kind, regardless of whether or not the statistical analysis is done in good faith, it is ultimately up to you to ask reasonable questions about the data and potential confounding variables in the experimental data.

Controlled Experiments: Data by Design

Suppose you wanted to know whether an agricultural crop would have higher yields if a different amount of fertilizer was used. This kind of question would be ideal for a controlled experiment. The purpose of controlled experiments is to reveal the response of one variable (crop yield, the response variable) to changes in another variable (level of fertilization, the explanatory variable). In a controlled experiment the researcher attempts to control the environment of the experiment so that the effect of one variable on another can be isolated and measured. In these studies there is a **control group** and an **experimental group**. Ideally, there is no initial difference between the two groups. During the experiment a **treatment** is applied to the experimental group.

The exact form of the treatment will depend on the particular experiment. If the experimental group were an agricultural crop, a treatment might be applying a given level of fertilizer or perhaps a difference in the amount of water that is applied to the crop. Assuming the experiment is of sufficient size, a cause and effect relationship between the **explanatory variable** and the **response variable** in the experiment can potentially be established. The effect of the treatment can be measured by comparing the response variable in the control and experimental groups.

Comparative Experiments

Isolating the effects of one variable on another means anticipating potentially confounding variables and designing a controlled experiment to produce data in which the values of the confounding variables are regulated. In the physics example in the previous section, the confounding variables are the mathematical knowledge and ability of those students who self-selected to take calculus before physics. To control for these *biases*, students could be randomly assigned to take the calculus course before the physics course. By randomly assigning students to take the calculus course before the physics course, the bias associated with mathematical knowledge and ability of the two groups should be removed. If mathematical knowledge and ability are controlled, and the experiment has a significant sample size, any difference in physics scores could be attributed to beneficial effect of the calculus course. An experimental design in which experimental units (students in this case) are randomly assigned to two different treatments is called a **completely randomized design**.

Response Variable: Students' grades in the physics course

Explanatory Variable: Whether students take calculus before physics

Randomization is often used as a method of controlling bias and is an important principle in the design of experiments.

> ### Response Variable
>
> A **response variable** measures the outcome of interest in a study.
>
> DEFINITION

> ### Explanatory Variable
>
> An **explanatory variable** causes or explains changes in a response variable.
>
> DEFINITION

Example 2.1.1

Suppose a new species of tomato has been genetically engineered to increase yields. The question: Does the new species produce higher yields?

Solution

In this experimental design, the plots of tomatoes will be divided into two groups, one that contains the new species and another that contains the unaltered variety. The plots containing the genetically engineered variety will be the treatment group, and the plots containing the standard variety will be the control group. If the experiment is properly performed, any change in the response variable (yield) can be attributed to the explanatory variable (genetic engineering) and not to other variables that are controlled. The untangling of variables at the data-gathering stage makes the analysis of the data much easier. There is no better way to establish a causal relationship.

Plot 1	Plot 2	Plot 3	Plot 4
Plot 5	Plot 6	Plot 7	Plot 8
Plot 9	Plot 10	Plot 11	Plot 12
Plot 13	Plot 14	Plot 15	Plot 16

Variables like rainfall, amount of sunshine, or type of soil can affect the yield of tomatoes. These variables must be controlled in the experiment so that differences in yields between plots can be attributed just to the genetically-engineered species. One possible method of controlling for these variables is to create small plots in the same field all with similar soil types. Several plots of each type of tomato are planted. Each plot contains only one type of tomato. Rainfall is measured and supplemented with irrigation to assure that each plot has the same amount of water. By controlling for these variables in this manner, we can say that any differences noted in the yield (response variable) between the genetically-engineered variety (treatment group) and the unaltered variety (control group) is due to genetic improvements (explanatory variable).

The Before and After Study

The before and after study also contains a comparative experiment. The control group and the experimental group are initially identical. The response variable is measured in the control group at the beginning of the study, and then a treatment is applied to the control group. After the treatment is applied, the control group becomes the experimental group. The response variable is again measured after the treatment has been applied. If the treatment affects the response variable then there should be a difference between the value of the response variable for the control and experimental groups, presumably caused by the treatment.

Example 2.1.2

Does an SAT preparation course improve performance on the SAT?

Solution

A group of high school students take the SAT. Then they are given an SAT preparation course. They retake the SAT. If the group's second SAT performance improves, then it may be related to the SAT preparation course.

Explanatory variable: SAT preparation course

Response variable: SAT scores

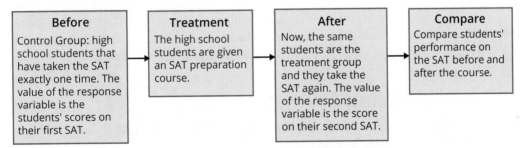

In this experiment there is only one group of students. Suppose there were two groups of students, one that had taken the course (treatment group) and one that had not (the control group). Could you assign any difference in results solely to the SAT preparation course? Because of potential differences in the cognitive abilities of the two groups of students, this experiment would be much more vulnerable to the justifiable criticism that the differences in student cognitive ability caused the difference in the group's SAT performance rather than the SAT preparation course. However, by using the before and after method we have only one group of students and cognitive ability is controlled.

The Placebo Effect

A difficult problem arises in experiments involving people. In clinical trials of some drug or medical treatment, patients often respond favorably to any treatment, including a "dummy" or "fake" treatment. These fake treatments are called **placebos**.

Placebos

One might think that the effectiveness of placebos should be close to zero; this, however, is not the case. Studies have shown that up to 62% of headache sufferers, 58% of those suffering from sea sickness, and even 39% of those suffering from postoperative wound pain showed symptoms of relief when given a placebo. This is a stunning revelation of the effect of psychology on our mind and body.

An intriguing but ethical question for you to ponder is this: If placebos can be 62% effective for curing headaches, would or should a physician treat a headache with a placebo only?

Placebos

A **placebo** is a fake treatment that has the potential to cause a response.

DEFINITION

In medical research, a placebo is a pill that contains none of the drug that is being tested. It has been shown in several pain studies that placebos relieve pain in 30% to 40% of patients, even though the placebo has no active ingredients. The placebo effect is not confined to medicine. Similar effects have been noticed in psychological research in which the subjects seem to try to help the researcher prove some conclusion.

One of the more interesting experiments contaminated by this effect was the Hawthorne Study conducted at the Western Electric Company's Hawthorne Works in Chicago between 1927 and 1932. The studies were initiated to determine the effect of lighting on worker productivity. Lighting was increased in stages, and the investigators found that each time lighting increased, worker output increased. The investigators were suspicious that another effect might be causing worker productivity to improve. So, workers were told lighting was to be increased when, in fact, it was decreased. Despite the decrease, worker output increased again. Clearly there was some other variable affecting worker output.

The workers wanted the study to be *successful,* and their desire was confounding the experiment. Instead of discovering the expected relationship between worker output and lighting, the investigators found that the social system and the employees' roles within that system had a great deal more to do with worker productivity than lighting. The Hawthorne Study has been credited with introducing psychology to the work place. It also points out the hazards of measurement, even in a controlled experiment.

Double-Blind Studies

The placebo effect is prevalent in medical studies, and another data gathering methodology is used to counteract it.

Double-Blind Study

Double-blind studies are used to counteract the placebo effect. In a double-blind study the subjects are not told whether they are members of the treatment group or the control group. The evaluators (the persons that measure the response variable) are not told whether their subjects are members of the control or experimental group.

DEFINITION

Until recently, ulcers in the upper intestine were a rather common illness. A new treatment for ulcers was proposed. This treatment involved gastric freezing and required the patient to swallow a deflated balloon with tubes attached. A refrigerated solution was then pumped through the balloon for an hour. The idea behind this therapy was to cool the stomach wall and reduce the amount of acid produced. Initially, the results looked promising and the treatment was used for several years. However, none of the initial studies were double-blind.

In the double-blind study half the patients were given the procedure and the other half were given a placebo treatment, which included swallowing the balloon, but no cooling solution was injected into the balloon. In the double blind study patients that had the placebo treatment actually did better than the ones that received the real treatment. Gastric freezing was eventually abandoned as a treatment for upper-intestinal ulcers.

Observational Studies

Observational data comes about by measuring "what is." If you are trading stocks, the market data you receive is observational. It is simply what is happening in the marketplace at the time. Census data is observational; it is a measure of how things are in a specific geographic area at a given point in time. There is no experimentation to see how manipulating one variable will affect another variable, or variables. Virtually all of the data we routinely encounter is observational. Examples regularly appearing in the newspaper include:

- stock, commodity, bond, option, and currency market data

- almost all federal government data, including census, economic, and educational

- virtually all local and state government data

- sports data

The data described above is often collected to satisfy state and government regulation as well as for business purposes. These data values are not the result of a designed experiment.

Observational studies can be extremely vulnerable to confounding variables. For example, the effect of vitamin C has been the subject of controversy for some time. Numerous claims of beneficial health effects from regularly consuming vitamin C have been made. However, Enstrom, Kemin, and Klein ("Vitamin C Intake and Mortality," *Epidemiology*, May 1992) in an observational study with 10,000 participants noted that males in their study who supplemented their diets with 500 milligrams of vitamin C each day (on average) lived approximately six years longer than those who did not take the vitamin. Females taking this dosage of vitamin C (on average) lived approximately one year longer. Although this study was quite large, it does not prove that vitamin C causes increased longevity. If the data had come from a controlled experiment the strength of the study's conclusion would be much more powerful. The Vitamin C study is an observational study because the subjects were not chosen randomly for the control and treatment groups. If the experiment were conducted as a controlled experiment, the control group would be given a placebo and the treatment group would be given vitamin C.

Untangling Variables in an Observational Study

Untangling variables is difficult. It is much better to untangle data (with respect to the effects of one variable on another) in a controlled experiment before doing the analysis. But, sometimes the data has already been collected and there is no choice. In 1973, the Graduate Division at the University of California, Berkeley, carried out an observational study on gender bias in admissions to the Graduate School. There were 8442 men and 4321 women who applied for admission. Of the men that applied, 3714 were subsequently accepted, and 1512 of the women were accepted. Given that almost twice as many men applied to the graduate program, it is reasonable to expect that more men would be accepted.

Double-Blind Studies

Double-blind studies are the gold standard in design of experiments for new drug therapies. The Food and Drug Administration has a gauntlet of "phases" that a new drug must pass through before it can be offered to the market. The last of these phases, Phase III, consists of clinical trials. Only about 1 in 3 drugs makes it to Phase III clinical trials. Phase III trials have between 300 and 3000 participants. All the participants have the condition the drug is intended to treat. If it is possible, Phase III trials are conducted as double-blind studies.

To make a reasonable comparison, the first thing that is needed is to adjust for the difference in application rates between men and women. Comparing the percentage of each group that was accepted will take care of this problem. Nearly 44% of the men and 35% of the women were admitted. These admission statistics suggested there was "statistical" support for the idea of discrimination against women.

The graduate school admission process at UC Berkeley was done by major. If there was a discrimination against women, those departments that were discriminating would stand out when the admissions data was examined on a departmental basis. But when the data was examined, the investigator did not find what was expected.

	Table 2.1.1 - College Acceptance Rates			
	Men		**Women**	
Major	**Number of Applicants**	**Percent Admitted**	**Number of Applicants**	**Percent Admitted**
I	825	62	108	82
II	560	63	25	68
III	325	37	593	34
IV	417	33	375	35
V	191	28	393	24
VI	373	6	341	7

Suppose the data in Table 2.1.1 represents the six largest majors on the Berkeley campus.

In all but two of the majors, women were admitted more frequently than men. Not only were women not being discriminated against, but there appears to be potential discrimination against men in Major I. How could this completely opposite conclusion be true? A close examination of the data shows that in the majors with the largest percentage admitted (the easiest to get into) there were many male applicants and very few female applicants. The majors that had very low acceptance rates (difficult to be admitted) had relatively very few men and many women applying. Thus, the variable major field of study was **confounding** the variable gender in the original analysis and **biasing** the original conclusion. This is one of the most well-known examples of a phenomenon called Simpson's paradox, which states that the relationship between two variables can be heavily affected by a third variable.

Bias

Bias is the tendency to overestimate or underestimate the value of a certain population parameter.

DEFINITION

The original conclusion was the result of the fact that women were applying to the most difficult departments for admission, not because of sex discrimination. By separating the data by major, the analyst was able to **control** for the confounding variable, choice of major, and remove the bias. When it is possible to remove the effect of one variable, we are said to be **controlling for** that variable. The Berkeley data illustrates a subtle problem in the comparison of two or more proportions.

In this instance the analyst was able to untangle the two variables, but this is not always the case. Unless the data is gathered with a controlled experiment, it may not be possible to untangle the effects of the causal factors.

Surveys

A great deal of the statistical information presented to us is the result of surveys.

Often we will see in the news that one of the major polling organizations, Gallup, Harris, ABC-Washington Post, and NBC-New York Times, is reporting findings on various topics, from the approval rating of the President to the popularity of a television show.

In some instances, the purpose of a survey is purely descriptive, as those described above. However, in many cases the researcher is interested in discovering a relationship. Because virtually all surveys produce observational data, survey research belongs to the discovery steps (one and two) of the scientific method. Sometimes a plausible relationship is discovered and a designed experiment is undertaken to more convincingly demonstrate the relationship.

A famous observational study, known as the Framingham Study, recorded various data on 4,500 middle-aged men. The men were followed for many years with the hope of uncovering what factors relate to the development of heart disease. It was discovered that the development of heart disease seemed to be associated with obesity, heavy smoking, and high blood pressure. Because of the large number of participants and the researcher's ability to control for potentially confounding variables after the data was collected, this research influenced many physicians to work with their patients to control the three **causal** factors found in the study.

Even Hollywood studios do survey research. The survey shown in Figure 2.1.3 is used by a major studio. Looking at the questions that are posed you can see they want data on *why you came to the movie* and *what you liked about it*. Collecting this data on a wide variety of movies gives the studio insight into what makes a movie successful, the importance of stars, and what other factors have universal appeal.

Steps to Consider When Conducting a Survey

1. Have specific goals.
2. Consider alternatives for collecting data.
3. Select samples to represent the population.
4. Match the question wording to the concepts being measured.
5. Pretest questionnaires.
6. Construct quality checks.
7. Use statistical analysis and reporting techniques.
8. Disclose all methods used to conduct the survey.

Source: American Association for Public Opinion Research

Figure 2.1.3

SAMPLE MOVIE SURVEY

Please complete the first 9 questions of this survey before the movie begins and questions 10 through 14 after the movie.
Please give the completed questionnaire to the persons collecting them at the exits.

1. Indicate the <u>one item</u> in the list below that was most influential in your decision to see the movie. (Check one)

    <u>Newspaper</u>: Ad..( )1   <u>Radio</u>:   Ad..( )1
    　　　　　　Review.................................( )2   　　　　　Review......................................( )2
    　　　　　　Article ....( )3

    <u>Magazine</u>: Ad..( )4   <u>Around Town</u>: Received a Complimentary Pass................( )3
    　　　　　　Review.................................( )5   　　　　　　Coming Attractions.........................( )4
    　　　　　　Article ....( )6   　　　　　　Poster or Billboard ....( )5

    <u>Television</u>: Commercial..........................( )7   　　　　　　The soundtrack album....................( )6
    　　　　　　Review.................................( )8   　　　　　　Recommended from a friend or relative ....( )7
    　　　　　　MTV or other Music Videos........( )9   　　　　　　Computer on-line service................( )8
    　　　　　　Other cable ....( )0   　　　　　　Internet ....( )9
    　　　　　　Talk Show, other ....( )x   　　　　　　Other: ....( )0

2. Which of the following were important to you in deciding to come to this movie? (Mark as many as apply)

    Tony Curtis ....( )1   Billy Wilder, the producer...............( )4   The visual effects ....( )7
    Marilyn Monroe ....( )2   The story ....( )5   The reviews ....( )8
    Jack Lemmon ....( )3   The drama ....( )6   Other ....( )9

3. What is your age? (Check one)

    Under 12 ....( )1   30 to 34 ....( )7
    12 to 14....................( )2   35 to 39 ....( )8
    15 to 17....................( )3   40 to 44 ....( )9
    18 to 20....................( )4   45 to 49 ....( )0
    21 to 24....................( )5   50 to 59 ....( )x
    25 to 29....................( )6   60 & over..................................( )y

4. What is the last grade of school you completed?

    Some high school or less ....( )1
    Completed high school ....( )2
    Some college/currently in college ....( )3
    Completed 2 year college ....( )4
    Completed 4 year college ....( )5
    Currently in/completed post-grad.............( )6

5. Are you...(Check One)

    Male................( )1
    Female ....( )2

6. What is your ethnic background? (Check One)

    African-American............( )1   Caucasian ....( )4
    Asian.............................( )2   Native American ....( )5
    Hispanic.........................( )3

7. What is your marital status? (Check one)

    Single....................................( )1
    Married ....( )2
    Divorced/Separated ....( )3
    Widowed..............................( )4

8. Before today, how familiar were you with the storyline? Very familiar...( )1   Somewhat familiar...( )2   Not at all familiar...( )3

9. How many times before today have you seen the movie?

    None..............................( )1   Once ....( )2   Twice..............................( )3   Three or more times. ....( )4

XXXXXXXXX COMPLETE QUESTIONS 10 THROUGH 14 AFTER THE MOVIE XXXXXXXXXX

10. How would you rate the movie?

    Excellent ....( )1
    Very Good ....( )2
    Good ....( )3
    Fair.....................................( )4
    Poor....................................( )5

11. Would you recommend the movie?

    Definitely ....( )1
    Probably..............................( )2
    Probably Not.......................( )3
    Definitely Not ....( )4

12. How did the movie measure up to your expectations?

    Better than expected ....( )1
    About what I expected...............( )2
    Not as good as expected ....( )3

13. Which of the following words or phrases best describe the movie you just saw? (Mark as many as apply)

    Entertaining...........................( )1   Worn-out theme ....( )1   Well acted.......................................( )1
    Boring/dull ....( )2   Surprising...................................( )2   Not enough drama...........................( )2
    Dramatic................................( )3   Too long ....( )3   Has a good story..............................( )3
    Interesting settings ....( )4   Different/original........................( )4   Unrealistic ....( )4
    Too slow in parts................( )5   Not my kind of movie ....( )5   Educational ....( )5
    Offensive ....( )6   Controversial ....( )6   Nothing new/done before................( )6
    Confusing...............................( )7   Moved just right ....( )7   Thought provoking..........................( )7
    Interesting characters ....( )8   Humorous...................................( )8   Too predictable ....( )8
    Too silly/stupid...................( )9   Good cast ....( )9   Believable..( )9
    Action packed......................( )0   In bad taste ....( )0   Depressing.......................................( )0

14. Would you pay to see this movie again?   Yes...( )1   No..( )2

2.1 **Exercises**

Basic Concepts

1. What are the two fundamental problems of measurement?

2. When measurements are used to help solve a problem, what desirable characteristics should the measurements possess?

3. Name and briefly describe three measurement systems commonly used in business.

4. When you encounter any type of data, what three questions should you ask to determine the quality of the measurements?

5. What is the scientific method?

6. What is a confounding variable?

7. How does statistics interact with the steps in the scientific method?

8. Name and briefly describe the two main branches of statistics.

9. What is the decision-making method?

10. What is different between the scientific method and the decision-making method?

11. Are problems that can be solved by collecting data always the result of a system malfunction? Explain.

12. Give an example of how statistics can be used to improve a process.

13. What are fuzzy concepts? What are the measurement problems associated with fuzzy concepts?

14. Give an example of a tool that has been widely accepted as an instrument used to measure a fuzzy concept.

15. What are the two ways of obtaining data?

16. What are the dangers of making conclusions based on poorly collected data?

17. How do you treat the problem of a confounding variable?

18. Explain the difference between the control group and the experimental group in a controlled experiment.

19. What is an explanatory variable?

20. What is a response variable?

21. What is bias? How can it be controlled?

22. What is a completely randomized design? What are the advantages of using a completely randomized design?

23. What is a before and after study?

24. What is the placebo effect? Give an example.

25. What is a double-blind study?

26. How do observational studies differ from controlled experiments?

27. What kinds of problems can be associated with an observational study?

28. Researchers use surveys for two main purposes. Name and give an example of each.

Exercises

29. Specify whether the following variables are well-defined or not. Justify your answer.

   a. Height   **c.** Hot   **e.** Beauty

   b. Weight   **d.** Temperature

30. A researcher has developed a test that reportedly measures intelligence. The test includes questions such as:

What is the lowest common denominator of the fractions $\frac{5}{32}$ *and* $\frac{6}{9}$?

Who invented the digital computer?

Is it reasonable to measure intelligence with these questions? Discuss.

31. A hotel manager is interested in getting feedback from guests. Two variables of interest to the manager are cleanliness and aesthetics of the rooms. Discuss what problems you would encounter when measuring those variables.

32. Suppose you want to determine the proportion of college students in the state of Virginia that pay more than $500 per year on textbooks. Using the scientific method, how would you conduct the experiment?

33. The manager of an electronics company was interested in determining the reason for the increase in sales volume over the last three years. The manager randomly selected data on the advertising budget, number of salespeople, and average product costs. When examining the data, the manager found that her average product costs were fairly stable but the advertising budget steadily increased over the last two years along with the number of salespeople. Are there any confounding variables in this study? If so, what are they and why do you consider them confounding?

34. A company that produces bulbs for projectors wanted to conduct an experiment to determine the length of life of its bulbs. The company's leading competitor's bulbs have an average life of 1000 hours. The company sampled its bulbs and found that the average life of the bulbs was 1200 hours. Thus, the company has concluded and advertises that its bulbs last longer than the competition by at least 100 hours. Were the results of this experiment an example of descriptive or inferential statistics? Explain your answer.

35. The health and social problems associated with obesity can be a severe hindrance in attaining many of life's goals. Methods for treating obesity were compared in "One Year Behavioral Treatment of Obesity: Comparison of Moderate and Severe Caloric Restriction and the Effect of Weight Maintenance Therapy," in the *Journal of Consulting and Clinical Psychology*. In the study, a group of 25 women, each of whom was at least 25 kilograms (kg) overweight, were randomly split into two groups. The first group received behavior therapy and was placed on a 1200 calorie per day diet for a period of one year. The second group received behavior therapy and was placed on a 420 calorie per day diet for the first 16 weeks of the year. Then they returned to a 1200 calorie per day diet for the remainder of the year. At the end of a 26-week period, the average weight lost was 11.86 kg for the first group and 21.45 kg for the second group. But after 52 weeks, the average weight lost was 10.94 kg for the first group and 12.18 kg for the second group.

    a. Why is this study an example of a controlled experiment?

    b. What is the explanatory variable?

    c. What is the response variable?

    d. Is there a control group in the study? Explain.

    e. Suppose that the data was gathered from an observational study instead of from a controlled experiment. How would this affect the conclusions that might be made from the study?

36. An article appearing in the *New England Journal of Medicine* investigated whether the academic performance of asthmatic children being treated with the drug Theophylline was inferior to a non-asthmatic group. In one part of the study, 72 children were identified as being treated for asthma. For each child with asthma, a non-asthmatic sibling was also identified. (The use of sibling controls allows for control of family environment and certain genetic factors on academic achievement.) All 144 children were then given a test to measure academic achievement. There were no significant differences on the test between the two groups.

    a. Why is this study an example of a controlled experiment?

    b. What is the explanatory variable?

    c. What is the response variable?

    d. Is there a control group in the study? Explain.

    e. Suppose that the data was gathered from an observational study instead of from a controlled experiment. How would this affect the conclusions that might be made from the study?

37. A small clinical pilot study was conducted by a research team from Harvard Medical School and the School of Public Health. Fifteen individuals in the early stages of Multiple Sclerosis were fed bovine myelin, a substance containing two antigens thought to be the target of the immune system's attack in Multiple Sclerosis. Another fifteen were given a placebo. In the study, fewer members of the group fed bovine myelin had major attacks of the disease.[1]

    a. Which phase of the Scientific Method best describes this study?

    b. Is this an observational study or a controlled experiment?

    c. What is the response variable?

    d. What is the explanatory variable?

    e. Which group is the treatment group?

    f. Which group is the control group?

38. London scientists conducted a study to determine if chocolate can trigger migraines. Twelve migraine-prone subjects were given a peppermint-laced chocolate candy and eight migraine-prone subjects were given a peppermint-laced placebo made of carob, peppermint, and vegetable fat. Five subjects from the group given chocolate developed a migraine headache within one day. No one from the group given the placebo developed a migraine in the same time period.[2]

    a.   Which phase of the Scientific Method best describes this study?

    b.   Is this an observational study or a controlled experiment?

    c.   What is the response variable?

    d.   What is the explanatory variable?

    e.   Which group is the treatment group?

    f.   Which group is the control group?

39. Jacob normally plays basketball three days a week and has begun to develop patellar tendinitis, which is inflammation in the patellar tendon and results in nagging knee pain. In an effort to relieve his knee pain, Jacob decides to take a week away from playing basketball and rest his knee. However, after about four days, his friend offers him an analgesic rub and insists that his knee will feel better in two to three days. After using the analgesic rub for a couple of days, Jacob's knee begins to feel better. Did the analgesic rub work? Explain how confounding variables might have played a role on Jacob's knee getting better.

40. The Nurse's Health Study conducted on 87,245 women at Boston's Brigham and Women's Hospital revealed that women who eat a cup of beta carotene-rich food a day have 40 percent fewer strokes and 22 percent fewer heart attacks than those who consume a quarter of a cupful per day.[3]

    a.   Which phase of the Scientific Method best describes this study?

    b.   Is this an observational study or a controlled experiment?

    c.   What is the response variable?

    d.   What is the explanatory variable?

    e.   Which group is the treatment group?

    f.   Which group is the control group?

41. A religious group conducted a survey with two of the questions asking "Do you go to church?" and "Are you happy?" After conducting the survey, the group concluded that those who go to church are generally happier than those that do not go to church. Do you think going to church makes one happier? Describe how confounding variables could play a role with the conclusion drawn by the religious group.

42. In May 2011, Internet Explorer reversed its trend in the United States and gained usage share (the percentage of users using a particular Internet browser). In June of 2011, the trend reversal became global. Internet Explorer gained 0.57% in June across all operating systems with Internet Explorer 8.0 gaining 0.86% globally. The gains for Internet Explorer came primarily at the expense of Mozilla Firefox (−0.51%). Google Chrome's pace of usage

share gains slowed to +0.2% for June.[4] The gains for IE were the largest in Europe and Asia:

Internet Explorer in Europe: +0.88%

Internet Explorer in Asia: +0.81%

This increase may be the result of a marketing campaign. In early June, Microsoft launched their "Confidence" campaign aimed at showing the security features of Internet Explorer 8.

    a.   Are the results stated above likely to have come from an observational study?

    b.   How can Microsoft (and other companies) benefit from this information?

43. A survey was conducted by an investment firm asking participants the following questions: "Are you financially secure?" and "Do you independently make decisions about your investments?" After analyzing the data from the survey, the firm concluded that people who make investment decisions independently tend to be not as financially secure as those who make decisions with the help of an investment advisor. What confounding variables could have played a role in this conclusion?

2.2   **Data Classification**

Data or variables can be categorized in several ways:

- discrete or continuous
- level of measurement
- quantitative or qualitative

Since the kind of data available affects the types of analyses that can be performed, it is important to recognize data attributes.

Discrete and Continuous Data

Suppose that observations are taken on two variables: the number of brothers and sisters (siblings) that a child has and the height of the child. In looking at the data, one difference is that the number of brothers and sisters are whole numbers, whereas the heights of children are decimal-valued. Since it is impossible for a family to have 3.167 children, or any fractional number for that matter, there are gaps in the values that the variable "Number of siblings" can assume.

Number of siblings	2	3	5	2	6
Height of child	40.12	44.64	51.27	47.08	59.51

The sibling data in the table is **discrete**. While the data representing siblings can only assume integer values, it would be misleading to create the impression that a discrete variable can only assume integer values. Discrete data may assume decimal values. For example, a variable that takes only the values 1, 1.5, 2, 2.5 is discrete.

> **Discrete**
>
> Data in which the observations are restricted to a set of values (such as 1, 2, 3, 4) that possess gaps is called **discrete**.
>
> DEFINITION

The height data in the table is **continuous**. It may appear that the heights of children are discrete, since values appear to only take on values up to the second decimal place. However, it is only the inadequacy of the measuring instrument that creates the illusion. The first height is listed as 40.12 inches, but the actual height of the first child may be 40.119723412... inches. If the measuring device can only detect differences in the hundredth place, then all measurements will be given to the hundredth place. Any digits beyond the hundredth place will be ignored. But just because these digits are ignored doesn't mean they don't exist.

> **Continuous**
>
> Data that can take on any value within some interval is called **continuous**.
>
> DEFINITION

Level of Measurement

Like most things in life, data comes in different qualities. Some measurements are purely numerical and are based on well-defined standards, such as pounds, inches, dollars, and percentages. On the other hand, some measurements are exceedingly *fuzzy* and the standard of measure is ill-defined, if at all. For example, consider the response to the following evaluation:

What is your opinion of the musicians's performance?

1–very disappointing 2–disappointing 3–satisfactory 4–good 5–extraordinary

Someone's *good* response may be equal to someone else's *extraordinary*. There can be no guarantee of a common scale and thus the level of consistency between measurements is unreliable. This type of data is very fuzzy and of much lower quality than measurements on some standard scale, such as pounds or inches.

> **Level of Measurement**
>
> The quality of data is referred to as its **level of measurement**.
>
> DEFINITION

Note

When analyzing data you must be exceedingly conscious of the data's level of measurement because many statistical analyses can only be applied to data that possess a certain level of measurement.

The terms used to describe the quality of data are nominal, ordinal, interval, and ratio.

Because of different levels of measurement, not all data is created equally. Unfortunately, once data is in numerical form, many believe that a number is a number is a number. And everyone knows that you can add, subtract, multiply, and divide numbers. But for some measurements, adding, subtracting, multiplying, and dividing are simply meaningless.

Standard mathematical operations (such as addition and subtraction) are not defined for nominal and ordinal data, and consequently, many forms of statistical analysis (descriptive and inferential) are not appropriate.

Nominal Data

Nominal scales are categorical. Each subject belongs to one category. For example, sex (male or female) and hair color (blond, brunette, or redhead) are examples of nominal variables. If the sex variable is coded numerically, say female = 1, male = 0, then what do the numbers mean?

Nominal

Data that represents whether a variable possesses some characteristic is called **nominal**.

DEFINITION

Is it meaningful to add, subtract, multiply, or divide these numbers? Let's try addition:

$$1 \quad + \quad 0 \quad = \quad 1$$
$$\text{female} \quad + \quad \text{male} \quad = \quad \text{female}$$

Is it meaningful to add a female and a male and get a female? If it is, it is certainly a bizarre interpretation.

Let's try subtraction.

$$1 \quad - \quad 0 \quad = \quad 1$$
$$\text{female} \quad - \quad \text{male} \quad = \quad \text{female}$$

Is it meaningful to subtract a male from a female and get a female? If this kind of mathematics works, it doesn't say a lot for males!

Similarly absurd conclusions can be reached for multiplication and division. For strictly nominal data, none of the arithmetic operators can be applied. Statistically speaking, only some graphical and a very few numerical statistical procedures can be applied to nominal data.

Ordinal Data

Ordinal data allows for ranking of the data values. For example, consider a response to the fill in the blank question.

Frosty Pops taste _____.

1–very bad   2–bad   3–fair   4–good   5–very good

Ordinal Data

Ordinal data represents categories that have some associated order.

DEFINITION

These responses are ordered on the basis of an individual's impression of the goodness of Frosty Pops. The response *bad* is perceived to be better than *very bad*, and *good* better than *fair*, and so forth. If numerical codes are used to represent the responses, should the properties of addition, subtraction, multiplication, and division be applied to them? Let's try addition.

$$1 \quad + \quad 1 \quad + \quad 1 \quad + \quad 1 \quad + \quad 1 \quad = \quad 5$$
$$\text{very bad} + \text{very bad} + \text{very bad} + \text{very bad} + \text{very bad} = \text{very good}$$

Get Out of Here Aristotle

"Aristotle maintained that women have fewer teeth than men; although he was twice married it never occurred to him to verify this statement by examining his wives' mouths."
–Bertrand Russell

The Greek philosopher Aristotle held that one could develop all the laws that govern the universe by pure thought and that it was unnecessary to obtain measurements that would confirm the validity of these laws. Perhaps this explains why he never bothered to count his wives' teeth. The goal of Aristotelian science was to explain *why* things happen. Modern science was born when Galileo began trying to explain *how* things happen. Galileo's approach originated the method of controlled experiments which form the basis of scientific investigation. Controlled experiments yield data, and statistics allows people to think with that data. If Aristotle had been right, there wouldn't be a very large demand for statistics.

This means that if you thought that a Frosty Pop tasted *very bad* (1) you should eat five of them, and doing so would be equivalent to eating something that you thought was *very good* (5). Addition of ordinal values is not reasonable. And for that matter, neither is subtraction, division, and multiplication. So the only difference between ordinal and nominal data is that ordinal data possesses order. Here again, like nominal data, only a very limited number of statistical analyses can be performed.

Note that ordinal data is also nominal, but it also possesses the additional property of ordinality.

Interval Data

> ### Interval
>
> If the data can be ordered and the arithmetic difference is meaningful, the data is **interval**.
>
> DEFINITION

One example of interval data is temperature (measured on the Fahrenheit scale).

$$48 \text{ degrees } - 45 \text{ degrees } = 3 \text{ degrees}$$
$$72 \text{ degrees } - 69 \text{ degrees } = 3 \text{ degrees}$$

In the case above, the difference between the temperatures is three degrees, and it is true that the difference in kinetic energy between 48 and 45 degrees is the same as the difference between 72 and 69 degrees.

Interval data also has another interesting property, an arbitrary zero value, or in other words, a zero value that was defined as such for no particular reason. You don't have to be a mathematician to appreciate the usual meaning of the zero concept, having zero dollars means that you do not have any money. However, a temperature of zero degrees on the Celsius or Fahrenheit scales does not mean there is no kinetic energy, and thus in the case of temperature, zero has been arbitrarily selected. In fact, the Celsius temperature scale places the value of zero at a temperature equivalent to 32 degrees Fahrenheit.

One implication of an arbitrary zero point is that the ratio of two variables has no meaning. For example, the kinetic energy associated with a temperature of four degrees on the Fahrenheit scale is not twice so great as the kinetic energy associated with a temperature of two degrees. The property that distinguishes interval data is the notion that equal intervals represent equal amounts. For example, the interval between four degrees and one degree represents the same difference in kinetic energy as the difference between 71 degrees and 74 degrees.

Interval data is numerical data that possesses both the property of ordinality and the interval property.

Ratio Data

> ### Ratio Data
>
> **Ratio data** is similar to interval data, except that it has a meaningful zero value.
>
> DEFINITION

The operations of addition, subtraction, multiplication, and division are reasonable on ratio data. Many of the variables we commonly encounter are ratio variables: volumes, heights, weights, pressure. Being aware of the data's level of measurement is an extremely important part of any statistical analysis, since many statistical measures that are meaningful for interval and ratio data are not meaningful for ordinal and nominal measurements.

Example 2.2.1

Is money a ratio variable?

Say a friend had $40 and you had $20.

$$\frac{\$40}{\$20} = 2$$

According to the ratio we just computed your friend has twice as much money as you. Is this really true? Money is a ratio variable because ratios (quotients) are meaningful. If someone does have $40 and you have $20, they do have twice as much money as you.

Qualitative and Quantitative Data

Data is sometimes categorized as qualitative or quantitative.

Qualitative

Qualitative data is measured on a nominal or ordinal scale.

DEFINITION

Quantitative

Quantitative data is measured on an interval or ratio scale.

DEFINITION

2.2   **Exercises**

Basic Concepts

1. What is qualitative data? Give an example.

2. What is quantitative data? Give an example.

3. Which levels of measurement are associated with qualitative data? Which levels are associated with quantitative data?

4. What is the difference between discrete and continuous data?

5. What is a level of measurement?

6. What are the four levels of measurement? Give an example of each.

7. For which level(s) of measurement is arithmetic appropriate?

8. What is the primary difference between nominal and ordinal data?

9. What is an arbitrary zero value? Which level of measurement has this property?

10. What is the fundamental difference between interval and ratio data?

Exercises

11. Identify the following variables as discrete or continuous.

    a. The number of doctors who wash their hands between patient visits.

    b. The amount of liquid consumed by the average American each day.

    c. The weight of a newborn baby at a local hospital.

    d. The time it takes a person to react to a stimulus.

    e. The number of voters who favor a particular candidate.

12. Identify the following variables as discrete or continuous.

    a. The number of on-time flights at the Hartsfield-Jackson International Airport in Atlanta.

    b. The height of skyscrapers in New York City.

    c. The price of General Electric's common stock.

    d. The temperature of US cities.

    e. The number of alcoholics who are men.

13. The results of a study investigating the nutritional status of mid-nineteenth century Americans were reported in "The Height and Weight of West Point Cadets: Dietary Changes in Antebellum America," in the *Journal of Economic History*. The data is based upon physical examination lists for West Point applicants from 1843 to 1894. Some of the information obtained from each cadet were his height, weight, the state from which the cadet was appointed, the occupation of the father, the income of the parents, and the type of home residence (city, town, or rural) of the cadet.

    a. List the different variables measured on the cadets.

    b. Which variables are quantitative and which are qualitative?

    c. Give the levels of measurement for these variables.

    d. Why is some method of data summary necessary here?

14. The major television networks regularly conduct polls in order to ascertain the feelings of Americans on current political issues. In May of 1993, such a poll was conducted by ABC concerning United States involvement in Bosnia. The respondent's gender, political affiliation, and opinion (approve, disapprove, or no opinion) on how President Clinton was handling the situation in Bosnia represented some of the information supplied by the respondent on the survey. Each respondent was also asked to rate the job that the news media had done (excellent, good, not so good, poor) in covering the situation in Bosnia.

    a. List the different variables measured on the respondents.

b. Which variables are quantitative and which are qualitative?

c. Give the levels of measurement for these variables.

d. What are some problems associated with collecting data in polls such as the one described in this exercise?

15. Under most states' auto lemon laws, dealers or car makers must replace defective autos that aren't successfully repaired after three attempts or that remain in the shop for 30 days. The table below shows data for Hawaii for the year 2010, weighing car makers' lemons against statewide market share.[5] Assume the "lemon index" is the share of the complaints divided by the total market share for each manufacturer.

Lemon Index: Hawaii, 2010			
Best	**Lemon Index**	**Worst**	**Lemon Index**
Toyota (includes Lexus)	0.212	Chrysler (includes Dodge and Jeep)	6.512
Honda	0.462	Kia	2.750
Ford (includes Lincoln)	0.868	GM (includes Chevrolet, GMC, Buick)	2.375
Nissan (includes Infinity)	1.056	BMW	2.129
Mazda	1.833	Hyundai	2.000

Answer the following questions for the variable "Lemon Index."

a. Is the data quantitative or qualitative? Why?

b. What is the highest level of measurement the data could have?

16. Determine the level of measurement (nominal, ordinal, interval, or ratio) for each of the following variables.

a. The temperature (in degrees Fahrenheit) of patients with pneumonia.

b. The age at which the average male marries.

c. Client satisfaction survey responses: Poor, Average, Good, and Excellent.

d. The region of the U.S. in which an individual lives: North, South, East, or West.

e. The number of people with a Type A personality.

17. Determine the level of measurement (nominal, ordinal, interval, or ratio) for each of the following variables.

a. The time it takes for a student to complete an exam.

b. Majors of randomly selected students at a university.

c. The category which best describes how frequently a person eats chocolate: Frequently, Occasionally, Seldom, Never.

d. The number of pounds of snack food eaten by an individual in his or her lifetime.

18. Given the table below on browser usage, what is the highest level of measurement that the data could have? Justify your answer.

Browser Usage Share (%)				
Month	Google Chrome	Mozilla Firefox	Internet Explorer/ Microsoft Edge	Apple Safari
January 2016	68.4	18.8	6.2	3.7
February 2016	69.0	18.6	6.2	3.7
March 2016	69.9	17.8	6.1	3.6
April 2016	70.4	17.5	5.8	3.7
May 2016	71.4	16.9	5.7	3.6
June 2016	71.7	17.0	5.6	3.3
July 2016	71.9	17.1	5.2	3.2
August 2016	72.4	16.8	5.2	3.2
September 2016	72.5	16.3	5.3	3.5
October 2016	73.0	15.7	5.2	3.6
November 2016	73.8	15.3	5.2	3.5
December 2016	73.7	15.5	4.8	3.5

2.3 Time Series Data vs. Cross-Sectional Data

Time Series Data

Recall from Chapter 1, the science of statistics is divided into two categories: descriptive statistics and inferential statistics. Fundamental to the concept of statistical inference is the notion of population – the total collection of measurements.

Time Series

Time series data originates as measurements usually taken from some process over equally spaced intervals of time.

DEFINITION

Because measurements are taken over time, the concept of a population gets a little blurry. Suppose we want to examine the divorce rate in the United States since 1895. What is the population we are studying?

Presumably the members of the population under study would be the residents of the United States. But in 1895 there were only about 65 million people in this country. Now there are over 323 million. Moreover, none of the 65 million that were around in 1895 are alive today, so the population from which the divorce data is drawn is certainly not fixed. In addition, cultural and sociological conditions that prevailed in 1895 were substantially different from those today. Why is this important? If a population doesn't contain a fixed set of members or subjects, how can inferences be made about it? The concept of population is not sufficiently broad to cope with time series measurements.[6]

Table 2.3.1 - Divorce Rate in the U.S. 1900–2015 (per 1000 Total Population)			
Year	Divorce Rate	Year	Divorce Rate
1900	0.7	1996	4.3
1905	0.8	1997	4.3
1910	0.9	1998	4.2
1915	1.0	1999	4.1
1920	1.6	2000	4.0
1925	1.5	2001	4.0
1930	1.6	2002	3.9
1935	1.7	2003	3.8
1940	2.0	2004	3.7
1945	3.5	2005	3.6
1950	2.6	2006	3.7
1955	2.3	2007	3.6
1960	2.2	2008	3.5
1965	2.5	2009	3.5
1970	3.5	2010	3.6
1975	4.8	2011	3.6
1980	5.2	2012	3.4
1985	5.0	2013	3.3
1990	4.7	2014	3.2
1995	4.4	2015	3.1

Time series data originates from processes. Processes can be divided into two categories: stationary and nonstationary. All time series that are interesting vary, and the nature of the variability determines how the process is characterized. In a **stationary process** the time series varies around some central value and has approximately the same variation over the series. In a **nonstationary process** the time series possesses a **trend** — the tendency for the series to either increase or decrease over time.

Example 2.3.1

A batting average represents the percentage of the time a player gets on base as a result of a hit. In major league baseball the better players have batting averages between .300 and .400, which means they get on base as a result of a hit between 30% and 40% of the time. The following table is a list of the batting average champions of the American League since 1970.[7] Glancing at a plot of the data suggests the conditions for stationary seem to be met. The time series seems to be wobbling around a central value and the dispersion around the central value is reasonably constant throughout the series. Thus, the series appears to be stationary.

American League Batting Champions Batting Average					
Year	Player	BA	Year	Player	BA
1970	Alex Johnson	0.329	1994	Paul O'Neill	0.359
1971	Tony Oliva	0.337	1995	Edgar Martinez	0.356
1972	Rod Carew	0.318	1996	Alex Rodriguez	0.358
1973	Rod Carew	0.350	1997	Frank Thomas	0.347
1974	Rod Carew	0.364	1998	Bernie Williams	0.339
1975	Rod Carew	0.359	1999	Nomar Garciaparra	0.357
1976	George Brett	0.333	2000	Nomar Garciaparra	0.372
1977	Rod Carew	0.388	2001	Ichiro Suzuki	0.350
1978	Rod Carew	0.333	2002	Manny Ramirez	0.349
1979	Fred Lynn	0.333	2003	Bill Mueller	0.326
1980	George Brett	0.390	2004	Ichiro Suzuki	0.372
1981	Carney Lansford	0.336	2005	Michael Young	0.331
1982	Willie Wilson	0.332	2006	Joe Mauer	0.347
1983	Wade Boggs	0.361	2007	Magglio Ordóñez	0.363
1984	Don Mattingly	0.343	2008	Joe Mauer	0.328
1985	Wade Boggs	0.368	2009	Joe Mauer	0.365
1986	Wade Boggs	0.357	2010	Josh Hamilton	0.359
1987	Wade Boggs	0.363	2011	Miguel Cabrera	0.344
1988	Wade Boggs	0.366	2012	Miguel Cabrera	0.330
1989	Kirby Puckett	0.339	2013	Miguel Cabrera	0.348
1990	George Brett	0.329	2014	José Altuve	0.341
1991	Julio Franco	0.341	2015	Miguel Cabrera	0.338
1992	Edgar Martinez	0.343	2016	José Altuve	0.338
1993	John Olerud	0.363	2017	José Altuve	0.346

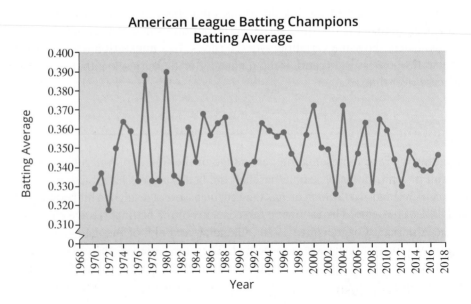

American League Batting Champions Batting Average

Example 2.3.2

Look at the wildfire data in the following table. The variation in the data, graphed below, seems to be increasing over time, and the central value around which those variations occur is also increasing. Thus the series seems to meet the conditions of a nonstationary series.[8]

Acres Burned by Wildfires			
Year	Acres	Year	Acres
1983	1,323,666	2000	7,393,493
1984	1,148,409	2001	3,570,911
1985	2,896,147	2002	7,184,712
1986	2,719,162	2003	3,960,842
1987	2,447,296	2004	8,097,880
1988	5,009,290	2005	8,689,389
1989	1,827,310	2006	9,873,745
1990	4,621,621	2007	9,328,045
1991	2,953,578	2008	5,292,468
1992	2,069,929	2009	5,921,786
1993	1,797,574	2010	3,422,724
1994	4,073,579	2011	8,711,367
1995	1,840,546	2012	9,326,238
1996	6,065,998	2013	4,319,546
1997	2,856,959	2014	3,595,613
1998	1,329,704	2015	10,125,149
1999	5,626,093	2016	5,509,995

Acres Burned (in Millions of Acres)

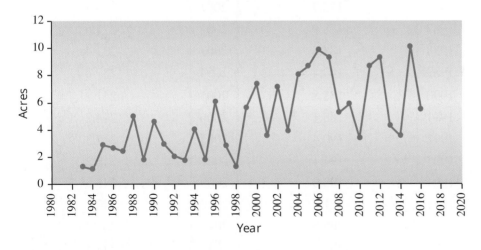

Example 2.3.3

Look at the divorce rate data in Table 2.3.1 at the beginning of the section. The graphed data in the figure below suggests that there is strong evidence of an upward trend until about 1980, and then the data begins to trend downward after 1980.

However, the data never seems to gravitate towards a central value, thus the time series is nonstationary. (**Note:** this data is not affected by population increases over the years since it is given in divorces per 1000 total population residing in the country.)

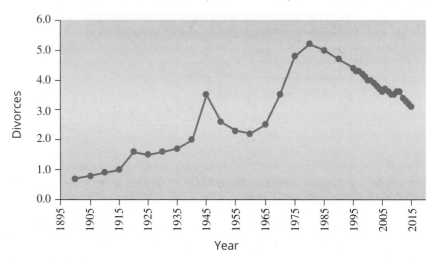

Divorces per 1000 People

Example 2.3.4

The U.S. is a large country that depends greatly on the use of automobiles for transportation. Let's look at the data on automobile registration and see if there are any trends.[9]

Vehicle Registration in the U.S. 1985–2014			
Year	Number of Vehicles (in millions)	Year	Number of Vehicles (in millions)
1985	171.7	2000	221.5
1986	175.7	2001	230.4
1987	178.9	2002	229.6
1988	184.4	2003	231.4
1989	187.4	2004	237.2
1990	188.8	2005	241.2
1991	188.1	2006	244.2
1992	190.4	2007	247.3
1993	194.1	2008	248.2
1994	198.0	2009	246.3
1995	201.5	2010	242.1
1996	206.6	2011	253.2
1997	207.8	2012	253.6
1998	211.6	2013	255.9
1999	216.3	2014	260.4

The graph below reveals an obvious upward trend in vehicle registration. The trend is probably attributable to population increases during the period.

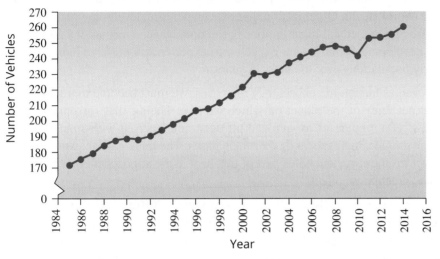

US Motor Vehicle Registration (in millions)

Data Resources

We live in a data rich society. Anyone with access to a personal computer can access thousands of different databases throughout the internet. These databases are packed full of observational data.

The companion site for this textbook, stat.hawkeslearning.com, provides numerous links to data resources. However, some of the largest, most credible, and most commonly used databases are:

- The World Bank
- World Health Organization
- Data.gov (Data regarding the U.S.)
- Organisation of Economic Cooperation and Development (OECD)
- UNdata (United Nations)
- The CIA World Factbook
- Amazon Web Services

Cross-Sectional Data

Cross-Sectional Data

Cross-sectional data are measurements created at approximately the same period of time.

DEFINITION

For example, consider the life expectancy at birth in 2015 for selected countries given in Table 2.3.2.[10]

Table 2.3.2 - Life Expectancy at Birth 2015	
Country	**Life Expectancy**
Afghanistan	61
Australia	83
Botswana	66
Egypt	71
Guatemala	72
Japan	84
Kenya	63
Sierra Leone	46
Spain	83
Sri Lanka	75
Sweden	82
United Kingdom	81
United States	79

The data represents cross-sectional measurements since the measurements were made in the same time period (2015). People in Japan are expected to live on the average until age 84, about 5 years longer than the average for Americans. Developed countries such as Australia and the United States generally have higher life expectancies than developing countries such as Sri Lanka and Kenya. But according to the World Health Organization, life expectancies in developing countries are on the rise due to medical interventions based on advanced technology and drugs. In fact, developing countries are expected to experience a massive increase in their elderly populations over the next 25 years.

However, as human life expectancy increases, we must become more aware of the life expectancy of the planet on which we live. The air that surrounds the earth consists of a mixture of oxygen and nitrogen, interspersed with small amounts of carbon dioxide, methane, and other trace gases. The trace gases capture heat as the sun warms the earth and holds part of that heat in the atmosphere in what is known as the "greenhouse effect."

These gases prevent the sun's heat from simply hitting the ground and being re-channeled back into space. For most of the last several thousand years, the earth's greenhouse gases have been stable. The most abundant trace gas, carbon dioxide, was processed by plants and maritime organisms at approximately the same rate as it was given off by other organisms, until about the time of the Industrial Revolution starting in the late 18th century. The natural world's ability to absorb carbon dioxide has been unable to keep up, and consequently the level of carbon dioxide in the atmosphere has been rising. A time series of annual increases in the atmosphere of major greenhouse gases reveals a disturbing trend.[11]

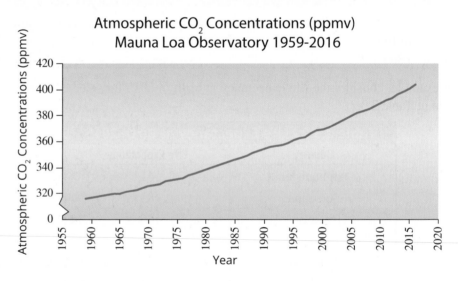

The U.S. produces about 15% of the world's carbon dioxide. Table 2.3.3 shows the greenhouse emissions of each state on a per capita basis sorted from the highest emissions to the lowest.[12] However, the data in the table below can lead to some confusing conclusions. Are the people of Wyoming really the largest contributors to the US CO_2 levels? And are the people of California and New York really the least CO_2 polluting? Both conclusions seem very unlikely. So, what might be confounding the data as presented? The state of Wyoming as a whole produces an average amount of greenhouse emissions. However, it is the least populous state in the country, thus driving up the emissions per capita. Conversely, the state of California produces the second most greenhouse emissions of any state (behind Texas), but it is also the most populous state in the nation. This causes the emissions per capita to be a much smaller number. Population size is confounding the data in the table. So, how might you reasonably compare two states?

Table 2.3.3 - CO_2 Emissions per Capita by State (in metric tons) 2014			
State	**CO_2 Emissions per Capita**	**State**	**CO_2 Emissions per Capita**
Wyoming	111.55	Colorado	16.95
North Dakota	74.81	Michigan	16.31
West Virginia	52.47	Tennessee	15.69
Alaska	47.17	South Carolina	15.39
Louisiana	44.50	Delaware	14.24
Montana	31.51	Arizona	13.79
Kentucky	31.19	Georgia	13.76
Indiana	30.81	Nevada	13.02
Nebraska	27.51	Hawaii	12.82
Oklahoma	26.92	New Jersey	12.78
Iowa	26.78	North Carolina	12.64
Texas	26.29	Maine	12.52
Alabama	25.05	Virginia	12.42
New Mexico	24.07	Florida	11.41
Kansas	23.97	New Hampshire	11.25
Arkansas	23.13	Washington	10.40
Utah	21.90	Maryland	10.38
Missouri	21.66	Idaho	10.18
Mississippi	21.28	Rhode Island	10.08
Ohio	19.75	Connecticut	9.77
Pennsylvania	18.94	Oregon	9.56
Illinois	18.12	Massachusetts	9.49
South Dakota	17.91	Vermont	9.38
Wisconsin	17.47	California	9.26
Minnesota	17.24	New York	8.61

2.3   Exercises

Basic Concepts

1. What are time series measurements?

2. What problems are associated with the concept of population when studying time series data?

3. What is a stationary process?

4. What is a nonstationary process?

5. What is a trend? If a time series has an 'upward trend' what does this mean?

6. What is cross-sectional data?

7. What is the difference between cross-sectional data and time series data?

Exercises

8. Consider the following graph of long-term interest rates (10-year treasury notes) and inflation rates:[13]

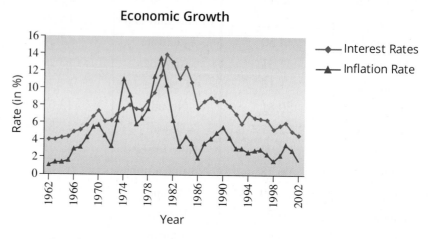

a. Are the long-term interest rates presented above time series or cross-sectional data?

b. Are the inflation rates presented above time series or cross-sectional data?

c. For each of parts **a.** and **b.**, if the data is time series data, does it appear to be stationary or nonstationary?

9. Consider the following graph of total exports.[14]

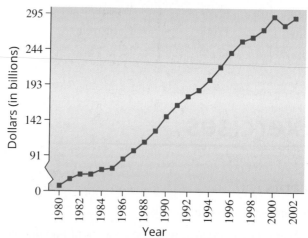

a. Is the data time series or cross-sectional?

b. If the data is time series data, does it appear to be stationary or nonstationary?

10. The following table shows the annual average crude oil price from 1946 through 2011.[15] Prices are adjusted for inflation to April 2011 prices using the Consumer Price Index (CPI-U) as presented by the Bureau of Labor Statistics. Inflation adjusted prices were at an all-time high in 1980, reaching $102.26 dollars per barrel. Crude oil prices reached an all-time low in 1998 (lower than the price in 1946!) when the price per barrel dipped to $16.44. Using the data in the table, discuss if the data set contains time series or cross-sectional data. Also, discuss the data and make some inferences. That is, can you explain some of the fluctuations in the oil prices?

Annual Average Domestic Crude Oil Prices ($ per Barrel)					
Year	Nominal	Inflation Adjusted (April 2011)	Year	Nominal	Inflation Adjusted (April 2011)
1946	1.63	18.49	1979	25.10	77.05
1947	2.16	21.73	1980	37.42	102.26
1948	2.77	25.92	1981	35.75	88.55
1949	2.77	26.17	1982	31.83	74.24
1950	2.77	25.90	1983	29.08	65.69
1951	2.77	24.00	1984	28.75	62.26
1952	2.77	23.47	1985	26.92	56.28
1953	2.92	24.50	1986	14.44	29.62
1954	2.99	25.04	1987	17.75	35.13
1955	2.93	24.57	1988	14.87	28.32
1956	2.94	24.35	1989	18.33	33.24
1957	3.14	25.12	1990	23.19	39.80
1958	3.00	23.38	1991	20.20	33.36
1959	3.00	23.15	1992	19.25	30.85
1960	2.91	22.15	1993	16.75	26.09
1961	2.85	21.44	1994	15.66	23.76
1962	2.85	21.19	1995	16.75	24.73
1963	2.91	21.39	1996	20.46	29.32
1964	3.00	21.75	1997	18.64	26.12
1965	3.01	21.47	1998	11.91	16.44
1966	3.10	21.48	1999	16.56	22.30
1967	3.12	21.04	2000	27.39	35.76
1968	3.18	20.53	2001	23.00	29.23
1969	3.32	20.36	2002	22.81	28.50
1970	3.39	19.65	2003	27.69	33.86
1971	3.60	20.00	2004	37.66	44.81
1972	3.60	21.44	2005	50.04	57.57
1973	4.75	23.87	2006	58.30	65.03
1974	9.35	42.58	2007	64.20	69.51
1975	12.21	51.00	2008	91.48	95.25

Annual Average Domestic Crude Oil Prices ($ per Barrel)					
Year	Nominal	Inflation Adjusted (April 2011)	Year	Nominal	Inflation Adjusted (April 2011)
1976	13.10	51.78	2009	53.48	55.96
1977	14.40	53.41	2010	71.21	73.44
1978	14.95	51.58	2011 (Partial)	86.84	–

11. Do you think the pay of executives working for digital companies increases/ decreases as the company's stock price increases/decreases? Examine the following table.[16]

CEO Compensation and Stock Performance						
Exec	Salary/ Bonus ($)	Stock/ Options ($)	Other Non-Equity Compensation ($)	Total 2007 Compensation ($)	Change from 2006 Compensation (%)	2007 Stock Performance (%)
Tom Rogers (Tivo)	800,000	6,200,000	495,075	7,495,075	+102	+32
Mel Karmazin (Sirius)	5,250,000	–	18,743	5,268,743	+23	−23
Paul Sagan (Akamai)	403,651	3,554,264	497,362	4,455,277	−40	−48
Reed Hastings (Netflix)	850,000	1,568,307	270	2,418,577	+5	−6
Rob Glaser (RealNetworks)	1,169,384	643,400	354,200	2,166,984	−26	−45
Bobby Kotick (Activision Blizzard)	899,560	1,188,467	–	2,088,027	+6	+49
Magid M. Abraham (comScore)	421,952	1,125,000	–	1,546,952	+185	−16
Barry Diller (IAC)	500,000	–	927,429	1,427,429	+270	+21
John S. Riccitiello (Electronic Arts)	750,000	–	625,350	1,375,350	−37	−38
Steve Ballmer (Microsoft)	1,340,833	–	10,001	1,350,834	N/A	0
Wayne T. Gattinella (WebMD)	830,000	–	9214	839,214	+6	+10

What type of data is in the Salary/Bonus column? What do you think about executive salaries as a function of the company's stock performance? Justify your responses.

CR   **Chapter Review**

Key Terms and Ideas

- The Scientific Method
- Confounding Variable
- The Decision-Making Method
- Fuzzy Concepts
- Observational Experiment
- Controlled Experiment
- Control Group
- Experimental Group
- Treatment
- Explanatory Variable
- Response Variable
- Completely Randomized Design
- Before and After Study
- The Placebo Effect
- Double-Blind Study
- Observational Study
- Bias

- Simpson's Paradox
- Surveys
- Level of Measurement
- Nominal Data
- Ordinal Data
- Interval Data
- Ratio Data
- Qualitative Data
- Quantitative Data
- Discrete Data
- Continuous Data
- Time Series Data
- Stationary Process
- Nonstationary Process
- Trend
- Cross-Sectional Data

Additional Exercises

1. Suppose you were the administrator of a public school system. What kinds of variables would you measure and how would you collect the measurements on the following subjects:

    a. Student learning

    b. School discipline

    c. Teacher preparation

    d. Absenteeism (pupil and teacher)

    e. Cafeteria food quality

2. The head of the Veterans Administration has been receiving complaints from a Vietnam Veterans organization concerning disability checks. The organization claims that checks are continually late. The checks are to arrive no later than the tenth of each month.

    a. What variables would you measure to explore this problem?

    b. How would you collect measurements on these variables?

3. A family member has unexpectedly bequeathed you a sizable sum of money.

    a. What criteria might you wish to evaluate in deciding how to invest the money?

    b. What data might be useful in your considerations?

4. Flying Eagle Airlines advertises that it surpasses all other airlines in flights that arrive on time. A competitor states that it has a better on-time record than any other airline. Can they both be correct? Explain.

5. Two local grocery stores both claim to have the lowest prices in town. Develop a measurement that you believe could be used as a criterion to determine which store actually has the lowest prices.

6. At the end of 2001, the United States had 32.9 million people living in poverty according to the Census Bureau (www.census.gov). This was an increase of 1.3 million from the previous year. Poverty was defined by the Census Bureau as having a cash income less than $14,255 a year. The Census Bureau does not include in their income measurement any part of $167 billion spent on Medicaid, a federal program by which medical care is provided to the poor. The Census Bureau only includes $34.9 billion out of the $205 billion spent annually on public welfare. Forty percent of those classified as impoverished own their own homes. How do you think poverty should be defined?

7. The quality movement has compelled American businesses to address the problem of measuring customer satisfaction. How would you measure customer satisfaction if you owned a car dealership?

8. Identify the following variables as discrete or continuous.

    a. Average test score on a test ranging from 0 to 100

    b. Number of boot errors on a computer

    c. Investment ratios for earnings per share

    d. Energy usage in a production process

9. Determine the level of measurement for each of the following variables.

    a. Golf score in relation to par

    b. SAT score

    c. Rating from 1 to 5 of quality of service in a restaurant

    d. Make and model of a vehicle

    e. The number of students with a business major

10. According to a Danish researcher, if you drop your average daily activity level by taking elevators instead of stairs, by parking your car in the closest space, or by never walking to run errands, you increase your risk of diabetes, heart disease, and premature death. The researcher studied two groups of healthy men (eight in the first group with an average age of 27 and an average body mass index (BMI) of 22.9, which is well within the normal range; and ten in the second group with an average age of 23.8 years and a BMI of 22.1). In addition to age and BMI, researchers also collected information such as number of steps per day (each group of men was fitted with pedometers), height, weight, and race. With the first group of men, the researchers asked that they reduce their daily activity (steps) by taking cars on short trips and elevators instead of stairs. The insulin levels were also measured for each group and the researchers found that with the reduced activity, insulin levels rose by nearly 60 percent after two weeks of inactivity, thus increasing the risk of diabetes and heart disease. However, the good news is that by increasing activity over a two-week period of time, one can begin to reduce his or her risk of diabetes and heart disease.[17]

  a. List the different variables measured in this study.

  b. Which variables are quantitative and which are qualitative?

  c. Of the variables that are quantitative, are they discrete or continuous?

  d. Give the levels of measurement for these variables.

  e. Why is some method of data summary necessary here?

11. Consider the world production of crude oil given in millions of barrels per day.[18]

World Production of Crude Oil			
Year	Total World Production (Millions of Barrels per Day)	Year	Total World Production (Millions of Barrels per Day)
1980	63.987	1995	70.274
1981	60.602	1996	71.919
1982	58.098	1997	74.160
1983	57.934	1998	75.656
1984	59.568	1999	74.853
1985	59.172	2000	77.768
1986	61.407	2001	77.686
1987	62.086	2002	76.994
1988	64.380	2003	79.598
1989	65.508	2004	83.105
1990	66.426	2005	84.595
1991	66.399	2006	84.661
1992	66.564	2007	84.543
1993	67.091	2008	85.507
1994	68.590	2009	84.389

  a. What is the level of measurement of the data?

  b. Is the data time series or cross-sectional? If the data is time series, plot the data. Does the series appear to be stationary or nonstationary? Explain your answer.

12. Consider the graph of the number of respondents (in percentages) who think things in the U.S. are now on the wrong track versus those that think the economy is going in the right direction. The data was collected using a survey asking the question, *In general, are you satisfied or dissatisfied with the way things are going in the United States at this time?*[19]

Right Direction or Wrong Track?

a. Are the opinions on the outlook of the economy presented in time series or cross-sectional data? Justify your answer.

b. If the data is time series data, does the series appear to be stationary or nonstationary? Explain your answer.

13. Can you think of a process that would yield measurements that did not have any variability? Would studying such a process be very interesting?

14. One of the measurements that population experts use in predicting trends in population growth is the fertility rate. The total fertility rate is sometimes defined as the number of likely births one woman will have in her lifetime. The accompanying table gives the fertility rate from 1934 to 2005.[20] If the data is time series data, plot the data in a line chart. Make observations based on the graph as to whether the series is stationary or nonstationary. If the time series is nonstationary, identify any noticeable trends.

Fertility Rates					
Year	**Fertility Rate**	**Year**	**Fertility Rate**	**Year**	**Fertility Rate**
1934	2.294	1958	3.693	1982	1.829
1935	2.250	1959	3.705	1983	1.803
1936	2.207	1960	3.654	1984	1.806
1937	2.236	1961	3.629	1985	1.843
1938	2.288	1962	3.474	1986	1.836
1939	2.238	1963	3.333	1987	1.871
1940	2.301	1964	3.208	1988	1.933
1941	2.399	1965	2.928	1989	1.977
1942	2.628	1966	2.736	1990	2.081
1943	2.718	1967	2.573	1991	2.073
1944	2.568	1968	2.477	1992	2.065

Fertility Rates					
Year	**Fertility Rate**	**Year**	**Fertility Rate**	**Year**	**Fertility Rate**
1945	2.491	1969	2.465	1993	2.046
1946	2.943	1970	2.480	1994	2.036
1947	3.274	1971	2.267	1995	2.019
1948	3.109	1972	2.010	1996	2.040
1949	3.110	1973	1.879	1997	2.000
1950	3.091	1974	1.835	1998	2.030
1951	3.267	1975	1.774	1999	2.070
1952	3.355	1976	1.738	2000	2.056
1953	3.418	1977	1.790	2001	2.034
1954	3.537	1978	1.760	2002	2.013
1955	3.574	1979	1.808	2003	2.043
1956	3.682	1980	1.840	2004	2.046
1957	3.760	1981	1.815	2005	2.054

15. One of the problems associated with the management of solid waste is the NIMBY (not in my backyard) syndrome. In separate surveys taken in 1988, 1989, and 1990 the National Solid Waste Management Association asked, *Would you object to a new landfill in your community?* The percentage response is given in the table below.

Survey Results			
Survey Date	**Don't Object**	**Object**	**Not Sure**
March 1990	36	59	5
February 1989	23	65	12
February 1988	30	62	8

    a. What is the level of measurement of the survey data?

    b. Is the data time series or cross-sectional?

    c. What other information would be useful in evaluating the results of the study?

16. In a recent study of four leading anesthetics, three hundred patients were randomly selected and assigned to be given one of the four products during a surgery. One of the products performed significantly better than the rest. Is this an observational study or a controlled experiment?

17. In the fall of 1999, Hurricane Floyd swept through eastern Carolinas causing billions of dollars of damage. Suppose you were the finance manager for one of the insurance companies which insured primarily residential housing. You need to be sure that adequate funds are available to pay the anticipated claims. The morning after the hurricane you sit in your office in Hartford, Connecticut, and begin wondering what kind of data you might collect in order to anticipate the company's financial obligations resulting from the hurricane. What variable(s) would you measure, and how would you collect the measurements?

18. Do seat belts affect the types and degree of injuries sustained in an automobile crash? What kind of data should you obtain to answer this question? Will the data be experimental or observational?

19. An article on the BBC website titled "Higher temperatures linked to EU asylum figures" discusses a study which found that as temperatures rise above average in agricultural areas, more people are seeking refuge abroad. The researchers believe these "weather shocks" happen due to decreased agricultural yield, which in turn damages national GDP. They also believe the heat increases aggressive behavior. The lead author of the study told BBC News "I feel very confident that what we discovered for 2000-2014 is a causal relationship between weather and asylum applications." Discuss how you would establish this link.

"No human experience is without meaning or unworthy of analysis."

— Primo Levi

3 CHAPTER
Visualizing Data

Introduction

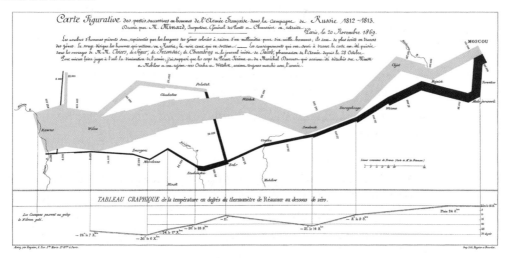

Effective visualization enables you to see a perspective of the data in its totality. The graph above depicts Napoleon's march into Russia from 1812 to 1813 during the Napoleonic Wars. Given the sophisticated computer graphing programs that exist, it may be surprising to know that the image above is considered one of the best data visualizations ever produced. The route Napoleon took to Moscow is traced in light brown on the map. His return from Moscow is traced in black. The width of the trace depicts the size of the French army at each location on the map in proportion to the original size of the army which began with 425,000 troops. Looking at the map, you can see that Napoleon had lost about 60% of his troops when he finally got to Moscow. His return from Moscow obliterated all but 10,000 of his remaining troops. The graph was created in 1869 by a French civil engineer named Charles Joseph Minard. In great artistic and storytelling visualizations like Minard's, the story of Napoleon's invasion of Russia in 1812 and the disastrous consequences to the French army pours out of the graphic. The data display makes an unforgettable point about the loss of life during this campaign.

Data is a representation of real life. There is a truth to it. In the case of the Minard graph, it was a morbidly brutal truth for the French army. For data analysts, the question is always: how much truth can be squeezed out of the data? Usually the first step in the "squeezing" process is data visualization.

Data visualization is used for two purposes: exploring data looking for the "truth" of it; and telling a story about what has been found. The visualization methods in the exploratory and storytelling processes are mostly the same. However, you may create hundreds of different visualizations while you are exploring the data but you will only settle on a few of the best visualizations for the storytelling part. This chapter will focus on the exploratory part of data analysis. However, we have included a supplement on our companion website that discusses the artistic and perspective aspects of visualization.

There are hundreds of ways to visualize data, and each one has a specific purpose. On our companion website, *stat.hawkeslearning.com*, you will find several resources that catalog different methods of visualizing data as well as some of the "greatest hits" in data visualization. Our focus in this chapter is to provide the basic visualization tools and develop graphical reasoning.

3.1   Frequency Distributions

Statistics exists because of variation. The statistician's job is to comprehend variation by looking for structure. Frequency distributions are one method of examining a data set's structure. To examine structural characteristics, ask questions such as,

- *Where are most of the observations located?*

- *Does the data cluster around one central point or are there several points that data seems to cluster around?*

- *Does the data seem to be uniformly spread out over some interval or bunched in some range?*

These questions all relate to the concept of "distribution".

Frequency Distribution

A **frequency distribution** is a summary technique that organizes data into classes and provides in tabular form a list of the classes along with the number of observations in each class.

DEFINITION

The process of refining information is interesting. The analyst begins with individual data, then organizes that data by counting the number of observations in each classification. In Table 3.1.1, the individual data consists of population counts in each state for the years 2010 and 2016. By comparing the state populations in 2016 with the populations in 2010, the percentage of population change can be computed for each state over the 6-year period.[1]

⋮ **Data**

The complete data set can be found on stat. hawkeslearning.com under **Data Sets > Population Count 2010 and 2016**.

Table 3.1.1 - Population of Individual States in 2010 and 2016				
Geographic Area	**Population Estimate**		**Change, 2010 to 2016**	
	April 1, 2010	**July 1, 2016**	**Number**	**Percent**
Alabama	4,780,131	4,863,300	83,169	1.7
Alaska	710,249	741,894	31,645	4.5
Arizona	6,392,301	6,931,071	538,770	8.4
Arkansas	2,916,025	2,988,248	72,223	2.5
California	37,254,522	39,250,017	1,995,495	5.4
Colorado	5,029,324	5,540,545	511,221	10.2
• • •				

When the population change data is classified in the frequency distribution (see Table 3.1.2), the actual magnitudes of the data values disappear. Losing information may not seem to be a desirable result, but without some lumping together it is difficult to comprehend large amounts of data.

Table 3.1.2 - Frequency Distribution of Population Change in States	
% Change in Population	**Frequency**
Below 0	2
0 to 1.9	15
2 to 3.9	6
4 to 5.9	11
6 to 7.9	7
8 to 9.9	4
10 to 11.9	3
12 +	2

With the frequency distribution, we are able to see the broader structure of the data. It is now easy to see that most 6-year state population changes are between 0% and 8%. Further, population changes above 12% and below 0% are uncommon. Without the organization that a frequency distribution provides, these conclusions would be more difficult to establish. If there were 10,000 data values instead of 50, it would be much more difficult to make similar conclusions.

There are two major steps in the construction of a frequency distribution.

Constructing a Frequency Distribution

1.   Choose the classifications.

2.   Count the number in each class.

PROCEDURE

For simple data, such as the results from tossing a coin, the choice of classifications is easy. Heads is one category and tails the other. However, for continuous data, such as weights, heights, and volumes, the choice of classification scheme becomes less obvious, since there are an enormous number of possibilities. There are two requirements that should be met when setting up the categories for classification: the categories must be both *mutually exclusive* and *exhaustive*. Essentially, this means categories should not overlap and should cover all possible values.

Since choosing the classification depends on whether the data is qualitative (nominal or ordinal) or quantitative (interval or ratio), the discussion of frequency distributions will be presented on the basis of these data types. This section will present how to construct a frequency distribution for qualitative data, and Section 3.3 will introduce constructing frequency distributions for quantitative data.

Qualitative Frequency Distributions

To construct a qualitative frequency distribution, choose the categories to classify the data. In many instances, the problem at hand will suggest the classification scheme. For example, in the coin-tossing example there are only two classes, heads and tails. If we are classifying students by class level, then we have four classes: freshmen, sophomores, juniors, and seniors. For qualitative data, it would be unusual if a reasonable set of categories is *not* relatively obvious.

After the categories have been chosen, count the items belonging to each class in order to construct the frequency distribution.

Example 3.1.1

Louis Harris and Associates Inc. conducted a poll of 1250 adults to determine *How Americans Grade the School System*. There were 24 questions in the original survey, producing a total of 30,000 pieces of data (24·1250). Without some way of summarizing, this data would not produce usable information.

The first question in the survey was: *In general, how would you rate the quality of American public schools?* The frequency of each response category is shown in the table on the left. The frequency distribution for the second question involving *a lack of parental involvement with a child's education* is given in the table on the right. The summary tables are much more informative than looking at 1250 observations for each question.

Frequency Distribution of Responses		Frequency Distribution of Responses	
In general, how would you rate the quality of American public schools?		**How serious is a lack of parental involvement with a child's education?**	
Excellent	462	**Very serious**	700
Pretty good	288	**Somewhat serious**	325
Only fair	225	**Not very serious**	112
Poor	225	**Not a problem**	75
Not sure	50	**Not sure**	38

In the next two tables, relative frequency distributions are calculated. In those tables, the frequencies are converted into percentages. These are defined as **relative frequencies**, i.e., the proportion relative to the total. They are valuable in assessing the data quickly in terms we use frequently. (See Section 3.3 for an additional discussion of relative frequency distributions.)

Relative Frequency Distribution of Responses		Relative Frequency Distribution of Responses	
In general, how would you rate the quality of American public schools?		**How serious is a lack of parental involvement with a child's education?**	
Excellent	37%	**Very serious**	56%
Pretty good	23%	**Somewhat serious**	26%
Only fair	18%	**Not very serious**	9%
Poor	18%	**Not a problem**	6%
Not sure	4%	**Not sure**	3%

As one can see in the tables above, the majority of adults who participated in the poll rate the quality of American public schools as *Pretty good* or *Excellent*. The poll also reveals that the lack of parental involvement with a child's education is considered *Very serious* or *Somewhat serious* by 82% of the adults who took the poll. Summarizing qualitative data using a frequency distribution table or a relative frequency distribution table, allows the researcher to make conclusions about the data without having to view each observation.

3.1 **Exercises**

Basic Concepts

1. From a comprehension standpoint, what are the advantages of visual images over the written word?

2. What are the two purposes of data visualization?

3. Describe the purpose of a frequency distribution.

4. What are the basic questions to ask when examining the structure of a data set?

5. What are the two steps to constructing a frequency distribution?

6. In the construction of a frequency distribution, what are the two requirements that the classification categories must meet?

Exercises

7. Using the House Style variable from the Mount Pleasant Real Estate data set from the web resource, consider the following.

   a. What level of measurement does the data possess?

   b. Is the data qualitative or quantitative?

   c. Construct a frequency distribution for the House Style variable.

Data

stat.hawkeslearning.com
Data Sets > Mount Pleasant Real Estate Data

8. Parkinsonism is an affliction of the aged and is frequently caused by Parkinson's disease, Alzheimer's disease, or other illnesses. The results from a recent study on Parkinsonism were reported in "Prevalence of Parkinsonian Signs and Associated Mortality in a Community Population of Older People," *New England Journal of Medicine*. A sample of 467 people, all 65 years of age or older, was selected from East Boston, Massachusetts. Each person was clinically evaluated and various signs of Parkinsonism, if any, were noted. The following table is a frequency distribution for some of the signs of Parkinsonism.

Signs of Parkinsonism	
Sign	**Frequency**
Reduced arm swing	210
Prolonged turning	153
Right leg rigidity	141
Left leg rigidity	154
Slow finger taps	197
Shuffling gait	83

   a. What level of measurement does the data possess?

   b. What percent of the sample suffered from left leg rigidity? Round your answer to two decimal places.

   c. Add up the frequencies. Why does the sum of the frequencies exceed the total sample size of 467?

d.   Suppose 30 people suffer from both left leg rigidity and right leg rigidity. How many people in the sample suffer from rigidity in at least one of their legs?

9.   A small commuter airline in the West keeps records of complaints received from its customers. Complaints for March and July are listed in the following table.

Customer Complaints		
Type of Complaint	**March**	**July**
Tickets cost too much	11	15
Stewardess did not provide blankets	8	3
Schedules not convenient	12	17
Plane often late	17	16
Seats too stiff	3	3
Airplane too hot	6	20
Airplane too cold	8	5
Poor reservation system	5	5
Plane interior looks shabby	5	6

a.   Classify the items by the following categories: comfort, price, service, and schedule, and develop a qualitative frequency distribution.

b.   Classify the items by the following categories: plane, personnel, building/equipment, and other, and develop a qualitative frequency distribution.

c.   Would another person necessarily assign the same items to the same categories as you have? Discuss the implications of this when reviewing data collected and distributed by someone else for open answer questions.

d.   Do the categories chosen in parts **a.** and **b.** meet the requirement that categories be mutually exclusive and exhaustive? Discuss.

3.2   Displaying Qualitative Data Graphically

Graphical analysis is a trade-off. We lose sight of the individual observations (the row data). In return we are able to see a representation of the totality of observations. The trade is almost always beneficial since a well-designed graph gives our visual processing system the kind of image it processes best, a picture.

Because a set of data can be graphically represented in many different ways, selecting and creating graphical displays requires a certain amount of artistic judgment.

Several types of graphs and tabular displays will be discussed in this chapter. Bar charts, stacked bar charts, and pie charts are effective, visually appealing methods of graphically displaying qualitative data. A quick look at publications such as *Time*, *USA Today*, *The Wall Street Journal*, *Scientific American*, and *Forbes* provides convincing evidence of the frequent and beneficial usage of these data visualization techniques.

Bar Charts

Bar charts are often used to illustrate a frequency distribution for qualitative data.

> ## Bar Chart
>
> The **bar chart** is a simple graphical display in which the length of each bar corresponds to the number of observations in a category.
>
> **DEFINITION**

Bar charts are valuable as presentation tools and are especially effective at reinforcing differences in magnitudes, since they permit the visual comparison of data by displaying the magnitude of each category by a vertical or horizontal bar. Figure 3.2.1 is a bar chart constructed from the *lack of parental involvement* question in Example 3.1.1.

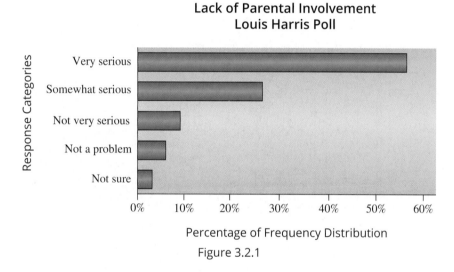

Figure 3.2.1

∽ **Technology**

For instructions on how to create a bar chart in Excel, Minitab, or other technologies please visit stat.hawkeslearning.com and navigate to **Technology Instructions > Graphs > Bar Charts.**

The Aesthetics of Bar Chart Construction

Bar chart construction requires numerous layout decisions such as size, use of color, and label locations. These decisions are frequently made on a trial-and-error basis. However, certain conventions have been developed that improve the quality and effectiveness of the charts. They are presented below as suggestions, not rules. Actually, several of the points are general in nature and would serve as useful guidelines in the construction of any graph.

- Bar charts can be constructed horizontally or vertically. Customarily, horizontal orientation is used for categories that are descriptively labeled, and vertical (or columnar) orientation is used for categories that are numerical. It is important to remember that this idea is only a suggestion. If you believe that a vertical bar chart is more appealing, use it.

- If the categories have some associated order, they maintain that order in the bar chart. Otherwise, the categories may be listed alphabetically, in either ascending or descending order, or in some other pattern related to the nature of the data.

- Miscellaneous or "other" categories should be listed at the bottom of the chart (if oriented horizontally) or at the far right (if oriented vertically).

- The difference in bar length is the principal visual feature in comparing differences in category amounts. Consequently, scales for the axes should be chosen that will most effectively allow for the desired comparisons. *Unless there is a good reason, the axis used to measure the bars should start at zero.* Otherwise, the axis can be stretched to exaggerate differences in the bar lengths. For example, suppose the data in the following table were plotted.

Table 3.2.1 - Sales Performance	
Salesperson	**Total Sales (in thousands of dollars)**
Susan	187
William	201
Beth	207
Rob	193

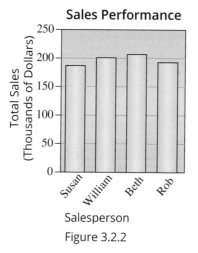

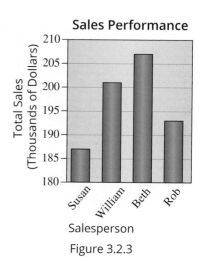

Figure 3.2.2

Figure 3.2.3

Figures 3.2.2 and 3.2.3 are plots of the same data (Table 3.2.1). What a difference axis scaling can make on perception! Figure 3.2.3 starts the *y*-axis at 180 instead of zero. If you want to emphasize similarity, use Figure 3.2.2 to do the job. If you want to emphasize differences, use Figure 3.2.3. However, it is difficult to imagine any legitimate reason for using Figure 3.2.3 to represent the data. Axis stretching is often employed to mislead. *When you see an axis that does not start at zero, you should be a bit skeptical as to the conclusions the author intends for you to make.*

- Bar widths should be chosen that are pleasing visually and should not be allowed to vary within a particular chart.

- Appropriate shading, crosshatching, and coloring of the bars can help in presenting the data. Many spreadsheet programs incorporate sophisticated graphing programs which make changes in shading, color, and crosshatching patterns extremely easy.

- The spacing between bars can dramatically affect the perception of the graph. Spacing should be set at approximately one-half the width of a bar. This, however, is not a rigid rule. Artistic judgment is needed.

- Gridlines extended into the body of the chart are often useful and may be included if deemed helpful. Study Figure 3.2.4 and Figure 3.2.5. Both bar charts illustrate the same data. Notice that the readability of the graph in Figure 3.2.5 is improved by adding vertical gridlines.

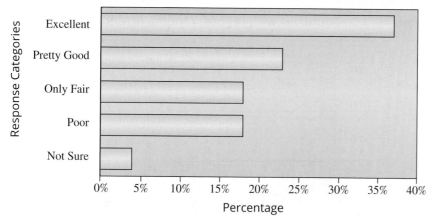

Figure 3.2.4

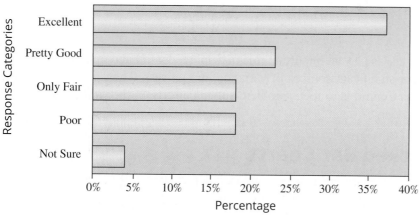

Figure 3.2.5

- If there is sufficient room on the graphs, labels should be provided for each bar (category) and for each axis.

- Notes on sources of data or other footnotes should be given below the chart.

One of the themes of this chapter is that a graph can be an analytical device and a presentation tool. Simple graphics are fine for certain analytical purposes, but if you are trying to make a point, then a higher standard is required to create visual impact. Designing effective graphics is not just about making things look better; graphics can help the reader comprehend information. Using graphics well can emphasize meaning and organize content.

Pareto Charts

The order in which the categories of a bar chart are displayed does not matter unless you want to create a **Pareto chart**. Figure 3.2.6 is an example of a Pareto chart for the countries with the highest cinema attendance in 2014.[2]

Pareto Chart

The **Pareto chart** is a bar graph whose bars are arranged in decreasing order of frequency.

DEFINITION

The following Pareto chart shows the cinema attendance in 2014 for 15 selected countries.

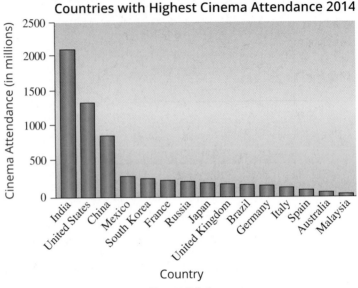

Countries with Highest Cinema Attendance 2014

Figure 3.2.6

⌀ **Technology**

For instructions on how to create a Pareto chart in Excel, Minitab, or other technologies, please visit stat.hawkeslearning.com and navigate to **Technology Instructions > Graphs > Pareto Charts**.

Pareto charts play an important role in helping identify and rank potential problem areas or significant sources of variation in a process. Their purpose in Statistical Process Control is to focus problem-solving efforts on the *vital few* instead of the *trivial many*.

Stacked Bar Charts

Stacked bar charts are an interesting variation on the standard bar chart. The number of medals (gold, silver, and bronze) won during the 2014 Winter Olympics for selected countries is given in Figure 3.2.7.

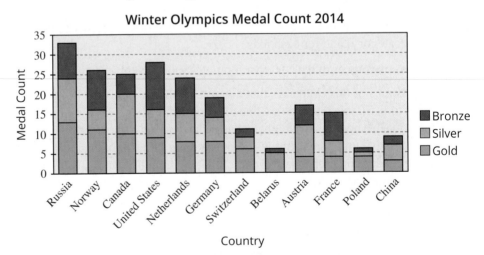

Winter Olympics Medal Count 2014

Figure 3.2.7

Without the stacked bar chart, the reader would have to view either three different charts tallying medal counts for the 2014 Winter Olympics or a much "busier" chart plotting each medal on the horizontal axis above each country like in Figure 3.2.8.

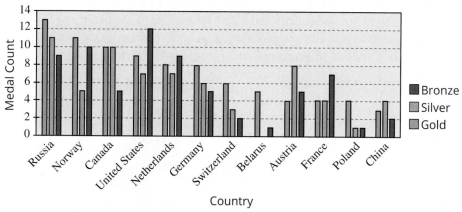

Figure 3.2.8

Pie Charts

We have just seen how bar charts are used as a means of expressing frequency distributions. Pie charts can perform the same function.

> ## Pie Chart
>
> A **pie chart** (or **circle graph**) is a graph used to display categorical data as slices of a circle. The size of each slice is proportional to the amount or frequency in each category. The proportion of the total that each slice represents is often displayed as a percentage on the chart. These percentages should total 100%.
>
> **DEFINITION**

∽ **Technology**

For instructions on how to create a pie chart in Excel, Minitab, or other technologies, please visit stat.hawkeslearning.com and navigate to **Technology Instructions > Graphs > Pie Charts.**

The circle represents the total "pie" available, and the slices are proportional to the amount in each category. One of the advantages of the pie chart is the ability to easily compare the total in each of the classifications to the total number of observations.

One common use of pie charts is to display how some set of assets is spent. One of the biggest asset pies in the world is the budget of the United States government. In 2015 government outlays were in the neighborhood of 3.36 trillion dollars. If the budget is split into five categories, the percentages spent in 2015 in each category are provided in Table 3.2.2. While the table provides the information, it is not visually interesting. A pie chart will enable you to improve the presentation of the information in Table 3.2.2.[3]

Table 3.2.2 - Percentage Spent by the Federal Government in 2015	
Category	**Percentage Spent**
Social Security	38%
Medicare and Health	28%
National Defense	16%
Other Programs	12%
Net Interest	6%

The pie chart in Figure 3.2.9 tells an interesting story about how our tax dollars are spent. In a glance at the pie chart, your eyes are drawn to two of the biggest slices, a 38% slice going to Social Security and a 28% slice going to Medicare and Health. If you would like to look at current information on how government monies are spent, go explore the Office of Management and Budget on the White House website.

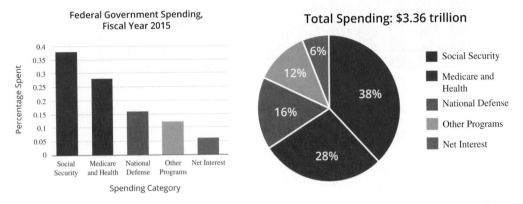

Figure 3.2.9

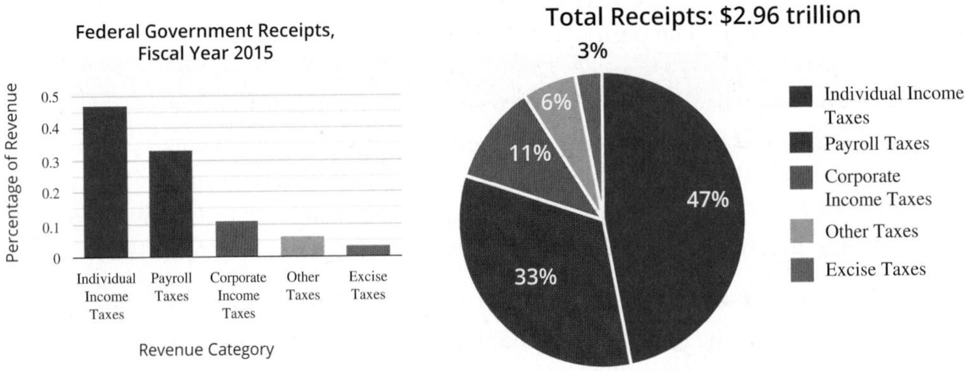

Figure 3.2.10

A pie chart showing where government revenues originate is given in Figure 3.2.10. In order to determine from the pie chart how much was spent in a particular category, multiply the total amount by the percentage given for that category in the pie chart. For example, to find the amount of government receipts contributed by individual income taxes, multiply the total amount of government receipts ($2.96 trillion) by the percentage contributed by individual income taxes (47%). This means that $2.96 \cdot 0.47 = \$1.3912$ trillion of all government receipts come from individual income taxes.

Although pie charts are useful displays of categorical data, they have their limitations. Once the number of categories rises above ten, the information conveyed by a pie chart is less meaningful. As Figure 3.2.11 and Figure 3.2.12 demonstrate, when the number of employees increases from 5 to 40, using a pie chart to show the percentage of sales for each employee is not as informative.

Percentage of Sales
(5 Employees)

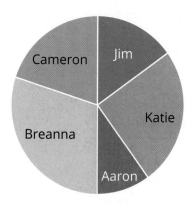

Figure 3.2.11

Percentage of Sales
(40 Employees)

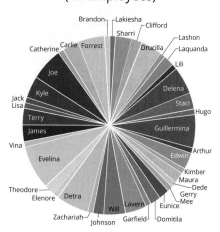

Figure 3.2.12

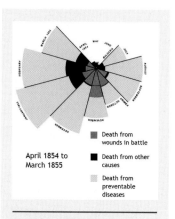

April 1854 to
March 1855

■ Death from
wounds in battle

■ Death from other
causes

□ Death from
preventable
diseases

A Passion for Compassion

In the 19th century, statistics was not widely seen as an applicable skill. That is, until Florence Nightingale came onto the scene. When she arrived at the front line of the Crimean War, she was appalled by the situation. The mortality rate was too high, and the hospitals were in complete disarray. She immediately set about organizing what little records were kept, and started to gather a lot of new data. Upon analyzing this new data, she discovered that the majority of deaths that were occurring in British military hospitals were due to preventable diseases. Using this new information, Nightingale was able to present a case to Parliament for improving the sanitary practices in British hospitals. She utilized data analysis and visualization to literally save thousands of lives, and in the process, her "rose diagram", also known as a "coxcomb chart", became an iconic data visualization.

3.2 **Exercises**

Basic Concepts

1. What are some benefits of graphing?

2. What is the major disadvantage of graphing?

3. Describe the types of data that a bar chart would be useful in displaying.

4. Where should miscellaneous categories be displayed in a bar chart?

5. Explain how axis scales on bar charts can be misleading.

6. What is a stacked bar chart?

7. Why would a stacked bar chart be preferred over a normal bar chart?

8. What is a pie chart?

Exercises

9. A consumer magazine uses bar charts to compare four popular brands of automobiles. This particular bar chart represents a comparison of the miles per gallon (mpg) for the four brands.

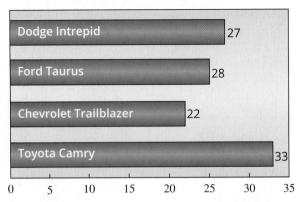

a. What is wrong with this picture?

b. Evaluate the bar chart using the guidelines suggested in the section on the aesthetics of bar chart construction.

⁙ **Data**

stat.hawkeslearning.com
**Data > Employee
Satisfaction**

10. The following frequency distribution is for the Employee Satisfaction data set from the web resource.

Frequency Distribution of Employee Salaries			
Department	**High Salary**	**Medium Salary**	**Low Salary**
Accounting	74	358	335
HR	45	335	359
IT	83	609	535
Management	225	180	225
Marketing	80	402	376
Product Management	68	451	383
Research and Development	51	364	372
Sales	269	2099	1772
Support	141	1147	942
Technical	201	1372	1147
Total	**1237**	**7317**	**6446**

a. Construct a bar chart for the number of employees with high salaries by department.

b. Construct a bar chart for the number of employees with medium salaries by department.

c. Construct a bar chart for the number of employees with low salaries by department.

d. Construct a stacked bar chart for the number of employees with low, medium, and high salaries by department.

e. Construct a pie chart for the number of employees with high salaries.

f. Construct a pie chart for the number of employees with medium salaries.

g. Construct a pie chart for the number of employees with low salaries.

h. What did you learn from the charts created in parts **a.** through **g.**?

11. Consider the following data regarding the average expenditure on healthcare per person for various countries.[4]

Healthcare Costs Around the World per Capita, 2014	
Country	**Expenditure per Capita ($)**
Australia	6031
Canada	5292
Denmark	6463
Finland	4612
France	4959
Germany	5411
Iceland	4662
Ireland	4239
Japan	3703
Sweden	6808
Switzerland	9674
United Kingdom	3935
United States	9403

a. Construct a bar chart for the average healthcare cost per person for the various countries.

b. What did you learn from the chart?

12. Consider the following data regarding professions with high projected growth rates for the years 2016 through 2026.[5]

Occupation Growth Rates	
Occupation	**Projected Increase 2016–2026**
Solar photovoltaic installers	105%
Wind turbine service technicians	96%
Home health aides	47%
Personal care aides	37%
Physician assistants	37%
Nurse practitioners	36%
Statisticians	33%
Physical therapist assistants	31%

a. Construct a bar chart for the projected growth rates of the various occupations.

b. What did you learn from the chart?

13. Consider the following data regarding the methods which consumers use to pay for items purchased in a particular store.

Payment Methods	
Method of Payment	**Relative Frequency**
Cash	81.1%
Checks	7.6%
General-Purpose Credit Cards	5.5%
Proprietary Credit Cards	5.3%
Debit Cards	0.5%

a. Construct a bar chart for the relative frequencies of the various methods of payment.

b. Construct a pie chart for the relative frequencies of the various methods of payment.

c. Comment on any information about the relative frequencies of the various methods which you were able to ascertain by examining the charts.

3.3 Constructing Frequency Distributions for Quantitative Data

When data is qualitative (nominal or ordinal), selecting the categories for display is relatively easy. However, selecting categories for quantitative data is not particularly obvious, since using different schemes can dramatically affect the perception of the data. The fundamental decision in constructing a frequency distribution is selecting the number of classes.

Example 3.3.1

A data set containing the heart rates of 50 students is given below. However, looking at the individual data is not very revealing. Even with only 50 observations, there are just too many data values to get a good idea of the measurements. Instead of trying to examine or analyze 50 data values, a frequency distribution is given in Table 3.3.1, which provides a summary of the heart rate data. Examining the frequency distribution, an analyst can look at a table that has only five categories and five frequencies, thus reducing the complexity.

Heart Rates (per min.) of 50 Students

77	84	79	90	67	84	82	74	88	75
69	81	94	68	65	86	78	79	79	70
83	83	84	82	93	80	81	80	87	80
62	98	77	83	82	80	82	73	85	77
77	79	81	70	72	85	84	80	74	83

Table 3.3.1 - Frequency Distribution of Heart Rates

Heart Rate	Number of Students
57–66	2
67–76	10
77–86	32
87–96	5
97–106	1

With the frequency distribution, we are able to see the broader structure of the data. It is now easy to see that the overwhelming majority of the heart rates are between 77 and 86 beats per minute. Further, heart rates above 96 and below 67 are uncommon. These conclusions would be considerably more difficult to establish without the organization that the frequency distribution provides.

The purpose of a frequency distribution is to condense a set of data into a meaningful summary form. The major steps in constructing a frequency distribution are as follows.

Constructing a Frequency Distribution

1. **Determine how many classes should be in the distribution.** Choosing the number of classes is arbitrary and should depend on the amount of data available. The more data available, the more classes that can be used. Generally, fewer than four classes would be too much compression of the data, and greater than 20 classes provides too little summary information.

2. **Determine the class width.** In some cases, the data set easily lends itself to natural divisions, such as decades or years. At other times, we must choose divisions for ourselves. You will want to choose a width so that the classes formed present a clear representation of the data and include all values in the data set. The width of each class should be the same whenever possible; exceptions may occur for the beginning and ending intervals. There is really no perfect formula for class width that will work for every data set. However, a good starting point for class width is to divide the difference between the maximum observation and minimum observation by the number of classes.

$$\text{Class Width} = \frac{\text{Maximum Value} - \text{Minimum Value}}{\text{Number of Classes}}$$

Class endpoints with fractional values will make the graph harder to understand. If possible, try to keep the width to an integer value by rounding the class width up to the next largest integer or choosing an integer value close to the calculated class width that makes sense.

Continued...

PROCEDURE

Constructing a Frequency Distribution (continued)

3. **Find the class limits.** The **lower class limit** is the smallest number that can belong to a particular class, and the **upper class limit** is the largest number that can belong to a class. Using the minimum data value, or a smaller number, as the lower limit of the first class is a good place to start. However, judgment is required. You should choose the first lower limit so that reasonable classes will be produced. After choosing the lower limit of the first class, add the class width to it to find the lower limit of the second class. Continue until you have the desired number of lower class limits. The upper limit of each class is determined such that the classes do not overlap. Once you create your classes, if there are any data values that fall outside the class limits, you must adjust either the class width or your choice for the first lower class limit.

4. **Determine the frequency of each class.** Make a tally mark for each data value in the appropriate class. Count the marks to find the total frequency for each class. Summing the frequencies in each class together should equal the total number of observations in the data set.

PROCEDURE

Suppose we wanted to create a frequency distribution from the heart rate data in Example 3.3.1. If there are to be five classes, determine a class width.

$$\text{Class Width} = \frac{\text{Maximum Value} - \text{Minimum Value}}{\text{Number of Classes}} = \frac{98 - 62}{5} = \frac{36}{5} = 7.2$$

Class endpoints with fractional values will make the data harder to interpret. If possible, try to keep the class width to an integer value. If the calculated class width is 7.2, you might try a class width in the range of 8 to 10. An interval width of 10 is used throughout the heart rate example.

Generally, class widths should be equal. To form the first interval, take the smallest value in the data and use that value or round it down to an appropriate value. The exact value selected is arbitrary. In the example, we have selected the starting point of the first class as 57. However, 55, 58, or 60 could just as easily have been used, since the smallest data value is 62. If 57 is selected as the beginning point for the first interval, then the first class will span the interval 57 to 66. Adding the class width to the lower class limit creates the next interval. So, our classes are 57–66, 67–76, 77–86, 87–96, and 97–106. Now tally the data in each interval and you have the frequency distribution in Table 3.3.1.

The frequency distribution given in Table 3.3.1 is just one way of organizing the data. There are three other distributions that can be calculated from the frequency distribution: relative frequency, cumulative frequency, and cumulative relative frequency. Each gives a slightly different perspective on the data.

Relative Frequency Distribution

Relative frequency represents the proportion of the total observations in a given class. The **relative frequency distribution** enables the reader to view the number in each category in relation to the total number of observations. Relative frequency is a standardizing technique. Converting the frequency in each class to a proportion in each class enables us to compare data sets with different numbers of observations.

Relative Frequency

The **relative frequency** of any class is the number of observations in the class divided by the total number of observations:

$$\text{Relative Frequency} = \frac{\text{Number in Class}}{\text{Total Number of Observations}}$$

DEFINITION

Table 3.3.2 - Heart Rate Relative Frequency Distribution	
Heart Rate	**Relative Frequency**
57–66	2/50 = 0.04
67–76	10/50 = 0.20
77–86	32/50 = 0.64
87–96	5/50 = 0.10
97–106	1/50 = 0.02

Table 3.3.2 shows the relative frequencies of the heart rate data. Using this table it is easy to see that 64% of the observed heart rates are between 77 and 86 beats per minute.

Cumulative Frequency Distribution

The cumulative frequency distribution gives the reader an opportunity to look at any category and determine immediately the number of observations that belong to a particular category and all categories below it.

Cumulative Frequency

The **cumulative frequency** is the sum of the frequency of a particular class and all preceding classes.

DEFINITION

Table 3.3.3 - Heart Rate Cumulative Frequency Distribution		
Heart Rate	**Frequency**	**Cumulative Frequency**
57–66	2	2
67–76	10	12
77–86	32	44
87–96	5	49
97–106	1	50

In this example, the reader can easily see in Table 3.3.3 that 49 out of 50 heart rates are less than or equal to 96 beats per minute.

Cumulative Relative Frequency

To obtain the cumulative relative frequency, add the relative frequencies of all preceding classes to the relative frequency of the current class.

Cumulative Relative Frequency

The **cumulative relative frequency** is the proportion of observations in a particular class and all preceding classes.

DEFINITION

Table 3.3.4 - Heart Rate Cumulative Relative Frequency

Heart Rate	Relative Frequency	Cumulative Relative Frequency
57–66	0.04	0.04
67–76	0.20	0.24
77–86	0.64	0.88
87–96	0.10	0.98
97–106	0.02	1.00

From the cumulative relative frequency in Table 3.3.4 it is easy to see that 88% of the heart rates are less than or equal to 86.

3.3 Exercises

Basic Concepts

1. What are the fundamental decisions in constructing frequency distributions for quantitative data?

2. Describe the general guidelines for selecting the number of classes for a quantitative frequency distribution.

3. What is a good starting point for determining the class width?

4. What is a relative frequency distribution? How do you calculate relative frequencies from raw frequencies?

5. What is a cumulative frequency distribution?

6. What is a cumulative relative frequency distribution?

Exercises

7. A business magazine was conducting a study into the amount of travel required for mid-level managers across the U.S. Seventy-five managers were surveyed for the number of days they spent traveling each year.

Mid-Level Manager Travel					
Days Traveling	0–6	7–13	14–20	21–27	28–34	35 and above
Frequency	15	21	27	9	2	1

   a. Construct a relative frequency distribution.

   b. Construct a cumulative frequency distribution.

8. In November 2017, the closing prices for the stocks in the Dow Jones Industrial Average were as follows. Construct a frequency distribution for the stock prices.

Dow Jones Industrial Average Closing Prices	
Stock	**Closing Price (Dollars)**
3M	203.56
American Express	86.14
Apple	164.05
Boeing	240.33
Caterpillar	118.28
Chevron	108.76
Cisco	32.30
Coca-Cola	45.78
Disney	101.50
DowDuPont	70.15
Exxon Mobil	76.57
General Electric	25.14
Goldman Sachs	225.88
Home Depot	150.78
IBM	144.08
Intel	35.09
Johnson & Johnson	131.03
JPMorgan Chase	91.70
McDonald's	159.81
Merck	63.83
Microsoft	73.94
Nike	53.36
Pfizer	33.96
Procter & Gamble	92.53
Travelers Companies Inc.	119.90
United Technologies	117.92
UnitedHealth	199.75
Verizon	47.92
Visa	103.90
Wal-Mart	78.37

9. Every year, the average temperatures of 100 selected U.S. cities are published by the National Oceanic and Atmospheric Administration. The average temperature (°F) for the month of October for 15 randomly selected cities from the list of 100 are listed in the following table.

Average Temperatures (°F)				
68.5	50.9	67.5	57.5	56.0
47.1	50.1	65.8	51.5	49.5
75.2	56.0	62.3	53.0	46.1

a. Construct a frequency distribution for the average temperatures for the month of October.

b. Construct a relative frequency distribution for the average temperatures for the month of October.

c. Construct a cumulative frequency distribution for the average temperatures for the month of October.

 Data

stat.hawkeslearning.com
Data > California DDS Expenditures

10. Using the California DDS Expenditures data set from the web resource, perform the following.

a. Construct a frequency distribution with 8 classes for the Expenditures variable.

b. Construct a relative frequency distribution for the expenditures using the frequency distribution from part **a.**

c. Construct a cumulative frequency distribution for the expenditures.

3.4   Histograms and Other Graphical Displays of Quantitative Data

A **histogram** is a common graphical method that reveals the distribution of a set of data. Histograms are often constructed based on frequency distributions of quantitative data. Histograms look similar to bar graphs, but are used to analyze quantitative data rather than qualitative data.

> ### Histogram
>
> A **histogram** is a graphical representation of a frequency or relative frequency distribution. The horizontal scale corresponds to classes of quantitative data values and the vertical scale corresponds to the frequency or relative frequency of each class.
>
> DEFINITION

Each of the classes in the frequency distribution is represented by a vertical bar whose height is proportional to the frequency of the class interval. The horizontal boundaries of each vertical bar correspond to the class boundaries. Once the frequency distribution has been calculated, all the information necessary for plotting a histogram is available. In Figure 3.4.1, the histogram is created from the frequency distribution of the heart rate data in Table 3.3.1 of the previous section.

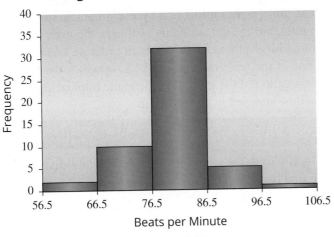

Figure 3.4.1

You can quickly see that most of the heart rates are in the third class interval from 76.5 to 86.5. The center of the data appears to be near 80 and the data appears to have a mound shape with most of the data in the middle.

Histograms are one of the more frequently used statistical tools. A histogram is not only easy to interpret, it also reveals a great deal about the structure of the data. You can quickly see that most of the heart rates are in the second and third classes (66.5 to 86.5). By examining the histogram, one can determine the shape of the distribution of the data. That is, the data could be **symmetric** or **skewed**.

Symmetric vs. Skewed

If you split the histogram of a distribution down the center, and the left and right sides of the histogram are approximately mirror images of one another, the distribution is said to be **symmetric**.

A **skewed distribution** is a nonsymmetric (or asymmetric) distribution that extends more to one side than the other. The distribution is said to be **skewed to the right** (or positively skewed) if the tail to the right of the peak of the distribution is longer than the tail to the left of the peak. The distribution is said to be **skewed to the left** (or negatively skewed) if the tail to the left of the peak of the distribution is longer than the tail to the right of the peak.

DEFINITION

When we look at a histogram, what features are important?

1. Is the distribution of the data symmetric or skewed?

Skewed Right   Skewed Left

2. Is it bell-shaped?

3. Does the distribution have several peaks or modes?

4. Where is the center of the distribution?

5. Are there outliers, data values that are very different from the others?

☍ Technology

For instructions on how to create a histogram in Excel, Minitab, or other technologies, please visit stat.hawkeslearning.com and navigate to **Technology Instructions > Graphs > Histograms.**

Stem-and-Leaf Plot

The **stem-and-leaf plot** (or **stemplot**) is a hybrid graphical method. The plot is similar to a histogram, but the data remains visible to the user. Like all graphical displays, the stem-and-leaf plot is useful for both ordering and detecting patterns in the data. It is one of the few graphical methods in which the individual data is not lost in the construction of the graph. As the name implies, there is a "stem" to which "leaves" will be attached in some pattern.

Stem-and-Leaf Plot

The **stem-and-leaf plot** is a graph representing quantitative data that separates each data value into two parts: the stem and the leaf.

DEFINITION

Consider the following data: 97, 99, 108, 110, and 111. If we are interested in the variation of the last digit, the stem and leaves are as shown in Table 3.4.1 and displayed in Figure 3.4.2. The leaves in this case are the *ones* digit and the stems are the *tens* and *hundreds* digits. All of the data values that have common stems are grouped together, and their leaves branch out from the common stem.

Table 3.4.1 - Data, Stems, and Leaves

Data	Stem	Leaf
97	09	7
99	09	9
108	10	8
110	11	0
111	11	1

Stem-and-Leaf Plot

Stem	Leaf
09	7 9
10	8
11	0 1
Key: 10	8 = 108

Figure 3.4.2

Notice the key at the bottom of the stem-and-leaf plot to show how the data is to be read from the plot. It is also important to keep the spacing between the leaves consistent.

If we are interested in the variation of the last two digits, the stem and leaves are shown in Table 3.4.2 and displayed in Figure 3.4.3. The leaves in this case are the *tens* and *ones* digits and the stems are the *hundreds* digits. Again all of the data values that have common stems are grouped together, and their leaves branch out from the common stem.

Table 3.4.2 - Data, Stems, and Leaves		
Data	Stem	Leaf
97	0	97
99	0	99
108	1	08
110	1	10
111	1	11

Stem-and-Leaf Plot

Stem	Leaf
0	97 99
1	08 10 11
Key: 1	08 = 108

Figure 3.4.3

Deciding which part to make the stem and which part to make the leaf depends on the focus or purpose of the analysis. Sometimes the choice of stem and leaf is easy. With the heart rate data, using the *tens* digit as the stem will break the data into four classes. Figure 3.4.4 shows a stem-and-leaf plot of the heart rate data using the tens digit as the stem.

Stem-and-Leaf Plot	
Stem	Leaf
6	7 9 8 5 2
7	7 9 4 8 9 7 3 7 9 0 2 7 0 5 4 9
8	4 4 2 1 6 3 3 4 2 0 1 0 3 2 0 2 1 5 4 0 3 0 5 7 8
9	0 4 3 8
Key: 9	0 = 90 bpm

Figure 3.4.4

It is often advantageous to place the leaves of a stem-and-leaf plot in numerical order. Ordering the leaves in the heart rate data pictured above gives us Figure 3.4.5.

Ordered Stem-and-Leaf Plot	
Stem	Leaf
6	2 5 7 8 9
7	0 0 2 3 4 4 5 7 7 7 7 8 9 9 9 9
8	0 0 0 0 0 1 1 1 2 2 2 2 3 3 3 3 4 4 4 4 5 5 6 7 8
9	0 3 4 8
Key: 9	0 = 90 bpm

Figure 3.4.5

Example 3.4.1

Construct a stem and leaf plot that compares the annual home run production Babe Ruth and Barry Bonds hit per season.[6]

Barry Bonds					
Year	1986	1987	1988	1989	1990	1991
HR	16	25	24	19	33	25
Year	1992	1993	1994	1995	1996	1997
HR	34	46	37	33	42	40
Year	1998	1999	2000	2001	2002	2003
HR	37	34	49	73	46	39
Year	2004	2005	2006	2007		
HR	45	5	26	28		

Babe Ruth					
Year	1914	1915	1916	1917	1918	1919
HR	0	4	3	2	11	29
Year	1920	1921	1922	1923	1924	1925
HR	54	59	35	41	46	25
Year	1926	1927	1928	1929	1930	1931
HR	47	60	54	46	49	46
Year	1932	1933	1934	1935		
HR	41	34	22	6		

Solution

Home runs Hit per Season: Babe Ruth vs Barry Bonds		
Ruth		**Bonds**
0 4 3 2 6	0	5
1	1	6 9
9 5 2	2	5 4 5 6 8
5 4	3	3 4 7 3 7 4 9
1 6 7 6 9 6 1	4	6 2 0 9 6 5
4 9 4	5	
0	6	
	7	3
Key: 0	6	1 = 60 HR for Ruth, 61 HR for Bonds

Note that in order to compare the two sets of data more readily, we needed to use the same stems for each. This was accomplished in this example by sharing the common stems and creating one plot instead of two separate ones. This is commonly referred to as a **side-by-side** (or **back-to-back**) **stem-and-leaf plot**.

The Ordered Array

An **ordered array** is a listing of all the data in either increasing or decreasing magnitude. Data listed in increasing order are said to be listed in **rank order**. If listed in decreasing order, they are listed in **reverse rank order**. Listing the data in an ordered way can be very helpful. It allows you to scan the data quickly for the largest and smallest values, for large gaps in the data, and for concentrations or clusters of values.

Example 3.4.2

The personnel records for a clothing department store located in the local mall are examined, and the current ages for all employees are noted. There are 25 employees, and their ages are listed in the following table. It is desired that their ages be placed in rank order.

Ages of Employees												
32	21	24	19	61	18	18	16	16	35	39	17	22
21	60	18	53	18	57	63	28	20	29	35	45	

Solution

Ages (Ordered)												
16	16	17	18	18	18	18	19	20	21	21	22	24
28	29	32	35	35	39	45	53	57	60	61	63	

It is always a good idea to get a look at the ordered array of the data early in your analysis. Examining the ranked data produces a good intuitive sense for the data. Looking at the ordered array, it is evident that over half of the employees are younger than 25 and only three employees are 60 or older. We can also easily see that the youngest employee is 16 years old and the oldest employee is 63 years old. Ordering the data makes it easy to analyze the data quickly and easily.

Ordered arrays are easy to create. Virtually all statistics, spreadsheet, and database programs enable the user to quickly sort the data in ascending or descending order. If a spreadsheet or database program is not available, a stem-and-leaf plot can be helpful in sorting the data.

Dot Plots

A **dot plot** is a graph where each data value is plotted as a point (or a dot) above a horizontal axis. If there are multiple entries of the same data value, they are plotted one above the other. Dot plots are useful when you are interested in where the data is clustered and which values occur most often.

Technology

In Microsoft Excel, the Sort tool allows the user to sort any number of data values in ascending or descending order. To learn how to do this with Excel , or with other technologies, please visit stat.hawkeslearning.com and navigate to **Technology Instructions > Data Manipulation > Sorting**.

Example 3.4.3

The following table contains the number of wins by baseball's Chicago Cubs for a recent 50 year period. Use this data to construct a dot plot.

⌘ Technology

For instructions on how to create a dot plot in Excel, Minitab, or other technologies, please visit stat.hawkeslearning.com and navigate to **Technology Instructions > Graphs > Dot Plot.**

Wins by the Chicago Cubs (1967–2016)									
61	85	67	68	78	76	73	81	85	87
66	97	88	90	84	77	71	79	77	84
73	83	89	67	49	93	96	80	66	92
97	75	79	65	73	77	77	64	75	84
103	71	66	88	76	77	70	38	75	83

Solution

We plot each data value on the axis. For values where there are multiple entries, such as for 77, we stack the points on top of one another.

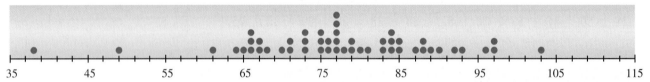

Chicago Cubs Wins

From the dot plot we see that most values occur between 64 and 97 and the value that occurs most frequently is 77.

By way of comparison, the dot plots for a few other teams are given below.

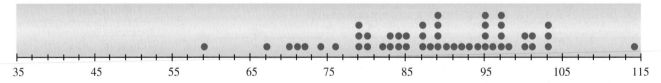

NY Yankees Wins

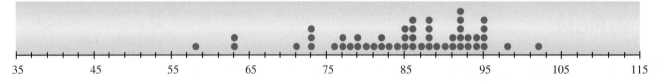

LA Dodgers Wins

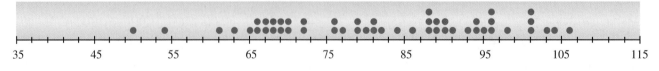

Atlanta Braves Wins

Time Series Plots

A good example of time series data is the census measurements taken every decade since 1790. The population of the United States has been growing steadily since the first census as shown in Table 3.4.3.[7] Interestingly, the change in population between 2000 and 2010 was 27.3 million, which is greater than the entire population of the United States in 1850.

Table 3.4.3 - US Census Data		
Year	Population	Population (in millions)
1790	3,929,214	3.9
1800	5,308,483	5.3
1810	7,239,881	7.2
1820	9,638,453	9.6
1830	12,866,020	12.9
1840	17,069,453	17.1
1850	23,191,876	23.2
1860	31,443,321	31.4
1870	38,558,371	38.6
1880	50,189,209	50.2
1890	62,979,766	63.0
1900	76,212,168	76.2
1910	92,228,496	92.2
1920	106,021,537	106.0
1930	123,202,624	123.2
1940	132,164,569	132.2
1950	151,325,798	151.3
1960	179,323,175	179.3
1970	203,211,926	203.2
1980	226,545,805	226.5
1990	248,709,873	248.7
2000	281,421,906	281.4
2010	308,745,538	308.7

In a line graph, time is always labeled on the horizontal axis, with the variable being measured labeled on the vertical axis. Points are then plotted for each time period, and a line is drawn that connects each consecutive point. In Figure 3.4.6, each of the points is plotted with the year on the horizontal axis and the corresponding population (in millions) on the vertical axis.

⌀ **Technology**

For instructions on how to create a line graph using Excel, Minitab, or other technologies, please visit stat.hawkeslearning.com and navigate to **Technology Instructions > Graphs > Line Graph.**

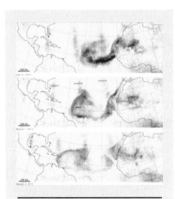

How the Sahara Feeds the Amazon Jungle

The Sahara is one of the most desolate stretches of land on the planet, yet it breathes life into one of our most fertile jungles. It was a story that few people even knew existed until a group of researchers lead by Dr. Hongbin Yu, a research scientist at NASA's Goddard Space Flight Center, looked at the data. In 2015, the research group published a study that used satellite imagery to quantify the annual amount of phosphorous contained in Saharan dust that was swept into the atmosphere by winds, and transported over the Atlantic to the Amazon Basin. They created three-dimensional simulation models that allowed them to visualize the plumes of dust traveling over the ocean, and then they measured the trace amounts of phosphorous that remained in the dust from when water used to cover the Sahara. Phosphorous is vital in the growth of vegetation, and it is in low supply in tropical regions, making the link between the desert and the jungle vital to the stability of the global ecosystem. This is just one example of how our planet creates ecological balance, and it showcases how much we have left to learn about the place we call home. This discovery is only the beginning of a much larger revolution, and through the increased collection and analysis of data, we may one day be able to tell the true story about the ways of our world.

Source: NASA's Goddard Space Flight Center

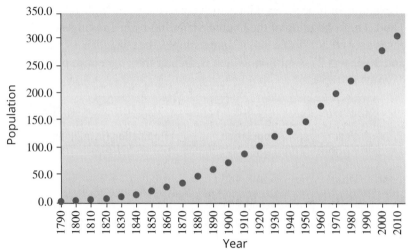

Figure 3.4.6

In Figure 3.4.7, a line segment connects consecutive points in the time series to give a line graph. From the line graph we can easily see that the series is nonstationary, and that there is an upward trend in the data.

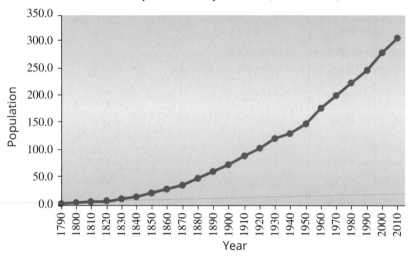

Figure 3.4.7

Does it make sense to draw a histogram for a nonstationary time series? We could create a histogram of the population data we have been examining, but it would not reveal anything very interesting. For a nonstationary time series (a time series with a trend), a histogram is usually not warranted.

It is not uncommon to see time series graphs with multiple sets of data plotted. It is also not uncommon to see two vertical axes used if the data sets have different scales. In Figure 3.4.8, both the sea level change and the global temperature change since 1901 are shown on the same graph. The vertical scale on the left refers to the change in sea level. The vertical scale on the right refers to the change in global temperature. By plotting both sets of data on the same graph, we can see the trend that the two sets of data share.

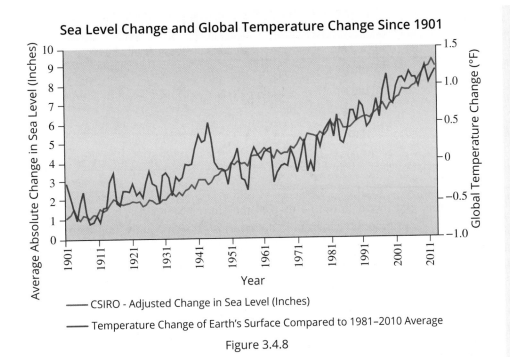

Figure 3.4.8

Geospatial Graphs

For centuries, humans have used maps to portray information about specific places or regions. Today, it is very common to see data that is associated with some type of geographic location such as zip codes, county codes, states, countries, or even specific longitudes and latitudes. This association allows us to layer the data values on top of a map of a certain area, or satellite image, ultimately providing us with a greater understanding of how different regions compare to one another based on a variety of different variables.

Choropleth maps are one type of geospatial graph that has become very popular, although their use dates back to the early 19th century. Choropleth maps utilize shades of color to measure a variable across several pre-defined areas, and those areas can be anywhere on a map as long as they are pre-defined and have data associated with them. Choropleth maps are similar to heat maps; however, heat maps use the given data to define regions whereas choropleth maps come with predefined regions with which data is already associated. An example of a heat map would be weather radar, where the shaded region is dynamically defined by the amount and type of precipitation in an area rather than by state or county lines.

Suppose we are interested in visualizing obesity in different regions of the United States. The Center for Disease Control (CDC) provides a county level data set containing the number of people in each county who are above the obesity threshold. For our inquiry, we are only interested in two columns of the full data set: the county code, or FIPS Code, and the number of people in a county who are obese in the year 2016. A preview of the data we will use is in Table 3.4.4.[8]

Note

You frequently hear data visualization specialists refer to encoding data into a graphic. For example, in a histogram the data is encoded into different categories. If you are creating a choropleth map, the data is encoded spatially by placing the data in a region (usually county, state, or country). The magnitude of the data is usually represented by a color shade. So, the data is encoded in two dimensions.

Data

To download the full US County data set, please go to the web resource at **Data > US County Data.**

Table 3.4.4 - Number of Obese Adults by US County	
FIPS Code	**Number of Obese Adults 2016**
1001	15,884
1003	47,117
1005	10,653
1007	7,611
1009	17,347
. . .	

We want to plot this data onto a map of the United States. Each FIPS Code can be used to determine the geographic boundaries of each county, and then we will shade each county region on a map of the U.S. based on the number of adults who are obese in that area. A lighter shade will indicate that the number of obese adults is smaller, and a darker shade will indicate that the number is higher.

County Obesity Population 2016

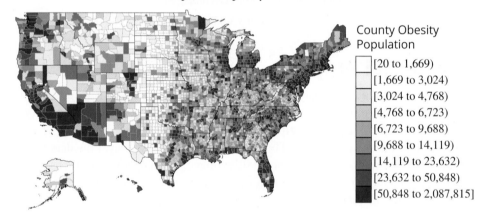

County Obesity Population

[20 to 1,669)
[1,669 to 3,024)
[3,024 to 4,768)
[4,768 to 6,723)
[6,723 to 9,688)
[9,688 to 14,119)
[14,119 to 23,632)
[23,632 to 50,848)
[50,848 to 2,087,815]

Figure 3.4.9

⌁ Technology

Choropleth maps can be useful when comparing multiple locations. To learn how to create a county level choropleth map of the United States, please visit stat.hawkeslearning.com and navigate to **Technology Instructions > Graphs > Choropleth Map (County)**.

Figure 3.4.9 suggests that the majority of obese adults in the United States reside in the Southwest and Northeast, and that the Midwest and Central Plains areas don't have very many obese adults at all. By looking at the legend to the right, you can see that there is an extremely wide range from the lowest class to the highest. This is because some counties contain millions of residents, while others contain as few as a couple hundred. So, for many of the rural counties in the center of the country, even if every single person in the county was obese, they still would not compare with, say, Los Angeles County which has a total population of nearly 10 million.

Note

On our companion website, stat.hawkeslearning. com, there is a link to a number of beautiful map visualizations offering several perspectives on the locations of every McDonald's restaurant in the United States.

It is inaccurate to rank the counties simply by the total number of obese adults, and doing so will lead to faulty or incomplete conclusions. In order to get a better understanding of how the counties truly compare to one another, we need to **normalize** the values being graphed. Since our variable of interest in Figure 3.4.10, number of obese adults, is a subset of the total population in each county, we can use the total population in each county to find the percentage in each county that is obese. This can be done by dividing the number of people in a county who are obese by the total county population, however, the US County data set provides the percentages for us. A preview of the updated data set, with the new variable of interest, is shown in Table 3.4.5.[9]

Table 3.4.5 - Percentage of Obese Adults by US County	
FIPS Code	**Percentage of Obese Adults 2016**
1001	30.5
1003	26.6
1005	37.3
1007	34.3
1009	30.4
. . .	

Using our new data, we generate the following map.

County Obesity Percentages 2016

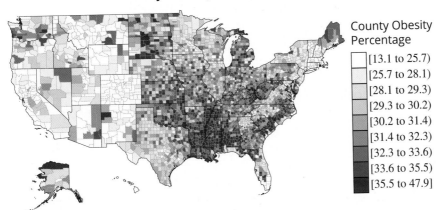

County Obesity
Percentage

[13.1 to 25.7)
[25.7 to 28.1)
[28.1 to 29.3)
[29.3 to 30.2)
[30.2 to 31.4)
[31.4 to 32.3)
[32.3 to 33.6)
[33.6 to 35.5)
[35.5 to 47.9]

Figure 3.4.10

As you can see, Figure 3.4.10 is substantially different from Figure 3.4.9, and comes along with an entirely new set of conclusions. If we had used Figure 3.4.9 to come to a conclusion, we would have assumed that the Southwest and Northeast regions are the areas in the country that struggle with obesity the most. However, once we normalized our obesity variable by making it a ratio of the total county population, Figure 3.4.10 seems to suggest that it is actually the Southeast and the Midwest that struggle with obesity the most. The data shows that these regions have a higher percent of adults who are obese relative to their total population than the Northeast and Southwest do. This is a prime example of why it is necessary to normalize data when making comparisons.

3.4 **Exercises**

Basic Concepts

1. What is the main characteristic of data that a histogram reveals?

2. Describe the type of data that could be usefully described with a histogram.

3. True or false: A frequency distribution contains all of the information needed to construct a histogram.

4. List the important features to look for when studying a histogram.

Absence of Evidence is Not Evidence of Absence

During the London cholera outbreaks of the mid-1800s, thousands of people died within a relatively short period. At the time, the prevailing theory regarding how cholera was spread was called the miasma theory. It stated that the disease was spread through "bad air" that emanated from rotting organic matter. However, Dr. John Snow suspected that unsanitary water from the River Thames was the true culprit. Unfortunately, germ theory had not been developed yet, so Dr. Snow didn't fully understand how the alternative transmission method worked. In 1854, Dr. Snow utilized sampling and data visualization to illustrate that most of the cholera outbreaks happening at the time were occurring in houses that were close to the water pump on Broad Street. Still, the skeptics endured. However, even though his examination of the water was absent of evidence for harmful microbes, that does not mean that the microbes themselves were absent. Over a decade later, Louis Pasteur would officially propose germ theory, vindicating the work of Dr. Snow.

5. Explain why the stem-and-leaf plot is sometimes called a "hybrid graphical method."

6. Identify the advantages of a stem-and-leaf plot.

7. Consider the following data value: 39. What would be the stem and the leaf for this value if we identified the stem as the tens digit? What would be the stem and the leaf if we identified the stem as the hundreds digit?

8. When constructing a stem-and-leaf plot, how do you determine which part to make the stem and which part to make the leaf?

9. What is an ordered array?

10. What are some advantages of the ordered array?

11. What is a dot plot?

12. What are some advantages of using a dot plot?

13. How can the most frequently occurring value be identified by studying a dot plot?

14. Why is it important to plot time series data?

15. The time variable is always graphed on which axis?

16. What is a choropleth map?

Exercises

17. In November 2017, the closing prices (in dollars) for stocks in the Dow Jones Transportation Average were as follows.

Closing Prices	
Stock	**Closing Price ($)**
Alaska Air Group (ALK)	66.90
American Airlines (AAL)	49.15
Avis Budget Group (CAR)	36.04
C.H. Robinson Worldwide (CHRW)	80.65
CSX (CSX)	51.14
Delta Air Lines (DAL)	50.17
Expeditors International of Washington (EXPD)	60.86
FedEx (FDX)	217.00
J.B. Hunt Transport Services (JBHT)	104.39
JetBlue Airways (JBLU)	20.03
Kansas City Southern (KSU)	106.24
Kirby (KEX)	62.20
Landstar System (LSTR)	98.80
Matson (MATX)	27.64
Norfolk Southern (NSC)	128.29
Ryder System (R)	78.69
Southwest Airlines (LUV)	55.28

Closing Prices	
Stock	**Closing Price ($)**
Union Pacific (UNP)	117.15
United Continental Holdings (UAL)	59.84
United Parcel Service (UPS)	114.41

a. Construct a frequency distribution for the closing prices.

b. Construct a histogram for the closing prices.

18. Using the San Francisco Salaries - 2014 data set from the web resource, create a histogram and frequency distribution for the variable TotalPayBenefits and use them to answer the following questions. For the histogram and frequency distribution, use $30,000 for the minimum value and $480,000 for the maximum value. Use class widths of $50,000.

⁝ **Data**

stat.hawkeslearning.com
Data Sets > San Francisco Salaries 2014

a. What is the level of measurement of the variable?

b. How many of the laborers earn more than $130,000 per year?

c. What percent of the laborers earn at most $130,000 per year? Round your answer to one decimal place.

d. What percent of the laborers earn more than $230,000 per year? Round your answer to one decimal place.

19. A chemist is interested in knowing the amount of alcohol contained in American-brewed beers. To study this, the chemist uses data containing information about several different kinds of American-brewed beers, and evaluates the alcohol by volume for each. Using the Beers and Breweries data set from the web resource, perform the following:

⁝ **Data**

stat.hawkeslearning.com
Data Sets > Beers and Breweries

a. Construct a frequency distribution for the alcohol by volume (ABV) variable. Use 0.001 for the minimum value and 0.130 for the maximum value. Use bin widths of 0.010.

b. Construct a relative frequency distribution for the ABV. Round the relative frequencies to four decimal places.

c. Construct a histogram of the relative frequency distribution.

d. Comment on any information about the alcohol by volume in American-brewed beers which you were able to ascertain by examining the distributions and the histogram.

20. Consider the assets (in billions of dollars) of the 10 largest commercial banks listed in the following table.

Assets (Billions of Dollars)				
216.9	138.9	115.5	110.3	103.5
98.2	76.4	64.0	53.5	49.0

a. Construct a frequency distribution for the assets (in billions of dollars) of the 10 largest commercial banks.

b. Construct a relative frequency distribution for the assets (in billions of dollars) of the 10 largest commercial banks.

c.   Construct a histogram of the relative frequency distribution.

d.   Comment on any information about the assets (in billions of dollars) of the 10 largest commercial banks which you were able to ascertain by examining the distributions and the histogram.

21.   Fifty hospitals in a western state were polled as to their basic daily charges for a semi-private room. The results are listed in the following table, rounded to the nearest dollar.

Daily Charges for Semi-Private Rooms (Dollars)									
125	135	148	156	248	215	156	148	135	149
178	156	135	125	214	256	258	265	156	148
123	147	189	199	189	248	215	259	158	235
268	269	158	198	147	258	269	239	288	199
179	179	189	169	258	178	257	249	259	259

a.   What level of measurement does the data possess?

b.   Does the data need to be normalized?

c.   Construct a stem-and-leaf display for the data using the tens digits as the stems.

d.   Comment on the shape of the distribution.

22.   The data in the following table are the toxic emissions (in thousands of tons) for 10 states in the United States.[10]

Toxic Emissions (Thousands of Tons)									
206	147	441	128	127	133	422	152	114	134

a.   Construct a stem-and-leaf display for the data using the hundreds digits as the stems.

b.   Comment on any information about the toxic emissions (in thousands of tons) of the 10 states that you were able to ascertain by examining the stem-and-leaf display.

23.   Consider the following highway miles per gallon for 19 selected models of mini-compact, sub-compact, and compact cars.

Miles per Gallon									
26	46	36	31	28	28	27	38	42	36
37	33	23	29	37	34	29	40	28	

a.   Construct a stem-and-leaf display for the data.

b.   Comment on any information about the highway mpg of the selected models which you were able to ascertain by examining the stem-and-leaf display.

24.   An instructor is interested in comparing exam scores for fraternity and non-fraternity males in her class. Meaningful comparisons between two sets of data can be made using a side-by-side stem-and-leaf display. To illustrate this, note the following display summarizing the scores.[11]

Leaf (Non-Fraternity)	Stem	Leaf (Fraternity)
	0	9
2	1	4 0 8
	2	5 7 9 4 5 5 1
3 9	3	2 6 6 9 7 7 3 2 1 6 0
	4	2 7 5
5 6 4 8 9 9 0 2	5	4 7 6 7
4 4 7 8 1 0 3 2 2 6 8 9	6	6 8 9 9 5
5 4 7 8 4 3 8 8 9 1	7	3 4 2 7 8 6 7 4 3
2 9 7 4	8	4 5 3 8 9 9 6 4 2 1 1 4 5
4 2	9	4 3 5 1 6 7 7 0 3

a.   What level of measurement does the data possess?

b.   Based upon the stem-and-leaf display, compare the two groups. Think of the several ways in which this can be done.

c.   Suppose that 60% is considered a passing score on the exam. What percent of the fraternity students passed the exam? Non-fraternity students?

d.   If someone scores 90 or higher on the exam, they will be exempt from taking the next exam. What percent of the fraternity students will be exempt from taking the next exam? Non-fraternity students?

25.   *Fortune* magazine publishes a list of the top 100 best companies to work for. For the top 10 companies on this list, the average annual employee salaries are given in the following table (in thousands of dollars).

Average Salaries (Thousands of Dollars)									
121	122	136	74	118	101	114	61	95	132

a.   Construct a stem-and-leaf display for the data using the tens digits as the stems.

b.   Comment on any information about the average annual salaries (in thousands of dollars) of the top 10 companies which you were able to ascertain by examining the stem-and-leaf display.

c.   Construct an ordered array of the average annual salaries in rank order.

d.   Does the ordered array provide any additional insight into the nature of the data?

26.   Use the table of data below to complete the following.

a.   Construct a dot plot of the data.

b.   Which data value occurs most often?

23	19	15	20	17
16	18	14	23	22
19	23	19	16	25
17	20	21	23	24

27. Listed in the following table is the number of passing attempts per game by Super Bowl champion Aaron Rodgers in the 2010 NFL season.

    a. Construct a dot plot of the data.

    b. Which data value occurs most often?

Passing Attempts by Aaron Rodgers				
31	29	45	17	46
33	34	34	34	31
35	30	11	37	28

28. The following line graph displays the total IRA and Keogh accounts (in billions of dollars) in the U.S., charted from June 1990 to June 2011.[12]

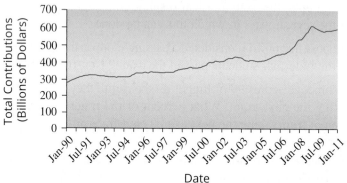

    a. What conclusions can you make regarding the total contributed to the accounts?

    b. Is the data time series data?

    c. If the data is time series data, is the series stationary or nonstationary?

29. The following chart contains LIBOR (which stands for London Interbank Offered Rate) data for January 2011 through May 2011. LIBOR is the average interest rate that banks in London charge when lending funds to other banks. The line graphs in the figure represent 1 month, 3 month, 6 month, and 12 month interest rates.[13]

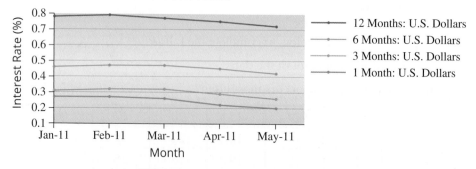

    a. Examine the chart and discuss the data. What conclusions can you make?

b. If the data is time series data, is it a stationary or nonstationary time series? Explain your reasoning.

30. The Gallup Poll frequently obtains responses to the question, *At the present time, do you think religion as a whole is increasing its influence on American life or losing its influence?* The percent of the respondents who answered "increasing" is given below for various polls.

Survey Responses										
Year	2009	2005	2001	1995	1992	1991	1990	1988	1986	1984	1982
Percent	25	49	71	38	27	27	33	36	48	42	41
Year	1980	1978	1977	1975	1974	1970	1969	1968	1965	1962	1957
Percent	35	37	37	39	31	14	14	19	33	45	69

    a. What level of measurement do the responses to the question possess?

    b. Construct a time series plot for the data.

    c. What conclusions can you make from the plot?

31. The following table gives the number of immigrants (in thousands) and the average annual immigration rate per 1000 people in the U.S. population for the decade ending in the year given.

Annual Immigration (per 1000 People)										
Year	1900	1910	1920	1930	1940	1950	1960	1970	1980	1990	2000
Number	3688	8795	5736	4107	528	1035	2515	3322	4493	7338	9095
Rate	5.3	10.4	5.7	3.5	0.4	0.7	1.5	1.7	2.1	2.9	3.2

    a. What levels of measurement do the three variables in this exercise possess?

    b. Construct a time series plot of the number of immigrants per decade.

    c. Find the percent change in the number of immigrants from the decade ending in 1900 to the decade ending in 2000.

    d. Find the percent change in the average annual immigration rate per 1000 people in the U.S. population from the decade ending in 1900 to the decade ending in 2000. Compare your answer to that which you obtained in part **c.** Can you explain why these answers are different?

3.5   Analyzing Graphs

Graphs that help us visualize data can either be enlightening, in the sense that they gives us insight and understanding of a set of data, or misleading, either intentionally or unintentionally. When you see graphs in the media, you need to be cautious to ensure the data has been accurately represented by the graph. This section will help you analyze graphs for accuracy and appropriate presentation of the given information. Here are a few key ideas to consider when interpreting information displayed in graphical form.

> **Statistics Can Be Cool!**
>
> There is a YouTube video entitled "The best stats you've ever seen" with millions of views. The video is presented by Hans Rosling who was a global health expert. Mr. Rosling created some amazing data visualization about the state of the world, especially the "developing world".
>
> If you want to see a statistical presentation that is truly inspiring, you will enjoy this video!

Graph Labeling

Every graph should be properly labeled with an appropriate title that tells you what type of information is being displayed. Also, if the graph has a horizontal and vertical axis, these should be labeled and should include the unit of measurement when necessary for the understanding of the data. For example, in Figure 3.5.1 shown below, the title does not provide enough information about the data. Why were those countries chosen? Do they have relatively high or low prison populations compared to the rest of the world? Furthermore, we do not know whether this information is relevant to modern times. Is this data for a specific year? The countries are labeled along the horizontal axis, but note that the vertical axis is just labeled *Population*. We have no idea what the values along the vertical axis represent. Is the prisoner population in units of thousands, millions, or billions? In fact, this chart shows the countries with the top ten highest prisoner populations for the year 2016. The unit for the vertical axis should be thousands, which means that the United States had a prison population of approximately 2217 thousand, or 2.217 million, in the year 2016. Without these seemingly small pieces of information, the graph is not very informative. It is also good practice to use the largest possible unit for the scale of an axis, which in this case is correctly chosen to be thousands.

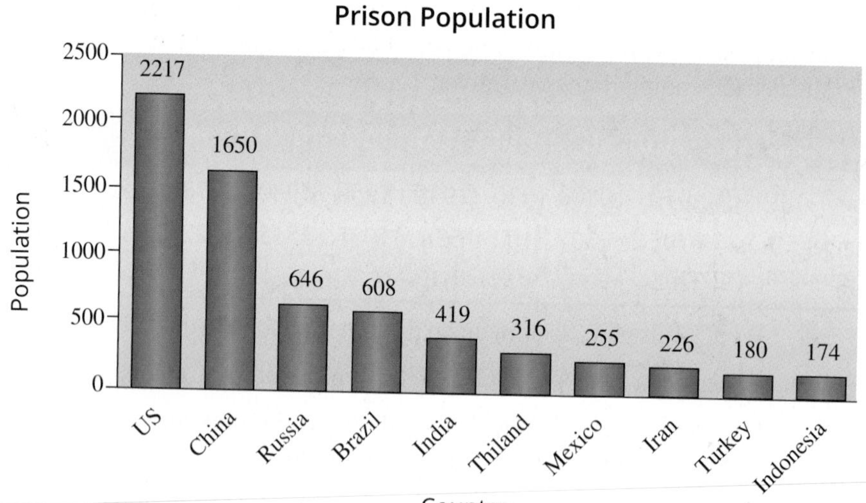

Figure 3.5.1

Sources

When examining graphs in the media it is very important to consider the source of the information, i.e., who is telling the story. What good is a graph if the underlying data is not credible? The data on the US population from 1790 to 2010 from the previous section came from census data collected by the U.S. Census Bureau, which is a highly reputable source of information. Generally, sources such as government entities and scientific journals are fairly reliable. When looking at the credibility of your data, keep in mind the old quote, "Large skepticism leads to large understanding. Small skepticism leads to small understanding. No skepticism leads to no understanding."

Appropriateness of a Graph

Throughout this chapter we have looked at a wide variety of graphs. What we want to consider now is the *appropriateness* of a graph. In other words, we want to be able to determine whether the type of graph being used is best suited for the data being displayed. For example, let's contrast the different uses of line graphs and bar graphs. In the previous section, we looked at the US population since 1790 and chose to display that data using a line graph. We could have just as easily used the bar graph shown in Figure 3.5.2.

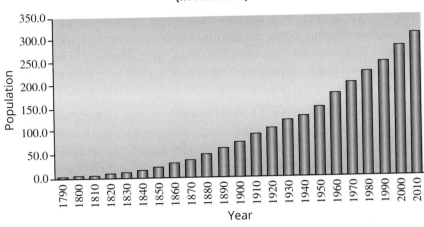

Figure 3.5.2

The bar graph also shows the increasing trend of the US population over time, but the trend is better seen using a line graph. The lengths and widths of the bars in the bar graph are somewhat distracting, and obscure the change in population from one time period to the next.

Bar graphs and pie charts are often interchangeable when displaying qualitative data, but if you want to accurately display the categories as parts of a whole, the pie chart will give the best representation, as it allows you to visually compare the slices of the "pie" very quickly. However, the pie chart becomes less effective as the number of categories increases as was depicted in Section 3.2.

Scaling of Graphs

Another important feature to keep in mind when analyzing graphs is whether a graph is scaled appropriately. If you stretch or shrink the scale on either axis, the shape of the graph can change dramatically, and thus affect the interpretation of the graph. For example, suppose that we change the scale for Figure 3.2.9 on federal government spending to range from 0 to 0.8 instead of 0 to 0.4.

Note

Our companion website, stat.hawkeslearning.com, has a link to a video called "The Art of Data Visualization" that was produced by PBS. While no particular data sets are featured in the video, it displays interesting data driven art and information. The video is only about seven minutes long and is worth taking a quick look.

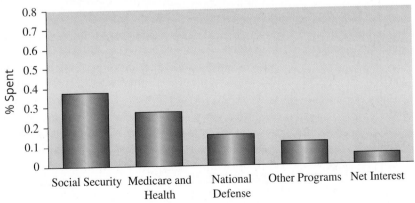

Figure 3.5.3

Note

There is a very good TED Talk video on YouTube entitled "The Beauty of Data Visualization" by David McCandless. In the video, McCandless presents interesting data and a number of "normalization" techniques that are creative.

Note that Figure 3.5.3 now minimizes the differences among the five spending categories compared to the original graph. The large amount of "white space" in the graph is a good indicator that the scale may not be appropriate for the data. Therefore, when analyzing a graph make sure that the scale represents the data well.

Data Transformations

It is often useful to transform data by replacing a variable in the data set by a function of that variable so that the distribution is easier to work with or interpret. For example, if the data set contains a variable x, we can transform the distribution of the data by replacing x with some function of x, such as the square root of x or the logarithm of x.

In fact, we have already applied a transformation to one of the geospatial graphs in the previous section. Recall that, due to the massive variance in US county populations, we could not accurately compare the obesity prevalence between counties when we measured the number of obese people in each county. To account for this, we applied a function to our data that transformed the variable of interest, the *number* of obese people in a county, into the *percentage* of obese people in a county. The function divided the number of obese people in a county by the total county population, multiplied the quotient by 100, and resulted in the percentage of the county population that was obese. The alternate perspective of the data then allowed us to easily compare counties since the variable of interest was **normalized** by total county population.

In this section, we will focus on another transformation, the log transformation, which is one of the most common transformations in statistics. The log transformation is often used to help "unclutter" data points for visualization purposes. When the data is tightly grouped together, it can be hard to visualize and make inferences about individual data points. Log transformations numerically "stretch" the portion of the axis closest to zero, and "compress" the portion of the axis farthest from zero. This allows us to better visualize each individual point while also maintaining the underlying relationship between the variables being graphed. The log transformation also allows us to visualize relative change as opposed to absolute change.

Data

The full Amazon stock price data set can be found on stat.hawkeslearning.com under **Data Sets > Amazon Stock Price.**

Figure 3.5.4 shows the price per share of Amazon stock since its initial public offering (IPO) in May 1997. No transformation is applied to the data which means that the graph shows absolute change.

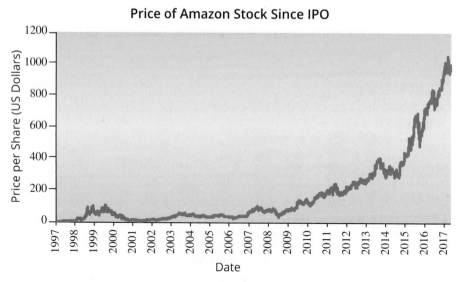

Figure 3.5.4

As you can see, Amazon has experienced massive success over the years. However, this graph seems to suggest that Amazon didn't really hit its stride until about 2010.

In terms of data visualization, logarithms can be used to determine relative change between observations. As you can see in Figure 3.5.4, Amazon's stock price starts to become very substantial starting in 2010. In fact, the difference between the stock price in May 2015 and the price in May 2016 is a larger number than the maximum stock price was in any year prior to 2011. When we compare every data point to the original base, the stock price in May 1997, it becomes very hard to compare relative performances from year to year; a good amount of growth in the late 1990s and early 2000s would not be considered very good after 2010. However, transforming our price variable by applying a log function will allow us to analyze Amazon's yearly performance relative to the stock price for each year. After applying the log function to the y-axis of the previous graph, we generate Figure 3.5.5 which tells the story in a slightly different way.

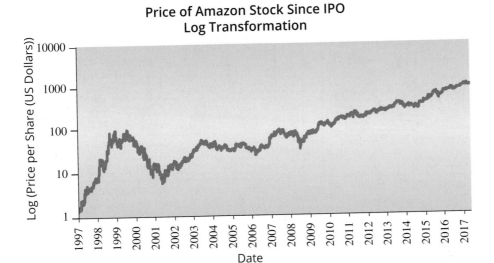

Figure 3.5.5

Notice that the y-axis of Figure 3.5.5 now portrays the price variable in factors of 10 as opposed to a continuous unit scale. It turns out that Amazon experienced its most rapid period of relative growth in the years immediately following its IPO. However, notice that the stock price began to sharply decline in 1999. This was when the dot-com bubble "burst". When the bubble burst, thousands of internet companies went out of business. Fortunately, Amazon's business model was built for long-term growth, and it allowed the company to survive the downward economic trend. In 2001, Amazon turned its first profit and restored the confidence of investors. Since then, Figure 3.5.5 reveals that Amazon continues to experience steady year over year growth on the log scale.

Misleading Graphs

An issue related to scaling that is often used to mislead readers is to start the vertical scale at some value other than zero. We saw this earlier with the sales performance data in Section 3.2. By starting the scale on the vertical axis at $180,000 and using increments of $5,000, the sales performance differences were exaggerated (see Figures 3.2.2 and 3.2.3).

One type of graph commonly used in the media is a pictograph, because it is visually appealing and simple to understand. A **pictograph** is basically a bar graph that uses pictures of objects in place of the bars. For example, the graph on the left in Figure 3.5.6 shows a potentially misleading pictograph of the top five countries ranked in order by the amount of forest area they contain. The bars in this bar chart are represented by trees. Note how as the amount of forest area increases, the trees expand with regard to width and height, thus giving the illusion that the amount of increase is much larger than it is in reality. This is a common problem with pictographs found in the media. Often when the size of the object is increased or decreased, the change is not simply one-dimensional. So be very cautious when looking at data displayed with a pictograph to make sure the graph isn't misleading by representing increases or decreases along one dimension (height of the bar) using an object that is changing in area or volume. The graph on the right represents the correct way to scale a pictograph by only changing the heights of the trees.

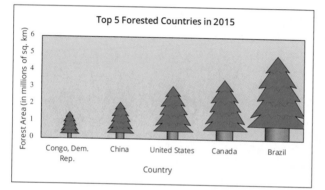 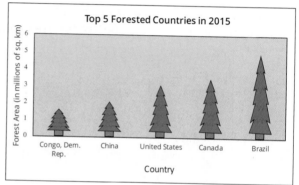

Figure 3.5.6

3.5 **Exercises**

Basic Concepts

1. Why is it important to label and title graphs properly?

2. What types of sources are reliable?

3. Why is the scaling of a graph important?

4. Why are data transformations useful?

Exercises

5. Do you see any issues with the scales used on the axes of the graph depicting banana prices per pound in July?[14] Why or why not?

Price of Bananas per pound in July

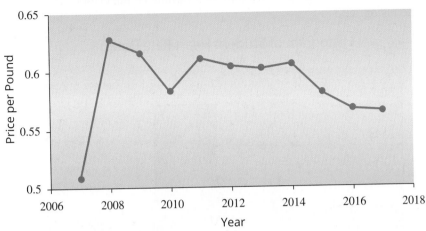

6. Using the San Francisco Salaries 2014 data set from the web resource, create a histogram for the variable TotalPayBenefits and answer the following:

    a. Does the distribution of the data in the histogram look bell-shaped, skewed right, or skewed left?

    b. Construct a new histogram for the variable LogTotalPayBenefits, which is a log transformation of the variable TotalPayBenefits.

    c. Does the distribution of the data in the log transformed histogram look bell-shaped, skewed right, or skewed left?

∷ **Data**

stat.hawkeslearning.com
Data Sets > San Francisco Salaries 2014

7. The US median home price increased from $219,600 in November 2010 to $318,700 in November 2017, as shown in the following pictograph.[15]

    a. What was the percentage increase in US median home price between November 2010 and November 2017?

    b. Is the pictograph shown an accurate depiction of this increase? Why or why not?

    c. How could you improve the pictograph so that it accurately represents the information?

US Median Home Price

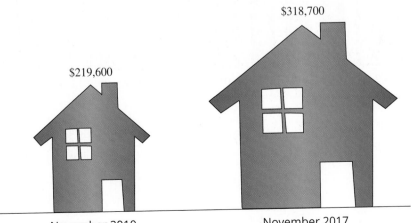

8. The following histogram uses the heart rate data from Example 3.3.1 but has different classes than were used in the example. What errors can you find in the histogram?

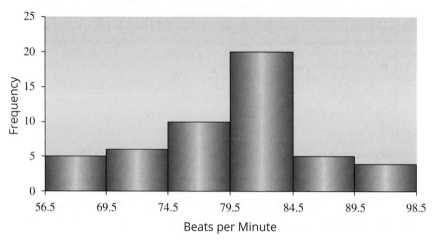

Histogram of Student Heart Rate Data

9. The number of robberies in North Charleston, SC is depicted in two different graphs below.[16] Use these graphs to answer the following.

   a. Which graph do you feel better represents the data? Why?

   b. If you lived in North Charleston, how concerned would each of these graphs make you feel? Explain.

   c. Approximately how many times taller is the 2016 bar compared to the 2013 bar in Graph B? How many times more robberies were there actually in 2016 compared to 2013?

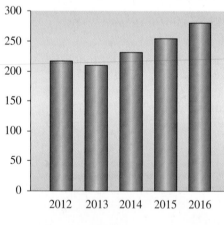

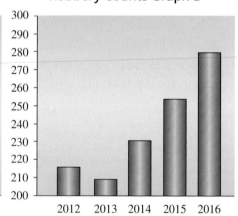

CR   **Chapter Review**

Basic Concepts

1. From a comprehension standpoint, what are the advantages of visual images over the written word?

2. What are some of the benefits of graphing?

3. What is the major disadvantage of graphing?

4. Describe the purpose of a frequency distribution.

5. Describe in general terms the types of data that a bar chart would be useful in displaying.

6. What is a stacked bar chart?

7. Describe the type of data that could be usefully described with a histogram.

8. What are some advantages of the ordered array?

9. Why is it important to plot time series data?

Key Terms and Ideas

- Frequency Distribution
- Bar Chart
- Stacked Bar Chart
- Pie Chart
- Relative Frequency
- Cumulative Frequency
- Cumulative Relative Frequency
- Histogram
- Class Boundaries

- Symmetric Distribution
- Skewed Distribution
- Stem-and-Leaf Display
- Ordered Array
- Rank Order
- Reverse Rank Order
- Dot Plot
- Time Series Plot
- Line Graph

Key Formulas	
	Section
Class Width	3.3
$$\dfrac{\text{Maximum Value} - \text{Minimum Value}}{\text{Number of Classes}}$$	
Relative Frequency	3.3
$$\dfrac{\text{Number in Class}}{\text{Total Number of Observations}}$$	

Additional Exercises

1. The table below contains median family incomes in the United States for the years 1997 through 2016.[17]

Median Family Income					
Year	Income ($)	Percent Change	Year	Income ($)	Percent Change
1997	66,503	–	2007	71,024	2.2
1998	68,808	3.5	2008	68,581	–3.4
1999	70,392	2.3	2009	67,218	–2.0
2000	70,732	0.5	2010	66,310	–1.4
2001	69,689	–1.5	2011	65,051	–1.9
2002	68,972	–1.0	2012	65,064	0.0
2003	68,745	–0.3	2013	67,461	3.7
2004	68,692	–0.1	2014	67,552	0.1
2005	69,062	0.5	2015	71,590	6.0
2006	69,528	0.7	2016	72,707	1.6

   a. What graphical methods would be useful in displaying the data?

   b. Graph the data.

   c. Write a short paragraph describing the data.

2. The following data represent income of households headed by adults 25 years and older, tabulated by educational attainment.[18]

Income and Educational Attainment									
Educational Attainment	Under $5000	$5000 – $9999	$10,000 – 14,999	$15,000 – 24,999	$25,000 – 34,999	$35,000 – 49,999	$50,000– 74,999	$75,000 & Over	Median Income
Elementary	16.3%	26.7%	17.2%	19.7%	9.9%	6.4%	2.9%	0.8%	$11,730
< 8 Years	18.4	27.9	17.3	18.1	8.9	5.9	2.7	0.7	10,884
8 Years	13.7	25.2	17.1	21.7	11.0	7.0	3.1	1.0	12,999
High School	6.8	12.4	12.0	21.8	17.8	17.0	9.5	2.8	23,382
1 – 3 Years	10.9	19.4	14.9	22.2	14.2	11.2	5.6	1.6	16,727
4 Years	5.4	10.0	11.0	21.6	19.0	18.9	10.8	3.2	25,910
College	2.6	4.3	5.8	15.1	16.3	22.7	20.1	13.2	38,337
1 – 3 Years	3.6	6.6	8.1	18.7	18.1	22.6	16.1	6.1	31,865
4 Years +	1.8	2.5	4.1	12.4	14.9	22.8	23.0	18.5	43,952

   a. What graphical methods would be useful in displaying the data?

   b. Use a graphics program to display the data.

   c. Discuss any conclusions you made from your graph(s).

3. Where do business school students most want to work? A CNNMoney list ranks companies that MBA students want to work for most after getting their degree. It can be seen that men and women have different desires when it comes to employment after business school. The table below shows seven of the top companies students want to work for and the percentage of students that ranked the particular company in their top 5.[19]

Most Desired Companies		
Company	Percent of Men	Percent of Women
Google	22.36	21.72
Goldman Sachs	17.76	5.81
Johnson & Johnson	5.68	11.41
Bain & Company	12.89	7.88
Apple Computer	12.80	11.01
Nike	8.06	9.04
J.P. Morgan	12.08	4.44

   a. What graphical method do you think would be most useful in summarizing this data? Explain your answer.

   b. Graph the data using the method you identified in part **a.**

   c. Write a short paragraph describing the data, making conclusions from the graph you constructed in part **b.**

4. The following data give the percentage of people in the U.S. holding more than one job in a one-year period. Graph the data using a method that would contrast the difference between men and women in this situation.[20]

Percentage Holding More Than One Job		
Year	Men	Women
1970	7.0%	2.2%
1979	5.9%	3.5%
1989	6.4%	5.9%
1999	5.7%	5.6%
2003	5.2%	5.4%

5. *Billboard* magazine, in cooperation with Arbitron, produces a national radio format rating. The following data were gathered from radio listeners 12 and older.

Radio Formats						
	Mon – Fri 6 AM – 10 AM	Mon – Fri 10 AM – 3 PM	Mon – Fri 3 PM – 7 PM	Mon – Fri 7 PM – 12 AM	Mon – Sun 12 AM – 6 AM	Mon – Sun 6 AM – 12 AM
Adult Contemporary	17.2%	19.7%	17.7%	15.0%	16.2%	20.0%
News/Talk	17.9	13.1	12.5	14.3	5.3	15.6
Country	13.0	13.2	13.2	10.3	11.7	14.3

Radio Formats						
	Mon – Fri 6 AM – 10 AM	Mon – Fri 10 AM – 3 PM	Mon – Fri 3 PM – 7 PM	Mon – Fri 7 PM – 12 AM	Mon – Sun 12 AM – 6 AM	Mon – Sun 6 AM – 12 AM
Album Rock	10.0	10.4	10.9	9.8	18.7	10.2
Top 40	8.9	9.7	10.9	12.9	14.3	4.7
Urban	7.5	7.6	8.9	14.1	11.8	7.1
Oldies	6.0	6.8	6.9	6.5	4.3	10.2
Classic Rock	4.7	3.6	3.7	3.9	6.1	2.9
Spanish	4.5	4.2	3.7	2.2	4.9	4.2
Adult Standards	3.4	4.2	3.7	2.7	0.3	2.8
Religious	2.1	1.7	1.8	1.8	1.3	2.5
Classical	1.4	1.7	1.7	1.9	0.5	2.3
Easy Listening	0.9	1.1	0.9	0.8	0.2	1.2
Modern Rock	1.0	1.1	1.3	1.6	2.4	0.4
Adult Alternative	1.5	1.9	2.2	2.2	2.0	1.6

    a.   What kinds of graphs would be appropriate for displaying the data? Explain your choices.

    b.   Graph a column of the data. Briefly analyze your graph.

    c.   Create a graph that would be useful in visually comparing two columns of the data. Briefly analyze your graph.

  6. The Caribbean has been a favorite vacation spot for affluent North Americans and Europeans, especially during the winter months. The following table lists the number of tourists during the first six months of the year for a number of Caribbean destinations.

Number of Tourists			
	U.S.	Canada	Europe
Antigua & Barbuda	53,811	10,709	18,591
Aruba	94,028	1320	4681
Barbados	105,236	51,830	34,562
Bermuda	250,390	21,241	11,715
Bonaire	12,210	352	2266
Cayman Islands	81,180	3791	3025
Curacao	15,186	572	6543
Guadeloupe	15,596	10,654	25,409
Trinidad & Tobago	29,110	12,470	11,820

    a.   Create a stacked bar graph that shows where tourists from the U.S., Canada, and Europe travel in the Caribbean.

b. Create three separate bar charts, one for American tourists, one for Canadian tourists, and one for European tourists, that show the number of people traveling to each Caribbean destination.

7. The following table contains a list of the top 20 global corporations, ranked by the amount spent on research and development in 2009.[21]

			Amount Spent on Research and Development (R&D) in 2009 (Millions of Dollars)		
Rank	Company	R&D Spending	Spending as a % of Sales	Headquarters Location	Industry
1	Roche Holding	9120	20.1	Europe	Healthcare
2	Microsoft	9010	15.4	N. America	Software and Internet
3	Nokia	8240	14.4	Europe	Computing and Electronics
4	Toyota	7822	3.8	Japan	Auto
5	Pfizer	7739	15.5	N. America	Healthcare
6	Novartis	7469	16.9	Europe	Healthcare
7	Johnson & Johnson	6986	11.3	N. America	Healthcare
8	Sanofi-Aventis	6391	15.6	Europe	Healthcare
9	GlaxoSmithKline	6187	13.9	Europe	Healthcare
10	Samsung	6002	5.5	S. Korea	Computing and Electronics
11	General Motors	6000	5.7	N. America	Auto
12	IBM	5820	6.1	N. America	Computing and Electronics
13	Intel	5653	16.1	N. America	Computing and Electronics
14	Merck	5613	20.5	N. America	Healthcare
15	Volkswagen	5359	3.7	Europe	Auto
16	Siemens	5285	5.1	Europe	Industrials
17	Cisco Systems	5208	14.4	N. America	Computing and Electronics
18	Panasonic	5143	6.4	Japan	Computing and Electronics
19	Honda	4996	5.4	Japan	Auto
20	Ford	4900	4.1	N. America	Auto

a. For comparative purposes, which of the two columns reporting R&D spending is more useful, and why?

b. What types of graphs would be useful in presenting this data? Explain your answers.

c. Develop a histogram for the spending as a percent of sales.

d. Use computer software to develop pie charts for the headquarters location and industry categories of the top 20 global R&D spenders.

8. In New York, a group of women challenged the state's ban on topless sunbathing. The legal issue was whether the ban was discriminatory. During the controversy, the Gallup poll conducted a survey asking the following question: *Do you think women should be permitted to sunbathe topless on public beaches, if they choose to, or do you think topless sunbathing on public beaches should be banned?*

Response to Survey Question				
	Permitted	**Banned**	**No Opinion**	**Number of Interviews**
National	33%	63%	4%	1001
Gender				
Male	50	45	5	500
Female	18	79	3	501
Age				
18 – 29	47	51	2	219
30 – 49	39	58	3	411
50 – 64	18	76	6	206
65 +	18	77	5	357
Region				
East	39	59	2	247
Midwest	34	62	4	254
South	25	71	4	301
West	38	57	5	199
Community				
Urban	42	55	3	345
Suburban	35	62	3	351
Rural	23	72	5	298
Race				
White	33	64	3	871
Non-white	39	57	4	121
Education				
College Grads	46	48	6	288
Some College	35	62	3	233
No College	28	69	3	475
Sex/Education				
Male/College	56	40	4	238
Male/No College	45	49	6	238
Female/College	26	70	4	264
Female/No College	13	85	2	237

a. Suggest two different types of graphs that might be useful in graphing the data.

b. Create two different graphs using the data.

c. Write a short paragraph describing the data.

9. The nation's political identification (Republican, Democrat, or Independent) changes over time. The data in the following table represent Harris poll results on political identification from 1977 to 2008.[22]

	Nation's Political Identification (Percent of the Population) 1977–2008						
Year	Republican	Democrat	Independent	Year	Republican	Democrat	Independent
1977	21	48	25	1993	29	38	27
1978	22	43	30	1994	32	37	26
1979	22	41	31	1995	31	36	28
1980	24	41	29	1996	30	38	26
1981	28	39	28	1997	29	37	26
1982	26	40	28	1998	28	37	27
1983	26	41	27	1999	29	36	26
1984	27	40	24	2000	29	37	23
1985	30	39	26	2001	31	36	22
1986	30	39	25	2002	31	34	24
1987	29	38	28	2003	28	33	24
1988	31	39	25	2004	31	34	24
1989	33	40	23	2005	30	36	22
1990	33	38	25	2006	27	36	24
1991	32	37	26	2007	26	35	23
1992	30	36	29	2008	26	36	31

a. What types of graphs would be useful in visualizing this data? Explain your answer.

b. Construct two different types of graphs from the data.

c. Examine the data and write a short paragraph on your conclusions.

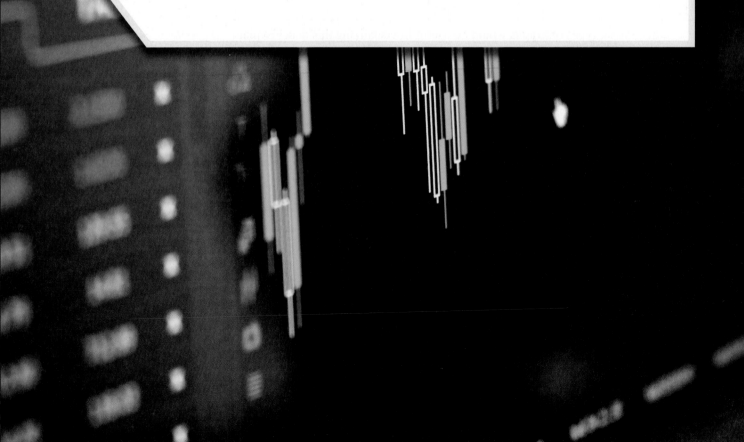

"To be is to be the value of a variable."
— Willard Van Orman Quine

4

CHAPTER

Describing and Summarizing Data from One Variable

Introduction

Frequency distributions, bar charts, pie charts, and histograms can be informative visual tools for examining the big picture when analyzing data. But there is a lack of exactness in the language that we use to describe these graphs. Suppose we say that one data set is more compact than another. This only leads to the question, *How much more compact is it?* Graphical analysis is ill-equipped to answer that question precisely.

If we examine Figure 4.1 and Figure 4.2, we notice the two histograms are somewhat similar, but there is a clear difference in the underlying data. To more precisely describe the differences, we need summary measures to characterize specific data attributes.

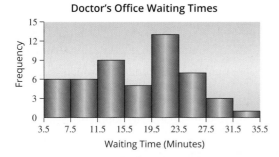

Figure 4.1

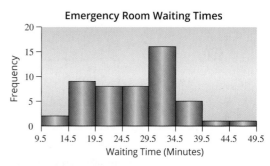

Figure 4.2

Attributes for Summarizing Data

To adequately summarize a set of data, a data analyst might ask the following questions.

- Location: Where is the center of the data?

- Dispersion: Is the data widely scattered or tightly grouped around the central point?

- Shape: Is the data spread symmetrically about the central value? Is the data unbalanced (e.g., are the values much larger than the mean, but not much smaller)?

- Does the data tend to cluster in several groups?

PROPERTIES

Different types of measurements will be developed for each of the attributes listed above. For example, the mean (average) and the median measure the **location** or **central tendency** of a data set. Both of these statistical measures are trying to tell us something about the location of the middle of the data, but they use different ideas for defining that notion of middle.

From the morning paper to the evening news, general concepts are translated into specific statistical measures. Some examples are listed here.

- Poverty rates in 2016 ranged from a low of 7.3% in New Hampshire to a high of 20.8% in Mississippi.[1]

- In 2016, Maryland ($78,945) and Alaska ($76,440) had median household incomes that were among the highest; Mississippi had the lowest ($41,754).[2]

- In 2016, 22.9% of 18 to 34-year-olds living in households, lived in their parents' home.[3] (Compare this to 14.7% in 1975.)

- The median price of an existing home in the U.S., as of August 2017, was $253,500.[4]

- The average hourly manufacturing earnings in the U.S. in August 2017 was $20.90. (Compare this to the average of $14.84 in 2002.)[5]

Such measures are examples of **numerical descriptive statistics**.

Numerical Descriptive Statistics

Numerical descriptive statistics are numerical summaries of quantitative data.

DEFINITION

There is a distinction between measures that are applied to populations and measures that are applied to samples.

Parameter vs. Statistic

A **parameter** is a numerical measure that describes a characteristic of a *population*.

A **statistic** is a numerical measure that describes a characteristic of a *sample*.

DEFINITION

In most instances a data analyst will not know what the population parameters are, since the cost and/or feasibility of obtaining all the population data is usually prohibitive. Inferential statistics involves making conclusions regarding a population using data from a sample.

Inferential Statistics

Inferential statistics is concerned with making conclusions or inferences about population parameters using sample statistics.

DEFINITION

There are many formulas in this chapter that you will have to spend some time examining to appreciate. In most cases, the concepts which motivate these formulas are simple. Yet if these concepts are either ignored or forgotten, statistics becomes a meaningless assortment of symbols, instead of a useful problem-solving and decision-making tool.

 Data

The complete tuition data set can be found on stat.hawkeslearning.com under **Data Sets > Tuition**.

The data in Table 4.1 displays the first six rows of the annual tuition costs of 400 colleges for the academic year (AY) 2016-2017. Looking at 400 pieces of data without using a graphical representation would be confusing. (It seems 400 measurements would contain a great deal of information, yet the sheer volume of the data obscures comprehension.) It's the old problem of not being able to see the forest for the trees.[6]

Table 4.1 – The Cost of a Year's Tuition at 400 Colleges and Universities, AY 2016–2017									
10,632	27,650	34,140	17,000	22,950	24,140	21,304	13,432	23,429	8,282
41,072	14,616	10,587	27,080	25,020	13,590	19,137	10,560	4,944	16,138
31,598	49,644	11,320	26,200	10,430	26,500	12,494	6,900	3,450	31,420
10,266	12,996	11,700	24,390	13,830	19,247	17,133	12,003	4,895	22,467
25,152	15,000	21,830	24,200	23,130	27,492	17,339	25,166	18,056	17,276
17,136	29,994	6,999	12,123	28,800	10,860	24,461	16,841	24,268	18,954
. . .									

Looking at a histogram of the data (see Figure 4.3) is always a good first step. But, we need to learn more. To do this, we use statistical tools designed to reveal the data's fundamental characteristics. These statistical tools answer important questions such as, *Where is the center of the data?* and *How dispersed is the data?*

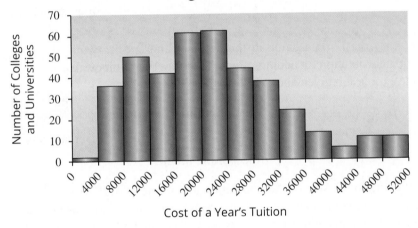

Histogram of Tuition Data

Cost of a Year's Tuition

Figure 4.3

4.1   **Measures of Location**

To your question concerning the whereabouts of Tom Stevens, a mutual friend responds, "In the library." The answer is informative in that it provides general information about Tom's whereabouts. Even though you don't know what part of the library he is in, the information does provide a focal point—a location of sorts. The information may also permit some inferences regarding what Tom is doing.

Statistically speaking, the idea of location is similar to knowing that Tom is in the library. If we think of a data set as a group of data values that cluster around some central value, then this central value provides a focal point for the data set—a location of sorts. Unfortunately, the notion of *central value* is a vague concept, which is as much defined by the way it is measured as by the notion itself. There are several statistical measures that can be used to define the notion of center: the arithmetic mean, weighted mean, trimmed mean, median, and mode.

The Arithmetic Mean

The **arithmetic mean** is one of the more commonly used statistical measures. It appears every day in newspapers, business publications, and frequently in conversation. For example, after receiving a grade on a test, you might be curious about how the rest of the class performed. You might ask the instructor, *What was the average on the test?* The term *average* is often associated with the arithmetic mean, which is more commonly referred to as just the **mean**.

> ### Arithmetic Mean
>
> Suppose there are n observations in a data set, consisting of the observations $x_1, x_2, ..., x_n$; then the **arithmetic mean** is defined to be
>
> $$\frac{1}{n}\left(x_1 + x_2 + ... + x_n\right).$$
>
> **DEFINITION**

If we use some common mathematical notation, the formula can be simplified to

$$\frac{\sum x_i}{n}$$

where x_i is the ith data value in the data set and $\sum$ (pronounced *sigma*) is a mathematical notation for adding values. There are two symbols that are associated with the expression given above:

$$\mu = \frac{1}{N}\left(x_1 + x_2 + ... + x_N\right) \text{ the \textbf{population mean}, and}$$

$$\bar{x} = \frac{1}{n}\left(x_1 + x_2 + ... + x_n\right) \text{ the \textbf{sample mean}.}$$

Here N refers to the size of the population and n refers to the size of the sample. Otherwise, the calculations are made in precisely the same way. The Greek letter μ, representing the population mean, is pronounced *mu*, and the symbol $\bar{x}$, representing the sample mean, is pronounced *x-bar*.

⌘ Technology

To find summary statistics, such as the sample mean, we can use the 1-Var Stats option on the TI-83/84 Plus calculator or we can use other technologies. The calculator results are shown here. For instructions please visit stat.hawkeslearning.com and navigate to **Technology Instructions > Descriptive Statistics > One Variable**.

```
1-Var Stats
x̄=9
Σx=36
Σx²=390
Sx=4.69041576
σx=4.062019202
↓n=4
```

```
1-Var Stats
↑n=4
 minX=4
 Q1=5.5
 Med=8.5
 Q3=12.5
 maxX=15
```

Example 4.1.1

Calculate the sample mean of the following sample data values: 4, 10, 7, 15.

Solution

$$x_1 = 4, x_2 = 10, x_3 = 7, x_4 = 15, \text{ and } n = 4.$$

Note that

$$\bar{x} = \frac{\sum x_i}{n} = \frac{4 + 10 + 7 + 15}{4} = \frac{36}{4} = 9.$$

The sample mean is 9. But why does adding up a group of numbers and dividing by the number of numbers measure central tendency? As unlikely as it sounds, the answer is related to balancing a scale.

Deviation

Given some point *A* and a data point *x*, then *x* − *A* represents how far *x* **deviates** from *A*. This difference is also called a **deviation**.

DEFINITION

Let's calculate the deviations from the mean (9) for the data in Example 4.1.1. Examining the deviations from the mean in Table 4.1.1, we can see the deviations on the left side (−5 and −2) and right side (1 and 6) are in balance. In fact, the mean is considered a point of centrality because the deviations from the mean on the positive side and the negative side are equal (see Figure 4.1.1). The sample mean can be interpreted as a center of gravity.

Table 4.1.1 – Deviations from the Mean	
Data (x_i)	**Deviations from the Mean (x_i - 9)**
4	−5
10	1
7	−2
15	6
TOTAL	$\sum (x_i - 9) = 0$

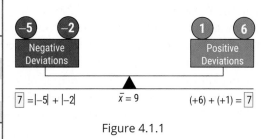

Figure 4.1.1

On the other hand, if we calculate the deviations about any other value the deviations do not balance. For example, assume the central value is 8. The deviation from the alleged central value, 8, for each data value is calculated in Table 4.1.2 and shown in Figure 4.1.2.

The positive deviations (+2 and +7) are not counterbalanced by the negative deviations (−4 and −1). A desirable characteristic of a central value would be to have the positive and negative deviations equal to each other in absolute value.

Table 4.1.2 – Deviations from the Mean	
Data (x_i)	**Deviations from 8 (x_i - 8)**
4	−4
10	2
7	−1
15	7
TOTAL	$\sum (x_i - 8) = 4$

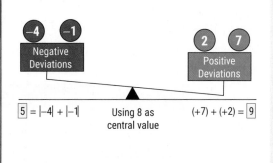

Figure 4.1.2

Although the arithmetic mean is frequently used, there are times when it should not be employed. *Since the mean requires that the data values be added, it should only be used for quantitative data.* Furthermore, if one of the data values is extremely large or small relative to the others, this data value could be considered an **outlier**. An outlier can have a dramatic impact on the value of the mean and dramatically affect

Will Rogers Phenomenon

Will Rogers was an American showman who unwittingly left a lasting impression on the mathematical community when he made a humorous remark regarding migration during the American Depression of the 1930s. He joked: "When the Okies left Oklahoma and moved to California, they raised the average intelligence level in both states." The idea played on the stereotype of the time that Californians were not particularly intelligent, and anyone migrating from any other state to California would raise the average intelligence of California. As it turns out, his joke is mathematically plausible. In fact, the phenomenon occurs so regularly in fields such as medical diagnostics that it was named the "Will Rogers Phenomenon" by Dr. Alvan Feinstein in 1985. The underlying principles of the phenomenon are quite simple. Suppose there are two sets of values; Set 1 has a mean of 50 and Set 2 has a mean of 30. Now, suppose we take five values between 35 and 40 out of Set 1; this will, by definition, raise the mean of Set 1 since the removed values were below the original mean. Now, if we insert those values removed from Set 1 into Set 2, it will, by definition, raise the mean of Set 2 since the inserted values are greater than the original mean of Set 2.

A Knower of the Secret of the Dice

Oftentimes, it is easy for us to take simple mathematical concepts, such as the mean, for granted. However, imagine living in a time when these concepts were not so formally defined. The people with the ability to perform these seemingly basic functions were hailed as the magicians of their time.

An ancient Indian story recounts how King Rtuparna, known to be a frequent gambler, estimated the number of leaves and fruit on two large branches of a tree by using the leaves and fruit of a single twig as the average. He then multiplied the number of leaves and fruit on the single twig by the estimated number of twigs on each branch, and his estimation turned out to be very close to the actual value. When asked how he was able to do this, he replied, "Know that I am a knower of the secret of the dice, and therefore adept in the art of enumeration."

The invention and practice of estimation and measurement are arguably some of the most important milestones in human history, and it might come as a surprise that many of the concepts we use today stemmed from gambling scenarios. Technology, cartography, healthcare, and many other facets of our modern lives are almost entirely supported by our ability to estimate the parameters of a population by using descriptive and inferential statistics.

its value as a measure of central tendency. (See Section 4.3 for further discussion of outliers.)

Outliers and Resistant Measures

An **outlier** is a data value that is extremely different from other measurements in the data set. Statistical measures which are not affected by outliers are said to be **resistant**.

DEFINITION

The mean is *not* a **resistant measure**.

Weighted Mean

The weighted mean is similar to the arithmetic mean except it allows you to give different weights (or importance) to each data value. The weighted mean gives you the flexibility to assign weights when you find it inappropriate to treat each observation the same. The weights are usually positive numbers that sum to one, with the largest weight being applied to the observation with the greatest importance. The weights can be determined in a variety of ways, such as the number of employees, the market value of a company, or some other objective or subjective method. There are occasions in which it is easier to assign the weights without worrying that they will sum to one. If you are concerned about your weights summing to one, you can make your weights sum to one by dividing each weight by the sum of all the weights.

Weighted Mean

The weighted mean of a data set with values $x_1, x_2, x_3, ..., x_n$ is given by

$$\bar{x} = \frac{w_1 x_1 + w_2 x_2 + ... + w_n x_n}{w_1 + w_2 + ... + w_n} = \frac{\sum (w_i x_i)}{\sum w_i}$$

where w_i is the weight of observation x_i.

FORMULA

Example 4.1.2

Meghan is a freshman in college and she received the following grades for her first semester.

Meghan's Grades		
Course	**Grade**	**Credit Hours**
Psychology 101	B	3
Probability and Statistics	A	4
Anatomy I	C	5
English 101	A	3

A grade of A is worth 4 points on a 4-point scale. A grade of B is worth 3 points and a grade of C is worth 2 points.

a. Calculate Meghan's GPA using the credit hours as weights. Round to two decimal places.

b. If Meghan's goal was to have a GPA of 3.4, what grade did she need to make in the Anatomy I class to reach her goal?

Solution

a. To calculate Meghan's GPA we use the weighted mean formula with the numerical grade point values as the *x*-values and the credit hours as weights.

$$\bar{x} = \frac{\sum(w_i \cdot x_i)}{\sum w_i} = \frac{3 \cdot 3 + 4 \cdot 4 + 2 \cdot 5 + 4 \cdot 3}{3 + 4 + 5 + 3}$$

$$= \frac{9 + 16 + 10 + 12}{15} = \frac{47}{15}$$

$$\approx 3.13$$

b. To determine the grade that Meghan needed in the Anatomy I class to reach her goal of a 3.4 GPA, let *x* represent the grade in the weighted mean formula.

$$\bar{x} = 3.4 = \frac{3 \cdot 3 + 4 \cdot 4 + x \cdot 5 + 4 \cdot 3}{15}$$

$$= \frac{9 + 16 + 5x + 12}{15} = \frac{37 + 5x}{15}$$

Solving this equation for *x* gives us the following result.

$$3.4(15) = 37 + 5x$$
$$51 = 37 + 5x$$
$$51 - 37 = 5x$$
$$14 = 5x$$
$$2.8 = x$$

Since the grading scale only uses integers, Meghan would have had to make 3 points or a grade of B on her Anatomy I class for a GPA of 3.4.

◆

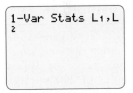

Technology

To find the weighted mean we use the `1-Var Stats` option on the TI-83/84 Plus calculator with the numerical grade point value in L1 and credit hours in L2. The results are shown below. We can also utilize other technologies to calculate the weighted mean. For instructions please visit stat.hawkeslearning.com and navigate to **Technology Instructions > Descriptive Statistics > Two Variable**.

The Trimmed Mean

Since outliers can have an enormous effect on the value of the mean, the mean's usefulness as a typical measure of a set of data is diminished if the data contains outliers.

> **Trimmed Mean**
>
> The **trimmed mean** is a modification of the arithmetic mean which ignores an equal percentage of the highest and lowest data values in calculating the mean.
>
> **DEFINITION**

Finding the 10% Trimmed Mean

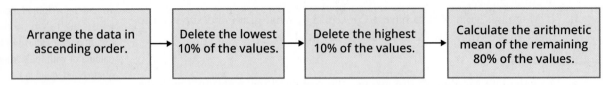

| Arrange the data in ascending order. | → | Delete the lowest 10% of the values. | → | Delete the highest 10% of the values. | → | Calculate the arithmetic mean of the remaining 80% of the values. |

Before calculating the trimmed mean, the data is arranged in ascending order of magnitude. A 10% trimmed mean uses the middle 80% of the data values. It is calculated by removing the top 10% *and* the bottom 10% of the data values, then finding the arithmetic average of the remaining values. If the data set does not contain any outliers, the mean and the trimmed mean will be similar. Unlike the arithmetic mean, the trimmed mean is not affected by outliers and is considered a resistant measure.

Measuring Figure Skating Performances

Almost every figure skating competition has some scoring controversy. The Winter Olympics of 2002 were no exception. French judge, Marie-Reine Le Gougne, said she was "pressured to vote a certain way" when she scored the Russian couple, Elena Berezhnaya and Anton Sikharulidze, over the Canadian pair, Jamie Sale and David Pelletier. In addition, very few people understood exactly how Sarah Hughes won the gold medal and how Michelle Kwan dropped to third after leading the event.

For almost a century figure skating has used a scoring method that is similar to the methodology of the trimmed mean in order to remove bias. Skaters were scored on a 0 to 6 scale. The highest and the lowest score are discarded (the data is trimmed) and the resulting "score" is computed. The intent of trimming the data is to avoid bias caused by judges with nationalistic or political agendas. The International Skating Union is replacing this scoring method with similar methods that attempt to remove biases in judge's scores.

Example 4.1.3

Consider the following data taken from a poll on how many text messages a person sent in a day.

$$16 \quad 18 \quad 20 \quad 21 \quad 23 \quad 23 \quad 24 \quad 32 \quad 36 \quad 42$$

$$\text{mean} = 25.5$$

Find the 10% trimmed mean.

Solution

Since there are 10 observations, removing the highest 10% and lowest 10% means removing only one observation from each end of the data. That is,

$$10\% \text{ of } 10 = 0.1 \cdot 10 = 1.$$

Note that the data is already sorted. If the mean is calculated without including the values 16 and 42, the resultant measure is called the 10% trimmed mean.

$$\cancel{16} \quad 18 \quad 20 \quad 21 \quad 23 \quad 23 \quad 24 \quad 32 \quad 36 \quad \cancel{42}$$

$$10\% \text{ trimmed mean} = \frac{18 + 20 + 21 + 23 + 23 + 24 + 32 + 36}{8} = 24.625$$

If there had been 100 data values, the largest 10% and smallest 10% (a total of 20 data values) would have been removed before the mean was calculated.

Example 4.1.4

Consider the same data set, except the last data value is replaced with an outlier.

$$16 \quad 18 \quad 20 \quad 21 \quad 23 \quad 23 \quad 24 \quad 32 \quad 36 \quad 490$$

$$\text{mean} = 70.3$$

Find the 10% trimmed mean.

Solution

Since there are 10 observations, removing the highest 10% and lowest 10% means removing only one observation from each end of the data.

$$\cancel{16}\ \ 18\ \ 20\ \ 21\ \ 23\ \ 23\ \ 24\ \ 32\ \ 36\ \ \cancel{490}$$

$$10\%\text{ trimmed mean} = \frac{18+20+21+23+23+24+32+36}{8} = 24.625$$

As expected, the trimmed mean is not affected by the addition of the outlier, while the mean increased dramatically. This is why the trimmed mean is considered to be a **resistant measure**.

◆

The Median

The median of a set of data provides another measure of center that is different from a "mean". It is a simple idea. To find the median, place the data in ascending order and then find the observation that has an equal number of data values on either side. That is, half of the observations are less than the median and half of the observations are greater than the median. The median is the middle value.

Median

The **median** of a set of observations is the measure of center that is the middle value of the data when it is arranged in ascending order. The same number of data values lie on either side of the median.

DEFINITION

To determine the median of a set of data, we use the following steps.

Finding the Median of a Data Set

1. Arrange the data in ascending order.
2. Determine the number of values in the data.
3. Find the data value in the middle of the data set.
4. If the number of data values is odd, then the median is the data value that is exactly in the middle of the data set.
5. If the number of data values is even, then the median is the mean of the two middle observations in the data set.

PROCEDURE

Example 4.1.5

Consider the following goal tallies from eleven games played by the Charleston Battery soccer team.

$$2,\ 3,\ 5,\ 4,\ 1,\ 7,\ 3,\ 3,\ 1,\ 2,\ 6$$

Find the median.

☁ Technology

To find summary statistics, such as the median, we can use the 1-Var Stats option on the TI-83/84 Plus calculator, Microsoft Excel, or we can use other types of technology. The calculator and Excel results are shown here. For instructions please visit stat.hawkeslearning.com and navigate to **Technology Instructions > Descriptive Statistics > One Variable**.

Column1	
Mean	3.363636364
Standard Error	0.591957113
Median	3
Mode	3
Standard Deviation	1.963299634
Sample Variance	3.854545455
Kurtosis	-0.466246885
Skewness	0.636683254
Range	6
Minimum	1
Maximum	7
Sum	37
Count	11

```
1-Var Stats
↑n=11
 minX=1
 Q₁=2
 Med=3
 Q₃=5
 maxX=7
```

Solution

First, the data set must be ordered,

$$1, \ 1, \ 2, \ 2, \ 3, \ 3, \ 3, \ 4, \ 5, \ 6, \ 7$$

Since the data set contains an odd number of values, 11, the middle observation in the ordered array must be the sixth observation. Since the median is the sixth observation, the median value is 3.

$$1, \ 1, \ 2, \ 2, \ 3, \ \mathbf{3}, \ 3, \ 4, \ 5, \ 6, \ 7$$

Example 4.1.6

Consider the following ten test scores from a student taking a high school calculus class.

$$65, \ 98, \ 76, \ 83, \ 94, \ 79, \ 88, \ 72, \ 90, \ 85$$

Find the median.

Solution

If there are an even number of observations, average the two center values in the ordered data set.

$$65, \ 72, \ 76, \ 79, \ \mathbf{83}, \ \mathbf{85}, \ 88, \ 90, \ 94, \ 98$$

To find the median, average the fifth and sixth observations.

$$\frac{83 + 85}{2} = 84 \text{ (the median)}$$

The median possesses a rather obvious notion of centrality, since it is defined as the central value in an ordered list. It is not affected by outliers and is therefore a resistant measure. For example, if we replaced 98 with 200,000,000 in the data set from the previous example, the median would not change at all. The median does possess one limitation: it cannot be applied to nominal data. In order to calculate the median, the data must be placed in order. To accomplish this task meaningfully, the level of measurement must be at least ordinal. Unless the data set is skewed or contains outliers, the median and the mean usually have similar values.

The Mode

The **mode** is another measure of location. It is not used as frequently as the mean or the median, and its relation to the "central tendency" concept and the values of the mean and median are not predictable. The mode is the only measure of location that can be used for nominal data. Of the three measures of location, the mode is used the least due to the limited information it provides. Sometimes sorting the data (in ascending or descending order) makes it easier to find the mode.

Mode

The **mode** of a data set is the most frequently occurring value.

DEFINITION

When reporting the mode for numerical data, do not round. The value of the mode should be the same as the original data value.

Example 4.1.7

Find the mode of the following data regarding the number of power outages reported over a period of eleven days.

> 0, 1, 4, 3, 9, 8, 10, 0, 1, 3, 0

Solution

Since the value of 0 occurs more than any other value, it is the mode. In this instance, as a measure of location, the modal value is not a particularly appealing choice. However, as noted previously, the mode does possess one very favorable property—it is the only measure of location that can be applied to nominal data. Therefore, for nominal measurements like color preferences, it would be perfectly reasonable to discuss the modal color.

Suppose we added one more value to the data set in Example 4.1.7. If this value were a 1, then both 0 and 1 would be repeated three times and there would be two modes. When this occurs, the data is said to be **bimodal**. Any time a data set has more than two modes, it is said to be **multimodal**. If all observations in a data set occur with the same frequency, the data set has **no mode**.

The Relationship between the Mean, Median, and Mode

Oftentimes, the shape of the data determines how the mean, median, and mode are related. For a bell-shaped distribution, the mean, median, and mode are identical.

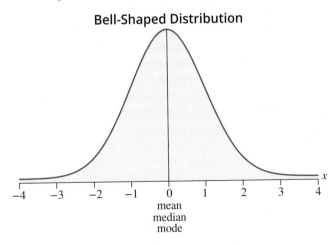

Bell-Shaped Distribution

Figure 4.1.3

Certainly, not all data produces distributions that follow a bell-shaped curve. If the distribution of the data has a long tail on the right, it is said to be skewed to the right, or positively skewed. Conversely, if the distribution has a long tail on the left, it is said to be skewed to the left, or negatively skewed. If the data is positively skewed, the median will be smaller than the mean. If the data is negatively skewed, the mean will be smaller than the median.

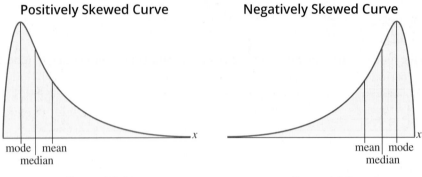

Figure 4.1.4   Figure 4.1.5

Where does the mode fall on these graphs? The area containing the greatest number of observations contains the mode. That area is represented by the large peak in the curve. In Figure 4.1.4 and Figure 4.1.5 the obvious peaks in the curves are the portions of the distributions that will contain the mode. The highest point on the curve will be the mode of the distribution. Notice that in a bell-shaped distribution (Figure 4.1.3), the mode is equal to the mean and median. If the distribution is positively skewed (Figure 4.1.4), the mode is less than the mean and median. If the distribution is negatively skewed (Figure 4.1.5), the mode is greater than the mean and median.

Selecting a Measure of Location

The objective of using descriptive statistics is to provide measures that convey useful summary information about the data. When selecting a statistic to represent the central value of a data set, the first thing to consider is the type of data being analyzed.

The arithmetic mean is used so frequently that its computation is almost a knee-jerk reaction to analyzing data. Unfortunately, it is not always a reasonable measure of centrality or location. Table 4.1.3 defines the applicable levels of measurement for each measure of location. Table 4.1.4 defines the sensitivity to outliers for each measure of location. When the data is qualitative (nominal or ordinal), the mean should not be calculated and, if the data is quantitative and contains outliers, the mean does not convey the notion of typical value as well as some other measures. The only time in which the mean should be used without any explanation is when the distribution of the data is symmetrical or nearly so. In that event, the mean and median should be approximately the same value.

Table 4.1.3 – Applicable Level of Measurement	Qualitative		Quantitative	
	Nominal	**Ordinal**	**Interval**	**Ratio**
Mean			✓	✓
Median		✓	✓	✓
Mode	✓	✓	✓	✓
Trimmed Mean			✓	✓

Table 4.1.4 – Sensitivity to Outliers	**Not Sensitive**	**Very Sensitive**
Mean		✓
Median	✓	
Mode	✓	
Trimmed Mean	✓	

The median is also a good measure of central tendency. It is not sensitive to outliers and can be applied to data gathered from all levels of measurements except nominal.

If the level of measurement of the data is interval or ratio and there are no outliers, the mean is a reasonable choice. If the data set appears to have any unusual values, then the trimmed mean or the median would be more appropriate.

If the level of measurement is nominal or ordinal (the data are qualitative), appropriate measures of center are limited. If the data is ordinal, then the median is the best choice. If the data is nominal, there is only one choice, the mode. The mode is applicable to all data types, although it is not very useful for quantitative data.

Time Series Data and Measures of Centrality

We discussed two types of time series data in Chapter 2, stationary and nonstationary. Stationary time series wobbled around some central value, so calculating a central value is perfectly reasonable, and the methods we previously discussed are applicable. A nonstationary time series is another story. Nonstationary time series possess trend. That means there is no central value for the time series. Instead, the series trends in one direction or another. Computing a central value using the methods discussed earlier would be inappropriate for such data.

Table 4.1.5 shows the first six rows of the data on average US gas price from 1991 to 2015. In this nonstationary time series, the central value of the process is trending upward as shown in Figure 4.1.6. One way to capture this movement is with a **moving average**.

Table 4.1.5 – Average US Gas Price 1991-2015 (in dollars per gallon)			
Year	**Average US Gas Price**	**2-Period Moving Average**	**3-Period Moving Average**
1991	1.14		
1992	1.13	1.135	
1993	1.11	1.120	1.127
1994	1.11	1.110	1.117
1995	1.15	1.130	1.123
1996	1.23	1.190	1.163
. . .			

⋮ Data

The complete US gas price data set can be found on stat.hawkeslearning.com under **Data Sets > US Gas Price**.

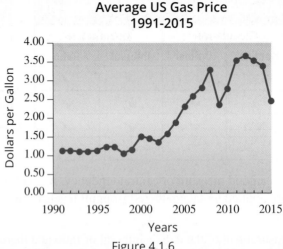

Figure 4.1.6

Moving Average

A **moving average** is obtained by adding consecutive observations for a number of periods and dividing the result by the number of periods included in the average.

DEFINITION

A moving average can be used to forecast the new level of a series over time or as a descriptive method. By averaging just two or three periods at a time we can still see long-term trends, but at the same time smooth out some of the short-term variability in the time series. How the average is associated with a specific period is dependent on its purpose. We will assume the moving average is to be used as a method of forecasting the next level of the time series. Suppose a two-period moving average is calculated for the gas price data and is used to specify the level of the series at a given point in time. The two-period moving average for 1992 averages the values of the time series in 1991 and 1992.

$$\frac{1.14 + 1.13}{2} = 1.135$$

Similarly, the two-period moving average for 1993 would be the average of the time series values in 1992 and 1993.

$$\frac{1.13 + 1.11}{2} = 1.120$$

Since data is not available for 1989 or 1990, the three-period moving average for 1991 cannot be calculated. The three-period moving average associated with 1993 is the average of the time series values in 1991, 1992, 1993.

$$\frac{1.14 + 1.13 + 1.11}{3} = 1.127$$

And, the three-period moving average for 1994 would be the average of the time series values in 1992, 1993, and 1994.

$$\frac{1.13 + 1.11 + 1.11}{3} = 1.117$$

The chart in Figure 4.1.7 displays the time series, the two-period moving average, and three-period moving average. Both of the averages follow the time series quite closely. However, notice that the two-period moving average follows the actual data values more closely than the three-period moving average.

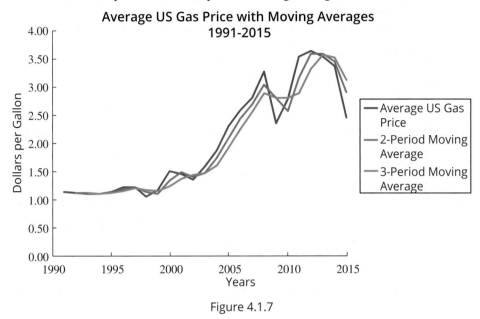

Figure 4.1.7

4.1   **Exercises**

Basic Concepts

1. Describe the difference between statistics and parameters.

2. Describe three major attributes used in summarizing a data set.

3. What are numerical descriptive statistics and why are they important?

4. Identify and describe five measures of location. List the advantages and disadvantages of each.

5. What is a resistant measure?

6. Describe a situation in which using the weighted mean as a measure of location would be appropriate.

7. What does it mean if we say that a data set is positively skewed? Negatively skewed?

8. Explain why the mean should not be calculated for a nonstationary time series.

9. What is a moving average? When is it useful?

Exercises

10. Calculate the mean, median, 10% trimmed mean, and the mode for the following data.

| 90.25 93.83 91.41 92.27 90.89 99.12 92.88 97.74 |
| 96.28 95.33 91.16 94.30 95.51 92.27 97.63 95.94 |
| 90.95 94.76 92.27 92.88 |

⸭ Data

stat.hawkeslearning.com
Data Sets > US Violent Crime by State

11. Using the US violent crime rate data by state found on the companion website, calculate the mean, median, mode, and 20% trimmed mean for the year 2014. Round your answers to 2 decimal places.

12. Using the US violent crime rate data from the previous problem, remove Washington D.C. (District of Columbia) from the data and then calculate the mean, median, mode, and the 20% trimmed mean for the year 2014. Round your answers to 2 decimal places.

13. Calculate the mean, median, the 10% trimmed mean, and the mode for the following data.

| 2 22 6 18 10 14 12 12 16 8 |

14. Discuss the usefulness of each of the measures of central tendency with respect to the following situations.

    a. A company is considering a move into a regional market for specialty soft drinks. In analyzing the size of the containers that his competitors are currently offering, would the company be more interested in the mean, median, or mode of their containers?

    b. The creative director for an advertising agency is trying to target an ad campaign that will be shown in one city only. Would he be more interested in the mean or median family income in the city?

    c. A young economist was assigned the task of comparing the interest rates on ninety day certificates of deposit (CDs) in three major cities. Should she compare the mean, median, or modal interest for the banks in the three cities?

    d. A telephone company is interested in knowing how customers rate their service: excellent, good, average, or poor. Would the company be more interested in studying the mean, median, or mode of the customer service ratings?

15. Discuss the usefulness of each of the measures of central tendency with respect to the following situations.

    a. A doctor is interested in analyzing the increase in systolic blood pressure caused by a certain antibiotic. Would the doctor be more interested in studying the mean, median or mode of the systolic blood pressures?

b. A car manufacturer is trying to decide in what colors it should offer its new sports coupe. In analyzing the preferred colors of other sports coupes, would the manufacturer be more interested in the mean, median, or mode of the colors?

c. A manufacturer of chocolate bars is interested in knowing how people rate its chocolate: the best, above average, average, below average, or the worst. Would the company be more interested in the mean, median, or mode of the ratings?

d. A realtor is interested in studying the prices of recent home sales in an area which has many diverse neighborhoods. Would the mean, median, or mode of the prices of recent home sales be the best measure of central tendency?

16. Using the Amazon stock price data set from the companion website, perform the following calculations. The Excel "Filter" feature is useful when only trying to view a portion of the data based on a condition. Round your answers to 2 decimal places.

a. Calculate the mean daily closing stock price in the year 2016.

b. Calculate the median daily closing stock price in the year 2016.

c. Calculate the mode of the daily closing stock price in the year 2016.

d. Calculate the 10% trimmed mean of the daily closing stock price in the year 2016.

e. Calculate and graph a 3-day moving average of the daily closing price for the years 1997–2017.

f. Which measure of central tendency do you think best describes the center of the data set? Why?

⁘ **Data**

stat.hawkeslearning.com
Data Sets > Amazon Stock Price

⌀ **Technology**

To learn how to filter data in Excel, please visit stat.hawkeslearning.com and navigate to **Technology Instructions > Data Manipulation > Filtering**.

17. A tour guide informs his group that the "average" temperature at their destination is 60 degrees Fahrenheit. Once they arrive, they discover that the daytime highs are about 120 degrees Fahrenheit and the nighttime lows are about 0 degrees Fahrenheit. Do you feel that the tour guide accurately described the temperatures to the group? Discuss.

18. A worker is participating in a test on a new machine. Her daily production, measured in numbers of units, for the twenty-day test is listed below. On days 4 and 5, the worker was ill and went home shortly after coming to work.

Daily Production									
Day	1	2	3	4	5	6	7	8	9	10
Units	100	104	117	20	20	111	105	106	115	101
Day	11	12	13	14	15	16	17	18	19	20
Units	101	102	115	116	113	103	104	119	118	108

a. What level of measurement does the data possess?

b. Compute the mean, 10% trimmed mean and the 20% trimmed mean.

c. Considering the worker's illness, which measure computed in part **b.** best describes the production capability of the machine? Discuss.

19. Using the CO_2 emissions data set from the companion website, answer the following questions.

    a. What level of measurement does the data possess?

    b. For the United States, compute the mean, 10% trimmed mean, and the 20% trimmed mean for CO_2 emissions (metric tons per capita) between the years 1960 and 2014. Round your answers to three decimal places.

20. Consider the following monthly sales for a small clothing store in a resort community.

Monthly Sales			
Month	**Sales ($)**	**Month**	**Sales ($)**
January	100,500	July	200,000
February	120,000	August	185,000
March	133,000	September	175,000
April	145,000	October	120,000
May	160,000	November	180,000
June	180,000	December	330,000

    a. Draw a line graph of the data.

    b. Calculate the two-period moving averages for the data.

    c. Calculate the three-period moving averages for the data.

    d. Add line graphs for the two-period moving averages and three-period moving averages to the graph which you constructed in part **a.**

    e. Which series of data (the original sales data, the two-period moving averages, or the three-period moving averages) do you think best represents sales for the year? Why?

21. A student earned scores of 95, 97, 88, 92, and 100 on their first five homework assignments of the semester. The student then missed an assignment and received a 0. The student needs an average of 90 or above to have an overall homework grade of A. The maximum grade for any homework assignment is 100 and there is one homework assignment remaining in the course.

    a. Is it still possible for the student to earn an A average for homework?

    b. What score would the student need on the final homework assignment to do so?

    c. What is the best overall grade the student can earn for their homework?

22. A course is set up such that attendance counts for 5% of the final grade, homework counts for 15%, quizzes count for 20%, and there are midterm and final exams that each count for 30% of the final grade. Before the final exam, a student has an attendance score of 100, a homework average of 80, a quiz average of 75, and a score of 77 for the midterm exam. The student wants to make a B in the course, which would require an overall average of at least an 82. To get a B in the course, what score does the student need to make on the final exam? Round your answer up to the nearest integer.

23. Consider the following average monthly balances for one bank customer for January through March. Calculate the weighted average balance for the three-month period. Note that each average monthly balance must be weighted by the number of days in that month on a non-leap year. Round to the nearest cent.

Average Monthly Balances for a Bank Customer (January through March)	
Month	**Average Monthly Balance**
January	$1885.67
February	$1312.92
March	$2001.53

24. Using the US County data set on the companion website, calculate the percentage of the total US population that has at least a high school diploma by utilizing the weighted mean. Use the At.Least.High.School.Diploma variable, which is the percentage of a county population with at least a high school diploma, as the data values, and use the Total.Population variable as the weights.

⋮ **Data**

stat.hawkeslearning.com
Data Sets > US County Data

4.2   **Measures of Dispersion**

Suppose all people looked alike, all cars looked alike, everyone wore the same kind of clothes, and there was only one kind of hamburger (plain). Without diversity it would be a boring world and a world in which statistics would be of little value. Since much of statistics is devoted to describing, analyzing, and explaining variability, understanding how variability is measured is essential to understanding statistics.

The concept of **variability** (also referred to as **dispersion** or **spread**) is as vague as the concept of central tendency. And vague concepts lead to different measurement ideas. The same issues that are important in evaluating location measures are meaningful in evaluating measures of dispersion.

Many of the good measures of dispersion use the concept of deviation from the mean. If the mean is a focal point or base, use it as a common basis from which to measure variation. The distance that a point is from its mean is called a **deviation from the mean**. A data set and its deviations from the mean are calculated in Table 4.2.1.

Table 4.2.1 – Calculating Deviations from the Mean	
Mean = 10	
Data Values	**Deviations from the Mean (Data – Mean = Deviation)**
3	$3 - 10 = -7$
12	$12 - 10 = 2$
20	$20 - 10 = 10$
15	$15 - 10 = 5$
0	$0 - 10 = -10$

Because the mean is the point at which the sum of the positive deviations equals the sum of the absolute values of the negative deviations, the deviations will always sum to zero. Many of the variability measures we will discuss average these deviations in some form.

The Range

The range is a primitive measure of spread that does not use the deviation concept. It is highly sensitive to outliers and consequently, not a resistant measure.

Range

The **range** is the difference between the largest and smallest data values.

DEFINITION

Example 4.2.1

Calculate the range of the following data set consisting of the number of times the television channel was changed in a 1-hour time span.

$$4, \ 6, \ 16, \ 9, \ 24, \ 8, \ 12, \ 1$$

Solution

The largest value equals 24 and the smallest value equals 1. Thus, the range is calculated as

$$\text{Range} = 24 - 1 = 23.$$

The problem with the range is that it is affected by outliers, and it does not bring all the information in the data directly to bear on the problem of measuring variation.

Mean Absolute Deviation (MAD)

One of the ways of obtaining information about the spread of a set of data is to analyze the deviations from the mean. If instead of adding the raw deviations, suppose the absolute values of the deviations (which can be interpreted as distance from the mean) are summed and divided by the number of deviations. This new measure computes the average distance from the mean for the data set. This measure is called the **mean absolute deviation**. If data set A has a larger average deviation than B, then it is reasonable to believe that data set A has more variability than data set B.

Mean Absolute Deviation

The sample mean absolute deviation (MAD) is given by

$$\text{MAD} = \frac{\sum |x_i - \bar{x}|}{n}.$$

FORMULA

Example 4.2.2

Suppose six people participated in a 1000-meter run. Their times, measured in minutes, are given below.

> 5, 10, 9, 11, 9, 7

The mean time is 8.5 minutes. In the table shown below we do the basic calculations for the mean absolute deviation.

Solution

	Calculating Mean Absolute Deviation		
Time (Minutes)	Deviation $x_i - \bar{x}$	Absolute Deviation $\lvert x_i - \bar{x} \rvert$	% of Total Deviation
5	5 − 8.5	3.5	35%
10	10 − 8.5	1.5	15%
9	9 − 8.5	0.5	5%
11	11 − 8.5	2.5	25%
9	9 − 8.5	0.5	5%
7	7 − 8.5	1.5	15%
	TOTAL	10.0	100%

$$\text{Mean Absolute Deviation} = \frac{10.0}{6} \approx 1.7 \text{ minutes}$$

Thus, on average, the points are 1.7 units from the mean. Note that the contribution to the sum of the deviations is proportional to the size of the deviation. That is, if one absolute deviation is twice as large as another, it contributes twice as much to the value of the statistic. For example, compare the data point 7, which is 1.5 units from the mean, to the data point 11, which is 2.5 units from the mean. The percentage contribution to the total deviation is 15% for 7 and 25% for 11, which is in proportion to their respective distances from the mean. A variability measure in which each data value contributes proportionally to its distance from the mean seems reasonable.

The mean absolute deviation is sensitive to outliers and is not a resistant measure, as demonstrated in the following example.

Example 4.2.3

Suppose the value 200 is added to the data set given in Example 4.2.2.

The mean is drastically affected, increasing from 8.5 to 35.86. In the table below we redo the basic calculations for the mean absolute deviation. What effect, if any, does the value of 200 have on the MAD?

Solution

Calculating Mean Absolute Deviation		
Data	**Deviation $x_i - \bar{x}$**	**Absolute Deviation $\left|x_i - \bar{x}\right|$**
5	5 – 35.86	30.86
10	10 – 35.86	25.86
9	9 – 35.86	26.86
11	11 – 35.86	24.86
9	9 – 35.86	26.86
7	7 – 35.86	28.86
200	200 – 35.86	164.14
	TOTAL	**328.30**

$$\text{Mean Absolute Deviation} = \frac{328.3}{7} \approx 46.9 \text{ minutes}$$

The mean absolute deviation changes dramatically, increasing to 46.9. Therefore, the mean absolute deviation is sensitive to outliers and is not a resistant measure. The mean absolute deviation is a very intuitive measure of variation, but is not used very often.

Variance and Standard Deviation

The **variance** and **standard deviation** are the most common measures of variability. Since the standard deviation is computed directly from the variance, our discussion will center on the variance. Like the MAD, the variance and standard deviation provide numerical measures of how the data varies around the mean. If the data is tightly packed around the mean, the variance and standard deviation will be relatively small. On the other hand, if the data is widely dispersed about the mean, the variance and standard deviation will be relatively large.

The Introduction of Variance

Carl Gauss (1777-1855) was a German mathematician that introduced the notion of variance. However, some believe that the work may have been prepared by Tycho Brahe while he was working on the problem of trying to estimate the position of a star using a series of measurements of its location. Both men lived highly interesting, yet quite contrasting, lives. Gauss was a child prodigy that rose out of poverty while Brahe was a Dutch nobleman and astronomer. The Wikipedia articles outlining their lives and accomplishments are fascinating and well worth reading.

Variance

The **variance** of a data set containing the complete set of *population* data is given by

$$\sigma^2 = \frac{\sum\left(x_i - \mu\right)^2}{N},$$

and is called the **population variance**.

The **variance** of a data set containing *sample* data is given by

$$s^2 = \frac{\sum\left(x_i - \bar{x}\right)^2}{n - 1},$$

and is called the **sample variance**.

FORMULA

Both of these definitions can be construed to be averages, although at first glance it may not be readily apparent. That is, for the population variance, we are adding up the sum of the squared deviations and dividing by the number of items that are added. Thus, the population variance is the average squared deviation from the mean. For the sample variance, we are dividing by $n-1$ because it gives us an unbiased estimate of the population variance.

It is usually not necessary to compute a variance using manual methods, except to become familiar with the definition.

☌ **Technology**

For instructions on how to calculate variance using either a TI-83/84 Plus calculator, Microsoft Excel, or other technologies, please visit stat.hawkeslearning. com and navigate to **Technology Instructions > Descriptive Statistics > One Variable.**

Example 4.2.4

Given the following times in minutes of 6 persons running a 1000-meter course, compute the sample variance.

> 5, 10, 9, 11, 9, 7

Solution

We previously computed the mean of this sample as 8.5. In the table below we do the basic calculations needed to compute the sample variance.

Data	Deviation $x_i - \bar{x}$	Squared Deviation $(x_i - \bar{x})^2$	% of Total Squared Deviation
5	$5 - 8.5 = -3.5$	12.25	52.13%
10	$10 - 8.5 = 1.5$	2.25	9.57%
9	$9 - 8.5 = 0.5$	0.25	1.06%
11	$11 - 8.5 = 2.5$	6.25	26.60%
9	$9 - 8.5 = 0.5$	0.25	1.06%
7	$7 - 8.5 = -1.5$	2.25	9.57%
	TOTAL	**23.5**	**100%**

Calculating the Sample Variance

$$s^2 = \frac{\sum (x_i - \bar{x})^2}{n-1} = \frac{23.5}{5} = 4.7 \text{ squared minutes}$$

Thus the average squared deviation of the data is 4.7 squared minutes. The phrase "squared minutes" in the last sentence may seem a bit odd. No one carries out transactions in square minutes, or square dollars, or square tons, so it is difficult to interpret the significance of the measurement in this form. That is why the standard deviation exists. It converts the measure into the original units by taking the square root of the variance.

Column1	
Mean	8.5
Standard Error	0.885061203
Median	9
Mode	9
Standard Deviation	2.167948339
Sample Variance	4.7
Kurtosis	0.067904029
Skewness	-0.794947105
Range	6
Minimum	5
Maximum	11
Sum	51
Count	6

```
1-Var Stats
 x̄=8.5
 Σx=51
 Σx²=457
 Sx=2.167948339
 σx=1.979057015
↓n=6
```

```
1-Var Stats
↑n=6
 minX=5
 Q₁=7
 Med=9
 Q₃=10
 maxX=11
```

Standard Deviation

The **standard deviation** is also a measure of how much the data varies around the mean. It is found by taking the square root of the variance.

DEFINITION

Baseball Players, Better or Worse?

In the history of Major League Baseball (MLB), the last time someone hit above .400 was Ted Williams in 1941. Before that, Ty Cobb had hit .420 in 1911. Finally, in 1980 George Brett came close but hit only .390. From this it appears that with time hitting for high averages is becoming more difficult. Is this then evidence of progress or lack of progress? The late evolutionary biologist Stephen Jay Gould, himself an avid baseball fan, had an interesting statistical angle to this riddle. He computed and observed: (1): The yearly batting averages have remained more or less stable (around .267) over the history of the league. (2): The annual standard deviations have declined steadily over the same period. (3) Finally, the yearly batting averages are all normally distributed. Gould then computed the z-scores for all three players and observed they were all well above 4.0.

His conclusions: Hitting has improved since the standard deviations of the averages are getting smaller. The best hitters are still at the fence of the normal distribution (though different ones) and are the best of their times. Therefore, apparent decline (disappearance of .400 hitters) is actually a sign of improvement! (Through lowered standard deviation.) Less can actually be more in some situations!

Source: Gould, S. J. (1986). Entropic homogeneity isn't why no one hit .400 any more. Discover, August, 60-66.

Since there are two measures of variance, there will be two standard deviations, one for population data and one for sample data.

$$\sigma = \sqrt{\sigma^2} \quad \text{the population standard deviation}$$
$$s = \sqrt{s^2} \quad \text{the sample standard deviation}$$

From the example,

$$s = \sqrt{4.7 \text{ minutes}^2} \approx 2.17 \text{ minutes.}$$

It is important to remember these symbols (σ and s), since the standard deviation is a fundamental statistical concept.

Describing the standard deviation in an intuitive way is not easy. It is not the average deviation from the mean (which always equals 0), although in most cases it will be reasonably close to the mean absolute deviation. The fact is that the standard deviation is the square root of the average squared deviation. It is not an intuitive concept! Certainly a reasonable question at this juncture is, if the standard deviation is not very intuitive, why use it to measure deviation? Part of the answer lies in the fact that it is expressed in the same units as the data. The variance is an important theoretical measure of variability because it has "nice" mathematical properties (in contrast to the more intuitive MAD).

The standard deviation can be used to measure how far data values are from their mean. You will often see that the majority of data values lie within one standard deviation of the mean. Furthermore, relatively few data values will be more than two standard deviations from the mean.

The variance and standard deviation both suffer from the same problem as the mean; they are very sensitive to outliers. Suppose the value 200 was added to the data in Example 4.2.2. The sample variance would increase from 4.7 to 5242.81; the new sample variance (which includes the outlier 200) then is 1115 times as large as the original variance. The standard deviation increases from 2.17 to 72.4. The presence of the outlier tarnishes the interpretation of the standard deviation as a measure of variability.

Another interesting property of the variance is that values farther from the mean contribute a disproportionate amount to the value of the statistic. In Example 4.2.4, one data point, 5, which is 3.5 units from the mean, contributes over 50% of the variation in the data (see the column labeled % of Total Squared Deviation in Table 4.2.4). Compare this to the data point 7, which is 1.5 units from the mean yet only contributes 9.57% to the total variation. The reason that 5 contributes so heavily to the total variation is because the deviations are squared. By squaring the deviations, values further from the mean have a disproportionate effect on the sum of the squared deviations.

> ### Properties of the Standard Deviation
>
> - The standard deviation is always nonnegative. It is zero only if all the data values are exactly the same.
> - The standard deviation can increase dramatically if there are one or more outliers in the data.
> - The standard deviation is expressed in the same units as the original data values.
>
> **PROPERTIES**

While there are a number of descriptive tools available for summarizing variability, the variance and standard deviation are the most frequently used statistics.

Dispersion and Time Series Data

If a time series is stationary, then the methods discussed in this section can be used to measure dispersion. However, if the series is nonstationary, the dispersion measures we have discussed are not applicable. Measuring variation in a nonstationary time series is beyond the scope of this text.

Using the Standard Deviation

Although the standard deviation is not an especially intuitive concept, knowing the mean and standard deviation of a data set provides a great deal of information about the data. If the histogram of the measurements is bell-shaped, the **empirical rule** describes the variability of a set of measurements. **Chebyshev's Theorem** is a more general rule describing the variability of *any* set of data regardless of the shape of its distribution.

Empirical Rule

The empirical rule is so named because the given percentages are actually observed in practice. This rule doesn't apply to all distributions, only those that are symmetrical and bell-shaped.

> ### Empirical Rule
>
> If the distribution of the data is bell-shaped, then
>
> - About 68% of the data should lie within 1 standard deviation of the mean.
> - About 95% of the data should lie within 2 standard deviations of the mean.
> - About 99.7% of the data should lie within 3 standard deviations of the mean.
>
> **PROPERTIES**

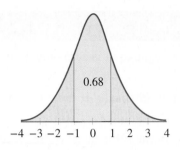

Figure 4.2.1 – One Sigma

One sigma rule: If the distribution of the data is bell-shaped, about 68% of the data should lie within one standard deviation of the mean.

A deviation of more than one sigma from the mean is to be expected about once in every three observations.

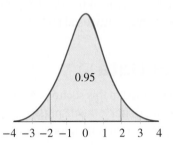

Figure 4.2.2 – Two Sigma

Two sigma rule: If the distribution of the data is bell-shaped, about 95% of the data should lie within two standard deviations of the mean.

A deviation of more than two sigma from the mean is to be expected about once in every twenty observations.

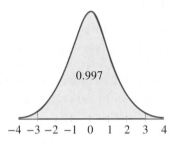

Figure 4.2.3 – Three Sigma

Three sigma rule: If the distribution of the data is bell-shaped, about 99.7% of the observations should lie within three standard deviations of the mean.

A deviation of more than three sigma from the mean is to be expected about once in every 370 observations, slightly less than 0.3% of the time.

Example 4.2.5

Suppose a group of high technology stocks has an average earnings per share of $6.26, with a standard deviation of $1.37. If the data possesses a bell-shaped distribution, which interval contains 68% of the earnings? Which interval contains 95% of the earnings?

Solution

Using the one sigma rule, we will capture 68% of the observations.

$$\$6.26 \pm \$1.37$$

```
        −$1.37      +$1.37
    (       |       )
   4.89    6.26    7.63
```

Using the one sigma rule results in an interval from $6.26 − $1.37 to $6.26 + $1.37. Doing the arithmetic produces an interval from $4.89 to $7.63.

To capture 95% of the earnings, use the two sigma rule, $6.26 \pm 2 \cdot 1.37. Doing the arithmetic results in an interval from $3.52 to $9.00.

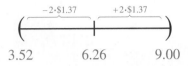

Note that to increase the percentage of data captured from 68% to 95% requires an interval that is twice as large.

Chebyshev's Theorem

It is important to remember that *the empirical rule applies only to bell-shaped distributions.* For *any* distribution, regardless of shape, Chebyshev's Theorem may be used, although its results are much more approximate.

Chebyshev's Theorem

The proportion of any data set lying within k standard deviations of the mean is at least

$$1 - \frac{1}{k^2}, \text{ for } k > 1.$$

If $k = 2$ at least $1 - \frac{1}{2^2} = \frac{3}{4}$ (or 75 %) of the data values lie within 2 standard deviations of the mean, for any data set.

If $k = 3$ at least $1 - \frac{1}{3^2} = \frac{8}{9}$ (or 88.9 %) of the data values lie within 3 standard deviations of the mean, for any data set.

DEFINITION

Note that k does not have to be an integer value. If $k = 1.5$, at least $1 - \frac{1}{1.5^2} = \frac{5}{9}$ (or approximately 55.6%) of the data values will lie within 1.5 standard deviations of the mean for any data set.

Example 4.2.6

The age distribution histogram for New Jersey in 2017 is shown in the graph. The mean of the data is 37.2, while the standard deviation is 22. What can we conclude from Chebyshev's Theorem using $k = 2$?

New Jersey

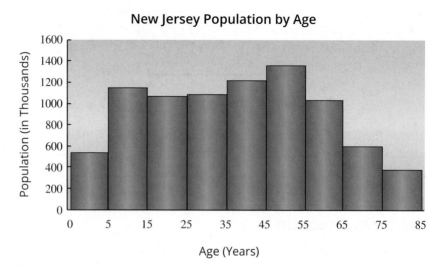

Solution

Because we are interested in $k = 2$, we will look at the values two standard deviations above and below the mean.

Two standard deviations above the mean is

$$\mu + 2\sigma = 37.2 + 2(22) = 81.2,$$

and two standard deviations below the mean is

$$\mu - 2\sigma = 37.2 - 2(22) = -6.8.$$

Because age cannot be negative, we have a natural boundary so we will consider this as zero.

Therefore, by Chebyshev's Theorem, we can say that at least 75% of the population of New Jersey is between 0 and 81.2 years old. It is doubtful that this revelation will become breaking news.

The Coefficient of Variation

Sometimes a data analyst wants to compare the variation of two or more data sets. The **coefficient of variation** is a unit-free statistical measure that enables the comparison of the variation in two or more data sets.

Coefficient of Variation

For population data, the measure is defined as $CV = \left(\dfrac{\sigma}{\mu} \cdot 100 \right) \%,$

and for sample data, $CV = \left(\dfrac{s}{\bar{x}} \cdot 100 \right) \%.$

FORMULA

When comparing the variation of data sets, many times the units of measure will be different. The coefficient of variation standardizes the variation measure, by dividing it by the mean. The division has one interesting side effect, the unit of measure is removed from the statistic.

One of the primary focuses of quality control in manufacturing is the reduction in variation of the output of the process. A bolt manufacturer wants to compare the variability of two bolt manufacturing processes. One process creates bolts with a mean length of 2.5 cm and a standard deviation of 0.2 cm. Is this process more variable than one that produces a bolt that has a mean length of 1 inch and a standard deviation of 0.052 inches?

Using the coefficient of variation as our measure of variability allows us to compare the two processes although the measurements are in different units.

$$CV_{Bolt\ 1} = \frac{0.2}{2.5} \cdot 100 = 8.0\%$$

$$CV_{Bolt\ 2} = \frac{0.052}{1} \cdot 100 = 5.2\%$$

The coefficient of variation for Bolt 1 is 8.0%. This means that the variation is 8% of the mean value. The coefficient of variation for Bolt 2 is 5.2% of the mean. Therefore, the process used to make Bolt 2 is less variable than that for Bolt 1.

4.2 Exercises

Basic Concepts

1. Describe three measures of variation. Discuss the strengths and weaknesses of each.

2. What does the standard deviation measure?

3. Why are the variance and standard deviation more commonly used as measures of variability than the MAD?

4. Explain how the variance can be construed as an average.

5. True or False: The variance and standard deviation are resistant measures.

6. When is it appropriate to calculate the variance of a time series?

7. What is the empirical rule? When is it appropriate to use?

8. What is Chebyshev's Theorem?

Exercises

9. Find the missing age in the following set of four student ages.

Student Ages		
Student	Age	Deviation from the Mean
A	19	−4
B	20	−3
C	?	+1
D	29	+6

Who is King of the Hill?

In 1961, Wilt Chamberlain, won the National Basketball Association (NBA) rebounding title with 27 rebounds per game. In 1992, the colorful Dennis Rodman won the same title with 18.7 rebounds per game. Common sense suggests that professional basketball in the 1990's is played at a much higher level than in the 1960's. So why have the rebounding leader's number fallen? Is it another case of "less is more"?

Researchers investigating this interesting puzzle used two other variables: Number of rebounding opportunities available (this had gone down since the field goal percent has increased historically) and the average number of minutes played per game, which has also fallen. Thus, when we adjust the actual rebounds obtained by the rebounding leaders to the number of minutes played and the total number of rebounds available, we see a completely different picture.

The adjusted rebound numbers for Chamberlain and Rodman are 35.42 and 51.06, respectively.

Source: Chatterjee, S., Brooks, G. and Yilmaz, M. R. (1997). Who is the Greatest Rebounder of All Time? Chance, 10, 1, 22-25.

10. Find the missing weight in the following data set.

Weights		
Person	Weight	Deviation from the Mean
A	144	−20
B	156	−8
C	?	+1
D	176	+12

Data

stat.hawkeslearning.com
Data Sets > Super Bowl Stats

11. Since Super Bowl football games are a sample of all NFL football games, use the Super Bowl Stats data set from the companion website to calculate the following.

   a. Calculate the sample variance of the variable Winner_Rush Attempts. Round your answer to three decimal places.

   b. Calculate the sample standard deviation of the variable Winner_Rush Attempts. Round your answer to three decimal places.

   c. Calculate the range of the variable Winner_Rush Attempts.

   d. What are some of the factors which might contribute to the variation in the observations?

Data

stat.hawkeslearning.com
Data Sets > Super Bowl Stats

12. Since Super Bowl football games are a sample of all NFL football games, use the Super Bowl Stats data set from the web resource to calculate the following.

   a. Calculate the sample variance of the variable Loser_Rush Attempts. Round your answer to three decimal places.

   b. Calculate the sample standard deviation of the variable Loser_Rush Attempts. Round your answer to three decimal places.

   c. Calculate the range of the variable Loser_Rush Attempts.

   d. What are some of the factors which might contribute to the variation in the observations? Try to use different factors than the ones used in the previous exercise.

13. The interest rates on 30 year mortgages offered by seven randomly selected banks in a large metropolitan area are recorded below.

> 7.5% 8.0% 7.0% 7.25% 8.5% 8.25% 7.75%

   a. Calculate the sample variance of the interest rates.

   b. Calculate the sample standard deviation of the interest rates.

   c. Calculate the range of the interest rates.

   d. What are some of the factors which might contribute to the variation in the observations?

14. A researcher has hypothesized that female college students are more disciplined than male college students. The researcher believes that a reasonable measure of discipline is performance on a statistics test in terms of both absolute scores

and consistency of scores. Seven male statistics students and seven female statistics students are randomly selected and their scores on a statistics test are observed.

Statistics Test Scores							
Males	65	100	75	45	85	73	95
Females	75	80	95	85	82	72	49

a.   Calculate the average test score for male students and female students separately.

b.   Calculate the variance of the test scores for male students and female students separately.

c.   Calculate the standard deviation of the test scores for male students and female students separately.

d.   Do you think that the data tend to support the hypothesis that female college students are more disciplined than male college students based on the researcher's measurement?

e.   What do you think about this particular measurement of discipline?

15.   Consider the following market values of two portfolios of stocks at five randomly selected times during a year.

Market Values ($)					
Portfolio A	150,000	155,000	145,000	160,000	140,000
Portfolio B	130,000	175,000	100,000	150,000	195,000

a.   What level of measurement does the data possess?

b.   What statistical criteria might you use to select the better portfolio? Justify your answer.

c.   Calculate the statistics you proposed in part **b.**

d.   Which portfolio has the least amount of risk? Why?

16.   Add 20 to each of the following data values.

> 81   99   97   81   85   86
>
> 99   93   96   83   82   91

a.   Compute the mean and standard deviation for both the original data and the adjusted data.

b.   Compare the mean and standard deviation of the adjusted data to the mean and standard deviation of the original data.

c.   Describe the effect of adding a constant value to each member of a data set on the mean and standard deviation of the data.

17. Adjust the following data values by subtracting 20 from each data value.

> 745   789   712   764   736
> 758   722   773   751   741

    a. Calculate the mean and variance for the original and adjusted data.

    b. Compare the mean and the variance of the adjusted data to the mean and the variance of the original data.

    c. Describe the effect of subtracting a constant value from each member of a data set on the mean and variance of the data.

18. The average score on a pre-employment test is 26 with a standard deviation of 7. Using Chebyshev's Theorem, state the range in which at least 88.89% of the data will reside.

19. The daily average number of phone calls to a call center is 972 with a standard deviation of 127. Using Chebyshev's Theorem, state the range in which at least 75% of the data will reside.

20. There is an annual chowder eating contest in a small New England town. The average amount of chowder eaten at the contest was 32 ounces with a variance of 64 ounces. Given that one hundred people participated in the contest, find:

    a. the approximate number of people who ate between 24 and 40 ounces of chowder.

    b. the approximate number of people who ate between 16 and 48 ounces of chowder.

    c. What assumptions did you make about the amount of chowder eaten by each contestant in answering parts **a.** and **b.**?

21. The manager of a local diner has calculated his average daily sales to be $4500 with a standard deviation of $750.

    a. In what range can the manager expect his daily sales to be 68% of the time?

    b. In what range can the manager expect his daily sales to be 95% of the time?

    c. In what range can the manager expect his daily sales to be 99.7% of the time?

    d. What assumption did you make about daily sales when answering parts **a.**, **b.**, and **c.**?

22. A management consulting firm is evaluating the salary structure for a large insurance company. The goal of the study is to develop salary ranges for each of the possible job grades within the company. The company and the firm have agreed that a reasonable salary range for each job grade can be determined by finding the salary range in which 95% of the current salaries for that job grade fall. The average salary and the standard deviation of the salaries are listed in the table below for three of the job grades.

Salary ($)			
Job Grade	25	33	40
$\bar{x}$	35,000	55,000	70,000
s	8,000	2,000	5,000

a. Determine the appropriate salary ranges for the three job grades.

b. What assumption did you make about the salaries in each of the job grades in answering part **a.**?

23. A consumer interest group is interested in comparing two brands of vitamin C. One brand of vitamin C advertises that its tablets contain 500 mg of vitamin C. The other brand advertises that its tablets contain 250 mg of vitamin C. Tablets for each brand are randomly selected and the milligrams of vitamin C for each tablet are measured with the following results.

Vitamin C Content (mg)		
	Brand A (500 mg)	Brand B (250 mg)
$\bar{x}$	500	250
s	10	7

a. Calculate the coefficient of variation for Brand A.

b. Calculate the coefficient of variation for Brand B.

c. Which brand more consistently produces tablets as advertised? Explain.

24. A manufacturer of bolts has two different machines. One machine is used to produce 1/4 inch bolts; the other machine is used to produce 1/2 inch bolts. It is very important that the machines consistently produce bolts of the correct diameters, or the bolts will not fit on the corresponding nuts. In order to compare the two machines, management randomly selects bolts produced from each machine and computes the average diameter of the bolts and the standard deviation of the bolts. The results of the study are shown in the table below.

Bolt Diameter		
	Machine X $\left(\dfrac{1}{4}" \right)$	Machine Y $\left(\dfrac{1}{2}" \right)$
$\bar{x}$	0.25"	0.50"
s	0.03"	0.05"

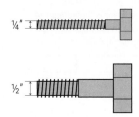

a. Calculate the coefficient of variation for Machine X.

b. Calculate the coefficient of variation for Machine Y.

c. Which machine more consistently produces bolts of the correct diameter? Explain.

4.3 Measures of Relative Position, Box Plots, and Outliers

Suppose you want to know where an observation stands in relation to other values in a data set. For example, on many standardized tests such as the SAT, GMAT, and ACT, the test scores themselves are rather meaningless unless they are associated with some measure that tells you how well you did relative to others taking the same test. There are two principal methods of communicating relative position: **percentiles** and **z-scores**. Both of these methods are data transformations which change the scale of the data in some way.

Caution

It is important to remember that when you find the value of ℓ, this result is not the percentile. It is the location of the percentile in the ordered array.

Percentiles

The most commonly used measure of relative position is the percentile. In fact, we have already discussed the 50th percentile; it is the median. For example, in data sets that do not contain significant quantities of identical data, the 30th percentile is a value such that about 30 percent of the values are below it, and around 70 percent are above it.

Finding the Pth Percentile

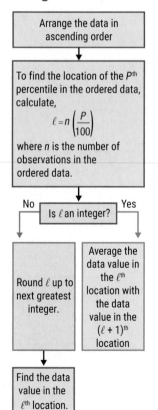

Arrange the data in ascending order

To find the location of the Pth percentile in the ordered data, calculate,

$$\ell = n\left(\frac{P}{100}\right)$$

where n is the number of observations in the ordered data.

No — Is ℓ an integer? — Yes

Round ℓ up to next greatest integer.

Average the data value in the ℓth location with the data value in the $(\ell + 1)^{\text{th}}$ location

Find the data value in the ℓth location.

Figure 4.3.1

P^{th} Percentile

Given a set of data $x_1, x_2, ..., x_n$, the **P^{th} percentile** is a value, say x, such that approximately P percent of the data is less than or equal to x and approximately $(100 - P)$ percent of the data is greater than or equal to x.

DEFINITION

To determine the Pth percentile, perform the following steps.

Finding the Pth Percentile

To determine the Pth percentile:

Form an ordered array by placing the data in order from smallest to largest.

To find the location of the Pth percentile in the ordered array, let

$$\ell = n\left(\frac{P}{100}\right)$$

where n is the number of observations in the ordered data.

If ℓ is not an integer, then round ℓ up to the next greatest integer. For example, if $\ell = 7.1$, then round ℓ up to 8 and find the data value in the ℓth location. If ℓ is an integer value, then average the data value in the ℓth location with the data value in the $(\ell + 1)^{\text{th}}$ location.

PROCEDURE

For example, if the result of calculating (and rounding up) ℓ is 15, then the desired percentile would be the fifteenth value in the ordered list.

Example 4.3.1

Find the 50th percentile for the following data on the number of spelling errors found on 7 pages of a web site.

> 3, 5, 0, 1, 9, 2, 7

Solution

Number of observations, $n = 7$.

The percentile, $P = 50$.

The location of the percentile, $\ell = 7 \cdot \left(\dfrac{50}{100} \right) = 3.5$.

Since the location of the percentile is not an integer, the value is rounded up to 4. Thus, the fourth observation in the ordered array is the 50th percentile.

$$0, \ 1, \ 2, \ \boxed{3}, \ 5, \ 7, \ 9$$
$$\uparrow$$
$$\text{fourth observation}$$

Therefore, the median value (which is the 50th percentile) is 3.

Example 4.3.2

Suppose that 40 members of your company are given a screening test for a new position. These scores are reported in the table on the left below. To inform potential employees of their screening test performance you may wish to report various percentiles for the test scores. Find the 10th and 88th percentiles for the test.

Test Scores				Ordered Test Scores			
67	45	18	82	18	43	54	66
45	54	61	55	21	44	55	67
63	47	21	31	21	45	55	69
58	46	43	49	27	45	56	70
34	71	69	56	29	46	57	71
54	80	73	77	31	47	58	73
27	70	41	29	32	48	61	77
66	32	44	33	33	49	62	80
21	64	52	81	34	52	63	81
48	55	57	62	41	54	64	82

Solution

In order to calculate the percentiles, the data must be placed in an ordered array (Ordered Test Scores). To compute the 10th percentile, its position in the ordered array must be determined. The number of observations is $n = 40$. The percentile is $P = 10$. The location of the percentile is found by

$$\ell = 40 \cdot \left(\frac{10}{100} \right) = 4.$$

Interpreting Percentiles

When students take the SAT, they receive a copy of their scores as well as the percentile they fall into. This percentile can sometimes be confusing. If a student receives a score of 620 on the Critical Reading section, they would fall into the 84th percentile. This means that they received a higher score than 84 percent of the students. The same score in the Mathematics section would place the student into the 80th percentile. Receiving a score of 800 on Critical Reading or Mathematics will put the student in the 99th percentile.

Since ℓ is an integer, the 4th and 5th observations in the array must be averaged. Since the fourth data value is 27 and the fifth data value is 29, then the 10th percentile is calculated as follows.

$$10^{\text{th}} \text{ percentile} = \frac{27 + 29}{2} = 28$$

To determine the 88th percentile, first calculate its location in the ordered array.

$$\ell = 40 \cdot \left(\frac{88}{100} \right) = 35.2$$

Since the location is not an integer, its value is rounded up to 36. The 36th observation in the ordered array will correspond to the 88th percentile. The 36th value in the table of ordered scores is 73, so 73 is the 88th percentile.

A slightly different problem connected with percentiles involves taking a raw score and determining its corresponding percentile. Raw scores are usually not very meaningful. If someone scores a 50 on the screening test in the previous example, is that substantially less or about the same as someone who scored a 67 on the same test? To compare these two scores find the percentile of each.

Percentile

The **percentile** of some data value x is given by

$$\text{percentile of } x = \frac{\text{number of data values less than or equal to } x}{\text{total number of data values}} \cdot 100.$$

FORMULA

Note that when finding the percentile of a specific value, if there are multiple occurrences of that value in the data, they all need to be counted in the numerator in order to calculate the percentile. To determine the percentile for a score of 50, the number of data values less than or equal to 50 must be counted. Since there are 18 data values less than or equal to 50, the resulting percentile would be

$$\text{percentile of a score of } 50 = \frac{18}{40} \cdot 100 = 45.$$

Hence a score of 50 on the screening test corresponds to the 45th percentile. Thus, approximately 45 percent of the scores are less than or equal to 50. Next, compute the percentile for a score of 67.

$$\text{percentile of a score of } 67 = \frac{32}{40} \cdot 100 = 80$$

A score of 67 on the screening test corresponds to the 80th percentile. The score was better than or equal to 80 percent of all other scores on the test. By computing percentiles, we have changed the data's scaling. We see the data from a new perspective. Using percentiles, it is clear that a score of 67 is significantly better than a score of 50. The 17 point difference in raw score is translated into a 35 percent differential on the percentile scale.

Quartiles

> ## Quartiles
>
> The 25th, 50th, and 75th percentiles are known as **quartiles** and are denoted as Q_1, Q_2, and Q_3 respectively.
>
> **DEFINITION**

Quartiles serve as markers that divide a set of data into four equal parts. Q_1 separates the lowest 25 percent, Q_2 represents the median (50th percentile), and Q_3 marks the beginning of the top 25 percent of the data.

Since quartiles are nothing more than percentiles (25th, 50th and 75th), the same methods used to construct percentiles will also produce quartiles. For the screening test data in the previous example, the location of the 25th percentile would be

$$\ell = 40 \cdot \left(\frac{25}{100} \right) = 10.$$

Since the location is an integer, we average the 10th and 11th observation in the ordered data to find the 25th percentile.

$$Q_1 = 25^{th} \text{ percentile} = \frac{41 + 43}{2} = 42$$

Therefore, we would expect 25 percent of the data to be less than or equal to 42.

The location of the 50th percentile is given by

$$\ell = 40 \cdot \left(\frac{50}{100} \right) = 20.$$

Since the location is an integer, we must average the 20th and 21st observations in order to calculate the percentile.

$$Q_2 = 50^{th} \text{ percentile} = \frac{54 + 54}{2} = 54,$$

which means that approximately half the data are at or below 54.

The location of the 75th percentile is given by

$$\ell = 40 \cdot \left(\frac{75}{100} \right) = 30.$$

Since the location is an integer, we average the 30th and 31st observations in the ordered array.

$$Q_3 = 75^{th} \text{ percentile} = \frac{64 + 66}{2} = 65$$

This means that approximately 75 percent of the data are less than or equal to 65. The quartiles are useful descriptions of data. They provide a good idea of how the data vary. The **interquartile range** is a measure of dispersion that is calculated using the first and third quartiles.

The Zen of Statistics

Douglas Hofstadler in his book *Godel, Escher, Bach* describes Zen as an attitude in which words and truth are incompatible, or at least that no words can capture truth. If we think of the collected data as truth, statistics is a language whose "words" are pictures and numerical measures which seek to describe that "truth." Despite our best efforts, the statistical language suffers from the same inadequacies as our own language. We ignore the totality of the data in order to summarize it. There is a tradeoff—the loss of the "truth" for a better understanding.

Interquartile Range

The **interquartile range** is a measure of dispersion which describes the range of the middle fifty percent of the data. It is calculated as follows.

$$IQR = Q_3 - Q_1$$

FORMULA

For the screening test data, the interquartile range is $65 - 42 = 23$, indicating that the middle 50 percent of the data spans a 23-unit range.

Box Plots – Graphing with Quartiles

A very important use of quartiles is in the construction of box plots. As the name implies, box plots are graphical summaries of the data which, when constructed, have a box-like shape. They provide an alternative method to the histogram for displaying data. **Box plots** are a graphical summary of the central tendency, the spread, the skewness, and the potential existence of outliers in the data. Figure 4.3.2 displays a box plot of the screening test data from Example 4.3.2.

Box Plot of Screening Test Scores

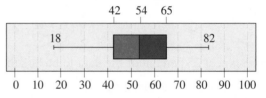

Figure 4.3.2

The box plot is constructed from five summary measures: the largest data value (maximum), the smallest data value (minimum), the 25th percentile (Q_1), the 75th percentile (Q_3), and the median (Q_2).

5-Number Summary

For a set of data, the 5-number summary consists of the following five values:

1. Minimum
2. First quartile, Q_1
3. Second quartile, Q_2, or the median
4. Third quartile, Q_3
5. Maximum

DEFINITION

The lower boundary of the box is the 25th percentile, which is 42 for the screening test data. The upper boundary of the box is the 75th percentile, which is 65 for the screening test data. The median is marked with a line through the box. The median of the test scores data is 54. Notice that the box itself represents the middle 50% of the data, and the length of the box is the interquartile range.

In Figure 4.3.2, a line is drawn from the 25th percentile to the smallest test score of 18, and another line is drawn from the 75th percentile to the largest score of 82. These lines are often referred to as "whiskers." Adding "whiskers" to the box plot creates a **box and whisker plot**. The box plot for the screening test scores shows that the test score data is slightly skewed to the left. Why? Because the whisker extending from Q_1 appears to be longer than the whisker that extends from Q_3.

Procedure for Constructing a Box Plot

1. Determine the 5-number summary for the data set.
2. Draw a scale that includes the minimum and maximum data values.
3. Construct a box extending from Q_1 to Q_3.
4. Draw a line through the box at the value of the median.
5. Draw lines extending from Q_1 to the minimum and from Q_3 to the maximum.

PROCEDURE

Detecting Outliers

The concept of an outlier is an arbitrary concept. What you consider an outlier and what someone else considers an outlier may not be the same thing. However, one definition of an outlier which has gained some acceptance is developed in the context of a box plot.

Outlier

A data point is considered an **outlier** if it is 1.5 times the interquartile range above the 75th percentile or 1.5 times the interquartile range below the 25th percentile.

DEFINITION

If there is an outlier in the data set, the whiskers are drawn to the largest or smallest data point which is within 1.5 times the interquartile range from the box, and the outliers are marked with a point. For example, suppose test scores of 110 and 2 were added to the screening test data in Example 4.3.2. For the screening test data, a point is considered an outlier if it is

- larger than the 75th percentile + 1.5 times the interquartile range = 66 + 1.5(25) = 103.5 or
- smaller than the 25th percentile − 1.5 times the interquartile range = 41 −1.5(25) = 3.5.

Box Plot with Added Test Scores

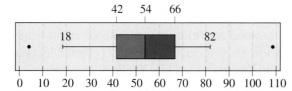

Figure 4.3.3

Since 110 is larger than 103.5, it is considered an outlier. Since 2 is smaller than 3.5, it is considered an outlier. Figure 4.3.3 shows the box plot of the screening test data with the outliers incorporated. Notice that the whiskers did not change because 82 and 18 are still the largest and smallest observations within 1.5 times the

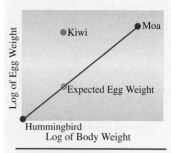

Kiwi Eggs Are Outliers!

Both animal and plant kingdoms offer spectacularly odd and beautiful sights. A kiwi bird (one of many interesting life forms from New Zealand) lays eggs that are close to 25% of their body weight and sometimes lays two or three such eggs at a time. For birds, eggs usually correspond to about 5% of the bird's weight among all species.

If you draw a graph relating (log) egg weights against (log) body weight you get a so-called hummingbird-moa curve (moa, an extinct ostrich-like bird of the New Zealand area.) In this curve, the kiwi shows up as an outlier. Using the kiwi body weight (of about 5 lb) one expects an egg weight of about 55 to 100 grams while the real weight of kiwi eggs is about 400 to 435 grams matching an expected body weight of about 40 lb. Why? And what accounts for such an anomaly?

The most reasonable explanation provided by biologists is that kiwis and moa birds are members of the same species except the kiwis have dwarfed through their evolutionary history. A subarea of biology called "allometry" states that as body size decreases the internal organs decrease relatively slowly which supports the dwarfism hypothesis. The kiwis have lost body weight but not their internal womb structure which still holds large eggs. Outliers are important because they force you to think about your data more seriously.

Source: Gould, S. J. (1991). "Of Kiwi Eggs and the Liberty Bell" in Bully For Brontosaurus, W.W. Norton and Company, New York.

interquartile range from the box. This type of box plot is often referred to in statistical software packages as a **modified box plot**.

Although the box plot can be used to display data for a single variable, the histogram is probably more useful for this purpose. The real power of the box plot is the ease with which it allows the comparison of several variables. Consider the data from the number of wins per baseball team given in Chapter 3. The four variables are displayed by the box plots in Figure 4.3.4. It is easy to see from the box plots that the center of the Yankees' number of wins is higher than that for the Dodgers, which has a higher center than the center of both the Braves and the Cubs. Note the existence of outliers for both the Cubs and the Dodgers. Also, it appears that the spread of the data, or the variation within the observed values, is not the same for all four variables. This type of comparison will be used in later chapters to help confirm assumptions which must be made about the data in order to perform statistical inference.

Technology

Microsoft Excel is capable of creating a multitude of different charts. For instructions on how to create a box plot, or box and whisker plot, using Excel or other technologies, please visit stat.hawkeslearning. com and navigate to **Technology Instructions > Graphs > Box Plot.**

Box Plot of the Number of Franchise Wins per Season 1967-2016

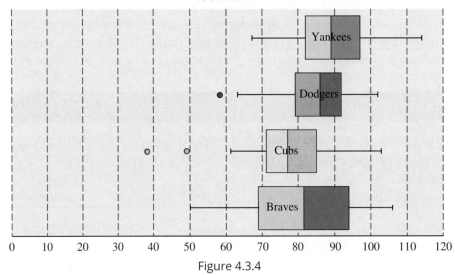

Figure 4.3.4

Example 4.3.3

Education attainment seems to have a positive association with a person's income.[7] The amount of education a person has can be divided into five categories.

1. Less than a high school diploma
2. High school graduate, no college
3. Some college or associate degree
4. Bachelor's degree only
5. Advanced degree

The categories are ordered according to educational attainment. The vertical box plots in the figure below show the distributions of personal income per each level of education, for individuals age 25 and older. Rather than extending the whiskers to the smallest and largest income values in each category, the whisker endpoints represent the 10th and 90th percentiles. What conclusions can be drawn from this figure?

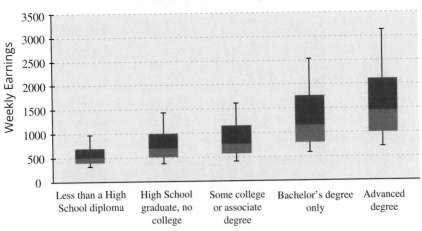

Education and Earnings 2016

Solution

It is rather obvious from this figure that more education equates to higher earnings. Also, there is a lot of spread in the last two box plots as shown by the longer lengths of the boxes. This is probably due in part to the market demands for degrees in scientific disciplines, especially computer science.

An interesting set of data is that of the violent crime rate in the United States. The crime rate is defined as the number of reported violent crimes per 100,000 residents. The data from 2010 to 2014 is shown in Figure 4.3.5. Note that there is an outlier for each year. The outlier for each year belongs to the same region of the United States—Washington D.C. Although it may seem that the box plots in the figure suggest a different level of criminality in Washington D.C., it should be noted that there are about 700,000 residents in the district, but commuters from the surrounding suburbs of Maryland and Virginia increase the city's population to over a million during the work week. The crime rate, therefore, may be confounded by the influx of people coming into the area on a daily basis. Usually, outliers that are very far away from the central grouping of data, such as the crime rate in Washington D.C., are removed from the data before any analysis takes place so that the extreme values associated with the outliers do not skew the results.

⋮⋮ Data

The full US violent crime data set can be found on stat.hawkeslearning.com under **Data Sets > US Violent Crime by State.**

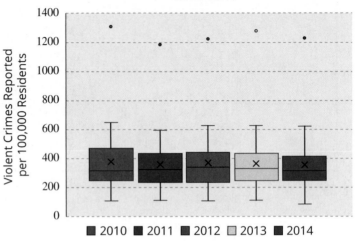

US Violent Crime Rate (per 100,000 Residents)
2010-2014

Figure 4.3.5

z-Scores

The **z-score** is a standardized measure of relative position with respect to the mean and variability (as measured by the standard deviation) of a data set.

---

z-Score

The **z-score** transforms a data value into the number of standard deviations that value is from the mean.

$$z = \frac{x - \mu}{\sigma}$$

FORMULA

Describing a data value by its number of standard deviations from the mean is a fundamental concept in statistics that is found throughout this book. It is used as a standardization technique, a yardstick, to describe properties of data sets and to compare the relative values of data from different data sets.

Example 4.3.4

Suppose you scored an 86 on your biology test and a 94 on your psychology test. The mean and standard deviations of the two tests are given in the following table.

Test Scores		
Course	**Mean**	**Standard Deviation**
Biology	74	10
Psychology	82	11

What are the z-scores for your two tests? On which of the tests did you perform relatively better?

Solution

The z-score for the biology test is $z = \dfrac{86 - 74}{10} = 1.20.$

The z-score for the psychology test is $z = \dfrac{94 - 82}{11} = 1.09$.

On the biology test you scored 1.2 standard deviations above the mean, compared to only 1.09 standard deviations above the mean for the psychology test. Even though the raw score on the psychology test is larger than the raw score on the biology test, relative to the means and variability in the data sets, the performance on the biology test was slightly better. Once again, changing the scale of the data has beneficial effects. It enables the comparison of two measurements that are drawn from different populations.

Properties of a z-Score

- If a z-score is negative, the corresponding data value is less than the mean.

- Conversely, if a z-score is positive, the corresponding data value is greater than the mean.

- The z-score is a unit-free measure. That is, regardless of the original units of measurement (centimeters, meters, or kilometers), an observation's z-score will be the same.

PROPERTIES

4.3   **Exercises**

Basic Concepts

1. What are two methods for describing relative position?

2. If a data value is calculated to be the 72nd percentile, what does this mean?

3. Describe how to find the percentile of a particular value.

4. What are quartiles? Are they equivalent to percentiles? If so, how?

5. What is the interquartile range? What does it measure?

6. What are the advantages of using a box plot to display a data set?

7. What are the key calculations needed in order to construct a box plot?

8. What is an outlier? How can outliers be identified?

9. What is a z-score? Why is it useful?

Exercises

10. Using the "safety_score" variable in the OECD Better Life Index 2016 data set, answer the following questions.

    a. What level of measurement does the data possess?

    b. Calculate the 20th percentile.

    c. Calculate the 95th percentile.

    d. Interpret the meaning of each of these percentiles.

 Data

stat.hawkeslearning.com
Data Sets > OECD Better Life Index 2016

∷ **Data**

stat.hawkeslearning.com
Data Sets > OECD Better Life Index 2016

11. Use the OECD data from the previous problem to calculate the following. Round your answers to the nearest whole number.

   a. Determine the percentile rank for Ireland's safety_score.

   b. Determine the percentile rank for Chile's safety_score.

∷ **Data**

stat.hawkeslearning.com
Data Sets > US County Data

12. Using the "Adult.smoking" variable in the US County Data set, answer the following questions.

   a. What level of measurement does the data possess?

   b. Calculate the 20th percentile. Round your answer to three decimal places.

   c. Calculate the 95th percentile. Round your answer to three decimal places.

   d. Interpret the meaning of each of these percentiles.

∷ **Data**

stat.hawkeslearning.com
Data Sets > US County Data

13. Use the US County Data from the previous problem to find the following.

   a. Determine the percentile rank for Lee County, Kentucky's Adult.smoking percentage. Round to the nearest whole number.

   b. Determine the percentile rank for Ozaukee County, Wisconsin's Adult. smoking percentage. Round to the nearest whole number.

14. Subjects in a marketing study were shown a film and at the end of the film were given a test to measure their recall. The scores are listed below.

> 97 31 61 49 61 85 35 57 31 26 27 40 86 78 28 61
> 87 62 92 58 38 95 81 68 64 72 45 57 84 100

   a. What level of measurement does the data possess?

   b. Calculate Q_1, the first quartile.

   c. Calculate Q_2, the second quartile.

   d. Calculate Q_3, the third quartile.

   e. Explain the meaning of these percentiles in the context of the marketing study.

   f. Calculate the interquartile range.

   g. Construct a box plot for the test scores. Are there any outliers?

   h. Compute the z-score for a test score of 81.

   i. Compute the z-score for a test score of 62.

   j. Explain what the z-scores in parts **h.** and **i.** are measuring.

15. Use the marketing study data from the previous problem to find the following.

   a. Determine the percentile rank for the subject who scored 49.

   b. Determine the percentile rank for the subject who scored 95.

∷ **Data**

stat.hawkeslearning.com
Data Sets > Moneyball

16. Using the on-base percentage (OBP) variable from the Moneyball data set, answer the following questions.

   a. What level of measurement does the data possess?

b.   Calculate Q_1, the first quartile. Round your answer to three decimal places.

c.   Calculate Q_2, the second quartile. Round your answer to three decimal places.

d.   Calculate Q_3, the third quartile. Round your answer to three decimal places.

e.   Explain the meaning of these percentiles in the context of the on-base percentages.

f.   Calculate the interquartile range.

g.   Construct a box plot for the on-base percentages. Are there any outliers?

h.   Compute the z-score and percentile for an on-base percentage of 0.280. Round the z-score to three decimal places and the percentile to the nearest whole number.

i.   Compute the z-score and percentile for an on-base percentage of 0.355. Round the z-score to three decimal places and the percentile to the nearest whole number.

j.   Explain what the z-scores in parts **h.** and **i.** are measuring.

17.   Using the on-base percentage (OBP) variable from the previous problem, find the following.

a.   Determine the percentile rank for the Chicago Cubs in the year 2012. Round to the nearest whole number.

b.   Determine the percentile rank for the New York Yankees in the year 2012. Round to the nearest whole number.

18.   Consider a set of data in which the sample mean is 64 and the sample standard deviation is 21. For the following specific values, calculate the z-score and interpret the results.

a. $x = 80$ **b.** $x = 64$ **c.** $x = 40$

19.   A statistics student scored a 75 on the first exam of the semester and an 82 on the second exam of the semester. The average score and standard deviation of scores for the two exams are given in the following table. On which exam did the student perform relatively better?

Test Scores		
Statistic	First Exam	Second Exam
μ	74	85
σ	10	7

20.   A hospital measures babies' heights when they are born in both inches and centimeters. Eight baby girls are randomly selected and the following heights are recorded in both inches and centimeters.

Newborn Heights								
Baby	1	2	3	4	5	6	7	8
Inches	17.75	18.50	19.25	19.75	20.25	20.50	20.50	20.75
Centimeters	45.09	46.99	48.90	50.17	51.44	52.07	52.07	52.71

a. Calculate the mean height in inches and centimeters for the baby girls.

b. Calculate the standard deviation of the heights of baby girls in both inches and centimeters.

c. Calculate the z-score for the height of Baby Girl 3 measured in inches.

d. For Baby Girl 3, calculate the z-score for the heights measured in centimeters.

e. Consider the z-scores calculated in parts **c.** and **d.** Are the z-scores as you expected them to be? Explain.

4.4   Data Subsetting

Looking at the 2016–2017 tuition data presented in Table 4.1 of the introduction with a histogram using fewer intervals gives a slightly different picture. Figure 4.4.1 provides some idea about the **location** and **dispersion** of the data, but nothing specific. Histograms are outstanding at defining the **shape** of a set of data.

Where is the Central Value of the Tuition Data?

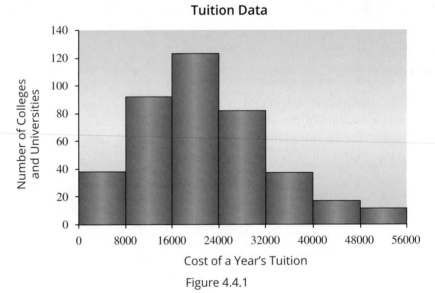

Figure 4.4.1

There are several measurements that can be used to describe the location or central value of the tuition data (see Table 4.4.1). The mode is not considered because the data is quantitative and there are a large number of observations. Moreover, the mode is not a very informative measure of central tendency. Since the mean of the data is somewhat larger than both the median and the 10% trimmed mean, the choice of central value in this case will make a difference. The histogram suggests that the difference is due to the skewness of the data to the right caused by schools with tuition costs greater than $40,000. As mentioned previously, the mean is more sensitive to the presence of outliers than either the median or the trimmed mean. So, which one of the three candidate measurements should be considered as the central value of the data?

The choice isn't easy. You are justified in selecting any of the three statistical measures. However, because of the difference between the mean and the other two measures, reporting two measures (the 10% trimmed mean and the median) would not be a bad idea. If only one measure is reported, identify the measure as the mean or the median rather than the average. The term average is a bit too ambiguous in current usage.

Table 4.4.1 – Tuition Data	
Location Measurement	**Value**
Mean	$21,680.11
Median	$20,694.50
10% Trimmed Mean	$20,863.72

Describing Dispersion of the Tuition Data

Several measurements which assess variation have been discussed, including variance, standard deviation, mean absolute deviation, and percentiles. Since the variance and standard deviation are different forms of the same measurement, usually only the standard deviation is reported. For the tuition data, a reasonable description of dispersion for the 400 values would be given by the following statistics.

Table 4.4.2 – Tuition Data	
Standard Deviation	$10,927.19
Minimum	$2,260.00
First Quartile	$13,099.50
Median	$20,694.50
Third Quartile	$28,469.50
Maximum	$50,080.00

Table 4.4.3 – Percentiles for the Tuition Data	
Percentile	**Value**
100th (maximum)	$50,080.00
95th	$45,240.50
90th	$36,291.00
75th	$28,469.50
50th	$20,694.50
25th	$13,099.50
10th	$8,200.00
5th	$6,071.00
0th (minimum)	$2,260.00

The original histogram of the tuition data, which is repeated below in Figure 4.4.2, reveals a heavy concentration of tuition costs from $4000 to $32000, with the distribution being skewed to the right. If you have ever researched colleges, perhaps to determine which ones to apply to, then you already know that tuition costs vary widely from one institution to another. What might be the reason(s) for the heavy concentration in tuition costs in the lower two-thirds of the data range? Looking at the shape of this histogram, it appears that there may be multiple underlying distributions. If we could separate these distributions, we might be able to get a clearer picture of the tuition data. One potential variable that may explain some of the variability in tuition costs is that some schools are state-supported and others are privately funded. This supposition of the variability in tuition costs could be checked rather easily if the data is divided or **subsetted** into private and state-supported schools.

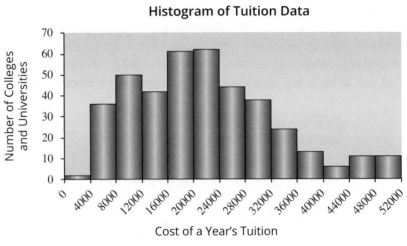

Figure 4.4.2

Data Subsetting

The original data contained the annual tuition cost of private and state-funded institutions. Out-of-state tuition was used for the state-supported schools.

Subsetting

The structure of a set of data is often exposed by using another variable to break the data into smaller groups. This is called **subsetting.**

DEFINITION

A natural structuring of the tuition data can be obtained by subsetting the data into private and state-supported institutions.

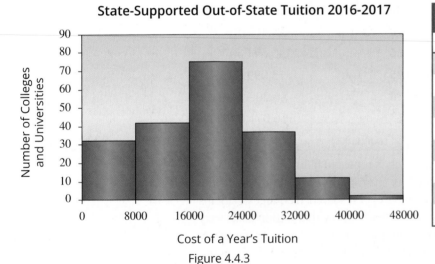

Figure 4.4.3

State-Supported Institutions	
(Out-of-State Tuition _n_ = 200)	
Mean Tuition	$18,330.62
Median Tuition	$18,348.00
Trimmed Mean	$17,951.60
Standard Deviation	$9,094.56
Minimum	$2,260.00
Q_1	$10,500.00
Q_3	$23,138.50
Maximum	$45,002.00

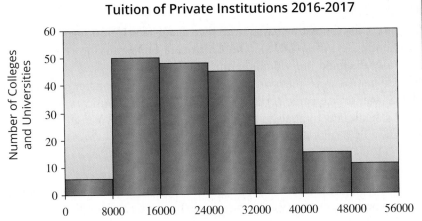

Figure 4.4.4

Private Institutions (*n* = 200)	
Mean Tuition	$25,016.43
Median Tuition	$23,215.00
Trimmed Mean	$24,143.90
Standard Deviation	$11,606.17
Minimum	$4,940.00
Q_1	$15,548.00
Q_3	$32,148.00
Maximum	$50,080.00

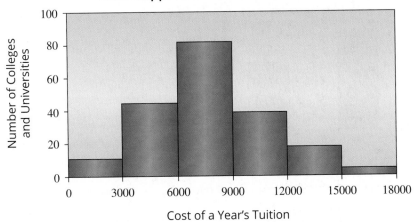

Figure 4.4.5

State-Supported Institutions:	
(In-State Tuition *n* = 200, not included in the original data set)	
Mean Tuition	$7,861.69
Median Tuition	$7,463.50
Trimmed Mean	$7,732.26
Standard Deviation	$3,315.27
Minimum	$1,800.00
Q_1	$5,645.00
Q_3	$10,009.00
Maximum	$17,514.00

The data subsetting suggests that the heavy concentration of tuition costs in the lower two-thirds of the data range that was evident in the histogram in Figure 4.4.2, is the result of merging data from different kinds of educational institutions. Once the data is subsetted, we can see different pictures of tuition costs. Looking at the mean costs for each group, from a tuition point of view, state-supported schools are substantially less expensive than private schools. There is a mean difference of almost $7000 in annual tuition fees between private schools and the out-of-state tuition charged by state-supported colleges. There is roughly a $17,000 mean annual tuition difference between private colleges and in-state tuition at state-supported schools.

Another data characteristic should stimulate our interest. One of the data values for state-supported, out-of-state tuition is $45,002. Is this a mistake? The *z*-score for this data value is

$$z = \frac{45002 - 18330.62}{9094.56} = 2.93,$$

which would indicate that the value may be an outlier. Any value that is 2.93 standard deviation units from the mean is worth investigating. In this case the value is correct. The tuition cost corresponds to the University of Michigan in Ann Arbor.

⋮ **Data**

The full California DDS data set can be found on stat.hawkeslearning.com under **Data Sets > California DDS Expenditures.**

Example 4.4.1

A few years ago, a discrimination lawsuit was filed against the California Department of Developmental Services (DDS). The California DDS provides funding for developmentally-disabled individuals within the state. The lawsuit claimed that White Non-Hispanics were receiving more funding than Hispanics. If this was true, the DDS would face some serious legal and financial ramifications, so they hired several statisticians to analyze the data behind the issue. Were these claims of discrimination by a state department actually true?

Solution

First, we will create box plots to visualize how the lawsuit arose. We will look at the relationship between ethnicity and expenditure by plotting expenditure grouped by the different ethnicities.

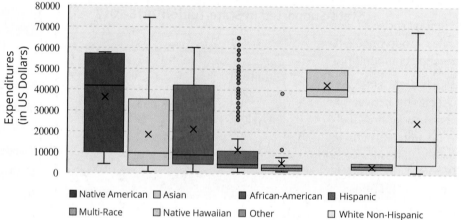

California DDS Expenditure by Ethnicity

If the data is examined on a purely ethnic basis, then the figure above suggests that there is discrimination towards multiple different ethnic groups. But, now we need to think about any variables that could be confounding this picture.

The statisticians discovered that age played a massive role in the expenditure per person, because more costs are associated with caring for older developmentally-disabled individuals. To account for the variation in expenditure between different ages, the statisticians decided to subset the whole data set into six different age groups, and then examine the expenditure by ethnicity within each age group to see if the discrimination claim still held true. The box plots in the following figure illustrate their findings.

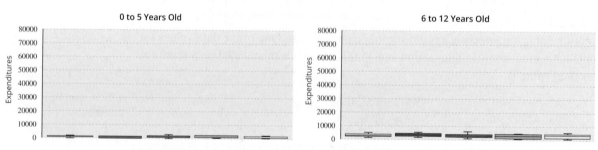

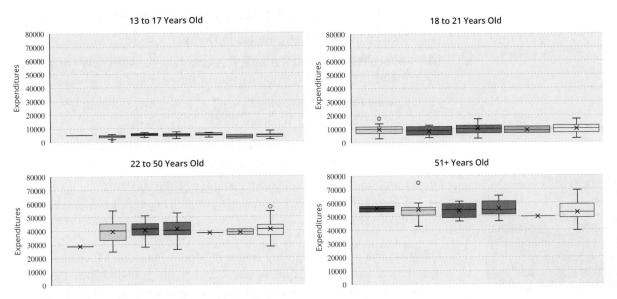

To the surprise of many involved, the box plots were roughly the same for each ethnic group once age was considered. There was no evidence of discrimination once the confounding variable "age" was accounted for.

This is a classic example of Simpson's paradox, which states that the perceived association between two variables (ethnicity and expenditures per person in this case) can be drastically affected by a third variable. When the data is partitioned by the third variable (age in our case) the "alleged" relationship may not exist or be just the opposite. We encountered this in Chapter 2 when we discussed the gender discrimination lawsuit regarding admissions at the University of California, Berkeley. When analyzing data, it is good to keep in mind Oscar Wilde's cautionary quote, "the truth is rarely pure, and never simple". We must always be very cautious when attributing causation.

4.4   **Exercises**

Basic Concepts

1. Describe the purpose of data subsetting.

2. Describe a data set where data subsetting should be implemented. What are the disadvantages of not subsetting the data?

3. What is Simpson's paradox?

Exercises

4. Suppose you are a craft beer lover taking a trip to Denver on business and you want to be sure to stop at one of the local breweries while you are there. Using the Beers and Breweries data set from the companion website, subset the data to only show beers brewed in Denver, Colorado, and answer the following questions.

   a.   What level of measurement do each of the variables represent?

∞ **Technology**

To learn how to perform calculations on a filtered data set, please visit stat.hawkeslearning. com and navigate to **Technology Instructions > Data Manipulation > Subset Calculations.**

⠿ **Data**

stat.hawkeslearning.com **Data Sets > Beers and Breweries**

    b.   What variables other than City could be used to subset the data?

    c.   How many craft breweries are in Denver?

    d.   Which craft beer has the highest Alcohol by Volume (ABV) of the beers brewed in Denver? Give the name of the beer and the brewery.

    e.   For the Renegade Brewing Company, how many different IPA styles of beer do they make? What are they?

    f.   What is the mean and standard deviation of the ABV values for the craft beers made by the Wynkoop Brewing Company?

    g.   Calculate the coefficient of variation of the ABV values for both the Renegade and Wynkoop breweries. Which brewery has more consistent ABV values?

Data

stat.hawkeslearning.com
Data Sets > Mount Pleasant Real Estate Data

5. Suppose you are looking for a house in Mount Pleasant, SC, which is near Charleston, and you have limited your search to three subdivisions: Park West, Dunes West, and Carolina Park. Using the Mount Pleasant Real Estate data set from the companion website, answer the following questions.

    a.   What level of measurement do each of the variables represent?

    b.   Which variables could be used to subset the data?

    c.   How could you subset the data using quantitative variables such as List Price and Acreage?

    d.   How many different house styles are represented in these three subdivisions? What are the styles?

    e.   How many of the houses are newly built (2015–2017)? Which subdivision has the most new homes?

    f.   What is the average price of new homes (2015–2017) in Carolina Park? Round your answer to the nearest whole dollar.

    g.   For all new homes (2015–2017) in the three subdivisions, what is the minimum and maximum priced homes and in which subdivision are they?

    h.   What is the price per square foot of the two homes in part **g.**?

    i.   What variables do you think may contribute to the high price of the house with the maximum price?

4.5　**Analyzing Grouped Data**

All of the statistical measurements we have discussed so far presume that individual data measurements are readily available. However, there may be instances in which only a frequency distribution of the data is available. When data is presented in that form, it is called **grouped data.** It is important to be able to compute measures such as the mean and standard deviation for this type of data. Note that because the raw data observations are not available, the measures will be approximate.

The strategy for finding the mean of grouped data involves finding the midpoint of each of the classes in the frequency distribution and then weighting each of these midpoints by the number of observations in the class.

Mean of Grouped Data

The population **mean of grouped data** is given by

$$\mu = \frac{\sum (f_i M_i)}{N}$$

where

f_i = the number of observations in the ith class,

N = the total number of observations in all classes, $N = \sum f_i$, and

M_i = the midpoint of the ith class.

The sample mean of grouped data is given by

$$\bar{x} = \frac{\sum (f_i M_i)}{n},$$

where n is the number of observations in the sample.

FORMULA

We can also estimate the variance and standard deviation of grouped data using the following formulas.

Variance of Grouped Data

The population **variance of grouped data** is given by the following expression.

$$\sigma^2 = \frac{\sum (M_i - \mu)^2 f_i}{N}$$

The corresponding formula for the sample variance is as follows.

$$s^2 = \frac{\sum (M_i - \bar{x})^2 f_i}{n-1}$$

where n equals the total number of observations in the sample.

FORMULA

There are also computational formulas that can be used to calculate the variance of grouped data. These formulas may make it easier to calculate the variance by hand. These formulas will be used in the example that follows. We do highly recommend the use of technology instead of manual calculations when possible.

Computational Formulas for the Variance

The computational formulas for the population and sample variances of grouped data are as follows.

$$\sigma^2 = \frac{\sum f_i M_i^2 - \dfrac{\left(\sum f_i M_i\right)^2}{N}}{N} = \frac{\sum f_i M_i^2}{N} - \left(\frac{\sum f_i M_i}{N}\right)^2$$

$$s^2 = \frac{\sum f_i M_i^2 - \dfrac{\left(\sum f_i M_i\right)^2}{n}}{n-1}$$

FORMULA

⊗ **Technology**

To find the mean and standard deviation of grouped data we can use the 1-Var Stats option on the TI-83/84 Plus calculator with midpoints in L1 and frequencies in L2. The calculator results are shown below. We can also perform the calculations using other technologies. For instructions please visit stat.hawkeslearning.com and navigate to **Technology Instructions > Descriptive Statistics > Two Variable**.

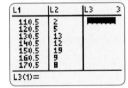

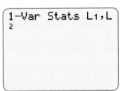

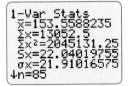

Example 4.5.1

The table below presents the systolic blood pressure reading of 85 patients, in grouped form. Compute the mean and standard deviation for this data.

Grouped Blood Pressure Data	
Systolic Blood Pressure	**Frequency** f_i
106 – 115	2
116 – 125	5
126 – 135	13
136 – 145	12
146 – 155	19
156 – 165	9
166 – 175	8
176 – 185	8
186 – 195	7
196 – 205	2

Solution

To compute the mean and standard deviation, the midpoints of each interval must be calculated. The class midpoint is determined as follows.

$$\text{midpoint} = \frac{\text{lowerclass boundary + upperclass boundary}}{2}$$

The midpoints as well as the other required calculations are presented below.

Systolic Blood Pressure	Midpoint M_i	Frequency f_i	$f_i \cdot M_i$	M_i^2	$f_i \cdot M_i^2$
105.5 – 115.5	110.5	2	221.0	12210.25	24420.50
115.5 – 125.5	120.5	5	602.5	14520.25	72601.25
125.5 – 135.5	130.5	13	1696.5	17030.25	221393.25
135.5 – 145.5	140.5	12	1686.0	19740.25	236883.00
145.5 – 155.5	150.5	19	2859.5	22650.25	430354.75
155.5 – 165.5	160.5	9	1444.5	25760.25	231842.25
165.5 – 175.5	170.5	8	1364.0	29070.25	232562.00
175.5 – 185.5	180.5	8	1444.0	32580.25	260642.00
185.5 – 195.5	190.5	7	1333.5	36290.25	254031.75
195.5 – 205.5	200.5	2	401.0	40200.25	80400.50
TOTAL		**85**	**13052.5**	**250052.5**	**2045131.25**

Calculating Mean and Variance of Grouped Data

Assuming the data is population data, the mean systolic blood pressure for the 85 patients is calculated as follows.

$$\mu = \frac{\sum f_i M_i}{N} = \frac{13,052.5}{85} \approx 153.56$$

The variance of the grouped data is calculated using the computational formula.

$$\sigma^2 = \frac{\sum f_i M_i^2 - \frac{\left(\sum f_i M_i\right)^2}{N}}{N}$$

$$= \frac{2,045,131.25 - \frac{13,052.5^2}{85}}{85} \approx 480.06$$

To find the population standard deviation we would then take the square root of the variance, 480.06, to obtain 21.91.

If the data was sample data, then the sample variance would be calculated.

$$s^2 = \frac{\sum f_i M_i^2 - \frac{\left(\sum f_i M_i\right)^2}{n}}{n-1}$$

$$= \frac{2,045,131.25 - \frac{13,052.5^2}{85}}{84} \approx 485.77$$

The sample standard deviation would then be the square root of 485.77 or 22.04.

It is important to remember that the calculation of the mean and standard deviation are approximate. That is, if the individual data is available, the actual mean and standard deviation would likely differ from the measures calculated using the grouped data.

4.5 **Exercises**

Basic Concepts

1. When analyzing group data, are the measurements exact? Why or why not?

2. What calculations are required in order to analyze grouped data?

Exercises

3. A client of a commercial rose grower has been keeping records on the shelf-life of a rose. The client sent the frequency distribution to the grower. Calculate the mean and variance for the shelf-life given the following frequency distribution.

Rose Shelf-Life	
Days of Shelf-Life	**Frequency**
1 – 6	2
7 – 12	3
13 – 18	9
19 – 24	6
25 – 30	3
31 – 36	1

4. A frequency distribution for the Beers and Breweries data set from the companion website is shown below. Use the frequency distribution to perform the following.

Data

Data Sets > Beers and Breweries

ABV Frequencies	
ABV	**Frequency**
0.0010–0.017	1
0.0175–0.033	6
0.0335–0.049	402
0.0495–0.065	1228
0.0655–0.081	565
0.0815–0.097	146
0.0975–0.113	45
0.1135–0.129	3

a. Calculate the average ABV of all beers based on the frequency distribution. Round your answer to three decimal places.

b. Calculate the variance of the ABVs of the different beers based on the frequency distribution. Round your answer to four decimal places.

c. Calculate the standard deviation of the ABVs of the different beers based on the frequency distribution. Round your answer to three decimal places.

4.6 **Proportions and Percentages**

Proportions

A **proportion** is one of the more common summary measures of a set of data. A proportion can be expressed as a fraction or a percentage.

> ### Proportion
>
> A **proportion** measures the fraction of a group that possesses some characteristic.
>
> **DEFINITION**

To calculate a proportion, simply count the number in the group that possess the characteristic of interest and divide the count by the number in the group. Let

X = the number that possess the characteristic,

N = the number in the population,

n = the number in the sample, then

$p = \dfrac{X}{N}$ the population proportion, and

$\hat{p} = \dfrac{X}{n}$ the sample proportion.

The symbol $\hat{p}$ is pronounced "p-hat".

Example 4.6.1

Suppose your statistics class is composed of 48 students of which 4 are left-handed. What proportion of the class is left-handed?

There are 48 pieces of data in the class. Think of the data as composed of 0s and 1s. Any left-handed person will be a 1, and any right-handed person will be a 0. In our data set, there are four 1s and forty-four 0s.

$$\text{Assuming } x_i = \begin{cases} 1 & \text{if person is left-handed} \\ 0 & \text{if person is right-handed} \end{cases}$$

$$\text{then } \sum x_i = 1+1+1+1+0+0+\cdots+0 = 4.$$

In the notation we used earlier, X equals the number that possess the characteristic. Therefore,

$$X = \sum x_i = 4, \text{ and}$$

$$p = \frac{X}{N} = \frac{4}{48} \approx 0.083.$$

Then 0.083 is the proportion of people in the class that are left-handed.

In the previous example, the proportion of people in the class who are left-handed could have been reported as a percentage. Instead of saying that 0.083 is the proportion of people in the class that are left-handed, it could be stated that 8.3% of people in the class are left-handed.

Example 4.6.2

Suppose you have been playing softball and have kept records on each plate appearance. According to your records you have batted 216 times. Of those 216 plate appearances, you have walked 24 times, gotten on base by a fielding error 7 times, and reached base on a hit 64 times. Let's compute your batting average, which is a proportion. The batting average is the proportion of times you reached base on a hit, excluding walks and errors. In this case the number in the group of at bats we will consider is

$$N = \text{Plate appearances } - \text{ Walks } - \text{ Bases by fielding errors}$$
$$= 216 - 24 - 7$$
$$= 185 \text{ at bats.}$$

The proportion of times you got a hit (excluding walks and errors) is

$$p = \frac{64}{185} \approx 0.346.$$

Hence your batting average is 0.346.

For the softball example, you would not convert 0.346 to a percentage because batting averages are always reported as a proportion. In Major League Baseball (MLB) statistics, the zero in front of the decimal point is usually omitted in batting averages. So, if you were in MLB your batting average would be reported as .346.

This chapter has been devoted to summarizing data. Yet with the exception of the mode, none of the summary methods discussed should be applied to nominal data. Using proportions is one of the few summary methods available for analyzing qualitative data.

4.6   **Exercises**

Basic Concepts

1. What is a proportion?

2. What is the difference in notation between a population and a sample proportion?

3. Other than the mode, proportions are one of the few summary methods available to analyze what type of data?

Exercises

4. *Science News*, Vol. 143 reported some "depressing news for low-cholesterol men." A study conducted at the University of California, San Diego found that among men age 70 and older in the low cholesterol group (concentration of less than 160 mg of cholesterol per deciliter of blood), nine of 75 reported symptoms of mild depression. Calculate the sample proportion of men age 70 and older in the low cholesterol group who reported symptoms of mild depression.

5. A study conducted at Virginia Commonwealth University in Richmond indicates that many older individuals can shed insomnia through psychological training. A total of 23 insomnia sufferers averaging age 67 years old completed eight weekly sessions of cognitive-behavior therapy. After the therapy, 13 participants enjoyed a substantially better night's sleep. Calculate the sample proportion of insomnia sufferers who enjoyed a better night's sleep after the therapy.[2]

6. A study was conducted to explore the relationship between smoking and depression. Researchers interviewed 995 smokers and asked them if they had ever experienced severe depression. 250 of those surveyed said that they had experienced severe depression. Calculate the sample proportion of smokers who experienced severe depression.

7. Researchers conducted a study of the relationship between baldness and heart disease. Of 600 men age 21–54 who had just suffered their first heart attack, 50 were found to have vertex scalp baldness (hair loss from the top of the head). Calculate the sample proportion of men age 21–54 who had just suffered their first heart attack and also experienced vertex scalp balding.

8. Using the Beers and Breweries data set from the companion website, consider the following questions. Round your answers to three decimal places.

    a. What proportion of beers are brewed in Colorado?

    b. What proportion of beers are brewed in California?

    c. What is the overall proportion of beers brewed in Colorado or Texas?

 Data

Data Sets > Beers and Breweries

9. According to a study administered by the National Bureau of Economic Research, half of Americans would struggle to come up with $2000 in the event of a financial emergency. The majority of the 1900 Americans surveyed said they would rely on more than one method to come up with emergency funds if required. In the survey, 532 people said that they "certainly" would not be able to cope with an unexpected $2000 bill if they had to come up with the money in 30 days, and 418 people said they "probably" would not be able to cope.[2]

    a. What percentage of Americans "certainly" would not be able to produce $2000 in the event of an emergency according to the study?

    b. What percentage of Americans would "probably" not be able to pay a $2000 bill in 30 days if required?

    c. What does this say about the savings habits of Americans?

10. What college football conference has the right to brag about putting players in the NFL? The following table displays the results of the first round draft picks broken down by conference. Use the data to answer the following questions. Round answers to three decimal places where appropriate.

First Round NFL Draft Picks by Conference	
Football Conference	**Number of Players**
SEC	397
Big Ten	373
Pac-12	291
ACC	237
Big 12	171
Independent	78
MAC	76
Other	95

    a. What proportion of first round draft picks are from the SEC?

    b. What proportion of first round draft picks are from the "Other" conferences category?

    c. Is it true that a player in the SEC has a better chance of being drafted in the NFL than a player from a different conference? Explain.

11. It is no secret that Wall Street firms compete aggressively to lure their high end clients to their firms. Having more high-end clients translates into fees and revenues that turn into profits. A survey of 150 high-end clients asked what lured them to their respective Wall Street firm. The following table shows the results.

High-End Client Response	
Perk Received	**Client Response**
Lucrative Golf Outings	12
Lavish Dinners	8
Free Private Jet Use	33
Prime Seats at Sports Events	20
Other	22
No Perk Received	30

    a. Which type of perk appears to be most successful in luring clients?

    b. What proportion of clients were lured to a Wall Street firm by the perk identified in part **a.**?

    c. What proportion of clients did not receive a perk at all?

    d. Given that these perks aren't inexpensive, what conclusion can you make about providing perks to clients? Explain.

CR   **Chapter Review**

Key Terms and Ideas

- Numerical Descriptive Statistics
- Parameters
- Statistics
- Inferential Statistics
- Measures of Location (Central Tendency)
- Arithmetic Mean
- Sample Mean
- Population Mean
- Deviation
- Weighted Mean
- Trimmed Mean
- Median
- Resistant Measure
- Mode
- Bimodal
- Multimodal
- Positively Skewed (Skewed to the Left)
- Negatively Skewed (Skewed to the Right)
- Moving Average
- Variability (Dispersion or Spread)

- Deviation from the Mean
- Range
- Mean Absolute Deviation
- Population Variance
- Sample Variance
- Population Standard Deviation
- Sample Standard Deviation
- Empirical Rule
- Chebyshev's Theorem
- P^{th} Percentile
- Percentile
- Quartile
- Interquartile Range
- Outlier
- z-Score
- Shape
- Subsetting
- Coefficient of Variation
- Mean of Grouped Data
- Variance of Grouped Data
- Population Proportion
- Sample Proportion

Key Formulas	
	Section
Arithmetic Mean	4.1
$\dfrac{1}{n}\left(x_1 + x_2 + \cdots + x_n\right)$	
Population Mean	4.1
$\mu = \dfrac{1}{N}\left(x_1 + x_2 + \cdots + x_N\right) = \dfrac{\sum x_i}{N}$	

Key Formulas	
	Section
Sample Mean $$\bar{x} = \frac{1}{n}\left(x_1 + x_2 + \cdots + x_n\right) = \frac{\sum x_i}{n}$$	4.1
Weighted Mean $$\bar{x} = \frac{w_1 x_1 + w_2 x_2 + \cdots + w_n x_n}{w_1 + w_2 + \cdots + w_n} = \frac{\sum\left(w_i \cdot x_i\right)}{\sum w_i}$$	4.1
Range $$\text{maximum value} - \text{minimum value}$$	4.2
Mean Absolute Deviation $$\text{MAD} = \frac{\sum\left|x_i - \bar{x}\right|}{n}$$	4.2
Population Variance $$\sigma^2 = \frac{\sum\left(x_i - \mu\right)^2}{N}$$	4.2
Sample Variance $$s^2 = \frac{\sum\left(x_i - \bar{x}\right)^2}{n-1}$$	4.2
Population Standard Deviation $$\sigma = \sqrt{\sigma^2}$$	4.2
Sample Standard Deviation $$s = \sqrt{s^2}$$	4.2
Empirical Rule **One Sigma Rule:** $\mu \pm 1\sigma$ contains about 68% of the data **Two Sigma Rule:** $\mu \pm 2\sigma$ contains about 95% of the data **Three Sigma Rule:** $\mu \pm 3\sigma$ contains about 99.7% of the data	4.2
Chebyshev's Theorem The proportion of any data set lying within k standard deviations of the mean is at least $1 - \dfrac{1}{k^2}$ for $k > 1$.	4.2

Key Formulas

	Section
Coefficient of Variation	4.2

$$\text{Population data: } CV = \left(\frac{\sigma}{\mu} \cdot 100 \right)\%.$$

$$\text{Sample data: } CV = \left(\frac{s}{\bar{x}} \cdot 100 \right)\%.$$

	Section
Location of the Pth Percentile	4.3

$$\ell = n\left(\frac{P}{100} \right)$$

	Section
Percentile	4.3

$$\text{percentile of } x = \frac{\text{number of data values less than or equal to } x}{\text{total number of data values}} \cdot 100$$

	Section
Location of Q_1	4.3

$$\ell = n\left(\frac{25}{100} \right)$$

	Section
Location of Q_2	4.3

$$\ell = n\left(\frac{50}{100} \right)$$

	Section
Location of Q_3	4.3

$$\ell = n\left(\frac{75}{100} \right)$$

	Section
Interquartile Range	4.3

$$\text{IQR} = Q_3 - Q_1$$

	Section
Outlier	4.3

Data value greater than $Q_3 + 1.5 \cdot \text{Interquartile Range}$

or

Data value less than $Q_1 - 1.5 \cdot \text{Interquartile Range}$

	Section
z-Score	4.3

$$z = \frac{x - \mu}{\sigma}$$

Key Formulas	
	Section

Mean of Grouped Data

Population data: $\mu = \dfrac{\Sigma(f_i M_i)}{N}$

Sample data: $\bar{x} = \dfrac{\Sigma(f_i M_i)}{n}$

4.5

Variance of Grouped Data

Population data: $\sigma^2 = \dfrac{\Sigma(M_i - \mu)^2 f_i}{N}$

Sample data: $s^2 = \dfrac{\Sigma(M_i - \bar{x})^2 f_i}{n-1}$

4.5

Computational Formulas for the Variance of Grouped Data

Population Data: $\sigma^2 = \dfrac{\Sigma(f_i M_i^2)}{N} - \left(\dfrac{\Sigma(f_i M_i)}{N}\right)^2$

Sample Data: $s^2 = \dfrac{\Sigma(f_i M_i^2) - \dfrac{(\Sigma(f_i M_i))^2}{n}}{n-1}$

4.5

Class Midpoint

$M_i = \dfrac{\text{lower class boundary} + \text{upper class boundary}}{2}$

4.5

Population Proportion

$p = \dfrac{X}{N}$

4.6

Sample Proportion

$\hat{p} = \dfrac{X}{n}$

4.6

Additional Exercises

1. A carpenter is attempting to repair a porch and needs twenty boards which are eight feet long. The salesman at the hardware store says he has twenty boards that "average" eight feet long. When the carpenter checks what he has bought, there are ten boards at six feet and ten boards at ten feet. Do you feel the salesman accurately represented the lengths? Discuss.

2. The maximum heart rates achieved while performing a particular aerobic exercise routine are measured (in beats per minute) for 9 randomly selected individuals.

Maximum Heart Rates (BPM)								
145	155	130	185	170	165	150	160	125

   a. Calculate the sample variance of the maximum heart rate achieved.

   b. Calculate the sample standard deviation of the maximum heart rate achieved.

   c. Calculate the range of the maximum heart rate achieved.

   d. What are some of the factors which might contribute to the variation in the observations?

   e. Create a box plot of the data.

   f. What is the percentile associated with a BPM of 145?

3. A sample of teenagers was asked how many times they went to the movies in the past 3 months. The frequency distribution table summarizes the results.

Teenager Movie Visits			
Number of Visits	**Frequency**	**Number of Visits**	**Frequency**
0	13	6	0
1	18	7	3
2	11	8	3
3	7	9	0
4	4	10	2
5	3		

   a. What proportion of the sample visited the movies at least 3 times in the previous 3 months?

   b. Find the mean and standard deviation of the number of visits using the formulas for grouped data.

   c. Compute the interval one standard deviation about the mean.

   d. Find the percent of data falling in the interval one standard deviation about the mean.

   e. Is the percent of the data falling in the interval one standard deviation about the mean close to what the Empirical Rule predicts? What is the reason for the discrepancy, if any?

4. A high school math teacher summarized the 35 math SAT scores for the students in her calculus class. The mean for the class was 521 and the median was 535. The range of the scores was 235 and the highest score in the entire class was 675. Approximately 40% of the class scored higher than 562. State whether each of the following is true or false.

    a. The 45th percentile exceeds 540.

    b. The lowest score in the class was 440.

    c. The z-score for a score of 510 is a negative number.

    d. The third quartile exceeds 562.

    e. The percentile rank of 562 is 40.

5. Consider the following number of defective circuit boards produced by two different machines on seven randomly selected days.

Defective Circuit Boards							
Machine A	2	3	7	4	5	1	0
Machine B	2	3	4	3	4	2	4

    a. Calculate the average number of defective circuit boards produced by each machine.

    b. Calculate the variance of the number of defective circuit boards produced by each machine.

    c. Calculate the standard deviation of the number of defective circuit boards produced by each machine.

    d. Which machine do you think is better? Why?

    e. Is there another way of approaching this problem?

6. A basketball coach has one remaining scholarship to offer and has narrowed his choice to two players. Listed in the following table are the points scored per game over the last season for each player.

Points Scored		
Game Number	Braudrick	Douglas
1	27	35
2	34	21
3	29	50
4	25	28
5	28	missed
6	35	32
7	31	29
8	33	missed
9	33	23
10	25	35
11	28	31
12	32	36
TOTAL	360	320

a. What level of measurement does the data possess?

b. What statistical criteria might you use to select the better player? Justify your answer.

c. Calculate the statistics you proposed in **b.**

d. Which player is more consistent? Why?

e. What biases or errors might be present in the data?

f. Is there another way of approaching this problem?

7. Consider the literacy data given in the following table.[8]

Literacy Rates			
Country	Literacy Rate (%)	Country	Literacy Rate (%)
Australia	99.0	Luxembourg	99.0
Bolivia	90.7	Mexico	92.8
Canada	99.0	Netherlands	99.0
Denmark	99.0	Peru	89.6
France	99.0	Saudi Arabia	85.0
India	74.0	United States of America	99.0
Kenya	73.0	Zimbabwe	91.2

a. What is the mean literacy rate for these selected countries?

b. What is the standard deviation of these literacy rates?

c. How many countries in this group would we expect to have literacy rates between one standard deviation below the mean and one standard deviation above the mean?

d. How many countries in this group actually have literacy rates between one standard deviation below the mean and one standard deviation above the mean?

e. What assumption did you make in answering part **c.** above?

8. A manufacturer considers her production process to be "in control" if the proportion of defective items is less than 3%. She randomly selects 200 items and determines that 9 of the items are defective.

a. Calculate the sample proportion of defective items.

b. Based on the sample, do you think it is reasonable for the manufacturer to conclude that the production process is "out of control"? Why or why not?

9. Late in the summer of 1996, Tiger Woods became a professional golfer. This highly publicized event followed a sensational college career at Stanford University, where Tiger won three United States Amateur championships. Tiger was not a professional very long before he had his first win on the pro tour, the Las Vegas Invitational. He received a total of $297,000 for his accomplishment. The prize money (in thousands) for the top 40 finishers in the tournament are given below:

Tournament Prize Money (Thousands of Dollars)							
297.0	60.2	46.2	31.3	21.4	14.5	10.7	8.5
178.2	60.2	31.3	31.3	14.5	14.5	10.7	8.5
95.7	46.2	31.3	24.7	14.5	14.5	8.5	8.5
95.7	46.2	31.3	21.4	14.5	14.5	8.5	8.5
60.2	46.2	31.3	21.4	14.5	10.7	8.5	8.5

a. Find the mean.

b. Find the median.

c. Find the mode.

d. Find the 10% trimmed mean and compare it to the mean and the median.

e. Comment on the skewness of the distribution.

10. A pharmacist is interested in studying the relationship between the amount of a particular drug in the bloodstream (in mg) and reaction time (in seconds) of subjects taking the drug. Ten subjects are randomly selected and administered various doses of the drug. The reaction times (in seconds) are measured 15 minutes after the drug is administered with the following results.

Reaction Times			
Amount of Drug (mg)	Reaction Time (Seconds)	Amount of Drug (mg)	Reaction Time (Seconds)
1	0.5	6	0.8
2	0.7	7	0.9
3	0.6	8	0.6
4	0.7	9	0.9
5	0.8	10	1.0

Analyze the data collected for the study by answering the following questions:

a. Do the variables selected for measurement seem appropriate for answering the question the pharmacist is interested in?

b. What biases or errors might be present in the data?

c. What level of measurement (nominal, ordinal, interval, ratio) do the data possess?

11. Our galaxy, the Milky Way, is 120,000 light years across and contains over 200 billion stars. But, the universe has an estimated 2 trillion galaxies. In the 1930s it was unknown whether the galaxies were moving away from one another (i.e. the universe was expanding) or moving toward one another (contracting). The astronomer Edwin Hubble attempted to measure the rate at which the galaxies were moving and discovered they were moving apart. He originally estimated they were moving apart at the rate of 500 km/s/Mpc or about 160 km/sec per million-light-years from Earth, which was called Hubble's constant. As new telescopes have come online and new methods and technologies have become available, Hubble's constant has been reestimated. The current contenders are a team at the European Space Agency which estimates the constant at 67.8 km/s/Mpc, while another team has estimated the constant at 73.24 km/s/Mpc. A recent *Science* magazine article said, "the two values are separated by a gulf of 3.4 sigma."

a.   What is the value of sigma in this case?

b.   What questions would you like to ask about this conclusion?

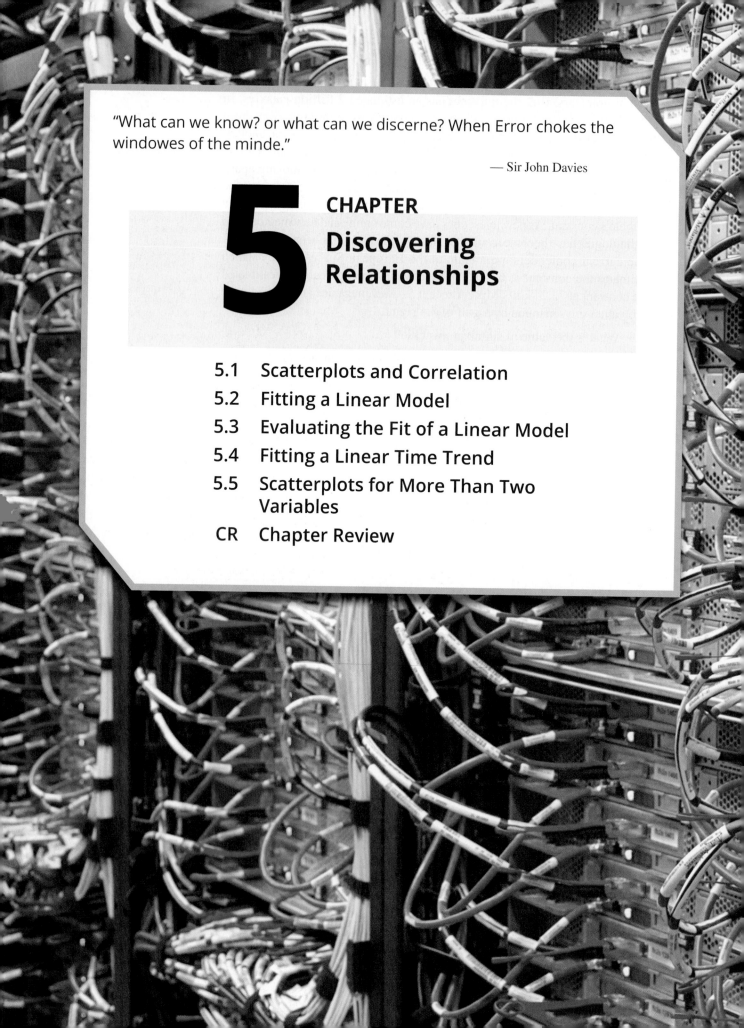

"What can we know? or what can we discerne? When Error chokes the windowes of the minde."

— Sir John Davies

5 CHAPTER
Discovering Relationships

Introduction

In the early part of the twentieth century bacteriologists went to great lengths to protect their cultures against contaminants, especially a common mold that killed entire cultures. That mold and its effects must have been seen thousands of times, but in the 1920s a London doctor, Alexander Fleming, realized that the annoying mold was actually the bacteria killer medical researchers were struggling to find. The mold was penicillin. Fleming's discovery followed a change in perception; the *facts* had not changed, but their meaning had. The discovery of the relationship between penicillin and the destruction of bacteriological organisms in the body eventually produced immeasurable benefits. Fortunately, we don't always have to rely on a sudden flash of insight to develop new relationships. Statistical tools can aid in the discovery of relationships.

Thinking about relationships is something that everyone does. Why, for example, does an admissions counselor want to know the relationship between SAT scores and college performance? The admissions counselor's task is to select students who will be successful at that college. If college performance is related to SAT scores and the relationship can be specified explicitly, then SAT scores can be used to *predict* performance. Consequently, the relationship would be helpful in selecting students for admission. On the other hand, if SAT scores are not useful in predicting college performance, then they should not be considered very important in the admission decision. Discovering whether SAT scores are related to college performance could improve the admissions process.

Most students view grades as important and work to make good grades for self-satisfaction and to enhance career opportunities. Because grades are perceived as important, students often wonder about the relationship between the amount of time spent studying and the grade received. If study time is related to the grade received, a student could use the relationship to *predict* a grade based on study time. In addition, if the student is able to predict their grade in this way, the student could adjust their study time to obtain whatever grade is desired. Being able to predict a low grade could lead to corrective action and an improvement in grade point average. The ability to predict often leads to the ability to control.

5.1   **Scatterplots and Correlation**

In earlier chapters, all of the statistical summary measurements, like the mean, variance, and proportions, were concerned with describing **univariate** data (measurements of one variable).

Bivariate Data

To understand the relationship between two variables, data on both variables needs to be collected. This type of data is called **bivariate** data.

> ### Bivariate Data
>
> **Bivariate** data is data in which two variables are recorded or measured on an entity.
>
> **DEFINITION**

The 2014 data on high school completion and crime rate contains 50 bivariate data pairs, one pair for each state, on high school completion rate and crime rate. A subset of that data is shown in Table 5.1.1.[1,2] The overall crime rate is further broken down into violent crimes and property crimes. As you can see from the data in the table, the high school completion rates are much lower in some states. The same data problems we discussed when analyzing one variable are now doubled. How was the data obtained? What exactly does the data measure? Is the data measured accurately?

:·: **Data**

The full high school completion and crime rate data set can be found on stat.hawkeslearning.com under **Data Sets > High School Completion and Crime Rate.**

Table 5.1.1 – High School Completion and Crime Rate 2014				
State	**High School Completion**	**Crime Rate (Per 100,000)**	**Violent crimes (Per 100,000)**	**Property Crimes (Per 100,000)**
Alabama	86	3605.0	427.4	3177.6
Alaska	71	3395.8	635.8	2760.0
Arizona	76	3597.4	399.9	3197.5
Arkansas	87	3818.1	480.1	3338.0
		. . .		
Virginia	85	2126.5	196.2	1930.3
Washington	78	3991.3	285.2	3706.1
West Virginia	85	2336.7	302.0	2034.7
Wisconsin	89	2378.6	290.3	2088.3
Wyoming	79	2160.2	195.5	1964.7

Every 10 years, the US Census Bureau publishes the high school completion rate for each state. Deciding how to measure something as apparently simple as the high school completion rate can be unexpectedly complex. If a basketball player's free throw percentage is 70%, that means that out of all free throws shot, 70% of them were made. But if the high school completion rate in Arizona is 76%, what does that mean? Does it mean that 76% of high school seniors graduated from high school? Does it mean that 76% of those who are of graduation age actually graduated? Or is there some other meaning? As a matter of fact, the Census Bureau takes the number of high school graduates (including those with GEDs) and divides by the total population of 18-year-olds to obtain those percentages.

What Level of Measurement (Nominal, Ordinal, Interval, or Ratio) Does the Data Possess?

The level of measurement of the data will determine how the relationship between two variables is analyzed. If the data is nominal or ordinal, the two methods discussed in this chapter (correlation and regression) will not be applicable. We will discuss how to handle qualitative bivariate data in Chapter 17.

How Is Data to Be Collected—through Observation or through a Controlled Experiment?

There is a strong link between how we collect data and what we can expect to do with it. The data on high school completion and crime rate is observational, hence it is vulnerable to **confounding**, which is the undesirable effect of other variables on the measurements. (We will discuss the effect of confounding later in the chapter.) If experimental methods are used to gather the data, any causal relationship between the variables can be more reliably estimated.

Looking for Patterns in the Data

Detecting a relationship between two variables often begins with a graph. In the case of bivariate data, a **scatterplot** (or **scatter diagram**) is the traditional exploratory graphical method used to display the relationship between two variables.

Scatterplot

A **scatterplot** is a graph used to display the relationship between two quantitative variables measured on the same entity. Data pairs (x, y) representing the two variables are plotted as a single point on a graph with x (the **explanatory variable**) along the horizontal axis and y (the **response variable**) along the vertical axis.

DEFINITION

When examining a scatterplot we are trying to draw conclusions concerning the overall pattern of the plotted data points. Does the data roughly follow a linear pattern? Is the pattern upward sloping or downward sloping? Are the data values tightly clustered in the pattern or widely dispersed? Are there significant deviations from the pattern?

A number of different scatterplots are shown in the following figures. In the first two scatterplots (Figures 5.1.1 and 5.1.2) the data is strongly related and, in fact, the data points follow a linear pattern. In Figure 5.1.1, the slope of the linear relationship is positive, that is, as the x variable increases the y variable also increases. In Figure 5.1.2, the relationship is negative; as the x variable increases, the y variable decreases. This is also called an **inverse relationship**.

Inverse Relationships

When there is an **inverse relationship** between two variables, as one variable increases, the other variable decreases and vice versa.

DEFINITION

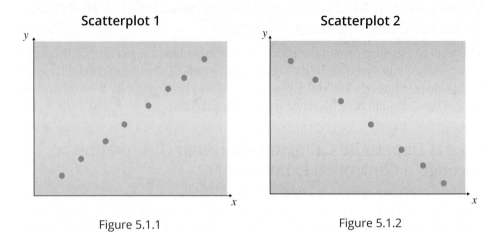

Figure 5.1.1

Figure 5.1.2

Figures 5.1.3 and 5.1.4 show less obvious relationships between the two variables. Figure 5.1.3 reveals a very imprecise relationship between x and y, although as x increases, y tends to increase. The relationship between x and y is much more apparent in Figure 5.1.4 than in Figure 5.1.3.

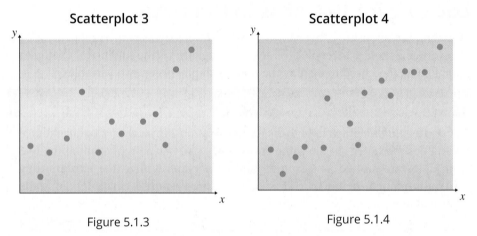

Figure 5.1.3

Figure 5.1.4

Figure 5.1.5 reveals a downward sloping relationship between x and y. That is, as x increases y tends to decrease. The inverse relationship is not as exact as the relationship in Figure 5.1.2. In Figure 5.1.6, there is no apparent relationship between x and y. That is, there is no tendency for y to increase or decrease as x increases.

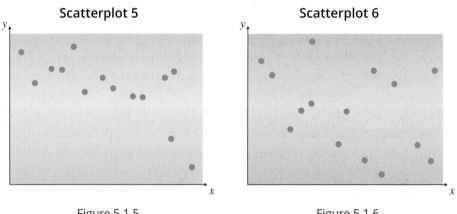

Figure 5.1.5

Figure 5.1.6

Let's explore the data in Table 5.1.1 with a scatterplot. Examining Figure 5.1.7 reveals a somewhat downward sloping relationship. That is, as crime increases, high school completion rates tend to decline.

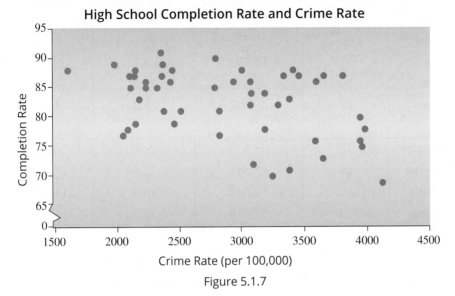

Figure 5.1.7

While the inverse relationship between crime rate and high school completion rate is apparent, the relationship is not very strong. For example, note that in Table 5.1.1 Wyoming has a relatively low crime rate, but it has a lower high school completion rate as well. The fact that there appears to be a negative relationship between crime and high school completion rates does not prove that high rates of crime cause low high school completion rates, or vice versa—even though such a conclusion may seem reasonable.

Wyoming

There are many potential variables in this observational data that could affect high school completion rates. In fact, there are many socioeconomic factors which affect high school completion rates. Some potential variables like parental involvement, as well as many other important factors, are difficult to measure. However, the US Department of Education collects data on state school systems, such as average teacher salaries, average pupil/teacher ratios, and yearly expenditure per student. These factors may have some effect on high school completion rates. For example, many people expect high school completion rates to be higher in states that have higher teacher salaries and higher expenditures per student. Further, it would be reasonable to expect that as the average number of pupils per teacher rises, high school completion rates may fall.

When data on several variables is recorded about an entity, it is called a **case** or an **observation**. In Table 5.1.2, each state (entity) has four variables recorded, and thus there are 50 cases. Looking down at line 1, we see the following.

Alabama

| **Alabama** | 86 | $49,375 | 15.6 | $8,797 |

We could have also used any other state as an example of a case.

:: **Data**

The full data set of factors affecting high school completion can be found on stat.hawkeslearning.com under **Data Sets > Factors Affecting HS Completion Rate.**

Table 5.1.2 – Factors that could Affect High School Completion Rates for 2013–2014				
States	**Completion Rate**	**Average Teacher's Salary ($)**	**Pupil/Teacher Ratio**	**Expenditure per Student ($)**
Alabama	86	49,375	15.6	8,797
Alaska	71	65,891	8.7	20,117
Arizona	76	45,335	17.7	7,461
Arkansas	87	48,493	8.0	9,573
. . .				
Washington	78	53,512	20.0	10,055
W. Virginia	85	45,887	15.5	12,859
Wisconsin	89	54,648	16.0	11,424
Wyoming	79	57,318	11.7	16,127

High School Completion Rate and Average Teacher Salary

The anticipated positive relationship between teacher salary and high school completion rate is not evident in Figure 5.1.8. In fact, the graph does not suggest any relationship. On the surface, high school completion rate does not seem to be affected by the magnitude of the average teacher salary, a somewhat surprising finding.

New York

California

Figure 5.1.8

Finding no relationship at all between two variables can be quite interesting, especially if a relationship is anticipated.

High School Completion Rate and Pupil/Teacher Ratio

The pupil/teacher ratio measures the load placed on each teacher. In California the average number of students assigned to a teacher is 20.2, while in New York the average is 10.9. Presumably, a smaller pupil/teacher ratio would permit an instructor to provide more individual attention, thereby increasing the quality of instruction.

However, Figure 5.1.9 below suggests that no relationship between pupil/teacher ratio and high school completion rate exists. That is, high school completion rate is unaffected by the magnitude of the average number of students per teacher. Incidentally, cross-cultural studies confirm this relationship. Students in Japan, for example, are frequently taught in classes containing 30–40 students, yet these students consistently score within the highest range in math and science.

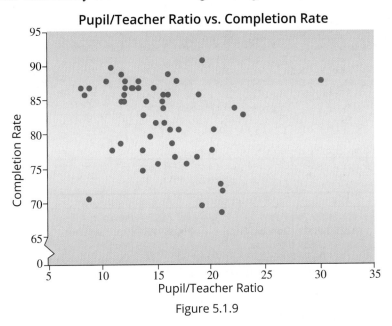

Figure 5.1.9

High School Completion Rate and Expenditure per Pupil

International tests have indicated for some time that American students are not keeping pace with other students throughout the world in math and science. One of the solutions that has been suggested is to increase the money spent on education. Figure 5.1.10 suggests there is no apparent relationship between high school completion rate and expenditure per pupil.

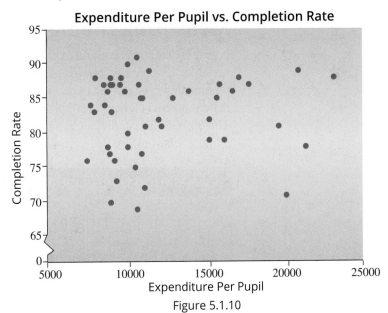

Figure 5.1.10

Perhaps other variables are confounding the relationship, but on the surface, at least, this lack of relationship has important implications for educational policy. This is an instance in which the purpose of exploring the relationship is not to develop a predictive model, but rather to understand whether there is a relationship or not. If there is a relationship, is it positive or negative? What is the strength of the relationship?

Technology

For instructions on how to calculate descriptive statistics using various technologies, please visit stat.hawkeslearning.com and navigate to **Technology Instructions > Descriptive Statistics > One Variable.**

Figure 5.1.11 provides a table of summary measures using Minitab for the variables discussed. Similar output from Excel can be found in Figure 5.1.12.

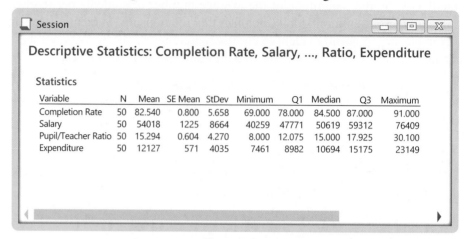

Figure 5.1.11

Completion Rate		Salary		Pupil/Teacher Ratio		Expenditure	
Mean	82.54	Mean	54017.78	Mean	15.294	Mean	12126.78
Standard Error	0.800107136	Standard Error	1225.228529	Standard Error	0.603894909	Standard Error	570.5658125
Median	84.5	Median	50619	Median	15	Median	10694
Mode	87	Mode	#N/A	Mode	15.6	Mode	15175
Standard Deviation	5.657611813	Standard Deviation	8663.674015	Standard Deviation	4.270181853	Standard Deviation	4034.509551
Minimum	69	Minimum	40259	Minimum	8	Minimum	7461
Maximum	91	Maximum	76409	Maximum	30.1	Maximum	23149
Count	50	Count	50	Count	50	Count	50

Figure 5.1.12

Measuring the Degree of Linear Relationship

A scatter diagram is a useful exploratory tool for detecting relationships between two variables. Eventually, however, a researcher will want to know the strength of the relationship between the two variables. In 1896, Karl Pearson developed a measure called the **correlation coefficient**, r, to measure the degree of linear relationship. The correlation coefficient is an index number used to summarize the strength of a linear relationship.

Correlation Coefficient

$$r = \frac{1}{n-1}\left\{\sum_{i=1}^{n}\left(\frac{x_i - \overline{x}}{s_x}\right)\left(\frac{y_i - \overline{y}}{s_y}\right)\right\} \qquad -1 \leq r \leq +1$$

FORMULA

There are two familiar expressions in the formula for the correlation coefficient:

$$\frac{y_i - \overline{y}}{s_y},$$

which is a z-score that shows how far y deviates from its mean measured in standard deviation units (s_y is the standard deviation of y), and

$$\frac{x_i - \overline{x}}{s_x},$$

which is a z-score that shows how far x deviates from its mean measured in standard deviation units (s_x is the standard deviation of x).

Summing the products of these **deviation measures** for each data pair determines the sign of the correlation coefficient.

Note: The formula presented for the correlation coefficient is difficult to calculate by hand. Often, you will see the correlation coefficient presented as the following computational formula. However, there are many statistical software programs that can calculate the correlation coefficient, so it is not often that you will need to do it by hand.

Computational Formula for the Correlation Coefficient

The computational formula for the correlation coefficient is as follows.

$$r = \frac{n\sum x_i y_i - \left(\sum x_i\right)\left(\sum y_i\right)}{\sqrt{n\sum x_i^2 - \left(\sum x_i\right)^2}\sqrt{n\sum y_i^2 - \left(\sum y_i\right)^2}}$$

FORMULA

Positive Relationships

When r is positive, there is a tendency for y to increase as x increases. If both of the deviations are positive, then each of the observations is above its mean. If both are negative, then each is below its mean. In a positive linear relationship, when one of the variables is above its mean, the other variable tends to be above its mean. Similarly, if one variable is below its mean, the other tends to be below its mean. Such is the case in Figure 5.1.12.

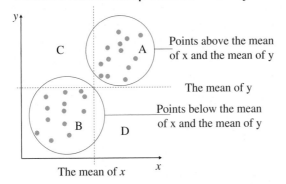

Figure 5.1.13

The points in the group labeled **A** are points whose x-values are greater than the mean of x and whose y-values are greater than the mean of y. Since for each point in group **A**, the deviations $x_i - \overline{x}$ and $y_i - \overline{y}$ will be positive numbers, the expression

$$\left(\frac{x_i - \overline{x}}{s_x}\right)\left(\frac{y_i - \overline{y}}{s_y}\right)$$

will be the product of two positive numbers, which will be *positive*.

The points in the group labeled **B** are points whose x-values are below the mean of x and whose y values are below the mean of y. Since $x_i - \bar{x}$ and $y_i - \bar{y}$ will both be negative numbers for members of this group, the expression

$$\left(\frac{x_i - \bar{x}}{s_x} \right) \left(\frac{y_i - \bar{y}}{s_y} \right)$$

will be the product of two negative numbers, which will be *positive*.

Since all the points fall into either group **A** or **B**, all the products in the summation are positive. Thus, the correlation measure (r) will have a positive value for an upward sloping (positive) relationship. Now, let's look at a downward sloping relationship.

Negative Relationships

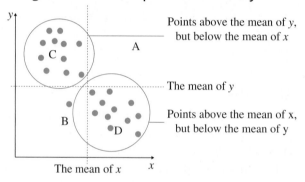

Negative Relationship between x and y

Points above the mean of y, but below the mean of x

A

The mean of y

Points above the mean of x, but below the mean of y

B

D

C

The mean of x

Figure 5.1.14

In downward sloping (negative) relationships, a value above the mean for one variable will tend to be associated with a value below the mean for the other. In Figure 5.1.14, for every point in group **C** the y-values are above the mean of y, but the x-values are below the mean of x. In group **D** the reverse is true. This kind of relationship is often called an **inverse relationship**. You see this kind of relationship quite often. For example, consider the relationship between price and quantity sold. For virtually all *normal* goods, as the price increases, the quantity sold will decrease. Examining the correlation measure for negative relationships reveals that the product in the summation,

$$\left(\frac{x_i - \bar{x}}{s_x} \right) \left(\frac{y_i - \bar{y}}{s_y} \right)$$

will be negative for points in groups **C** and **D**. Since all but one of the points belong to groups **C** and **D**, then the summation will consist of mostly negative values for

$$\left(\frac{x_i - \bar{x}}{s_x} \right) \left(\frac{y_i - \bar{y}}{s_y} \right);$$

therefore, the value of the correlation coefficient will be negative.

Many calculators and all statistics programs will compute the correlation coefficient, r, so it is unlikely that you will need to manually compute the measure.

Properties of the Correlation Coefficient

- The correlation coefficient, r, measures the degree of *linear* relationship; i.e., how well the data clusters around a line. If the scatterplot indicates a relationship that is not linear, you cannot use r to measure the strength of the relationship.

- The value of r is always between -1 and $+1$. (It is a unitless measurement.)

- A value of r near -1 or $+1$ means the data is tightly bundled around a line.

- Positive association is indicated by $r > 0$ and an upward sloping relationship.

- Negative association is indicated by $r < 0$ and a downward sloping relationship.

- A value of r near zero means there is no linear relationship between x and y.

- It does not matter whether you correlate y with x or x with y; you will still get the same value for r.

- If either variable is converted to different units, the value of r will not change.

- As a statistical measure, r is very sensitive to the presence of outliers. A single outlier can drastically affect the value of r.

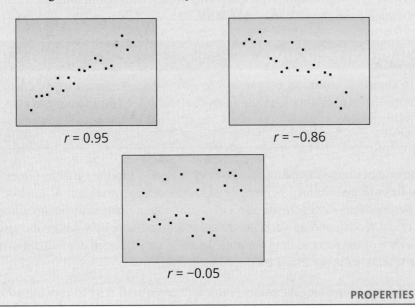

$r = 0.95$

$r = -0.86$

$r = -0.05$

PROPERTIES

Baldness and Heart Attacks

Newsweek Magazine reported the results of a medical study that identified increased risk of heart attack with male pattern baldness. This kind of information based on correlation can be useful in the sense that men with pattern baldness can be extra vigilant about possible heart attacks.

The medical researchers that studied this problem came to the conclusion that there may be a third variable, often called a lurking variable, which is a male hormone that induces both pattern baldness and propensity to increased heart attack risk. This finding opened new research questions that centered around finding such a male hormone.

Avoiding Some Correlation Pitfalls

A high correlation does not imply causation. Suppose that a high correlation has been observed between the weekly sales of ice cream and the number of snake bites each week. It seems unlikely that ice cream sales would cause snakes to bite people or that more snake bites would cause higher ice cream sales. Yet when the data is analyzed, you may find an unexpectedly high correlation. If the two variables aren't actually related, what could explain such an observed relationship?

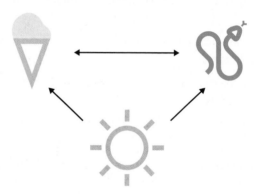

The apparent relationship is an illusion caused by a phenomenon called **common response**. That is, both variables are related to a third variable. In this case the high temperatures in the summer cause increases in both ice cream sales and reptile activity. The high summer temperatures would be confounding the relationship between ice cream sales and snake bites.

Common Response

In statistics, **common response** refers to the phenomenon where changes in both the explanatory and the response variables result from a change in a third variable.

DEFINITION

Sometimes this confounding effect is referred to as a lurking variable. Observational studies are particularly vulnerable to confounding variables. A good design of experiment can minimize the effect of confounding. Some statisticians differentiate between a confounding variable and a lurking variable by whether the researcher is aware of the confounding variable. Lurking variables are confounding variables the researcher is not aware of.

Correlating summary measures (such as means) will tend to provide an inflated correlation measurement. Ignoring the variation of the individual values magnifies the correlation measure and gives a somewhat distorted view of the underlying relationship.

Suppose there is good reason to believe that a causal relationship exists between two variables, but when a correlation is performed the value of the correlation is near zero, indicating no association. Does the lack of correlation between the two variables prove no relationship exists? There are several reasons two related variables might not have a high correlation.

Quadratic Relationship

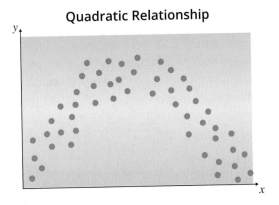

Figure 5.1.15

A low correlation could mean that no *linear* relationship exists. In Figure 5.1.15 the relationship between x and y does not follow a linear pattern. The correlation measure for these points is going to be very close to zero. Yet, there does appear to be a very strong relationship between x and y. The kind of relationship exhibited by this data is called a **quadratic relationship**.

Quadratic Relationship

A **quadratic relationship** is a mathematical relationship between two variables that follows the form of a quadratic equation (degree = 2). A scatterplot of the data will look like a parabola.

DEFINITION

Another problem that can produce a low correlation is confounding. **Confounding** occurs when more than one variable affects the response variable, and the effects of the variables cannot be distinguished from each other. Suppose that the variable y is dependent on x. Thus, as x changes, it produces changes in y. Such a relationship should produce a significant correlation measure between the two variables. But , as is illustrated in Figure 5.1.16, suppose there is another variable z, which also affects y. As z changes so does y. It is certainly possible that changes in z will mask the changes caused by x. A good design of the experiment can minimize or eliminate the effects of confounding variables.

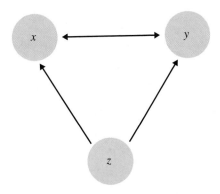

Figure 5.1.16

The range of x-values selected for a study can also significantly affect the value of the correlation coefficient. If the range of the x-values is large, the correlation will usually be greater than if the range of the *x*-values is small, as shown in Figure 5.1.17.

If the points below **A** in Figure 5.1.18 were removed and the points above **B** were removed from the data (as shown in Figure 5.1.17), the correlation between *x* and *y* will be considerably weaker. Thus, when looking at correlation data, you should ask if the data is complete.

Small Range of *x*-Values

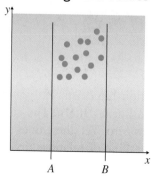

Figure 5.1.17

Complete Data

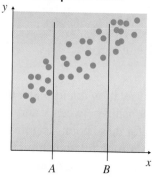

Figure 5.1.18

Sometimes unrelated variables are highly correlated. When this occurs the variables are said to have a **spurious** correlation. For example, over a short period of time, daily pizza sales and the number of penguins in Antarctica might be related. However, it is doubtful that a significant change in the penguin population will cause a change in pizza sales, or vice versa. The following graphs display some interesting spurious correlations that have been discovered.[3]

Cheese Consumption and Golf Course Revenue

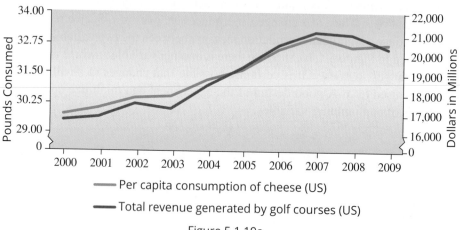

Figure 5.1.19a

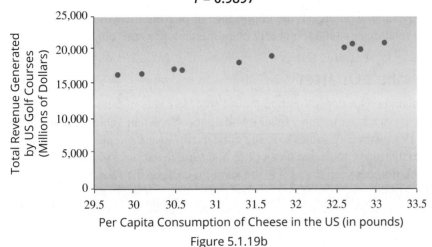

Figure 5.1.19b

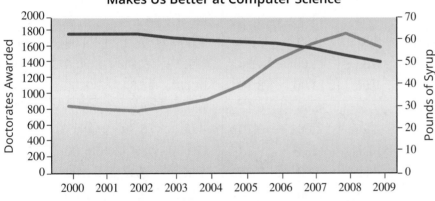

Computer science doctorates awarded (US)

US per capita consumption of high fructose corn syrup (in pounds)

Figure 5.1.20a

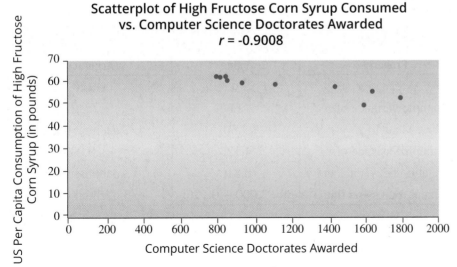

Figure 5.1.20b

**Francis Galton
1822–1911**

Galton was the ninth child of a wealthy English family in Birmingham, England. He did extensive traveling early in his life and became interested in heritability of human traits. He was also greatly influenced by his first cousin, Charles Darwin. He believed that physical characteristics such as weight, height, intelligence, as well as some personality traits were inherited. He collected data on these traits measuring mother and father and their children and found some interesting results. Tall fathers, for example, tended to have shorter children than themselves. Short fathers tended to have children that were taller than themselves. He also found this same property in seeds of wheat. He named this phenomena regression toward the mean. This is how the term regression entered statistics.

Galton was partially responsible for the development of the correlation coefficient. He needed some method of assessing the strength of the physical relationships between parents and their children. He enlisted a young English statistician named Karl Pearson to work on a measure that could be used to determine association. It was Pearson that developed the correlation coefficient for this purpose. It is unclear exactly what role Galton played in developing the correlation coefficient, however in social science literature Galton is recognized as a co-developer of the statistic.

There are several websites devoted entirely to spurious correlations. You may enjoy entering the term "spurious correlations" into a search engine and perusing the results.

This next example points out the importance of plotting the variables suspected of having a relationship, and to not rely on numerical measures alone.

Anscombe's Quartet

The Anscombe Quartet is a famous set of four data sets presented in 1973 by the statistician Francis Anscombe. In all four data sets (shown in Table 5.1.3 and labeled I, II, III, IV), all the x variables have the same mean (9) and sample variance (11). All the y variables have the same mean (7.5) and sample variance (4.125). In addition, the correlation between x and y is the same in each of the four data sets (0.816).

Table 5.1.3 – Anscombe's Quartet							
I		II		III		IV	
x_1	y_1	x_2	y_2	x_3	y_3	x_4	y_4
10.00	8.04	10.00	9.14	10.00	7.46	8.00	6.58
8.00	6.95	8.00	8.14	8.00	6.77	8.00	5.76
13.00	7.58	13.00	8.74	13.00	12.74	8.00	7.71
9.00	8.81	9.00	8.77	9.00	7.11	8.00	8.84
11.00	8.33	11.00	9.26	11.00	7.81	8.00	8.47
14.00	9.96	14.00	8.10	14.00	8.84	8.00	7.04
6.00	7.24	6.00	6.13	6.00	6.08	8.00	5.25
4.00	4.26	4.00	3.10	4.00	5.39	19.00	12.50
12.00	10.84	12.00	9.13	12.00	8.15	8.00	5.56
7.00	4.82	7.00	7.26	7.00	6.42	8.00	7.91
5.00	5.68	5.00	4.74	5.00	5.73	8.00	6.89

By examining the summary statistics of the four data sets in Table 5.1.4, a data analyst might conclude that the data sets were quite similar. However, if we look at the scatterplots of the four data sets in Figure 5.1.21, we observe four quite different structures in the x and y variables as well as in the relationship between the x and y variables.

Table 5.1.4 – Summary Statistics		
Property	**Value**	**Accuracy**
Mean of x	9	exact
Sample variance of x	11	exact
Mean of y	7.50	to 2 decimal places
Sample variance of y	4.125	+/- 0.003
Correlation between x and y	0.816	to 3 decimal places
Linear regression line	$y = 3.000 + 0.500x$	to 3 decimal places

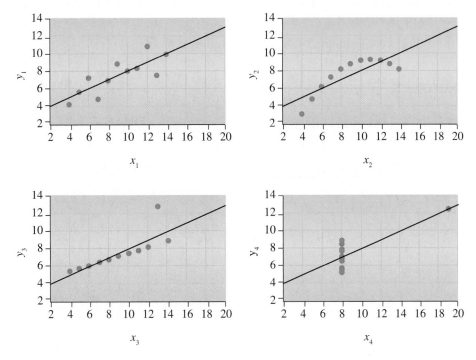

Figure 5.1.21

The Anscombe Quartet brings out an important data analytic principle. No matter what kind of numeric data is being analyzed, it is critically important to plot it before making any conclusions. For single variables, an analyst should at least be looking at histograms and box plots. When we begin to look for relationships in bivariate or multivariate data, creating scatterplots to display the relationship between the variables is more important than calculating summary measures of linear relationship, i.e., the correlation coefficient.

5.1   **Exercises**

Basic Concepts

1. Give an example of a situation in which knowledge of a relationship between two variables is desired.

2. If a relationship can be uncovered, what are the potential benefits?

3. What is bivariate data? How is bivariate data different from univariate data?

4. What graphical tool is often used in the discovery of relationships?

5. What sort of questions should you ask when studying a graphical representation of bivariate data?

6. If bivariate data exhibits an inverse relationship, what does that mean?

7. How do you measure the exact relationship between two variables?

8. In what range is the value of r when bivariate data exhibits a positive relationship? A negative relationship?

9. If the value of *r* is small, does this always mean that no relationship exists? Explain.

10. What is confounding? Why is confounding a problem?

Exercises

11. Answer the following questions regarding the overall pattern of the data for each of the scatterplots.

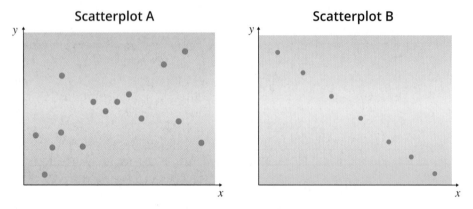

   a. Does the pattern roughly follow a linear pattern?

   b. Is the pattern upward sloping or downward sloping?

   c. Are the data values tightly clustered in the pattern or widely dispersed?

   d. Are there significant deviations from the pattern?

12. Answer the following questions regarding the overall pattern of the data for each of the scatterplots.

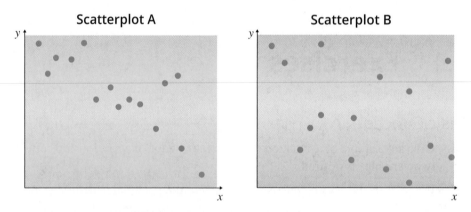

   a. Does the pattern roughly follow a linear pattern?

   b. Is the pattern upward sloping or downward sloping?

   c. Are the data values tightly clustered in the pattern or widely dispersed?

   d. Are there significant deviations from the pattern?

13. In the story of Moneyball, Billy Beane and Paul DePodesta initially calculated that 95 wins in a season was necessary for the Oakland A's to make it into the playoffs. Next, they wanted to understand the relationship between overall season run differential (the number of runs scored in a season minus the number of runs allowed) and the number of games won in a season. Go to the companion website and download the Moneyball data set. Beane and DePodesta performed this analysis in 2002, so they only had data up to the year 2001. Subset the data set to only include data for the years 1962–2001.

Data

stat.hawkeslearning.com
Data Sets > Moneyball

a. Analyze the data collected for the study by answering the following questions:

   i. What questions might Beane and DePodesta be trying to answer?

   ii. Do the variables selected in the data set seem appropriate for answering the question?

   iii. What biases or errors might be present in the data?

   iv. What level of measurement (nominal, ordinal, interval, ratio) does each variable possess?

   v. How is the data collected – through observation or controlled experiment?

b. Plot the data points for the variables RD (run differential) and W (wins) on a scatterplot.

c. Based on the scatterplot in part **b.**, answer the following questions regarding the overall pattern of the data.

   i. Does the data roughly follow a linear pattern?

   ii. Is the pattern upward sloping or downward sloping?

   iii. Are the data values tightly clustered in the pattern or widely dispersed?

   iv. Are there significant deviations from the pattern?

14. A pharmacist is interested in studying the relationship between the amount of a particular drug in the bloodstream (in mg) and reaction time (in seconds) of subjects taking the drug. Ten subjects are randomly selected and administered various doses of the drug. The reaction times (in seconds) are measured 15 minutes after the drug is administered with the following results:

Reaction Time of a Drug										
Amount of Drug (mg)	1	2	3	4	5	6	7	8	9	10
Reaction Time (in sec)	0.5	0.7	0.6	0.7	0.8	0.8	0.9	0.6	0.9	1.0

a. Analyze the data collected for the study by answering the following questions:

   i. Do the variables selected for measurement seem appropriate for the study of interest?

   ii. What biases or errors might be present in the data? What confounding variables could impact the conclusion?

      iii. What level of measurement (nominal, ordinal, interval, ratio) does the data possess?

      iv. How is the data collected—through observation or controlled experiment?

  b. Plot the data points on a scatterplot.

  c. Based on the scatterplot in part **b.**, answer the following questions regarding the overall pattern of the data.

      i. Does the pattern roughly follow a linear pattern?

      ii. Is the pattern upward sloping or downward sloping?

      iii. Are the data values tightly clustered in the pattern or widely dispersed?

      iv. Are there significant deviations from the pattern?

15. Illustrate, using a scatterplot, a data set that would have a correlation coefficient of 1.

16. Illustrate, using a scatterplot, a data set that would have a correlation coefficient of -1.

17. Describe the relationships indicated by the correlation coefficients as tightly clustered in a positive linear fashion, tightly clustered in a negative linear fashion, loosely clustered in a positive linear fashion, loosely clustered in a negative linear fashion, or no linear relationship.

  a. $r = 0.9$ **d.** $r = -0.5$

  b. $r = 0.5$ **e.** $r = 0$

  c. $r = -0.9$

  f. What assumption did you make about the scatterplots in answering **a.** through **e.**?

18. Describe the relationships indicated by the correlation coefficients as tightly clustered in a positive linear fashion, tightly clustered in a negative linear fashion, loosely clustered in a positive linear fashion, loosely clustered in a negative linear fashion, or no linear relationship.

  a. $r = 0.8$ **d.** $r = -0.4$

  b. $r = 0.4$ **e.** $r = 0.1$

  c. $r = -0.8$

  f. What assumption did you make about the scatterplots in answering **a.** through **e.**?

19. Sometimes the following descriptions are assigned to the correlation coefficient:

$r = 0$	no linear relationship
$-0.5 < r < 0$	weak negative linear relationship
$0 < r < 0.5$	weak positive linear relationship
$-0.8 < r \leq -0.5$	moderate negative linear relationship
$0.5 \leq r < 0.8$	moderate positive linear relationship
$-1.0 < r \leq -0.8$	strong negative linear relationship
$0.8 \leq r < 1.0$	strong positive linear relationship
$r = 1$	exact positive linear relationship
$r = -1$	exact negative linear relationship

Describe the relationships indicated by the correlation coefficients below using the descriptions defined above.

a. $r = 0.9$ **d.** $r = -0.5$

b. $r = 0.5$ **e.** $r = 0$

c. $r = -0.9$

f. What assumption did you make about the scatterplots in answering **a.** through **e.**?

20. Describe the relationships indicated by the correlation coefficients below using the descriptions defined in problem 8 above.

a. $r = 0.8$ **d.** $r = -0.4$

b. $r = 0.4$ **e.** $r = 0.1$

c. $r = -0.8$

f. What assumption did you make about the scatterplots in answering **a.** through **e.**?

21. Using the Super Bowl Stats data set from the companion website, consider the following:

a. Construct a scatterplot using the variables Winner_First Downs and Winner_Total Yards.

b. Does there appear to be a negative or positive relationship between the variables?

c. Compute the correlation coefficient.

⠿ **Data**

stat.hawkeslearning.com
Data Sets > Super Bowl Stats

22. Using the OECD Better Life Index 2016 data set from the companion website, consider the following:

a. Construct a scatterplot using the variables self_reported_health and satisfaction_score.

b. Determine the correlation coefficient.

c. Describe the relationship indicated by the correlation coefficient and the scatterplot.

⠿ **Data**

stat.hawkeslearning.com
Data Sets > OECD Better Life Index 2016

23. The following variables have high positive linear correlations. Is it reasonable to conclude that an increase in one variable causes an increase in the other variable? Explain what could be causing this apparent relationship.

a. Height and vocabulary

b. Absenteeism from school and sale of cough syrup

c. Sale of turkey and sale of toys

24. The following variables have high positive linear correlations. Can we conclude that an increase in one variable causes an increase in the other variable? Explain what could be causing this apparent relationship.

a. Sale of air conditioners and sale of tomatoes

b. Sale of greeting cards and sale of chocolates

c. The Number of wrecks on a local highway and absenteeism from work

5.2 Fitting a Linear Model

Building a Model

Consider the problem of deciding how long to study for an upcoming test. If we knew the exact relationship between time spent studying and the grade received, it could be useful in allocating study time. But the exact relationship between these variables is unknown and different for each course.

For most students the model relating study time to test performance is subjective, relying on past experience and data from other students. Is there any benefit from defining an exact relationship between study time and the grade received on a test? Essentially, knowing an exact relationship between study time and grade received would allow a student to choose his or her grade by allocating study time appropriately. How do you define an *exact* relationship? One method of defining a precise relationship between two or more variables is with the use of a mathematical model. Suppose, for example, that the relationship between test score and study time was given by the following linear equation.

$$\text{Test Score} = 45 + 3.8 \text{ (Hours of Study Time)}$$

If this mathematical model is accurate, then a student would be able to control his or her destiny. If a person studied for 10 hours, according to the model his or her test score would be:

$$\text{Test Score} = 45 + 3.8 \text{ (10)} = 83.$$

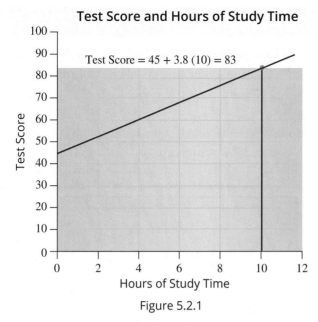

Figure 5.2.1

To get a higher test score, then study for 12 hours.

$$\text{Test Score} = 45 + 3.8\,(12) = 90.6$$

Figure 5.2.1 shows a graphical depiction of the relationship. Since the relationship is known in advance, students would be able to control their grade by choosing their study time appropriately. In fact, if the exact relationship were known in advance, taking the test would be necessary only as an intellectual exercise, since the grade would already be determined by the time studied and the model. Admittedly, there is no model that can precisely predict a test score solely on the basis of time studied since there are many other variables that affect test scores. But suppose a model were available which, although imperfect, fairly reliably predicted test scores based on hours studied.

$$\text{Test Score} = 45 + 3.8\,(\text{Hours of Study Time}) + \text{Error}$$

The new model introduces the possibility of error. Now, if someone studies 10 hours, the model would predict

$$\text{Test Score} = 45 + 3.8\,(10) + \text{Error} = 83 + \text{Error}.$$

The predicted test score would still be 83, but there is an unknown random error associated with the prediction. If the error is reasonably small (say, at most 5 points), then the prediction will still be useful for planning purposes. But if the error is too large, then it will be difficult to rely on the model's predictions. If a model admits the possibility of an error, then gauging the expected magnitude of the error is essential in determining the model's usefulness. Estimating the mean and variance of the errors will be an important part of determining model utility. A model with a mean error of zero and small variation in the error terms would be desirable and should yield useful predictions. The model we have been using is simple. If two variables appear to be related in a straight line manner, we can use a **linear equation** to model their relationship.

Linear Relationship

A **linear relationship** is graphically described as a line. Mathematically, a line is a set of points that satisfy the functional relationship

$$y = mx + b$$

where **m** is the **slope** of the line and **b** is the point where the function crosses the y-axis, which is called the **y-intercept**.

DEFINITION

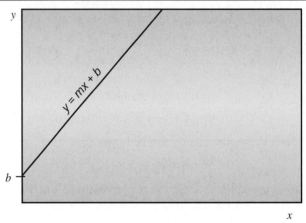

Figure 5.2.2

The slope determines if the line slopes upward (positive slope) or if the line slopes downward (negative slope). The relationship specified in Figure 5.2.3 is the linear equation

$$y = 5x + 3.$$

Slope   Intercept

In this case, $m = 5$ and $b = 3$.

Once the relationship is specified, y is completely determined by the value of x. If $x = 10$, then

$$y = 5 \cdot 10 + 3 = 53.$$

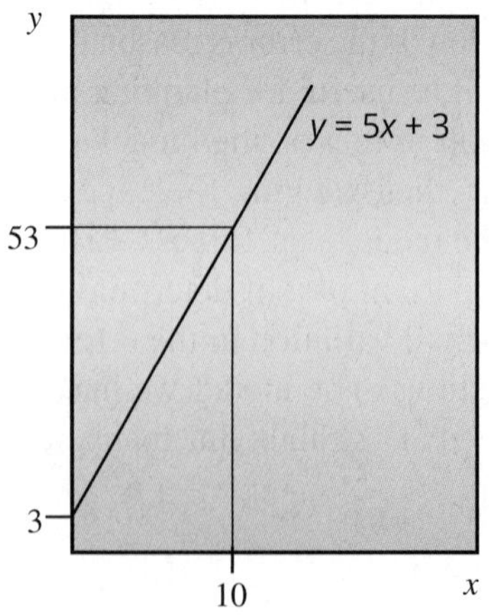

Figure 5.2.3

Very few observed relationships are exactly linear, although many follow an inexact linear pattern.

The slope and the intercept are called the **parameters** of the linear equation. The parameters completely define the equation of the line. Developing a model to fit real-world measurements is not trivial. Nature doesn't cooperate by requiring all relationships to be straight lines. Seldom, in fact, do pairs of measurements fall on perfectly straight lines. If a linear relationship exists, the data will have some general tendency to move together, or in opposite directions, as in Figure 5.2.4. In the following sections we will look at ways of measuring the degree of a linear relationship between two variables, as well as estimating the parameters (slope and intercept) of a line for a specific set of data.

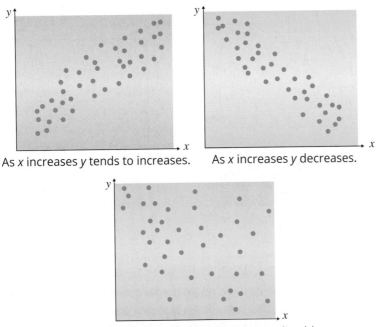

As *x* increases *y* tends to increases.   As *x* increases *y* decreases.

As *x* increases *y* does not change in a predictable way.

Figure 5.2.4

Defining a Linear Relationship

In the previous section, the correlation coefficient was used to measure the degree of linear relationship between two variables. However, it does not describe the exact linear association between *x* and *y*. That is the role of **regression analysis**. By determining a specific relationship between *x* and *y*, we may be able to use *x* to help predict *y*.

What does it mean to specify a linear relationship between two variables?

Before beginning, let's recall the equation of the line. Earlier in this section, we defined the equation of a line to be

$$y = mx + b$$

where *m* is the slope, and *b* is the *y*-intercept.

However, traditional statistics uses different symbols for the slope and intercept in the equation of the line. Instead of *b*, let b_0 be the symbol used to describe the *y*-intercept and b_1 be the symbol used to represent the slope of the line. Using this new set of symbols, the equation of the line becomes

$$y = b_0 + b_1 x.$$

By providing b_0 and b_1, the relationship between x and y is completely specified. The linear equation relating x to y is also referred to as a **mathematical model**. Note that the value of y is completely dependent on the value of x. Consequently, the y variable is called the **dependent variable**. The x variable in the model is called the **independent variable**.

For example, letting $b_0 = 3$ and $b_1 = 2$, specifies the line

$$y = 3 + 2x.$$

Figure 5.2.5 shows this relationship.   Figure 5.2.6 shows this relationship.

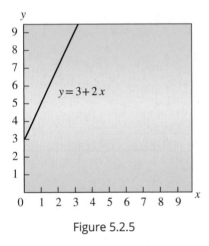

Figure 5.2.5

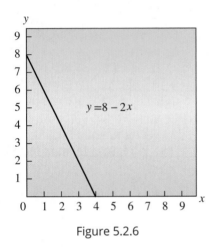

Figure 5.2.6

Letting $b_0 = 8$ and $b_1 = -2$ specifies the line $y = 8 - 2x$.

The data in Figure 5.2.7 seems to be related. Specifying the relationship between x and y with a linear model means finding a line that best fits the data in some way. The problem is that there are many lines that could be interpreted as fitting the data.

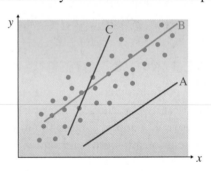

Figure 5.2.7

Which one of the lines in Figure 5.2.7 do you think best fits the data? Clearly, Line A doesn't do a very good job. The points don't cluster around the line at all. Lines B and C are very different lines, and they both seem to go through the data in some sense. Line B seems to fit the data much better than Line C, but is it the best line? To find the best line, we must come up with a method of summarizing how close each line is to the data. The closeness measure can then be used as a criterion to choose between various lines.

How Do We Measure How Close a Line Is to the Data?

One possible method of choosing the best fitting line is to use the line to predict the y-value for each observation. The superior line is the one that does the best job of predicting the observed y-values. Let's look at a small data set.

x	2	4	5	8	9
y	3	2	6	5	8

We plotted this data in Figure 5.2.8 and then tried to draw a line through the points. Notice that there is no straight line that passes through all of the data points. However, one line that seems to fit the data reasonably well is

$$y = 1 + 0.7x.$$

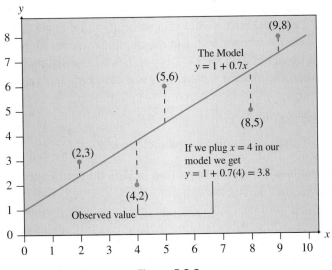

Figure 5.2.8

Although other lines might do a better job of fitting the data, let's see how well this line predicts the y-values. In order to evaluate how well a given line fits the data we must construct a method of measuring how well any line fits the data. If a reasonable measurement is developed, it can serve as a decision-making criterion which will enable us to look for the *best* line. To develop the appropriate criterion we need to examine the purpose of the **regression line**

$$y = b_0 + b_1 x.$$

Although the exact method of estimation has not been discussed, once the coefficients of the model $\left(b_0 \text{ and } b_1\right)$ are estimated, they become constants. The value of x is selected by the user of the model. Once the coefficients are estimated and the value of x is chosen, the corresponding value of y is completely determined. For instance, if $x = 2$, then using the model $y = 1 + 0.7x$, the predicted y-value is

$$y = 1 + 0.7(2) = 2.4.$$

If we take each of the observed values of x in the data and use the regression line to predict the corresponding value of y, we can compare the model's predicted value of y for each x, to the actual value of y for each x. These calculations are presented in Table 5.2.1.

Table 5.2.1 – Observed vs. Predicted Values				
Observed x	**Observed** y	**Predicted** y $y = 1 + 0.7x$	**Observed** y **– Predicted** y = **Error**	**Error**^{2}
2	3	$2.4 = 1 + 0.7(2)$	$3 - 2.4 = 0.6$	0.36
4	2	$3.8 = 1 + 0.7(4)$	$2 - 3.8 = -1.8$	3.24
5	6	$4.5 = 1 + 0.7(5)$	$6 - 4.5 = 1.5$	2.25
8	5	$6.6 = 1 + 0.7(8)$	$5 - 6.6 = -1.6$	2.56
9	8	$7.3 = 1 + 0.7(9)$	$8 - 7.3 = 0.7$	0.49
			$\sum \text{error} = -0.6$	$\text{SSE} = \sum \text{error}^2 = 8.90$

The purpose of the model is to predict y for some given value of x. According to the model, y should be 2.4 when $x = 2$. But the model is wrong. In the first historical observation, the observed data for $x = 2$ is $y = 3$, not 2.4 as the model predicts. The difference between the observed value of y and the predicted value of y is called the model's **error**.

For the first observation, the error is given by

$$\text{error} = \text{observed } y - \text{predicted } y = 3 - 2.4 = 0.6.$$

The errors reflect how far each observation is from the line. Examining the errors suggests how well the line fits the data.

If we incorporate the notion of error in our model, it becomes

$$y = b_0 + b_1 x + \text{error}.$$

Once the possibility of error has been acknowledged, the notation in the estimated model changes when the error term is not included.

$$\hat{y} = b_0 + b_1 x.$$

Specifically, the dependent variable is referred to as $\hat{y}$ (pronounced y *hat*), the predicted value of y. The symbol y is reserved for the observed value of y. The error for the model for any observation of the error is given by

$$\text{error} = y - \hat{y}.$$

One possible criterion that could be used to compare different lines that might fit the data would be to sum all the errors and choose the line with the smallest sum. But as you can see in the previous table, some of the larger positive errors were canceled out by equally large negative errors. It is possible to develop a line that has a small sum of errors, but the errors themselves are quite large. Thus, the sum of the errors is not the criterion we have been looking for, but it is close. By squaring the error terms and then adding the squared errors, there are no negative errors to cancel out the positive ones.

Let's examine the measurement of the **sum of squared errors (SSE)**.

Sum of Squared Errors (SSE)

The **sum of squared errors (SSE)** is given by

$$\text{SSE} = \sum \text{error}_i^2 = \sum \left(y_i - \hat{y}_i \right)^2 = \sum \left(y_i - \left(b_0 + b_1 x_i \right) \right)^2.$$

FORMULA

SSE can be used as a criterion for selecting the best fitting line through a set of points. If SSE is zero, then the model fits the data exactly and the observed data must lie in a straight line. If Line A's SSE is larger than Line B's, then Line B fits the data better than Line A. For the model we have been studying, the value of SSE is 8.90. Without studying other possible lines, there is no way to judge whether this is a large or small value for SSE. However, if there were a method that would find the *best* line (the line with the least sum of squared errors), then our problem would be solved. This best line would be called the **least squares line** since it would have the smallest SSE.

Finding the Least Squares Line

To define a line you must specify its slope and y-intercept. Fortunately, the problem of finding the least squares line was solved by Karl Gauss several hundred years ago. The equations for determining the slope and intercept are given as follows.

Slope and y-Intercept of the Least Squares Line

$$b_1 = \frac{n\left(\sum x_i y_i\right) - \sum x_i \sum y_i}{n\left(\sum x_i^2\right) - \left(\sum x_i\right)^2} \quad \text{and}$$

$$b_0 = \frac{1}{n}\left(\sum y_i - b_1 \sum x_i\right)$$

FORMULA

The x and y referred to in the expressions are the observed data values of x and y, respectively. You may never have to use these formulas, since many calculators and computer programs compute the coefficients of the least squares line. However, should manual calculation become necessary, the slope coefficient b_1 must be calculated prior to calculating b_0.

Estimating a Linear Relationship

Anyone who has ever purchased a car knows that a relationship exists between the price of a car and its age. In Table 5.2.2, data on age and asking price of a Honda Civic LX sedan has been gathered from fourteen classified car ads in a local newspaper.

Adrien-Marie Legendre 1752–1833

In 1806 Legendre was investigating the orbits of comets and published a book on the subject. In the appendix he gave the method of least squares curve fitting. In 1809 Karl Gauss also published his version of the least squares method. Although acknowledging Legendre's work, Gauss claimed priority on the discovery. This greatly hurt Legendre who fought for many years to have his discovery recognized as his contribution to statistics.

Table 5.2.2 – Price of a Honda Civic LX Sedan			
Age (Years)	Asking Price	Age (Years)	Asking Price
1	17,850	4	14,460
1	18,000	4	13,586
2	15,195	5	13,050
2	16,995	5	13,495
2	15,625	6	9,150
3	14,935	6	9,950
3	14,879	6	10,995

∽ **Technology**

There are several spreadsheet and statistical software programs that make estimating regression equations very simple. For instructions on how to estimate a regression equation using various types of software, please visit stat.hawkeslearning.com and navigate to **Technology Instructions > Regression > Simple Linear Regression**.

Using the least squares equations, we can estimate the following coefficients:

$$b_0 \approx 19{,}198.32 \text{ (the } y\text{-intercept)}$$

and,

$$b_1 \approx -1412.23 \text{ (the slope).}$$

Therefore the model to estimate the price of the Honda Civic LX is:

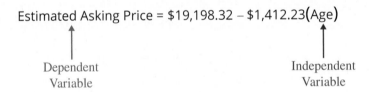

Estimated Asking Price = \$19,198.32 – \$1,412.23(Age)

Dependent Variable   Independent Variable

Figure 5.2.9 shows a graph of this model using the estimated coefficients.

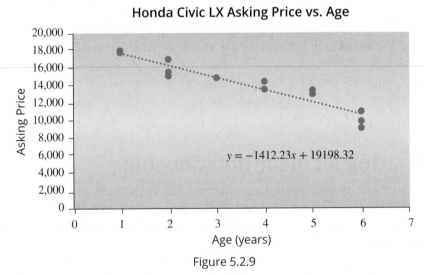

Figure 5.2.9

This model has a smaller SSE for this data than any other line. In Table 5.2.3 we examine the errors produced by the least squares model. Note that the sum of the errors equals zero.

Table 5.2.3 – Errors Produced by the Least Squares Model				
Age x	Asking Price y	Predicted y $\hat{y} = 19198.32 - 1412.23x$	Error = $y - \hat{y}$	Error^2
1	17,850	17786.09	63.91	4084.49
1	18,000	17786.09	213.91	45757.49
2	15,195	16373.86	−1178.86	1389710.90
2	16,995	16373.86	621.14	385814.90
2	15,625	16373.86	−748.86	560791.30
3	14,935	14961.63	−26.63	709.16
3	14,879	14961.63	−82.63	6827.72
4	14,460	13549.40	910.60	829192.36
4	13,586	13549.40	36.60	1339.56
5	13,050	12137.17	912.83	833258.61
5	13,495	12137.17	1357.83	1843702.31
6	9,150	10724.94	−1574.94	2480436.00
6	9,950	10724.94	−774.94	600532.00
6	10,995	10724.94	270.06	72932.40
			$\sum \text{error} = 0$	$\sum \text{error}^2 =$ 9055089.20

As you can see, in the building of a linear model, there is potential for a great deal of calculation. For most problems you will use some type of statistical analysis package or spreadsheet to compute the least squares coefficients as well as related statistics and diagnostic measures. These packages will compute a wealth of other summary and diagnostic measures concerning the estimated model.

Interpreting the Regression Equation

Using the estimated regression model, if the age of a car is 0, then the predicted asking price for a new Honda Civic LX is $19,198.32, the value of b_0.

Estimated Asking Price = $19,198.32 − $1,412.23 · (0) = $19,198.32

The value of b_0 is always interpreted as the average value of the dependent variable, in this case, the price of a Honda Civic LX, when the independent variable is set equal to zero, which is the cost of a *new* Honda Civic LX. Since b_1 is the estimated slope of the line, it is interpreted as the average change in the dependent variable, the price of a Honda Civic LX, for a one unit change in the independent variable (Age). In our example, the independent variable, Age, is expressed in years. Therefore, for every additional year in Age, the price of the car declines by $1,412.23. If this interpretation is correct, the model's predicted price for a two-year-old Honda Civic should be $1,412.23 greater than for a three-year-old Honda Civic.

If the Honda Civic is two years old, then $x = 2$, and

Estimated Asking Price = $19,198.32 − $1,412.23 · (2) = $16,373.86.

If the Honda Civic is three years old, then $x = 3$, and

Estimated Asking Price = $19,198.32 − $1,412.23 · (3) = $14,961.63.

Moneyball

In 1995, decisions by new management led the Oakland Athletics baseball team, or the A's, to be one of the poorest teams in professional baseball. In the early 2000s, Billy Beane, manager of the A's, decided that things needed to change. He needed better players for less money, but he needed help finding those players. Enter Paul DePodesta, a Harvard graduate who was hired to recruit players based on statistics rather than gut feeling. This removed any bias, and helped them focus on achieving their true goal, which Beane and DePodesta defined as making the playoffs. To make the playoffs, a team needs to win games; using data from previous years, DePodesta estimated that if a team won at least 95 out of 162 games, they almost certainly made the playoffs. To win a game, a team must score more runs than their opponent. Again, using data, DePodesta calculated that a team needed to score at least 135 more runs than they allowed to win 95 games and make the playoffs. But, coming up with the numbers was the easy part of the process. The A's now needed to bring in the players that could make these numbers into a reality. Beane and DePodesta highlighted stats that were largely undervalued by traditional scouts. Using simple linear regression models, the A's calculated the overall team statistics that were necessary to have a season run differential of 135, win 95 games, and thus make the playoffs. Then, they set about recruiting the players within their budget that helped them achieve their goal. The A's are still considered one of the most efficient teams when it comes to recruiting.

According to the model, the difference in price between a two-year-old and a three-year-old Honda Civic is exactly equal to the slope.

Difference in Asking Price = Slope	
Prediction for two-year-old car	$16,373.86
Prediction for three-year-old car	−$14,961.63
Difference	$1,412.23

Interpretation of b_0 and b_1

The intercept coefficient, b_0, is the average value of the dependent variable, y, when the independent variable, x, is equal to zero.

The slope coefficient, b_1, is the average change in the dependent variable, y, for a one unit change in the independent variable, x.

DEFINITION

5.2 Exercises

Basic Concepts

1. What is regression analysis?

2. What is the difference between a dependent and an independent variable?

3. What is the estimated linear regression equation and how is it used?

4. What is $\hat{y}$? How does this differ from y?

5. What is the technique used to estimate the linear regression coefficients?

6. What is the relationship between scatterplots and linear regression?

7. Why is it often difficult to accurately describe real world situations using a linear regression equation?

8. What is the sum of squared errors and what does it measure?

9. Explain why the best line is referred to as the least squares line.

10. What measure should be minimized in order to find the least squares line?

11. What is the equation for finding the slope of the least squares line?

12. What is the equation for finding the intercept of the least squares line?

13. When finding the least squares line manually, which must be calculated first: the slope or the y-intercept?

14. Interpret the intercept coefficient, b_0.

15. Interpret the slope coefficient, b_1.

Exercises

16. Suppose that a company wishes to predict sales volume based on the amount of advertising expenditures. The sales manager thinks that sales volume and advertising expenditures are modeled according to the following linear equation. Both sales volume and advertising expenditures are in thousands of dollars.

    Estimated Sales Volume $= 49.25 + 0.51($Advertising Expenditures$)$

    a. What is the dependent variable in this model? Explain.

    b. What is the independent variable in this model? Explain.

    c. What is the estimated sales volume for this company when the marketing department spends \$40,000 on advertising?

    d. If the company had a target sales volume of \$100,000, how much should the sales manager allocate for advertising in the budget?

    e. What is the sales manager forgetting to account for when using this linear equation to determine sales volume? What kinds of problems could this cause for the company?

17. Suppose the following estimated regression equation was determined to predict salary based on years of experience.

    Estimated Salary $= 25689.10 + 2148.35($Years of Experience$)$

    a. What is the dependent variable? What is the independent variable?

    b. What is the value that estimates b_0 in this particular equation?

    c. What is the value that estimates b_1 in this particular equation?

    d. What is the estimated salary for an employee with 15 years of experience?

18. Plot the following lines.

    a. $y = 2 + 3x$ c. $y = 9 - 2x$

    b. $y = 4 + 8x$ d. $y = x$

19. Plot the following lines.

    a. $y = 100 + 50x$ c. $y = 20 - 5x$

    b. $y = 0.5 + 0.7x$

20. Consider the following estimated regression equation.

    $$\hat{y} = 10x - 5$$

    a. Complete the following table.

Predicted Values					
x	2	5	7	9	10
y					

    b. Do these two variables appear to have a positive or negative relationship?

    c. For these two variables, what sign would you expect the correlation coefficient to have? Explain.

21. Consider the following data.

Observed Values					
x	0	1	5	6	8
y	2	4	9	7	8

a. Draw a scatterplot of the data.

b. Draw a line which you believe fits the data.

c. Suppose that $\hat{y} = 3 + 0.8x$ is a line that fits the data reasonably well. Complete the following table.

Observed and Predicted Values				
Observed x	Observed y	Predicted y	Error	Squared Error
0	2			
1	4			
5	9			
6	7			
8	8			

d. What is the sum of squared errors for this data?

Data

stat.hawkeslearning.com

Data Sets > Mount Pleasant Real Estate Data

22. Using the Mount Pleasant Real Estate data set from the companion website, consider the following:

a. Suppose we want to predict List Price based on Square Footage. Write the estimated regression equation in terms of List Price and Square Footage. (Assume the parameters of this model have not been estimated.)

b. Create a scatterplot using the List Price and Square Footage variables and draw a least squares regression line.

c. Suppose we determine that an equation that fits the data reasonably well is Estimated List Price $= -144{,}193 + 256.3753(\text{Square Footage})$. Using this equation, complete the following table. Round values to the nearest whole number.

Housing Prices and Square Footage				
Observed Selling Price	Observed Square Footage	Predicted Selling Price (Thousands of Dollars)	Error	Squared Error
375,000	1797			
423,600	2135			
448,315	1895			
515,250	2423			
556,400	2800			
600,500	3045			
583,620	3115			
683,025	3210			
635,250	3143			
615,300	2730			

Housing Prices and Square Footage				
Observed Selling Price	Observed Square Footage	Predicted Selling Price (Thousands of Dollars)	Error	Squared Error
731,410	3340			
860,750	3521			
835,000	4236			
815,500	3841			

    d.   Compute the sum of squared errors for the data in the table in part **c.** Round your answer to the nearest whole number.

    e.   Is there a variable other than Square Footage that might predict List Price more accurately? Create a scatterplot using that variable and List Price, and compare it to the plot in part **b.** Is the grouping tighter or more dispersed?

23. In the story of Moneyball, Billy Beane and Paul DePodesta determined that 95 wins out of 162 games was necessary in order for the Oakland A's to make it to the MLB playoffs. They also determined that there was a strong linear relationship between season run differential and the number of wins in a season. Using the Moneyball data set from the companion website, subset the data to only include data prior to the year 2002 (1962-2001), and answer the following questions.

    a.   What is the regression equation for predicting wins (W) using run differential (RD)?

    b.   What is the run differential necessary in order to win 95 games? Use the regression equation from part **a.** to calculate your answer. Do not round any values until the final answer. Round your final answer to the nearest whole number.

24. Consider the following data.

x	−2	−1	0	3	5
y	1	3	5	4	8

    a.   Plot the data points on a scatterplot.

    b.   Determine the least squares line. Use x as the independent variable.

    c.   Plot the least squares line on the scatterplot.

    d.   Use the model to compute the error for each data point.

25. Suppose a linear regression analysis produced the following equation relating an individual's salary to the current value of his or her home.

    Estimated Current Value of Home $= 52{,}331 + 3.14 \left(\text{Annual Salary} \right)$

    a.   Which of the variables in the model is the dependent variable?

    b.   Which of the variables in the model is the independent variable?

    c.   What would be the predicted current value of home for someone earning a salary of $32,000?

⋮ **Data**

stat.hawkeslearning.com
Data Sets > Moneyball

d. If a person earned $5000 additional income, how much of an increase in home value would be predicted?

e. In terms of the problem, interpret the estimate of the slope in the model.

f. In terms of the problem, interpret the estimate of the intercept in the model.

g. Do you believe annual salary is a causal factor in explaining the price of someone's home? Explain.

26. Suppose a linear regression analysis produced the following equation relating a basketball player's total points scored to the number of minutes played in a season.

$$\text{Estimated Points Scored} = -97.2 + 0.645(\text{Minutes Played})$$

a. Which of the variables in the model is the dependent variable?

b. Which of the variables in the model is the independent variable?

c. What would be the predicted value of total points scored for a basketball player who plays 500 minutes in a season?

d. If a basketball player played an additional 100 minutes, how much of an increase in total points scored would be predicted?

e. In the model, which of the coefficients is the slope?

f. In the model, which of the coefficients is the intercept?

g. Do you believe the number of minutes played is a causal factor in explaining the total points scored? Explain.

27. Suppose you were studying the educational level of husbands and wives (measured in number of years of education). You have randomly selected 10 couples and have obtained the data in the following table.

Education Level									
Husband	12	16	16	18	20	17	23	14	12	16
Wife	14	16	14	16	16	18	18	12	16	20

a. Suppose you wanted to predict the husband's years of education based on the wife's. Use the data to estimate the appropriate model.

b. Use the model in part **b.** to predict the husband's educational level if married to a woman with 16 years of education.

c. Suppose you wanted to predict the years of education for the wife based on the husband's years of education. Use the data to create the appropriate model. Did you get the same model as in part **b.**?

d. Use the model created in part **d.** to predict the wife's educational level if married to a husband with 16 years of education.

e. Do you believe there is a causal relationship between the two variables? If so, which direction is the causality? Does the husband's education cause the wife to have more or less education, or vice versa?

28. The graphs below describe stroke mortality related to blood pressure and age. Stroke mortality rate is pictured on a log scale with 95 percent confidence

intervals for each decade of age in relation to the estimated usual systolic and diastolic blood pressure at the start of that decade. For diastolic pressure, each age-specific regression line ignores the left-hand point (ie., at slightly less than 75 mmHg), for which the risk lies significantly above the fitted regression line (as indicated by the broken line below 75 mmHg). Use the graphs to answer the following questions.

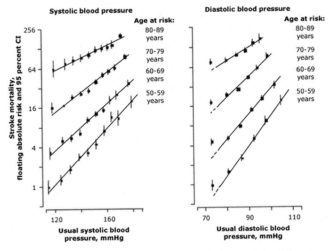

a.   What sign do you expect on the coefficient of the blood pressure term? Explain.

b.   What impact does blood pressure have on stroke mortality? Compare the impact of a change in systolic blood pressure versus diastolic blood pressure.

c.   What impact does age have on stroke mortality?

5.3   Evaluating the Fit of a Linear Model

The Importance of Errors

The usefulness of the regression model depends on the magnitude of the prediction errors you expect the model to produce. The Honda Civic model is

$$\text{Asking Price} = b_0 + b_1 \cdot \text{Age} + \text{error}.$$

Yet we ignored the error component in the previous section when we predicted the prices of the Honda Civic for different ages. For instance, when we predicted the price of a two-year-old Honda Civic, we found

$$\text{Estimated Asking Price} = \$19{,}198.32 - \$1412.23 \cdot (2) = \$16{,}373.86.$$

Since the model is not going to be a perfect predictor, we should incorporate the possibility of error in the model. Thus,

$$\text{Estimated Asking Price} = \$19{,}198.32 - \$1412.23 \cdot (2) + \text{error}$$
$$= \$16{,}373.86 + \text{error}$$

would have been a more precise statement. It is important to assess the magnitude of the error when the model is used for predictive purposes. If the errors are too large, then it will not be advantageous to use the model for prediction.

How Do We Assess the Magnitude of the Errors?

You may have wondered why we have been trying to predict observations that we already know. For example, an observation in the Honda Civic data was Age equal to 3 and Asking Price equal to $14,935. If we already know the price is $14,935 for this three-year-old Honda Civic, why try to predict it? Using the model to predict the observed outcomes of the dependent variable, y, produces error data that can be used to evaluate the errors the model produces. Knowledge of the errors will provide understanding of the predictive quality of the model.

How Do You Summarize the Errors a Model Produces?

For the Honda Civic model, the mean error is zero. This is true for all least squares models and hence the mean error won't provide any useful information. What about the average variation in the error terms? Large variation in the errors would indicate that a model's prediction is not very reliable. On the other hand, small variation in the errors would indicate that the model is capable of producing more trustworthy predictions.

Computing the variation of the error data is not very much different from computing the variation of any data set. Recall that the definition of sample variance is given by

$$s^2 = \frac{\sum (x_i - \bar{x})^2}{n-1}.$$

Since we are discussing errors, instead of using x as the variable name, let's use e. Using the new symbol and making a slight adjustment for degrees of freedom produces the definition for the **variance of the error**.

> ### Variance of the Error
>
> The variance of the error is given by
>
> $$s_e^2 = \frac{\sum (e - \bar{e})^2}{n-2} = \frac{\sum e^2}{n-2} = \frac{SSE}{n-2}.$$
>
> **FORMULA**

The symbol $\bar{e}$ refers to the mean of the errors. Because least squares is used to estimate the model, $\bar{e} = 0$, and therefore the term, $\bar{e}$, disappears from the definition. The numerator is divided by $n - 2$ (the degrees of freedom of the error data) instead of $n - 1$ to account for an additional constraint imposed by least squares estimation. In the Honda Civic data the variance of the errors is

$$s_e^2 = \frac{9055089.197}{14 - 2} \approx 754590.77$$

Statistics Can Be Cool!

Have you ever considered bragging about what you are learning in statistics? The evolution of regression methods has found its way into a very trendy and interesting field of study: machine learning. Since you are beginning to study regression methods and how they can be applied, you are also beginning to study a foundational component that is used in machine learning.

Machine learning is focused on predictive modeling. The field has borrowed an old statistical algorithm (regression) and is breathing some new life into it. There are plenty of resources on the internet related to machine learning; however, it is a technical subject, and you will need some basic knowledge of calculus, statistics, and programming to begin your adventure in the machine learning world.

and the **standard error** (standard deviation of the error terms) is given by

$$s_e = \sqrt{754590.77} \approx 868.67.$$

Table 5.3.1 – Summary Output				
Regression Statistics				
Multiple R	0.9515			
R Square	0.9053			
Adjusted R Square	0.8975			
Standard Error	868.6718			
Observations	14			
ANOVA				
	df	**SS**	**MS**	*F*
Regression	1	86613696.0169	86613696.0169	114.7823
Residual	12	9055089.1974	754590.7664	
Total	13	95668785.2143		
	Coefficients	**Standard Error**	*t* **Stat**	**P-value**
Intercept	19198.3224	524.9047	36.5749	0.0000
Age (Years)	−1412.2303	131.8160	−10.7137	0.0000

Table 5.3.1 shows the summary output from Microsoft Excel for the regression analysis of the Honda Civic data. Notice that the mean square error is given in the column labeled *MS* and the row labeled *Residual*. The standard error of the model is given in the *Regression Statistics* table and is labeled *Standard Error*.

Should you be satisfied with a model whose standard error is $868.67? It would certainly be more desirable if the model's standard deviation of error was only $100. If you know a great deal about the used car market (you have an intuitive model), then perhaps the current model would not be of value. However, if you are uninformed, the current model provides a basic understanding of the relationship between age and asking price.

What constitutes small and large variation of the errors is dependent on the nature of the problem. Using a model to predict the diameter of a valve to be used in a heart-lung machine is certainly going to produce a different idea of *small* than estimating the price of a car. It would be ideal to develop a measure that would summarize the degree of fit on some standardized scale.

The Coefficient of Determination

The goal in constructing most linear models is to use the independent variable, x, to explain or predict the dependent variable, y. The question we want to consider is, how much of the variation in y can be explained with the model? Before determining how much variation the model explains, it will be necessary to evaluate how much variability exists in the y variable. This quantity is called the **total sum of squares** (**Total SS**) and represents the total variation in the dependent variable (y).

> ### Total Sum of Squares (Total SS)
>
> The total variation in y is given by the **total sum of squares (Total SS)**.
>
> $$\text{Total SS} = \sum (y - \bar{y})^2$$
>
> **FORMULA**

If you think Total SS looks a great deal like the numerator of the formula for the sample variance, you are right. Total SS is the sum of the squared deviations about the mean of the independent variable y. If Total SS were divided by $n - 1$ it would be the sample variance of y.

What is an error?

An error $\left(y - \hat{y}\right)$ represents the model's inability to predict the variation in the dependent variable, y. If y didn't vary, for example if all the y's were 6, its value would be easy to predict and the model's errors would all be zero. Adding all the squared errors accumulates the total of all *unexplained* variation in y, which is denoted by **SSE**, the **sum of squared errors**.

$$\text{SSE} = \sum e^2 \quad \text{(Total of unexplained variation in } y\text{)}$$

The variation in y can be divided into two categories, unexplained and explained. Total variation must equal the unexplained variation plus the explained variation.

$$\text{Total SS} = \text{Unexplained Variation} + \text{Explained Variation}$$

or

$$\text{Total SS} = \text{SSE} + \text{Explained Variation}$$

Denoting explained variation as **SSR (sum of squares of regression)** produces

$$\text{Total SS} = \text{SSE} + \text{SSR}$$

and solving this equation for SSR results in

$$\text{SSR} = \text{Total SS} - \text{SSE}.$$

The explained variation, SSR, is equal to the total variation minus the unexplained variation.

Interpreting SSR

It would be delightful if the model would explain all of the variability in the y values, but unless all the observed data points fall on a line, this will not happen. In virtually all models, there will be errors, i.e., unexplained variation. The difference between the total variation in y and the unexplained variation must be the variation that is explained by the regression model. That's why explained variation is called the sum of squares of regression, SSR.

In the Honda Civic example,

$$\text{Total SS} \approx 95,668,785 \text{ and } \text{SSE} \approx 9,055,089.$$

Therefore,

$$\text{SSR} = \text{Total SS} - \text{SSE} \approx 95,668,785 - 9,055,089 = 86,613,696.$$

Of the roughly 96 million units of total variation in y, the model explains about 87 million.

Coefficient of Determination

The proportion of variation explained by the model is called the **coefficient of determination** and is denoted as R^2.

$$R^2 = \frac{\text{explained variation}}{\text{total variation}} = \frac{\text{SSR}}{\text{Total SS}} = 1 - \frac{\text{SSE}}{\text{Total SS}}$$

The coefficient of determination is a value between 0 and 1, inclusive. That is, $0 \leq R^2 \leq 1$.

DEFINITION

The R^2 measurement summarizes the degree of fit of the linear model on a standardized scale. The largest value R^2 can attain is 1, which will occur when the model explains all the variation in y and consequently SSR = Total SS. The smallest value of R^2 is 0, which occurs when the model does not explain any of the variation in y and consequently, SSR = 0. Thus, the R^2 value is the proportion of the variation in y explained by the model.

For the Honda Civic data,

$$R^2 = \frac{86,613,696}{95,668,785} \approx 0.9053$$

In other words, the estimated model explains about 91 percent of the variation in car prices. That's very good. One of the interesting features of the R^2 statistic is the ability to compare the fit of two models. If one model explains 91 percent of the data and another explains 98 percent, then the second model is preferred, all other things being equal.

Example 5.3.1

The SAT has been used for years as a predictor of academic success. If SAT scores are predictors of academic success, they should be positively related to the grade point average upon graduation. Twenty-seven graduates of a state college were sampled and their grade point averages (GPA) upon graduation and SAT scores reported upon admission are recorded as paired data values in the following table.

Table 5.3.2 – SAT Scores and Graduating GPA							
Student	**SAT Verbal**	**SAT Math**	**SAT Total**	**College GPA**	**Predicted GPA**	**Error**	**Error Squared**
1	680	554	1234	3.42	2.8647	0.5553	0.30835809
2	486	562	1048	2.37	2.4741	−0.1041	0.01083681
3	500	564	1064	2.52	2.5077	0.0123	0.00015129
4	501	564	1065	2.25	2.5098	−0.2598	0.06749604
5	503	583	1086	2.9	2.5539	0.3461	0.11978521
6	503	571	1074	3.17	2.5287	0.6413	0.41126569
7	603	667	1270	2.76	2.9403	−0.1803	0.03250809
8	507	552	1059	2.21	2.4972	−0.2872	0.08248384

Data

The SAT Scores and Graduating GPA data set can be found on stat.hawkeslearning.com under **Data Sets > SAT Scores and Graduating GPA.**

	Table 5.3.2 – SAT Scores and Graduating GPA						
Student	SAT Verbal	SAT Math	SAT Total	College GPA	Predicted GPA	Error	Error Squared
9	607	554	1161	2.27	2.7114	−0.4414	0.19483396
10	509	654	1163	3.20	2.7156	0.4844	0.23464336
11	510	583	1093	2.83	2.5686	0.2614	0.06832996
12	612	558	1170	2.91	2.7303	0.1797	0.03229209
13	517	568	1085	2.74	2.5518	0.1882	0.03541924
14	519	668	1187	3.21	2.7660	0.4440	0.19713600
15	528	607	1135	2.40	2.6568	−0.2568	0.06594624
16	528	516	1044	3.41	2.4657	0.9443	0.89170249
17	536	559	1095	2.24	2.5728	−0.3328	0.11075584
18	668	648	1316	3.47	3.0369	0.4331	0.18757561
19	648	580	1228	2.70	2.8521	−0.1521	0.02313441
20	538	554	1092	2.80	2.5665	0.2335	0.05452225
21	638	624	1262	3.08	2.9235	0.1565	0.02449225
22	541	568	1109	2.08	2.6022	−0.5222	0.27269284
23	642	660	1302	3.39	3.0075	0.3825	0.14630625
24	542	554	1096	2.34	2.5749	−0.2349	0.05517801
25	593	664	1257	2.35	2.9130	−0.5630	0.31696900
26	643	571	1214	2.40	2.8227	−0.4227	0.17867529
27	548	573	1121	3.20	2.6274	0.5726	0.32787076
28	548	574	1122	2.59	2.6295	−0.0395	0.00156025
29	549	557	1106	2.37	2.5959	−0.2259	0.05103081
30	549	564	1113	2.34	2.6106	−0.2706	0.07322436

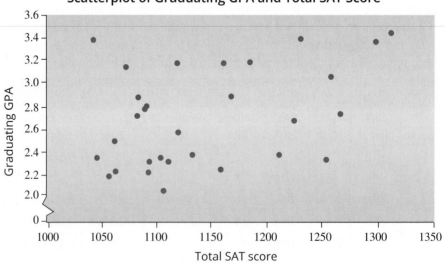

Scatterplot of Graduating GPA and Total SAT Score

The scatterplot of the data suggests that as SAT scores increase the GPA tends to increase, although there is a substantial amount of variability in the relationship. The upward sloping pattern of the data suggests a linear model could be constructed. However, a great deal of variation in the model's errors should be expected. What percent of the variation in final grade point average can be explained by the model relating total SAT score to graduating GPA?

Solution

Using the least squares method, the estimated model is given by

Estimated Graduating GPA = 0.2733 + 0.0021 (Total SAT Score).

SUMMARY OUTPUT				
Regression Statistics				
Multiple R	0.3996			
R Square	0.1597			
Adjusted R Square	0.1297			
Standard Error	0.4008			
Observations	30			
ANOVA				
	df	*SS*	*MS*	*F*
Regression	1	0.8548	0.8548	5.3218
Residual	28	4.4976	0.1606	
Total	29	5.3524		
	Coefficients	**Standard Error**	*t* **Stat**	**P-value**
Intercept	0.2733	1.0677	0.2560	0.7998
SAT Total	0.0021	0.0009	2.3069	0.0287

When we studied the Honda Civic model, a list of predicted values and errors for each observed value was given. Instead of providing a list of the errors for each of the observed values, let's summarize the errors from the model. In particular,

$$s_e^2 \approx 0.1606 \text{ and } s_e \approx 0.4008.$$

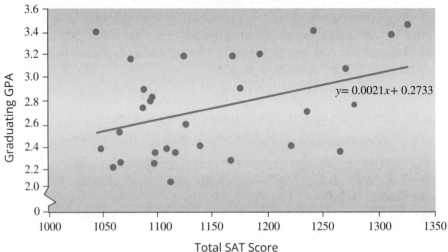

Scatterplot with Estimated Regression Line

$y = 0.0021x + 0.2733$

One of the differences in the Honda Civic model and the SAT/GPA model is the manner in which the models seem to fit the data. In the Honda Civic model, the data seemed to fit closely around the line, while in the SAT/GPA model the data is loosely clustered about the line. While *tight* and *loose* are interesting portrayals of the relative fit of the models to the data, it would be desirable to have a numerical measure to describe fit. R^2 is such a measure.

$$R^2 = \frac{SSR}{Total\ SS} \approx \frac{0.8548}{5.3524} \approx 0.1597$$

Thus, approximately 16% of the variation in graduating GPA is explained by the linear model.

Because R^2 is a unit-free measure, it can be used to compare the fit of two models. The SAT/GPA model only explains approximately 16% of the variation in the dependent variable. Compared to the Honda Civic model, which had an R^2 of about 0.9053, this model seems dramatically inferior. Using R^2 as a criterion, the Honda Civic model seems to have a substantially better fit (0.9053 vs 0.1597) than the SAT/GPA model. The real question is whether you can predict more accurately with the model than other available alternatives. If so, models with relatively low coefficients of determination, such as the SAT/GPA model, are useful. If you could develop a model to predict stock prices minute-by-minute, achieving an R^2 value of only 0.20, you could be a very wealthy person.

R^2 can also be found using the following computational formula.

Coefficient of Determination

The **coefficient of determination**, R^2, can be calculated using the equation:

$$R^2 = \left(\frac{n\sum x_i y_i - \sum x_i \sum y_i}{\sqrt{\left[n\sum x_i^2 - \left(\sum x_i\right)^2\right]\left[n\sum y_i^2 - \left(\sum y_i\right)^2\right]}} \right)^2$$

FORMULA

Normally you will not have to use this formula since calculators and computer programs can calculate the coefficient of determination. Recall the computational formula for the correlation coefficient that measures the degree of linear relationship between two variables.

$$r = \frac{n \sum x_i y_i - \left(\sum x_i \right) \left(\sum y_i \right)}{\sqrt{n \sum x_i^2 - \left(\sum x_i \right)^2} \sqrt{n \sum y_i^2 - \left(\sum y_i \right)^2}}$$

As we discovered in performing a regression analysis of the Honda Civic data. the coefficient of determination is the square of the correlation coefficient. The correlation coefficient can be found by either using the formula given previously or by taking the square root of the coefficient of determination, and adding the sign corresponding to the slope coefficient. Remember that the correlation coefficient takes values between -1 and 1, where negative values indicate a downward sloping relationship and positive values indicate an upward sloping relationship. The coefficient of determination takes values between 0 and 1 where values close to 0 indicate a weak linear relationship and values close to 1 indicate a strong linear relationship.

5.3   Exercises

Basic Concepts

1. Why is the magnitude of the prediction errors important when estimating a regression model?

2. What is the mean error for a least squares model?

3. Describe what the magnitude of the variation in the error terms tells us about the reliability of the regression model.

4. What is the variance of the error terms?

5. How many degrees of freedom are associated with the error term in a simple linear regression model?

6. What is the square root of the variance of the error term known as?

7. Describe where the summary statistics for the standard error and mean square error are found in a standard regression summary output in Microsoft Excel.

8. Is there a universal rule on how large is *large* with regard to standard error in a model?

9. What is estimated by the variance of the error term and what is estimated by the standard error?

10. What is the total sum of squares?

11. How are the total sum of squares and the sample variance related?

12. Define error in terms of a regression model.

13. What part of the simple linear regression model captures the unexplained variation?

14. Describe the total sum of squares in terms of explained and unexplained variation.

15. What is the sum of squares of regression?

16. Express SSR in terms of the total sum of squares and the sum of squared errors. Interpret this in terms of model variation.

17. Why will there be errors in virtually all regression models?

18. What is the coefficient of determination? What kinds of values can the coefficient of determination take?

19. Suppose that regression analysis is performed and the resulting model has an R^2 value of 0.856. Interpret this value.

20. How is the coefficient of determination related to the correlation coefficient?

Exercises

21. Consider the following summary output.

SUMMARY OUTPUT

Regression Statistics	
Multiple R	0.911653228
R Square	0.831111609
Adjusted R Square	0.79733393
Standard Error	0.253142413
Observations	7

ANOVA

	df	SS	MS	F
Regression	1	1.576737452	1.576737	24.60535
Residual	5	0.320405405	0.064081	
Total	6	1.897142857		

	Coefficients	Standard Error	t Stat	P-value
Intercept	4.021621622	0.181401491	22.16973	3.47E-06
X Variable 1	-0.22297297	0.044950802	-4.96038	0.004247

  a. What is the variance of the error terms for the data?

  b. What is the standard error of the model?

Data

stat.hawkeslearning.com
Data Sets > US County Data

22. Using the US County data set from the companion website, use the variables Diabetes.percent and Adult.obesity.percent to perform the following.

  a. Calculate the regression equation to predict Diabetes.percent using Adult.obesity.percent. Round values to 5 decimal places.

  b. What are b_0 and b_1? Round your answers to 5 decimal places.

  c. Using the information from parts **a.** and **b.**, complete the following table. Round Predicted Diabetes.percent and Error to 3 decimal places, and round Squared Error to 5 decimal places.

Observed versus Predicted Values				
Observed Adult.obesity. percent	Observed Diabetes. percent	Predicted Diabetes. percent	Error	Squared Error
0.408	0.173			
0.275	0.084			
0.375	0.115			
0.349	0.156			
0.312	0.070			
0.382	0.210			

    d. Compute the sum of squared errors for the table in part **c.** Round your answer to 5 decimal places.

    e. Compute the variance of the error term for the table in part **c.** Round your answer to 5 decimal places.

    f. Compute the standard error of the table in part **c.** Round your answer to 5 decimal places.

    g. Do you believe the estimates of b_0 and b_1 provide a reliable estimated regression equation for the data? Explain.

23. In the previous section, we used the Moneyball data set (1962-2001) to determine that a season run differential of about 135 runs was necessary for the Oakland A's to make it to the MLB playoffs. However, Coach Billy Bean and statistician Paul DePodesta needed to figue out how to make that run differential a reality. They found that two of the most statistically significant variables that contributed to the number of runs scored were on-base percentage and slugging percentage. Use the Moneyball data set from the companion website, subsetted to only include the years 1962-2001 since that was the only data available to Beane at the time, and perform the following.

⋰⋱ Data

stat.hawkeslearning.com
Data Sets > Moneyball

    a. Calculate the regression equation to predict runs scored (RS) using on-base percentage (OBP). Round values to 5 decimal places.

    b. Calculate the regression equation to predict runs scored (RS) using slugging percentage (SLG). Round values to 5 decimal places.

    c. Calculate the regression equation to predict runs allowed (RA) using opponent on-base percentage (OOBP). OOBP is only measured from 1999 on, so use data for the years 1999-2001 to estimate the equation. Round values to 5 decimal places.

    d. Calculate the regression equation to predict runs allowed (RA) using opponent slugging percentage (OSLG). OSLG is only measured from 1999 on, so use data for the years 1999-2001 to estimate the equation. Round values to 5 decimal places.

    e. Using the regression equation from part **a.** complete the following table. Round values to the nearest whole number.

Predicted RS using OBP				
Observed RS	**Observed OBP**	**Predicted RS**	**Error**	**Squared Error**
687	0.319			
897	0.350			
724	0.320			
923	0.354			
642	0.323			

f. Calculate the sum of squared errors and the standard error for the table in part **e.** Round answers to 3 decimal places.

g. Using the regression equation from part **d.** complete the following table. Round your answer to the nearest whole number.

Predicted RA using OSLG				
Observed RA	**Observed OSLG**	**Predicted RA**	**Error**	**Squared Error**
713	0.398			
806	0.440			
627	0.378			
968	0.494			
766	0.437			

h. Calculate the sum of squared errors and the standard error for the table in part **g.** Round answers to 3 decimal places.

24. A direct mail marketing company has been experimenting with the effect of price on sales. Five different direct mail prices have been sent to different sets of customers. They have carefully tracked the customers from each group and have recorded the proportion from each price category that purchased the product. The results are given in the following table.

Direct Mail					
Proportion That Purchased Product	0.032	0.028	0.026	0.015	0.009
Price of Product ($)	29.95	34.95	39.95	44.95	49.95

a. What level of measurement do the two variables in the table possess?

b. Specify the model that the marketing manager would be interested in estimating.

c. Which of the variables is the dependent variable in the model?

d. Which of the variables is the independent variable in the model?

e. Draw a scatterplot of the data.

f. Use the data in the table to estimate the model.

g. Predict the proportion that will buy the product if the price is $35.00.

h. Compute the mean error for the model you estimated in part **f.**

i. Determine the variance of the error term.

j. What is the coefficient of determination? Interpret this value in terms of the problem.

25. An economist is studying the relationship between income and savings. He has randomly selected seven subjects and obtained income and savings data from them. He wishes to use a simple linear regression model to predict savings based on annual income.

Income and Savings							
Income (Thousands of Dollars)	28	25	34	43	48	39	74
Savings (Thousands of Dollars)	0.2	0	0.8	1.2	3.1	2.1	8.3

    a. What level of measurement do the two variables in the table possess?

    b. Which of the variables is the dependent variable in the model?

    c. Which of the variables is the independent variable in the model?

    d. Draw a scatterplot of the data. Does the scatterplot suggest that a linear model is appropriate? Explain.

    e. Use the data to estimate the appropriate model.

    f. Predict the savings for someone who earns fifty thousand dollars annually.

    g. Interpret the meaning of the slope coefficient in the problem.

    h. What fraction of the variation in savings is explained by income?

26. Since 2009, the average term for a new-car loan was nearly 64 months. This leaves the buyer vulnerable to owing more on the car than it is worth. When applying for an automobile loan, it is oftentimes recommended to sign up for the shortest term you can afford. It is believed that along with one's credit rating, the length of the loan will help the buyer get a favorable interest rate. The following table contains interest rates and lengths of loans for 20 randomly selected auto purchases. Using the data in the table, answer the following questions.

Lengths of Loans and Interest Rates			
Months Financed	**Interest Rate (%)**	**Months Financed**	**Interest Rate (%)**
12	4.00	48	6.51
24	4.40	48	6.68
36	5.24	60	7.13
12	3.43	60	7.48
24	4.40	72	8.31
36	5.79	60	7.85
36	5.98	72	8.07
48	6.58	72	8.48
36	5.31	48	6.12
36	5.91	72	8.07

    a. Using statistical software, estimate the coefficients of the least squares regression equation.

    b. Interpret the meaning of the slope and the intercept in part **a.**

    c. Predict the interest rate for a person interested in a four-year auto loan.

    d. Should you use the model to predict interest rates for an eight-year loan? Justify your answer.

e. Determine the coefficient of determination and explain its meaning in terms of the problem.

f. Calculate the correlation coefficient for this model. What does it mean?

g. What interest rate would one expect to get if they were planning to apply for a five-year auto loan?

5.4 Fitting a Linear Time Trend

In Chapter 4, we discussed the notion that the mean is not a reasonable descriptor for nonstationary time series data. Recall that nonstationary time series do not meander around some central value. Instead, the data tends to get larger or smaller over time. How can you describe time series data that possesses a trend? For some time series, a **linear time trend** is a useful model. A linear time trend is nothing but a line that is used to model the changes in some phenomenon measured over time. In a linear time trend model, the independent variable is always a time index. The following example will illustrate the estimation of a linear time trend model.

Example 5.4.1

The following data is taken from the results of the 2013–2014 National Health and Nutrition Examination Survey (NHANES) of US adults age 20 and over who are above their recommended weight based on body mass index, or BMI. Body mass index, expressed as weight in kilograms divided by height in meters squared (kg/m^2), is commonly used to classify people as overweight (BMI 25.0–29.9), obese (BMI greater than or equal to 30.0), and extremely obese (BMI greater than or equal to 40.0). Based on BMI, the percent of overweight Americans from 1999 to 2014 is shown in the following table.[4]

Percent of Overweight American Adults							
Year	2000	2002	2004	2006	2008	2010	2012	2014
Percent Overweight	64.5	65.6	66.4	66.9	68.1	68.8	68.6	70.4

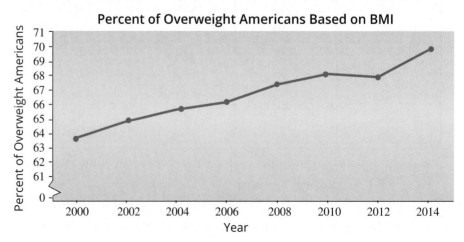

Percent of Overweight Americans Based on BMI

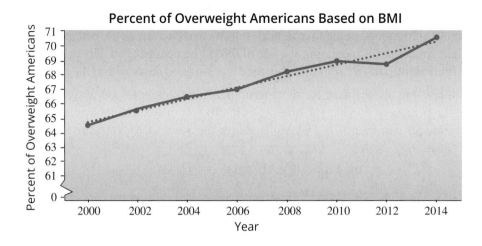

A graph of the data reveals an upward trend in the percent of overweight Americans. The data appears to be a nonstationary time series with an upward trend. To describe the data we will model the trend by fitting a line through the data with the notion of capturing how fast (on average) the series is changing over time. Estimating the slope of the line will provide the *average* rate of change per year in the percent of overweight Americans. The line is fitted using least squares estimates in exactly the same way as the other regression models we studied have been constructed. The independent variable in a linear trend model is always time. In this case, the dependent variable is the percent of overweight Americans.

The least squares equation is

Estimated % Overweight Americans = −705.5214 + 0.3851 (Year).

The computer output for the problem is given in the table below.

Summary Output				
Regression Statistics				
Multiple R	0.9830			
R Square	0.9660			
Adjusted R Square	0.9610			
Standard Error	0.3810			
Observations	8			
ANOVA				
	df	SS	MS	F
Regression	1	24.9172	24.9172	171.5380
Residual	6	0.8715	0.1453	
Total	7	25.7889		
	Coefficients	Standard Error	t Stat	P-value
Intercept	−705.5214	59.0152	−11.9550	0.00002
Year	0.3851	0.0294	13.0972	0.00001

Solution

The estimate of the slope of the line, 0.3851, tells us that on average the percent of overweight Americans is increasing at a rate of 0.3851 percent per year. Given how well the line fits the data ($R^2 = 96.6\%$), the trend line is a good descriptor of the data.

The trend line can also be used for short-term prediction. Suppose you wished to estimate the percent of overweight Americans in 2015. If the data is not available, the trend model can be utilized by substituting the year, 2015, into the least squares equation.

$$-705.5214 + 0.3851\,(2015) = 70.5\%$$

5.4   Exercises

Basic Concepts

1. Why is the mean not a reasonable descriptor for nonstationary time series data?

2. What is a linear time trend?

3. What is the independent variable in a linear trend model?

4. Is there a difference between the way the best fit line is determined for time series data and the way it is determined for other types of data?

Exercises

⸭ **Data**

stat.hawkeslearning.com
Data Sets > CO$_2$ Emissions

5. Using the CO_2 Emissions data set from the companion website, look at the CO_2 emissions per capita of the small island country of Trinidad and Tobago. Use the data to answer the following.

    a. Looking at the data for Trinidad and Tobago, do you believe the trend line will slope upward or downward?

    b. Suppose we are interested in constructing a linear trend model for the data. Identify the independent and dependent variables for this model.

    c. Write the general equation for the time trend model in terms of year and CO_2 emissions per capita.

    d. Use statistical software to estimate the least squares model for the data.

    e. Use this model to predict the CO_2 emissions per capita in Trinidad and Tobago in 2015.

    f. Can we determine the accuracy of this prediction? Explain.

6. Consider the following monthly sales data for an up-and-coming technology company.

	Sales Data		
Month	**Sales (Thousands of Dollars)**	**Month**	**Sales (Thousands of Dollars)**
1	321	7	698
2	542	8	710
3	540	9	799
4	581	10	821
5	641	11	833
6	700	12	850

a. Identify the independent and dependent variables for the linear time trend model.

b. Using statistical software, the following summary output was produced. Write the estimated regression equation.

SUMMARY OUTPUT

Regression Statistics	
Multiple R	0.949341195
R Square	0.901248704
Adjusted R Square	0.891373575
Standard Error	51.20789475
Observations	12

ANOVA

	df	SS	MS	F
Regression	1	239318.1818	239318.1818	91.26449427
Residual	10	26222.48485	2622.248485	
Total	11	265540.6667		

	Coefficients	Standard Error	t Stat	P-value
Intercept	403.7575758	31.51628057	12.81107949	1.57569E-07
Month	40.90909091	4.282219283	9.553245222	2.41268E-06

c. What is the mean square error for this model? The standard error?

d. Using this model, predict the company's sales for the 13th month.

e. What percent of the variation in sales is explained by the linear time trend model? Does this model seem to accurately fit the data?

7. Consider the following table containing unemployment rates for North Carolina and South Carolina in 2000 through 2010.[5]

	Unemployment Rates 2000–2010	
	Unemployment Rate (%)	
Year	North Carolina	South Carolina
2000	3.7	3.6
2001	5.6	5.2
2002	6.6	6.0
2003	6.5	6.7
2004	5.5	6.8
2005	5.3	6.8

Unemployment Rates 2000–2010		
	Unemployment Rate (%)	
Year	North Carolina	South Carolina
2006	4.8	6.4
2007	4.7	5.6
2008	6.2	6.8
2009	10.8	11.3
2010	10.6	11.2

a. Using statistical software, estimate the following linear time trend model and write the estimated regression equation using the least squares estimates for b_0 and b_1.

$$\text{N.C. Unemployment Rate} = b_0 + b_1\left(\text{Year}\right).$$

b. Using statistical software, estimate the following linear time trend model and write the estimated regression equation using the least squares estimates for b_0 and b_1.

$$\text{S.C. Unemployment Rate} = b_0 + b_1\left(\text{Year}\right).$$

c. Use the equations in parts **a.** and **b.** to estimate the unemployment rates for North and South Carolina in the year 2013.

d. What is the coefficient of determination for the regression model in part **a.**?

e. What is the coefficient of determination for the regression model in part **b.**?

f. Do you think that these regression models are reliable in predicting future unemployment rates? Of the two models, which seems to fit the data better?

∽ **Technology**

Graphing multivariate and multidimensional data within a single scatterplot can be useful in a variety of different scenarios. To learn how to graph more than two variables on a scatterplot using Tableau or other technologies, please visit stat.hawkeslearning.com and navigate to **Technology Instructions > Graphs > Multivariate/ Multidimensional**.

5.5   Scatterplots for More Than Two Variables

As displayed in Minard's graph of Napoleon's march in Chapter 3, it is often desirable to show more than two variables within the same graphic to determine if a relationship exists. However, a certain degree of creativity is required in order to figure out how to depict the desired variables within the spatial or dimensional limits. As each variable is added to the graph, a new method of reference must be associated with it. Scatterplots can be employed to portray relationships between more than two variables. Suppose we are interested in creating a graph that compares countries based on their citizens' personal earnings per year and the average number of years spent in the educational system. Using data from the Organisation for Economic Cooperation and Development (OECD) Better Life Index for 2016, we create the graph in Figure 5.5.1.

⋮⋮ **Data**

The full OECD Better Life Index 2016 data set can be found on stat.hawkeslearning.com under **Data Sets > OECD Better Life Index 2016**

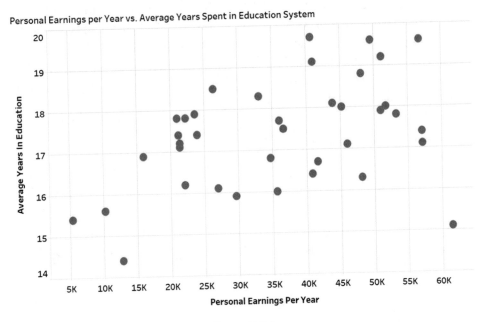

Figure 5.5.1

As Figure 5.5.1 suggests, there seems to be a positive relationship between the average number of years spent in the education system and personal earnings per year. In other words, as the number of years spent in the education system increases, so do personal earnings. However, suppose we are also interested in adding the satisfaction score of the citizens in each country. The OECD data set provides a satisfaction score for each country which purports to measure how happy the people living in that country are as reported by themselves. Since we have already used both of our axes for other variables, we need to find an alternative way to visually display the differences in the satisfaction scores. There are multiple different ways to accomplish this, however two of the most common methods include resizing each point on the graph based on the variable value, or assigning the values of the variable to a color scale and then coloring each point on the graph accordingly. In this case, we will use color to portray the differences in satisfaction between countries. After including our third variable as a color scale, the following plot is generated.

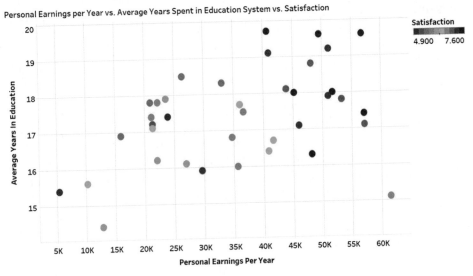

Figure 5.5.2

Now, Figure 5.5.2 allows us to look at the data in three dimensions and gain a better understanding of how these variables relate to one another. It appears that the wealthier, more educated countries also have the most satisfied citizens.

Perhaps we want to add in another variable that measures the perception of safety in a given country. The OECD data provides a safety score for each country based on the proportion of residents that said they would feel safe walking home alone. We will associate this variable with the size of each point, and generate the following graph.

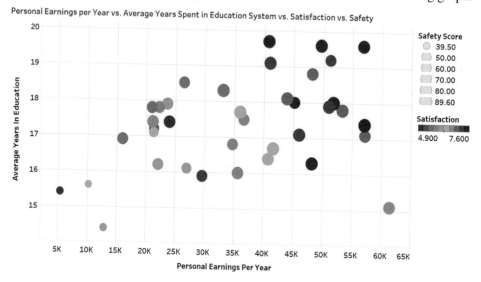

Figure 5.5.3

In Figure 5.5.3, we are looking at data in four dimensions. It seems that, in general, the wealthier, more educated, more satisfied countries also have a higher safety score. Thus, it would be reasonable to assume that wealth, education, and safety all contribute to a higher satisfaction rating in a given country.

As we just demonstrated, it is possible to cram large amounts of data into two-dimensional graphs, and such graphs can be wonderful tools that can be used for exploratory analysis in a variety of different areas. However, there are limitations to what can be visualized in a single graph. With each additional variable, more methods of measurement and presentation are needed. Furthermore, if we were analyzing a data set with thousands of observations, or rows, instead of just the 40 included in the OECD data, measurement methods like size begin to lose their visual effectiveness. When dealing with multivariate or multidimensional data, it is sometimes a better option to create several graphs with each one containing only a couple variables.

A superb example of using multivariate graphs for exploratory analysis can be demonstrated using the Trendalyzer tool found on Gapminder.org. Gapminder is a non-profit organization founded by Hans Rosling and supported by a coalition of economists, statisticians, and analysts, that promotes global development and education through the use of statistics. The Trendalyzer tool allows users to animate data over time and compare countries based on data provided by the World Bank, the UN, the World Health Organization, and many other sources. The Trendalyzer tool produces some of the most impressive statistical graphics the author of this book has ever seen.

Shown below is a screenshot of the Trendalyzer tool, with adjusted GDP per capita on the *x*-axis and life expectancy at birth on the *y*-axis, for the year 1800.

Notice that the *x*-axis employs a log transformation. Each data point is colored based on the region of the world the country is located in (green for The Americas, yellow for Europe, blue for Africa, red for Asia which includes Australia and Oceania), and the size of each point corresponds to the total population within that country.

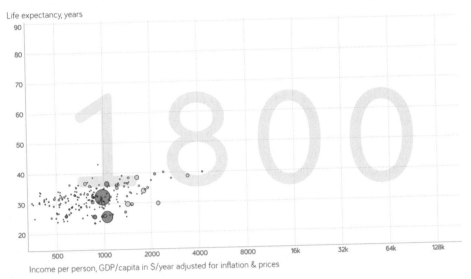

Now, here is a screenshot of the same graph, but for the year 2015.

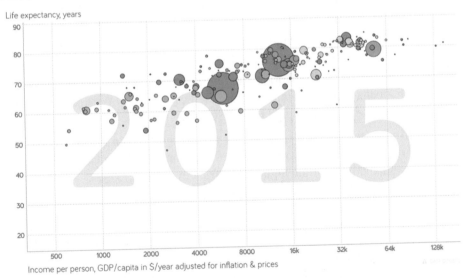

As you can see, a lot changed between 1800 and 2015. If you would like to see the animation from 1800 to 2015, go to the Gapminder website and experiment with the Trendalyzer tool yourself. Pay attention to countries that seem to stray from the central grouping, or from where they are expected to be, and note the year that this anomaly takes place. Once you have this information, do some research using your preferred search engine and try to come up with an explanation for the anomaly. You will be amazed at the amount of history that can be portrayed through the use of a seemingly simple scatterplot.

Dancing Data

Hans Rosling was one of the most renowned statisticians of the modern era, and arguably one of the most influential of all time. He was born in Sweden in 1948, and studied statistics and medicine at Uppsala University. Upon graduation, Rosling lived in India for a brief period before moving to Africa where he would spend the next 20 years serving as a medical officer. While there, he used data to help reveal the association between the outbreak of a paralytic disease called konzo, and the consumption of insufficiently processed cassava. After his tenure in Africa, Rosling returned to Sweden in 1996 to begin teaching at the Karolinska Institute. In 2005, he co-founded the Gapminder Foundation with the goal of using statistics to drive and expedite sustainable global development. One of the organization's main claims to fame is its development of the Trendalyzer software. Trendalyzer makes data "dance" by converting statistics over time into animated graphs that present a lot of information in a way that is easy to digest and understand. Hans Rosling passed away in February of 2017, but his legacy will continue to impact our entire planet well into the future.

5.5   **Exercises**

Basic Concepts

1. What are some methods of displaying measurements other than traditional axes?

2. What are the limitations of multivariable graphs?

3. What is Gapminder?

Exercises

☁ **Technology**

To learn how to use the Gapminder Trendalyzer tool, please visit stat. hawkeslearning.com and navigate to **Technology Instructions > Gapminder Trendalyzer**

4. Navigate to the Gapminder Trendalyzer tool in a web browser to answer the following questions. Make sure the *x*-axis is set to Adjusted GDP per Capita, and the *y*-axis is set to Life Expectancy.

   a. By looking at the graph for the year 2015, do you notice any patterns in the data?

   b. The American Civil War is arguably the most discussed event in American history. It is, by far, the bloodiest war the United States has ever experienced. An estimated 650,000 to 750,000 soldiers died during the Civil War, more than the American casualties from both World Wars, Korea, Vietnam, Iraq, and Afghanistan combined. Between the years 1860 and 1864, how much did the life expectancy in the United States decrease?

   c. In 1918, the entire world experienced a notable change. Describe what happens on the Gapminder graph in the year 1918. What was the cause of the worldwide event? Hint: Use a search engine to do some research.

   d. In the early 1990s, oil reserves were discovered in Equatorial Guinea which lead to a massive boost to the national GDP per Capita, and it has remained one of the highest in Africa ever since.

      i. From 1990 to 2008, how much did Equatorial Guinea's GDP per Capita increase?

      ii. How much did its Life Expectancy increase from 1990 to 2008?

      iii. In 2008, how does the life expectancy of Equatorial Guinea compare to countries with similar GDP per Capita?

CR   **Chapter Review**

Key Terms and Ideas

- Regression Analysis
- Dependent Variable (Response Variable)

- Independent Variable (Predictor Variable)
- Simple Linear Regression

- Simple Linear Regression Model
- Parameters
- Error Term
- Estimated Simple Linear Regression Equation
- Method of Least Squares
- Correlation Coefficient
- Sum of Squared Errors
- Least Squares Line
- Variance of the Error Terms
- Standard Error
- Total Sum of Squares
- Sum of Squares of Regression
- Coefficient of Determination

- Linear Time Trend
- Confidence Interval for β_1
- Testing a Hypothesis Concerning β_1
- Univariate Data
- Bivariate Data
- Scatterplot (Scatter Diagram)
- Linear Relationship
- Positive Relationship
- Negative Relationship (Inverse Relationship)
- Quadratic Relationship
- Common Response
- Confounding

Key Formulas	
	Section
Simple Linear Regression Model	5.2
$$y_i = \beta_0 + \beta_1 x_i + \varepsilon_i$$	
Estimated Simple Linear Regression Equation	5.2
$$\hat{y}_i = b_0 + b_1 x_i$$	
Sum of Squared Errors	5.2
$$\text{SSE} = \sum \left(y_i - \hat{y}_i \right)^2 = \sum \left(y_i - \left(b_0 + b_1 x_i \right) \right)^2$$	
Slope of the Least Squares Line	5.2
$$b_1 = \frac{n\left(\sum x_i y_i\right) - \sum x_i \sum y_i}{n\left(\sum x_i^2\right) - \left(\sum x_i\right)^2}$$	
y-Intercept of the Least Squares Line	5.2
$$b_0 = \frac{1}{n}\left(\sum y_i - b_1 \sum x_i\right)$$	

Key Formulas	
	Section
Mean Square Error $$s_e^2 = \frac{\sum\left(y_i - \hat{y}_i\right)^2}{n-2} = \frac{\text{SSE}}{n-2}$$	5.3
Standard Error $$s_e = \sqrt{\frac{\sum\left(y_i - \hat{y}_i\right)^2}{n-2}} = \sqrt{\frac{\text{SSE}}{n-2}}$$	5.3
Total Sum of Squares $$\text{Total SS} = \sum\left(y_i - \bar{y}\right)^2$$ $$\text{Total SS} = \text{SSE} + \text{SSR}$$	5.3
Sum of Squares of Regression $$\text{SSR} = \text{Total SS} - \text{SSE}$$	5.3
Coefficient of Determination $$R^2 = \frac{\text{SSR}}{\text{Total SS}} = 1 - \frac{\text{SSE}}{\text{Total SS}}$$ or $$R^2 = \left(\frac{n\sum x_i y_i - \sum x_i \sum y_i}{\sqrt{\left(n\sum x_i^2 - \left(\sum x_i\right)^2\right)\left(n\sum y_i^2 - \left(\sum y_i\right)^2\right)}}\right)^2$$	5.3
Correlation Coefficient $$r = \frac{n\sum x_i y_i - \sum x_i \sum y_i}{\sqrt{\left(n\sum x_i^2 - \left(\sum x_i\right)^2\right)\left(n\sum y_i^2 - \left(\sum y_i\right)^2\right)}}$$	5.3

Additional Exercises

1. Consider the following data:

x	1	2	3	4	5	6	7
y	1	4	9	16	25	36	49

   a.   Plot the data points on a scatterplot.

   b.   Determine the correlation coefficient.

   c.   Describe the relationship between x and y.

   d.   Determine the least squares line. Use x as the independent variable.

   e.   Plot the least squares line on the scatterplot.

   f.   Use the model to compute the error for each data point.

   g.   Determine the average value of the model's errors.

   h.   Determine the variance of the errors.

2. Consider the following data:

x	1	2	3	4	5	6	7
y	1	1.41	1.73	2	2.24	2.45	2.65

   a.   Plot the data points on a scatterplot.

   b.   Determine the correlation coefficient.

   c.   Describe the relationship between x and y.

   d.   Determine the least squares line. Use x as the independent variable.

   e.   Plot the least squares line on the scatterplot.

   f.   Use the model to compute the error for each data point.

   g.   Determine the average value of the model's errors.

   h.   Determine the variance of the errors.

3. The Road Warrior Trucking Company has kept careful records on ten hauls. The traffic manager has recorded the haul weight of each truck and its miles per gallon during ten runs with the intent of building a regression model. He wants to predict the miles/gallon for a haul based on the haul weight. The haul weights and miles/gallon information are given below. Haul weights are given in thousands of pounds.

Trucking	
Miles/Gallon	**Haul Weight (in thousands)**
4.6	36
4.8	33
5.1	31
4.0	42

Trucking	
Miles/Gallon	**Haul Weight (in thousands)**
4.7	33
5.2	30
4.5	37
4.6	37
4.2	40
4.5	36

a. What level of measurement do the two variables in the table possess?

b. What is the dependent variable in the model? [Hint, which variable does the traffic manager want to predict?]

c. What is the independent variable in the model?

d. Draw a scatterplot of the data. Based on the scatterplot, does a linear model seem appropriate?

e. Write the model in symbolic form. (Assume the parameters of the model have not been estimated.)

f. Use the data provided and estimate the coefficients of the linear model.

g. Interpret the coefficient of the independent variable.

h. Use the model to predict the miles/gallon for a truck hauling 38,000 pounds.

i. Do you believe there is a causal relationship between haul weight and the miles/gallon? If so, which direction is the causality? Do greater haul weights cause reduced mileage, or vice versa? Does the regression analysis prove the causality?

j. Compute the correlation coefficient of the data.

k. What fraction of the variation in miles per gallon is explained by the haul weight?

4. An agricultural research station is trying to determine the relationship between the yield of sunflowers and the amount of fertilizer applied. To determine the relationship, three different fields were planted. In each field four different plots were defined. In each plot a different amount of fertilizer was used. The plot assignments for the fertilizer application were randomly selected in each field.

Agricultural Research			
Pounds of Fertilizer (per acre)	**Pounds of Sunflower Seeds (per acre)**	**Pounds of Fertilizer (per acre)**	**Pounds of Sunflower Seeds (per acre)**
200	420	600	580
200	445	600	600
200	405	600	610
400	580	800	630
400	540	800	620
400	550	800	626

a. What level of measurement do the two variables in the table possess? Is the data developed through controlled experiment or is the data observational?

b. Draw a scatterplot of the data.

c. If a linear model is developed, which of the variables will be the dependent variable? Why?

d. Use least squares techniques to estimate the appropriate model.

e. Interpret the meaning of the slope coefficient in the model.

f. What fraction of the variation in pounds of sunflower seeds per acre can be explained by the amount of fertilizer used?

g. Predict the sunflower seed yield per acre if 500 pounds of fertilizer is applied.

5. Ten games were recently played in the National Football League. The number of passing yards and rushing yards, along with the winner (w) and loser (l) of the game, for the 20 participating teams is given below:

Game	Team	Rush	Pass	Outcome	Game	Team	Rush	Pass	Outcome
1	1	60	320	l	6	11	43	328	w
1	2	158	124	w	6	12	95	192	l
2	3	53	183	l	7	13	56	237	l
2	4	127	164	w	7	14	200	132	w
3	5	60	115	l	8	15	125	310	w
3	6	343	50	w	8	16	99	184	l
4	7	148	242	l	9	17	187	189	w
4	8	88	190	w	9	18	21	366	l
5	9	75	183	l	10	19	171	87	w
5	10	110	182	w	10	20	60	337	l

Before computing any statistics, if you compared winners and losers with respect to rushing and passing yardage, what would you expect to find? Compare the rushing and passing yards of winners and losers.

a. Make a scatterplot of rushing yards versus passing yards.

b. Compute the correlation coefficient for these two variables.

c. Create a new variable called total yards by adding rushing yards to passing yards.

d. Compute the correlation coefficient between rushing yards and total yards.

e. Compare the two correlation coefficients computed in this exercise. Why is there such a big difference between them?

6. Experimental results comparing two methods for estimating maximum aerobic speed were summarized in 'Comparison of Two Field Tests to Estimate Maximum Aerobic Speed', and reported in *The Journal of Sports Sciences*. The techniques compared were the treadmill test and the track test. Data from the 17 participants is given in the table below:

Maximum Aerobic Speed					
Subject	Track	Treadmill	Subject	Track	Treadmill
1	15	14	10	16	16
2	16	16	11	16	16
3	16	16	12	16	16
4	13	12	13	13	12
5	13	12	14	17	18
6	13	14	15	19	20
7	16	16	16	18	20
8	16	16	17	18	20
9	18	16			

a. Make a scatterplot of the results.

b. Does there appear to be a negative or positive relationship between the variables?

c. Compute the correlation coefficient for these two variables.

d. Create two new variables, V and W, where $V = $ Track/2 and $W = $ Treadmill/5.

e. Compute the correlation coefficient between V and W.

f. What appears to be the effect on the correlation coefficient of multiplying each variable by a constant value?

7. The following data is obtained on two quantitative variables:

x	876	516	598	789	734	667	682	714	598
y	50.1	88.2	80.7	39.6	20.5	40.9	30.6	22.9	34.8

a. Make a scatterplot of the data.

b. Does there appear to be a negative or positive relationship between the variables?

c. Compute the correlation coefficient.

d. Create two new variables, V and W, where $V = X - 700$ and $W = Y - 50$.

e. Compute the correlation coefficient between V and W.

f. What appears to be the effect on the correlation coefficient of subtracting a constant value from each of the variables?

8. The FBI releases crime statistics for cities categorized by population size. The table below gives data for cities containing different population groups. The robbery and murder rates are given for these cities together with their crime index and violent crime index. The trends for the crime index indicate the percent change in offenses known to law enforcement.

Crime Statistics				
City Population	Robbery Rate	Murder Rate	Crime Index	Violent Crime Index
Over 1,000,000	1.1	4.0	0.6	1.5
500,000 to 999,999	5.7	0.2	0.9	4.1
250,000 to 499,999	0.7	3.6	1.9	1.8
100,000 to 249,999	2.1	2.6	0.7	1.8
50,000 to 99,999	0.2	6.7	1.2	0.9
25,000 to 49,999	1.4	0.1	1.2	1.2
10,000 to 24,999	2.6	9.8	0.9	1.7
Under 10,000	1.4	14.7	1.2	1.8

a. In general, if we have k quantitative variables measured in a study, how many different correlation coefficients can be computed?

b. How many different correlation coefficients can be computed from the above data?

c. Which pair of variables appears to be most correlated?

d. Which pair of variables appears to be least correlated?

e. Do any pairs of variables appear to be negatively correlated?

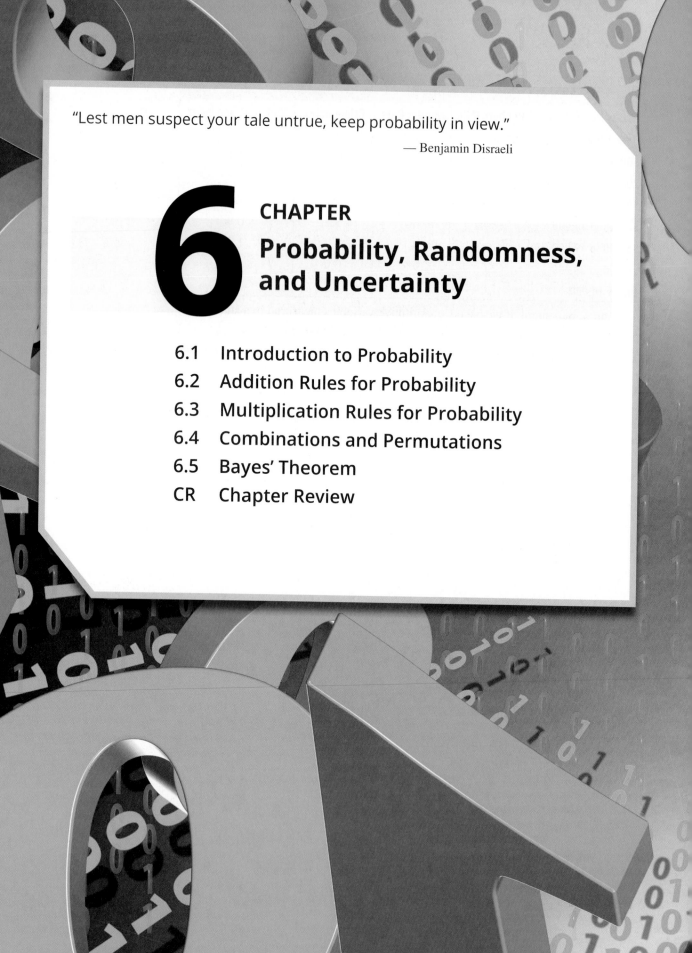

"Lest men suspect your tale untrue, keep probability in view."

— Benjamin Disraeli

6 CHAPTER
Probability, Randomness, and Uncertainty

Introduction

We all have to cope with uncertainty. Uncertainty is that uneasy feeling we get when our gas tank is nearly empty a few miles from the closest gas station. You remember in the past that your car continued to run when the gauge was even lower, but you are not quite sure it will this time. In everyday usage, the word *probably* describes an event or circumstance the speaker believes will occur. At the same time the speaker reserves the possibility that it may not occur. In this sense, *probably* reflects a strong but nonspecific degree of belief.

Probability is used to quantify uncertainty. If a person says he believes there is a 0.95 probability that his car will make it to a gas station before it runs out of gas, he has made a precise statement which, no doubt, reflects his past experiences and indicates a strong belief in his chances of finding a gas station. This statement is vastly different from the statement that there is a 0.40 probability the car will make it to a gas station, which casts considerably more doubt on his prospects. The probability statement provides more precise information than phrases like *maybe I'll make it, I might make it, or I should make it.* Therein lies its value.

Uncertainty doesn't necessarily have to be associated with events in the future. There can be plenty of uncertainty about the past. What was the Native American population of the continental United States in the year 1492? Nobody knows, so ascribing a probability to the statement *the population of Native Americans in 1492 was between 8 and 15 million* attaches someone's degree of belief to the statement.

The word **randomness** suggests a certain haphazardness or unpredictability. Randomness and uncertainty are both vague concepts that deal with variation. And even though these words are not synonyms, their discussion leads to the concept of probability.

A simple example of randomness involves a coin toss. Unless the person tossing the coin possesses magical powers, the outcome of the toss (heads or tails) is uncertain. Since the coin tossing experiment is unpredictable, the outcome is said to exhibit randomness. There are many different kinds of randomness.

Some are easily described, like the toss of a coin, and others are extraordinarily complex, like molecular motion or changes in stock prices.

Even though individual flips of a coin are unpredictable, if we flip the coin a large number of times, a pattern will emerge. For most coins, roughly half of the flips will be heads and half will be tails. This long-run regularity of a random event is described with probability. Our discussions of randomness will be limited to phenomena that in the short run are not exactly predictable but do exhibit long-run regularity.

6.1 **Introduction to Probability**

Games of chance, such as tossing a coin, provide a way to demonstrate some of the fundamental laws (rules) of probability. Statistically speaking, the playing of the game is called an **experiment**.

Random Experiment

A **random experiment** is defined as any activity or phenomenon that meets the following conditions.

1. There is one distinct outcome for each trial of the experiment.
2. The outcome of the experiment is uncertain.
3. The set of all distinct outcomes of the experiment can be specified and is called the **sample space**, denoted by S.

DEFINITION

Outcome

An **outcome** is any member of the sample space.

DEFINITION

If you were to toss a single coin there are only 2 outcomes {Head, Tail} in the experiment. The sample space of an experiment contains every potential outcome that could occur in one trial of the experiment. For a coin tossing experiment, the sample space would be $S = \{$Head, Tail$\}$. The sample space may be called the **outcome set**, since it contains all possible outcomes of an experiment. The result of a random experiment must be an outcome.

Event

An **event** is a set of outcomes.

DEFINITION

Examples of random experiments, events, and outcomes follow. These experiments will be used throughout the chapter to illustrate the laws of probability.

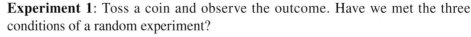

Experiment 1: Toss a coin and observe the outcome. Have we met the three conditions of a random experiment?

1. There will only be one outcome for each trial of the experiment since it is not possible to observe both a head and a tail on the same toss.
2. The outcome is unknown *before* the toss.
3. The sample space can be specified and contains two outcomes, $S = \{$Head, Tail$\}$.

Because each of the three conditions is satisfied, for all practical purposes, this experiment meets the conditions of a random experiment.

It is possible for a coin to land on its edge and thus neither be heads nor tails. Any theory, however, involves a certain degree of idealization, which means, in this case, that landing on an edge will not be considered a possible outcome.

Experiment 2: Toss a coin three times and observe the number of heads. Have we met the three conditions of a random experiment?

1. There will only be one outcome since, for example, it is not possible to have *exactly* one and *exactly* two heads on the same trial.

2. The outcome will be unknown *before* tossing the coin three times.

3. The sample space can be specified and is composed of eight outcomes:

$$S = \{TTT, TTH, THT, THH, HTT, HTH, HHT, HHH\}.$$

This experiment meets the conditions of a random experiment.

An **event** could be obtaining more than one head, which involves the following set of outcomes:

$$\{THH, HTH, HHT, HHH\}.$$

Experiment 3: Roll a die and observe the number of dots on the upper-most surface. Have we met the three conditions of a random experiment?

1. There will only be one outcome.

2. The value of the outcome is not known.

3. The sample space can be specified and is composed of outcomes,

$$S = \{1, 2, 3, 4, 5, 6\}.$$

This experiment meets the conditions of a random experiment.

An example of an **event** could be rolling an even number, which would be given by the set of outcomes, $\{2, 4, 6\}$.

Experiment 4: Assume we have a deck of playing cards consisting of 13 hearts, 13 clubs, 13 spades, and 13 diamonds. Draw a card from a well–shuffled deck and observe the suit of the card. Have we met the three conditions of a random experiment?

1. There will be only one outcome.

2. The suit will be unknown since the card will be drawn at random.

3. The sample space consists of the set of outcomes,

$$S = \{\text{heart, club, spade, diamond}\}.$$

This experiment meets the conditions of a random experiment.

If the random experiment involves drawing a card and observing a spade or a club, then the **event** would be given by the set of outcomes, $\{\text{spade, club}\}$.

Origins of Probability

Galileo performed one of the earliest probability analyses. Galileo was approached by an Italian nobleman who had observed that three dice were more likely to obtain a sum of 10 than a sum of 9 when thrown. Galileo became interested in the uncertainties of throwing dice and wrote a short work outlining his findings. Galileo's work set forth some of the theory of probability. The next step in the birth of probability came from the French.

A French nobleman, Chevalier de Mere, won quite a few francs by getting unwitting souls to bet him that he would not roll at least one six in a sequence of four tosses of a die. He then lost his profits by wagering that he would get at least one double 6 in a sequence of 24 tosses of two dice. Chevalier de Mere asked two of the leading mathematicians of the time, Pierre de Fermet (1601–1665) and Blaise Pascal (1623–1662), to consider his problem.

The exchange of letters between Fermat and Pascal led to some of the first analysis of random phenomena, and development of the first principles of probability theory.

The complete set of letters can be found in Oeuvres Complètes de Pascal, Volume III, pp. 220–236, Librairie Hachette, Paris, 1880.

The letters are also available online for digital viewing.

Experiment 5: Inspect a transistor to determine if it meets quality control standards. Have we met the three conditions of a random experiment?

1. There will be only one outcome.

2. The outcome of the experiment will be unknown if the transistor is selected from a manufacturing process that occasionally produces defective parts.

3. The sample space consists of the set of outcomes, $S = \{$meets standards, does not meet standards$\}$.

This experiment meets the conditions of a random experiment.

What Is Probability?

There are several competing ideas which seek to define the interpretation of probability, similar to the competing ideas which define the notion of central tendency (mean, median, mode, trimmed mean). In fact, there is a substantial conflict of ideas between the notions of statistical regularity and degree of belief. No simple answer exists for the question, *What is probability?* Probability remains an abstract concept for which there is no *true* meaning. Fortunately, the theory of probability does not require the interpretation of probabilities, just as in geometry, the interpretation of points, lines, and planes are irrelevant.

We will first discuss the two types of objective probabilities, the relative frequency approach and the classical approach. Afterwards, we will talk about the subjective approach to probability.

Relative Frequency Approach

Someone who wanted to determine the probability of getting a head on the toss of a coin could toss a coin a large number of times and observe the number of times that a head appeared. The probability could be computed as the number of times a head was observed divided by the number of times the coin was flipped. This is the relative frequency interpretation of probability.

Relative Frequency

If an experiment is performed n times, under identical conditions, and the event A happens k times, the **relative frequency** of A is given by the following expression.

$$\text{Relative Frequency of } A = \frac{k}{n}$$

If the relative frequency converges as n increases, then the relative frequency is said to be the **probability** of A.

DEFINITION

Let's flip a coin 42 times and observe the relative frequency of a head during those tosses.

Relative Frequency of Heads for 42 Flips						
Flip Number	1	2	3	4	5	6	7
Relative Frequency	1.00	0.5	0.6667	0.75	0.6	0.5	0.4286
Flip Number	8	9	10	11	12	13	14
Relative Frequency	0.375	0.4444	0.4	0.3636	0.4167	0.3846	0.3571
Flip Number	15	16	17	18	19	20	21
Relative Frequency	0.3333	0.375	0.4118	0.3889	0.3684	0.35	0.3810
Flip Number	22	23	24	25	26	27	28
Relative Frequency	0.3636	0.3478	0.375	0.36	0.3462	0.3333	0.3214
Flip Number	29	30	31	32	33	34	35
Relative Frequency	0.3448	0.3333	0.3548	0.375	0.3636	0.3529	0.3429
Flip Number	36	37	38	39	40	41	42
Relative Frequency	0.3611	0.3514	0.3421	0.3590	0.35	0.3415	0.3571

In Figure 6.1.1, you can see that the proportion of heads is very unstable during the first 15 flips. The proportion of heads begins to stabilize at around flip 20, although there is still some fluctuation in its value. Looking at the first 42 flips makes you wonder whether this is a "fair" coin, since heads is occurring only $0.3571(100)=35.71\%$ of the time. In Figure 6.1.2, which starts at about 200 flips, the proportion of heads becomes very stable. By flip number 296, there are 141 heads and 155 tails which equate to approximately a 0.4764 probability (or relative frequency) of heads. Although this is slightly less than the expected 0.5 for a "fair" coin, such a proportion is reasonable considering the randomness of the coin toss.

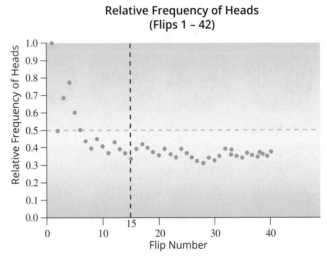

Figure 6.1.1

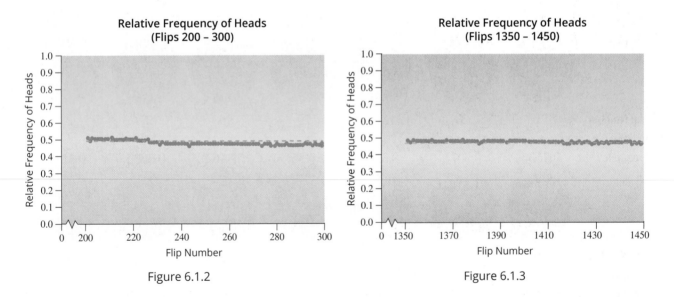

Figure 6.1.2   Figure 6.1.3

As can be seen in Figure 6.1.2 and Figure 6.1.3, the proportion of heads converges on some point which is close to 0.5. Figure 6.1.3 starts at about 1350 flips. As you can see, the proportion of heads remains very stable. At flip number 1450, there are 718 heads and 732 tails which equate to approximately a 0.4952 probability (or relative frequency) of heads.

What is the Relative Frequency of a Head on Our Coin?

Our best available guess is 0.4952, since it is the observed relative frequency of heads using all 1450 tosses.

$$\text{Relative Frequency of } A = \frac{k}{n} = \frac{718}{1450} \approx 0.4952$$

How good is this guess for the relative frequency of heads? Since the coin has been tossed a large number of times and the observed frequency is very stable, the guess should be very good.

Will the Observed Relative Frequency Ever Reach 0.5?

No mathematical or physical law requires the observed relative frequency to ever reach some predetermined level. But if the probability of observing a head was really 0.5, the observed relative frequency should closely approach this value after a large number of flips.

Pafnuty Chebyshev (1821–1894)

Chebyshev was a Russian mathematician who made contributions in probability, statistics, mechanics and number theory. His theorem is important in describing data, but it is also used to prove one of the more important theorems in probability theory, the weak law of large numbers. The law of large numbers demonstrates the stability of long-term results for averages of random events. In particular, as the sample size becomes large the sample mean will likely be close the population mean. Although you will not see the proof of this theorem, you will be using the idea when we discuss the Central Limit Theorem later in the book.

Summary

The experiment: Toss a coin and observe which side of the coin appears on top.

Duration of the experiment: Toss the coin 1450 times. $n = 1450$

Observe the event "getting a head": The event was observed 718 times. $k = 718$

Relative frequency of the event "getting a head":

$$A = \frac{k}{n} = \frac{718}{1450} \approx 0.4952$$

The relative frequency of a head seems to converge to the expected relative frequency of 0.5. This kind of convergence is sometimes called **statistical regularity**. Although the outcomes of the experiment may vary, in the long run the relative frequency of an outcome tends to some value, its probability. In probability theory this property is often stated as the **law of large numbers**.

Law of Large Numbers

As the number of repetitions of an experiment increases, the relative frequency of an event tends to approach the actual probability.

DEFINITION

Problems with the Relative Frequency Approach

The problem with the relative frequency approach to defining probability is that probability only exists for events that can be repeated under the same conditions. Coin, dice, and card experiments can easily be repeated. However, because of the strict requirements of identical and repeatable experiments, many events in which it would be desirable to have relative frequency probabilities do not satisfy the requirement of repetition. Whether the next satellite launch will be successful, or whether you will make an A in your statistics course are examples of experiments that are not repeatable under the exact same conditions. Thus, they are not appropriate for the application of the relative frequency idea. This perspective greatly limits the application of the relative frequency interpretation of probability. Despite its limitations, the relative frequency approach is a widely held interpretation of probability.

Classical Approach

The second objective approach commonly used in probability is the classical approach. **Classical probability** can be measured as a simple proportion: the number of outcomes that compose the event divided by the number of outcomes in the sample space, when it can be assumed that all of the outcomes are equally likely.

> ### Classical Probability
>
> Using the **classical approach** to probability, the probability of an event A, denoted $P(A)$, is given by
>
> $$P(A) = \frac{\text{number of outcomes in } A}{\text{total number of outcomes in the sample space}}.$$
>
> **DEFINITION**

Caution

When using the classical approach, always ensure that each outcome in the sample space is equally likely to occur.

Quantum Reality

From 1925 to 1927, Neils Bohr and Werner Heisnberg worked together to understand the ramifications of the new theory of quantum mechanics and revolutionized how we think about the universe. They proposed that the nature of reality is inherently probabilistic, an idea that is now referred to as the Copenhagen interpretation of quantum mechanics. One consequence of this interpretation is that an electron has a probability to be anywhere in the universe until it is measured and "forced" to be in one location. At the most fundamental level, the universe can only be understood in terms of probabilistic outcomes. This uncertainty prompted one of Einstein's most famous quotes, "I, at any rate, am convinced that He does not throw dice." Today, other interpretations of how the quantum world works have been entertained, but the probabilistic nature of the subatomic world remains a constant fixture.

Example 6.1.1

In **Experiment 2**, a coin was tossed three times and the number of heads was observed. The sample space consists of 8 outcomes {HHH, HHT, HTH, HTT, THH, THT, TTH, TTT}. Let A be the event of getting at least one head. What is $P(A)$?

Solution

Since the event A consists of 7 outcomes, {HHH, HHT, HTH, HTT, THH, THT, TTH}, and there are 8 equally likely outcomes in the sample space,

$$P(A) = \frac{7}{8} = 0.875.$$

In the previous example it was very easy to list the sample space of the experiment using a pattern to organize the outcomes. For experiments in which the sample space is large, it may be more difficult to ensure that no outcomes are omitted in the list. When an experiment, like the one above, is done in stages (each coin toss could be considered a stage), a **tree diagram** can be used to organize the outcomes in a systematic manner. The tree begins with the possible outcomes for the first stage and then branches extend from each of these outcomes for the possible outcomes in the second stage, and so on for each stage of the experiment. The sample space is found by following each branch of the tree to identify all the possible outcomes of the experiment.

For **Experiment 2**, the tree diagram of the experiment and the subsequent sample space is illustrated by the following figure.

Sample Space for Tossing a Coin Three Times

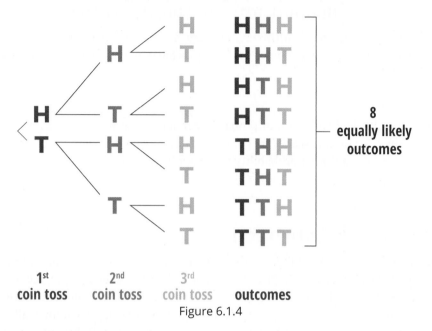

Figure 6.1.4

Example 6.1.2

In **Experiment 3**, let A be the event of observing an even number. What is $P(A)$?

Solution

Since there are 3 outcomes in A and 6 outcomes in the sample space,

$$P(A) = \frac{3}{6} = 0.5.$$

Example 6.1.3

In **Experiment 4**, let A be the event of drawing a heart. What is $P(A)$?

Solution

Since there are 13 outcomes in A (i.e., 13 hearts in a deck of cards) and 52 outcomes in the sample space (i.e., 52 cards in the deck) the probability of event A is as follows.

$$P(A) = \frac{13}{52} = \frac{1}{4} = 0.25$$

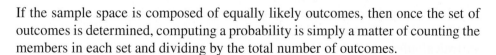

If the sample space is composed of equally likely outcomes, then once the set of outcomes is determined, computing a probability is simply a matter of counting the members in each set and dividing by the total number of outcomes.

It is very important to remember that the classical approach rests on the assumption of equally likely outcomes. If the assumption is not reasonable, some other method of determining the probability must be used.

Example 6.1.4

In **Experiment 2** a coin was tossed three times and the number of heads was observed. The outcomes in the sample space were as follows.

$$S = \{HHH, HHT, HTH, HTT, THH, THT, TTH, TTT\}$$

Could the sample space in this experiment have been formulated differently? Could, for example, the outcomes be defined as the number of heads in three tosses, $S = \{0, 1, 2, 3\}$?

Solution

Using the classical definition of probability requires that the outcomes be equally likely. Since the sample space $S = \{0, 1, 2, 3\}$ does not contain equally likely events, the classical definition of probability is not applicable.

Subjective Approach

The subjective viewpoint regards the probability of an event as a measure of the degree of belief that the event has occurred or will occur. Someone's degree of belief in some event will depend on his or her life experiences. Different life experiences produce different degrees of belief. Hence, the subjective approach must allow for differences in the degree of belief among reasonable people examining the same evidence. One of the significant advantages of this view is the ability to discuss the probability of events that cannot be repeated. Thus, a subjectivist would be willing to assign the probability of making an A in your statistics course. Someone who adopts the subjective view could use the frequency interpretation to influence the determination of a subjective probability. For example, suppose that a coin had been tossed 20,000 times and had come up heads 63% of the time. It would certainly be reasonable for a subjectivist to use this information in the formulation of a statement of probability about the outcome of the next toss.

Criticism of the Subjective Approach

If science is defined as finding out what is probably true, there should be a probability criterion on which all reasonable persons could agree. But if probability is subjective, how can it be used as a universally accepted criterion? Two reasonable persons might examine the same data and reach different conclusions about their degree of belief about some proposition.

Probability, Statistics, and Business

Most of the time, when working with samples, statisticians try to deduce from the samples the population parameters (means, proportions, variances, etc.) of certain variables. This process of making judgments about population parameters is called **statistical inference**.

Statistical Inference

Statistical inference involves the use of sample data to form generalizations or inferences about a population. Using sample data to estimate the values of population parameters is one form of statistical inference.

DEFINITION

Because samples are random, there is no guarantee that the sample will be representative of the population. If the sample is not representative, then using the sample mean as an estimate (inference) of the population mean would not be very wise. Probability is used to assess the quality of our inference. All statistical conclusions must be endowed with a degree of uncertainty. Because probability is used to assess the reliability of sample inferences, it is the foundation of all inferential statistics.

The probability concept also has many direct applications in business. When a manager wonders whether dropping a bid price by 5% will increase the probability of winning the bid, he or she is thinking about chance. Probability is also used as a criteria in designing and evaluating product reliability, evaluating insurance, inventory management, project management, and in the study of queuing theory (a probabilistic analysis of waiting lines).

Probability theory emerged from the need to better understand a game of chance. Business decisions, like games, have uncertain outcomes. In an effort to make better decisions, businesses spend considerable amounts of money trying to quantify uncertainty. This means trying to turn uncertainty into a probability. Insurance companies have historically done a good job quantifying uncertainty. In fact, a special kind of statistician, called an actuary, has emerged to assist in the development of insurance models which quantify uncertainty and aid in business decisions.

The next time you watch a 30-second commercial during the Super Bowl, consider the fact that a company has just spent on average $5 million for the air time plus a substantial amount of money developing the advertisement. Without knowing the effect of the advertisement in advance, extensive amounts of money are put at risk with an uncertain outcome. The manager making the decision uses subjective probability to assess the risk and reward.

Lloyd's of London

This very modern looking building is the home of the world's second largest commercial insurer and the sixth largest reinsurance group, Lloyd's of London. At Lloyd's, like all other insurers, risk is measured in probabilities, which are usually subjective. Lloyd's differs from other insurers in the kinds of policies they write. Lloyd's has written policies on nuclear reactors, space shuttle cargo, oil tankers, art treasures, kidnap and ransom, as well as the legs of ballerinas and football players.

Insurance has a very important place in commerce, and without it, many business activities would not be possible. If a shipping company could not insure its ships, raising the money to buy them would be virtually impossible. Insurance is big business. Lloyd's annual marine insurance premiums amount to more than $30 billion a year, and that represents little more than one-third of their aggregate income. In addition to sizable revenues, Lloyd's employs about 70,000 people. Lloyd's is a market, rather than an entity. It houses underwriters who evaluate insurance risk for the syndicates they represent. A syndicate is a group of individuals, called Names, who individually assume a small amount of risk in return for a commensurate portion of the premium. To become a Name you must have a net worth in excess of $550,000 (excluding the value of your home) and apply to Lloyd's committee for approval. For large policies, like an ocean cargo vessel, even a syndicate does not usually underwrite the entire policy; more often groups of syndicates each take a small percentage–thus further diluting each individual's risk.

6.1   **Exercises**

Basic Concepts

1. Describe randomness.

2. What is probability?

3. List the necessary conditions for a random experiment.

4. What is an outcome? What is an event?

5. What are the two approaches to objective probability?

6. What are some of the problems associated with the relative frequency approach?

7. What is the Law of Large Numbers?

8. Describe the classical approach to probability.

9. What is statistical inference?

10. Discuss the relationship between probability and statistics.

Exercises

11. Consider the following random experiment. A potato chip manufacturer is interested in determining if the brand of potato chip which it manufactures is preferred over three of its major competitors. Several customers are randomly selected and asked which brand of potato chip they prefer: Brand A, Brand B, Brand C, or Brand D.

    a. Determine the sample space for the experiment described.

    b. If the manufacturer makes Brand A, list the outcomes in the event $M = \{$customer does not prefer the manufacturer's brand$\}$.

12. Consider the following random experiment. A doctor is interested in determining whether or not his patients think that he listens attentively to what they are saying. He randomly selects several patients and administers an anonymous survey that asks which of the following categories best describes his attentiveness: Very Attentive, Somewhat Attentive, Not Attentive.

    a. Determine the sample space for the above experiment.

    b. Determine all possible outcomes for the event $A = \{$the doctor is not described as very attentive$\}$.

13. A gambler has made a weighted die. In order to decide which of the six sides is most likely to turn up, he tosses the die 33 times and notes the number of dots on the upper-most surface. The results of the experiment are shown in the following table.

Rolls of a Weighted Die										
1	2	1	3	1	4	1	5	6	3	1
3	1	5	1	2	1	3	1	2	1	2
2	1	3	5	1	2	1	2	1	4	6

    a. Using the relative frequency approach, what is the probability of observing each side?

    b. Assuming all outcomes have an equal payoff, which side do you think the gambler will bet on when the die is tossed?

14. Assume there are two red, two yellow, and two blue buttons in a hat. A button is drawn out of the hat, the color is noted, and the button is returned. This is repeated fifty times. The results are listed in the following table.

Button Drawing				
Yellow	Yellow	Red	Yellow	Red
Red	Red	Blue	Red	Blue
Blue	Red	Red	Yellow	Red
Red	Blue	Yellow	Red	Yellow
Yellow	Blue	Red	Blue	Red
Red	Red	Red	Red	Yellow
Blue	Yellow	Yellow	Blue	Red
Yellow	Red	Red	Red	Yellow
Red	Yellow	Yellow	Yellow	Red
Red	Red	Blue	Red	Blue

Using the relative frequency approach, what is the probability of drawing each color?

15. Twenty-five insurance agents are randomly selected and asked if they own a handgun. Twenty-two of those surveyed said that they do own a handgun. If an insurance agent is randomly selected from the sample, estimate the probability that the agent will own a handgun.

16. Thirty elementary school teachers are randomly selected and asked if they favor standardized testing of elementary school children. Twenty of those surveyed said that they did favor standardized testing of elementary school children. If an elementary school teacher is randomly selected from the sample, estimate the probability that the teacher will favor standardized testing for elementary school children.

17. Fifty chief executive officers (CEOs) of publicly traded companies are randomly selected and their salaries are determined. Forty-five of the CEOs selected have salaries in excess of $500,000. If a CEO from one of the selected publicly traded companies is randomly selected from the sample, find the probability that the CEO will have a salary in excess of $500,000.

18. Forty emergency calls to which a local police department responded were randomly selected. Of the forty emergency calls fifteen were categorized as domestic arguments. Estimate the probability that the next emergency call to which the local police department responds will be a domestic argument.

19. For the following situations, decide which probability interpretation is most reasonable to use: relative frequency, subjective, or classical.

   a. Whether or not you will have a wreck on your next trip to the mall.

   b. Whether or not a car coming off the Ford assembly line will have a defect.

   c. The probability that you will graduate from college in four calendar years.

   d. Whether a person will be in an automobile accident during the next year.

   e. The probability that you will be dealt a full house from a well-shuffled deck of cards.

20. For the following situations, decide which probability interpretation is most reasonable to use: relative frequency, subjective, or classical.

    a. Suppose you have purchased a lottery ticket. Describe your chances of winning the lottery.

    b. The probability you will enjoy a vacation trip to Mexico.

    c. The probability your company's sales will exceed seven million dollars this year.

    d. One hundred people receive keys to a new car in a radio contest. Only one key actually fits the car. The probability that key number 25 will open the car door.

    e. The probability that you will get a ticket if you drive 70 mph on the interstate between work and home this coming Tuesday.

    f. The probability that the S&P 500 will increase or decrease by at least 25 points in one day.

21. A couple plans to have two children. Assume the sex of the child is equally likely.

    a. List all possible outcomes for the sexes of the two children.

    b. Find the probability that the couple will have 2 boys.

    c. Find the probability that the couple will have at least 1 girl.

22. Consider a student who is taking a multiple choice examination where there are five possible answers for each question. Since the student has not studied or attended any of the classes, the student decides to randomly guess at each question.

    a. Find the probability that the student will answer the first question correctly.

    b. Find the probability that the student will answer the first question incorrectly.

23. A game show contestant has to choose one of three doors to win a prize. Behind one door the prize is a trip to Hawaii; behind another door, the prize is a color TV; behind the final door, the prize is a bag of potatoes. If a contestant randomly selects a door,

    a. Find the probability that the contestant will win a trip to Hawaii.

    b. Find the probability that the contestant will not win a trip to Hawaii.

6.2 Addition Rules for Probability

Interpreting probabilities using the classical approach is a good way of thinking about the basic probability principles. In this section we will discuss certain laws that probabilities must obey, regardless of how probability is defined.

Probability Law 1

A probability of zero means the event cannot happen. (For example, the probability of observing three heads in two tosses of a coin is zero.)

DEFINITION

Probability Law 2

A probability of one means the event must happen. (For example, if we toss a coin, the probability of getting either a head or tail is one.)

DEFINITION

Probability Law 3

All probabilities must be between zero and one inclusively. The closer the probability is to 1, the more likely the event. The closer the probability is to 0, the less likely the event. For an event A this is expressed as follows.

$$0 \le P(A) \le 1$$

DEFINITION

Probability Law 4

The sum of the probabilities of all outcomes must equal one. That is, if $P(A_i)$ is the probability of event A_i, and there are n such outcomes, then

$$P(A_1) + P(A_2) + \cdots + P(A_n) = 1.$$

DEFINITION

There are a number of rules concerning the relationships between events that are useful in determining probabilities.

Compound event

A **compound event** is an event that is defined by combining two or more events.

DEFINITION

Suppose that the marketing director of *Sports Illustrated* believed that anyone who possessed an income greater than $50,000 or subscribed to more than one other sports magazine could potentially be a good prospect for a direct mail marketing campaign.

Let the event

   $A = \{$annual income is greater than $50,000\}$

   and

   $B = \{$subscribes to more than one other sports magazine$\}$.

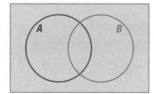

Figure 6.2.1

There are several different types of compound events. To illustrate the concepts, consider the two events A and B shown in the **Venn diagram** in Figure 6.2.1. A

Black Swan Events

Black Swan events are unexpected extreme events. The term stems from 16th century London: at this time, all known swans in the Euro-centric world were white. Subsequently, upon colonization of Western Australia, black swans were unexpectedly discovered. The term was popularized in Nassam Nicholas Taleb's book The Black Swan: The Impact of the Highly Improbable (2007). While the discovery of black swans did not adversely impact society, the black swan term today carries the connotations that the event is damaging, unexpected, and in hindsight, quite explainable. Two events occurring since 2000 that arguably qualify for black swan status are 9/11 and the disappearance of the MH-370 aircraft.

Statisticians quantify how rare events are via return periods. For example, if a 50-year earthquake at a fixed location has Richter magnitude 7.0, then the probability that a Richter magnitude 7.0 or greater earthquake occurs at the location over one year is roughly 1/50. Statisticians have a sub-discipline called extreme value theory that contains justifiable methods to estimate return periods (see Coles, 2001; An Introduction to Statistical Modeling of Extreme Values). This said, the field is often controversial and data void. Imagine trying to estimate a 200 year earthquake from only 50 years of data --- a 200-year earthquake event is probably not contained in the data record!

While extreme value statisticians seldom refer to black swan events, the term is common in financial and insurance settings today. There, it often simply serves as a reminder that unexpected rare events do happen and are difficult to quantify.

Courtesy of Robert Lund

Let's Make a Deal

A long time ago, back in the 70s, there was a television show called "Let's Make a Deal" starring Monty Hall as the host. This show produced an interesting problem in probability which someone submitted to Marilyn vos Savant which she answered in her column in Parade magazine. Incidentally, Ms. Savant is in the Guinness Book of World Records as having the highest recorded IQ (228). Here's the problem that was posed to Ms. Savant.

"Suppose you're on a game show, and you're given a choice of three doors: Behind one door is a car: behind the others, goats. You pick a door, say number 1, and the host, who knows what's behind the other doors, opens another door, say number 3, which has a goat. He then says to you, 'Do you want to pick door number 2?' Is it to your advantage to take the switch?"

Marilyn vos Savant answered the question in her column saying that it was to your advantage to switch. This set off a firestorm of mail telling Ms. Savant that she was incorrect. Much of this mail came from people with Ph.D.s behind their names. The New York Times printed a front page article in 1991 discussing the problem.

What do you think? To find the answer to this problem type "The Monty Hall problem" in your search engine and go to some of the web sites and try some of the simulations.

Venn diagram is a picture used to illustrate the relationship between two events (or sets). The rectangle represents the sample space and the circles represent events.

The set of outcomes in which either (or both) of these events occurs is called the **union** of the two sets.

Union

The **union** of the events A and B is the set of outcomes that are included in event A or event B or both. Symbolically, the union of A and B is denoted $A \cup B$ and is read "A union B."

DEFINITION

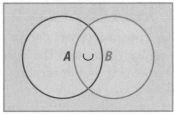

Figure 6.2.2

Notice in Figure 6.2.2 that the union includes all outcomes in either A or B.

Intersection

The **intersection** of the events A and B is the set of all outcomes that are included in both A and B. Symbolically, the intersection of A and B is denoted $A \cap B$ and is read "A intersect B."

DEFINITION

Suppose the marketing director was interested in persons who possessed an annual income greater than $50,000 and subscribed to more than one other sports magazine. That set would be called the intersection of A and B.

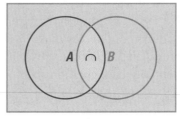

Figure 6.2.3

Notice in Figure 6.2.3 that the intersection includes only those outcomes in both A **and** B.

Two other useful concepts are the notions of **complement** of an event and events which are **mutually exclusive.**

Complement

The **complement** of an event A is the set of all outcomes in the sample space that are not in A. Symbolically, the complement of the set A will be written as A^c.

DEFINITION

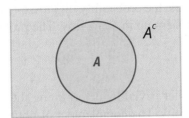

Figure 6.2.4

Notice in Figure 6.2.4 that the complement of event A includes all outcomes which are not in A. For the event $A = \{\text{annual income is greater than \$50,000}\}$, the complement of A would be

$$A^c = \{\text{annual income is less than or equal to \$50,000}\}.$$

Also note that $A \cup A^c = S$, which implies that $P(A) + P(A^c) = 1$.

The set relationships of complement, union, and intersection give rise to a number of probability laws.

Probability Law 5: Complement of an Event

The probability of A^c is given by $P(A^c) = 1 - P(A)$.

DEFINITION

Sometimes it is much easier to calculate the probability of the complement of an event, than the actual event.

Example 6.2.1

Consider the event $A = \{\text{annual income is greater than \$50,000}\}$. Suppose the probability of A is 0.08. Determine the probability of observing someone whose income is less than or equal to \$50,000.

Solution

$$P(\text{annual income is less than or equal to \$50,000}) = P(A^c)$$
$$= 1 - P(A)$$
$$= 1 - 0.08$$
$$= 0.92$$

Example 6.2.2

Consider an experiment to see how many tosses of a coin will be required to obtain the first head. The first head could be observed on the first toss or second toss, but there is no upper limit on the number of tosses that could be required. Therefore, the sample space for this experiment is the set of positive integers $\{1, 2, 3, \dots\}$. Not only is the sample space infinitely large, but there is another problem: the outcomes are not equally likely. This is a potentially ugly environment in which to compute a probability. But let's make matters slightly worse. Suppose we want to know the probability that it will require *at least* two tosses (i.e., two or more tosses) to get the first head. This means that we must compute the probability of 2 tosses

Winning the Lottery Twice!

In 1986 a woman won the N.J. State lottery twice and in 1988 a man in Pennsylvania also won the State lottery twice for a total of 5.4 and 6.8 million dollars respectively. The New York Times reported the odds to be 1 in 17 trillion? How is this to be explained?

When millions of people play a lottery daily it can be shown that the odds of winning twice are about 1 in 30 in a 4-month period and the odds are better than even in a 7-year period. Thus what appeared to be an almost theoretical impossibility, turns out to be quite a probable event. What one can say is that even when the probability of an event is very small, if there are millions of possibilities, then the rare event rarely remains rare. This is what has been called "The Law of Real Large Numbers" by Diaconis and Mosteller.

Source: Diaconis, P. and Mosteller, F. (1989). Methods for Studying Coincidences," Journal of the American Statistical Association, 84, 853-861.

Struck by Lightning

Many people have a greater chance of meeting someone who survived a lightning strike than someone who won the lottery. There are an estimated 1800 new thunderstorms being created around the world every minute and the odds against someone being struck by lightning is 606,944 to one. Unless you are Roy C. Sullivan. Mr. Sullivan was a former U.S. park ranger who was struck by lightning seven times in less than 36 years.

before the first head appears, the probability of 3 tosses to get the first head, and so on up to infinity and add them up in some way. The problem is rather insidious if approached directly.

Solution

The problem becomes rather trivial by determining the complement of the event and computing its probability. The complement of obtaining the first head in two or more tosses is getting a head on the first toss. The probability of getting a head on the first toss is 0.5, assuming the coin is fair. Therefore, we have the following.

$$P(\text{two or more tosses to obtain the first head}) = 1 - P(\text{head on the first toss})$$
$$= 1 - 0.5$$
$$= 0.5$$

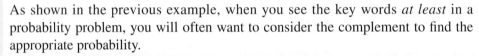

As shown in the previous example, when you see the key words *at least* in a probability problem, you will often want to consider the complement to find the appropriate probability.

Another topic that is often discussed when talking about probability, and which involves the complement of an event, is **odds**, as in *the odds of that horse winning the race are 3 to 1*. You often hear this terminology at casinos and racetracks instead of statements about the probability of an event occurring. There are two types of odds often considered in gambling situations.

Odds

The **odds in favor of** an event A occurring is given by $\dfrac{P(A)}{P(\text{not } A)} = \dfrac{P(A)}{P(A^c)}$.

The **odds against** an event A occurring is given by $\dfrac{P(\text{not } A)}{P(A)} = \dfrac{P(A^c)}{P(A)}$.

DEFINITION

Remember, that $P(A^c) = 1 - P(A)$. So, if $P(A) = 0.4$, then $P(A^c) = 1 - 0.4 = 0.6$.

Therefore, the odds in favor of A are $\dfrac{0.4}{0.6} = \dfrac{4}{6} = \dfrac{2}{3}$, which is typically written as 2 to 3 or 2:3.

If you are given the odds in favor of an event A as $n{:}m$, then the probability of that event can be calculated by

$$P(A) = \frac{n}{n+m}.$$

So, a horse with 3:1 odds of winning has a $\dfrac{3}{3+1} = \dfrac{3}{4} = 0.75$ probability of winning the race. A horse with 3:1 odds against winning would have a 0.25 probability of winning the race.

Example 6.2.3

In the game of American roulette, the roulette wheel contains the numbers 1 through 36, alternating between red and black. There are two green spaces numbered 0 and 00.

  a. Calculate the probability of the roulette ball landing on a red pocket.
  b. Calculate the probability of the roulette ball not landing on a red pocket.
  c. Calculate the odds in favor of the roulette ball landing on red.

Solution

  a. Since there are 18 red pockets and 38 possible pockets on which to land, the probability of landing on red is given by

$$P(\text{red}) = \frac{18}{38}.$$

  b. The probability of not landing on a red pocket is found by

$$P(\text{not red}) = 1 - \frac{18}{38} = \frac{20}{38}.$$

  Note that 20 is the sum of the 18 black pockets and the two green pockets.

  c. The odds in favor of the roulette ball landing on red is therefore,

$$\frac{P(\text{red})}{P(\text{not red})} = \frac{18}{38} \div \frac{20}{38} = \frac{18}{38} \cdot \frac{38}{20} = \frac{18}{20} = \frac{9}{10} \text{ or } 9{:}10.$$

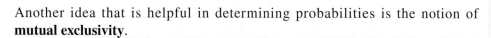

Another idea that is helpful in determining probabilities is the notion of **mutual exclusivity**.

Mutually Exclusive

Two events are **mutually exclusive** if they have no outcomes in common.

DEFINITION

Mutual exclusivity is also called **disjointedness**. Figure 6.2.5 represents two **disjoint** events.

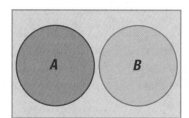

Figure 6.2.5

Probability Law 6: Union of Mutually Exclusive Events

If the events A and B are mutually exclusive, then

$$P(A \cup B) = P(A) + P(B).$$

DEFINITION

Mutually Exclusive

Two events are mutually exclusive if they cannot occur at the same time.

For example, if you were to select one card from a standard deck, the two outcomes:

  • The card is a Jack
  • The card is a Seven

are mutually exclusive, because you cannot select a card that is both a Jack and a Seven.

However, the two outcomes:

  • The card is a Jack
  • The card is a Club

are not mutually exclusive, because you can select a card that is both a Jack and a Club.

Probability Law 7: Intersection of Mutually Exclusive Events

If the events A and B are mutually exclusive, then

$$P(A \cap B) = 0.$$

DEFINITION

Example 6.2.4

Suppose that $P(A) = 0.27$ and the $P(B) = 0.19$. If A and B are mutually exclusive, what is the probability of $A \cup B$?

Solution

Since these are mutually exclusive events,

$$P(A \cup B) = P(A) + P(B) = 0.27 + 0.19 = 0.46.$$

There is a more generalized rule that eliminates the assumption of exclusivity between the events.

Probability Law 8: The General Addition Rule

For any two events A and B,

$$P(A \cup B) = P(A) + P(B) - P(A \cap B).$$

DEFINITION

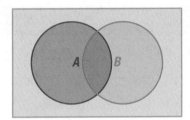

Figure 6.2.6

The general addition rule is identical to Probability Law 6 when the events are mutually exclusive, since A intersect B will be an empty set whose probability will be zero. In cases where A and B intersect, the probability of the intersection must be subtracted since it is contained once in A and once in B, and therefore has been added in twice.

Example 6.2.5

Suppose that the marketing manager mentioned earlier believed that the probability that someone earns more than \$50,000 is 0.2 and the probability that someone will subscribe to more than one sports magazine is 0.3. If the probability of finding someone in both categories is 0.08, what is the probability of finding someone who is earning over \$50,000 or subscribes to more than one sports magazine?

Solution

The problem involves the union of two events. Using the same event names (A and B) as in previous examples, the desired probability is

$$P(A \cup B) = P(A) + P(B) - P(A \cap B) = 0.2 + 0.3 - 0.08 = 0.42.$$

Therefore, the probability of finding someone who is earning over \$50,000 or subscribes to more than one sports magazine, or both is 0.42.

6.2 **Exercises**

Basic Concepts

1. What laws must probability obey, regardless of the methodology used to derive the probabilities?

2. Suppose you are taking a test next week. Interpret each of the following statements.

   a. P(receiving an A on the test) $= 0$

   b. P(receiving an A on the test) $= 1$

3. What is a compound event?

4. Draw a Venn diagram to represent the intersection of three events.

5. Define the following set operations: union, intersection, and complement.

6. If you know the probability of two events, what else must you know in order to calculate the probability of *one event or the other*?

7. If two events A and B are mutually exclusive, what is $P(A \cap B)$?

Exercises

8. Determine if the following values could be probabilities. If the value cannot be a probability, explain why.

   a. 0

   b. $\dfrac{36}{25}$

   c. $\dfrac{7}{8}$

   d. -0.4

   e. 0.23

9. Determine if the following values could be probabilities. If the value cannot be a probability, explain why.

   a. 1

   b. $\dfrac{15}{16}$

   c. $\dfrac{4}{3}$

   d. 0.99

   e. -0.05

10. Interpret the following probabilities with respect to the occurrence of some event.

    a. $P(\text{event}) = 0$ **d.** $P(\text{event}) = 65\%$

    b. $P(\text{event}) = 1.0$ **e.** $P(\text{event}) = -1.0$

    c. $P(\text{event}) = 0.45$

11. Find the following probabilities.

    a. The probability of an event that must happen.

    b. The probability of an event that cannot happen.

    c. The probability of having a boy or a girl in a single birth.

    d. The probability of rolling a two and a five in a single toss of a die.

12. Find the following probabilities related to odds.

    a. If the odds in favor of an event A occurring is 3:5, what is the probability of event A?

    b. If the odds against an event A occurring is 3:5, what is the probability of event A?

13. The annual premium amounts charged by life insurance companies to their clients are set very carefully. If the amount is too high, the client will take his or her business to another company. If it is too low, the insurance company may not make enough profit to stay in business. In order to properly determine a premium, the company often relies on life tables. These tables allow one to compute the probabilities of death at various ages. They are constructed only after collecting and reviewing extensive data on age at death from a large group of people. A life table is normally constructed assuming that 100,000 people are alive at age 0. This number is simply a reference value used to make comparisons throughout the table. Other numbers could be used. The table then gives the number of people of the original 100,000 that are alive at the beginning of various years of life. In order for the insurance company to optimally set premiums, a separate table should be constructed for the different genders and races. The following abbreviated life table is valid only for females.

Life Table						
Year	0	1	5	10	15	20
Number Alive	100,000	99,090	98,912	98,815	98,716	98,477
Year	25	30	35	40	45	50
Number Alive	98,204	97,897	97,500	96,958	96,097	94,766
Year	55	60	65	70	75	80
Number Alive	92,623	89,449	84,565	77,772	68,200	55,535

    a. What is the probability that a newborn female lives until the age of 40?

    b. What is the probability that a newborn female dies before she reaches the age of 50?

14. A mail order company classifies its customers by gender and location of residence. The market research department has gathered data from a random sample of 759 customers.

Mail Order Customers		
	Gender	
Location	**Male**	**Female**
Suburban	196	298
Urban	92	173

  a. What is the probability that a customer is male?

  b. What is the probability that a customer is female?

  c. What is the probability that a customer is a suburban male?

  d. What is the probability that a customer is an urban female?

  e. What is the probability that a customer is a suburban male or an urban female?

  f. What is the probability that a customer is urban?

  g. What is the probability that a customer is not a suburban female?

  h. What approach to probability did you use to calculate your answers?

  i. Are the events {customer is urban} and {customer is suburban} mutually exclusive? Explain.

15. A large life insurance company is interested in studying the insurance policies held by married couples. In particular, the insurance company is interested in the amount of insurance held by the husbands and the wives. The insurance company collects data for all of its 1000 policies where both the husband and the wife are insured. The results are summarized in the following table.

Life Insurance Coverage				
		Amount of Life Insurance on Husband ($)		
		0–50,000	50,000–100,000	100,000–150,000	More than 150,000
Amount of Life Insurance on Wife ($)	0–50,000	400	200	50	50
	50,000–100,000	50	50	30	30
	100,000–150,000	20	10	25	25
	More than 150,000	20	10	15	15

  a. For a randomly selected policy, what is the probability that the husband will have between $50,000 and $100,000 of insurance?

  b. For a randomly selected policy, what is the probability that the wife will have between $100,000 and $150,000 of insurance?

  c. For a randomly selected policy, what is the probability that the wife will have more than $150,000 of insurance or the husband will have more than $150,000 of insurance?

d. For a randomly selected policy, what is the probability that the wife will have between $0 and $50,000 of insurance and the husband will have between $0 and $50,000 of insurance?

e. For a randomly selected policy, what is the probability that the wife will not have between $0 and $50,000 of insurance?

f. For a randomly selected policy, what is the probability that the husband will have more than $50,000 of insurance?

g. What approach to probability did you use to calculate your answers?

h. Are the events {the wife has more than $150,000 in insurance} and {the husband has between $50,000 and $100,000 of insurance} mutually exclusive? Explain.

6.3 Multiplication Rules for Probability

Researchers often want to examine a limited portion of the sample space. For example, consider the question of whether cigarette smoking harms those that are indirectly exposed to the smoke. Suppose that 3% of women who do not smoke die of cancer. However, if a nonsmoking woman is married to a smoking husband (not to be confused with a husband who is on fire), the probability of dying of cancer is 0.08 or 8%. This probability is a **conditional probability**, because the sample space is being limited by some condition – in this case, limited to only wives of smoking husbands. In this instance, the dramatic effect of a smoking husband on cancer rates is readily evident.

P(a nonsmoking woman dies of cancer)

P(a nonsmoking woman dies of cancer given that her husband smokes)

Similarly, the results from a market survey indicate that 39% of the customers surveyed believe a product is of high quality. However, if the analysis is limited to only women, 54% of women surveyed believe the product is of high quality. Based on the survey, it appears that women have a much higher regard for the company's product than men. The difference in attitude would probably be something that could affect how the company spends its marketing dollars.

The notion of conditional probability is defined as follows.

> **Conditional Probability**
>
> The probability that an event will occur given that some other event has already occurred or is certain to occur, is a **conditional probability**.
>
> DEFINITION

To compute a conditional probability, apply the following rule.

Probability Law 9: Conditional Probability

The **conditional probability** of event A occurring, given that event B has already occurred is

$$P(A|B) = \frac{P(A \cap B)}{P(B)}$$

The notation $P(A|B)$ is read as *the probability of A given the occurrence of B*. The vertical bar within a probability statement will always mean *given*.

DEFINITION

The events A and B can be reversed in the preceding rule to compute $P(B|A)$. Note that since we are finding the conditional probability of A, given that B has occurred, $P(B) \neq 0$.

$$P(A|B) = \frac{P(A \cap B)}{P(B)}$$

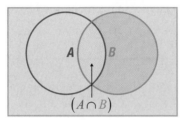

Figure 6.3.1

Example 6.3.1

Suppose a marketing research firm has surveyed a panel of consumers to test a new product and produced the following **cross tabulation** indicating the number of panelists that liked the product, the number that did not like the product, and the number that were undecided.

Market Research Survey				
Age	**Like**	**Not Like**	**Undecided**	**Total**
18–34	213	197	103	513
35–50	193	184	67	444
Over 50	144	219	83	446
Total	**550**	**600**	**253**	**1403**

If an individual is between 35 and 50 years old, what is the probability that he or she will like the product?

Solution

Let the events

A = {like the product},

and

B = {age between 35 and 50}.

Then the desired probability can be formulated as

$$P(A|B) = \frac{P(A \cap B)}{P(B)}$$

The $P(A \cap B)$ is called a joint probability since it is the probability of the occurrence of more than one event. To compute the $P(A \cap B)$ use the empirical approach; that is,

$$P(A \cap B) = \frac{193}{1403} \approx 0.1376.$$

Similarly, $P(B)$ can be computed as

$$P(B) = \frac{444}{1403} \approx 0.3165.$$

Consequently, $P(A|B)$ is

$$P(A|B) = \frac{0.1376}{0.3165} \approx 0.4348.$$

Note that this answer could have also been obtained by simply dividing 193 by 444.

Example 6.3.2

Out of 300 applicants for a job, 212 are male. Of the male job applicants, 110 have served in the military.

 a. What is the probability that a randomly chosen applicant has served in the military, given that he is male?

 b. If 152 of the applicants have served in the military, what is the probability that a randomly chosen applicant is male, given that the applicant has served in the military?

Solution

 a. The question asks for $P(\text{military service}|\text{male})$. Thus, in order to use the formula for conditional probability, we need to find $P(\text{male and military service})$ and $P(\text{male})$. There are 300 applicants total, so the probability of choosing an applicant who is male and has served in the military is $\frac{110}{300}$. Similarly, the probability of choosing a male applicant is $\frac{212}{300}$. Thus, we calculate the conditional probability as follows.

$$P(\text{military service}|\text{male}) = \frac{P(\text{male and military service})}{P(\text{male})} = \frac{\dfrac{110}{300}}{\dfrac{212}{300}} = \frac{110}{212} \approx 0.5189$$

 b. For this question we want to calculate $P(\text{male}|\text{military service})$. We know from part **a.** that the probability of choosing one of the 300 applicants who is male and has served in the military is $\frac{110}{300}$. Also, we know that the probability that a randomly chosen applicant has served in the military is $\frac{152}{300}$. Using the formula for conditional probability, we have the following.

$$P\big(\text{male}\big|\text{military service}\big) = \frac{P\big(\text{male and military service}\big)}{P\big(\text{military service}\big)} = \frac{\dfrac{110}{300}}{\dfrac{152}{300}} = \frac{110}{152} \approx 0.7237$$

As you can see, $P\big(A\big|B\big)$ is not necessarily the same as $P\big(B\big|A\big)$.

An extremely important concept in statistical analysis is **independence**. It describes a special kind of relationship between two events. Two events are said to be independent if knowledge of one event does not provide information of the other event's occurrence. In other words, the occurrence of one event does not affect the occurrence of another event if the events are independent.

Example 6.3.3

Conduct the experiment of rolling a fair die two times. Consider the two events

$A = \{$rolling a six on the first roll of a fair die$\}$, and

$B = \{$rolling a four on the second roll of a fair die$\}$.

Are these two events independent?

Solution

Since knowledge of the outcome of the first roll does not help one make an inference about the outcome of the second roll, the two events are independent.

Symbolically the idea of independence is expressed in the following definition.

Independent

Two events, A and B, are **independent** if and only if

$$P\big(A\big|B\big) = P(A) \text{ and } P\big(B\big|A\big) = P(B).$$

DEFINITION

In many cases, regarding the independence of two events, intuition and common sense will lead you to the correct determination. There are situations in which independence can only be discovered by formal application of the definition.

Probability Law 10: Multiplication Rule for Independent Events

If two events, A and B, are independent, then

$$P(A \cap B) = P(A) \cdot P(B).$$

If n events, $A_1, A_2, ..., A_n$, are independent, then

$$P(A_1 \cap A_2 \cap ... \cap A_n) = P(A_1) \cdot P(A_2) \cdot ... \cdot P(A_n).$$

DEFINITION

The above multiplication rule for independent events is sometimes called the **product rule**. The rule simply states that the probability of the joint occurrence of mutually independent events is the product of their probabilities.

Example 6.3.4

A coin is flipped and a fair die is rolled. Find the probability of getting a head on the coin and an even number on the die.

    a. Use a tree diagram to find the probability.
    b. Use Probability Law 10 to find the probability.

Solution

    a. The tree diagram for flipping a coin and rolling a fair die is given below. Note that there are 12 equally likely outcomes. The three outcomes outlined in red are those where the coin toss results in a head and the roll of the die results in a 2, 4, or 6, an even number. The probability is therefore

$$P(\text{head, even number}) = \frac{3}{12} = \frac{1}{4}.$$

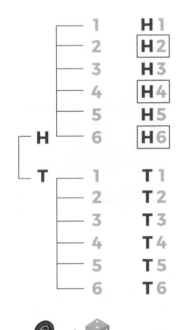

coin toss   die roll

    b. Since the event of tossing a coin is independent of the event of rolling a fair die, we can use Probability Law 10 and multiply the probabilities of the two events together.

$$P(\text{head, even number}) = P(\text{head}) \cdot P(\text{even number}) = \frac{1}{2} \cdot \frac{3}{6} = \frac{1}{4}$$

Notice that regardless of the approach you take to find the solution, you get the same result. In the next example we will look at an extension to three events.

Example 6.3.5

A coin is flipped, a die is rolled, and a card is drawn from a standard deck of 52 cards. Find the probability of getting a tail on the coin, a five on the die, and a jack of clubs from the deck of cards.

Solution

Since the three events (flipping a coin, rolling a die, and selecting a card) are independent, we can use the product rule.

We know the following.

$$P(\text{tails on the coin}) = \frac{1}{2} \quad P(\text{five on the die}) = \frac{1}{6} \quad P(\text{jack of clubs}) = \frac{1}{52}$$

Therefore, we can calculate the probability as follows.

$$P(\text{tail on coin} \cap \text{five on die} \cap \text{jack of clubs}) = P(\text{tail on coin}) \cdot P(\text{five on die}) \cdot P(\text{jack of clubs})$$

$$= \frac{1}{2} \cdot \frac{1}{6} \cdot \frac{1}{52} = \frac{1}{624} \approx 0.0016$$

So the probability of getting tails on the coin, rolling a five, and then selecting the jack of clubs is about 0.0016.

Example 6.3.6

Choose two cards from a standard deck, replacing the first card and shuffling before choosing the second one. What is the probability of choosing a king and then a queen?

Solution

Because the first card is replaced before the second card is drawn, the probability of the second event occurring is not affected by the outcome of the first event. That is, the two events are independent. Therefore, we can calculate the probability using the product rule as follows.

$$P(\text{king and queen}) = P(\text{king}) \cdot P(\text{queen}) = \frac{4}{52} \cdot \frac{4}{52} = \frac{16}{2704} \approx 0.0059$$

Example 6.3.7

This is an actual case that stirred up quite a controversy.

People vs. Collins (1968)

On June 18, 1964, at about 11:30 AM, Mrs. Juanita Brooks was assaulted and robbed while walking through an alley in the San Pedro area of Los Angeles. Mrs. Brooks described her assailant as a young woman with a blond pony tail. At about the same time, John Bass was watering his lawn and witnessed the assault. He described the assailant as a Caucasian woman with dark-blond hair. As she ran from the alley she jumped into a yellow automobile driven by a black man with a mustache and a beard.

Several days later the police arrested two individuals based on the descriptions provided by the assailant and the witness. The two suspects were eventually charged with the crime. During the trial the prosecution called a professor of mathematics to testify. The prosecutor set forth the following probabilities for the characteristics of the assailants.

Assailant Characteristics Data	
Characteristic	**Probability**
Yellow automobile	0.10
Man with mustache	0.25
Girl with ponytail	0.10
Girl with blonde hair	0.33
Black man with beard	0.10
Interracial couple in a car	0.001

How did the prosecution use these probabilities to argue its case?

Solution

If the events are assumed to be independent, then the product rule can be used to calculate the likelihood of observing their joint occurrence.

P(Yellow automobile ∩ Man with mustache ∩ Girl with ponytail ∩ Girl with blond hair ∩ Black man with beard ∩ Interracial couple in car)

$= (0.10)(0.25)(0.10)(0.33)(0.10)(0.001)$

$= 0.0000000825$

Based on the product rule, the mathematician testified that there was about a 1 in 12 million chance that a couple selected at random would possess these characteristics. The prosecution added that the probability was the chance that "any other couple possessed the distinctive characteristics of the defendants." The jury convicted the defendants. On appeal, the Supreme Court of California reversed the decision, based on two main points. First there was no proof offered that the probabilities used in the probability calculation were correct and there was no evidence that the events were independent. Second, the prosecution's evidence pertaining to a randomly selected couple was not pertinent to the problem of the existence of any other couple possessing the same characteristics.

Example 6.3.8

In a production process, a product is assembled by using four different independent parts (A, B, C, and D). In order for the product to operate properly, each part must be free of defects. The probabilities of the parts being nondefective are given by $P(A) = 0.9$, $P(B) = 0.7$, $P(C) = 0.8$, and $P(D) = 0.9$.

   a. What is the probability that all four parts are defective?
   b. What is the probability that the product does not work?

Solution

   a. For all parts to have defects, we need to find the probability of the intersection of the complement for each of the parts. That is,

$$P(\text{all four parts have defects}) = P\left(A^c \cap B^c \cap C^c \cap D^c\right).$$

    Since each part operates independently of the others, the probability that all four parts are defective is the product of the probability of each of the part's complement.

$$P(\text{all four parts have defects}) = P\left(A^c\right) \cdot P\left(B^c\right) \cdot P\left(C^c\right) \cdot P\left(D^c\right)$$
$$= (1-0.9)(1-0.7)(1-0.8)(1-0.9) = 0.0006$$

    Thus, the probability that all four parts have defects is 0.0006, or 0.06%.

   b. The probability that the product does not work is the probability that at least one of the parts does not work (since each part must be free of defects for the product to work).

$$P(\text{product does not work}) = P(\text{at least one part does not work})$$
$$= 1 - P(\text{all parts work})$$
$$= 1 - P(A \cap B \cap C \cap D)$$
$$= 1 - (0.9)(0.7)(0.8)(0.9) = 1 - 0.4536 = 0.5464$$

    Thus, there is nearly a 55% chance that the product will not work.

What does it mean if two events are not independent? One obvious response is to say that they are **dependent**, a term that is just as much a part of statistical vocabulary as independent. If events are dependent, they are related; the nature of the relationship and whether the relationship can be used for predictive purposes are problems often examined by statisticians.

During the course of a business negotiation, both negotiators may exhibit numerous types of idiosyncratic behavior. If they have jewelry, they might manipulate it. If they smoke cigarettes, they might play with their lighters or packs of cigarettes. Are their mannerisms independent of the importance of the issue they are negotiating? Does the negotiator tend to play with jewelry when he or she has a strong position? Good negotiators will pick up dependencies and use the information to their advantage. However, the concept of association implied by dependence must not be confused with the idea of causation. It may be that one of the events does indeed cause the other, but the fact that they are not independent (dependent) is not evidence of causation.

When two events are not independent, then the occurrence of one influences the occurrence of the other. For example, consider drawing two cards from a standard card deck **without replacement**, which means that the first card is not replaced in the deck before the second card is drawn. When a multistage experiment is performed without replacement, the outcome from the first stage affects the occurrence of the second, and so forth. The events are not independent. Instead, they are said to be dependent. To calculate the probability of dependent events occurring, we still multiply the probabilities, but we must take into account the outcome of the first stage when calculating the probability of the second event occurring.

Example 6.3.9

What is the probability of drawing a king and then a queen from a standard deck if the cards are drawn *without replacement*?

Solution

This situation is essentially the same as drawing two cards at the same time from the deck. Let's think of this experiment as having two stages for ease in calculation. We start by first determining the probability of drawing a king from the deck. Since there are 4 kings in a deck of 52 cards, this probability is

$$P(\text{king}) = \frac{4}{52} = \frac{1}{13}.$$

What is the probability of now drawing a queen? Since we are holding a king in our hand, there are still 4 queens left in the deck, but there are only 51 cards left to choose from in the deck. Therefore, the probability of drawing a queen, given we have already drawn a king and we did not place the king back in the deck before drawing our second card, is calculated as $\frac{4}{51}$.

We can now find the probability of drawing a king and a queen, *without replacement*, by multiplying the two probabilities together.

$$P(\text{king and queen, without replacement}) = P(\text{king}) \cdot P(\text{queen} \mid \text{king})$$

$$= \frac{1}{13} \cdot \frac{4}{51} = \frac{4}{663} \approx 0.0060$$

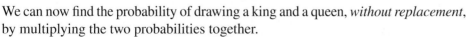

Basketball and Dependence

If we were playing basketball and made a large number of consecutive shots, then there might be a temptation to boast of our skills. Alternatively, someone might suggest that you were on a lucky streak. Two psychologists examined the lucky streak phenomenon by analyzing the sequence of made and missed shots by professional basketball players. The selected players made roughly 50 percent of their shots. Their analysis found that there was no evidence of the *hot hand*– that is, there was no evidence of a dependent relationship between the consecutive shots. They did not find more long streaks of made baskets than would be expected to occur by chance.

Notice that this value is slightly different than the value we obtained in Example 6.3.6 where we drew the cards **with replacement**. There is a slightly higher probability of drawing a king and then a queen, if the king is not placed back into the deck before the second draw. This example helps us to develop a formula for calculating the probability of dependent events.

Probability Law 11: Multiplication Rule for Dependent Events

If two events, A and B, are **dependent**, then

$$P(A \cap B) = P(A) \cdot P(B \mid A) = P(B) \cdot P(A \mid B)$$

DEFINITION

Example 6.3.10

Assume that there are 17 men and 24 women in the Lions Club. Two members are chosen at random each year to serve on the hospitality committee. What is the probability of choosing two members at random and the first being a man and the second being a woman?

Solution

Note that since we are choosing two members, the first choice will influence the probability for the second choice, assuming we do not want to choose the same member twice. This means we are dealing with dependent events. We want to find $P(\text{man and woman})$, which according to the Multiplication Rule for Probability Law 11, equals $P(\text{man}) \cdot P(\text{woman} \mid \text{man})$. When the first member is picked, there are 17 men out of 41 members. When the second member is picked, we assume that we have already picked a man, so that leaves all 24 women, but only 40 remaining members. The calculation is as follows.

$$P(\text{man and woman}) = P(\text{man}) \cdot P(\text{woman} \mid \text{man}) = \frac{17}{41} \cdot \frac{24}{40} \approx 0.2488$$

6.3   Exercises

Basic Concepts

1. Define conditional probability.

2. How do you calculate the conditional probability $P(A \mid B)$?

3. Explain the difference between dependent and independent events.

4. Are mutually exclusive events dependent or independent? Explain your answer.

5. If events A and B are independent, what is $P(A \mid B)$ equal to?

6. What is the product rule?

7. In the case *People v. Collins* an appeals court overturned the conviction. What flaws did the appeals court detect in the case against the accused assailants?

8. What does it mean to sample with replacement?

Exercises

9. The following table was given in Section 6.2 Exercise 14.

Mail Order Customers		
	Gender	
Location	Male	Female
Suburban	196	298
Urban	92	173

a. Given that the customer is a male, what is the probability that he is urban?

b. Given that the customer is urban, what is the probability that he is male?

c. Given that the customer is female, what is the probability that she is suburban?

d. Given that the customer is suburban, what is the probability that the customer is a woman?

10. The following table was given in Section 6.2, Exercise 15.

Life Insurance Coverage					
		Amount of Life Insurance on Husband ($)			
		0–50,000	50,000–100,000	100,000–150,000	More than 150,000
Amount of Life Insurance on Wife ($)	0–50,000	400	200	50	50
	50,000–100,000	50	50	30	30
	100,000–150,000	20	10	25	25
	More than 150,000	20	10	15	15

a. Given the wife has between $100,000 and $150,000 of insurance, what is the probability that the husband has more than $150,000 of insurance?

b. Given the wife has between $0 and $50,000 of insurance, what is the probability that the husband has between $0 and $150,000 of insurance?

c. Given that the husband has between $0 and $50,000 of insurance, what is the probability that the wife will have more than $150,000 of insurance?

d. Given that the husband has more than $150,000 of insurance, what is the probability that the wife will have more than $150,000 of insurance?

11. A computer software company receives hundreds of support calls each day. There are several common installation problems, call them A, B, C, and D. Several of these problems result in the same symptom, *lock up* after initiation. Suppose that the probability of a caller reporting the symptom *lock up* is 0.7 and the probability of a caller having problem A and a *lock up* is 0.6.

a. Given that the caller reports a lock up, what is the probability that the cause is problem A?

b. What is the probability that the cause of the malfunction is not problem A given that the caller is experiencing a lock up?

12. A television advertising representative has determined the following probabilities based on past experience. The probability that an individual will watch an ad during the Super Bowl is 0.10. Given that the individual watches the ad, the probability that the individual will buy the product is 0.005. It is also known that the probability that an individual would buy the product is 0.02. Given that an individual buys the product, find the probability that the individual watched the television ad during the Super Bowl.

13. Medical researchers have determined that there is a 2% chance that an individual will have a gene which gives him a predisposition for heart disease. Given that an individual has the gene, the probability that heart disease will develop is 25%. It is also known that the probability that an individual has heart disease is 12%.

    a. Find the probability that an individual will have the gene and develop heart disease.

    b. Given that a person has heart disease, what is the probability that they have the gene?

14. Use the table given in Exercise 9.

    Are the events {customer is urban} and {customer is suburban} independent? Explain.

15. Use the table given in Exercise 10.

    Are the events {the husband has more than $150,000 in insurance} and {the wife has more than $50,000 in insurance} independent? Explain.

16. Suppose you were flipping a coin. What is the probability that you would observe a head:

    a. on two consecutive flips?

    b. on three consecutive flips?

    c. on four consecutive flips?

    d. on 100 consecutive flips?

17. Suppose an atomic reactor has two independent cooling systems. The probability that Cooling System A will fail is 0.01 and the probability that Cooling System B will fail is 0.01. What is the probability that both systems will fail simultaneously?

18. Mandy is 30, and the probability that she will survive until age 65 is 0.90. Ashley is 45, and the probability that she will survive until age 65 is 0.95.

    a. Find the probability that both Mandy and Ashley will survive until age 65.

    b. Find the probability that only Mandy will survive until age 65.

    c. Find the probability that neither Mandy nor Ashley will survive until age 65.

    d. What assumption about the lives of Mandy and Ashley did you make in answering the above questions?

19. An insurance company is considering insuring two large oil tankers against spills. The limit of the liability on the coverage is $10,000,000. The company believes that the probability of an oil spill requiring the maximum liability coverage during the policy period is 0.001 per tanker.

    a. What is the probability that neither tanker would have a spill requiring the maximum liability coverage during the policy period?

    b. What is the probability that only one tanker would have a spill requiring the maximum liability coverage during the policy period?

    c. What is the probability that both tankers would have spills requiring the maximum liability coverage during the policy period?

20. Coin flipping can be used to model other real life phenomena and aid in certain probability calculations. An example of this would be to compute the probability that the World Series ends in some specified number of games. The World Series is a best of seven game series played at the end of the regular baseball season between the champion of the American League and the champion of the National League. The first team to win four games is declared the champion of baseball for that year. If we assume the probability of either team winning a game is approximately 0.5 and the games are independent events, the probability that the series ends in either 4, 5, 6, or 7 games can be computed.

    a. What is the probability that the series ends in exactly 4 games? Write the sample space consisting of 16 equally likely outcomes similar to the sample space resulting from tossing a coin four times.

    b. What is the probability that the series ends in exactly 5 games?

    c. Assume the probability that the series ends in exactly 6 games is $\frac{5}{16}$. Use this information together with your answers to the first two parts of this problem to compute the probability that the series ends in exactly 7 games.

21. Drug usage in the workplace costs employers incredible amounts of money each year. Drug testing potential employees has become so prevalent that drug users are finding it extremely hard to find jobs. Drug tests, however, are not completely reliable. The most common test used to detect drugs is approximately 98% accurate. To decrease the likelihood of making an error, all potential employees are screened through two tests, which are independent, and each has about 98% accuracy.

    a. If a person were drug-free, what is the probability he or she would fail both tests?

    b. If a person were a drug user, what is the probability he or she would pass both tests?

22. Suppose you draw two cards out of a standard deck without replacement. What is the probability that you draw the ace of spades and then another spade?

23. Dr. Hawkes's statistics class has 42 students, classified by academic year and gender as follows.

Dr. Hawkes Statistics Class		
	Male	**Female**
Freshman	9	13
Sophomore	4	5
Junior	4	2
Senior	2	3

Dr. Hawkes must choose two students at random for a special presentation.

a. What is the probability that a sophomore male and then a freshman female are chosen?

b. What is the probability that two males are chosen?

24. Daniel likes to keep a jar of change on his desk. Currently his jar contains 26 pennies, 19 nickels, 11 dimes, and 16 quarters. What is the probability that Daniel reaches in and randomly grabs a quarter and then a nickel?

6.4 Combinations and Permutations

To compute certain probabilities, such as the probability of having winning numbers in the state lottery, requires the ability to count the number of possible outcomes for a given experiment or a sequence of experiments.

However, often it is impractical to list out all the possibilities. Therefore, we will develop some techniques to facilitate our counting.

The Fundamental Counting Principle

E_1 is an event with n_1 possible outcomes and E_2 is an event with n_2 possible outcomes. The number of ways the events can occur in sequence is $n_1 \cdot n_2$. This principle can be applied for any number of events occurring in sequence.

PROCEDURE

Example 6.4.1

A local office supply store offers ballpoint pens from three different manufacturers. Each manufacturer's pens come in either red, blue, black, or green and either fine or medium tip is available for each color. How many different pens does the store carry?

Solution

$$\underset{\left(\substack{\text{number of} \\ \text{manufacturers}}\right)}{3} \cdot \underset{\text{(color of ink)}}{4} \cdot \underset{\text{(types of tips)}}{2} = \underset{\text{(different pens)}}{24}$$

Example 6.4.2

Most nonpersonalized license plates in the state of Utah consist of three numbers followed by three letters (excluding I, O, and Q). How many license plates are possible?

Solution

There are ten digits (0–9) possible for each of the first three characters. Likewise, there are 23 letters possible for the last three characters. Therefore, we have:

$$10 \quad \cdot \quad 10 \quad \cdot \quad 10 \quad \cdot \quad 23 \quad \cdot \quad 23 \quad \cdot \quad 23 \quad = \quad 12{,}167{,}000$$

(digit) (digit) (digit) (letter) (letter) (letter) (possible license plates)

Example 6.4.3

You have a stack of 5 textbooks: English, History, Statistics, Geology, and Psychology. How many ways can you arrange these textbooks on a shelf?

Solution

Because you can put each book on the bookshelf only once, you have five possible choices for the first book. Similarly, there are four possible choices for the second book, three possible choices for the third book, two possible choices for the fourth book and only one book left for the fifth book. Using the Fundamental Counting Principle, we have

$$5 \cdot 4 \cdot 3 \cdot 2 \cdot 1 = 120 \text{ possible arrangements.}$$

Permutations

The product $5 \cdot 4 \cdot 3 \cdot 2 \cdot 1$ in the previous example is a special type of product called a **factorial**. Factorials occur so frequently that they have their own notation as follows.

Factorial

Suppose n is a positive whole number. Then,

$$n! = n \cdot (n-1) \cdot (n-2) \cdot \ldots \cdot 3 \cdot 2 \cdot 1.$$

FORMULA

$n!$ is read as *n factorial*. Note from the previous example that $n!$ represents the number of ways to arrange n items.

Using this notation, $5! = 5 \cdot 4 \cdot 3 \cdot 2 \cdot 1 = 120$.

☁ Technology

To find the factorial of a number using the TI-83/84 Plus calculator, we enter the number and use the ! option under the PRB (probability) menu. For instructions please visit stat.hawkeslearning.com and navigate to **Technology Instructions > Counting > Factorial**.

We have seen how the Fundamental Counting Principle and factorial notation can help us when counting ordered arrangements. These ordered arrangements are called **permutations**.

Permutation

A **permutation** is a specific order or arrangement of objects in a set. There are $n!$ permutations of n unique objects.

DEFINITION

Note

$0! = 1$ by definition.

Example 6.4.4

To complete your holiday shopping, you need to go to the bakery, department store, grocery store, and toy store. If you are going to visit the stores in sequence, how many different sequences exist?

Solution

This is a permutation problem because the order in which you visit the stores matters. Note that there are 4 stores to visit. By the permutation definition there are $4! = 24$ sequences.

There are times when not all objects in a set will be used for a permutation problem. Consider the following example.

Example 6.4.5

At a local fast food restaurant, the door to the kitchen is secured by a five button lock, labeled 1, 2, 3, 4, 5. To open the door, the correct three digit code must be pushed, but each button can only be pushed once. How many different codes are possible?

Solution

This is a permutation problem of 5 objects, but we are selecting only 3 at a time. There are 5 buttons available for the first character in the code, 4 for the second and 3 for the third. Therefore, there are

$$5 \cdot 4 \cdot 3 = 60 \text{ possible codes.}$$

⌒ **Technology**

To find a permutation using the TI-83/84 Plus calculator, we enter the total number of objects and use the nPr option under the PRB (probability) menu. For instructions please visit stat.hawkeslearning.com and navigate to **Technology Instructions > Counting > Permutation.**

```
7 nPr 3
            210
```

In the previous example, we had a permutation of 5 objects taken 3 at a time. In general,

---

Permutation

The number of permutations of n unique objects in which k are selected at a time and repetition is not allowed is given by

$$_nP_k = \frac{n!}{(n-k)!}$$

Note that some alternate notations for permutations that you may see are P_k^n and $P(n,k)$.

FORMULA

Example 6.4.6

Seven sprinters have advanced to the final heat at a track meet. How many ways can they finish in first, second, and third place?

Solution

Because we have seven sprinters and the order (first, second, third) is important, we need to find the number of permutations of 7 objects selecting 3 at a time.

$$_7P_3 = \frac{7!}{(7-3)!} = \frac{7!}{4!} = \left(\frac{7 \cdot 6 \cdot 5 \cdot 4 \cdot 3 \cdot 2 \cdot 1}{4 \cdot 3 \cdot 2 \cdot 1}\right) = 7 \cdot 6 \cdot 5 = 210$$

There are times when we are interested in finding the number of permutations where some of the objects are duplicates. For instance, consider the word EYE.

If we interchange the two E's, the resulting permutation is not distinguishable from the original. To count the number of distinguishable permutations, we need the following formula.

Distinguishable Permutations

If given n objects, with n_1 alike, n_2 alike, ... , n_k alike, then the number of **distinguishable permutations** of all n objects is $\dfrac{n!}{(n_1!n_2!n_3!...n_k!)}$ **FORMULA**

Example 6.4.7

How many distinguishable permutations can be made from the word *Mississippi*?

Mississippi

Solution

There are 11 letters in the word *Mississippi*, one M, four I's, four S's, and two P's. So there are,

$$\frac{11!}{(1!4!4!2!)} = 34,650$$

distinguishable permutations of the letters in *Mississippi*.

Combinations

We have just looked at counting where order or arrangement mattered. But there are many situations, such as a winning lottery number, where the order is not important. If we want a count where the order is *not* important, then we have a **combination** problem.

Combinations

A **combination** is a collection or grouping of objects where the order is *not* important.   **DEFINITION**

The number of combinations of the n objects selecting k at a time can be found as follows.

Combination

The number of combinations of n unique objects selecting k at a time and repetition is not allowed is given by

$$_nC_k = \frac{n!}{(n-k)!k!}$$

Note that some alternate notations for combinations that you may see are C_k^n and $C(n,k)$.

FORMULA

Example 6.4.8

⚭ Technology

To find a combination using the TI-83/84 Plus calculator, we enter the total number of objects and use the nCr option under the PRB (probability) menu. For instructions please visit stat.hawkeslearning.com and navigate to **Technology Instructions > Counting > Combination.**

In South Carolina's *Palmetto Cash 5* lottery, a player selects five different numbers from 1 to 38 (inclusive). If the numbers selected match the player's numbers in any order, the player wins.

a. What is the total number of winning combinations?

b. What is the probability of winning?

Solution

a. Because we have 38 unique numbers and 5 will be selected at a time, we have:

$$_{38}C_5 = \frac{38!}{(38-5)!5!} = \frac{38!}{33!5!} = \frac{38 \cdot 37 \cdot 36 \cdot 35 \cdot 34 \cdot 33!}{33!5!} = 501{,}942$$

```
38 nCr 5
            501942
1/Ans
    1.992262054E-6
```

b. The probability of winning with any one combination is

$$\frac{1}{501{,}942} \approx 0.000002.$$

It is important to remember that permutations are used when order is important, and combinations are used when order is not important.

Concept		Formula
Fundamental Counting Principle	If one event has n_1 outcomes and another event has n_2 outcomes, the number of ways the events can occur in sequence is the product of n_1 and n_2. (This principle can be applied for any number of events occurring in sequence.)	$n_1 \cdot n_2$
Factorial	$n!$ is the product of each of the positive whole numbers from 1 to n.	$n! = n(n-1)(n-2)\cdots(3)(2)(1)$

Concept		Formula
Combination	A collection or grouping of objects where order is not important.	The number of combinations of n unique objects selecting k at a time and repetition is not allowed is given by the following formula. $$_nC_k = \frac{n!}{(n-k)!\,k!}$$
Permutation	A specific order or arrangement of objects.	The number of arrangements for n objects when order is important is given by n factorial: $n!$.
	The number of permutations of n unique objects selecting k at a time and repetition is not allowed.	$$_nP_k = \frac{n!}{(n-k)!}$$
	Given n objects with n_1 alike, n_2 alike, ..., n_k alike, then the number of distinguishable permutations is given by the formula to the right.	$$\frac{n!}{(n_1!)(n_2!)(n_3!)\cdots(n_k!)}$$

6.4   **Exercises**

Basic Concepts

1. What is the Fundamental Counting Principle?

2. What is a factorial and how is it calculated?

3. Describe the difference between permutations and combinations.

4. Give an example of a situation in which you would need to calculate the number of distinguishable permutations.

Exercises

5. The blue plate lunch at a local cafeteria consists of an entrée, a side item, and a desert. If there are 6 choices for an entrée, 5 choices for a side item, and 4 choices for a dessert, how many different lunches are available?

6. You are interested in buying a home in a new subdivision. The builder offers 3 basic floor plans, each with 4 possible arrangements for the garage, and siding in 6 different colors. How many different homes can be built?

7. Compute each of the following.

    a. 1!

    b. 3!

    c. 5!

    d. 7!

8. Compute each of the following.

   a. 2!

   b. 4!

   c. 6!

   d. 8!

9. A DJ needs to select 6 songs from a CD containing 12 songs to compose an event's musical lineup. How many different lineups are possible?

10. In how many ways can 11 kids be picked for the 9 positions on a baseball team?

11. How many distinguishable permutations can be made from the word STATISTICS?

12. How many distinguishable permutations can be made from the word SASSAFRAS?

13. A person tosses a coin 11 times. In how many ways can he get 9 heads?

14. How many 5 card hands can be dealt from a deck of 52 cards?

15. There are eight people hosting a party. Three people are needed to decorate for the party. How many ways can the decorating crew be chosen?

16. There are eight people hosting a movie party. One person must set up the food, another must rent the movies, and someone else needs to bring the drinks. In how many ways can these tasks be assigned?

17. In how many ways can a graduate student fulfill her degree requirements in statistics if 10 classes are needed from a choice of 15 classes?

18. The Johnson family is planning their vacation. Each of the five family members is allowed to nominate three places they would like to visit. If they want to visit four different places during the trip, in how many ways can they plan their trip, assuming that no family members choose the same place?

19. When painting a canvas at an art studio, James wants to use 3 different colors from the palette of 30 colors. How many different color combinations can he choose from?

20. Kara was born on 11/21/1992. She would like to make an eight-digit password using all of the digits in her birth date. How many different eight-digit passwords could she create?

21. Employees at a local software company need a unique seven-digit code to access the building. The manager wants to make each person's code from the company's phone number, 555-8212.

   a. If there are 509 employees who need codes, will the manager have enough unique codes using only the digits in the phone number?

   b. Would there be enough ten-digit codes if he used the area code, 516, as well?

22. Which of the following words would produce the greatest number of different five-letter arrangements? (**Hint:** Think before you calculate!)

    a. TEARS

    b. STOPS

    c. TESTS

    d. ROOST

23. The engineering club at a local high school must choose 2 representatives from each of the sophomore, junior, and senior classes to attend a national convention. If there are 6 sophomores, 5 juniors, and 7 seniors in the club, in how many ways can the group be chosen for the convention?

24. A local pizza parlor makes calzones with up to five different filling ingredients: cheese, ham, pepperoni, onions, and mushrooms. In how many different ways can the calzone be made?

6.5   **Bayes' Theorem**

We discussed conditional probability and independence in Section 6.3. **Bayes' Theorem** (also referred to as **Bayes' Rule** or **Bayes' Law**) is a clever way of obtaining a conditional probability given new information. The additional information is obtained for a subsequent event and is used to revise the initial probability. We begin with an example.

Example 6.5.1

Suppose that 85% of all passengers in an airport fly on a major airline, while the remaining 15% fly on a small airline. Of those passengers traveling on a major airline, suppose we know that 65% are traveling for business. Of those passengers traveling on a small airline, 25% are traveling for business. (Notice that even though we only talk about business passengers, there are also implied non-business passengers as well.) Now a business passenger is selected at random. What is the probability that the business passenger traveled on a major airline?

Solution

Let's first define the events associated with this problem.

$$M = \text{Major Airline}$$
$$S = \text{Small Airline}$$
$$B = \text{Business Passenger}$$

Here are the probabilities given to us in the problem.

$$P(M) = 0.85$$
$$P(S) = 0.15$$
$$P(B \mid M) = 0.65$$
$$P(B \mid S) = 0.25$$

To determine the probability that the selected business passenger traveled on a major airline, we need to find the probability $P(M \mid B)$. Using the four probabilities above and Bayes' Theorem, we proceed as follows.

$$P(M \mid B) \;=\; \frac{P(M \cap B)}{P(B)}$$

By the definition of a conditional probability.

$$=\; \frac{P(M \cap B)}{P(B \cap M) + P(B \cap S)}$$

The denominator says that all business passengers travel either on a major airline or on a small airline; those are the only two alternatives and they are mutually exclusive. Thus, $P(B)$ is equivalent to the denominator.

$$=\; \frac{P(M) \cdot P(B \mid M)}{P(M) \cdot P(B \mid M) + P(S) \cdot P(B \mid S)}$$

The numerator and denominator result from rearranging the conditional probability formula and solving for the probability of the intersection of two events. Note that $P(M \cap B)$ is equal to both $P(M) \cdot P(B \mid M)$ and $P(B) \cdot P(M \mid B)$ by the definition of conditional probability.

$$=\; \frac{0.85 \cdot 0.65}{0.85 \cdot 0.65 + 0.15 \cdot 0.25}$$

Substitute the probability values given in the problem.

$$=\; \frac{0.5525}{0.59} = 0.936 \approx 94\%$$

Therefore, we know that if the passenger was traveling for business, there is about a 94% chance that he or she will be traveling on a major airline.

Notice how the conditional probability of 94% is not intuitive. It is called the **posterior probability**. The **prior probability** of a passenger traveling on a major airline of 85% has been increased to 94%, given the information that the passenger was traveling for business purposes.

The following is a formal statement of Bayes' Theorem.

Bayes' Theorem

Let A be an event and B_1, B_2, ..., B_N be N mutually exclusive and collectively exhaustive events. Then Bayes' Theorem states,

$$
\begin{aligned}
P(B_i \mid A) &= \frac{P(B_i \cap A)}{P(A)} \\[2mm]
&= \frac{P(B_i \cap A)}{P(A \cap B_1) + P(A \cap B_2) + \cdots + P(A \cap B_N)} \\[2mm]
&= \frac{P(B_i) \cdot P(A \mid B_i)}{P(B_1) \cdot P(A \mid B_1) + P(B_2) \cdot P(A \mid B_2) + \cdots + P(B_N) \cdot P(A \mid B_N)} \\[2mm]
&= \frac{P(B_i) \cdot P(A \mid B_i)}{\sum_{i=1}^{N} P(B_i) \cdot P(A \mid B_i)}
\end{aligned}
$$

THEOREM

Let's look at another example using Bayes' Theorem.

Example 6.5.2

Let D be the event that a person has a rare disease. Suppose that the rare disease has an incidence rate of 1% in the population, $P(D) = 0.01$. $\overline{D}$ is the event that a person does not have the rare disease (i.e., the complement of D). Suppose a machine is used to diagnose the disease. Let C be the event that the disease is confirmed as the diagnosis. Suppose that the probability of the machine falsely confirming the disease when one doesn't have it is $P(C \mid \overline{D}) = 0.15$, called a *false positive*; while $P(C \mid D) = 0.95$, which says that the machine correctly confirms the disease with an accuracy of 95%. Now, suppose that the machine confirms that a person has the disease. What is the probability that the person actually has the disease? In other words, what is $P(D \mid C)$?

Solution

Here are the probabilities given to us in the problem.

$$
\begin{aligned}
P(D) &= 0.01 \\
P(\overline{D}) &= 0.99 \\
P(C \mid D) &= 0.95 \\
P(C \mid \overline{D}) &= 0.15
\end{aligned}
$$

To find the probability that a person with a positive diagnostic result actually has the disease we proceed as follows.

$$P(D|C) = \frac{P(D \cap C)}{P(C)}$$

$$= \frac{P(D \cap C)}{P(C \cap D) + P(C \cap \overline{D})}$$

$$= \frac{P(D) \cdot P(C|D)}{P(D) \cdot P(C|D) + P(\overline{D}) \cdot P(C|\overline{D})}$$

$$= \frac{0.01 \cdot 0.95}{0.01 \cdot 0.95 + 0.99 \cdot 0.15}$$

$$= \frac{0.0095}{0.0095 + 0.1485} = \frac{0.0095}{0.1580} \approx 0.06$$

This is somewhat of an assuring result in that you have only a 6% chance of having the disease even though the machine yielded a positive diagnostic.

6.5 Exercises

Basic Concepts

1. Briefly explain the relationship between conditional probability and Bayes' Theorem.

2. What is the difference between prior and posterior probabilities?

3. What is Bayes' Theorem?

4. How is Bayes' Theorem used to "revise" a probability based on additional information?

Excercises

5. In a production line, 8% of all items produced are defective. 75% of all defective items are fully inspected, while 10% of all non-defective items go through a complete inspection. Given that an item is completely inspected, what is the probability that it is defective?

6. The issue of Corporate Tax Reform has been cause for much debate in the United States, especially in the House Ways and Means Committee as well as the Senate Finance Committee. Among those in the legislature, 45% are Republicans and 55% are Democrats. It is reported that 30% of the Republicans and 70% of the Democrats favor some type of Corporate Tax Reform to prevent American companies from operating in foreign countries. Suppose a member

of Congress is randomly selected and they are found to favor some type of corporate tax reform. What is the probability that this person is a Democrat?

7. Males and females are observed to react differently to sad, emotional movies. It has been observed that 70% of the females say they cry at some point during those types of movies, whereas only 40% of the males admit to crying during those types of movies. A group of 40 people, of whom 25 are female, was shown a sad, emotional movie and the subjects were asked if they cried. A response picked at random from the 40 indicated that they cried. What is the probability that it was a male?

8. As items come to the end of a production line, an inspector chooses which items are to go through a complete inspection. Eight percent of all items produced are defective. Sixty percent of all defective items go through a complete inspection, and 20% of all good items go through a complete inspection. Given that an item is completely inspected, what is the probability that it is defective?

9. Two teaching methods for a business statistics class, online and face-to-face, are available during the course of an academic year. The failure rate (students that receive below a C− and thus, will have to repeat the course) is 4% for the online class and 8% for the face-to-face class. However, the online class is more expensive and hence is offered only 25% of the time. (The face-to-face class is offered the other 75% of the time.) A student takes the statistics class via one of the methods of delivery but failed the course. What is the probability that the student took the online class?

10. A personnel director has two lists of applicants for jobs. List 1 contains names of 15 women and 5 men whereas List 2 contains the names of 5 women and 12 men. A name is randomly selected from List 1 and added to List 2. A name is then randomly selected from the augmented List 2. Given that the name selected is that of a man, what is the probability that a woman's name was originally selected from List 1?

CR   **Chapter Review**

Key Terms and Ideas

- Probability
- Randomness
- Random Experiment
- Sample Space
- Compound Event
- Union
- Intersection

- Complement
- Dependent Events
- Sampling with Replacement
- Sampling without Replacement
- Multiplication Rule for Independent Events or Product Rule
- Outcome

- Event
- Subjective Probability
- Objective Probability
- Odds in Favor of
- Odds Against
- Mutual Exclusivity
- Union of Mutually Exclusive Events
- Multiplication Rule for Dependent Events
- Fundamental Counting Principle
- Factorial
- Law of Large Numbers

- Relative Frequency
- Statistical Regularity
- Classical Probability
- Statistical Inference
- Intersection of Mutually Exclusive Events
- The Addition Rule
- Conditional Probability
- Independent Events
- Combination
- Permutation
- Distinguishable Permutation
- Bayes' Theorem
- Probability Laws 1-11

Key Formulas	
	Section
Relative Frequency	**6.1**
If an experiment is performed n times and event A happens k times, then $$\text{Relative Frequency of } A = \frac{k}{n}.$$	
Classical Probability	**6.1**
$$P(A) = \frac{\text{number of outcomes in } A}{\text{total number of outcomes in the sample space}}$$	
Probability Law 3	**6.2**
$$0 \le P(A) \le 1$$	
Probability Law 4	**6.2**
$$P(A_1) + P(A_2) + \cdots + P(A_n) = 1$$	
Probability Law 5	**6.2**
$$P(A^c) = 1 - P(A)$$	

Key Formulas	
	Section

Odds   6.2

The odds in favor of an event A occurring is given by

$$\frac{P(A)}{P(\text{not } A)} = \frac{P(A)}{P(A^c)}.$$

The odds against an event A occurring is given by

$$\frac{P(\text{not } A)}{P(A)} = \frac{P(A^c)}{P(A)}.$$

Union of Mutually Exclusive Events   6.2

$$P(A \cup B) = P(A) + P(B)$$

Intersection of Mutually Exclusive Events   6.2

$$P(A \cap B) = 0$$

The Addition Rule   6.2

$$P(A \cup B) = P(A) + P(B) - P(A \cap B)$$

Independent Events   6.3

Two events are independent if and only if

$$P(A|B) = P(A) \text{ and } P(B|A) = P(B).$$

Conditional Probability   6.3

$$P(A|B) = \frac{P(A \cap B)}{P(B)}$$

Multiplication Rule for Independent Events   6.3

If two events, A and B, are independent, then

$$P(A \cap B) = P(A) \cdot P(B).$$

If n events, $A_1, A_2, ..., A_n$, are independent, then

$$P(A_1 \cap A_2 \cap ... \cap A_n) = P(A_1) \cdot P(A_2) \cdot ... \cdot P(A_n).$$

Multiplication Rule for Dependent Events   6.3

If two events, A and B, are dependent, then

$$P(A \cap B) = P(A) \cdot P(B \mid A) = P(B) \cdot P(A \mid B)$$

Key Formulas	
	Section
The Fundamental Counting Principle If E_1 is an event with n_1 possible outcomes and E_2 is an event with n_2 possible outcomes, the number of ways the events can occur in sequence is $n_1 \cdot n_2$.	6.4
n Factorial $$n! = n \cdot (n-1) \cdot (n-2) \cdot \ldots \cdot 3 \cdot 2 \cdot 1$$	6.4
Permutation $$_nP_k = \frac{n!}{(n-k)!}$$	6.4
Combination $$_nC_k = \frac{n!}{(n-k)!\,k!}$$	6.4
Number of Distinguishable Permutations $$\frac{n!}{(n_1!)(n_2!)(n_3!)\cdots(n_k!)}$$	6.4
Bayes' Theorem $$P(B_i|A) = \frac{P(A|B_i)P(B_i)}{P(A|B_1)P(B_1) + P(A|B_2)P(B_2) + \cdots + P(A|B_k)P(B_k)}$$ where B_i is the ith event out of k mutually exclusive and collectively exhaustive events.	6.5

Additional Exercises

1. A couple plans to have three children.

    a. List all possible outcomes for the sexes of the three children.

    b. Find the probability that the couple will have three girls.

    c. Find the probability that the couple will have at least one boy.

2. 671 registered voters were surveyed and asked their political affiliation and whether or not they favor a national healthcare policy. The results of the survey are displayed in the table below.

Survey Results			
Position on National Healthcare	**Democrat**	**Independent**	**Republican**
Favor	161	40	130
Do Not Favor	110	40	190

If one of the surveyed voters is randomly selected, answer the following questions.

a. What is the probability that the voter will be a Republican?

b. What is the probability that the voter will not favor a national healthcare policy?

c. What is the probability that the voter will be a Democrat or an Independent?

d. What is the probability that the voter will be a Democrat and favor a national healthcare policy?

e. Given that the voter is a Republican, what is the probability that the voter will favor a national healthcare policy?

f. If the voter does not favor a national healthcare policy, what is the probability that the voter is an Independent?

g. Are the events {voter is a Democrat} and {voter favors national healthcare policy} independent? Explain.

3. A roulette wheel has 38 outcomes labeled 1 through 36 plus 0 and 00. The wheels are supposed to be designed so that each outcome is equally likely. The numbers 0 and 00 are often referred to as house numbers because the only way that a player can win when these outcomes are observed is by directly betting on the numbers. A great deal of the money wagered on a roulette wheel is wagered on odd or even numbers, or columns or rows of numbers. The numbers 0 and 00 are not in any row or column, nor are they odd or even.

a. What is the probability of observing an even number (0 and 00 are neither odd nor even)?

b. What is the probability of observing a number between 1 and 12, inclusive?

c. What is the probability of observing 0 or 00?

d. What is the probability of observing a 4?

e. What is the probability of not observing 7, 13, or 21?

4. A survey of customers in a particular retail store showed that 10% were dissatisfied with the customer service. Half of the customers who were dissatisfied dealt with Bill, the senior customer service representative. If Bill responds to 40% of all customer service inquiries in the retail store, find the following probabilities.

a. The probability that a customer will be unhappy, given that the representative was Bill.

b. The probability that the service representative was not Bill, given that the customer complained.

5. A package of documents needs to be sent to a given destination, and it is important that it arrive within one day. To maximize the chances of on-time delivery, three copies of the documents are sent via three different delivery services. Service A is known to have a 90% on-time delivery record, Service B has an 88% on-time delivery record, and Service C has a 91% on-time delivery record. Assuming that the delivery services and their records are independent, what is the probability that at least one copy of the documents will arrive at its destination on time?

6. A boxcar contains six complex electronic systems. Two of the six are to be randomly selected for thorough testing and then classified as defective or not defective. If two of the six systems are actually defective:

   a. find the probability that at least one of the two systems tested will be defective.

   b. find the probability that both are defective.

7. Odds in favor of and odds against are often used to express chances of occurrences. For example, if the odds are 5 to 2 that it will rain tomorrow then we would be wise to carry an umbrella with us.

   a. What are the odds of rolling a six when a single die is thrown?

   b. What are the odds against getting a head when a coin is tossed?

   c. What are the odds against getting 3 consecutive heads when a coin is tossed 3 times?

   d. Suppose the odds in favor of your favorite athletic team winning this weekend are 8 to 3. What is the probability that they will win?

8. Consider a well-shuffled deck of cards with 13 hearts, 13 spades, 13 clubs, and 13 diamonds.

   a. Find the probability that the first card dealt is a heart.

   b. Find the probability that the first card dealt is a spade.

   c. Find the probability that the first card dealt is not a spade.

   d. If you know that the first card dealt will not be a spade, find the probability that it will be a heart.

   e. Suppose you saw the bottom card, and it was the queen of hearts. What is the probability that the first card dealt will be a heart?

9. A box contains eighteen large marbles and ten small marbles. Each marble is either green or white. Twelve of the large marbles are green and four of the small marbles are white. If a marble is randomly selected from the box, what is the probability that it is white or large?

10. User passwords for a certain computer network consist of four letters followed by two numbers. How many different passwords are possible?

11. Hydraulic assemblies for landing coming from an aircraft rework facility are each inspected for defects. Historical records indicate that 8% have defects in shafts only, 6% have defects in bushings only, and 2% have defects in both shafts and bushings. One of the hydraulic assemblies is selected randomly. What is the probability that:

   a.   the assembly has a bushing defect?

   b.   the assembly has a shaft or bushing defect?

   c.   the assembly has exactly one of the two types of defects?

   d.   the assembly has neither type of defect?

12.   Robin is assigned the task of setting the passwords for every computer at her office. Depending on the computer, the guidelines differ as to how the password can be set. How many different four-digit passwords using the digits 0–9 can she create under each of the following guidelines?

   a.   The passwords must be odd and greater than 3000.

   b.   The passwords must be even and greater than 4000.

   c.   The passwords must be even and less than 5000.

13.   Suppose that there are eight employees at the farmer's market in downtown Charleston, SC. One employee is needed to serve as a cashier, one is needed to wash produce, and one is needed to restock. In how many ways can these tasks be assigned?

14.   Maggie has ten pieces of jewelry in her jewelry case, and she wants to take four pieces with her on a business trip. In how many ways can she select the jewelry for her trip?

15.   A machine at the local department store is filled with children's toys. The machine is filled with 28 dinosaurs, 35 balls, 18 rubber snakes, and 41 small stuffed animals. Suppose your four children want to each get a toy from the machine, and they want 2 dinosaurs and 2 small stuffed animals. Find the probability that you get what you want on the first 4 tries. (This requires some thought. Don't undercount!)

"It is a truth, very certain, that when it is not in our power to determine what is true we ought to follow what is most probable."
— Rene Descartes (1596 -1650)

7 CHAPTER
Discrete Probability Distributions

Introduction

The notions of randomness and uncertainty were introduced in Chapter 6. This chapter extends those ideas by developing concepts to describe a pattern of randomness for an entire set of outcomes produced by some random phenomenon. In the coin tossing experiment the description was rather easy. The totality of outcomes contained only two values, *heads* or *tails*. Probabilities for these events were constructed by assuming a fair coin and by applying the classical definition of probability.

Example 7.1

Probability distribution for the outcome of a coin toss.

Tossing a Coin	
Outcome	**Probability**
Heads	0.5
Tails	0.5

To analyze more complex random phenomena requires a method of organizing information about random processes and a vocabulary to describe the organizational concepts. Two such descriptive notions will be introduced in this chapter: random variables and probability distributions.

Random variables considered in this chapter will be quantitative. Outcomes will have numerical values. Specifically, a probability distribution connects a probability to each value the random variable can assume.

Random Variable

A **random variable** is a numerical outcome of a random process.

DEFINITION

Probability Distribution

A **probability distribution** is a model which describes a specific kind of random process.

DEFINITION

Probability distributions are the best descriptors of random processes. For "real world" random processes they are often difficult to obtain.

7.1   Types of Random Variables

Quantitative random variables are classified as discrete or continuous classes. This categorization refers to the types of values that outcomes of the random variable can assume. Discrete random variables are analyzed in this chapter, and the next chapter discusses the continuous variety.

In defining random variables, there is a naming convention. Capital letters, such as X, will be used to refer to the random variable, while small letters, such as x, will refer to specific values of the random variable. Often the specific values will be subscripted: $x_1, x_2, ..., x_n$.

Discrete Random Variables

With a discrete random variable, you can count the number of outcomes that a random variable might possess.

Discrete Random Variable

A **discrete random variable** is a random variable which has a countable number of possible outcomes.

When describing a discrete random variable, you should do the following.

1.   State the variable.

2.   List all of the possible values of the variable.

3.   Determine the probabilities of these values.

DEFINITION

In fact, the values that many discrete random variables assume are the counting numbers from 0 to N, where N depends upon the nature of the variable.

Example 7.1.1

Random Phenomenon: Toss a die and observe the outcome of the toss.

1.   *Identify the random variable*: $X =$ the outcome of the toss of a die.

2.   *Range of values*: Integers between 1 and 6, inclusive.

In this instance, $x_1 = 1, x_2 = 2, ..., x_6 = 6$. Although the value of the random variable is the same as the subscript in this case, there is usually no relationship between the two.

3.   *Probability distribution*: The outcomes of the toss of a die and their probabilities are given below. The probabilities are deduced using the classical method and the assumption of a fair die.

Tossing a Die						
Value of X	1	2	3	4	5	6
Probability	$\frac{1}{6}$	$\frac{1}{6}$	$\frac{1}{6}$	$\frac{1}{6}$	$\frac{1}{6}$	$\frac{1}{6}$

Not all discrete random variables have probability distributions that are easy to determine. In examples 7.1.2 and 7.1.3, neither random variable has an easily determined probability distribution.

Example 7.1.2

Random Phenomenon: The number of defective integrated circuits received in a batch of 1000. Each outcome of the random variable is a numerical measure whose range of values is given below.

1. *Identify the random variable*: $X =$ the number of defective integrated circuits in a batch of 1000.

2. *Range of values*: Integers between 0 and 1000, inclusive, where $N = 1000$. If symbols were chosen to represent the values they could be given as $x_1 = 0$, $x_2 = 1$, ..., $x_{N+1} = 1000$.

3. *Probability distribution*: Unknown.

Example 7.1.3

Random Phenomenon: The head nurse of the pediatric division of the Sisters of Mercy Hospital is trying to determine the capacity requirement for the nursery. She realizes that the number of babies born at the hospital each day is a random variable. She will have to develop a description of the randomness in order to develop her plan.

1. *Identify the random variable*: $X =$ the number of babies born at Sisters of Mercy Hospital each day.

2. *Range of values*: Integers from 0 to some large positive number.

3. *Probability distribution*: Unknown, but could be estimated using the relative frequency idea from Section 6.1 in conjunction with historical data on hospital births at Sisters of Mercy.

Continuous Random Variables

Heights, weights, volumes, and time measurements, for example, are usually measured on a continuous scale. These measurements can take on any value in some interval.

Continuous Random Variable

A **continuous random variable** is a random variable that can assume any value on a continuous segment(s) of the real number line.

DEFINITION

Example 7.1.4

Random Phenomenon: A local restaurant has an express policy that states that lunch will be served within 15 minutes of ordering, or it will be free. Obviously, the restaurant is keenly interested in not giving away its product and in delivering on its

Note

For continuous random variables, we specify probabilities with probability density functions.

promise of a timely lunch. But the length of time to prepare each meal varies because of the difference in preparation times of each dish, the load on the kitchen, and the experience of the chefs and waitresses. Since time is measured on a continuous scale and the variability of meal preparation is not predictable, the time between ordering and receiving a meal is considered to be a continuous random variable.

1. *Identify the random variable*: X = the time between ordering a meal and receiving it.

2. *Range of values*: From 0 to ∞ (infinity). Note that X is measured on a continuous scale.

3. *Probability density*: Unknown, but could be approximated using historical data.

7.1 Exercises

Basic Concepts

1. What is a random variable?

2. What is a probability distribution?

3. Do all random variables have probability distributions?

4. What are the two types of random variables discussed in this section? What distinguishes the two types?

Exercises

5. Classify the following as either a discrete random variable or a continuous random variable.

   a. The number of pages in a standard math textbook.

   b. The amount of electricity used daily in a home.

   c. The number of customers entering a restaurant in one day.

   d. The time spent daily on the phone after supper by a teenager.

   e. Campers at a state park over Labor Day weekend.

6. Classify the following as either a discrete random variable or a continuous random variable.

   a. The speed of a train.

   b. The possible scores on the SAT exam.

   c. The number of pizzas eaten on a college campus each day.

   d. The daily takeoffs at Chicago's O'Hare Airport.

   e. The highest temperatures in Maine and Florida tomorrow.

7. Classify the following as either a discrete random variable or a continuous random variable.

    a.   The number of emergency phone calls received per day by a local fire department.

    b.   The speed of pitches of major league baseball pitchers.

    c.   The weight of a lobster caught in Maine.

    d.   The number of defective circuits on a computer chip.

    e.   The time it takes for a 5-year battery to die.

8. Classify the following as either a discrete random variable or a continuous random variable.

    a.   The total points scored per football game for a local high school team.

    b.   The daily price of a stock.

    c.   The interest rate charged by local banks for 30-year mortgages.

    d.   The number of times a backup of the computer network is performed in a month.

    e.   The amount of sugar imported by the U.S. in a day.

7.2   Discrete Random Variables

So far, the random variable concept is so general that it is not very useful by itself. What would make it useful is to determine what numerical values the random variable could assume and to assess the probabilities of each of these values. That information defines a probability distribution for a discrete random variable.

Discrete Probability Distribution

A **discrete probability distribution** consists of all possible values of the discrete random variable along with their associated probabilities.

Discrete probability distributions always have two characteristics.

   1. The sum of all of the probabilities must equal 1.

   2. The probability of any value must be between 0 and 1, inclusively.

DEFINITION

The association of the possible values with their respective probabilities can be expressed in three different forms: in a table, in a graph, and in an equation.

Example 7.2.1

Consider the random phenomenon of tossing a coin three times and counting the number of heads. What is the probability distribution for the number of heads observed in three tosses of a coin?

Fat the Butch

John Scarne, in his book *Scarne's Complete Guide to Gambling*, tells a story about a New York City gambler named Fat the Butch. It seems Fat the Butch lost $49,000 in virtually the same game that led Chevalier de Mere to his famous consultation with Pascal and Fermat. In this particular game another well-known gambler offered Fat the chance to bet $1000 that he would not roll one double six in 21 tosses of the dice. After 12 hours of dice rolling, Fat lost $49,000 and decided to quit. Later, Scarne discussed the fact that Fat needed 24.6 rolls to break even and that he had a significant expected loss on each play. According to Scarne, Fat shrugged his shoulders and said, "Scarne, in gambling you got to pay to learn, but $49,000 was a lot of dough to pay just to learn that."

Solution

The random variable is $X =$ the number of heads in three tosses of a coin.

Tossing a Coin		
Number of Heads, x	**$P(X = x)$**	**Simple Events**
0	$\frac{1}{8}$	TTT
1	$\frac{3}{8}$	HTT, THT, TTH
2	$\frac{3}{8}$	HHT, HTH, THH
3	$\frac{1}{8}$	HHH
Total	$\sum P(X = x_i) = 1.0$	

The probabilities given above can be deduced using the classical approach to probability and are given in the table above.

Example 7.2.2

K. J. Johnson is a computer salesperson. During the last year he has kept records of his computer sales for the last 200 days.

Frequency Distribution					
Sales	0	1	2	3	4
Frequency	40	20	60	40	40

He recognizes that his daily sales constitute a random process and he wishes to determine the probability distribution for daily sales. From the probability distribution he would like to determine the following.

a. The probability that he will sell at least 2 computers each day.
b. The probability he will sell at most 2 computers each day.

Solution

The random variable is $X =$ the number of computers sold each day.

The probabilities for this random variable are computed in the following table based upon 200 days of sales data obtained from Mr. Johnson's records using the relative frequency concept.

Probability Distribution						
Computer Sales, x	0	1	2	3	4	**Total**
Probability, $P(X = x)$	$\frac{40}{200} = 0.2$	$\frac{20}{200} = 0.1$	$\frac{60}{200} = 0.3$	$\frac{40}{200} = 0.2$	$\frac{40}{200} = 0.2$	$\sum P(X = x_i) = 1.0$

a. The probability that Mr. Johnson will sell at least 2 computers each day is calculated as follows.

$$P(X \geq 2) = P(X = 2) + P(X = 3) + P(X = 4) = 0.3 + 0.2 + 0.2 = 0.7$$

b. The probability that Mr. Johnson will sell at most 2 computers each day is calculated in the following way.

$$P(X \leq 2) = P(X = 0) + P(X = 1) + P(X = 2) = 0.2 + 0.1 + 0.3 = 0.6$$

Example 7.2.3

An investor has decided that she will purchase a stock if there is at least a 50% chance that the price of the stock will be more than $32 in thirty days. Assuming the price of the stock 30 days from now is described in the table below, should the investor purchase the stock?

Stock Prices								
x	30.0	30.5	31.0	31.5	32.0	32.5	33.0	
P(X = x)	0.05	0.10	0.20	0.25	0.20	0.15	0.05	$\sum P(X = x_i) = 1.0$

Solution

The random variable is: $X =$ the price of a stock 30 days hence.

Based on the probability distribution, the probability that the stock price will be more than $32 in thirty days is calculated as follows.

$$P(X > 32) = P(X = 32.5) + P(X = 33.0) = 0.15 + 0.05 = 0.20$$

Since the probability that the price of the stock will be more than $32 in thirty days is only 20%, the investor should not purchase the stock.

Where Do Probability Distributions Come From?

In the examples given above, the probability distributions are given. But in the *real world* there are very few instances in which the probability distribution is conveniently available. Substantial effort is usually required to obtain the probability distribution. Probabilities are determined using the same techniques described in Chapter 6: classical, relative frequency, or subjective.

Sometimes, however, you get lucky. The random variable you wish to analyze either conforms to or can be approximated by an experiment that has a known probability distribution. Four well-known discrete probability distributions will be discussed later in this chapter: uniform, binomial, Poisson, and hypergeometric.

Each of the discrete distributions possesses a **probability distribution function**. These functions assign probabilities to each value of the random variable.

Example 7.2.4

The following function is a discrete probability distribution function.

$$P(X=x) = \begin{cases} \dfrac{x^2}{30}, & \text{if } x = 1,2,3,4 \\ \\ 0 & \text{elsewhere} \end{cases}$$

Summarize the probability distribution for this function.

Solution

To determine the probability for a value, use the value as the argument to the function. For example, to determine the probability that $X = 3$, calculate

$$P(X = 3) = \frac{3^2}{30} = \frac{9}{30}.$$

The probability that $X = 4$ can be calculated similarly.

$$P(X = 4) = \frac{4^2}{30} = \frac{16}{30}$$

The resulting probability distribution is summarized in the table below.

Probability Distribution	
x	**P(X = x)**
1	$\dfrac{1}{30}$
2	$\dfrac{4}{30}$
3	$\dfrac{9}{30}$
4	$\dfrac{16}{30}$
Total	$\sum P(X = x_i) = \dfrac{30}{30} = 1$

Note that the distribution possesses the essential properties of all probability distributions; that is, the probabilities sum to one, and all the probabilities are between 0 and 1.

Expected Value

The notion of expected value is one of the most important concepts in the analysis of random phenomena. Expected value is important because it is a summary statistic for a probability distribution that can be used as a criterion for comparing alternative decisions in the presence of uncertainty. Conceptually, expected value is closely allied with the notion of mean or average.

The expected value of a random variable should be very close to the mean value of a large number of observations from the random process, and the larger the number of observations collected the more likely the mean of the observations will be close to the expected value. It should not be interpreted as the value of the random variable we *expect* to see. In fact, for discrete random variables the expected value is rarely one of the possible outcomes of the random variable.

Expected Value

The **expected value** of the random variable X is the mean of the random variable X. It is denoted $E(X)$ and is given by computing the following expression

$$\mu = E(X) = \sum \left[x \cdot p(x) \right]$$

where $p(x) = P(X = x)$.

DEFINITION

Essentially the expected value is a weighted average, in which each possible value of the random variable is weighted by its probability.

Table 7.2.1 - Calculating K.J. Johnson's Expected Number of Sales per Day		
x	**p(x)**	**x·p(x)**
0	0.2	0
1	0.1	0.1
2	0.3	0.6
3	0.2	0.6
4	0.2	0.8
Total		$E(X) = 2.1$

$$E(X) = \sum \left[x \cdot p(x) \right] = 0(0.2) + 1(0.1) + 2(0.3) + 3(0.2) + 4(0.2) = 2.1$$

The expected value of the probability distribution given in Example 7.2.2 is computed in Table 7.2.1. In the long run, the expected number of sales per day from this distribution should average about 2.1.

Using Expected Values to Compare Alternatives

Plato believed that happiness was the result of rational behavior. He would appreciate expected value analysis, since it is a rational method of comparing alternatives that involve uncertainty.

Example 7.2.5

Suppose you are confronted with two investment alternatives that possess uncertain outcomes described by the probability distributions given in the table below. Which option should you choose?

∽ Technology

Notice that an expected value is just a weighted mean where the weights sum to 1. For instructions on calculating a weighted mean using a TI-83/84 Plus calculator, or other technologies, please visit stat.hawkeslearning.com and navigate to **Technology Instructions > Descriptive Statistics > Two Variable**.

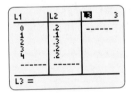

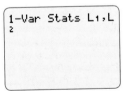

Solution

Investment Alternatives			
Option A		**Option B**	
Profit (Dollars)	Probability	Profit (Dollars)	Probability
−2000	0.2	−3000	0.2
0	0.1	−1000	0.1
1000	0.3	2000	0.2
2000	0.3	3000	0.3
4000	0.1	4000	0.2

$$E(X_A) = \sum \left[x_A \cdot p(x_A) \right]$$
$$= (-2000)0.2 + (0)0.1$$
$$+ (1000)0.3 + (2000)0.3$$
$$+ (4000)0.1$$
$$= \$900$$

$$E(X_B) = \sum \left[x_B \cdot p(x_B) \right]$$
$$= (-3000)0.2 + (-1000)0.1$$
$$+ (2000)0.2 + (3000)0.3$$
$$+ (4000)0.2$$
$$= \$1400$$

Because of the randomness of the profit variable, it is difficult to evaluate the investments by merely *eyeballing* the two distributions. However, by calculating the expected values of the two alternatives, the information in each distribution is condensed to a single value. This value characterizes the center of the distribution and facilitates comparison. The expected values of Options A and B are $900 and $1400, respectively. Thus, in the long run Option B would be $500 more profitable. The phrase *in the long run* is a significant qualifier. It means that under repeated investments with the same profit and probability structure, you would receive an average profit of $1400 from Option B. But on any one investment in Option B, you may lose as much as $3000 or make as much as $4000.

Variance of a Discrete Random Variable

While Option B has a greater expected value, it seems to have greater risk than Option A. Option B offers a greater chance of making a substantial gain, but it also has the potential for significant loss as well. The expected value of a distribution measures only one dimension of the random variable, namely its central value. To gauge the variability of a random variable we need another measure similar to the variance measure previously constructed but one which accounts for the difference in probabilities of the variable.

Variance and Standard Deviation of a Discrete Random Variable

The **variance of a discrete random variable** X is given by the following formula.

$$\sigma^2 = V(X) = \sum \left[(x - \mu)^2 \, p(x) \right]$$

The **standard deviation of a discrete random variable** X is therefore,

$$\sigma = \sqrt{V(x)} = \sqrt{\sum (x - \mu)^2 \, p(x)}.$$

DEFINITION

Note

Sometimes it is easier to calculate the variance of a discrete random variable using the computational formula

$$\sigma^2 = V(X) = \sum \left[x^2 \cdot p(x) \right] - \mu^2.$$

Both formulas are equivalent.

Once again, the variance can be considered an average. In this case it is the weighted average of the squared deviations about the mean. This is very similar to the computations for the sample variance (s^2) and population variance (σ^2) given by

$$s^2 = \frac{\sum (x - \bar{x})^2}{N - 1} \quad \text{and} \quad \sigma^2 = \frac{\sum (x - \mu)^2}{N},$$ respectively. The larger the variance the more variability in the outcomes.

To manually compute the variance of the random variable, it's often a good idea to construct a table.

Example 7.2.6

The calculation of the variances for the random variables described in Example 7.2.5 is given in the tables below.

Solution

Variance of Option A		
Option A		
Profit (Dollars)	Probability	$(x - \mu)^2 \, p(x)$
−2000	0.2	$(-2000 - 900)^2 \, 0.2 = 1{,}682{,}000$
0	0.1	$(0 - 900)^2 \, 0.1 = 81{,}000$
1000	0.3	$(1000 - 900)^2 \, 0.3 = 3{,}000$
2000	0.3	$(2000 - 900)^2 \, 0.3 = 363{,}000$
4000	0.1	$(4000 - 900)^2 \, 0.1 = 961{,}000$
	Total	$\sigma^2 = V(X) = 3{,}090{,}000$

Technology

Recall that the standard deviation is included in the output of the 1-Var Stats option on the TI-83/84 Plus calculator. For instructions on how to do this on a calculator, or using other technologies, please visit stat.hawkeslearning.com and navigate to **Technology Instructions > Descriptive Statistics > Two Variable**.

```
1-Var Stats
 x̄=900
 Σx=900
 Σx²=3900000
 Sx=
 σx=1757.839583
↓n=1
```

The standard deviation is computed by taking the square root of the variance. In this instance, the standard deviation of Option A is given by

$$\text{Standard Deviation} = \sqrt{V(X)} = \sqrt{3{,}090{,}000} = 1757.8.$$

Variance of Option B		
Option B		
Profit (Dollars)	Probability	$(x - \mu)^2 p(x)$
−3000	0.2	$(-3000 - 1400)^2\, 0.2 = 3{,}872{,}000$
−1000	0.1	$(-1000 - 1400)^2\, 0.1 = 576{,}000$
2000	0.2	$(2000 - 1400)^2\, 0.2 = 72{,}000$
3000	0.3	$(3000 - 1400)^2\, 0.3 = 768{,}000$
4000	0.2	$(4000 - 1400)^2\, 0.2 = 1{,}352{,}000$
	Total	$\sigma^2 = V(X) = 6{,}640{,}000$

The standard deviation of Option B is given by

$$\text{Standard Deviation} = \sqrt{6{,}640{,}000} \approx 2576.8.$$

A larger standard deviation reflects greater variability in profits and increased risk. When variance is considered, the decision becomes more difficult. The option with the largest expected value (Option B) is also the option with the greatest risk. Hence, the decision maker must subjectively evaluate the trade-off between greater expected return and increased risk.

7.2   **Exercises**

Basic Concepts

1. Discrete probability distributions always have two characteristics; what are they?

2. What is the value of describing a random variable with a probability distribution?

3. Identify three different ways to express possible values of a random variable along with their associated probabilities.

4. How is a probability distribution created?

5. Identify four discrete probability distributions to be discussed in this chapter.

6. What is a probability distribution function?

7. Why is the notion of expected value one of the most important concepts in the analysis of random phenomena?

8. True or False: The expected value of a random variable is usually one of the possible outcomes of the random variable.

9. Suppose the expected value of a random variable was known to be 6.3. Interpret the meaning of the expected value.

10. Give an example of a situation in which expected value would be useful to compare alternatives, other than the one used in the section.

11. How is the variability of a random variable related to risk?

Exercises

12. Determine whether or not the following distribution is a probability distribution. If the distribution is not a probability distribution, give the characteristic which is not satisfied by the distribution.

x	1	2	3
P(X = x)	$\frac{1}{3}$	$\frac{2}{3}$	$\frac{1}{3}$

13. Determine whether or not the following distribution is a probability distribution. If the distribution is not a probability distribution, give the characteristic which is not satisfied by the distribution.

x	−2	2	3
P(X = x)	0.25	0.50	0.25

14. Tell whether or not the following distribution is a probability distribution. If the distribution is not a probability distribution, give the characteristic which is not satisfied by the distribution.

x	2	3	4	5
P(X = x)	0.30	−0.50	0.50	0.70

15. Determine whether or not the following distribution is a probability distribution. If the distribution is not a probability distribution, give the characteristic which is not satisfied by the distribution.

x	5	10	15
P(X = x)	0.46	0.25	0.25

16. Determine whether or not the following distribution is a probability distribution. If the distribution is not a probability distribution, give the characteristic which is not satisfied by the distribution.

x	−10	−5	3	8
P(X = x)	0.18	0.39	0.08	0.35

17. Determine whether or not the following distribution is a probability distribution. If the distribution is not a probability distribution, give the characteristic which is not satisfied by the distribution.

x	100	200	300
P(X = x)	−0.10	0.50	0.50

18. Determine whether or not the following distribution is a probability distribution. If the distribution is not a probability distribution, give the characteristic which is not satisfied by the distribution.

$$P(X = x) = \frac{x}{16}, \text{ for } x = 1, 2, 3, 4, 5$$

19. Determine whether or not the following distribution is a probability distribution. If the distribution is not a probability distribution, give the characteristic which is not satisfied by the distribution.

$$P(X = x) = \frac{x^2}{30}, \text{ for } x = 1, 2, 3, 4$$

20. Find the expected value, the variance, and the standard deviation for a random variable with the following probability distribution.

x	−5	−2	0	2	5
p(x)	0.06	0.15	0.58	0.18	0.03

21. Find the expected value, the variance, and the standard deviation for a random variable with the following probability distribution.

x	400	420	440	460	480	500
p(x)	0	0.1	0.1	0.2	0.2	0.4

22. A regional hospital is considering the purchase of a helicopter to transport critical patients. The relative frequency of X, the number of times the helicopter is used to transport critical patients each month, is derived for a similarly sized hospital and is given in the following probability distribution.

x	0	1	2	3	4	5	6
p(x)	0.15	0.20	0.34	0.19	0.06	0.05	0.01

   a. Find the average number of times the helicopter is used to transport critical patients each month.

   b. Find the variance of the number of times the helicopter is used to transport critical patients.

   c. Find the standard deviation of the number of times the helicopter is used to transport critical patients.

   d. Find the probability that the helicopter will not be used at all during a month to transport critical patients.

   e. Find the probability that the helicopter will be used at least once to transport critical patients.

   f. Find the probability that the helicopter will be used at most twice to transport critical patients.

   g. Find the probability that the helicopter will be used more than three times to transport critical patients.

23. Based on past experience, an architect has determined a probability distribution for X, the number of times a drawing must be examined by a client before it is accepted.

x	1	2	3	4	5
$p(x)$	0.1	0.2	0.3	0.2	0.2

    a. Find the average number of times a drawing must be examined by a client before it is accepted.

    b. Find the variance of the number of times a drawing must be examined by a client before it is accepted.

    c. Find the standard deviation of the number of times a drawing must be examined by a client before it is accepted.

    d. What is the probability that a drawing must be examined five times before being accepted by the client?

    e. Find the probability that the drawing must be examined at least twice before being accepted by the client.

    f. Find the probability that a drawing must be examined at most three times before being accepted by the client.

    g. Find the probability that a drawing must be examined less than twice before being accepted by the client.

24. The manager of a retail clothing store has determined the following probability distribution for X, the number of customers who will enter the store on Saturday.

x	10	20	30	40	50	60
$p(x)$	0.10	0.20	0.30	0.20	0.10	0.10

    a. Find the expected number of customers who will enter the store on Saturday.

    b. Find the standard deviation of the number of customers who will enter the store on Saturday.

    c. Find the variance of the number of customers who will enter the store on Saturday.

    d. Find the probability that more than 30 customers will enter the store on Saturday.

    e. Find the probability that at most 20 customers will enter the store on Saturday.

    f. Find the probability that at least 40 customers will enter the store on Saturday.

    g. What is the probability that exactly 10 customers will enter the store on Saturday?

25. An entrepreneur is considering investing in a new venture. If the venture is successful, he will make $50,000. However, if the venture is not successful, he will lose his investment of $10,000. Based on past experience, he believes that there is a 40% chance that the venture will be successful.

    a. Use the information in the problem to determine the probability distribution of the amount of money to be made (or lost) on the venture.

    b. Determine the expected amount of money to be made on the venture.

    c. Determine the standard deviation of the amount of money to be made on the venture.

26. An investor is considering two alternative investment options with the following payoff distributions.

	Option 1			Option 2		
Payoff	−$100,000	$30,000	$100,000	−$20,000	$0	$20,000
P(Payoff)	$\frac{1}{3}$	$\frac{1}{3}$	$\frac{1}{3}$	0.25	0.50	0.25

    a. Calculate the expected payoff for each of the investment options.

    b. Calculate the standard deviation of the payoff for each of the investment options.

    c. Which investment option would you choose? Explain.

27. A cereal manufacturer has two new brands of cereal which it would like to produce. Because resources are limited, the cereal manufacturer can only afford to produce one of the new brands. A marketing study produced the following probability distributions for the amount of sales for each of the new brands of cereal.

Cereal A		Cereal B	
Sales	**P(Sales)**	**Sales**	**P(Sales)**
$150,000	0.2	$10,000	0.40
$200,000	0.3	$300,000	0.40
$300,000	0.3	$600,000	0.10
$400,000	0.2	$1,000,000	0.10

    a. What are the expected sales of each of the new brands of cereal?

    b. What is the standard deviation of the sales for each of the brands of cereal?

    c. If both of the brands of cereal cost the same amount to produce, which brand of cereal do you think the cereal manufacturer should produce? Explain.

7.3   **The Discrete Uniform Distribution**

The **discrete uniform distribution** is one of the simplest probability distributions. Each value of the random variable is assigned identical probabilities. There are many situations in which the discrete uniform distribution arises.

Example 7.3.1

What is the probability distribution for the outcome of the throw of a single six-sided die?

Solution

If the die is *fair*, then each of the outcomes is equally likely and thus we have a uniform distribution in which all probabilities equal $\frac{1}{6}$. The probability distribution is given below.

Throwing a Die						
x	1	2	3	4	5	6
P (X = x)	$\frac{1}{6}$	$\frac{1}{6}$	$\frac{1}{6}$	$\frac{1}{6}$	$\frac{1}{6}$	$\frac{1}{6}$

Example 7.3.2

Suppose a purchasing agent has just received a pricing and delivery schedule from a new vendor. The delivery schedule was quoted as 1 to 4 weeks. The purchasing agent wishes to construct a probability distribution for the time until delivery.

Solution

Without any prior information, the agent believes any time frame is as likely as any other. Hence, the number of weeks until delivery will be assumed to be a uniform distribution. Therefore, the probability distribution of the random variable $X =$ the number of weeks until delivery is as shown in the following table.

Delivery Distribution			
x	1	2	3	4
P (X = x)	$\frac{1}{4}$	$\frac{1}{4}$	$\frac{1}{4}$	$\frac{1}{4}$

Over time the purchasing agent will undoubtedly revise the distribution as more information is gathered about the company's delivery schedule.

Example 7.3.2 illustrates an important principle in the application of the discrete uniform distribution. That is, when there is little or no information concerning the outcome of a random variable, the discrete uniform distribution may be a reasonable initial alternative.

7.3   **Exercises**

Basic Concepts

1. What is the most significant property of the discrete uniform distribution?

2. Under what circumstances is the uniform distribution often used as an initial alternative?

Exercises

3. A classmate walks into class and states that he has an extra ticket to a rock concert on Friday night. He asks everyone in the class to put their name on a piece of paper and put it in a basket. He plans to draw from the basket to choose the person who will attend the concert with him. If there are 16 people in class that night, what is your chance of being chosen to attend the concert?

4. Sharlene has just put a down payment on a lot in a small subdivision. There are 10 lots in the subdivision and all are approximately 0.25 acres in size. Five builders have been contracted by the subdivision manager to each build two homes in order to finish the subdivision in 6 months. Sharlene's uncle is one of the builders contracted by the subdivision manager. What is the probability that Sharlene's uncle will be the builder that builds her house?

5. You order some clothing online and get an estimated delivery date of June 6–June 11. You know you will be out of town June 8th and 9th and are a little concerned about the package arriving when you are away. Assuming the delivery date follows a discrete uniform distribution, what is the likelihood your package will be delivered while you are out of town?

6. An experiment consists of tossing a coin and rolling a six-sided die simultaneously.

    a.   List the sample space for the experiment.

    b.   What is the probability of getting a head on the coin and the number 3 on the die?

    c.   What is the probability of getting a tail on the coin and at least a 4 on the die?

7. Given the following discrete uniform probability distribution, find the expected value and standard deviation of the random variable.

x	0	1	2	3	4
$P(X = x)$	$\frac{1}{5}$	$\frac{1}{5}$	$\frac{1}{5}$	$\frac{1}{5}$	$\frac{1}{5}$

7.4 The Binomial Distribution

The binomial distribution arises from experiments with repeated two-outcome trials, where only one of the outcomes is counted. Experiments of this kind are rather common in the business world. In market research a survey respondent (a trial) will either recognize a company's brand or will not. The number that recognize the brand out of a fixed sample size is a count that may be modeled as a **binomial random variable**.

Some examples of binomial random variables include:

- The number of left-handed persons in a sample of 200 unrelated people.
- The number of correct guesses out of 20 True or False questions when you randomly choose an answer.
- The number of winning scratch-off lottery tickets when you purchase 15 of the same type.

Experiments are required to meet several conditions in order to qualify as a binomial experiment.

Binomial Experiment

A **binomial experiment** is a random experiment which satisfies all of the following conditions.

1. There are only two outcomes on each trial of the experiment. (One of the outcomes is usually referred to as a *success*, and the other as a *failure*.)
2. The experiment consists of n identical trials as described in condition 1.
3. The probability of success on any one trial is denoted by p and does not change from trial to trial. (**Note:** The probability of a failure is $1 - p$ and also does not change from trial to trial.)
4. The trials are independent.
5. The binomial random variable is the count of the number of successes in n trials.

DEFINITION

A binomial random variable is formed by counting the number of successes in n trials of an experiment with two outcomes. One of the simplest of binomial random variables is produced by tossing a coin.

Example 7.4.1

Toss a coin 4 times and record the number of heads. Is the number of heads in 4 tosses a binomial random variable?

Solution

1. There are only two outcomes, heads or not heads.
2. The experiment will consist of 4 tosses of a coin. (Hence, $n = 4$.)
3. The probability of getting a head (success) is $\frac{1}{2}$ and does not change from trial to trial. (Hence, $p = \frac{1}{2}$.)

4. The outcome of one toss will not affect other tosses.

5. The variable of interest is the count of the number of heads in 4 tosses.

All the conditions of a binomial experiment are met, so the number of heads in 4 tosses of a coin is a binomial random variable. The probability distribution for this experiment is given in the following table.

Tossing a Coin		
Events	**Number of Heads**	**Probability**
TTTT	0	$\frac{1}{16}$
HTTT, THTT, TTHT, TTTH	1	$\frac{4}{16}$
HHTT, HTHT HTTH, THHT, THTH, TTHH	2	$\frac{6}{16}$
THHH, HTHH, HHTH, HHHT	3	$\frac{4}{16}$
HHHH	4	$\frac{1}{16}$

The probability distribution could be derived using classical methods described in the previous chapter. To derive the binomial distribution by listing the simple events is unnecessarily tedious (see Example 7.4.1). Instead of tossing the coin four times, suppose the coin is tossed 10 times in the experiment. The number of outcomes for an experiment with 10 tosses would be 1024, and an experiment with 20 tosses would require listing a staggering 1,048,576 outcomes. Fortunately, there is a far simpler method of obtaining the probability distribution. The **binomial probability distribution function** provides a relatively simple method of calculating binomial probabilities.

Note

An alternate notation often used is

$$P(X = x) = C_x^n p^x (1-p)^{n-x}.$$

Binomial Probability Distribution Function

The **binomial probability distribution function** is

$$P(X = x) = {}_nC_x p^x (1-p)^{n-x}$$

where ${}_nC_x$ represents the number of possible combinations of n objects taken x at a time (without replacement) and is given by

$${}_nC_x = \frac{n!}{x!(n-x)!} \quad \text{where } n! = n(n-1)(n-2)\cdots 2 \cdot 1 \quad \text{and } 0! = 1;$$

n = the number of trials,

p = the probability of a success, and

x = the number of successes in n trials.

FORMULA

To calculate a binomial probability, the parameters of the distribution (n and p), as well as the value of the random variable, must be specified. For example, to determine the probability of 3 heads in 4 tosses of a coin, you would substitute the values $x = 3$, $n = 4$, and $p = \frac{1}{2}$ into the binomial probability distribution function as follows.

$$P(X = 3) = {}_4C_3 \left(\frac{1}{2}\right)^3 \left(1 - \frac{1}{2}\right)^{4-3}.$$

Since, ${}_4C_3 = \dfrac{4!}{3!(4-3)!} = \dfrac{4 \cdot 3 \cdot 2 \cdot 1}{3 \cdot 2 \cdot 1 \cdot (1)} = 4$, then

$$P(X = 3) = 4 \left(\frac{1}{2}\right)^3 \left(\frac{1}{2}\right) = \frac{4}{16} = 0.25.$$

The probability that 2 heads would be tossed would be computed in a similar manner.

$$P(X = 2) = {}_4C_2 \left(\frac{1}{2}\right)^2 \left(1 - \frac{1}{2}\right)^{4-2} = \frac{4!}{2!2!}\left(\frac{1}{2}\right)^2 \left(\frac{1}{2}\right)^2 = \frac{6}{16} = 0.375.$$

The complete distribution can be computed by substituting the remaining values of the random variable into the probability distribution function.

Table 7.4.1 - Tossing a Coin					
Number of Heads	0	1	2	3	4
Probability	$\frac{1}{16}$	$\frac{4}{16}$	$\frac{6}{16}$	$\frac{4}{16}$	$\frac{1}{16}$

The coin toss is a classical binomial experiment easily related to the rules of a binomial experiment. In many instances the relationship of an experiment to the binomial definition is not as clear.

Example 7.4.2

Roll a single six-sided die 4 times and record the number of sixes observed. Does the number of sixes rolled in 4 tosses of a die meet the conditions required of a binomial random variable? Construct the probability distribution for this experiment.

Solution

1. The experiment either produces a six or not, and thus satisfies the two-outcome requirement. (At first glance, there appears to be a problem. There are six sides to a die and there would appear to be six possible outcomes rather than the two required for a single trial of a binomial experiment.)

2. The experiment is repeated 4 times. Hence, the number of trials equals four ($n = 4$).

3. The probability of getting a six, a success, is $p = \frac{1}{6}$. (This probability assumes that the die is fair.)

4. The probability remains constant from trial to trial. (One roll of the die does not affect other rolls.)

5. If X is the "number" of sixes in 4 rolls, then it has a binomial distribution.

⌘ **Technology**

To find a binomial probability we use the `binompdf` function on the TI-83/84 Plus calculator. The results are shown below. For instructions please visit stat.hawkeslearning.com and navigate to **Technology Instructions > Binomial Distribution Binomial Probability (pdf)**.

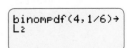

⌘ **Technology**

To find a binomial probability distribution using the TI-83/84 Plus calculator we can store the output of the `binompdf` function in a list. The results are shown below. For instructions on how to do this using a calculator, or using other technologies, please visit stat.hawkeslearning.com and navigate to **Technology Instructions > Binomial Distribution > Binomial Probability Distribution**.

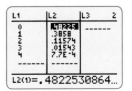

To obtain the probability distribution for X, use the binomial probability distribution function with parameters $n = 4$ and $p = \frac{1}{6}$.

$$P(X = 0) = {}_4C_0\left(\frac{1}{6}\right)^0\left(1 - \frac{1}{6}\right)^{4-0} = (1)(1)\left(\frac{5}{6}\right)^4 \approx 0.4823$$

$$P(X = 1) = {}_4C_1\left(\frac{1}{6}\right)^1\left(1 - \frac{1}{6}\right)^{4-1} = (4)\left(\frac{1}{6}\right)\left(\frac{5}{6}\right)^3 \approx 0.3858$$

$$P(X = 2) = {}_4C_2\left(\frac{1}{6}\right)^2\left(1 - \frac{1}{6}\right)^{4-2} = (6)\left(\frac{1}{6}\right)^2\left(\frac{5}{6}\right)^2 \approx 0.1157$$

$$P(X = 3) = {}_4C_3\left(\frac{1}{6}\right)^3\left(1 - \frac{1}{6}\right)^{4-3} = (4)\left(\frac{1}{6}\right)^3\left(\frac{5}{6}\right)^1 \approx 0.0154$$

$$P(X = 4) = {}_4C_4\left(\frac{1}{6}\right)^4\left(1 - \frac{1}{6}\right)^{4-4} = (1)\left(\frac{1}{6}\right)^4\left(\frac{5}{6}\right)^0 \approx 0.0008$$

⬙ Technology

Probabilities of a binomial random variable can also be found using technology such as a TI-83/84 Plus calculator, Microsoft Excel, Minitab, or R. Detailed directions for each of these may be found on stat.hawkeslearning.com under **Technology Instructions > Binomial Distribution**.

Throwing a Die					
x	0	1	2	3	4
Probability	0.4823	0.3858	0.1157	0.0154	0.0008

The calculations required to produce the distribution were reasonably simple in this case. However, if there had been forty cases rather than four, the determination of the probabilities would have been rather burdensome, at best. Binomial tables containing a large collection of binomial distributions have been constructed in order to avoid tedious calculations. These tables are found in Appendix A, Table E.

Example 7.4.3

The US Land Management Office regularly holds a lottery for the lease of government lands. Your company has won the rights to 12 leases. Historically, about 10% of these lands possess sufficient oil reserves for profitable operation. Construct the distribution for the number of leases that will be profitable. What is the probability that at least one of the leases will be profitable?

Solution

Binomial Table $n = 12$, $p = 0.10$			
x	**P(X = x)**	**x**	**P(X = x)**
0	0.2824	7	0.0000
1	0.3766	8	0.0000
2	0.2301	9	0.0000
3	0.0852	10	0.0000
4	0.0213	11	0.0000
5	0.0038	12	0.0000
6	0.0005		

Instead of laboriously computing the distribution, use the binomial tables in Appendix A, Table E. The binomial parameters are $n = 12$ and $p = 0.10$. Let X equal the number of profitable leases. The table above shows the binomial distribution for X. Note that the probabilities for 7 through 12 are given as 0.0000. This does not mean that the probability is 0, because it is possible that 7 or more of the leases could be profitable, albeit a rather small probability. (The probability, however, is so small that it is not significant in the fourth decimal place.)

The probability that none of the leases will be profitable is equal to the probability that $X = 0$, which is 0.2824. Hence, the probability that at least one of the leases will be profitable is one minus the probability that none of the leases will be profitable or $1 - 0.2824 = 0.7176$.

Example 7.4.4

According to a recent national poll, about 40% of Americans believe in ghosts. Assuming this percentage is accurate, if 20 people were randomly selected and asked if they believed in ghosts, what is the probability that 12 or more would say they do?

Solution

For this problem $n = 20$, $p = 0.4$, and x ranges from 12 to 20. So, nine probabilities must be calculated and added together to answer the question. This could be done using the binomial probability distribution function, but it would be cumbersome. Instead, use one of the binomial tables in Appendix A. Table E contains binomial probabilities for each value of x where p ranges from 0.1 to 0.9 and n ranges from 1 to 20.

To determine the answer, find the following individual probabilities in Table E and add them together.

$$
\begin{aligned}
P(X \geq 12) &= P(X = 12) + P(X = 13) + \cdots + P(X = 20) \\
&= 0.0355 + 0.0146 + \cdots + 0.0000 \\
&= 0.0565
\end{aligned}
$$

Alternately, use the cumulative binomial probability table (Table E) to find the cumulative probability where $x = 11$, $n = 20$, and $p = 0.4$, and subtract this probability from 1.

$$P(X \geq 12) = 1 - P(X \leq 11) = 1 - 0.9435 = 0.0565.$$

Technology such as Microsoft Excel or the TI-83/84 Plus calculator can also be used to obtain the probability. Note that if the value of p does not appear in the tables, then you must use technology or the binomial probability distribution function to calculate the probability.

☁ Technology

The answer to Example 7.4.3 can be easily found using the `binompdf` function on the TI-83/84 Plus calculator. Full instructions are available on stat.hawkeslearning.com under **Technology Instructions > Binomial Distribution > Binomial Probability (pdf)**.

```
binompdf(12,.1,0
)
         .2824295365
1-Ans
         .7175704635
```

☁ Technology

The probability can be found using Excel or R by calculating 1-(cumulative probability for $x=11$). For full instructions on calculating cumulative binomial probabilities, please visit stat.hawkeslearning.com and navigate to **Technology Instructions > Binomial Distribution > Binomial Probability (cdf)**.

Excel

fx	=1-BINOM.DIS (11,20,0.4, TRUE)	
	D	E
	0.056526	

R

```
> 1-pbinom(11,20,0.4)
[1] 0.05652637
```

The Shape of a Binomial Distribution

Binomial Distribution for *n* = 12 and *p* = 0.1

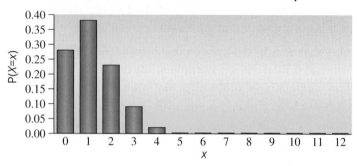

Figure 7.4.1

Binomial distributions have taken various shapes in the previous problems. The shape of the distribution depends upon the parameters n and p. If p is small, the distribution tends to be skewed with a tail on the right, (i.e., there are more successes when x is smaller) as is the case in Example 7.4.3 (see Figure 7.4.1).

Binomial Distribution for *n* = 9 and *p* = 0.5

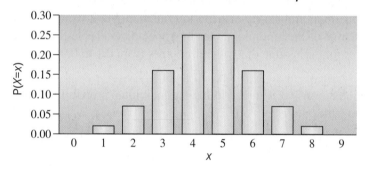

Figure 7.4.2

If p is near 0.5, the distribution is symmetrical. The graph in Figure 7.4.2 displays the probabilities for $n = 9$ and $p = 0.5$.

Binomial Distribution for *n* = 20 and *p* = 0.7

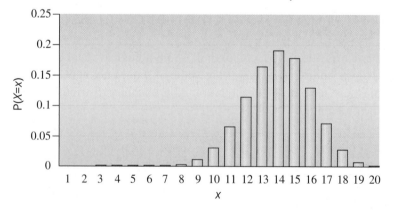

Figure 7.4.3

If p is large, the distribution tends to be skewed with a long tail on the left (i.e., there are more successes when x is larger). The graph in Figure 7.4.3 displays the binomial probabilities for $n = 20$ and $p = 0.7$.

The Expected Value and Variance of a Binomial

To calculate the expected value of a binomial random variable would require a substantial number of arithmetic operations. Fortunately, you can avoid this calculation by utilizing a special characteristic of the binomial distribution.

Expected Value of a Binomial Random Variable

The **expected value** of a binomial random variable can be computed using the expression

$$\mu = E(X) = np,$$

where n and p are the parameters of the binomial distribution.

FORMULA

It is important to remember that this formula is only valid for binomial random variables. Also, there is a simple method for obtaining the variance for binomial random variables.

Variance and Standard Deviation of a Binomial Random Variable

To find the **variance** of a binomial random variable, use the expression

$$\sigma^2 = V(X) = np(1 - p).$$

Therefore, the **standard deviation** of a binomial random variable is given by

$$\sigma = \sqrt{V(X)} = \sqrt{np(1 - p)}.$$

FORMULA

Example 7.4.5

Compute the expected value and the variance of the number of profitable leases in Example 7.4.3.

Solution

Since the random variable is binomial, we can use the shortcuts given on the previous page. Since $n = 12$ and $p = 0.1$, the expected value is given by the following expression.

$$\begin{aligned}\mu = E(X) &= np \\ &= 12(0.1) \\ &= 1.2\end{aligned}$$

The variance is

$$\begin{aligned}\sigma^2 = V(X) &= np(1 - p) \\ &= 12(0.1)(0.9) \\ &= 1.08,\end{aligned}$$

which implies that the standard deviation is $\sqrt{1.08} \approx 1.039$.

Thus, if groups of 12 oil leases were purchased with the same probability of success (0.10 probability of a profitable lease), then the average number of profitable leases per group of 12 would be 1.2 and the standard deviation would be 1.039 leases.

7.4 **Exercises**

Basic Concepts

1. Describe the characteristics of a binomial experiment.

2. What are the parameters of a binomial probability model?

3. Give an example of a binomial experiment, other than the one used in the section.

4. What is the formula for the binomial probability distribution function?

5. What influences the shape of the binomial probability distribution?

6. How do you calculate the expected value of a binomial random variable? The variance? The standard deviation?

Exercises

7. Calculate $_nC_x$ for each of the following combinations of x and n.

   a. $n = 5, x = 4$ **c.** $n = 15, x = 1$

   b. $n = 10, x = 8$ **d.** $n = 20, x = 0$

8. Calculate $_nC_x$ for each of the following combinations of x and n.

   a. $n = 4, x = 2$ **c.** $n = 18, x = 15$

   b. $n = 12, x = 8$ **d.** $n = 23, x = 20$

9. The random variable X is a binomial random variable with $n = 9$ and $p = 0.1$.

   a. Find the expected value of X.

   b. Find the standard deviation of X.

   c. Find the probability that X equals 2. (Use the formula for $P(X = x)$.)

   d. Find the probability that X is at most 3.

   e. Find the probability that X is at least 2.

   f. Find the probability that X is less than 5.

10. The random variable X is a binomial random variable with $n = 12$ and $p = 0.8$.

    a. Find the expected value of X.

    b. Find the standard deviation of X.

    c. Find the probability that X equals 7. (Use the formula for $P(X = x)$.)

   d. Find the probability that X is at most 4.

   e. Find the probability that X is at least 1.

   f. Find the probability that X is more than 10.

11. A real estate agent has ten properties that she shows. She feels that there is a ten percent chance of selling any one property during a week. The chance of selling any one property is independent of selling another property.

   a. What probability model would be appropriate for describing the number of properties sold each week?

   b. Compute the expected number of properties to be sold in a week.

   c. Compute the standard deviation of the number of properties sold each week.

   d. Compute the probability of selling one property in one week.

   e. Compute the probability of selling five properties in one week.

   f. Compute the probability of selling at least three properties in one week.

12. A small commuter airline is concerned about reservation no-shows and, correspondingly, how much they should overbook flights to compensate. Assume their commuter planes will hold 15 people. Industry research indicates that 20% of the people making a reservation will not show up for a flight. Whether or not one person takes the flight is considered to be independent of other persons holding reservations.

   a. What probability model would be appropriate for the number of passengers that actually take the flight?

   b. If the airlines decide to book 18 people for each flight, how often will there be at least one person who will not get a seat?

   c. If they book 17 people, how often will there be at least one person who will not get a seat?

   d. If they book 16 people, how often will there be at least one person who will not get a seat?

   e. If they book 18 people for each flight, how often will there be one or more empty seats?

   f. If they book 17 people, how often will there be one or more empty seats?

   g. If they book 16 people, how often will there be one or more empty seats?

   h. Based on the results from parts **b.** to **g.** above, which booking policy do you prefer? Explain your answer.

13. Seven plants are operated by a garment manufacturer. They feel there is a ten percent chance for a strike at any one plant and the risk of a strike at one plant is independent of the risk of a strike at another plant. Let X = the number of plants of the garment manufacturer that strike.

   a. Determine the probability distribution for X.

   b. Interpret the results for $P(X=0)$, $P(X=4)$, and $P(X=7)$.

   c. Compute the expected value of X.

d. Compute the standard deviation for *X*. Is this value large in relation to the expected value? In what units is the standard deviation expressed?

14. A company that makes traffic signal lights buys switches from a supplier. Out of each shipment of 1000 switches, the company will take a random sample of 10 switches. Let *X* equal the number of defective switches in the sample.

a. The company has a policy of rejecting a lot if they find any defective switches in the sample. What is the probability that the shipment will be accepted if, in fact, 2% of the switches are actually defective?

b. What is the probability that the shipment will be accepted if the percent of defective switches is actually 5%?

c. The company decides to change their policy and will accept the lot if they find no more than one defective switch. Repeat parts a. and b. for this new policy.

15. Parents have always wondered about the sex of a child before it is born. Suppose that the probability of having a male child was 0.5, and that the sex of one child is independent of the sex of other children.

a. Determine the probability of having exactly two girls out of four children.

b. What is the probability of having four boys out of four children?

16. A certain aspirin is advertised as being preferred by 4 out of 5 doctors. If the advertisement is assumed to be true, answer the following questions.

a. What is the probability that at least half of ten doctors chosen at random will prefer this brand of aspirin?

b. What is the probability that 9 out of 10 of the doctors will prefer this brand?

17. In manufacturing integrated circuits, the yield of the manufacturing process is the percentage of good chips produced by the process. The probability that an integrated circuit manufactured by the Ace Electronics Company will be defective is $p = 0.05$. If a random sample of 15 circuits is selected for testing, answer the following questions.

a. What is the probability that no more than one integrated circuit will be defective in the sample?

b. What is the expected number of defective integrated circuits in the sample?

18. The Alvin Secretarial Service procures temporary office personnel for major corporations. They have found that 90% of their invoices are paid within 10 working days. If a random sample of 12 invoices is checked, answer the following questions.

a. What is the probability that all of the invoices will be paid within 10 working days?

b. What is the probability that six or more of the invoices will be paid within 10 working days?

19. An experiment consists of rolling a pair of dice 10 times. On each roll the sum of the dots on the two dice is noted.

    a. Find the probability that on any roll of the two dice the sum of the dots is either 7 or 11.

    b. Find the probability that in the 10 rolls of the pair of dice, a 7 or 11 occurs 5 times.

    c. Find the probability that in the 10 rolls of the pair of dice, a 7 or 11 does not occur at all.

    d. Find the mean and variance of the number of times we see a 7 or 11 in the 10 rolls of the dice.

20. "Would you say you eat to live or live to eat?" was asked to each person in a sample of 1001 adults in a Gallup Poll taken in April 1996. Seventy-four percent of the respondents answered eat to live, 23% answered live to eat, and 3% had no opinion. Assuming these percents are accurate, find the probability, in 12 randomly chosen adults, that the number who would answer "eat to live" is:

    a. exactly 7.

    b. no more than 10.

    c. at most 11.

    d. at least 3.

7.5   The Poisson Distribution

The binomial random variable requires a fixed number of repetitions of the experiment, where the outcomes are either successes or failures. The **Poisson distribution** is similar to the binomial in that the random variable represents a count of the total number of successes. The major difference between the two distributions is that the Poisson does not have a fixed number of trials. Instead, the Poisson uses a fixed interval of time or space in which the number of successes are recorded. Thus, there is no theoretical upper limit on the number of successes, although large numbers of successes are not very likely.

The word *success* in the Poisson context can sometimes take on rather morbid connotations. Many phenomena that have been observed to follow the distribution are associated with violence and carnage. For example, the randomness exhibited by the number of airplane crashes, oil tanker spills, and car accidents in some fixed period of time seems to conform to the randomness described by a Poisson random variable.

Fortunately, not all applications are so bleak. In business environments a great many variables seem to follow a pattern of randomness similar to that described by the Poisson distribution. One of the Poisson's principal areas of use in business is the analysis of waiting lines. Other random phenomena, such as airplane arrivals, trucks arriving at a loading dock, users logging on to a computer system, or the number of defects in a given surface area, can be modeled with a Poisson distribution. These variables are often of interest in determining personnel requirements, inventories, and quality control.

Poisson Random Variable

In order to qualify as a **Poisson random variable** an experiment must meet two conditions.

1. Successes occur one at a time. That is, two or more successes cannot occur at exactly the same point in time or at exactly the same point in space.

2. The occurrence of a success in any interval is independent of the occurrence of a success in any other interval.

DEFINITION

If these two conditions are met, it can be proven that the random variable for the number of successes follows the Poisson probability distribution function.

Poisson Probability Distribution Function

The Poisson probability distribution function is given by

$$P\left(X = x\right) = \frac{e^{-\lambda}\lambda^{x}}{x!}, \text{ for } x = 0, 1, 2, \ldots$$

where

$e = 2.71828\ldots$, and

λ = the mean number of successes.

FORMULA

Technology

To find a Poisson probability distribution using the TI-83/84 Plus calculator we can store the output of the `poissonpdf` function in a list. The results are shown below. For instructions on how to do this using a calculator, or using other technologies, please visit stat.hawkeslearning.com and navigate to **Technology Instructions > Poisson Distribution > Poisson Probability Distribution**.

The Poisson distribution has only one parameter, λ, pronounced *lambda*. One peculiar feature of the distribution is that the variance of the distribution is equal to the mean. That is, $\mu = \lambda$ and $\sigma^2 = \lambda$.

Tables for the Poisson distribution are found in Appendix A, Table F. The tables give $P(X = x)$ for particular values of x and λ. Probabilities of a Poisson random variable can also be found using technology such as a TI-83/84 Plus calculator, Microsoft Excel, or Minitab.

The shape of the Poisson distribution varies dramatically with the parameter λ. If λ is small, say 0.3, then the corresponding distribution is found in Table 7.5.1 and displayed in Figure 7.5.1.

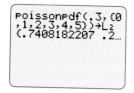

Table 7.5.1 $\lambda = 0.3$	
x	**P (X = x)**
0	0.7408
1	0.2222
2	0.0333
3	0.0033
4	0.0003
5	0.0000

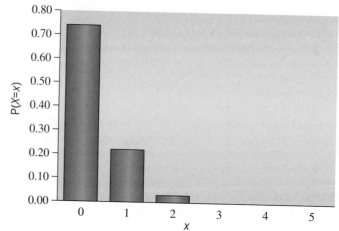

Figure 7.5.1

As λ increases to 3 (see Table 7.5.2), the distribution in Figure 7.5.2 exhibits a mound shape with skewness.

Table 7.5.2 $\lambda = 3$	
x	**P (X = x)**
0	0.0498
1	0.1494
2	0.2240
3	0.2240
4	0.1680
5	0.1008
6	0.0504
7	0.0216
8	0.0081
9	0.0027
10	0.0008
11	0.0002
12	0.0001

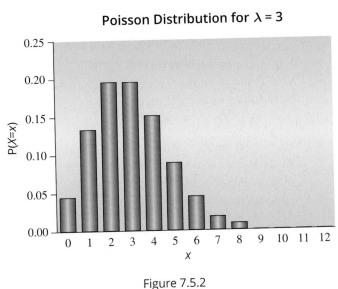

Poisson Distribution for $\lambda = 3$

Figure 7.5.2

As λ becomes even larger, say $\lambda = 12$, the distribution begins to closely resemble a bell-shaped distribution as shown in Figure 7.5.3.

Poisson Distribution for $\lambda = 12$

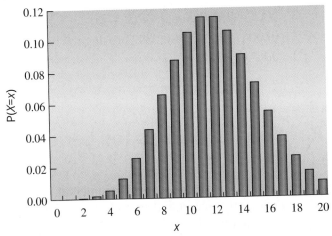

Figure 7.5.3

Kicked by Horses

The Poisson distribution is particularly useful in explaining statistical regularities in the occurrence of rare events. One classic and interesting example of this was presented by an economist and statistician named Ladislaus Bortkiewicz in his book, *The Law of Small Numbers*, published in 1898. In this book, he examined data for the number of soldiers killed by being kicked by a horse in each of 14 Prussian calvary corps during the period 1875-1894. It may not feel intuitive that something so rare and obscure could be condensed to a simple statistical model, but in fact the Poisson formula predicts these deaths quite well.

There were 196 deaths from being kicked by horses on record across 280 trials (14 corps x 20 years). Dividing 196/280 gives a mean (λ) of 0.7 deaths by horses per corps per year. Assuming a Poisson distribution, you would expect to see 97 instances of 1 horse kick death in a corps during a one year period, and 34 instances of 2 horse kick deaths. The records show that 91 instances of 1 death by horse occurred and 32 instances of 2! This example was found to be quite compelling and really popularized the Poisson distribution.

☁ **Technology**

To find a Poisson probability we use the `poissonpdf` function on the TI-83/84 Plus calculator. The results are shown below. For instructions on how to do this using a calculator, or using other technologies, please visit stat.hawkeslearning.com and navigate to **Technology Instructions > Poisson Distribution > Poisson Probability (pdf)**.

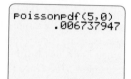

☁ **Technology**

For instructions on how to find Poisson probabilities using a calculator, or other technologies, please visit stat.hawkeslearning.com and navigate to **Technology Instructions > Poisson Distribution > Poisson Probability (cdf)**.

Poisson Random Variables for Time

Most Poisson applications relate to the number of occurrences of some event in a specific duration of time.

Example 7.5.1

Suppose a bank has one automatic teller machine. Customers arrive at the machine at a rate of 20 per hour and according to a Poisson pattern.

a. What is the probability that no one will arrive in a 15-minute interval?

b. What is the probability that in a 15-minute period at least 3 persons will use the automated teller machines?

Solution

a. Let X = the number of arrivals in a 15-minute period.

This problem contains one of the standard techniques used in working with Poisson random variables, that is, translating the arrival rate to correspond to the desired time interval. In this problem, the rate is given at 20 per hour which corresponds to a rate of 5 per $\frac{1}{4}$ hr. Thus, $\lambda = 5$ and the desired probability is $P(X = 0) = \dfrac{e^{-5}5^0}{0!}$, or $P(X = 0) = 0.0067$.

The probability could also have been found directly by using the table in Appendix A or technology.

b. What is the probability that in a 15-minute period at least 3 persons will use the automated teller machines?

$$
\begin{aligned}
P(X \geq 3) &= 1 - P(X \leq 2) \\
&= 1 - \big(P(X = 0) + P(X = 1) + P(X = 2)\big) \\
&= 1 - \big(0.0067 + 0.0337 + 0.0842\big) \text{ (using the Poisson table)} \\
&= 1 - 0.1246 = 0.8754
\end{aligned}
$$

Poisson Random Variables for Length or Space

Instead of counting the number of successes in a time interval, there are a number of applications of the Poisson that measure the number of successes in some area or length. The average number of successes in the area or length will define the parameter of the Poisson random variable.

Example 7.5.2

The telephone company is considering purchasing optical cable from Optica, Inc. The company wishes to replace approximately 100,000 feet of conventional cable with optical fiber. Since optical fiber is very difficult to repair, it is important that the number of optical cable defects are minimized. Optica claims that on average there is one defect per 200,000 feet of cable. What is the probability that the replaced cable will contain no defects?

Solution

Let X = the number of defects in 100,000 feet of optical cable.

Based on previous experience, we assume that the number of defects are approximated by a Poisson distribution with Poisson parameter as follows.

$$\lambda = \frac{100,000}{200,000} = \frac{1}{2} \text{ (the average number of defects per 100,000 feet of cable)}$$

Using the tables provided in Appendix A, Table F,

$$P(X = 0) = 0.6065.$$

⌾ Technology

A Poisson probability can also be found using the POISSON.DIST function in Excel. For instructions please visit stat.hawkeslearning.com and navigate to **Technology Instructions > Poisson Distribution > Poisson Probability (pdf)**.

fx	=POISSON.DIST(0,0.5,FALSE)	
	D	E
	0.606531	

7.5   Exercises

Basic Concepts

1. How is the Poisson distribution similar to the binomial distribution?

2. What are the two conditions that an experiment must meet in order to be considered a Poisson random variable?

3. What are some uses of the Poisson probability model in the real world?

4. What is the Poisson probability distribution function?

5. What is the parameter of the Poisson probability model?

6. What is the expected value of a Poisson random variable? The variance? The standard deviation?

Exercises

7. Suppose that, on average, 5 students enrolled in a small liberal arts college have their automobiles stolen during the semester. What is the probability that exactly 2 students will have their automobiles stolen during the current semester?

8. The number of calls received by an office on Monday morning between 8:00 AM and 9:00 AM has a Poisson distribution with λ equal to 4.0.

   a. Determine the probability of getting no calls between eight and nine in the morning.

   b. Calculate the probability of getting exactly five calls between eight and nine in the morning.

   c. What will be the expected number of calls received by the office during this time period? What is the variance?

   d. Graph the probability distribution of the number of calls using values from Appendix A, Table F.

9. The director of a local hospital is studying the occurrence of medication errors. Medication errors are deemed to occur when a patient is given the wrong amount of medication or the wrong medication is given to a patient. Based on past experience, the director believes that medication errors follow a Poisson process with an average rate of 2 per week. (For the following problems, assume that 1 month = 4 weeks.)

   a. What is the probability that there are no medication errors in one week?

   b. What is the probability that there are no medication errors in one month?

   c. Find the average number of medication errors in one week.

   d. Find the average number of medication errors in one month.

   e. Find the standard deviation of the number of medication errors in one month.

   f. How likely is it that at least 4 medication errors will be observed in one month?

10. The number of weaving errors in a 20 ft by 10 ft roll of carpet has a Poisson distribution with $\lambda = 0.1$.

   a. Using Appendix A, Table F, construct the probability distribution for the carpet.

   b. What is the probability of observing less than 2 errors in the carpet?

   c. What is the probability of observing more than 5 errors in the carpet?

11. A bank is evaluating their staffing policy to assure they have sufficient staff for their drive-up window during the lunch hour. If the number of people who arrive at the window in a 15-minute period has a Poisson distribution with $\lambda = 5$, answer the following questions.

   a. How many people are expected to arrive during the lunch hour?

   b. What is the probability that no one will show up during the lunch hour of 12:00 PM to 1:00 PM?

   c. What is the probability that more than 6 people will show up in any 15-minute period?

12. An aluminum foil manufacturer wants to improve the quality of his product and is trying to develop a probability model for the flaws that occur in a sheet of foil. Assume that X, the number of flaws per square foot, has a Poisson distribution. If flaws occur randomly at an average of one flaw per 50 square feet, what is the probability that a box containing a 200 square foot roll will contain one flaw? More than one flaw?

13. A manufacturing company is concerned about the high rate of accidents that occurred on the production line last week. There were 6 accidents in the last week and this may require a report to be sent to the government agency for safety. Calculate the probability of 6 accidents occurring in a week when the average number of accidents per week has been 3.5. Assume that the number of accidents per week follows a Poisson distribution.

7.6 The Hypergeometric Distribution

The binomial and the hypergeometric random variables are very similar. Both random variables have only two outcomes on each trial of the experiment. They both count the number of successes in n trials of an experiment. The hypergeometric distribution differs from the binomial distribution in the lack of independence between trials, which also implies that the probability of success will vary between trials. In addition, hypergeometric distributions have finite populations in which the total number of successes and failures are known.

Hypergeometric Probability Distribution

The **hypergeometric probability distribution** can be used when sampling from a population of finite size N without replacement and it is known that there are k successes in the population (therefore, $N - k$ failures). The hypergeometric distribution is used to find the probability of x successes in a sample of size n.

DEFINITION

Because the binomial and hypergeometric are closely related, a small change in an experiment can switch the distribution of the random variable. A binomial experiment, such as counting the number of red cards drawn in 8 draws from a deck with replacement, can easily be modified to a hypergeometric by not replacing the cards. Since there are 26 red cards (successes) and 26 black cards (failures), the probability of drawing a red card on the first draw is $\frac{26}{52}$ or $\frac{1}{2}$. If a red card is drawn on the first draw and not replaced, the probability of drawing a red card on the next draw is slightly less $\frac{25}{51}$, since there is one less red card in the deck. If the next card drawn is also red, then the probability of a red card on the third draw will be diminished to $\frac{24}{50}$.

Hypergeometric Probability Distribution Function

The probability distribution function of the **hypergeometric distribution** is given by

$$P(X = x) = \frac{{}_kC_x \, {}_{N-k}C_{n-x}}{{}_NC_n},$$

where

k = the total number of successes possible in the population,

N = the size of the total population,

n = the size of the sample drawn,

x = the number of successes in the sample of size n, and

$$\text{maximum of } (0, n + k - N) \le x \le \text{ minimum of } (k, n).$$

FORMULA

> **Note**
>
> An alternate notation often used is
>
> $$P(X = x) = \frac{C_x^k \, C_{n-x}^{N-k}}{C_n^N}.$$

There cannot be more *successes* than there are potential successes in the population, nor can there be more successes than the total size of the sample. Thus, the maximum value of X is the smaller of k and n.

| Example 7.6.1 |

Technology

Hypergeometric probabilities can be found in Excel using the function HYPGEOM. DIST. The results for $P(X=2)$ are shown below. For instructions on how to do this using Excel, or using other technologies, please visit stat.hawkeslearning.com and navigate to **Technology Instructions > Hypergeometric Distribution**.

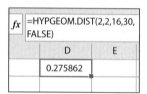

Suppose that a shipment from Piovan Semiconductor contains 30 memory chips of which two are bad. If a memory board requires 16 chips, what is the probability distribution for the number of defective chips on the memory board?

Solution

The random variable under consideration is given as

X = the number of defective chips on the memory board.

The parameters of the distribution are

$k = 2$ (a success in this case is a defective chip),

$N = 30$, and

$n = 16$.

The maximum value of X in this case is 2. Using the hypergeometric distribution function we can calculate the following probabilities.

$$P(X=0) = \frac{{}_2C_0 \; {}_{30-2}C_{16-0}}{{}_{30}C_{16}}$$
$$= \frac{(1)(30{,}421{,}755)}{145{,}422{,}675} = 0.209,$$

$$P(X=1) = \frac{{}_2C_1 \; {}_{30-2}C_{16-1}}{{}_{30}C_{16}}$$
$$= \frac{(2)(37{,}442{,}160)}{145{,}422{,}675} = 0.515, \text{ and}$$

$$P(X=2) = \frac{{}_2C_2 \; {}_{30-2}C_{16-2}}{{}_{30}C_{16}}$$
$$= \frac{(1)(40{,}116{,}600)}{145{,}422{,}675} = 0.276.$$

The distribution is summarized below.

Defective Memory Chips on the Memory Board Distribution	
x	**p(x)**
0	0.209
1	0.515
2	0.276

The Expected Value and Variance of a Hypergeometric Random Variable

It is apparent that the hypergeometric distribution can be rather tedious to calculate, based on the calculations above. Since there are no tables for the distribution, determining an expected value using the definition $\left(\sum x \cdot p(x)\right)$ would consume a considerable amount of time. Fortunately, there is a simpler method.

Expected Value of a Hypergeometric Random Variable

The **expected value** of a hypergeometric random variable can be obtained using the expression

$$\mu = E(X) = n\left(\frac{k}{N}\right).$$

FORMULA

Variance of a Hypergeometric Random Variable

The **variance** of a hypergeometric random variable is given by the expression

$$\sigma^2 = V(X) = n\left(\frac{k}{N}\right)\left(1 - \frac{k}{N}\right)\frac{(N-n)}{(N-1)}.$$

FORMULA

Example 7.6.2

Compute the expected value and variance for the random variable defined in Example 7.6.1.

Solution

$$E(X) = 16\left(\frac{2}{30}\right) = 1.067$$

$$V(X) = 16\left(\frac{2}{30}\right)\left(1 - \frac{2}{30}\right)\frac{(30-16)}{(30-1)} = 0.481$$

Thus, if the experiment were repeated many times, the average number of defective chips per board would be slightly greater than 1.

7.6 Exercises

Basic Concepts

1. How does the hypergeometric model differ from the binomial model?
2. What is the hypergeometric probability distribution function?
3. What are the parameters of the hypergeometric model?
4. How do you calculate the expected value of a hypergeometric random variable? The variance?

Exercises

5. Suppose a batch of 50 light bulbs contains 3 light bulbs that are defective. Let X = the number of defective light bulbs in a random sample of 10 light bulbs (where the sample is taken without replacement).

   a. What probability model would be appropriate for describing the number of defective light bulbs in the sample?

   b. Find the expected number of defective bulbs.

   c. Find the standard deviation of the number of defective bulbs.

   d. Find the probability that at least 1 of the bulbs sampled will be defective.

   e. Find the probability that at most 2 of the bulbs sampled will be defective.

   f. Find the probability that more than 3 of the bulbs sampled will be defective.

6. A small electronics firm has 60 employees. Ten of the employees are older than 55. An attorney is investigating a client's claim regarding age discrimination. The attorney randomly selects 15 employees without replacement and records the number of employees over age 55.

   a. What probability model would be appropriate for describing the number of employees over age 55 in a sample of 15 selected without replacement?

   b. Find the average number of employees over age 55 in the sample.

   c. Find the standard deviation of the number of employees over age 55 in the sample.

   d. Find the probability that at least 2 of the employees selected will be over age 55.

   e. Find the probability that less than 2 of the employees selected will be over age 55.

   f. Find the probability that at most 4 of the employees will be over age 55.

7. A bank has to repossess 100 homes. Fifty of the repossessed homes have market values that are less than the outstanding balance of the mortgage. An auditor randomly selects 10 of the repossessed homes (without replacement) and records the number of homes that have market values less than the outstanding balance of the mortgage.

   a. Find the expected number of homes the auditor will find with market values less than the outstanding balance of the mortgage. Find the standard deviation of the number of homes the auditor will find with market values less than the outstanding balance of the mortgage.

   b. What is the probability that all of the audited homes will have market values in excess of the outstanding balance of the mortgage?

   c. What is the probability that none of the audited homes will have market values in excess of the outstanding balance of the mortgage?

8. A small liberal arts college in the Northeast has 200 freshmen. Eighty of the freshmen are female. Suppose thirty freshmen are randomly selected (without replacement).

   a. Find the expected number of females in the sample.

   b. Find the standard deviation of the number of females in the sample.

   c. Find the probability that none of the selected students will be female.

   d. Find the probability that all of the selected students will be female.

CR   Chapter Review

Key Terms and Ideas

- Random Variable
- Probability Distribution
- Discrete Random Variable
- Continuous Random Variable
- Discrete Probability Distribution
- Probability Distribution Function
- Expected Value of a Discrete Random Variable
- Variance of a Discrete Random Variable
- Discrete Uniform Distribution
- Binomial Distribution
- Binomial Experiment
- Binomial Random Variable
- Binomial Probability Distribution Function
- Binomial Tables
- Expected Value of a Binomial Random Variable

- Variance of a Binomial Random Variable
- Standard Deviation of a Binomial Random Variable
- Poisson Distribution
- Poisson Random Variable
- Lambda
- Poisson Probability Distribution Function
- Poisson Tables
- Hypergeometric Distribution
- Hypergeometric Probability Distribution Function
- Expected Value of a Hypergeometric Random Variable
- Variance of a Hypergeometric Random Variable

Key Formulas	
	Section
Expected Value of a Discrete Random Variable X $$\mu = E(X) = \sum \left[x \cdot p(x) \right]$$ where $p(x) = P(X = x)$	7.2
Variance of a Discrete Random Variable X $$\sigma^2 = V(X) = \sum \left[(x - \mu)^2 \, p(x) \right]$$	7.2
Computational Formula for Variance of a Discrete Random Variable X $$\sigma^2 = V(X) = \sum \left[x^2 \cdot p(x) \right] - \mu^2$$	7.2
Binomial Probability Distribution Function $$P(X = x) = {}_nC_x \, p^x \, (1 - p)^{n-x}$$ where ${}_nC_x = \dfrac{n!}{x!(n-x)!}$, $n =$ the number of trials, $p =$ the probability of a success, and $x =$ the number of successes in n trials.	7.4
Expected Value of a Binomial Random Variable $$\mu = E(X) = np$$	7.4
Variance and Standard Deviation of a Binomial Random Variable $$\sigma^2 = V(X) = np(1 - p)$$ $$\sigma = \sqrt{V(X)} = \sqrt{np(1 - p)}$$	7.4
Poisson Probability Distribution Function $$P(X = x) = \frac{e^{-\lambda} \lambda^x}{x!}$$ where $e = 2.71828\ldots$ and $\lambda =$ the mean number of successes.	7.5
Hypergeometric Probability Distribution Function $$P(X = x) = \frac{{}_kC_x \, {}_{N-k}C_{n-x}}{{}_NC_n},$$ where $k =$ the total number of successes possible, $N =$ the size of the total population, $n =$ the size of the sample drawn, and $x =$ the number of successes in the sample of size n and maximum of $(0, n + k - N) \le x \le$ minimum of (k, n).	7.6

Key Formulas	
	Section
Expected Value of a Hypergeometric Random Variable	7.6
$$\mu = E(X) = n\left(\frac{k}{N}\right).$$	
Variance of a Hypergeometric Random Variable	7.6
$$\sigma^2 = V(X) = n\left(\frac{k}{N}\right)\left(1 - \frac{k}{N}\right)\frac{(N-n)}{(N-1)}.$$	

Additional Exercises

1. A statistics professor has determined the following probability distribution for X, the grade which a student will earn in a business statistics class.

Grade Distribution		
Grade	**x**	**P (X = x)**
A	4.0	0.15
B	3.0	0.35
C	2.0	0.25
D	1.0	0.15
F	0.0	0.10

   a. What is the average grade that a student will earn in a business statistics class?

   b. Find the variance of the grades that students will earn in a business statistics class.

   c. Find the standard deviation of the grades which students will earn in a business statistics class.

   d. What is the probability that a student will earn a grade of 4.0?

   e. Find the probability that a student will earn a grade of at least 2.0.

   f. Find the probability that a student will earn a grade of at most 1.0.

   g. Find the probability that a student will earn a grade of more than 3.0.

2. The US Department of Labor has issued a new set of guidelines governing certain work practices for employees. It estimates that only 20% of all firms will be subject to the new guidelines. To validate the estimate of the number of firms that will be affected by the new guidelines, the department randomly selects a sample of twenty firms for a study. Assuming their initial estimate of 20% is correct, answer the following questions.

    a.   What is the probability that 1 or fewer of the sampled firms will be subject to the new rules?

    b.   What is the probability that between 15 and 25 percent of the sampled firms will be subject to the rules?

    c.   One of the directors in the department remarked he thought that ten firms out of the sample would be subject to the rules. If the initial estimate is correct, what is the chance of this occurring?

3.   Historically, the probability that a library book will be returned in one week is $p = 0.50$. The head librarian for the University Staff Hospital library is monitoring a random sample of 10 books to determine if the historical proportion of the books returned within one week, 0.50, has changed. Assuming the historical return rate is still the same, answer the following questions.

    a.   What is the probability that between four and six books will be returned in one week?

    b.   What is the chance that eight or more books will be returned in one week?

    c.   What is the probability that only one book will be returned in one week?

4.   The number of fatalities resulting from automobile accidents for a 10-mile stretch of an interstate highway averages 1 per 100,000 automobiles. During a particular holiday weekend, 500,000 automobiles traveled over the 10-mile segment. Using a Poisson distribution, find the probability of each of the following.

    a.   No fatalities

    b.   3 fatalities

    c.   At least one fatality

5.   Compute the mean and variance for the following random variables.

    a.   The number of sixes obtained in 10 rolls of a single die.

    b.   The number of hearts in a 13-card bridge hand. (Draw 13 cards from a standard deck without replacement.)

    c.   The number of free throws made by a professional basketball player in his next 10 attempts. (Assume the player makes 88% of his free throws in the long run.)

    d.   The number of cracked eggs selected when randomly selecting 5 eggs from a 12-egg carton containing 2 cracked eggs.

    e.   The number of dots on the upper face when a single die is thrown.

6.   A manufacturer of digital cameras knows that a shipment of 30 cameras sent to a large discount store contains eight defective cameras. The manufacturer also knows that the store will choose two of the cameras at random, test them, and accept the shipment if neither one is defective.

    a.   Find the probability that at least one is defective.

    b.   What is the probability that the shipment is accepted?

7. In a certain shipment of sixteen radios, four are defective. Eight of the radios are selected at random without replacement. What is the probability that at least one of the eight radios is defective?

8. According to the American Hotel and Lodging Association (AH&LA), women accounted for 31% of business travelers in the year 2009.[1] Suppose that to attract these women business travelers, the AH&LA found that 80% of hotels offer hair dryers in the bathrooms. Consider a random and independent sample of 15 hotels.

    a. Based on the information given, how many of the 15 hotels are expected to offer hair dryers in the bathrooms?

    b. Find the probability that all of the hotels in the sample offer hair dryers in the bathrooms.

    c. Find the probability that more than 5 but less than 9 of the hotels in the sample offer hair dryers in the bathrooms.

9. A carnival has a game of chance: a fair coin is tossed. If it lands heads, you win $1, and if it lands tails, you lose $0.50. How much should a ticket cost to play this game if the carnival wants to break even?

10. You are working on a multiple-choice test which consists of 15 problems. Each of the problems has five answers, only one of which is correct. If you are totally unprepared for the test and are guessing, what is the probability that your first correct answer is within the first fifteen problems?

11. An automobile manufacturer is always trying to improve the quality of its vehicles. Assume that the number of defects per vehicle follows a Poisson distribution. If these defects occur randomly at an average rate of five per vehicle, what is the probability that a randomly selected vehicle will have at least one defect?

12. When proofreading a statistics textbook, one can expect to find a number of errors, whether they are typographical, symbolic, or even incorrect mathematical calculations. On average, a statistics textbook will contain 30 errors. What is the probability that when proofreading a text, one finds at least three errors? Assume that the number of errors found follows a Poisson distribution.

13. While on a shopping spree, you randomly select five smart watches from an electronics store that sells 20 smart watches. Of these 20 watches, 12 will last beyond the 1-year limited warranty and will not need to be replaced or repaired. What is the probability that at least three of the five smart watches selected will not last beyond the limited warranty period without needing to be replaced or repaired?

14. A jeweler was given a collection of twelve diamonds, of which three were synthetic (fake). If the jeweler selected two of these diamonds at random (without replacement), what is the probability that neither jewel is found to be synthetic?

15. L-Mart Inspections is a building inspection company. There were ten new commercial construction buildings completed in the last month and the sites are now available for inspection. L-Mart plans to inspect some of the new constructions for code violations and believes that half of the buildings will have violations.

    a. What probability model would be appropriate for describing the number of buildings in the sample that have code violations? Explain your answer.

    b. If L-Mart randomly selects four buildings to inspect, what is the probability that three of the buildings will have violations?

16. In the casino game of roulette, a wheel is spun and a ball is set in motion, ultimately coming to rest in one of the 38 slots on the wheel. Any slot is as likely as any other to capture the ball. Of the 38 slots, 18 are red, 18 are black, and 2 are green. Suppose the entry fee to play a single game is $1 and the participant bets on red. If the ball comes to rest in one of the red slots, he wins $1 in addition to getting back the original $1 entry fee. If the ball does not end up in a red slot, the $1 entry fee is lost. Let X denote the monetary gain when betting $1 on red, in a single game of roulette. Gain is defined as the amount won minus the fee to play.

    a. What are possible values of X?

    b. Is X a discrete or a continuous random variable? Explain.

    c. Construct the probability distribution of X.

    d. Find the expected value of X and interpret this number.

    e. Do you feel that in any casino games you would have a positive expected gain? Why?

17. An experiment consists of tossing two coins and a die simultaneously.

    a. List the 24 equally-likely simple events.

    b. Define the random variable X as the sum of the number of heads on the two coins and the number of dots on the die. What are the possible values of X?

    c. Construct the probability distribution of X in the form of a table.

    d. Find the expected value of X.

18. A pediatric nurse is studying the number of babies born at a hospital with congenital defects. The nurse believes that the number of babies born during a month with congenital defects follows a Poisson distribution with an average of one baby born with a congenital defect per month.

    a. Find the average number of babies born in one year with congenital defects.

    b. Find the standard deviation of the number of babies born in one year with congenital defects.

    c. Find the probability that no babies are born with congenital defects in one year.

    d. Find the probability that at least 1 baby is born with a congenital defect in a year.

    e. Find the probability that exactly 12 babies are born with a congenital defect in a year.

19. A lifelong beer drinker claims to be able to distinguish his favorite brand of beer, Sudriser, from all others. Two of his friends, doubtful of the claim, set up a taste test involving 4 brands of beer. Sudriser is poured into two mugs and each of the other 3 brands is also poured into 2 mugs, giving a total of 8 mugs of beer. The brand in each mug is written on a slip of paper taped to the bottom of the mug. The mugs are then arranged in a random order, and our friend is told to sample each mug and choose which 2 mugs contain Sudriser. Cheerfully, our friend complies.

Answer the following, assuming that the beer drinker really can't distinguish between beers.

   a.   What is the probability that the 2 mugs containing Sudriser are chosen?

   b.   What is the probability that at least one of the 2 mugs containing Sudriser is chosen?

   c.   What is the probability that the 2 mugs chosen contain the same brand?

   d.   What is the probability that the 2 mugs chosen contain different brands?

"Creativity is the ability to introduce order into the randomness of nature."

— Eric Hoffer

8 CHAPTER
Continuous Probability Distributions

Introduction

In the previous chapter, random variables were primarily counts of some phenomenon called a *success*. These counts could only take on discrete values, usually starting at zero. In this chapter, the focus will be on variables that take on any value in some continuum, that means a range of numbers on the real number line. The range of adult heights, for example, lies on a continuum between 26 and 100 inches.

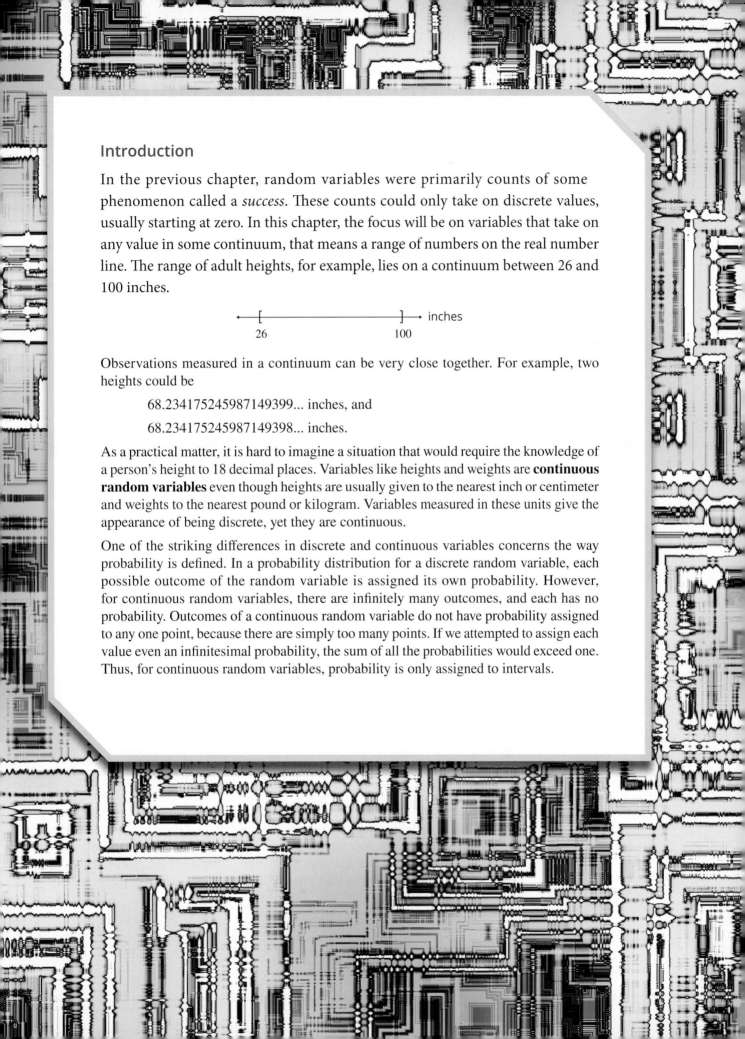

Observations measured in a continuum can be very close together. For example, two heights could be

       68.234175245987149399... inches, and

       68.234175245987149398... inches.

As a practical matter, it is hard to imagine a situation that would require the knowledge of a person's height to 18 decimal places. Variables like heights and weights are **continuous random variables** even though heights are usually given to the nearest inch or centimeter and weights to the nearest pound or kilogram. Variables measured in these units give the appearance of being discrete, yet they are continuous.

One of the striking differences in discrete and continuous variables concerns the way probability is defined. In a probability distribution for a discrete random variable, each possible outcome of the random variable is assigned its own probability. However, for continuous random variables, there are infinitely many outcomes, and each has no probability. Outcomes of a continuous random variable do not have probability assigned to any one point, because there are simply too many points. If we attempted to assign each value even an infinitesimal probability, the sum of all the probabilities would exceed one. Thus, for continuous random variables, probability is only assigned to intervals.

8.1   The Uniform Distribution

There are two types of uniform distributions, discrete and continuous. You already studied the discrete uniform distribution in Chapter 7. Conceptually both uniform distributions distribute probability evenly across a sample space. For the **continuous uniform distribution**, the probability density is spread out over some range from a to b, as shown in Figure 8.1.1.

Continuous Uniform Distribution

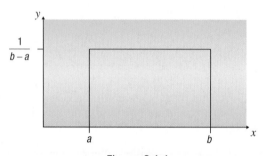

Figure 8.1.1

Uniform Probability Density Function

The **uniform probability density function** is given by

$$f(x) = \begin{cases} \dfrac{1}{b-a} & \text{for } a \leq x \leq b \\[2ex] 0 & \text{otherwise.} \end{cases}$$

The mean and standard deviation are given by the following expressions.

$$\mu = \frac{a+b}{2} \text{ and } \sigma = \frac{b-a}{\sqrt{12}}$$

FORMULA

Continuous random variables do not have probability distribution functions. Instead they have **probability density functions**, which are denoted by $f(x)$. The probability density function for the uniform random variable, its expected value (mean), and its standard deviation are given above. The parameters of the probability density function are the minimum and maximum values of the random variable and are referred to as a and b, respectively.

When the uniform probability density function is graphed, it produces a rectangle or square. The probability of observing a random variable in some interval is expressed as the area under the density function associated with the interval. Since the density for the uniform distribution produces a rectangle, calculating the probability of an interval is as simple as calculating the area of a rectangle, which does not require complicated geometry.

Example 8.1.1

The fire department records how long it takes each of its trucks to reach the scene of a fire. Suppose that distribution of arrival times is uniform with the minimum time being 2 minutes and the maximum 15 minutes. Let X equal the time it takes a truck to arrive at the scene of a fire after being called.

   a.   What is the probability that a truck will reach a fire scene within 5 to 10 minutes?
   b.   What is the expected time until arrival of the fire truck?
   c.   What is the standard deviation of truck arrival times?

Solution

   a.   For the uniform distribution, the probability is simply calculated using the formula for the area of a rectangle.

$$\text{Area} = \text{Height} \cdot \text{Width}$$

$\text{Height} = \dfrac{1}{b-a} = \dfrac{1}{15-2} = \dfrac{1}{13}$, and Width $= 10 - 5 = 5$, therefore

$$\text{Area} = \frac{1}{13} \cdot (5) = \frac{5}{13} \text{ and the } P(5 \le X \le 10) = \frac{5}{13}.$$

This is shown in the figure below.

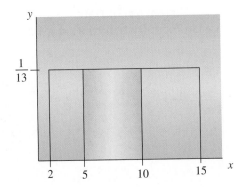

   b.   The expected value of a continuous uniform random variable is given by

$$E(X) = \mu = \frac{a+b}{2} = \frac{15+2}{2} = 8.5 \text{ minutes.}$$

Therefore, the expected time until arrival of the fire truck is 8.5 minutes.

   c.   The standard deviation of a continuous uniform random variable is given by

$$\sigma = \frac{b-a}{\sqrt{12}} = \frac{15-2}{\sqrt{12}} \approx 3.753 \text{ minutes.}$$

Therefore, the standard deviation of truck arrival times is approximately 3.753 minutes.

What does data from a uniform random variable look like?

While the density function for the uniform distribution has a flat top, a histogram of data from a uniformly distributed random process will not be so perfectly flat. Suppose that we generated 100 observations from a random process that was uniformly distributed between 2 and 15. Clearly, the frequency of each category is not identical (see Figure 8.1.2).

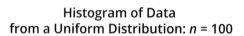
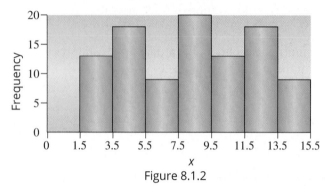

Figure 8.1.2

However, if we were to generate 1000 observations, the distribution would begin to level (see Figure 8.1.3).

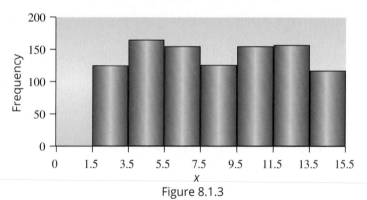

Figure 8.1.3

8.1   **Exercises**

Basic Concepts

1. Probability is defined differently for discrete and continuous random variables. Describe this difference.

2. How is the continuous uniform distribution different from the discrete uniform distribution?

3. What is the uniform probability density function?

4. Describe the shape of the density function for a uniform distribution.

Exercises

5. Suppose a continuous random variable is uniformly distributed between 10 and 70.

   a. What is the mean of the distribution?

   b. What is the standard deviation of the distribution?

   c. What is the probability that a randomly selected value will be above 45?

   d. What is the probability that a randomly selected value will be less than 30?

   e. What is the probability that a randomly selected value will be between 25 and 50?

   f. Find the probability that a randomly selected value will exactly equal 35.

6. Polar Bear Frozen Foods manufactures frozen French fries for sale to grocery store chains. The final package weight is thought to be a uniformly distributed random variable. Assume X, the weight of French fries, has a uniform distribution between 57 ounces and 63 ounces.

   a. What is the mean weight for a package?

   b. What is the standard deviation for the weight of a package?

   c. What is the probability that a store will receive a package weighing less than 59 ounces?

   d. What is the probability that a package will contain between 60 and 63 ounces?

   e. What is the probability that a package will contain more than 62 ounces?

   f. Find the probability that a package will contain exactly 60 ounces.

7. The annual growth in height of cedar trees is believed to be distributed uniformly between 6 and 11 inches.

   a. Draw a picture of the distribution of growth in height of cedar trees.

   b. What is the mean growth per year?

   c. What is the standard deviation of the growth per year?

   d. What is the probability that a randomly selected cedar tree will grow between 9 and 10 inches in a given year?

   e. Find the probability that a randomly selected cedar tree will grow less than 8 inches in a given year.

   f. Find the probability that a randomly selected cedar tree will grow more than 9 inches in a given year.

   g. Find the probability that a randomly selected cedar tree will grow exactly 7 inches in a given year.

8. A particular employee arrives to work sometime between 8:00 AM and 8:30 AM. Based on past experience the company has determined that the employee is equally likely to arrive at any time between 8:00 AM and 8:30 AM.

   a. On average, what time does the employee arrive?

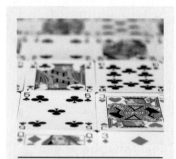

b.   What is the standard deviation of the time at which the employee arrives?

c.   If a call comes in for the employee at 8:10 AM find the probability that the employee will be there to take the call.

d.   Find the probability that the employee will arrive between 8:20 AM and 8:25 AM.

e.   Find the probability that the employee will arrive after 8:15 AM.

f.   Find the probability that the employee will arrive at exactly 8:10 AM.

8.2   The Normal Distribution

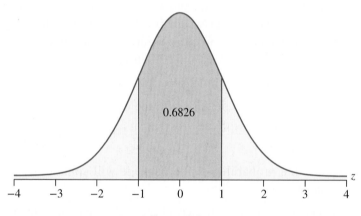

Figure 8.2.1

The **normal distribution**, originally called the Gaussian distribution, was named after Karl Gauss who published a work in 1833 describing the mathematical definition of the distribution. Gauss developed this distribution to describe the error in predicting the orbits of planets.

Normal distributions are all bell-shaped, but the bells come in various shapes and sizes. Since all normal distributions are symmetric, the mean, mode, and median are all equal.

Although normally distributed random variables can range in value from minus infinity to positive infinity, values that are a great distance from the mean rarely occur.

Properties of the Normal Distribution

The total area under any normal curve equals one.

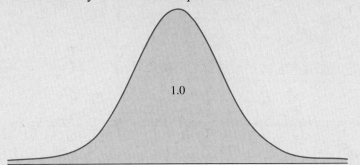

Within a fixed number of standard deviations from the mean, all normal distributions contain the same fraction of their probability.

The probability of a normal random variable being in some interval corresponds to the area under the curve bounded by the specified interval.

PROPERTIES

In Figure 8.2.1, the shaded area represents the probability of being within $\pm 1\sigma$ of the mean. Regardless of the shape of the normal distribution, the area under the curve and the probability of being within one standard deviation ($\pm 1\sigma$) of the mean equals 0.6826.

Figure 8.2.2 illustrates the area under the curve within two standard deviations of the mean. The probability of being within $\pm 2\sigma$ of the mean equals 0.9544 for every normal distribution.

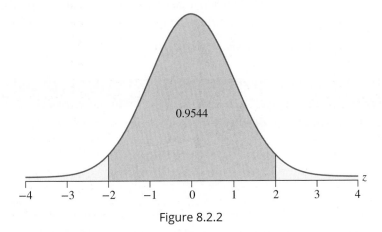

Figure 8.2.2

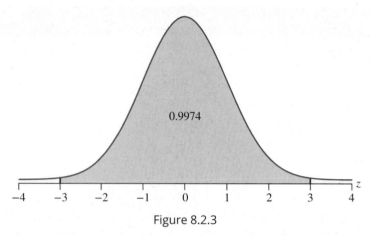

Figure 8.2.3

Figure 8.2.3 illustrates the area under the curve within three standard deviations of the mean. As you can see, virtually all the area under the curve is within three standard deviations of the mean. The probability of being within $\pm 3\sigma$ of the mean equals 0.9974.

Since the empirical rule given in Chapter 4 is based on the normal distribution, these results are identical to the empirical rule frequencies.

A number of non-normal random variables with bell shapes will be introduced in later chapters. In fact, the word *normal* can be somewhat misleading. The name suggests that the distribution is a fact of nature. It is not. However, many variables seem to possess a shape that resembles the normal distribution.

To be sure, the normal distribution is the preeminent distribution used in the statistical theory we will examine. Many statistical inference procedures either directly or indirectly have roots in normal theory. These procedures usually assume that the population from which a random sample is drawn is normally distributed.

Like other theoretical distributions, a normal distribution is completely defined by its probability density function.

> **Normal Probability Density Function**
>
> The **normal probability density function** is given by the following.
>
> $$f(x) = \frac{1}{\sigma\sqrt{2\pi}}\, e^{-\frac{(x-\mu)^2}{2\sigma^2}}$$
>
> **FORMULA**

At first glance, this function does not look very *normal*! The distribution has two parameters, μ and σ, which are the mean and standard deviation, respectively. The mean defines the location and the standard deviation determines the dispersion. Figure 8.2.4 illustrates several normal distributions with identical standard deviations. The only difference in the distributions is the central location, the mean.

Caution

Although a normal distribution has a bell shape, a bell shape does not imply a normal distribution.

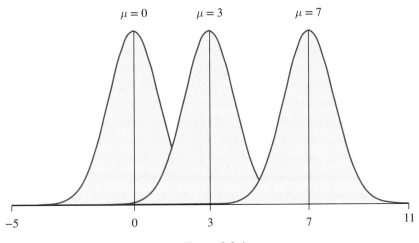

Figure 8.2.4

In Figure 8.2.5, there are several distributions with identical means, but with different standard deviations. Changing the standard deviation parameter can have rather significant effects on the shape of the distribution.

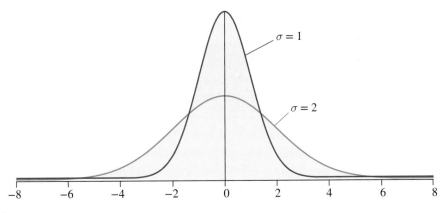

Figure 8.2.5

Looking at Data from Normal Distributions

The normal distribution is a theoretical construct with a bell shape. Therefore, it would not be unreasonable to expect data drawn from a normal population to exhibit the bell-shaped characteristic. In two small samples taken from a normal population, shown in Figures 8.2.6 and 8.2.7, the data does show a faint resemblance of a bell shape. But as you can see, the shapes of the histograms developed from these small samples are somewhat unpredictable, even though the bell-shaped pattern is to some extent apparent.

Bringing the Normal Distribution Out of the Closet

Adolphe Quetelet (1796-1874) was born in Belgium and received his doctorate from the University of Ghent in 1819. In 1824 he went to Paris for three months to study astronomy and was exposed to the theory of probability by LaPlace and Fourier.

Quetelet, however, became deeply interested in social science and believed the astronomers' error law and other laws of physics could be applied to phenomena in the social world. In 1844 Quetelet announced that the astronomers' error law (the normal distribution) could be applied to human features such as height, weight, and girth. He believed that models that astronomers were using could eventually be used in a new science of "social mechanics." Quetelet was instrumental in popularizing the normal distribution in disciplines other than astronomy.

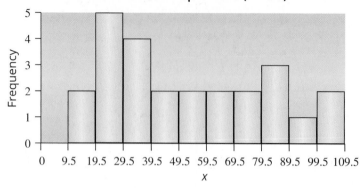

Figure 8.2.6

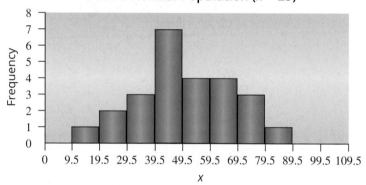

Figure 8.2.7

For large samples, the representation of the bell curve is usually more visible. While the large sample ($n = 200$) certainly is not a perfect bell curve, it is recognizable (see Figure 8.2.8).

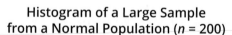

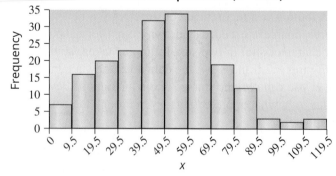

Figure 8.2.8

Using the probability density to determine the probability of some interval would be complicated. Fortunately, there is an easier way. A special normal distribution, called the **standard normal**, can be used to determine probabilities for any normal random variable. The standard normal distribution will be discussed in Section 8.3.

8.2   **Exercises**

Basic Concepts

1. How was the normal distribution developed?

2. Are the normal and uniform distributions probability models?

3. List the properties of the normal distribution.

4. What is the shape of the normal distribution?

5. What are the parameters of the normal distribution?

6. If the variance of a normal distribution is constant, what effect will changes in the mean have on the distribution?

7. If the mean of a normal distribution is constant, what effect will changes in the standard deviation have on the distribution?

Exercises

8. Sketch a normal curve and mark each of the following on the x-axis.

    a. μ **c.** $\mu - \sigma$

    b. $\mu + \sigma$

9. Sketch a normal curve and use labels to illustrate the empirical rule.

10. Sketch three normal curves on a single axis that have the same standard deviation but different means.

11. Sketch three normal curves on a single axis that have the same mean, but different standard deviations.

8.3   **The Standard Normal Distribution**

Given that the normal distribution is a function of two continuous parameters, μ and σ, there are an infinite number of combinations for μ and σ, and thus an infinite number of normal distributions. The **standard normal distribution** in Figure 8.3.1 is a special version of the normal distribution. This distribution provides a basis for computing probabilities for all normal distributions.

Standard Normal Distribution
The **standard normal distribution** is a normal distribution with a mean of zero and a standard deviation of one. $$\mu = 0 \quad \text{and} \quad \sigma = 1$$ <div align="right">**DEFINITION**</div>

Astronomy and the Normal Distribution

Although de Moivre derived the equation of the normal distribution as a consequence of problems involving the binomial distribution, Gauss and Laplace were inspired by their desire to predict the locations of planets, stars, meteors, and comets. Their predictions of the locations of celestial bodies produced errors and they needed to describe those errors. In the 19th century the normal distribution was referred to as the astronomers' error law. Much of the early scientific use of the normal distribution was for the analysis of errors.

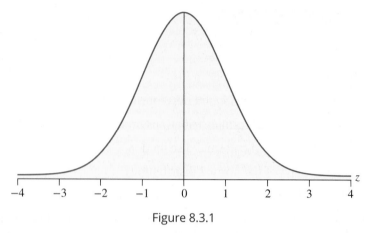

Figure 8.3.1

The technique used to translate any normal random variable into a standard normal random variable is called a **z-transformation** (or "standardizing" the random variable) and was discussed earlier in Chapter 4. Because the z-transformation gives the standard normal unique status among normals, the standard normal is also referred to as the **z-distribution**.

Tables A, B, and C in Appendix A contain probability calculations for various areas under the standard normal curve. Specifically, Tables A and B provide the probability that a standard normal random variable will be less than a specified value. Table C provides the probability that a standard normal random variable will be between 0 and a specified value. For example, to compute the probability that a standard normal random variable will be less than 1 (see Figure 8.3.2), look up the value 1.00 in Table B. The table value of 0.8413 is the area under the curve between negative infinity and 1, which is also the probability that the random variable will assume a value in that interval.

◌ Technology

A normal probability can also be easily found using technology, such as a TI-83/84 Plus calculator. For full instructions on computing normal probabilities using this and other technologies, visit stat.hawkeslearning.com and navigate to **Technology Instructions > Normal Distribution > Normal Probability (cdf)**.

```
normalcdf(-10ε6,
1)
         .8413447404
normalcdf(0,1)
         .3413447399
```

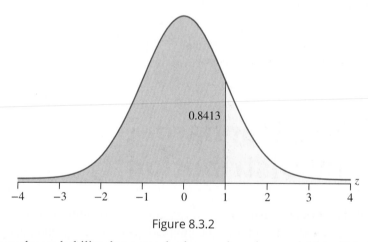

Figure 8.3.2

To compute the probability that a standard normal random variable will be between 0 and 1 (see Figure 8.3.3), look up the value 1.00 in Table C. The table value of 0.3413 is the area under the curve between 0 and 1, which is also the probability that the random variable will assume a value in that interval.

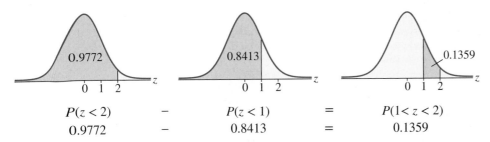

$P(z < 2)$ – $P(z < 1)$ = $P(1 < z < 2)$

0.9772   –   0.8413   =   0.1359

Again, drawing the picture proves to be invaluable in this example.

Now we are going to look at some examples similar to the ones we just completed but "in reverse". This time we will be given a particular area and asked to find the value of z (a z-score) that marks the cut-off point for that area under the normal curve.

Example 8.3.6

Given that z is a standard normal random variable, find the value of z for each situation.

    a. The area to the left of z is 0.9147.
    b. The area between 0 and z is 0.3665.
    c. The area to the left of z is 0.1469.
    d. The area to the right of z is 0.7967.

Solution

    a. First, draw a picture.

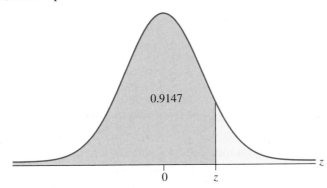

Note that this problem is slightly different from the previous one. In Example 8.3.5, you were asked to find a probability, given that you know the value of z. In this example, you are given a probability and asked to find the corresponding value of z. Recall that Table A and Table B in Appendix A give you the cumulative probability of the area less than some value of z.

Since the value of z shown in the figure above is positive (greater than 0), look in the body of Table B and find the probability value 0.9147. Once you've found the value (the probability), determine the corresponding value of z. In this case, the value of z is 1.37. So,

$$P(z < 1.37) = 0.9147$$

and the value of z is 1.37 with the area to the left of it being 0.9147.

∞ **Technology**

To find the value of z given a particular area with a TI-83/84 Plus calculator, use the invNorm function within the DISTR menu. For instructions, please visit stat.hawkeslearning.com and navigate to **Technology Instructions > Normal Distribution > Inverse Normal.**

```
invNorm(0.9147)
        1.370278443
invNorm(0.8665)
        1.10999774
invNorm(1-0.7967
)
        -.8298917332
```

b.   Again, draw a picture.

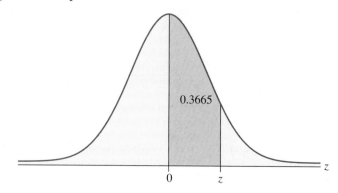

Recall that Table C gives us cumulative probabilities from 0 to z. Therefore, find 0.3665 in the body of Table C and locate the corresponding value of z. In this case,

$$P(0 < z < 1.11) = 0.3665.$$

So, the value of z corresponding to an area of 0.3665 between 0 and z is $z = 1.11$.

c.   Just as in parts **a.** and **b.**, a picture can be helpful.

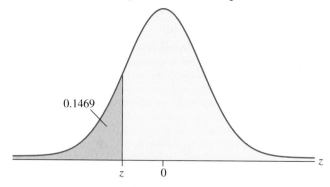

Please note that the value of z is to the left of 0. Thus, the value of z is going to be negative. Note that the area to the left of z represents the cumulative probability (in the above figure). So, to find the value of z, we only need to find 0.1469 in the body of Appendix A, Table A. The value of z with the area 0.1469 to the left of it is -1.05. That is, $P(z < -1.05) = 0.1469$.

d.   Once again, a picture can be very helpful.

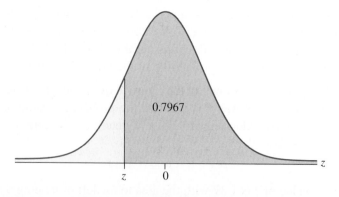

Note that from the picture, we have the area to the right of z. However, we know that the total area under the curve is 1. Thus, if the area to the right of z is 0.7967, then the area to the left of z is $1 - 0.7967 = 0.2033$. From the picture, it is clear that if we find 0.2033 in the body of Appendix A, Table A, the corresponding value of z is the value we are interested in. This value of z is -0.83. Therefore, the value of z with the area 0.7967 to the right is -0.83.

8.3   **Exercises**

Basic Concepts

1. What is the standard normal distribution? What are the parameters of the distribution?

2. Why is the standard normal distribution important?

Exercises

3. What proportion of the area under the standard normal curve falls between the following z-values?

   a.   0 and 0.67   **c.**   0 and 1.96
   b.   0 and 1.645   **d.**   0 and 2.575

4. What proportion of the area under the standard normal curve falls between the following z-values?

   a. -0.67 and 0   **c.** -1.96 and 0
   b. -1.645 and 0   **d.** -2.575 and 0

5. What proportion of the area under the standard normal curve falls between the following z-values?

   a. -0.85 and 0.85   **c.** -1.56 and 1.98
   b. -0.55 and 0.55   **d.** -2.23 and 2.96

6. What proportion of the area under the standard normal curve falls between the following z-values?

   a. -0.97 and 0.97   **c.** -1.95 and 2.28
   b. -0.54 and 1.82   **d.** -2.89 and 1.59

7. Using the standard normal tables in Appendix A, determine the following probabilities. Sketch the associated areas.

   a. $z \leq 0$ **c.** $z \leq -1$ **e.** $z \geq -1$
   b. $z \geq 0$ **d.** $z \leq 1$ **f.** $z \geq 1$

8. Using the standard normal tables in Appendix A, determine the following probabilities. Sketch the associated areas.

   a. $z \leq -0.44$

   b. $z \geq 0.44$

   c. $-0.44 \leq z \leq 0.44$

   d. $z \leq -0.67$

   e. $z \geq 0.67$

   f. $-0.67 \leq z \leq 0.67$

9. Using the standard normal tables in Appendix A, determine the following probabilities. Sketch the associated areas.

   a. $z \leq -1.28$

   b. $z \geq 1.28$

   c. $-1.28 \leq z \leq 1.28$

   d. $z \leq -1.96$

   e. $z \geq 1.96$

   f. $-1.96 \leq z \leq 1.96$

10. Using the standard normal tables in Appendix A, determine the following probabilities. Sketch the associated areas.

    a. $P(0 \leq z \leq 0.79)$

    b. $P(-1.57 \leq z \leq 2.33)$

    c. $P(z \geq 1.89)$

    d. $P(z \leq -2.77)$

11. Using the standard normal tables in Appendix A, determine the following probabilities. Sketch the associated areas.

    a. $P(0 \leq z \leq 1.24)$

    b. $P(-2.64 \leq z \leq 3.32)$

    c. $P(z \geq 3.22)$

    d. $P(z \leq -3.39)$

12. Find the value of z such that 0.05 of the area under the curve lies to the right of z.

13. Find the value of z such that 0.01 of the area under the curve lies to the right of z.

14. Find the value of z such that 0.10 of the area under the curve lies to the right of z.

15. Find the value of z such that 0.05 of the area under the curve lies to the left of z.

16. Find the value of z such that 0.01 of the area under the curve lies to the left of z.

17. Find the value of z such that 0.10 of the area under the curve lies to the left of z.

18. Find the value of z such that 0.7458 of the area under the curve lies between $-z$ and z.

19. Find the value of z such that 0.9505 of the area under the curve lies between $-z$ and z.

20. Find the value of z such that 0.90 of the area under the curve lies between $-z$ and z.

8.4 Applications of the Normal Distribution

Standardizing a Normal Random Variable

The following formula can transform any normal random variable into a standard normal random variable, z.

$$z = \frac{x - \mu}{\sigma}$$

where x is a normal random variable with mean μ and standard deviation σ.

FORMULA

If we look at the individual pieces, exactly how the transformation works is not very mysterious. First, the numerator $x - \mu$ centers the z-distribution around zero. By subtracting the mean of the random variable from each data value, the mean of the resulting random variable will be zero. A short example illustrates the point.

Suppose that a population contained the following data values shown in Table 8.4.1.

Table 8.4.1 - Deviations from the Mean	
Data Set A	**Data Set A - 6**
1	$1 - 6 = -5$
5	$5 - 6 = -1$
6	$6 - 6 = 0$
12	$12 - 6 = 6$
Mean = 6	Mean = 0

The data has a mean of six. If six is subtracted from each of the data values, the resulting deviations are shown in the second column of the table. The deviations have a mean of zero. Essentially the location of the data set has been shifted to zero. The interrelationship of the data points to one another has not changed. Try this experiment on larger sets of data to convince yourself that subtracting the mean from each value of a data set will produce a data set that always has a mean of zero.

The standard deviation of Data Set A is approximately 3.9370. Let's standardize each data value in Data Set A (see Table 8.4.2). The resulting z-values indicate how far the data values in Table 8.4.1 are from the mean, measured in standard deviation units. The first row of Table 8.4.2 shows that the data value 1 is -1.27 standard deviation units from the mean. The mean and standard deviation of the transformed values in Table 8.4.2 are zero and one, respectively. You can verify that the mean and standard deviation of the z-scores are actually zero and one. Compute the population standard deviation rather than the sample standard deviation (divide by n instead of $n - 1$ in the standard deviation formula).

Table 8.4.2 – Standardizing Data Set A		
Data	**Formula**	**Value of z**
1	$\dfrac{1-6}{3.9370} \approx$	-1.27
5	$\dfrac{5-6}{3.9370} \approx$	-0.25
6	$\dfrac{6-6}{3.9370} \approx$	0
12	$\dfrac{12-6}{3.9370} \approx$	1.52
6	Mean	0
3.9370	Standard Deviation	1

Now that we have seen how to convert any normal random variable into a standard normal random variable, let's apply it.

Example 8.4.1

Find the probability that a normal random variable with a mean of 10 and a standard deviation of 20 will lie between 10 and 40.

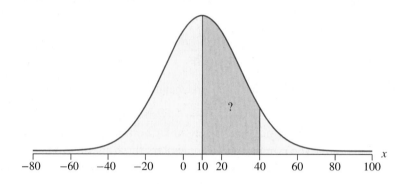

∞ Technology

To draw the area under a normal curve using the TI-83/84 Plus calculator, please see the instructions on stat.hawkeslearning.com under **Technology Instructions > Normal Distribution > Normal Probability Graph.**

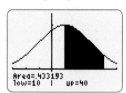

Solution

Standardizing the random variable X yields the following.

$$P(10 \leq x \leq 40) = P\left(\frac{(10-10)}{20} \leq \frac{x-\mu}{\sigma} \leq \frac{(40-10)}{20} \right) = P(0 \leq z \leq 1.5)$$

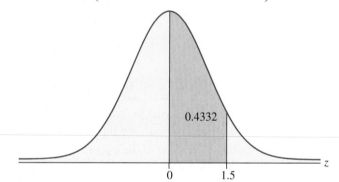

Once the problem has been converted to a problem involving z (see the figure above), the appropriate probability can be determined from the standard normal tables in Appendix A. From Table C,

$$P(0 < z < 1.5) = 0.4332.$$

Example 8.4.2

Find the probability that a normal random variable with a mean of 10 and standard deviation of 20 will be greater than 30.

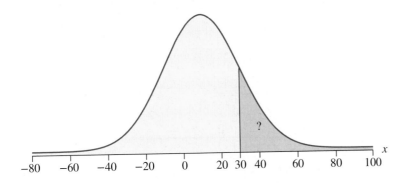

Solution

Standardizing the random variable, we have the following.

$$P(x > 30) = P\left(z > \frac{30 - 10}{20}\right)$$
$$= P(z > 1)$$

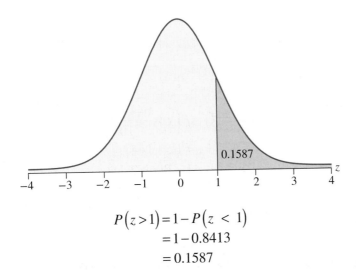

$$P(z > 1) = 1 - P(z < 1)$$
$$= 1 - 0.8413$$
$$= 0.1587$$

Technology

For instructions on computing the probability using a TI-83/84 Plus calculator visit stat.hawkeslearning.com and navigate to **Technology Instructions > Normal Distribution > Normal Probability (cdf)**.

```
normalcdf(30,10ε
6,10,20)
        .1586552596
normalcdf(1,10)
        .1586552596
```

Note that the x-value of 30 transformed into the z-value of 1. In other words, 30 is one standard deviation away from the mean.

Example 8.4.3

Suppose that a national testing service gives a test in which the results are normally distributed with a mean of 400 and a standard deviation of 100. If you score a 644 on the test, what fraction of the students taking the test exceeded your score?

Solution

Let X = a student's score on the test.

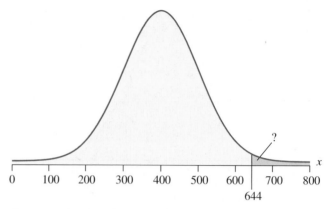

The first step is to standardize the random variable.

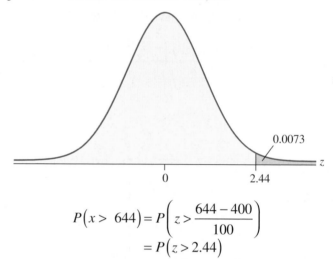

☁ **Technology**

To find the probability we use the `normalcdf` function on the TI-83/84 Plus calculator. For instructions, please visit stat.hawkeslearning.com and navigate to **Technology Instructions > Normal Distribution > Normal Probability (cdf).**

```
normalcdf(644,99
9999,400,100)
        .0073436327
```

$$P(x > 644) = P\left(z > \frac{644 - 400}{100}\right)$$
$$= P(z > 2.44)$$
$$= 1 - P(z < 2.44)$$
$$= 1 - 0.9927 = 0.0073$$

Thus, only 0.73% of the students scored higher than your score of 644.

Example 8.4.4

Suppose that for 132 shoppers making a purchase at a clothing store, the total each shopper will spend follows a normal distribution with a mean of $234 and a standard deviation of $94. What is the probability that the next purchase total will be between $100 and $150?

Solution

Let X = the purchase total. We are interested in the probability that x is between $100 and $150. Writing this probability statement and then standardizing the random variable x, we have the following.

$$P(100 < x < 150) = P\left(\frac{100 - 234}{94} < z < \frac{150 - 234}{94}\right) = P(-1.43 < z < -0.89)$$

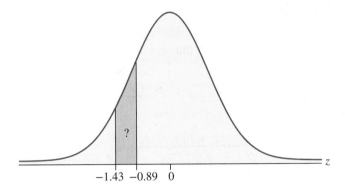

To find the probability that z is between -1.43 and -0.89, we will need to find the probability that z is less than -0.89 and subtract the probability that z is less than -1.43. Using Table A in Appendix A, we have the following.

$$P\left(-1.43 < z < -0.89\right) = P\left(z < -0.89\right) - P\left(z < -1.43\right) = 0.1867 - 0.0764 = 0.1103$$

Thus, there is approximately an 11% chance that the purchase will be between $100 and $150.

☁ **Technology**

For instructions on computing the probability using a TI-83/84 Plus calculator visit stat.hawkeslearning.com and navigate to **Technology Instructions > Normal Distribution > Normal Probability (cdf)**.

```
normalcdf(-1.43,
-0.89)
         .1103743504
```

Finding Values of a Normally Distributed Random Variable

In the previous section, we were asked for the value of z corresponding to an area under the normal curve, but a question could ask for the value of a normally distributed random variable X associated with some specified probability. Recall that the steps for finding the area under a normal curve when given a value of x are as follows.

1. Use the values of the mean and standard deviation to convert the value of x to a z-value.

2. Use the z-value to find the area under the standard normal curve.

When we want to find the value of a normally distributed random variable x given the area under a normal curve, we use the steps in reverse. First, we will rearrange the z-score formula, using algebra to solve for x, as shown.

$$z = \frac{x - \mu}{\sigma}$$
$$z \cdot \sigma = x - \mu$$
$$z \cdot \sigma + \mu = x$$

So $x = z \cdot \sigma + \mu$. Using this altered formula, the steps are as follows.

1. Use the given area under the standard normal curve to find the corresponding value of z.

2. Use the values of z, the mean, and the standard deviation to find the value of the random variable x by using the formula $x = z \cdot \sigma + \mu$.

Example 8.4.5

If a normal distribution has a mean of 28.0 and a standard deviation of 2.5, what is the value of the random variable X that has an area to its right equal to 0.6700?

Solution

Remember that we need to use the steps in reverse. Begin by using the given area to find the value of z.

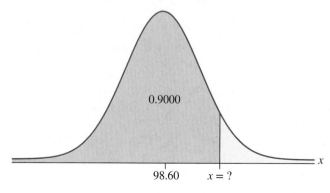

⬡ Technology

On the TI-83/84 Plus calculator, you can solve the problem without any intermediate calculations using the function invNorm(area, μ, σ). For instructions, please visit stat.hawkeslearning.com and navigate to **Technology Instructions > Normal Distribution > Inverse Normal**.

```
invNorm(1-0.6700
)
       -.4399131698
```

```
invNorm(1-0.6700
,28.0,2.5)
        26.90021708
```

Since we know that the area to the right of x is 0.6700, we also know the area to the left of x is $1 - 0.6700 = 0.3300$. Using Table A in Appendix A, we find the z-value corresponding to this area is $z \approx -0.44$. The final step is to use this z-score, along with the given values of the mean and standard deviation, to solve for x. Substituting these values into the formula for x we have the following.

$$x = z \cdot \sigma + \mu$$
$$= (-0.44)(2.5) + 28.0$$
$$= 26.9$$

This process is extremely helpful when we want to know the data values that represent cutoff points or mark certain intervals in our data set. A percentile is one type of "cutoff" for which we might want to find the value of the random variable.

Example 8.4.6

The body temperatures of adults are normally distributed with a mean of 98.60 °F and a standard deviation of 0.73 °F. What temperature represents the 90th percentile?

Solution

In order to determine the temperature that represents the 90th percentile, we first need to find the z-value that represents the 90th percentile.

Using technology, we determine this value to be $z \approx 1.281552$. Once we have the value of z, we can substitute into the formula given above to find x.

$$x = z \cdot \sigma + \mu$$
$$\approx (1.281552)(0.73) + 98.60$$
$$\approx 99.535533$$

Thus, a temperature of approximately 99.54 °F represents the 90th percentile.

⌀ Technology

To find the value of z given a percentile, use the invNorm function within the DISTR menu on a TI-83/84 Plus calculator. For instructions, please visit stat.hawkeslearning.com and navigate to **Technology Instructions > Normal Distribution > Inverse Normal**.

```
invNorm(0.9000)
        1.281551567
```

```
invNorm(0.90,98.
60,0.73)
        99.53553264
```

8.4　**Exercises**

Basic Concepts

1. Describe the connection between the z-transformation and the standard normal random variable.

Exercises

2. Calculate the z-value given $\mu = 15$, $\sigma = 2$, and $x = 19$. Indicate where the z-value would be on the standard normal distribution.

3. Calculate the z-value given $\mu = 0.023$, $\sigma = 0.001$, and $x = 0.020$. Indicate where the z-value would be on the standard normal distribution.

4. The random variable X has a normal distribution with a mean of 30 and a standard deviation of 5.

   a. Find the probability that x is between 25 and 35.

   b. Find the probability that x is greater than 40.

   c. Find the probability that x is less than 20.

5. The random variable X has a normal distribution with a mean of 200 and a standard deviation of 25.

   a. Find the probability that x is between 160 and 220.

   b. Find the probability that x is greater than 240.

   c. Find the probability that x is less than 150.

6. The Arc Electronic Company had an income of $200,000 last year. Suppose the mean income of firms in the industry for the year is $1,000,000 with a standard deviation of $500,000. If incomes for the industry are normally distributed, what proportion of the firms in the industry earned less than Arc?

7. A certain component for the newly developed electronic diesel engine is considered to be defective if its diameter is less than 8.0 mm or greater than 10.5 mm. The distribution of the diameters of these parts is known to be normal

with a mean of 9.0 mm and a standard deviation of 1.5 mm. If a component is randomly selected, what is the probability that it will be defective?

8. A television manufacturer is studying television remote control unit usage. One of the criteria they are measuring is the distance at which people attempt to activate the television set with the remote unit. They have discovered that activation distances are normally distributed with an average activation distance of six feet with a standard deviation of three feet. If a remote unit's maximum range is ten feet, what fraction of the time will users attempt to operate the remote outside of the operating limit?

9. According to the Bureau of Labor Statistics, the mean weekly earnings for people working in a sales related profession in 2010 was $631. Assume that the weekly earnings are approximately normally distributed with a standard deviation of $90.[1]

   a. What are the mean weekly earnings for people working in a sales related profession in 2010?

   b. If a salesperson was randomly selected, find the probability that his or her weekly earnings exceed $700.

   c. If a salesperson was randomly selected, find the probability that his or her weekly earnings are at most $525.

   d. If a salesperson was randomly selected, find the probability that his or her weekly earnings are between $400 and $615.

   e. Do you feel that it is reasonable to assume that the weekly earnings have a normal distribution? Why or why not?

10. The repair time for air conditioning units is believed to have a normal distribution with a mean of 38 minutes.

   a. What is the standard deviation of repair time if 40% of the units are repaired between 33 and 43 minutes?

   b. Using the value of the standard deviation that you calculated in **a.**, what is the probability that a repair will be longer than an hour?

   c. Using the value of the standard deviation that you calculated in **a.**, what is the probability that the repair time for an air conditioning unit will be less than 25 minutes?

11. VGA monitors manufactured by TSI Electronics have life spans which have a normal distribution with an average life span of 15,000 hours and a standard deviation of 2000 hours. If a VGA monitor is selected at random, find the following probabilities.

   a. The probability that the life span of the monitor will be less than 12,000 hours.

   b. The probability that the life span of the monitor will be more than 18,000 hours.

   c. The probability that the life span of the monitor will be between 13,000 hours and 17,000 hours.

12. A beer distributor believes the amount of beer in a 12-ounce can of beer has a normal distribution with a mean of 12 ounces and a standard deviation of 1 ounce. If a 12-ounce beer can is randomly selected, find the following probabilities.

   a. The probability that the 12-ounce can of beer will actually contain less than 11 ounces of beer.

   b. The probability that the 12-ounce can of beer will actually contain more than 12.5 ounces of beer.

   c. The probability that the 12-ounce can of beer will actually contain between 10.5 and 11.5 ounces of beer.

13. A statistics teacher believes that the final exam grades for her business statistics class have a normal distribution with a mean of 82 and a standard deviation of 8.

   a. Find the score which separates the top 10% of the scores from the lowest 90% of the scores.

   b. The teacher plans to give all students who score in the top 10% of scores an A. Will a student who scored a 90 on the exam receive an A? Explain.

   c. Find the score which separates the lowest 20% of the scores from the highest 80% of the scores.

   d. The teacher plans to give all students who score in the lowest 10% of scores an F. Will a student who scored a 65 on the exam receive an F? Explain.

14. In order for you to become a member of Mensa, a worldwide organization with approximately 100,000 members, your IQ score must be in the top 2%. The word *mensa* is Latin for "table," and was chosen to denote a group or round table of people with equal ability. In 1996, Mensa, which was founded by two British barristers, celebrated its 50th birthday. American Mensa Ltd., which was founded in 1960 has almost 50,000 members. Marilyn vos Savant, who is reputed to have the highest recorded IQ, is a member. Assuming that IQ scores have an approximately normal distribution with a mean and standard deviation of 100 and 15, respectively, answer the following questions.

   a. What IQ must one have in order to become a member of Mensa?

   b. What percent of all Americans have an IQ of at least 145?

   c. What percent of all members of Mensa have an IQ of at least 145?

   d. If Mensa decided to become more exclusive, and accepted only the top 1% instead of the top 2% as members, what IQ would one need in order to become a member of Mensa?

15. A farmer believes that the yields of his tomato plants have a normal distribution with an average yield of 10 lb and a standard deviation of 2 lb. The farmer would like to identify the plants which yield the highest 5% and save them for breeding purposes.

   a. Calculate the yield which separates the highest 5% of yields from the lowest 95% of yields.

b. If a tomato plant yielded 14 lb would it be kept for breeding purposes? Explain.

c. If a tomato plant yielded 13 lb would it be kept for breeding purposes? Explain.

8.5 **Assessing Normality**

Many of the statistical tests that are discussed in this book require that the data be a simple random sample from a population that has a *normal* distribution, or is at least approximately normal. If a histogram of the data is symmetric and bell-shaped, we can assume normality. However, the shape of a histogram can be hard to determine with a small sample of data. Therefore, we need additional ways to assess normality. One of these alternative methods is called a **normal probability plot** (or **normal quantile plot**).

Normal Probability Plot

A **normal probabilty plot** is a graph that plots the observed data (*x*) versus the **normal score** (*y*). The normal score is the expected *z*-score of the data values, assuming the data are normally distributed. The expected *z*-score of an observation depends on the number of observations in the data set, *n*.

DEFINITION

Assessing Normality

1. Graphically confirm the distribution of the sample data.

   a. If there are enough data values to draw a histogram, then the histogram of the data must follow a bell-shaped curve, or a "normal curve". If the shape of the histogram differs drastically from a bell shape, then we conclude that the data are not drawn from a normal distribution.

   b. For small data sets ($n \leq 30$), construct a normal probability plot. If the points on the normal probability plot do not follow a linear pattern, or if there is a systematic pattern that is not linear, then we conclude that the data are not drawn from a normal distribution.

2. Inspect the histogram or normal probability plot for outliers.

   a. The data must have no more than one outlier present. A single outlier could be the result of an error or some chance variation. However, since even a single outlier may affect results, we must reject normality if there are two or more outliers. A method to detect outliers was described in Section 4.3. Box plots of the data can also be used to detect outliers.

PROCEDURE

☁ **Technology**

Software programs which easily create normal probability plots include Minitab and R. Full directions are detailed on stat.hawkeslearning.com under **Technology Instructions > Graphs > Normal Probability Plot**.

The construction of a normal probability plot can be a tedious process if done by hand, however, there are several software programs that make the process much easier. In general, the steps for constructing a normal probability plot manually are as follows.

Constructing a Normal Probability Plot

1. Sort the data values so they are arranged from smallest to largest, and assign a rank to each value with 1 corresponding to the smallest value and n corresponding to the largest value.

2. Once sorted, compute the percentile occupied by each value using the formula

$$\frac{i-0.5}{n},$$

where i is the rank and n is the total number of data points.

3. Using the percentile computed in the previous step, find the corresponding z-value or z-score.

4. Create a scatter plot with the observed values on the horizontal axis, and the corresponding expected z-scores on the vertical axis.

PROCEDURE

Example 8.5.1

Suppose a tech company is offering computer-programming courses to the local community, and the courses are open to all ages. One of the course sections has 10 students enrolled with the ages shown below. Is there evidence to support the belief that the ages come from a normally distributed population?

Ages of Students Enrolled in the Course									
20	32	14	23	27	23	29	24	23	19

Solution

Since our data set is small, constructing a histogram will not tell us much about the distribution of the data. In order to get a better understanding of the shape of our data, we need to construct a normal probability plot. Usually, we would use a software application to construct a normal probability plot since the process can become tedious for large data sets. However, it is beneficial to understand how the process is carried out by hand. Since we are assessing a small data set, we will demonstrate the calculations below.

Steps 1–3

1. Sort the data values so they are arranged from smallest to largest, and assign a rank to each value.

2. Compute the percentile occupied by each value. For example, the value 20, which has rank 3, occupies the 25th percentile.

$$\frac{3-0.5}{10} = 0.25$$

3. Using the percentiles calculated in the previous step, find the corresponding z-scores using technology.

Age	Rank	Percentile	z-score
14	1	0.05	−1.645
19	2	0.15	−1.036
20	3	0.25	−0.674
23	4	0.35	−0.385
23	5	0.45	−0.126
23	6	0.55	0.126
24	7	0.65	0.385
27	8	0.75	0.674
29	9	0.85	1.036
32	10	0.95	1.645

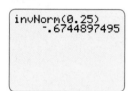

∞ Technology

The z-scores are calculated using the inverse normal. For instructions for varying technologies, please visit stat.hawkeslearning.com and navigate to **Technology Instructions > Normal Distribution > Inverse Normal**.

```
invNorm(0.25)
     -.6744897495
```

∞ Technology

For detailed instructions on creating a Normal Probability Plot using Excel please visit stat.hawkeslearning.com and navigate to **Technology Instructions > Graphs > Normal Probability Plot**.

Step 4

We create a scatter plot with ages on the horizontal axis and the corresponding z-scores on the vertical axis. This can be done by hand, or using a software application.

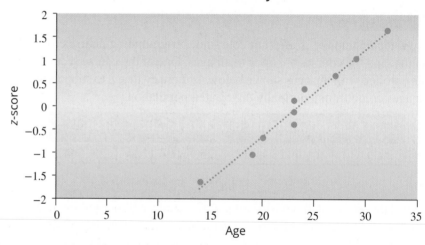

Normal Probability Plot

As we can see from the normal probability plot, the data points roughly follow a linear pattern. We cannot detect any outliers (any points very far removed from the majority on the plot). Therefore, we can conclude that the ages of students enrolled in the course come from a normally distributed population.

Example 8.5.2

Biostatisticians Dr. Robert R. Sokal and Dr. F. James Rohlf published a text titled *Biometry* which focused on the use of statistical methods in biological research.[2] Within that book, there was a data set regarding the wing lengths of houseflies in tenths of a millimeter. The length values are shown in the following table sorted from smallest to largest.

Note

The housefly population exceeds the human population 17:1.

Housefly Wing Lengths (tenths of a mm)									
36	41	42	43	45	46	47	48	49	51
37	41	42	44	45	46	47	48	49	51
38	41	42	44	45	46	47	48	49	51
38	41	43	44	45	46	47	48	49	51
39	41	43	44	45	46	47	48	50	52
39	41	43	44	45	46	47	48	50	52
40	42	43	44	45	46	47	48	50	53
40	42	43	44	45	46	47	49	50	53
40	42	43	44	45	46	47	49	50	54
40	42	43	44	45	46	48	49	50	55

⁖ Data

This data set may be accessed on stat.hawkeslearning.com under **Data Sets > Housefly Wing Lengths**.

Check whether the data are approximately normally distributed.

Solution

As the sample size is reasonably large, we start by creating a histogram so we can check to see if the distribution is symmetrical and bell-shaped.

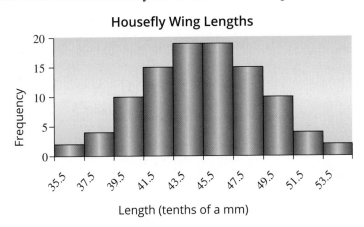

Housefly Wing Lengths

⌕ Technology

This histogram was created using Excel. For instructions on how to do this, visit stat.hawkeslearning.com and navigate to **Technology Instructions > Graphs > Histogram**.

Based on the histogram, we can assume the population is normally distributed.

By examining the beginning and end of the list of sorted data points, and also by examining the histogram, we find that there are no discernable outliers in the data set.

We are able to conclude that the population is normally distributed. With this knowledge, we can perform further statistical analysis using methods tailored to normally distributed populations.

Example 8.5.3

Dr. Thomas W. Schoener assembled a data set containing the bill-length ratios of several hundred different bird species.[3] The bill-length ratio is the ratio of the largest bill to the smallest bill measured in each population (in each species). For example, if a certain species had a bill-length ratio of 1.23, that means that the largest bill measured within that species was 1.23 times larger than the smallest bill measured within that species. Is there evidence to support the belief that bill-length ratio is normally distributed?

⁖ Data

The full data set can be retrieved from stat.hawkeslearning.com under **Data Sets > Bill Length**.

Solution

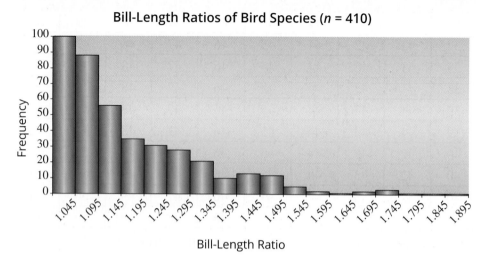

Bill-Length Ratios of Bird Species (*n* = 410)

Clearly, the histogram does not have a bell shape, so we would reject the belief that bill-length ratio is normality distributed.

Though the data set is large, let's examine what the normal probability plot looks like for this data.

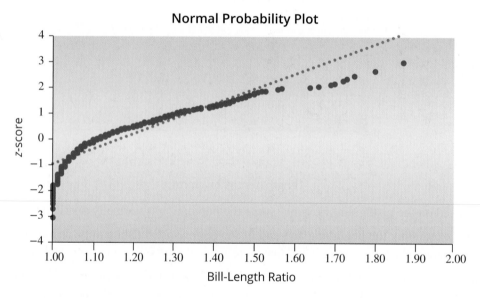

Normal Probability Plot

From the graph, we can see that the plotted points do not follow a linear trend. This particular pattern indicates that the data are skewed right and not normally distributed, confirming what we observed in the histogram.

Being able to assess the normality of a data set is of high importance in the field of statistics, and we will return to this topic when we begin discussing the various forms of statistical tests and models in later chapters.

8.5   **Exercises**

Basic Concepts

1. List two ways to graphically assess the normality of a data set. Under what conditions are each appropriate?

2. Describe the general procedure for creating a normal probability plot.

3. How should a normal probability plot look to indicate normality?

Exercises

⋰ **Data**

stat.hawkeslearning.com
Data Sets > Moneyball

⋰ **Data**

stat.hawkeslearning.com
Data Sets > Housefly Wing Lengths

4. Construct a histogram using the "BA" (batting average) column of the Moneyball data set. Can we assume batting averages have a normal distribution?

5. Create a normal probability plot of the housefly data from Example 8.5.2. What do you observe? Does the plot lead you to the same conclusion as the histogram?

6. A pharmaceutical company wants to test whether a new cold medication will perform better than an existing medication. Laboratory technicians observe a sample of 25 patients and record the number of hours it takes for each patient to feel symptom relief after taking the medicine. Before the company performs a test of the new medication against the current one, they need to know if the data are normally distributed. Use a normal probability plot to determine if the data appear to come from a population that is normally distributed.

3.00	1.50	0.20	1.62	1.06
3.01	2.45	0.66	1.94	0.21
1.51	3.08	5.37	6.96	1.32
0.79	7.20	1.36	4.45	3.29
1.74	3.87	1.90	3.50	3.09

7. Data on the total annual rainfall (in millimeters) in South Carolina was gathered by a weather station in Aiken, South Carolina from 2001-2015.[4] Use a normal probability plot to determine if the data appears to come from a population that is normally distributed.

Total Annual Rainfall in South Carolina					
Year	Total Precipitation (in millimeters)	Year	Total Precipitation (in millimeters)	Year	Total Precipitation (in millimeters)
2001	895.7	2006	1031.3	2011	991.8
2002	1106.9	2007	1002.7	2012	1089.5
2003	1681.3	2008	1321.6	2013	1584.0
2004	1003.6	2009	1434.0	2014	1070.2
2005	1166.1	2010	946.2	2015	1537.4

8. A professor is interested in examining the distribution of the grades his students received on the midterm exam.[5] There are 18 students in the class, and no time limit was given for the exam. Use a normal probability plot to determine if the students' grades are normally distributed.

80.8	81.7	81.7	81.7	81.7	82.5
83.3	83.3	84.2	84.2	85	86.7
86.7	87.5	87.5	90.3	90.4	90.8

9. A group of students and professors are studying conifers in the Pacific Northwest United States.[6] They take a sample of 25 Douglas Fir trees and record several metrics, including the circumference of the trunks (in meters). Use a normal probability plot to determine if the trunk circumference values are normally distributed.

4.97	0.45	0.40	0.15	2.84
6.65	0.62	0.39	0.86	1.24
4.93	0.64	0.62	2.22	2.23
0.29	0.18	0.27	1.97	2.45
0.19	0.55	0.41	2.85	9.09

10. A group of friends decide to run a marathon together. There are 16 runners in the group, and they are all in relatively good shape. Use a normal probability plot to determine if their marathon times are normally distributed.

4:07:58	4:18:34	4:21:15	4:24:23
4:08:07	4:18:40	4:22:17	4:25:12
4:16:28	4:19:39	4:23:52	4:25:14
4:17:30	4:19:45	4:23:55	4:26:34

8.6 Approximation to the Binomial Distribution

To approximate other distributions, the normal distribution can be very useful. Although it is a continuous distribution, it is used to approximate discrete distributions, specifically the binomial.

The Binomial Distribution

Calculating binomial probabilities can be quite time consuming if n is large. For example, suppose that you intend to sample 2000 subjects for a marketing research survey. If 50 percent of the population believes your product is superior to the competition's, what is the probability of obtaining 600 or fewer subjects who believe your company's product is superior?

$$P(X \leq 600) = P(X = 0) + P(X = 1) + P(X = 2) + \cdots + P(X = 599) + P(X = 600)$$

Determining the appropriate probability using the binomial distribution would require the calculation of 601 individual probabilities, many of which would have extremely large combinations such as the following.

$$_{2000}C_{400}\,0.5^{400}\left(1-0.5\right)^{1600}$$

Computing this and the other 600 similar calculations would be a formidable task. The normal distribution is useful in approximating binomial probabilities. The larger the binomial parameter, n, the more accurate the approximation. Determining the probability described above using the normal approximation is trivial in comparison to calculating the exact probability using the binomial.

Recall that the normal distribution is a function of two parameters, the mean and the standard deviation. Thus, if the normal distribution is used to approximate the binomial distribution, it seems reasonable that the mean and standard deviation of the normal should be the same as the mean and standard deviation of the binomial that is being approximated. Specifically, let

$$\mu = E\left(X\right) = np,\text{ and}$$

$$\sigma = \sqrt{V\left(X\right)} = \sqrt{np\left(1-p\right)}.$$

To approximate a binomial with $n = 20$ and $p = 0.5$ would require a normal distribution with

$$\mu = \left(20\right)\left(0.5\right) = 10,\text{ and}$$

$$\sigma = \sqrt{\left(20\right)\left(0.5\right)\left(1-0.5\right)} = \sqrt{5} \approx 2.2361.$$

In this example, the shapes of the distributions are quite similar and consequently the approximation will be good. This is illustrated in Figures 8.6.1 and 8.6.2.

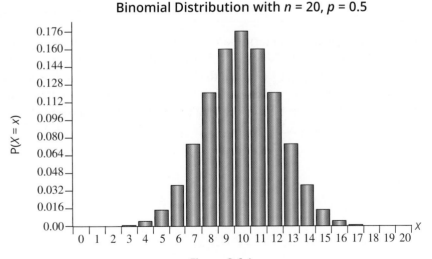

Binomial Distribution with $n = 20$, $p = 0.5$

Figure 8.6.1

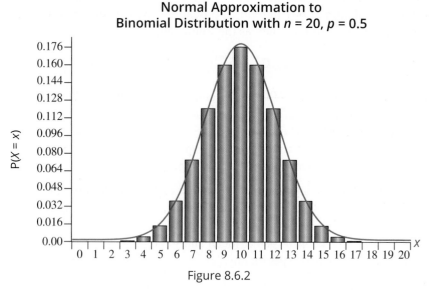

Figure 8.6.2

So, when should the normal distribution be used to approximate the binomial distribution? Generally, the approximation is reasonable when the mean of the binomial, np, is greater than or equal to 5 and $n(1 - p)$ is greater than or equal to 5. The approximation becomes quite good when np is greater than or equal to 10 and $n(1 - p)$ is greater than or equal to 10.

The normal approximation to the binomial can be improved by using **continuity correction**.

Continuity Correction

Continuity correction is used when a discrete distribution is approximated using a continuous distribution. To apply continuity correction, subtract or add 0.5 (depending on the question at hand) to a selected value in order to find the desired probability.

DEFINITION

Suppose that you wished to determine the probability that a binomial random variable ($n = 20$ and $p = 0.5$) is equal to 5. Recall that for a continuous random variable X, the probability that X is equal to some specific value is zero since there is no area under the curve for a single point, say $X = 5$. Therefore, to approximate the probability would require finding the area under the curve of a normal random variable Y between 4.5 and 5.5.

Normal Approximation to the Binomial, *n* = 20, *p* = 0.5

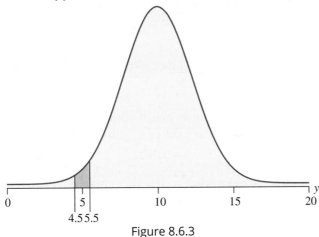

Figure 8.6.3

The continuity correction should be used whenever the normal distribution is used to approximate the binomial distribution. The following examples will illustrate how to approximate the binomial distribution using the normal distribution with continuity correction.

Example 8.6.1

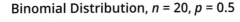

   a. Assuming $n = 20$ and $p = 0.5$, use a normal random variable (Y) to approximate the probability that a binomial random variable (X) is 5 or less.

   b. Using a normal distribution to approximate, find the probability that X is greater than 4.

Solution

   a. This implies finding the area of the rectangles for 0, 1, 2, 3, 4, and 5.

Binomial Distribution, *n* = 20, *p* = 0.5

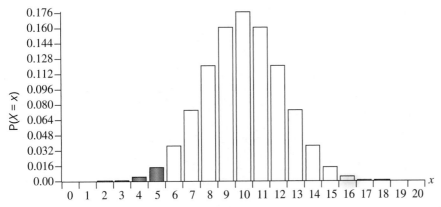

Instead of using the normal approximation $P(Y \leq 5)$, use the continuity correction $P(Y \leq 5.5)$ in order to accumulate all of the probabilities under the normal curve that correspond to the region $X \leq 5$.

To use the normal approximation the mean and standard deviation of the binomial must be calculated.

Note

The method of approximating the binomial with the normal distribution was developed in the 18th century before something like a calculator existed. Now it is practical to find the true probabilities using technology. However, it is still important to understand the normal approximation concept as we will use this idea later in Section 11.4.

∞ **Technology**

For directions on computing the exact binomial probability using a TI-83/84 Plus calculator, please visit stat.hawkeslearning.com and navigate to **Technology Instructions > Binomial Distribution > Binomial Probability (cdf)**.

```
binomcdf(20,0.5,
5)
        .0206947327
1-binomcdf(20,0.
5,4)
        .9940910339
```

$$\mu = E(X) = np = (20)(0.5) = 10$$
$$\sigma = \sqrt{np(1-p)} = \sqrt{(20)(0.5)(1-0.5)} = \sqrt{5} \approx 2.2361$$

Using the normal random variable Y with a mean of 10 and a standard deviation of 2.2361 to approximate the binomial using continuity correction,

$$P(Y \leq 5.5) = P\left(z \leq \frac{5.5-10}{2.2361}\right)$$
$$\approx P(z \leq -2.01)$$
$$= 0.0222.$$

Normal Approximation to the Binomial, $n = 20$, $p = 0.5$

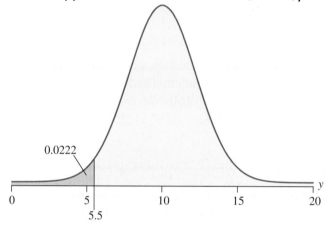

Thus, the probability that the binomial random variable is 5 or less is approximately 0.0222.

b.

Binomial Distribution, $n = 20$, $p = 0.5$

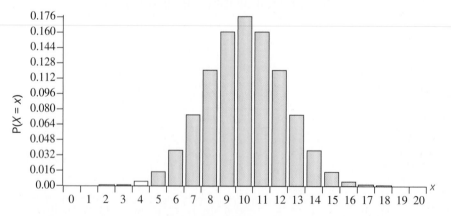

We are interested in the probability that a binomial random variable, X, is greater than 4. Since this is a discrete distribution, the probability that X is greater than 4 is equal to the probability that X is greater than or equal to 5. Thus, when using the normal approximation, we need to apply continuity correction and consider the probability that the normal random variable is greater than or equal to 4.5.

Using the normal random variable Y with a mean of 10 and a standard deviation of 2.2361 to approximate the binomial using continuity correction,

$$P(Y \geq 4.5) = P\left(z \geq \frac{4.5 - 10}{2.2361}\right)$$
$$\approx P(z \geq -2.46)$$
$$= 1 - P(z < -2.46)$$
$$= 1 - 0.0069$$
$$= 0.9931.$$

Normal Approximation to the Binomial, *n* = 20, *p* = 0.5

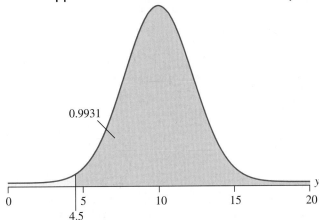

Thus, the probability that the binomial random variable is greater than 4 is 0.9931.

Example 8.6.2

An advertising agency hired on behalf of Tech's development office conducted an ad campaign aimed at making alumni aware of their new capital campaign. Upon completion of the new campaign, the agency claimed that 20% of alumni in the state were aware of the new campaign. To validate the claim of the agency, the development office surveyed 1000 alumni in the state and found that 150 were aware of the campaign. Assuming that the ad agency's claim is true, what is the probability that no more than 150 of the alumni in the random sample were aware of the new campaign?

Solution

Let X = the number of alumni that were aware of the campaign.

X is a binomial random variable with $n = 1000$ and $p = 0.20$.

So, $np = 200$ and $n(1 - p) = 800$. Therefore, the normal distribution is appropriate to use as an approximation to the binomial distribution.

The mean is $\mu = np = 200$ and the standard deviation is

$$\sigma = \sqrt{np(1 - p)} = \sqrt{160} \approx 12.6491.$$

We are interested in the probability that no more than 150 of the alumni in the sample were aware of the campaign, or $P(X \leq 150)$. However, since we are using the normal distribution to approximate the binomial, continuity correction must be applied.

Note

The z-value -3.91 is not listed in the tables given in Appendix A. However, using technology such as a calculator or computer software, it can be calculated that the actual probability is approximately 0.000046.

Let Y be a normally distributed random variable with a mean of 200 and a standard deviation of 12.6491. Applying continuity correction, we are interested in the following probability.

$$P(Y \leq 150.5) = P\left(z \leq \frac{150.5 - 200}{12.6491}\right) = P(z \leq -3.91) \approx 0.$$

Thus, if the marketing agency's claim is true, the probability that 150 or fewer alumni are aware of the campaign is practically zero. This would lead the development office to believe that the agency's claim is false.

The smaller the sample size, the more the binomial distribution deviates from the normal distribution. For this reason, continuity correction is especially useful for small sample sizes. Example 8.6.3 illustrates the difference that continuity correction makes when using the normal distribution to approximate the binomial.

Example 8.6.3

A popular restaurant near Tech's campus accepts 200 reservations on Saturdays, often the day of a home Tech football game. Given that many of the reservations are made weeks in advance of game day, the restaurant expects that about eight percent will be no-shows. What is the probability that the restaurant will have no more than 20 no-shows on the next Saturday of a football weekend?

Solution

Let X = the number of no-shows.

X is a binomial random variable with $n = 200$ and $p = 0.08$.

Since $np = 16$ and $n(1 - p) = 184$ are both greater than 10, the normal distribution can be used to approximate the binomial probability.

For the binomial, $\mu = np = 16$ and

$$\sigma = \sqrt{np(1-p)} = \sqrt{(200)(0.08)(1-0.08)} = \sqrt{14.72} \approx 3.8367.$$

Using the normal random variable Y with a mean of 16 and a standard deviation of 3.8367 to approximate the binomial without continuity correction results in

$$P(Y \leq 20) = P\left(z \leq \frac{20 - 16}{3.8367}\right) = P(z \leq 1.04) = 0.8508.$$

Using continuity correction,

$$P(Y \leq 20.5) = P\left(z \leq \frac{20.5 - 16}{3.8367}\right) = P(z \leq 1.17) = 0.8790.$$

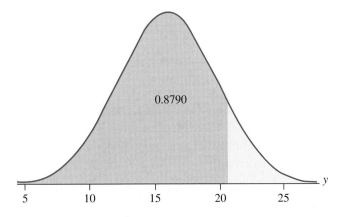

Normal Approximation to the Binomial, *n* = 200, *p* = 0.08

Thus, using the normal approximation and continuity correction, the probability that the restaurant will have no more than 20 no-shows is 0.8790. Notice that the continuity correction has a significant impact on the accuracy of the approximation. Using the binomial distribution, the exact probability is 0.8775.

Technology

For directions on computing the exact binomial probability using a TI-83/84 Plus calculator, please visit stat.hawkeslearning.com and navigate to **Technology Instructions > Binomial Distribution > Binomial Probability (cdf)**.

```
binomcdf(200,0.0
8,20)
        .877543355
```

8.6   **Exercises**

Basic Concepts

1. Why would you want to use the normal distribution to approximate a binomial distribution?

2. What are the parameters of a normal distribution used to approximate a binomial distribution?

3. What is continuity correction? How does it improve the normal approximation to the binomial?

Exercises

4. Consider the probability that fewer than 15 out of the 123 people watching a movie have already read the book. Assume that the probability of a given person having read the book is 40%. Verify that a normal distribution can be used to approximate the binomial probability, or show how the conditions have not been met.

5. Consider the probability that at most 2 out of 30 television sets on an assembly line are defective. Assume that the probability of a given television set being defective is 5%. Verify that a normal distribution can be used to approximate the binomial probability, or show how the conditions have not been met.

6. Management at a small engineering company is considering the addition of a company cafeteria area. A random sample of 50 persons out of the total number of persons employed by the firm will be surveyed to see if they are

in favor of the addition. Assume that the true percentage of persons that favor the addition is 90%.

a. Find the expected number of employees in the sample who will favor the addition of the cafeteria area.

b. Find the standard deviation of the number of employees in the sample who will favor the addition of the cafeteria area.

c. What is the probability that between 35 and 37 employees (inclusive) in the sample will favor the cafeteria?

d. What is the probability that more than 40 of the employees in the sample will favor the cafeteria?

e. What is the probability that at most 38 of the employees in the sample will favor the cafeteria?

7. The accounting department of a large corporation checks the addition of expense reports submitted by executives before paying them. Historically, they have found that 15% of the reports contain addition errors. An auditor randomly selects 60 expense reports and audits them for addition errors.

a. Find the expected number of reports in the sample that will have addition errors.

b. Find the standard deviation of the number of reports sampled that will have addition errors.

c. Find the probability that fewer than 10 of the sampled expense reports will have addition errors.

d. Find the probability that at least 30 of the sampled expense reports will have addition errors.

e. Find the probability that between 5 and 15 (inclusive) of the sampled expense reports will have addition errors.

8. A local electronics store purchased a market research study which suggests that 60 percent of all homes have DVD recorders/players. A sample of 200 homes is selected to confirm the study's findings. If the marketing study is correct, answer the following questions.

a. Find the expected number of homes sampled which will have DVD recorders/players.

b. Find the standard deviation of the number of homes in the sample which will have video recorders/players.

c. What is the probability that at most 80 of the sampled homes will have DVD recorders/players?

d. What is the probability that between 100 and 120 (inclusive) homes sampled will have DVD recorders/players?

e. What is the probability that at least 130 of the sampled homes will have DVD recorders/players?

9. Suppose a virus is believed to infect two percent of the population. If a sample of 3000 randomly selected subjects are tested, answer the following questions.

a. Find the expected number of subjects sampled that will be infected.

b. Find the standard deviation of the number of subjects sampled that will be infected.

c. What is the probability that fewer than 30 of the subjects in the sample will be infected?

d. What is the probability that between 40 and 80 (inclusive) of the subjects in the sample will be infected?

e. Find the probability that at least 70 of the subjects in the sample will be infected.

CR   **Chapter Review**

Key Terms and Ideas

- Continuous Random Variables
- Continuous Uniform Distribution
- Probability Density Function
- Uniform Probability Density Function
- Normal Distribution
- Normal Probability Density Function

- Standard Normal Distribution
- z-Distribution
- z-Score
- Standard Normal Random Variable
- Normal Probability Plot
- Normal Approximation to the Binomial Distribution
- Continuity Correction

Key Formulas	
	Section
Uniform Probability Density Function	8.1
$$f(x) = \begin{cases} \dfrac{1}{b-a} & \text{for } a \le x \le b \\ 0 & \text{otherwise} \end{cases}$$	
Expected Value for a Continuous Uniform Random Variable	8.1
$$\mu = E(x) = \dfrac{a+b}{2}$$	
Standard Deviation for a Continuous Uniform Random Variable	8.1
$$\sigma = \dfrac{b-a}{\sqrt{12}}$$	

Key Formulas	
	Section
Normal Probability Density Function	8.2

$$f(x) = \frac{1}{\sigma\sqrt{2\pi}}\, e^{-\frac{(x-\mu)^2}{2\sigma^2}}$$

Standardizing a Normal Random Variable	8.4

$$z = \frac{x - \mu}{\sigma}$$

Normal Approximation for the Binomial Distribution	8.6

If X is a binomial random variable where $np \geq 10$ and $n(1-p) \geq 10$, then X can be approximated by a normal distribution with $\mu = np$ and $\sigma = \sqrt{np(1-p)}$.

Additional Exercises

1. Using the standard normal tables, determine the following probabilities. Sketch the associated areas.

   a. $P(0 \leq z \leq 0.85)$ c. $P(z \geq 1.75)$

   b. $P(-1.25 \leq z \leq 2.25)$ d. $P(z \leq -2.75)$

2. Using the standard normal tables, determine the following probabilities. Sketch the associated areas.

   a. $P(0 \leq z \leq 1.00)$ c. $P(z \geq 3.25)$

   b. $P(-2.50 \leq z \leq 3.01)$ d. $P(z \leq -2.50)$

3. Find the value of z such that 0.99 of the area under the curve lies between $-z$ and z.

4. Find the value of z such that 0.80 of the area under the curve lies between $-z$ and z.

5. The weights of newborn baby boys born at a local hospital are believed to have a normal distribution with an average weight of 7.25 lb and a standard deviation of 1 lb. If a newborn baby boy, born at the local hospital, is randomly selected, answer the following questions.

   a. Find the probability that the weight of the newborn baby boy will be more than 8 lb.

   b. Find the probability that the weight of the newborn baby boy will be less than 6 lb.

   c.   Find the probability that the weight of the newborn baby boy will be between 6.5 lb and 8.5 lb.

   d.   Find the weight that separates the lowest 10% of the weights from the highest 90% of the weights. If babies in the lowest 10 percent of weights are kept for observation, would a baby that weighed 5 lb be kept for observation?

6. Medication errors in a hospital can be dangerous and expensive. Medication errors are defined as giving a patient a non-prescribed medication in any quantity or the improper dosage of a prescribed medication. Suppose the national average for medication errors is one out of every 1000 patients. A hospital believes that their medication error rate is comparable to the national average. If the hospital randomly selects 5000 patients, answer the following questions.

   a.   Find the expected number of patients in the sample that will have had a medication error.

   b.   What is the standard deviation of the number of patients in the sample that will have had a medication error?

   c.   What is the probability of observing one or more patients who have had medication errors in the sample?

   d.   What is the probability of observing two or more patients who have had medication errors in the sample?

   e.   Do you have any concerns about the accuracy of the probabilities you determined in parts **c.** and **d.**?

7. According to the 2011 Statistical Abstract of the United States, 20.5% of the scores on the critical reading portion of the SAT Reasoning Test exceeded 600.[7] Approximately 17.4% of the scores were less than 400, according to the same reference. Assuming that scores on the critical reading portion of the SAT are approximately normally distributed, what are the mean and the standard deviation of the scores on the critical reading portion of the SAT Reasoning Test?

8. The annual average per capita consumption of red meat in the United States in 2008 was 108.3 pounds, according to the 2011 Statistical Abstract of the United States.[8] This figure was down from a per capita average of 126.4 pounds in 1980. Assume that both in 2008 and 1980 the per capita amount of red meat consumed was a normal random variable with a standard deviation of 15 pounds.

   a.   In 1980, what percent of the population consumed at least 100 pounds of red meat?

   b.   In 2008, what percent of the population consumed at least 100 pounds of red meat?

   c.   In 1980, what percent of the population consumed at most 130 pounds of red meat?

   d.   In 2008, what percent of the population consumed at most 130 pounds of red meat?

   e.   Do you feel that it is reasonable to assume that the per capita amount of red meat consumed has a normal distribution? Why or why not?

9. A cell phone manufacturer has developed a new type of battery for its phones. Extensive testing indicates that the population battery life (in days) obtained by all batteries of this new type is normally distributed with a mean of 700 days and a standard deviation of 100 days. The manufacturer wishes to offer a guarantee providing a discount on batteries if the original battery purchased does not exceed the days stated in the guarantee. What should the guaranteed battery life be (in days) if the manufacturer desires that no more than 5% of the batteries will fail to meet the guaranteed number of days?

10. A machine used to regulate the amount of dye dispensed for mixing shades of paint can be set so that it discharges an average of μ milliliters of dye per can of paint. The amount of dye discharged is known to have a normal distribution with a variance equal to 0.0160. If more than 6 milliliters of dye are discharged when making a particular shade of blue paint, the shade is unacceptable. Determine the setting of μ so that no more than 1% of the cans of paint will be unacceptable.

11. The length of time required to complete a college achievement test is found to be normally distributed with a mean of 75 minutes and a standard deviation of 15 minutes. When should the test be terminated if we wish to allow sufficient time for 95% of the students to complete the test?

12. A manufacturing plant utilizes 3000 electric light bulbs that have a length of life that is normally distributed with a mean of 500 hours and a standard deviation of 50 hours. To minimize the number of bulbs that burn out during operation hours, all the bulbs are replaced after a given period of operation. How often should the bulbs be replaced if we want not more than 2% of the bulbs to burn out between replacement periods?

13. Howe's Finance Corporation provides financing for customers at an automotive dealership. The average loan amount is $24,000 with a standard deviation of $8000. Assuming that the loan amount is normally distributed, what is the probability that a randomly selected consumer buying a car will want to finance at least $20,000?

14. Suppose that the income of families in a large community follows a normal distribution. Two families are randomly selected and their incomes are $55,000 and $85,000, respectively. The two incomes correspond to z-scores of -0.5 and 2.0 respectively. Calculate the mean and standard deviation of the income of families in the neighborhood.

15. Suppose that the 30th percentile of a normal distribution is equal to 756 and that the 90th percentile of this normal distribution is 996. Find the mean and standard deviation of the normal distribution.

"By a small sample, we may judge the whole piece."
— Miguel de Cervantes from *Don Quixote de la Mancha*

9 CHAPTER
Samples and Sampling Distributions

Introduction

When you were a child, did you ever jump into a tub of water only to find out the tub was too hot? If you did, the next time before committing your tender body to the water, you would stick your big toe in first. And then you would make a decision about the temperature, without having to examine every drop of water in the tub. Essentially, you performed an informal statistical experiment: sampling and making an inference about the population of water in the tub. Humans have performed informal sampling and inference for a long time. It seems only evolutionary that a science (statistics) would develop to try to understand one of the most common of human experiences, sampling and inference.

The quality of all statistical analyses and procedures depends on the quality of the sample data. If the sample data is not representative of the population, analyzing the data and drawing conclusions from it will be unproductive, at best. This is a simple idea, and an important one. It suggests the beginning of any statistical investigation should be focused on the development of representative sample data. Interestingly, to obtain a representative sample requires the introduction of randomness in the sampling procedure.

The concern over the quality of sample data is brought about by the fact that this chapter begins a bridge from the study of probability to the study of statistical inference. One of the critical links between statistical inference and probability is the sampling distribution, which is the probability distribution of a statistic. In the ensuing chapter the language of probability will be used to help define the confidence associated with the statistical inferences that are made.

9.1 Random Samples

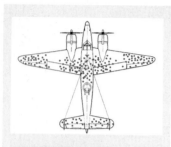
People do a lot of sampling every day. If someone buys a cup of coffee, that person does not have to drink the whole cup to determine whether the coffee is too hot. He or she takes a sample, a sip or two, then makes a decision. The sampling procedure produces as much information as sampling the entire cup and, if the coffee is too hot, with much less pain. Sampling is a fundamental component of existence. When we cross an intersection, we sample traffic in both directions before making the decision to cross. When driving a car, we visually sample traffic conditions, speed, and engine gauges. When we walk into a room, we sample the air for pleasing aromas or smells that might be related to hazardous conditions. Sampling is a good idea. It saves time and is less costly than performing a census on the entire population. (Imagine sniffing an entire room's worth of air!) If the sample is representative of the population, the information it provides can be almost as good as performing a census. The relevant question is, how do you select a sample that is representative of the population?

Drawing samples that are representative of a population is often quite difficult. One "sampling method" that is often seen in the media is **voluntary sampling**. Usually some question is posed to a large audience and people "volunteer" to participate in the sample. The internet has made this kind of "sampling" popular. However, this sampling method can often produce misleading results.

How bad can a voluntary sample be? In a survey of the readers of the syndicated advice column called *Ask Ann Landers*, the columnist asked her readers the question, *If you had it to do over again, would you have children*? Over 10,000 readers wrote in; 70% said 'No,' and many described the misery their children had brought them. Voluntary response of this kind overrepresents people with strong feelings, especially strong negative feelings. A national random sample on the same issue found that over 90% of parents would choose to have children again. Voluntary response can easily produce 70% 'No' in a sample when the truth about the population is close to 90% 'Yes.' Yet the media continue to conduct voluntary response polls and discuss them as if they provided useful information.

Ann Landers' sample is an extreme example of **selection bias**. Selection bias occurs when the sample that has been selected overrepresents or underrepresents some segments of the population it is intended to represent. In the case of Ann Landers' sample, the sampling bias was the result of parents with strong negative opinions feeling compelled to respond to the survey. For this reason, the majority of responses were negative. Voluntary or self-selected samples typically are not representative samples of a population.

Biased Sample

A **sample is biased** if it overrepresents or underrepresents some segment(s) of the population.

DEFINITION

Choosing a Representative Sample

In order to select a sample, a clear definition of the population is required. Otherwise, once the sample is selected, it is not clear what it represents. However, once the population is defined, the real work begins. A significant portion of the effort required to produce good samples goes into the creation of a **sampling frame**, which is a list containing all the members of the population. Once this list is available, it is possible to construct a **simple random sample**.

Sampling Frame

A **sampling frame** is a list which identifies all members of the population.

DEFINITION

Using Randomness to Remove Sample Bias

One of the more powerful methods of coping with bias is the use of randomness in the sampling process.

Simple Random Sample

A **simple random sample** from a finite population is one in which every possible sample of the same size n has the same probability of being selected.

DEFINITION

This definition implies that each member of the sampling frame has an equal chance of being selected for the sample. There are a number of ways of selecting a simple random sample. If the sampling frame is small, each member of the list can be assigned a unique number. These numbers can be placed in a hat and drawn *randomly*. Another technique is to use a **random number table**.

Random number tables are composed of random digits, arranged in groups of 4 or 5 to improve readability. To use the random number table, randomly pick a row and column in the table as a starting point and select the appropriate number of digits. The appropriate number of digits is based on the size of the sampling frame. If the size of the sampling frame is from 1 to 99, then two digits should be selected. If the size of the sampling frame is from 100 to 999, then three digits should be selected. It makes no difference whether the random numbers are selected across a row or down a column. Random numbers which have the correct number of digits, but which are larger than the frame, should be ignored. Once the appropriate random numbers have been selected, sample the items in the frame which correspond to the random numbers. The resulting sample will constitute a simple random sample.

Example 9.1.1

Select a simple random sample of 20 customer accounts from a sampling frame that contains 897 accounts.

Solution

If each account is given a number between 1 and 897, then three digits from the table can be used to indicate a specific account. Any consecutive three digits that are greater than 897 should be ignored. We can select the initial starting position as row three and column two, and select three digits across the row. Those accounts colored in red are selected.

The Missing Bullet Holes

Continued...

This led Wald to suggest the planes that didn't return were most likely hit in the areas that had no bullet holes on the returning planes, which were the engine and tail areas. And, that these were the portions of the plane that needed armor the most. This was an example of selection bias, particularly survivorship bias.

Wald's recommendations regarding the placement of armor was implemented and saved many lives. His spectacular insight into overcoming survivorship bias in this problem is legendary.

Picture by McGeddon - Own work, CC BY-SA 4.0, https://commons.wikimedia.org/w/index.php?curid=53081927

Note

"Finite" is the opposite of infinite. A finite population means that the number of items in the population can be counted.

Technology

Directions for obtaining random samples using technology can be found on stat.hawkeslearning.com under **Technology Instructions > Sampling > Random Samples.**

```
randInt(1,897,20
)
{815 132 462 36...
```

Random Number Table									
985	201	776	714	905	686	072	210	940	558
609	709	343	350	500	739	981	180	505	431
398	082	773	250	725	682	482	940	524	201
527	756	785	183	452	996	340	628	898	083
137	467	007	818	475	406	106	871	177	817
886	854	020	086	507	584	013	676	667	951
903	476	493	296	091	106	299	594	673	488
751	764	969	918	260	892	893	785	613	682
347	834	113	862	481	176	741	746	850	950
580	477	697	473	039	571	864	021	816	544

Lava Lamps, Randomness, and Your Bank Account

True randomness is something computers are not currently very good at creating. To generate "random" numbers, computers use an algorithm that produces pseudo-random numbers. A simple example of a pseudo-random number generator would be to take the current day of the month and add the current time in minutes to it, then find the digit of pi that corresponds to that "seed" number. For example, if the date is 7/4/2020 and the time is 10:48 AM, then the seed number would be 52 and the 52nd digit of pi is 5. Therefore, 5 would be the "random" number that this simple pseudo-random number generator returns.

Every digital transaction that occurs relies on encryption to protect your money. Encryption keys are a random string of characters. Encryption relies on non-predictable encryption keys. The problem with a pseudo-random number generator for encryption purposes is that if a hacker knows how the generator works, then they may be able to "predict" the encryption key and thus destroy the security that the encryption provides. If encryption keys are "predictable," all wire transfer and other online financial transactions would be vulnerable to fraud. For encryption purposes the security of the encryption key is directly associated with the true randomness of its key.

Continued...

While random number tables are still used in some applications, it is more common in practice that a random sample is chosen using some sort of random number generator. Excel, Minitab, and TI-83/84 Plus calculators all have their own functions to generate random numbers. These are sometimes referred to as **pseudo-random number generators** because the numbers are produced by a defined process, which means the "randomness" can be predicted. A number called a **seed** initializes the function, and every time that seed is used the function will give the same output (provided the inputs were also the same). While not truly random, a pseudo-random number generator is considered "good enough" for most purposes.

Random samples form the basis of almost all inferential statistics. But random sampling is not a haphazard, purposeless selection technique. On the contrary, removing potential selection bias is difficult, and randomness is the only tool for the job.

Suppose you want to obtain a random sample of students at your college. If 8000 students attend the college, deriving the sampling frame would be a formidable task. Fortunately, a college's student population is well-defined, and with the aid of a computer and the registrar's database, a random sample could be selected.

Well-defined populations are the exceptions, not the rule. Consider the problem of defining the sampling frame for the customer base of a retail shopping mall. Developing a clear definition of the mall's market area would be difficult. Assuming this could be done, developing the list of all potential customers in the market area would be almost impossible. There would be numerous sources that would have a large segment of the names (utility companies, phone companies, etc.), but however complete these lists may be, there will be people who will be omitted. The principal liability of the simple random sampling technique is the necessity of forming the sampling frame. There are sampling techniques that are designed to overcome the problem, one of which is called **cluster sampling**. This and other sampling techniques are discussed in Section 9.5.

9.1 **Exercises**

Basic Concepts

1. Why is the quality of sample data so important?

2. Why is randomness useful in sampling?

3. What is wrong with a voluntary sample?

4. What makes a sample biased?

5. What is a sampling frame and why is it important?

6. Discuss how you would draw a simple random sample of the people in your town.

7. True or False: Determining a well-defined population is easy when developing a sampling frame.

8. What is a pseudo-random number generator? How is it not completely random?

9. With regards to sampling, what is a seed?

Exercises

10. Obtain a random sample of 15 beers from the Beers and Breweries data set. Describe how you selected the sample.

11. Obtain a random sample of 12 houses (list the IDs) from the Dunes West subdivision in the Mount Pleasant Real Estate data set. Describe how you selected the sample.

12. A magazine reported the results of a survey in which readers were asked to send in their responses to several questions regarding good eating. Consider the reported results to the question, *How often do you eat chocolate?*

Survey Responses	
Category	**% of Responses**
Frequently	13
Occasionally	45
Seldom	37
Never	5

   a. Were the responses to this survey obtained using voluntary sampling techniques? Explain your answer.

   b. What types of biases may be present in the responses?

   c. Is 13% a reasonable estimate of the proportion of all Americans who eat chocolate frequently? Explain.

Lava Lamps, Randomness, and Your Bank Account

Continued...

If true randomness is required, the best place to find randomness is in nature.

Cloudflare is an internet security company that uses a wall of lava lamps to generate truly random strings for encryption. The chaotic nature of the fluid dynamics (the bubbles) in the lava lamps makes it impossible to predict what they will look like at any given moment. This enables Cloudflare to take billions of pictures of their wall of lava lamps and generate billions of truly random encryption strings from these pictures.

⋮ **Data**

stat.hawkeslearning.com
Data Sets > Beers and Breweries

⋮ **Data**

stat.hawkeslearning.com
Data Sets > Mount Pleasant Real Estate Data

13. A magazine reported the results of a survey in which readers were asked to send in their responses to several questions regarding anger. Consider the reported results to the question, *How long do you usually stay angry?*

Survey Responses	
Category	**% of Responses**
A few hours or less	48
A day	12
Several days	9
A month	1
I hold a grudge indefinitely	22
It depends on the situation	8

   a. Were the responses to this survey obtained using voluntary sampling techniques? Explain your answer.

   b. What types of biases may be present in the responses?

   c. Is 22% a reasonable estimate of the proportion of all Americans who hold a grudge indefinitely? Explain.

14. Students in a marketing class have been asked to conduct a survey to determine whether or not there is a demand for an insurance program at a local college. The students decide to randomly select students from the local college and mail them a questionnaire regarding the insurance program. Of the 150 surveys that were mailed, 50 students responded to the following survey item: *Pick the category which best describes your interest in an insurance program.*

Survey Responses	
Category	**% of Responses**
Very Interested	50
Somewhat Interested	15
Interested	10
Not Very Interested	5
Not At All Interested	20

   a. What types of biases may be present in the responses?

   b. Is 50% a reasonable estimate of the proportion of all students who would be very interested in an insurance program at the local college? Explain.

   c. Is 50% a reasonable estimate of the proportion of all business majors who would be very interested in an insurance program at the local college? Explain.

   d. What strategies do you think the marketing students could have used to get a less biased response to their survey?

   e. Suppose the program was created and only a few people registered. How could the survey question have been reworded to better predict actual enrollment?

15. National news programs often conduct opinion surveys by announcing some question on the air and advising viewers to respond to a Twitter poll. Suppose that a national news program asks its viewers to tweet responses to the following: *Women should be permitted to assume combat roles in the military.* The results of the particular survey were 34% *yes* and 66% *no.* Is it reasonable to believe that the results of the survey reflect the attitudes of the nation on this issue? What biases exist in this sampling method?

9.2   Introduction to Sampling Distributions

The notion of a statistic, such as the sample mean, as a random variable may seem odd. After all, when you studied descriptive statistics in Chapter 4, statistics were numbers, not variables. The focus, however, of Chapter 4 was to demonstrate techniques for summarizing data after it had been collected. When we consider a sampling distribution the "after the data has been collected" condition is dropped. A sampling distribution for the sample mean would describe the means of all possible samples of a particular sample size from a specified population. Since the value of the sample mean for any particular sample depends on the sample we draw, the sample mean is a random variable.

As we studied in Chapter 7, the best way to summarize outcomes of some random phenomena (in this case the sample mean) is with a probability distribution. The probability distribution which describes the distribution of the sample means is called the **sampling distribution of the sample mean**.

Although the discussion has focused on the sample mean, the same arguments could be applied to the sample variance, sample proportion, and sample standard deviation. All of these sample statistics have sampling distributions as well.

> ## Sampling Distribution of a Statistic
>
> The **sampling distribution of a statistic** (such as the sample mean or sample proportion) is the probability distribution of all values of the statistic when all possible samples of size *n* are taken from a population.
>
> **DEFINITION**

Statistical inference is the focus of a large portion of the remainder of this text. As we previously discussed, statistical inference uses statistics calculated from samples as the basis of an inference about the population. If the sample is representative, then the sample statistics (which are random variables that depend on which random sample is selected) ought to be close to their population counterparts. In other words, the sample mean ought to be close to the population mean, the sample proportion ought to be close to the population proportion, and the sample variance should be close to the population variance. Since sample statistics will be used as the basis of the statistical inference, we must know how those statistics vary from one sample to another. Once the variability of the sample statistic is understood, we will be able to make probability statements regarding our inferences.

Why Calculate the Sample Mean?

When analyzing ratio data, the first piece of summary information that an analyst wants to determine is the mean. For most populations, performing a census to determine the population mean is impractical. The only alternative is to use sample information. It seems reasonable that the sample mean, $\bar{x}$, would contain an enormous amount of information about the population mean, μ, and would thus be a sensible estimate of the population mean. Generally, if you wish to estimate a population value—be it the mean, variance, or proportion—the corresponding sample statistic will be a good **estimator**.

Point Estimator

A **point estimator** is a single-valued estimate calculated from the sample data, which is intended to be close to the true population value.

DEFINITION

Can you be sure that the sample mean will always be close to the population mean? When dealing with random variables, nothing is certain, but there are methods of reducing the probable error. To understand how this is achieved, we must examine how the sample mean varies.

9.2   Exercises

Basic Concepts

1. Is the sample mean always close to the population mean?
2. What is the sampling distribution of the sample mean?
3. Why is the sample mean a random variable?
4. What is a point estimator?

9.3   The Distribution of the Sample Mean and the Central Limit Theorem

Sample means vary because sample data vary from sample to sample. As an illustration, suppose that the quality control department wished to determine the average diameter of a shipment of valves that are used in the manufacture of respirators. Since measuring these valves is very time consuming, the quality control group has decided to select two from a batch of six. Suppose that the actual widths of the six valves are given in Table 9.3.1.

Table 9.3.1 - Valve Measurements	
Valve	**Diameter (cm)**
A	0.124
B	0.136
C	0.201
D	0.144
E	0.138
F	0.147

It is important to realize that the above set of data constitutes a population. The mean diameter of the population in Table 9.3.1 equals 0.1483 cm and the population standard deviation is 0.02465 cm.

$$\mu \approx 0.1483 \text{ cm}$$
$$\sigma \approx 0.02465 \text{ cm}$$

Both of these measures are considered population parameters. The diameters given in Table 9.3.1 are not known by the quality control group when the shipment arrives. Their job is to estimate the population average using a sample estimate, in this case using the sample mean from a sample of size two.

How many different samples of size two can be drawn? Assuming no replacement, there would be 15 possible samples of size two if order does not matter. A list of all possible samples and the resulting means is given in Table 9.3.2.

Table 9.3.2 - Valve Sample Measurements ($n = 2$)			
Sample Number	**First Observation**	**Second Observation**	$\bar{x}$
1 (A & B)	0.124	0.136	0.1300
2 (A & C)	0.124	0.201	0.1625
3 (A & D)	0.124	0.144	0.1340
4 (A & E)	0.124	0.138	0.1310
5 (A & F)	0.124	0.147	0.1355
6 (B & C)	0.136	0.201	0.1685
7 (B & D)	0.136	0.144	0.1400
8 (B & E)	0.136	0.138	0.1370
9 (B & F)	0.136	0.147	0.1415
10 (C & D)	0.201	0.144	0.1725
11 (C & E)	0.201	0.138	0.1695
12 (C & F)	0.201	0.147	0.1740
13 (D & E)	0.144	0.138	0.1410
14 (D & F)	0.144	0.147	0.1455
15 (E & F)	0.138	0.147	0.1425

The sample means in Table 9.3.2 vary and when something varies there are at least three questions to ask:

1. What is the central value of the variable?
2. What is the variability of the variable?
3. Is there a familiar pattern (distribution) to the variability?

What is the Central Value of $\bar{x}$?

Intuitively, you would expect the sample mean to be larger than μ some of the time and smaller than μ some of the time. For large samples, the distribution of $\bar{x}$ will be relatively symmetrical, and consequently $\bar{x}$ should be larger than μ about 50% of the time and smaller than μ about 50% of the time. But for small samples the distribution of the sample mean may not be symmetrical. This is the case for the sample means in Table 9.3.2. Ten of the fifteen means are below 0.1483, which is the population mean of the population of six valve diameters in Table 9.3.1. Generally, however, the sample means should be near the population mean, or symbolically $\bar{x}$ should be near μ. It can be shown theoretically that the mean of the sample means equals μ. In the example, the mean of the sample means is 0.1483, which equals the population mean. This is not a coincidence.

> ## Unbiased
>
> If the average value of an estimator equals the population parameter being estimated, the estimator is said to be **unbiased**.
>
> **DEFINITION**

Note

The sample median is an unbiased estimator of the population median if the distribution of the population is symmetric.

Estimators are similar to marksmen. When you shoot, you want to hit what you are shooting at. When you estimate, you want to get as close as possible to the population characteristic you are estimating. But, bullets do not always land exactly where the marksman aims. If the gun sights are properly adjusted, then the shots will be dispersed around the middle of the target area.

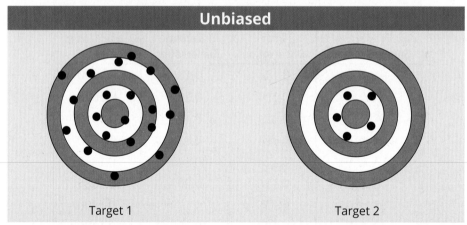

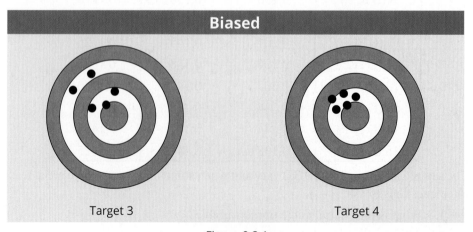

Figure 9.3.1

An estimator which produces estimates centered around the true value is said to be **unbiased**.

Unbiasedness is generally thought to be a good property of an estimator. Just as the ideal target rifle is one that would hit in exactly the same place every shot, the ideal estimator is one that is unbiased and has no variance. Because the mean of $\bar{x}$ equals μ, $\bar{x}$ is an unbiased estimator of μ.

Question

Do you think the sample range is an unbiased or biased estimator of the population range?

Unbiased Estimators

1. The sample mean, $\bar{x}$, is an unbiased estimator of μ.
2. The sample proportion, $\hat{p}$, is an unbiased estimator of p.
3. The sample variance, s^2, is an unbiased estimator of σ^2.

PROPERTIES

If an estimator is unbiased, its variability determines its reliability. If an unbiased estimator is extremely variable, then the individual estimates it produces may not be as close to the parameter being estimated as estimates produced by a biased estimator. Such is the case when you compare Target 4 (biased) to the unbiased Target 1. This is why it is important to not only consider the central value, but also the variability of a random variable, in this case the sample mean.

What is the Variability of $\bar{x}$?

The variability of an estimator reveals a great deal about the quality of that estimator. In order to assess how well the sample mean estimates the population mean, the variance of the sample means must be determined.

Variance and Standard Deviation of the Sample Mean: Infinite Population

It can be shown that for a population of infinite size the variance of $\bar{x}$ ($\sigma_{\bar{x}}^2$) equals

$$\sigma_{\bar{x}}^2 = \frac{\sigma^2}{n}$$

and the standard deviation is

$$\sigma_{\bar{x}} = \frac{\sigma}{\sqrt{n}}$$

where σ^2 is the population variance and n is the sample size.

FORMULA

We refer to $\sigma_{\bar{x}}$ as the **standard error of the mean**, generally called the **standard error**, which is the standard deviation of a point estimator. We will use the standard error of the mean to indicate how far the sample mean is from the population mean.

Suppose, for example, you were drawing a sample from a population whose variance is 0.00061. The variance of the sample means for samples of size $n = 2$ would be

$$\sigma_{\bar{x}}^2 = \frac{\sigma^2}{n} = \frac{0.00061}{2} \approx 0.00031.$$

Therefore, the standard deviation of the sample means for samples of size $n = 2$ would be

$$\sigma_{\bar{x}} = \frac{\sigma}{\sqrt{n}} = \sqrt{\sigma_{\bar{x}}^2} = \sqrt{\frac{0.00061}{2}} \approx 0.01746.$$

When we apply the Central Limit Theorem, we assume that the population has an **infinite** number of members. When we sample with replacement, the population becomes essentially infinite. However, in reality there are applications that involve sampling without replacement. For these **finite** populations, an adjustment needs to be made to $\sigma_{\bar{x}}$.

If the population is finite, as in Table 9.3.1, then the finite population correction factor $\left(\frac{N-n}{N-1}\right)$ must be applied to the calculation of the variance of the sample mean.

Note

The finite population correction factor should be used if n is greater than 5% of the finite population size, N.

Variance and Standard Deviation of the Sample Mean: Finite Population

For a **finite population** the variance of $\bar{x}$ is

$$\sigma_{\bar{x}}^2 = \frac{(N-n)}{(N-1)} \cdot \frac{\sigma^2}{n},$$

and the standard deviation is

$$\sigma_{\bar{x}} = \sqrt{\frac{(N-n)}{(N-1)}} \cdot \frac{\sigma}{\sqrt{n}},$$

where N = the size of the population and n = the size of the sample.

FORMULA

Correcting for the finite population represented in Table 9.3.1, the standard deviation of the sample mean for a sample of size 2 would be

$$\sigma_{\bar{x}} = \sqrt{\frac{(N-n)}{(N-1)}} \cdot \frac{\sigma}{\sqrt{n}} = \sqrt{\frac{(6-2)}{(6-1)}} \cdot 0.001746 \approx 0.01562.$$

Examining the formula for $\sigma_{\bar{x}}$, we note that as the size of the sample n increases, the variability of the sample mean decreases. The possibility of changing the variability of an estimator means the accuracy of the estimator can be manipulated. For example, suppose that instead of using a sample of size two, the quality control director decides to use a sample of size three. Six items chosen three at a time could produce 20 samples of size three. These samples and the means of each sample are shown in Table 9.3.3. The standard deviation of the sample means for $n = 3$ in Table 9.3.3 is 0.01102, using the finite population correction factor.

For both samples ($n = 2$ and $n = 3$) the mean of the sample means is 0.1483, which equals the population mean. But the standard deviation of the sample means for samples of size three is 0.01102, which is about 30% percent smaller than the standard deviation for samples of size two (0.01562).

For $n = 2$, $\sigma_{\bar{x}} = 0.01562$.

For $n = 3$, $\sigma_{\bar{x}} = 0.01102$.

Answer

Do you think the sample range is an unbiased or biased estimator?

The range is a biased estimator as most samples will not include the minimum or maximum values in the population. This means the sample range is expected to be less than the population range.

Since both estimators are unbiased and are centered around the population mean, the standard deviation of the estimator is a measure of how close the estimator (in this case the sample mean) is to the population mean. In other words, the lower $\sigma_{\bar{x}}$ is, the better the estimator is.

Table 9.3.3 - Valve Sample Measurements ($n = 3$)			
Sample Number	**First Observation**	**Second Observation**	**Third Observation**	**$\bar{x}$**
1 (A, B, & C)	0.124	0.136	0.201	0.153667
2 (A, B, & D)	0.124	0.136	0.144	0.134667
3 (A, B, & E)	0.124	0.136	0.138	0.132667
4 (A, B, & F)	0.124	0.136	0.147	0.135667
5 (A, C, & D)	0.124	0.201	0.144	0.156333
6 (A, C, & E)	0.124	0.201	0.138	0.154333
7 (A, C, & F)	0.124	0.201	0.147	0.157333
8 (A, D, & E)	0.124	0.144	0.138	0.135333
9 (A, D, & F)	0.124	0.144	0.147	0.138333
10 (A, E, & F)	0.124	0.138	0.147	0.136333
11 (B, C, & D)	0.136	0.201	0.144	0.160333
12 (B, C, & E)	0.136	0.201	0.138	0.158333
13 (B, C, & F)	0.136	0.201	0.147	0.161333
14 (B, D, & E)	0.136	0.144	0.138	0.139333
15 (B, D, & F)	0.136	0.144	0.147	0.142333
16 (B, E, & F)	0.136	0.138	0.147	0.140333
17 (C, D, & E)	0.201	0.144	0.138	0.161000
18 (C, D, & F)	0.201	0.144	0.147	0.164000
19 (C, E, & F)	0.201	0.138	0.147	0.162000
20 (D, E, & F)	0.144	0.138	0.147	0.143000

As in many problems, there is an accuracy versus dollars trade-off. Greater accuracy can be found by taking a larger sample, but larger samples cost more.

Suppose a population had a mean of 43,660 and a standard deviation of 2500. The distributions in Figure 9.3.2 are the distributions of the sample mean for samples of size 25, 100, and 200, respectively from this population. Based on the graphs in Figure 9.3.2, it seems that the estimator shown for $n = 200$ would be preferred. Because it has less variability, the estimates of μ from samples of $n = 200$ should be closer (on average) to μ.

The History of the Central Limit Theorem

Pierre-Simon Laplace is credited with the initial statement of the Central Limit Theorem in 1776. He developed the theorem while working on the probability distribution of the sum of meteor inclination angles.

Although the theorem is stated with respect to the sample mean, it is a more general theorem regarding the sum of random variables. If you add up a sufficiently large number of random variables the sum will be normally distributed.

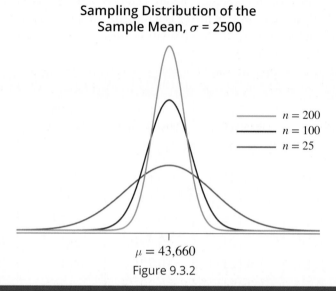

Figure 9.3.2

Characteristics of the Sample Mean

If an estimate of the population mean is required, the sample mean seems to possess two good characteristics.

1. The mean of sample means is the population mean. Another way of expressing this concept is to say that the expected value of $\bar{x}$ is equal to the population mean. Symbolically, this can be expressed as

$$E\left(\bar{x}\right) = \mu. \text{ (unbiasedness)}$$

2. If the sample size is increased, the variability of the sample mean decreases. This implies that the quality of the estimator tends to improve as the sample size increases.

$$\sigma_{\bar{x}} = \frac{\sigma}{\sqrt{n}}$$

PROPERTIES

The second characteristic has an important consequence for estimating a population characteristic. By choosing a sufficiently large sample size, an estimate can be obtained with some specified level of accuracy. Being able to predetermine the accuracy of an estimate is an important topic in statistics and will be discussed in the next chapter.

Is There a Familiar Pattern to the Variability?

The **Central Limit Theorem** is a very important theorem which summarizes the distribution of the sample mean. *The distribution of the sample mean becomes closer to a normal distribution as the sample size becomes larger, regardless of the shape of the population from which the sample is drawn.*

The most important feature of the Central Limit Theorem is that it can be applied to any population. Because the theorem does not have any distributional assumptions, it is widely applicable and is one of the cornerstones of statistical inference. Many of the statistical techniques discussed in subsequent chapters will have their theoretical basis in this theorem.

The Central Limit Theorem

If a sufficiently large random sample (i.e., $n > 30$) is drawn from a population with mean μ and standard deviation σ, the distribution of the sample mean will have the following characteristics.

1. An approximately normal distribution regardless of the distribution of the underlying population.

2. $\mu_{\bar{x}} = E(\bar{x}) = \mu$ (The mean of the sample means equals the population mean.)

3. $\sigma_{\bar{x}} = \dfrac{\sigma}{\sqrt{n}}$ (The standard deviation of the sample means equals the standard deviation of the population divided by the square root of the sample size.)

DEFINITION

The only restrictive feature of the theorem is that the sample size must be sufficiently large for the theorem to be applicable. Even if the distribution of the population deviates substantially from the normal distribution, a sample size greater than 30 will be sufficiently large to produce a sampling distribution for $\bar{x}$ that is approximately normal. This concept is illustrated in Figure 9.3.3.

If the population is known to be normally distributed, then the sampling distribution of $\bar{x}$ will be normally distributed for any sample size.

Once we have determined the sample size is sufficiently large, we can use the z-transformation we studied in Chapter 8 to calculate probabilities about the random variable $\bar{x}$. We can adapt the z-transformation to the random variable $\bar{x}$ as follows.

$$z = \frac{\bar{x} - \mu_{\bar{x}}}{\sigma_{\bar{x}}} = \frac{\bar{x} - \mu}{\sigma / \sqrt{n}}$$

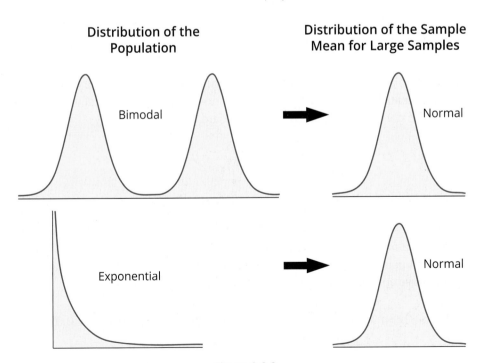

Figure 9.3.3

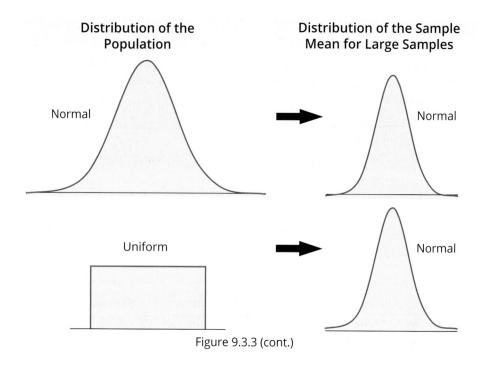

Figure 9.3.3 (cont.)

Using the Central Limit Theorem

Let's look at some examples using the Central Limit Theorem.

Example 9.3.1

Suppose a population has a mean of 30 and a variance of 25. If a sample size of 100 is drawn from the population, what is the probability that the sample mean will be larger than 31?

Solution

The information given in the problem is

$$\sigma^2 = 25 \quad n = 100 \quad \mu = 30.$$

In order to solve this problem, the sampling distribution of $\bar{x}$ must be determined. Using the Central Limit Theorem, the distribution of $\bar{x}$ will be normal with a mean equal to the population mean, 30, and a standard deviation given by

$$\sigma_{\bar{x}} = \frac{\sigma}{\sqrt{n}} = \frac{5}{\sqrt{100}} = 0.5.$$

The question that is being asked can be stated as follows:

$$P(\bar{x} > 31) = ?$$

Since $\bar{x}$ is a normal random variable, the probability that $\bar{x}$ is greater than 31 is determined using a z-transformation. The objective is to find the area under the normal curve corresponding to an $\bar{x}$ greater than 31.

$$P(\bar{x} > 31) = P\left(z > \frac{31-30}{0.5}\right) = P(z > 2) = 1 - P(z < 2) = 1 - 0.9772 = 0.0228$$

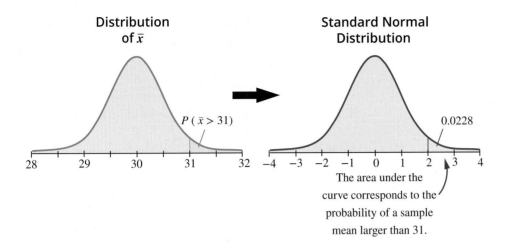

Distribution of $\bar{x}$

$P(\bar{x} > 31)$

28   29   30   31   32

Standard Normal Distribution

0.0228

−4 −3 −2 −1 0 1 2 3 4

The area under the curve corresponds to the probability of a sample mean larger than 31.

Example 9.3.2

Consider the same scenario as in Example 9.3.1 except that the mean is unknown. If the sample mean is used as an estimate of the population mean, what is the probability that the sample mean will be in error by at most one unit from the true mean?

Solution

The concept of using a statistic to estimate a population parameter introduces the concept of sampling error. In general, the sampling error is the difference between a sample statistic and the parameter that it is estimating. In the problem at hand, the error is given by $\mu - \bar{x}$ since we will be using $\bar{x}$ to estimate μ.

However, we are just as interested in negative errors as positive errors. Thus, to satisfy the condition that an error of less than one unit has been made, the condition $\left| \mu - \bar{x} \right| < 1$ must be satisfied.

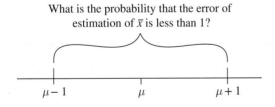

What is the probability that the error of estimation of $\bar{x}$ is less than 1?

$\mu - 1$ μ $\mu + 1$

$$P\left(\left|\mu - \bar{x}\right| < 1\right) = P\left(\mu - 1 < \bar{x} < \mu + 1\right)$$

$$= P\left(\frac{\mu - 1 - \mu}{\sigma_{\bar{x}}} < z < \frac{\mu + 1 - \mu}{\sigma_{\bar{x}}}\right)$$

An interesting and almost magical phenomenon happens when we use the z-transformation.

$$= P\left(\frac{-1}{\sigma_{\bar{x}}} < z < \frac{1}{\sigma_{\bar{x}}}\right)$$

$$= P\left(-2 < z < 2\right) \qquad \text{Since } \sigma_{\bar{x}} = 0.5.$$

$$= 0.9772 - 0.0228 = 0.9544$$

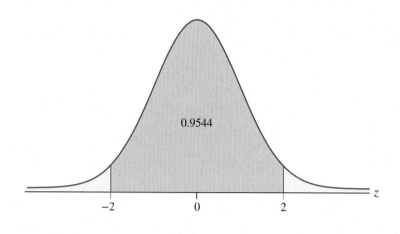

In the previous problem we were able to determine the probability of making an error of less than one unit *without knowing the mean of the population*. This probability (0.9544) tells us a lot about the likely quality of the estimate $\bar{x}$. The estimate of μ obtained from a sample of size 100 is more than just an estimate now, it is an estimate with a "level of confidence" in its quality.

9.3 Exercises

Basic Concepts

1. What is an estimator? Give an example.

2. What three questions should be asked when considering a random variable?

3. Explain the difference between a biased estimator and an unbiased estimator.

4. Give two examples of estimators that are unbiased.

5. Is an unbiased estimator always closer to the parameter being estimated than a biased estimator? Explain.

6. What is the standard error of the mean and what does it indicate?

7. What are two desirable characteristics of the sample mean?

8. Explain the Central Limit Theorem.

9. What effect does increasing the sample size have on the accuracy of an estimate?

Exercises

10. Suppose the random variable X has a mean of 20 and a standard deviation of 5. Calculate the mean and the standard deviation of the sample mean for each of the following sample sizes. (Assume the population is infinite.)

    a. $n = 35$

    b. $n = 50$

    c. $n = 75$

    d. What happens to the size of the standard deviation of the sample mean as the sample size increases?

11. Suppose the random variable X has a mean of 50 and a standard deviation of 10. Calculate the mean and standard error for each of the following sample sizes (assume the population is infinite).

    a. $n = 40$

    b. $n = 55$

    c. $n = 100$

    d. What happens to the size of the standard error as the sample size increases?

12. If there is a normally distributed random variable with a mean of 75 and a standard deviation of 22, what is the probability that the mean of a sample of size 19 will be greater than 80?

13. If a sample of size 40 is drawn from a population that has a mean of 276 and a variance of 81, what is the probability that the mean of the sample will be less than 273?

14. Suppose there is a normally distributed population with a mean of 250 and a standard deviation of 50. If $\bar{x}$ is the average of a sample of 36, find the following probabilities.

    a. $P(\bar{x} \leq 240)$

    b. $P(\bar{x} \geq 255)$

    c. $P(246 \leq \bar{x} \leq 260)$

    d. $P(234 \leq \bar{x} \leq 245)$

15. Suppose there is a normally distributed population with a mean of 100 and a standard deviation of 10. If $\bar{x}$ is the average of a sample of 50, find the following probabilities.

    a. $P(\bar{x} \leq 110)$

    b. $P(\bar{x} \geq 90)$

    c. $P(95 \leq \bar{x} \leq 115)$

    d. $P(85 \leq \bar{x} \leq 98)$

16. A company fills bags with fertilizer for retail sale. The weights of the bags of fertilizer have a normal distribution with a mean weight of 15 lb and standard deviation of 1.70 lb.

    a. What is the probability that a randomly selected bag of fertilizer will weigh between 14 and 16 pounds?

    b. If 35 bags of fertilizer are randomly selected, find the probability that the average weight of the 35 bags will be between 14 and 16 pounds.

17. A travel agency conducted a survey of the prices charged by ocean cruise ship lines and determined they were approximately normally distributed with a mean of $110 per day and a standard deviation of $20 per day.

    a. If an ocean cruise ship line is chosen at random, find the probability that it will charge less than $99 per day.

    b. What is the probability that the average charge for a randomly selected sample of 35 ocean cruise ship lines will be less than $99 per day?

18. The turkeys found in a particular county have an average weight of 15.6 pounds with a standard deviation of 4.00 pounds. Forty-five turkeys are randomly selected for a county fair.

    a. Find the probability that the average weight of the turkeys will be less than 14.5 pounds.

    b. What is the probability that the average weight of the turkeys will be more than 17 pounds?

    c. Find the probability that the average weight of the turkeys will be between 13 and 18 pounds.

19. The average score for a water safety instructor (WSI) exam is 75 with a standard deviation of 12. Fifty scores for the WSI exam are randomly selected.

    a. Find the probability that the average of the fifty scores is at least 80.

    b. Find the probability that the average of the fifty scores is at most 70.

    c. Find the probability that the average of the fifty scores is between 72 and 78.

20. A college food service buys frozen fish in boxes labeled 10 pounds. The true average weight of the boxes is 8 pounds with a standard deviation of 2 pounds. The food service director suspects that the boxes do not contain as much fish as advertised. He decides to inspect 40 boxes from the next shipment. If the average weight is less than 10 pounds he will reject the entire shipment. Find the probability that the food service director will not reject the shipment.

9.4 The Distribution of the Sample Proportion

There are many instances in which the variable of interest is a proportion. A manufacturer would be interested in knowing what fraction of his manufacturing components are defective. A marketing researcher would be interested in what proportion of persons on a mailing list will buy the company's product. A college would be concerned with the fraction of freshmen that may be in academic difficulty after the first year. Population proportions must be estimated just like population means. The symbols used to represent the population and sample proportions are

    p, the population proportion, and

    $\hat{p}$, the sample proportion.

Note

$\hat{p}$ is pronounced *p-hat*.

Determining the Sample Proportion

Suppose you are trying to determine what fraction of the students at your school smoke cigarettes at least once a week. If you select 120 students at random and 38 students in the sample smoke, then

$$\hat{p} = \text{proportion in the sample who smoke} = \frac{38}{120} \approx 0.3167.$$

In general, when calculating a proportion, the number in the sample that possess the characteristic of interest (in the previous example, this characteristic was smoking) goes in the numerator, and the size of the sample is placed in the denominator.

Sample Proportion

The sample proportion is given by

$$\hat{p} = \frac{x}{n},$$

where x is the number of observations in the sample possessing the characteristic of interest and n is the total number of observations in the sample.

FORMULA

Just as the sample mean was a good estimate of the population mean, the sample proportion is a good estimate of the population proportion. And just as the sample mean varied depending on the sample selected, the sample proportion varies depending on the selected sample.

Since $\hat{p}$ varies, three familiar questions must be examined.

1. What is the central value?
2. What is the variability?
3. Is there a familiar pattern to the variability?

What is the Central Value of $\hat{p}$?

The expected value of the sample proportion, $\hat{p}$, is the population proportion, p. Symbolically, this is expressed as

$$E\left(\hat{p}\right) = p.$$

Since the expected value of the estimator $\hat{p}$ is equal to p, then $\hat{p}$ is an unbiased estimator of p.

What is the Variability of $\hat{p}$?

Standard Deviation of the Sample Proportion

The standard deviation of $\hat{p}$ is given by

$$\sigma_{\hat{p}} = \sqrt{\frac{p(1-p)}{n}},$$

where p is the population proportion and n is the sample size.

FORMULA

Note that $\sigma_{\hat{p}}$ is affected by the values of p and n. The standard deviation of $\hat{p}$ decreases as n becomes larger. Also, the numerator reaches a maximum when $p = 0.5$ and declines as you move away from that figure. So for a fixed value of n, $\hat{p}$ has its greatest standard deviation when the population proportion equals 0.5. If the population proportion is unknown (which is usually the case), p can be estimated by $\hat{p}$, and the standard deviation of the sample proportion is estimated as

$$\sigma_{\hat{p}} \approx \sqrt{\frac{\hat{p}(1-\hat{p})}{n}}.$$

The sampling distribution of $\hat{p}$ approaches normality as n becomes sufficiently large, as illustrated in Figure 9.4.1. The sample size is generally considered "sufficiently large" if $np \geq 10$ and $n(1 - p) \geq 10$.

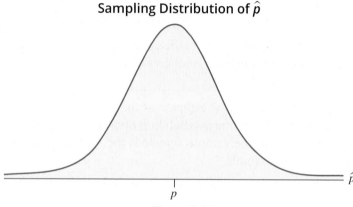

Sampling Distribution of $\hat{p}$

Figure 9.4.1

The sampling distribution of $\hat{p}$ is summarized below for both finite and infinite populations.

Sampling Distribution of the Sample Proportion

If the population is infinite and the sample is sufficiently large, the distribution of $\hat{p}$ has the following characteristics:

1. An approximately normal distribution.

2. $\mu_{\hat{p}} = E\left(\hat{p}\right) = p$. (The mean of the sample proportions equals the population proportion.)

3. $\sigma_{\hat{p}} = \sqrt{\dfrac{p(1-p)}{n}} \approx \sqrt{\dfrac{\hat{p}\left(1-\hat{p}\right)}{n}}$.

If the population is finite and the sample is sufficiently large, the distribution of $\hat{p}$ has the following characteristics:

1. An approximately normal distribution.

2. $\mu_{\hat{p}} = E\left(\hat{p}\right) = p$.

3. $\sigma_{\hat{p}} = \sqrt{\dfrac{N-n}{N-1}} \cdot \sqrt{\dfrac{p(1-p)}{n}} \approx \sqrt{\dfrac{N-n}{N-1}} \cdot \sqrt{\dfrac{\hat{p}\left(1-\hat{p}\right)}{n}}$,

where N is the size of the population.

DEFINITION

Since $\hat{p}$ is a good estimator of p, one of the natural questions to ask is, can limits be established for the error in estimation? Since the sampling distribution of $\hat{p}$ is known, determining probabilities for various errors of estimation can be determined.

Example 9.4.1

Suppose a sample of 400 persons is used to perform a taste test. If the true fraction in the population that prefers Pepsi is really 0.5, what is the probability that less than 0.44 of the persons in the sample will prefer Pepsi?

Solution

Assume the population from which the sample is drawn is extremely large and the finite population correction factor is not applicable. The distribution of $\hat{p}$ would then be normal with $E\left(\hat{p}\right) = 0.5$,

$$\sigma_{\hat{p}} = \sqrt{\frac{(0.5)(1-0.5)}{400}} = \sqrt{0.000625} = 0.025.$$

The probability that the sample proportion is less than 0.44 is given by

$$P\left(\hat{p}<0.44\right) = P\left(z<\frac{(0.44 - 0.5)}{0.025}\right)$$

$$= P(z < -2.40) = 0.0082.$$

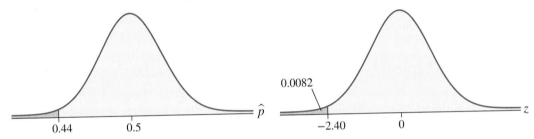

With the information we have developed thus far we can begin to draw conclusions (make inferences). If the true fraction of people in the population who prefer Pepsi is really 0.5, it is extremely unlikely (0.0082 is less than 1 in 100) to observe a sample proportion as low as 0.44. Suppose that you had to make a decision as to whether cola drinkers were indifferent between Pepsi and Coke. If they were indifferent, the fraction who prefer Pepsi should be around 0.5. If you used a sample of 400 people and observed a sample proportion of 0.438 that preferred Pepsi, which of the conclusions would you believe?

The indifference hypothesis
Conclusion A: Cola drinkers are indifferent between Pepsi and Coke. Stated another way, the proportion of persons that favor Pepsi is about 0.5.

The difference hypothesis
Conclusion B: Cola drinkers are not indifferent between Pepsi and Coke.

The likelihood of observing a sample with $\hat{p}$ less than 0.44 is very rare (0.0082) given that the true proportion who prefer Pepsi is $p = 0.5$. Most people would doubt the indifference hypothesis, Conclusion A, and select Conclusion B. The decision-making problem given above is really a statistical inference problem. Although the procedure for analyzing inference problems will be presented in a subsequent chapter, the problem illustrates the connection between probability and inference. To reach a decision (make the inference) we used the fact that if the true proportion is really 0.5, a proportion below 0.44 is highly improbable for a sample of 400.

Example 9.4.2

Suppose a sample of 500 is used to estimate the fraction of voters that favor a particular candidate. If the population proportion that favors the candidate is really 0.4, what is the probability that the error of estimation will be less than 0.05?

Solution

Since the true value of the population proportion is assumed to be 0.4, the value of $\hat{p}$ must fall between 0.35 and 0.45 in order for the error of estimation to be less than 0.05.

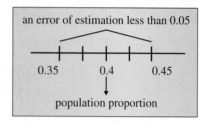

In order to determine the probability that $\hat{p}$ will fall in this interval, its distribution must be determined. Since the distribution of $\hat{p}$ is approximately normally distributed for large samples, the distribution of $\hat{p}$ will be approximately normal with

$$E\left(\hat{p}\right) = 0.4, \ \sigma_{\hat{p}} = \sqrt{\frac{\hat{p}(1-\hat{p})}{n}} = \sqrt{\frac{0.4\left(1-0.4\right)}{500}} = \sqrt{0.00048} \approx 0.0219.$$

To find the probability that $\hat{p}$ is within 0.05 of the true mean, we must find

$$P\left(p - 0.05 < \hat{p} < p + 0.05\right) = P\left(0.35 < \hat{p} < 0.45\right).$$

The Distribution of $\hat{p}$

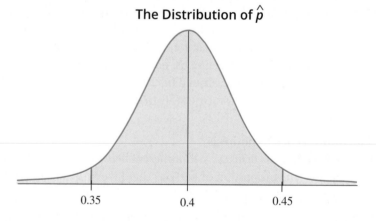

Using the z-transformation,

z-Distribution

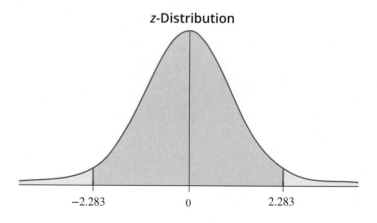

$$P\left(\frac{(0.35-0.4)}{0.0219} < z < \frac{(0.45-0.4)}{0.0219}\right)$$

$$= P\left(-2.283 < z < 2.283\right)$$

$$= P\left(z < 2.283\right) - P\left(z < -2.283\right)$$

$$= 0.9887 - 0.0113$$

$$= 0.9774$$

For a sample of 500, it is very probable (0.9774) that the error of estimation will be less than 0.05.

∽ **Technology**

For directions on calculating the probability using a TI-83/84 Plus calculator, please visit stat.hawkeslearning.com and navigate to **Technology Instructions > Normal Distribution > Normal Probability (cdf)**.

```
normalcdf(.35,.4
5,.4,.0219)
        .9775758823
```

9.4 **Exercises**

Basic Concepts

1. What does the symbol $\hat{p}$ represent?

2. What is the connection between $\hat{p}$ and p?

3. Is $\hat{p}$ an unbiased estimator? If so, of what?

4. What are the conditions that make the sample size n "sufficiently large" for a sample proportion?

5. Describe the sampling distribution of $\hat{p}$ if n is sufficiently large.

Exercises

6. A random sample of 40 electronic components has 5 defective components.

   a. Find the sample proportion of components that are defective.

   b. Find the sample proportion of components that are not defective.

7. A random sample of 100 employees of a large steel company has 30 females and 70 males.

   a. Find the sample proportion of female employees.

   b. Find the sample proportion of male employees.

8. Suppose that the true proportion of registered voters who favor the Republican presidential candidate is 0.45. Find the mean and standard deviation of the sample proportion for samples of the following sizes.

   a. $n = 30$

   b. $n = 45$

   c. $n = 65$

   d. What happens to the size of the standard deviation of the sample proportion as the sample size increases?

9. Suppose that the true proportion of Americans over 25 years old that have a 4-year college degree is 0.35. Find the mean and the standard deviation of the sample proportion for samples of the following sizes.

    a. $n = 38$
    b. $n = 52$
    c. $n = 75$

    d. What happens to the size of the standard deviation of the sample proportion as the sample size increases?

10. Suppose the true population proportion is $p = 0.50$. What is the probability that the sample proportion of a sample of size 20 will be greater than 0.60?

11. Suppose the true population proportion is $p = 0.30$. What is the probability that the sample proportion of a sample of size 60 will be less than 0.25?

12. Suppose that the true proportion of Americans who save at least 10% of their income is 0.15. If $\hat{p}$ is the sample proportion of Americans surveyed who save at least 10% of their income from a sample of size 68, find the following probabilities.

    a. $P\left(\hat{p} > 0.25\right)$
    b. $P\left(\hat{p} < 0.09\right)$
    c. $P\left(0.10 < \hat{p} < 0.20\right)$
    d. $P\left(0.18 < \hat{p} < 0.25\right)$

13. Suppose that the true proportion of airline pilots between the ages of 35 and 45 is 0.60. If $\hat{p}$ is the sample proportion of airline pilots between the ages of 35 and 45 from a sample of size 100, find the following probabilities.

    a. $P\left(\hat{p} > 0.55\right)$
    b. $P\left(\hat{p} < 0.45\right)$
    c. $P\left(0.50 < \hat{p} < 0.60\right)$
    d. $P\left(0.60 < \hat{p} < 0.75\right)$

14. The director of a radio station in a large metropolitan area believes that the proportion of young professionals (his target market) in the area who prefer country music has increased from 25% to 35%. The director randomly decides to select 50 young professionals and ask them if they prefer country to any other type of music. If the sample proportion is greater than 0.35, he will switch to a new format emphasizing country.

    a. If the true proportion of young professionals who prefer country has not changed, find the probability that the radio director will switch to the new format.

    b. If the true proportion of young professionals who prefer country has changed as the director suspects, find the probability that the radio director will switch to the new format.

15. The owner of a large office building plans on building a dedicated smoking area outside, but will not do so if less than 30% of his employees smoke. He decides to randomly select 50 of the workers in the building and ask them whether or not they smoke. If the sample proportion of workers who smoke is less than 0.30, the owner will not create the smoking area.

    a. Find the probability that the owner will not create the smoking area when the true proportion of smokers is 0.5.

b.   Find the probability that the owner will create the smoking area when the true proportion of smokers is 0.2.

16.   Eighty percent of the flights arriving in Atlanta for a large US airline are on time. If the FAA randomly selects 50 of the airline's flights, find the probability that:

   a.   at least 85% of the sampled flights will be on time.

   b.   at most 70% of the sampled flights will be on time.

   c.   between 75% and 85% of the sampled flights will be on time.

17.   Approximately 7% of the nation's public-school children in grades 2 through 5 take medication for attention deficit hyperactivity disorder (ADHD), a developmental disorder characterized by impulsiveness or difficulty concentrating or sitting still. The main treatment prescribed for ADHD is Ritalin, a relatively safe drug with few side effects. A sample of 286 students is taken.

   a.   Find the probability that at least 4% of the school children in the sample take medication for ADHD.

   b.   Find the probability that between 5% and 8% of the school children in the sample take medication for ADHD.

9.5   **Other Forms of Sampling**

Random sampling is an effective means of obtaining a sample that is representative of the population. As we discussed previously, acquiring an exact sampling frame for the population under study is a requirement for simple random sampling, a requirement which can be time-consuming and expensive. There are other sampling strategies that are designed to reduce the cost of sampling or add control to the sampling procedure. These techniques can be categorized as probability samples or non-probability samples.

Probability samples enable an analyst to determine the probable errors that an estimator might generate. Essentially, they allow the analyst a known degree of confidence in their estimation. All of statistical inference relies on probability sampling. **Non-probability samples** are convenient means of obtaining sample data. If data from a non-probability sample is used to estimate a population parameter, there is no statistical theory that helps define the potential error of the estimate, and hence no statement about an estimate's reliability can be made.

Non-Probability Samples

Non-probability samples come in several forms.

Judgment Sample

A sample in which the observations are selected by an expert in the field and not picked at random.

DEFINITION

Literary Digest

For the 1936 presidential election, Literary Digest conducted a poll to determine the winner. Over 10 million questionnaires were sent to those who owned automobiles and/or telephones. Over 2.4 million questionnaires were returned and Literary Digest predicted that Alf Landon would defeat Franklin D. Roosevelt with 57% of the vote. George Gallup also conducted a poll of 50,000 random voters and predicted Roosevelt as the winner. Many people laughed at Gallup because Literary Digest had been correctly predicting the outcome of the presidential election since 1916 and based its predictions on such a large sample. Gallup was correct and Roosevelt won with 62% of the vote. Where did Literary Digest go wrong? First, only those who were rich enough to afford the luxury of a car or phone were sampled. Also, those who were not happy with Roosevelt were more likely to respond. In the end, Literary Digest went bankrupt and Gallup started his own company.

One of the common uses of judgment samples is in auditing. When auditing a company's accounts receivable, an auditor may use a judgment sample to verify the accounts outstanding. The quality of the sample data is related to the competence of the expert. If the expert is good at what he or she does, this type of sampling can produce reasonable representations of the population and correspondingly good estimates of the population parameters.

Another type of non-probability sample is the **convenience sample**.

Convenience Sample

A sample of observations that are easily obtained and not random.

DEFINITION

As the name implies, a convenience sample is nothing more than a convenient group of observations. For example, the students in your statistics class would be a convenience sample of students in your college. Although convenience samples could be representative of the population, they tend to possess more bias than other forms of sampling. Consider your statistics class. It is likely that the class is dominated by some particular group of majors and has a disproportionate number of sophomores and juniors. Despite their shortcomings, convenience samples are convenient, and certainly a convenient sample is often better than no sample at all.

There are two disadvantages to using a convenience sample. First, it is difficult to determine how representative the sample is of the population, or if it is representative at all. Secondly, even though the convenience sample may not be representative of the population, statistical methods are often applied. Since it is not a probability sample, the results will lack validity and are questionable.

The worst forms of non-probability samples are the voluntary or self-selected samples. Those samples were discussed in Section 9.1.

Systematic Sampling

One type of sampling technique, the **systematic sample**, does not belong to probability or non-probability samples.

Systematic Sample

A sample in which you choose a starting point and then every k^{th} member of the population is included in the sample.

DEFINITION

For example, suppose a sample of 1000 names is to be selected from a mailing list that contains 80,000 names. If every 80th person in the mailing list is selected for inclusion in the sample, the result will be a sample of 1000 names. If the names are in random order, then the systematic sample will produce a random sample. Unfortunately, it is difficult to be sure that the list does not possess some pattern that would bias the sample. Still, systematic samples are regularly used in sampling mailing lists. They are also used in controlling production quality. Production-oriented quality control plans frequently call for the inspection (sample) of every k^{th} item on an assembly line. Conceptually, inspection of every k^{th} item is no different from sampling every k^{th} item from a mailing list. A sample using this technique is called an "almost random sample."

Systematic samples are generally good samples. But if there is some pattern in the sampling frame that corresponds to the sampling pattern, an unrepresentative sample can result. For example, suppose you wished to sample a list containing total daily sales. If you sampled every 7th item, the result would be a sample that contained sales from the same day of the week.

Cluster Sampling

Although simple random sampling may be feasible, the traveling cost required to obtain the sample information may be prohibitive. Suppose McDonald's wishes to perform quality control inspection on its franchises. If a random sample of 500 is drawn from the nearly 37,000 McDonald's scattered throughout the world, the quality inspection team could be in for quite a bit of traveling. Instead of selecting the stores individually, suppose we divide the world into 200 regions. Then we could select 20 of these regions and inspect every store in the region. This technique is called **cluster sampling**. Using this technique, an inspector would be required to travel much less and a substantial reduction in cost would result.

Clusters are not always geographic. Suppose you were interested in soliciting student opinion regarding bookstore prices. If everyone in your college had a 9 am class, one reasonable method of clustering would be to use each class as a cluster. Randomly select a set of clusters (classes) and interview each member of the selected cluster. The selection of clusters depends greatly on the population and variables of interest.

> ### Cluster Sampling
>
> **Cluster sampling** involves dividing the population into clusters, and randomly selecting a sample of clusters to represent the population. Cluster sampling is used when "natural" groupings are evident in the population.
>
> **DEFINITION**

Cluster sampling can be as effective as simple random sampling if the clusters are as heterogeneous as the population. Unfortunately, clusters are almost never as diverse as the population. If the clusters are geographic, people in the same geographic area tend to be less diverse than the population. If the clusters are not heterogeneous, cluster sampling is less efficient than simple random sampling for a given sample size. Generally, smaller cluster sizes will result in more representative samples.

In simple random sampling, constructing the sampling frame is frequently cumbersome. Cluster sampling simplifies the task, since the initial frame is composed only of clusters. Only those clusters selected as part of the sample must be completely enumerated and sampled.

Cluster sampling is a good alternative to simple random sampling when the population's geographic area is spread out over a large area or when the sampling frame for a simple random sample is difficult to construct.

Stratified Sampling

The fundamental goal of sampling is to obtain a sample that is representative of the population. Representative means that the characteristics of the population are proportionally represented in the sample. For example, if a population contained 60% females and 30% with blood type A, then it would be desirable for the sample to have 60% females and 30% with blood type A. Simple random samples make no guarantees regarding the constituency of the sample. If a random sample could be taken such that it was assured that the population characteristics were properly represented, the resulting samples would tend to be more representative of the population. This is precisely the objective of **stratified sampling**.

Stratified Sampling

In **stratified sampling**, the population is divided into **strata**, which are sub-populations. A **strata** can be any identifiable characteristic that can be used to classify the population. If the population consists of people, then strata could be sex, income, political party, religion, education, race, or location.

DEFINITION

Suppose you wished to estimate the average weight of some species. If it is known that males of the species are generally heavier than females, then stratifying the sample based on gender would provide a better estimate of the mean weight than a simple random sample of the same size. Stratification would mean that a fixed percentage of the sample observations would come from each gender. For humans, half the sample should be male and half should be female. The mean and variance from each gender would be calculated separately and combined to form the population estimate. The variance of each subgroup should be smaller than the variance of the population. When these variances are combined to form an estimate of the population variance, the resulting variance will be smaller than if a simple random sample had been used.

In summary, stratified sampling can provide greater accuracy if the population is heterogeneous, and sub-populations of the population can be identified that are relatively homogeneous.

9.5   Exercises

Basic Concepts

1. What are advantages and disadvantages of non-probability samples?

2. What is a judgment sample? Give an example not in the text of when a judgment sample would be appropriate.

3. What is a convenience sample? Are these samples usually representative of the population?

4. What are the worst forms of non-probability samples?

5. Explain the idea of systematic sampling. What are the advantages and disadvantages of this sampling procedure?

6. Explain the idea of cluster sampling. What are the advantages and disadvantages of this sampling procedure?

7. Explain the idea of stratified sampling. What are the advantages and disadvantages of this sampling procedure?

Exercises

8. An employee-owned company has 6000 female employees and 2000 male employees. The human resources department decides to develop a survey on several different benefit plans, including child care and retirement benefits, that they may offer employees in the future. The results of the survey are to be presented to the board of directors for consideration. Because the human resources department wants to be sure of equal representation of the sexes, it has decided to randomly select 500 females and 500 males. What kind of sampling method is the human resources department using? If the sample is used to make inferences regarding the desirability of various benefits packages for all employees, discuss any deficiencies in the sampling procedure.

9. Explain why a systematic sample is not a random sample.

10. Suppose you were instructed to draw a simple random sample from a metropolitan area in order to gain information on the citizens' view on a proposed amendment to the state constitution. To create a simple random sample, you must create a sampling frame. You have decided to use the telephone directory as your frame for the metropolitan area.

    a. Identify the population under consideration.

    b. What kinds of people will be omitted from your frame?

    c. What kinds of biases will be introduced in your sample as a consequence of the omission you described in part **b.**? Can you think of ways of compensating for the bias?

11. A social researcher in Florida wants to determine the average number of children per family in the state.

    a. What is the population of interest?

    b. What variable will be measured?

    c. What level of measurement is the variable of interest?

    d. Discuss the steps that would be necessary for each of the following sampling methods.

        i.   Simple random sampling

        ii.   Cluster sampling

        iii. Stratified sampling

    e. What sampling method do you believe would be the most cost-effective? Justify your answer.

12. A stock analyst wants to estimate the average yearly earnings of stocks on the New York Stock Exchange.

    a. What is the population of interest?

    b. Discuss the steps necessary to apply each of the following sampling methods.

        i.   Simple random sampling

        ii.   Cluster sampling

        iii. Stratified sampling

13. A news reporter in Orlando, Florida wants to conduct a survey to determine how local residents feel about the institution of a state income tax. Since there will be a lot of people from which to choose, he goes to Disney World and randomly selects individuals entering the complex. He asks the selected people whether or not they favor a state income tax in Florida. The responses to the survey are as follows.

Survey Responses	
Category	**% of Responses**
Favor a Florida State Income Tax	50
Do Not Favor a Florida State Income Tax	50

a. What sampling technique was used for this survey?

b. What biases may be present in the responses?

c. Is 50% a reasonable point estimate of the proportion of Orlando residents who favor the state income tax? Explain.

CR   Chapter Review

Key Terms and Ideas

- Sampling
- Sampling Distribution
- Voluntary Sampling
- Selection Bias
- Biased Sample
- Sampling Frame
- Simple Random Sample
- Random Number Table
- Sampling Distribution of the Sample Mean
- Point Estimator
- Unbiased Estimator
- Standard Error of the Mean

- Central Limit Theorem
- Population Proportion
- Sample Proportion
- Sampling Distribution of the Sample Proportion
- Error of Estimation
- Probability Samples
- Non-Probability Samples
- Judgment Sample
- Convenience Sample
- Systematic Sampling
- Cluster Sampling
- Stratified Sampling

Key Formulas

Key Formulas	
	Section
Standard Deviation of the Sample Mean: Infinite Population $$\sigma_{\bar{x}} = \frac{\sigma}{\sqrt{n}}$$ where σ is the population standard deviation and n is the sample size.	9.3
Standard Deviation of the Sample Mean: Finite Population $$\sigma_{\bar{x}} = \sqrt{\frac{(N-n)}{(N-1)}} \cdot \frac{\sigma}{\sqrt{n}}$$ where N = the size of the population and n = the size of the sample.	9.3
Characteristics of the Sample Mean 1. $E(\bar{x}) = \mu$ 2. $\sigma_{\bar{x}} = \frac{\sigma}{\sqrt{n}}$	9.3
Central Limit Theorem If a sufficiently large random sample $(n > 30)$ is drawn from a population with mean μ and standard deviation σ, the distribution of the sample mean will have the following characteristics. 1. An approximately normal distribution regardless of the distribution of the underlying population. 2. $\mu_{\bar{x}} = E(\bar{x}) = \mu$ 3. $\sigma_{\bar{x}} = \frac{\sigma}{\sqrt{n}}$	9.3
Sample Proportion $$\hat{p} = \frac{x}{n}$$ where x is the number of observations in the sample possessing the characteristic of interest and n is the total number of observations in the sample.	9.4
Standard Deviation of the Sample Proportion: Infinite Population If the population is infinite and the sample is sufficiently large $(np \geq 10$ and $n(1-p) \geq 10)$, $$\sigma_{\hat{p}} = \sqrt{\frac{p(1-p)}{n}} \approx \sqrt{\frac{\hat{p}(1-\hat{p})}{n}}$$ where p is the population proportion and n is the sample size.	9.4

Key Formulas

	Section
Standard Deviation of the Sample Proportion: Finite Population	9.4

If the population is finite and the sample is sufficiently large $\left(np \geq 10 \text{ and } n(1-p) \geq 10\right)$,

$$\sigma_{\hat{p}} = \sqrt{\frac{N-n}{N-1}} \cdot \sqrt{\frac{p(1-p)}{n}} \approx \sqrt{\frac{N-n}{N-1}} \cdot \sqrt{\frac{\hat{p}(1-\hat{p})}{n}}$$

where N is the size of the population.

Additional Exercises

1. A national news network is interested in the opinion which Americans have regarding a national health care policy. During the evening news they display a 900-telephone number and ask their viewers to call in and respond to the question: *Do you favor a national health care policy in the U.S.?*

Survey Responses	
Category	**% of Responses**
Yes	45
No	45
Do not have enough information to decide	10

    a.   What type of sampling technique was used for this survey?

    b.   What type of biases may be present in the responses?

    c.   Is 45% a reasonable estimate of the proportion of all Americans who favor a national health care policy? Explain.

2. An entrepreneur wants to open a new Indian restaurant in a resort community. To determine if there is a market for the new restaurant, the entrepreneur decides to conduct a survey.

    a.   What is the population of interest to the entrepreneur?

    b.   Can you think of any good sources for a sampling frame?

    c.   What are the shortcomings (if any) of the sources you picked for the sampling frame?

3. A paint manufacturer is developing a new type of paint. Test panels were exposed to various corrosive conditions to measure the protective ability of the paint. Based on the results of the test, the manufacturer has concluded that the mean life before corrosive failure for the new paint is 168 hours with a

standard deviation of 30 hours. If the manufacturer's conclusions are correct, find the probability that the paint on a sample of 60 test panels will have a mean life before corrosive failure of less than 150 hours.

4. Seventy-five percent of the students graduating from high school in a small Iowa farm town attend college. The town's Chamber of Commerce randomly selects 30 recent graduates and determines whether or not they will attend college.

   a. Find the probability that at least 80% of the surveyed students will be attending college.

   b. Find the probability that at most 70% of the surveyed students will be attending college.

   c. Find the probability that between 65% and 85% of the surveyed students will be attending college.

5. A biology professor is interested in the proportion of students at his college who are pre-med. majors. In his next class he asks for the students who are pre-med. majors to raise their hands. Fifty percent of the students raised their hands.

   a. What type of sampling technique was used for this survey?

   b. What type of biases may be present in the responses?

   c. Is 50% a reasonable point estimate of the proportion of students at the college who are pre-med. majors? Explain.

6. It is known that the percentage return for a group of stocks in the technology sector is normally distributed with a mean of 15 percent and a standard deviation of 22 percent. Suppose you selected a random sample of 10 stocks from this sector.

   a. What are the mean and standard deviation of $\bar{x}$?

   b. Find the interval containing 68.26% of all possible sample mean returns.

7. A restaurant wants to determine the average time to prepare meals for its customers. To aid in this process, the restaurant randomly selects the meal preparation time of 150 of its customers and finds that the average preparation time is 18 minutes with a standard deviation of eight minutes. Describe the distribution of the sample mean of preparation time for its customers.

8. With such a large number of people using text messages as a means of communication, a company is interested in determining the number of work hours lost due to text messaging. Based on a survey of 30 randomly selected employees (anonymously, of course), the company has determined that the average amount of time spent texting over a one-month period is 180 minutes with a standard deviation of 60 minutes.

   a. What is the probability that the average amount of time spent using text messages is more than 210 minutes in this one-month period?

   b. Thinking that it is practically impossible for her employees to spend, on average, three hours a month texting while at work, the manager conducts another survey. She randomly samples 45 employees and finds that the average amount of time spent texting while at work over a one-month period is less than 180 minutes. Is it reasonable to conclude that the average amount of time spent using text messaging has decreased since the initial survey? Justify your answer.

c. How might the data gathered from this sample not accurately depict the loss of productivity from text messaging?

9. Suppose that a random sample of size 64 was selected and the researcher found that the mean was 30 and the standard deviation was 4.

a. What is the probability that the sample mean is more than 31.25?

b. What assumptions were made in part **a.**?

10. A town is considering building a high school football stadium approximately one-half mile from a well-established housing development. The residents of the development opposed the stadium construction due to the noise coming from the stadium during games. In presenting their argument, the residents indicated that any noise more than 103 decibels would be unacceptable. Using a sample of 35 games previously played in the old arena, the town found that the average decibels were 100 with a standard deviation of 8 decibels.

a. What is the probability that a randomly selected game will generate noise in excess of 103 decibels at the stadium?

b. What is the probability that a randomly selected game will generate a noise level of exactly 103 decibels?

c. Suppose a compromise was made that required the noise level to be lower than 103 decibels 95% of the time. Will the mean level of the noise have to be lowered to comply with the new regulation? If so, by how much? Assume that the standard deviation remains at 8 decibels.

11. The town manager believes that 60% of the residents will approve the construction of the proposed high school football stadium. A random sample of 100 residents will be used to estimate the proportion of residents that will approve the construction.

a. Assuming that the town manager is correct and that $p = 0.6$, describe the sampling distribution of $\hat{p}$.

b. What is the probability that between 50% and 70% of the residents will approve the stadium construction?

12. It is believed that 90% of all adults and 85% of all kids between the ages of 12 and 17 have cellular phones. Suppose a sample of 500 adults and 400 kids was taken.

a. Describe the sampling distribution of the proportion of adults that have cellular phones. Assume that the stated probabilities above are true.

b. Describe the sampling distribution of the proportion of kids that have cellular phones. Assume that the stated probabilities above are true.

c. What is the probability that the sample proportion of adults having cell phones will be within 2% of the true proportion?

d. What is the probability that the sample proportion of kids having cell phones will be within 4% of the true proportion?

13. A survey of college students was conducted to learn about their attitudes toward alcohol abuse on college campuses. Sixty-two percent of student respondents indicated that they believe there was a high rate of alcohol abuse on college campuses. Suppose that a sample of 250 college students was taken. What is the probability that more than seventy percent believed that there was a high rate of alcohol abuse on college campuses?

14. A credit card issuer believes that 75% of college students between the ages of 18 and 22 have more than $5000 of credit card debt. The credit card issuer conducted a survey of 500 college students between the ages of 18 and 22.

    a. What is the probability that at least 70% of college students between the ages of 18 and 22 have credit card debt in excess of $5000?

    b. Assuming that the credit card issuer is correct, what is the probability that the proportion will be within three percent of the population proportion?

    c. What is the probability that the proportion will not be within three percent of the population proportion?

15. A marketing firm conducts a survey by mail with a 20% response rate. If the firm mailed 1000 surveys for a new study, what is the probability that at least 220 individuals will respond?

16. Suppose that it has been reported by a group of researchers that the average number of hours of TV viewing per household per week in the United States is 50.4 hours. Suppose the standard deviation is 11.8 hours, and a random sample of 42 U.S. households is taken.

    a. What is the probability that the sample average is more than 35 hours? If the sample average is actually more than 35 hours, what would it mean in terms of the figures presented by the researchers?

    b. Suppose the population standard deviation is unknown. If 71% of all sample means are greater than 49 hours and the population mean is still 50.4 hours, what is the value of the population standard deviation? Use a sample size of 42.

17. Are you grumpy, anxious, irritable? Do you view the past with regret and the future with dread? If so you may have a shorter version of the gene responsible for the brain's ability to use an important neurochemical, serotonin. Researchers, whose results were reported in *Science*, found that there is a positive relationship between having a generally pessimistic attitude and having the shorter version of this gene. Approximately 70% of the population suffer from this deficiency, according to the article. Assume a random sample of 200 people is chosen and for each person included in the sample it is determined whether or not the person has the shorter version of the gene.

    a. Find the probability that at least three-fourths of those sampled have the shorter version of the gene.

    b. Find the probability that at most 72% of those sampled have the shorter version of the gene.

    c. Find the probability that between 72% and 82% of those sampled have the shorter version of the gene.

"If you are distressed by anything external, the pain is not due to the thing itself, but to your estimate of it; and this you have the power to revoke at any moment."

— Marcus Aurelius Antoninus (121 AD - 180 AD)

10 CHAPTER
Estimation: Single Samples

Introduction

The importance of the statistical measures to a decision-making process depends on the confidence the decision maker has in the estimated values. How much faith can be placed in the accuracy of the estimate? Statistical inference permits the estimation of statistical measures (means, proportions, etc.) with a known degree of confidence. This ability to assess the quality of estimates is one of the significant benefits statistics brings to decision making and problem solving.

Applications of statistics are usually concerned with learning about populations or processes. Populations are described using summary measures called parameters, such as the mean, the variance, and the proportion. Processes are also described with summary measures and with various models. Unfortunately, determining the exact mean and variance of a population is seldom an easy task and often is not feasible. Statistical methods rely upon samples of the population to obtain information about the population's parameters. Whether the sample data will produce reliable information about a process or population depends on whether the sample is representative, which to a large degree depends on the methods used to collect the data.

Statistical Inference

Using properly drawn sample data to draw conclusions about the population is called **statistical inference**.

DEFINITION

The previous chapter concentrated on sampling and how the practice of drawing samples produces a statistic (e.g., the sample mean) that is a random variable. This chapter marks the beginning of statistical inference. It discusses the properties of sample summary statistics (sample means, sample proportions, etc.) as well as methods for assessing the reliability of those estimates.

All forms of statistical inference are tarnished with a degree of uncertainty. If samples are selected randomly, the uncertainty of the inference is measurable. *The ability to measure the confidence associated with an estimate is the value received for drawing random samples.* If samples are not selected randomly, there will be no known relationship between the sample estimates and the population parameters they purport to estimate. Henceforth, if a statistical technique requires a sample, assume the sample will be a random sample from a population or process.

This chapter is devoted to the one-sample problem. That is, a sample consisting of n measurements, $x_1, x_2, \ldots, x_n$, of some population will be analyzed with the objective of making inferences about the population. Inference will be introduced with the one-sample problem, not because it is the most common, but because the procedures and basic principles of inference are easier to understand.

10.1 Point Estimation of the Population Mean

What is an Estimator?

What is meant by the terms **estimator** and **estimate**?

Estimator
An **estimator** is a strategy or rule that is used to estimate a population parameter. If the rule is applied to a specific set of data, the result is an **estimate**. **DEFINITION**

The sample mean is an *estimator* of the population mean. A specific sample mean, $\bar{x}$, such as 103.4, is an *estimate* of a population mean (μ).

In this chapter we will study two different kinds of estimators, point and interval. A **point estimator** uses a single point to estimate a population parameter. For example, $\bar{x}$, is a *point estimator* of a population mean ($\bar{x} = 12.7$ is a *point estimate* of a population mean).

Table 10.1.1 - Point Estimators		
Point Estimator	**Parameter Being Estimated**	**Point Estimate**
$\bar{x}$	μ	$\bar{x} = 12.7$
$\hat{p}$	p	$\hat{p} = 0.37$
s	σ	$s = 6.4$

An **interval estimate** defines an upper and lower boundary for an interval that will hopefully contain the population parameter.

Point Estimation of the Population Mean

Like other statistical inference methods, estimation begins with the collection of data. Two important questions come to mind.

- How should the data be used to estimate the population mean?
- How can you tell a good estimator from a bad one?

Good estimators conform to the rules of horseshoes: the closer, the better. If the objective is to estimate a population mean, closeness is measured in terms of the distance the estimate is from the actual population mean.

One of the more puzzling questions is "How can you judge how accurate your estimate is without knowing the true value of the population parameter?" It's like shooting an arrow at a bull's-eye, without being able to see it. If you can't see the bull's-eye, how do you know how close you are?

> ## Important Note
>
> As estimation begins with the collection of data, a fundamental assumption for all statistical inference models is that the data for the inference is credible. Without credible data, any results from your inference are unsound.

Mean Squared Error

An estimator's average squared distance from the true parameter is referred to as its **mean squared error** (MSE). The mean squared error for the sample mean is given by:

$$\text{MSE}\left(\overline{x}\right) = E\left(\overline{x} - \mu\right)^{2}$$

FORMULA

A perfect estimator would have a mean squared error of zero, but there is no such thing as a perfect estimator. Since statistical estimators depend on data which is randomly drawn, estimates are random variables and will seldom be equal to the true population characteristic. The goal is to find an estimator whose average squared error is the smallest. Unfortunately, there are an infinite number of possible estimators and without restricting the kinds of estimators that will be considered, very little progress can be made.

One desirable restriction is **unbiasedness**. As was discussed in Chapter 9, to be an **unbiased estimator**, the expected value of the estimator must be equal to the parameter that is being estimated. For example, $\overline{x}$ is an unbiased estimator of the population mean since

$$E\left(\overline{x}\right) = \mu.$$

Unfortunately, there are many estimators that are unbiased estimators of the population mean: including the sample mean, sample median, or any single sample value. **Among unbiased estimators of the population mean, the sample mean has the smallest mean squared error**. There is no other unbiased estimator that can consistently do a better job of estimating the population mean.

The fact that the sample mean is a good estimator of the population mean should not be surprising, since you would expect most sample statistics to be reasonably good estimators of their population counterparts. One of the exceptions is the sample range, which is a poor estimator of the population range. In summary, the best estimator is the one that is unbiased and has the smallest mean squared error.

10.1 **Exercises**

Basic Concepts

1. What is statistical inference?

2. What is an estimator?

3. Explain, in your own words, the difference between the terms *estimator* and *estimate*.

4. What is the difference between a point estimate and an interval estimate?

5. Give three examples of point estimators. Identify the parameters being estimated by these estimators.

**The Father of Confidence Intervals
Jerzy Neyman
1894 – 1981**

Jerzy Neyman grew up in Poland. However, a significant part of Poland was under Russian control during his youth and Neyman received his training in mathematics in Russia.

In her book *Neyman:From Life* Constance Reid attributes the development of the confidence interval to Jerzy Neyman.

"During the years 1934-38 Neyman made four fundamental contributions to the science of Statistics. Each of them would have been sufficient to establish an international reputation, both for their immediate effect and for the impetus which the new ideas and methods had on the thinking of young and old alike. He put forward the theory of confidence intervals, the importance of which in statistical theory and analysis of data cannot be overemphasized.

His contribution to the theory of contagious distributions is still of great utility in the interpretation of biological data. His paper on sampling stratified populations paved the way for a statistical theory which, among other things, gave us the Gallup Poll. His work, and that of Fisher, each with a different model for randomized experiments, led to the whole new field of experimental design so much used in agriculture, biology, medicine, and physical sciences."

6. What are two important questions to consider when estimating a population mean?

7. What is mean squared error?

8. What is an unbiased estimator? Give an example.

9. Why is the sample mean considered the best point estimate of the population mean?

10. Are all estimators unbiased? Explain.

11. What are two characteristics of the best available estimate for a parameter?

10.2 Interval Estimation of the Population Mean

Rarely will a point estimate of the population mean result in a value which exactly matches the population mean, μ. In fact, the probability that a point estimate for the population mean exactly equals the population mean is zero for data drawn from continuous distributions. Yet, if an estimate is used for decision making, it is desirable that there be some indication of its potential error. One of the significant limitations of simply reporting a point estimate is the lack of information concerning the estimator's accuracy.

Interval estimates, however, are constructed to provide additional information about the precision of the estimate. An **interval estimator** is made by developing an upper and a lower boundary for an interval that will hopefully contain the population parameter. It would be easy to construct an interval estimator that would always contain the population parameter: for example, the interval from negative infinity to positive infinity. But this particular estimator would not contain any useful information about the location of the population parameter. In interval estimation, the smaller the interval for a given level of confidence, the better the estimator.

The seeds of a good interval estimator for the population mean can be found in Chapter 9, which defined how $\bar{x}$ should vary. Recall that if the sample size is reasonably large ($n > 30$), the Central Limit Theorem ensures that $\bar{x}$ has an approximate normal distribution with mean, μ, and standard deviation, $\dfrac{\sigma}{\sqrt{n}}$.

Sampling Distribution of $\bar{x}$

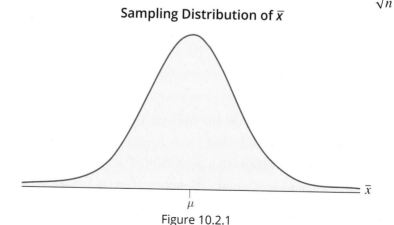

Figure 10.2.1

The sampling distribution can be used to develop an interval estimator. For the standard normal random variable,

$$P(-1.96 < z < 1.96) = 0.95.$$

Since $\bar{x}$ can be transformed into the standard normal random variable by using the z-transformation, $z = \dfrac{\bar{x} - \mu}{\sigma_{\bar{x}}}$, then by substitution,

$$P\left(-1.96 < \frac{\bar{x} - \mu}{\sigma_{\bar{x}}} < 1.96\right) = 0.95,$$

and with some algebraic manipulation we obtain

$$P\left(\bar{x} - 1.96\sigma_{\bar{x}} < \mu < \bar{x} + 1.96\sigma_{\bar{x}}\right) = 0.95.$$

If the sample size is greater than 30, there is a 0.95 probability that the sample mean will be within 1.96 standard deviations of the population mean **before a particular sample is selected**.

Sampling Distribution of $\bar{x}$

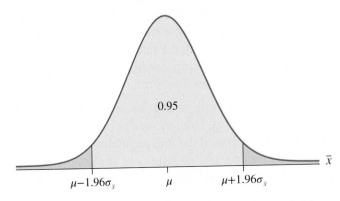

0.95

$\mu - 1.96\sigma_{\bar{x}}$ μ $\mu + 1.96\sigma_{\bar{x}}$

$\bar{x}$

Figure 10.2.2

Since we discussed the sampling distribution of the sample mean in Chapter 9, the idea of defining the probability that the sample mean should fall within some specified distance of the population mean is not a new one. The expression above does suggest a specific form for the interval since it provides an interval and the associated probability that the population mean will fall within the interval

$$\bar{x} \pm 1.96\,\sigma_{\bar{x}}.$$

However, the provision *before a particular sample is selected* modifies the interpretation of the interval for a specific sample. After the sample is selected, the sample mean is no longer a random variable. Suppose a simple random sample has been drawn from a population with a standard deviation of 200, and the following characteristics have been observed:

$\sigma = 200$, (given)

$n = 100$, (chosen by researcher)

$\bar{x} = 150$, (obtained from the sample).

Remember,

$$\sigma_{\bar{x}} = \frac{\sigma}{\sqrt{n}} = \frac{200}{\sqrt{100}} = \frac{200}{10} = 20.$$

The resulting interval would be

$$150 \pm 1.96(20).$$

That is,

$$150 - 1.96\,(20) \approx 110.8 \qquad 150 \qquad 150 + 1.96\,(20) \approx 189.2$$

Is the population mean, μ, inside this interval? If not, what fraction of the time will μ be inside the interval? Even though the interval is calculated using a technique that captures the population mean 95% of the time, it would not be appropriate, from a relative frequency point of view, to state that

$$P(\,110.8 < \mu < 189.2\,) = 0.95$$

since the population mean is an unknown but constant quantity. Either μ will always be inside the interval or will always be outside the interval. Then what information do we have about the interval? Since it was constructed from a technique that will include the true population mean in the interval 0.95 of the time, we are 95% confident in the technique. Hence, the term **confidence interval** is used to describe the method of construction rather than a particular interval.

In summary, a 95% confidence interval can be interpreted to mean that if all possible samples of a given size are taken from a population, 95% of the samples would produce intervals that captured the true population mean and 5% would not. In Figure 10.2.3 we have plotted, as line segments, the confidence intervals from 20 random samples. All but one of the intervals, number 5, captures the mean, μ.

Confidence Intervals from 20 Random Samples

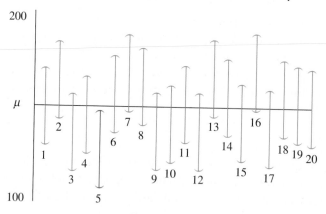

Figure 10.2.3

So far we have examined only the 95% confidence interval, yet the idea is a general one and can be extended to any specified degree of confidence.

In a practical sense, the selection of the degree of confidence depends upon the importance of the decision for which the confidence interval will be utilized. If we are launching a space vehicle, we would want to be very certain that the vehicle would have sufficient fuel to return safely. For other decisions, we might be willing to accept an 80% confidence of correctly estimating the population mean, especially if the cost of gathering additional data is large.

100(1 − α)% Confidence Interval for the Population Mean, σ Known

If σ is known and the sample is drawn from a normal population or $n > 30$, a **100(1 − α)% confidence interval for the population mean** is given by

$$\bar{x} \pm z_{\alpha/2} \frac{\sigma}{\sqrt{n}}.$$

FORMULA

The expression, $\bar{x} \pm z_{\alpha/2} \frac{\sigma}{\sqrt{n}}$, creates the "generalized" confidence interval shown below.

$$\left(\overline{}\right)$$

$$\bar{x} - z_{\alpha/2} \frac{\sigma}{\sqrt{n}} \qquad \bar{x} \qquad \bar{x} + z_{\alpha/2} \frac{\sigma}{\sqrt{n}}$$

The confidence interval can also be written as

$$\bar{x} - z_{\alpha/2} \frac{\sigma}{\sqrt{n}} < \mu < \bar{x} + z_{\alpha/2} \frac{\sigma}{\sqrt{n}}.$$

The term $z_{\alpha/2}$ represents the z-value required to obtain an area of $1-\alpha$ centered under the standard normal curve. The z-values for obtaining various $(1-\alpha)$ areas centered under the standard normal curve are given in Table 10.2.1 and graphed in Figure 10.2.4.

Table 10.2.1 - Critical Values of z	
Confidence $(1 - \alpha)$	$z_{\alpha/2}$
0.80	1.28
0.90	1.645
0.95	1.96
0.99	2.575

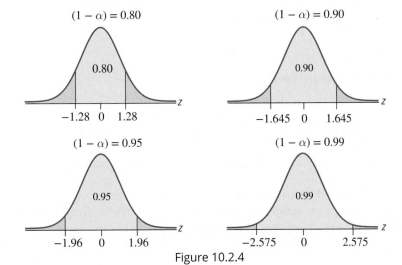

Figure 10.2.4

The role of the z-value in the confidence interval formula is to move the boundary points for the confidence interval the number of standard deviation units from the sample mean necessary to achieve the desired level of confidence. As the confidence interval formula demonstrates, the larger the desired confidence, the greater the number of standard deviations that must be used to form the boundary points for the confidence interval.

∞ **Technology**

The confidence intervals can be constructed with the TI-83/84 Plus calculator. For instructions please visit stat.hawkeslearning.com and navigate to **Technology Instructions > Confidence Intervals > z-Interval**.

Example 10.2.1

A random sample of 100 car engines has a mean weight of 425 pounds. Construct 80%, 90%, 95%, and 99% confidence intervals for the population mean if the standard deviation of the population is 900.

Solution

Since the random sample is from a population with a known standard deviation and n is greater than 30, we use the standard normal distribution to construct the confidence intervals.

$$n = 100, \text{ and}$$
$$\bar{x} = 425 \text{ lb}$$

80% Confidence Interval

$$425 \pm 1.28 \cdot \frac{900}{\sqrt{100}} \text{ or } 309.8 \text{ to } 540.2$$

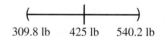

90% Confidence Interval

$$425 \pm 1.645 \cdot \frac{900}{\sqrt{100}} \text{ or } 276.95 \text{ to } 573.05$$

95% Confidence Interval

$$425 \pm 1.96 \cdot \frac{900}{\sqrt{100}} \text{ or } 248.6 \text{ to } 601.4$$

99% Confidence Interval

$$425 \pm 2.575 \cdot \frac{900}{\sqrt{100}} \text{ or } 193.25 \text{ to } 656.75$$

The intervals in Example 10.2.1 illustrate that to achieve more confidence we must pay a price. For a given sample size the only way to achieve greater confidence is to widen the interval. However, the resulting information provides a less precise location of the population mean.

So far, the confidence interval has been discussed as a way of placing bounds on the location of a parameter with a specific degree of confidence. But we can also think about the confidence interval as a means of describing the quality of a point estimate. Let's look at the expression for the confidence interval for the population mean.

Confidence Interval for μ

$$\underbrace{\overline{x}}_{\text{point estimate}} \quad \pm \quad \underbrace{z_{\alpha/2}\,\frac{\sigma}{\sqrt{n}}}_{\substack{\text{margin of error with} \\ \text{a specific level of} \\ \text{confidence}}}$$

Another interpretation of the confidence interval is given below the expression of the confidence interval of μ. The part of the expression that is added and subtracted to the point estimate, $z_{\alpha/2}\,\dfrac{\sigma}{\sqrt{n}}$, can be thought of as the **maximum error** in estimating μ using the point estimate $\overline{x}$ with a specified level of confidence. The maximum error of estimation is also referred to as the **margin of error, E**. Therefore, the confidence interval for the population mean above can also be written as $\overline{x} \pm E$.

For example, the 95% confidence interval in Example 10.2.1 was given as

$$425 \pm 1.96 \cdot \frac{900}{\sqrt{100}}$$
$$425 \pm 176.4.$$

We could say that we are 95% confident that the point estimate of μ, $\overline{x} = 425$, has an error of estimation no larger than 176.4 lb (or a margin of error of 176.4 lb). *Being able to assess the error of an estimate is one of the most useful applications of statistical methods.*

Example 10.2.2

An analyst is interested in investigating the average durability of the bladder within the soccer balls that his company manufactures. Suppose a random sample of 100 soccer balls is selected, and the balls are put through a pressure test to determine the PSI at which the bladder will burst. It is known from past experiences that the population standard deviation of the pressure at which a ball bursts is 13.25 PSI. The sample mean PSI necessary to pop a soccer ball is found to be 147.58 PSI. Calculate a 95 percent confidence interval for the population mean PSI necessary to pop a soccer ball.

Solution

From the information given, we know that

$$n = 100,\ \overline{x} = 147.58,\ \text{and}\ \sigma = 13.25.$$

We can either use a table to find the value of z, or we can use statistical software to speed up the process. For this example, we will utilize Minitab. Enter the summarized data into the appropriate Minitab dialogue box, and make sure the correct confidence level is specified. Once the calculations are executed, the following output will be returned.

⌁ **Technology**

For instructions on obtaining this Minitab output, please visit stat.hawkeslearning.com and navigate to **Technology Instructions > Confidence Intervals > *t*-Interval**.

William Sealy Gossett: The Student

Upon graduating from New College, Oxford with a strong understanding of mathematics, W.S. Gossett began working at the Guinness brewery in Dublin, Ireland. While working at Guinness, Gossett applied his statistical knowledge to find the best yielding varieties of barley, and in 1908, he developed the *t*-distribution. Few other statisticians at the time saw the merit in developing small-sample methods since most of their work required large data sets, however Gossett was convinced of the importance of his work. Unfortunately, Guinness had prohibited its employees from publishing papers to protect trade secrets, and thus did not originally allow Gossett to publish his findings. After convincing the brewery that his statistical methods would be of no use to competing breweries, Guinness allowed Gossett to publish his conclusions on the *t*-distribution, but only under the pseudonym, "Student", to avoid issues with other staff members. To this day, Gossett's most noteworthy achievement is known simply as the "Student's *t*-distribution."

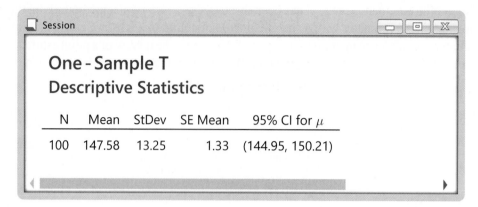

Under the column titled "95% CI for μ", two values are shown in interval format. These values are the endpoints for the 95% confidence interval. Therefore, the confidence interval for the population mean PSI necessary to pop a soccer ball is 144.95 to 150.21.

Interval Estimation of the Population Mean for a Normal Population with σ Unknown

In the last section we assumed that the population standard deviation is known. In practice this assumption is not very realistic, since the variance describes variability about the mean. If the population variance is known, the mean is usually also known, and there is no need to create an interval estimate for it. Why estimate something we already know?

If σ is not known and either the population is normally distributed or $n > 30$, the derivation of the confidence interval must be changed slightly.

Student's *t*-Distribution

Provided the population from which the sample is drawn is normally distributed or $n > 30$, the distribution of the quantity

$$t = \frac{\bar{x} - \mu}{\frac{s}{\sqrt{n}}}$$

where s is the standard deviation of the sample, has a **Student's *t*-distribution**.

FORMULA

The *t*-distribution is very much like the normal distribution (see Figure 10.2.5). It is a symmetrical, bell-shaped distribution with slightly thicker tails than a normal distribution. The shape of the *t*-distribution approaches the normal distribution as the degrees of freedom become larger.

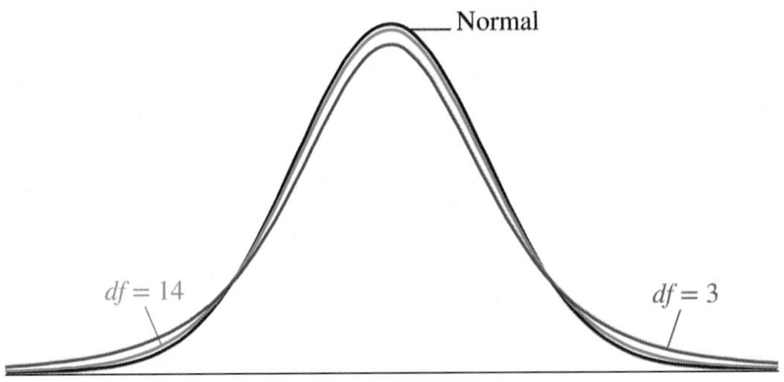

Figure 10.2.5

The t-distribution has one parameter, **degrees of freedom**. The number of degrees of freedom is the number of values from the sample that can vary after imposing restrictions on the data. For example, given the specific value for the mean of a set of data with $n = 5$, then four of the data values can vary freely, whereas the fifth one would be determined—it would have to have a particular value in order for the five data values to have the specified mean. Therefore, the number of degrees of freedom is equal to the sample size minus 1.

$$df = \text{number of sample observations} - 1 = n - 1$$

100(1 − α)% Confidence Interval for the Population Mean, σ Unknown

If σ is unknown and the sample is drawn from a normal population or $n > 30$, a $100(1 - \alpha)\%$ **confidence interval for the population mean** is given by

$$\bar{x} \pm t_{\alpha/2,\, n-1} \frac{s}{\sqrt{n}}$$

where $t_{\alpha/2,\, n-1}$ is the critical value for a t-distribution with $n - 1$ degrees of freedom which captures an area of $\frac{\alpha}{2}$ in the right tail of the distribution. For this confidence interval $E = t_{\alpha/2,\, n-1} \frac{s}{\sqrt{n}}$.

FORMULA

The form of the confidence interval is identical to the previous confidence interval for the mean of a population except that the z has been replaced by a t and σ has been replaced by s. The interpretation of the confidence interval is identical to the previous interval.

Example 10.2.3

A random sample of hours worked in a week by student interns is drawn from a normal population with unknown mean and variance. The seven data values sampled are as follows.

$$25, \ 19, \ 37, \ 29, \ 40, \ 28, \ 31$$

Construct a 95% confidence interval for the population mean.

Solution

Since we have $n < 30$, we should confirm the sample comes from an approximately normal distribution.

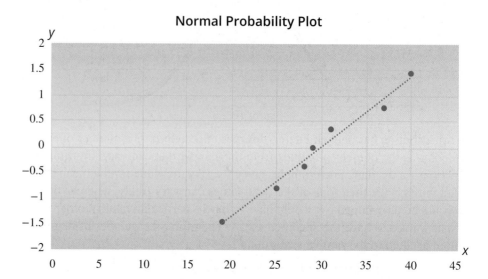

Normal Probability Plot

Since the normal probability plot of the data indicates an approximately normal distribution and the standard deviation of the population is unknown, the Student's t-distribution will be used to construct the confidence interval. The sample mean and standard deviation are $\bar{x} = 29.86$ hours and $s = 7.08$ hours, respectively. The degrees of freedom associated with the problem are

$$df = n - 1 = 7 - 1 = 6.$$

The t-value corresponding to 6 degrees of freedom and 95% confidence is given in Table D of Appendix A as $t_{0.025,\,6} = 2.447$. The general form of the confidence interval is given by

$$\bar{x} \pm t_{\alpha/2,\,n-1} \frac{s}{\sqrt{n}}.$$

Substituting the sample statistics and the critical value for the t-distribution into the confidence interval formula yields the following confidence interval for the population mean.

$$29.86 \text{ hours} \pm 2.447 \left(\frac{7.08}{\sqrt{7}} \right) \text{ hours}$$

$$29.86 \text{ hours} \pm 6.55 \text{ hours}.$$

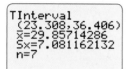

Thus, we are 95% confident that the interval 23.31 hours to 36.41 hours will contain the population mean. The confidence interval can also be written as

$$23.31 \text{ hours} < \mu < 36.41 \text{ hours}$$

or

$$(23.31 \text{ hours}, 36.41 \text{ hours}).$$

An alternate interpretation would be that we are 95% confident that the point estimate (29.86 hours) has a maximum error of estimation (or margin of error) of 6.55 hours.

Example 10.2.4

A manufacturing company is interested in the amount of time it takes to complete a certain stage of the production process. The project manager randomly samples 10 products as they come from the production line and notes the time of completion. The average completion time is 23.45 minutes with a sample standard deviation of 4.32 minutes. Based on this sample, construct a 95% confidence interval for the average completion time for that stage in the production process. Assume that the population distribution of the completion times is approximately normal.

Solution

Since the company wants to calculate a 95% confidence interval for the average completion time, μ, we know that $\alpha = 0.05$. We also have a sample size of $n = 10$ and thus, $n - 1 = 10 - 1 = 9$ degrees of freedom. Therefore, we use $t_{\alpha/2, n-1} = t_{0.025, 9} = 2.262$ from Table D in the Appendix.

We also know that the general form of the confidence interval for the population mean when σ is unknown and $n < 30$ is given by

$$\bar{x} \pm t_{\alpha/2, n-1} \frac{s}{\sqrt{n}}$$

$$23.45 \text{ min} \pm 2.262 \frac{4.32}{\sqrt{10}} \text{ min}$$

$$23.45 \text{ min} \pm 3.0901 \text{ min}$$

$$20.36 \text{ min to } 26.54 \text{ min.}$$

Thus, we are 95% confident that the true average completion time of that stage of the process is between 20.36 minutes and 26.54 minutes.

⟳ Technology

The margin of error can be found using Excel's CONFIDENCE.T function. Detailed instructions for constructing a confidence interval using Excel can be found on stat.hawkeslearning.com under **Technology Instructions > Confidence Intervals > *t*-Interval**.

fx	=CONFIDENCE.T (0.05,4.32,10)	
	D	E
	3.090342	

Interval Estimation of the Population Mean: A Summary

Finding a Confidence Interval for the Population Mean

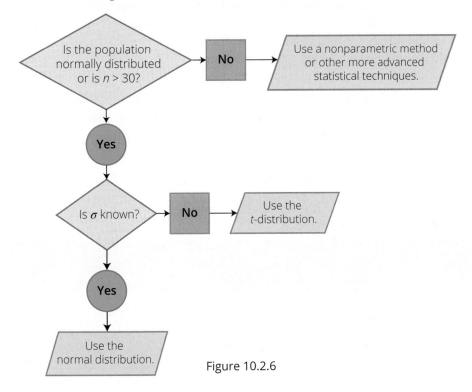

Figure 10.2.6

Precision and Sample Size for Estimating the Population Mean

The more accurate an estimate, the greater its potential value in decision making. The only way to accurately determine an unknown population parameter is to perform a census, though this is usually impractical because of cost or time considerations. Realistically, the best interval estimate a decision maker could hope for would be an interval with a small width and possessing a large amount of confidence. The width of the confidence interval defines the precision with which the population mean is estimated; the smaller the interval, the greater the precision. If the width of a confidence interval could be controlled, we could achieve estimates with a level of accuracy that is appropriate for the decision at hand. This is precisely what we plan to do in the next section.

Sample Size for σ Known

There are three components which affect the width of the confidence interval for the population mean:

$z_{\alpha/2}$ Represents the distance the confidence interval boundary is from the sample mean $\bar{x}$ in standard deviation units. The distance is related to the specific level of confidence.

σ Represents the population standard deviation.

n Represents the sample size.

As discussed previously, the level of confidence will affect confidence interval width. Although decision makers can vary the level of confidence in order to reduce/expand the confidence interval width, there is no real increase in the information. Changing the confidence only presents the information in a different form. The population standard deviation, σ, is a constant, it does not change. The sample size, however, is selected by the decision maker. The larger the sample, the smaller the width of the resulting confidence interval for some given level of confidence. Since the sample size can be enlarged, which reduces the width of the confidence interval, how large should the sample be? Taking too large a sample wastes money, while taking too small a sample produces an estimator that does not possess sufficient reliability.

The sample size should be selected in relation to the size of the maximum positive or negative error the decision maker is willing to accept or can afford. This can be achieved by setting the error equal to one-half the confidence interval width,

$$E = \text{margin of error} = z_{\alpha/2} \frac{\sigma}{\sqrt{n}}.$$

Solving this equation for n gives us the following formula for determining the sample size.

Sample Size Determination for Estimating a Population Mean

$$n = \left(\frac{z_{\alpha/2}\sigma}{E} \right)^2$$

FORMULA

Six Degrees of Separation: A Law of Small Worlds

What is the number of people a randomly chosen person in Omaha, Nebraska needs before she can find a connection with a randomly chosen person in New England? How many intervening people do you think separates you from the President of the United States? Unsuspecting readers might very well guess very large numbers but the actual numbers are quite small. The answer to both of these questions may very well be less than 6. Psychologists have done very ingenuous experiments and have actually calculated this degree of separation, and found the average to be six. What is amazing about this degree of separation is that it is equally true for the President and a sweet vendor in Bangladesh.

The question of the degree of separation has applications for the number of clicks that you need to make to get to a website that interests you, as well as the analysis of terrorists networks. The new science of social networks can shed useful light and derive general laws applicable to all of these questions.

By selecting a level of confidence and the maximum error, the relationship can be used to determine the sample size necessary to estimate the population mean with the desired accuracy. *In order to assure the desired level of confidence, always round the value obtained for the sample size up to the next integer.*

Example 10.2.5

Consider a population having a standard deviation of 15. We want to estimate the mean of the population. How large of a sample is needed to construct a 95% confidence interval for the mean of this population if the margin of error is equal to 1.5?

Solution

$$n = \left(\frac{z_{\alpha/2}\sigma}{E}\right)^2 = \left(\frac{1.96 \cdot 15}{1.5}\right)^2 = 384.16 \approx 385 \text{ (Always round up.)}$$

Rounding up, we have to have a sample size of 385 to ensure that we get at least a 95% confidence interval with a margin of error equal to 1.5.

Example 10.2.6

Suppose that a quality control manager at Argon Chemical Company wishes to measure the average amount of cleaning fluid the company is placing in their 12 ounce bottles. From previous studies, they believe their population standard deviation to be 0.3 ounces. How large a sample must be taken in order to be 95% confident of estimating the mean cleaning fluid in a 12 ounce bottle to within 0.05 ounces?

Solution

$$n = \left(\frac{z_{\alpha/2}\sigma}{E}\right)^2 = \left(\frac{1.96 \cdot 0.3}{0.05}\right)^2 = 138.30 \approx 139 \text{ (Always round up.)}$$

To be assured of finding the desired level of confidence, always round up. Thus, we are 95% confident that a sample of $n = 139$ observations would produce an estimate of the mean cleaning fluid in a 12 ounce bottle to within 0.05 ounces. Being able to know the accuracy of your estimate is one of the significant benefits of inferential statistics. In this case, if 139 bottles are measured, we will be 95% confident that the resulting sample mean is within five one-hundredths of an ounce of the true mean. That's close.

Sample Size for σ Unknown

In the previous discussion of sample size determination, σ was assumed to be known. This assumption is usually unreasonable in most problem-solving environments. The most obvious method for obtaining an estimate of σ is to take a small sample and use the sample standard deviation as an estimate of the population standard deviation. Replacing σ with s in the sample size determination relationship will provide an initial estimate of the required sample size.

Example 10.2.7

An airline's maintenance manager desires to estimate the average time (in hours) required to replace a jet engine in a Boeing 767. How large a sample would be necessary if the manager wishes to be 95% confident of estimating the mean to within one-quarter of an hour ($E = 0.25$). Assume a preliminary sample of size $n = 31$ has an average replacement time of 16.7 hours with a standard deviation of 4.3 hours.

Solution

Using the results from the initial sample,

$$n = \left(\frac{1.96 \cdot 4.3}{0.25} \right)^2 = 1136.50$$

$n = 1137$. (Always round up to assure the required confidence.)

Notice that while the sample data values are being collected they can be used to improve the estimate of the population standard deviation. For example, suppose the sample standard deviation after sampling the first 100 observations was 4.1. Using this estimate of s instead of 4.3 results in a sample size of 1034 compared to the original specification of 1137. The notion of modifying the sample size estimate as additional data is observed can be applied at regular intervals during the sampling process until the estimate of the standard deviation stabilizes.

10.2 **Exercises**

Basic Concepts

1. What is an interval estimator?

2. What is the distinction between probability and confidence?

3. What is the role of the z-value in the confidence interval expression?

4. Describe in words the ideas behind the construction of a confidence interval.

5. Consider the following statement: *If the sample size is greater than 30, then by the Central Limit Theorem there is a 0.95 probability that the sample mean will be within 1.96 standard deviations of the population mean before a particular sample is selected.* Explain why the phrase "before a particular sample is selected" is important here.

6. Explain what is wrong with the following expression: $P(111 < \mu < 189) = 0.95$.

7. What are the conditions required in order to construct a $100(1-\alpha)\%$ confidence interval using the expression $\bar{x} \pm z_{\alpha/2} \frac{\sigma}{\sqrt{n}}$?

8. Describe the effect on the width of a confidence interval as each of the following increases: n, $1 - \alpha$, α, $\bar{x}$.

9. What expression indicates the margin of error? Is this the same as the maximum error of estimation?

10. What is $\bar{x} \pm z_{\alpha/2} \frac{\sigma}{\sqrt{n}}$ an estimate of?

11. Why is the assumption that the population standard deviation is known when estimating the population mean not very realistic?

12. What effect does knowing the standard deviation of the population have on the construction of the confidence interval?

13. What is the Student's t-distribution?

14. What is the parameter of the t-distribution? How is it calculated?

15. What is the value of having a confidence interval with a small width?

16. Can a confidence interval be constructed with a width of your choice? Explain.

17. What is the margin of error? What is the connection between the expression for the margin of error and the equation to determine the sample size?

18. What is the difference between the method of determining the sample size when σ is known versus when σ is unknown?

19. Note that E and s can be viewed as measures of variation. Compare and contrast the meanings of E and s in layman's terms.

Exercises

20. Find $z_{\alpha/2}$ for the following levels of α.

    a. $\alpha = 0.05$ d. $\alpha = 0.04$

    b. $\alpha = 0.01$ e. $\alpha = 0.02$

    c. $\alpha = 0.10$ f. $\alpha = 0.08$

21. Find $z_{\alpha/2}$ for the following confidence levels.

    a.   98%   d.   96%

    b.   94%   e.   88%

    c.   92%   f.   85%

22. Construct a 90% confidence interval for the true mean of a normal population if a random sample of size 40 from the population yields a sample mean of 75 and the population has a standard deviation of 5.

23. A paint manufacturer is developing a new type of paint. Thirty panels were exposed to various corrosive conditions to measure the protective ability of the paint. The mean life for the samples was 168 hours before corrosive failure. The life of paint samples is assumed to be normally distributed with a population standard deviation of 30 hours. Find the 95% confidence interval for the mean life of the paint.

24. The chief purchaser for the State Education Commission is reviewing test data for a metal link chain which will be used on children's swing sets in elementary school playgrounds. The average breaking strength for a sample of 50 pieces of chain is 5000 pounds. Based on past experience, the breaking strength of metal chains is known to be normally distributed with a standard deviation of 100 pounds. Estimate the actual mean breaking strength of the metal link chain with 99% confidence.

25. Find the *t*-value such that 0.025 of the area under the curve is to the right of the *t*-value. Assume the degrees of freedom equal 13.

26. Find the *t*-value such that 0.01 of the area under the curve is to the right of the *t*-value. Assume the degrees of freedom equal 21.

27. Find $t_{\alpha/2,df}$ for the following combinations of α and *n*.

    a. $\alpha = 0.05$, $n = 15$ **d.** $\alpha = 0.05$, $n = 12$

    b. $\alpha = 0.01$, $n = 20$ **e.** $\alpha = 0.01$, $n = 18$

    c. $\alpha = 0.10$, $n = 8$ **f.** $\alpha = 0.10$, $n = 22$

28. A random sample, consisting of the values listed below, was taken from a normally distributed population. Assuming the standard deviation of the population is unknown, construct a 99% confidence interval for the population mean.

27.4	26.5	25.7	31.4
28.2	21.9	16.3	22.7
18.8	34.4	29.2	20.5

29. Construct an 80% confidence interval for the mean of a normal population assuming that the values listed below comprise a random sample taken from the population. The population standard deviation is unknown.

83.9	87.4	65.2	86.0	73.1
80.3	92.7	87.5	69.3	77.5
91.9	71.1	79.1	72.4	88.2

30. An FDA representative randomly selects 8 packages of ground chuck from a grocery store and measures the fat content (as a percent) of each package. The resulting measurements are given below.

13%	12%	14%	17%
15%	16%	18%	15%

    a.   Calculate the sample mean and the sample standard deviation of the fat contents.

    b.   Construct a 90% confidence interval for the true mean fat content of all the packages of ground beef.

    c.   What assumption did you make about the fat content in constructing your interval?

31. A hospital would like to determine the mean length of stay for its patients having abdominal surgery. A sample of 15 patients revealed a sample mean of 6.4 days and a sample standard deviation of 1.4 days.

    a.   Find a 95% confidence interval for the mean length of stay for patients with abdominal surgery.

    b.   Interpret this interval and state any assumptions that were made in the construction of the interval.

32. An independent group of food service personnel conducted a survey on tipping practices in a large metropolitan area. They collected information on the percentage of the bill left as a tip for 25 randomly selected bills. The average tip was 18.3% of the bill with a standard deviation of 2.7%.

    a. Construct an interval to estimate the true average tip (as a percent of the bill) with 99% confidence.

    b. Interpret the interval, and state any assumptions that were made in the construction of the interval.

33. A travel agent is interested in the average price of a hotel room during the summer in a resort community. The agent randomly selects 15 hotels from the community and determines the price of a regular room with a king size bed. The average price of the room for the sample was $115 with a standard deviation of $30.

    a. Construct an interval to estimate the true average price of a regular room with a king size bed in the resort community with 90% confidence.

    b. Interpret the interval, and state any assumptions that were made in the construction of the interval.

34. A technician working for the Chase-National Food Additive Company would like to estimate the preserving ability of a new additive. This additive will be used for Auntie's brand preserves. Based on past tests, it is believed that the time to spoilage for this additive has a standard deviation of 6 days. To be 90% confident of the true mean time to spoilage, what sample size will be needed to estimate the mean time to spoilage with an accuracy of one day?

35. A computer software company would like to estimate how long it will take a beginner to become proficient at creating a graph using their new spreadsheet package. Past experience has indicated that the time required for a beginner to become proficient with a particular function of the new software product has an approximately normal distribution with a standard deviation of 15 minutes. Find the sample size necessary to estimate the true average time required for a beginner to become proficient at creating a graph with the new spreadsheet package to within 5 minutes with 95% confidence.

36. A hot dog vendor is evaluating a downtown location by counting the number of people who walk past the prospective location on a particular day during lunch time (i.e. 11:00 AM to 2:00 PM). A preliminary study has indicated a standard deviation of about 30 people per lunch period. How many lunch periods will be needed to estimate the average number of people who walk past the prospective location during the lunch period to within 9 people with 90% confidence?

10.3 Estimating the Population Proportion

Estimating Population Attributes

An attribute is a characteristic that members of a population either possess or do not possess. Attributes are almost always measured as the **proportion** of the population that possess the characteristic.

Many decisions require a measure of a population attribute. Television and radio stations base their advertising charges on ratings reflecting the *percentage of television viewers who are watching a particular program.* A political analyst wants to know the *fraction of voters who favor a particular candidate.* A social researcher needs the *fraction of teachers who believe group learning is a beneficial instructional method.* An insurance company is interested in estimating the *fraction of their policies that will result in claims.* A quality control engineer is interested in the *percentage defective in a lot of goods.* A marketing researcher demands the *fraction of persons on a mailing list that will purchase the product as a result of a direct mail marketing campaign.* The items in italics are measures of attributes of some population. Researchers estimate the proportion of population members possessing those characteristics.

Estimating the proportion of the population that possess an attribute is straightforward. A random sample is selected and the sample proportion is computed as follows:

x = number in the sample that possess the attribute,

n = sample size, and

$\hat{p} = \dfrac{x}{n}$ proportion in the sample that posses the attribute.

The symbol p indicates the proportion in the population that possess the given attribute and $\hat{p}$ is the proportion in the sample that possess the attribute. Since $\hat{p}$ is computed from a random sample, $\hat{p}$ is a random variable whose value depends on which random sample is selected.

Example 10.3.1

Estimate the fraction of defective transistors in a lot containing 100,000 transistors. Suppose a sample of size 800 is drawn from the lot, and 5 transistors were found to be defective.

Solution

We have $x = 5$ and $n = 800$. Then

$$\hat{p} = \frac{5}{800} = 0.00625.$$

A natural question to ask is, "How good is the estimate of the fraction of defective transistors?" The answer to this question naturally arises in the discussion of interval estimation for proportions.

Interval Estimation of a Population Attribute

The concept of confidence intervals, used to apprise a decision maker of the reliability of estimates of a population mean, can also be applied to estimating proportions. In order to develop the confidence interval for a population proportion, the sampling distribution of the point estimate must be developed. (See Section 9.4 for review.) The random variable, $\hat{p}$, has a binomial distribution that can be approximated with a normal random variable.

Thus, the sample proportion, $\hat{p}$, is distributed normally with mean, p, and variance,

$$\sigma_{\hat{p}}^2 = \frac{p(1-p)}{n}.$$

The standard deviation of the sample proportion, $\hat{p}$, is denoted symbolically as $\sigma_{\hat{p}}$ and is given by

$$\sigma_{\hat{p}} = \sqrt{\frac{p(1-p)}{n}} \approx \sqrt{\frac{\hat{p}(1-\hat{p})}{n}},$$

where $\hat{p}$ is used as an estimate of p.

As before,

$$P(-1.96 < z < 1.96) = 0.95.$$

Substituting

$$z = \frac{\hat{p} - p}{\sigma_{\hat{p}}}$$

results in

$$P\left(-1.96 < \frac{\hat{p} - p}{\sigma_{\hat{p}}} < 1.96\right) = 0.95.$$

Manipulating the inequalities results in

$$P\left(\hat{p} - 1.96\,\sigma_{\hat{p}} < p < \hat{p} + 1.96\sigma_{\hat{p}}\right) = 0.95,$$

which suggests that the interval,

$$\hat{p} \pm 1.96\sigma_{\hat{p}},$$

would be a good choice of a 95% confidence interval for the population proportion. As before, the probability that the interval will contain the true population proportion is 0.95 *before a specific sample is drawn*. After a specific sample is drawn, the only available information about the interval is that the technique which generated it will bound the true proportion 95% of the time.

Note

The criteria that np and $n(1-p)$ must be greater than 10 is required to ensure that the normal distribution can be used as a good approximation to the binomial distribution.

100(1 − α)% Confidence Interval for the Population Proportion

If the sample size is sufficiently large, i.e., $np \geq 10$ and $n(1-p) \geq 10$, the $100(1-\alpha)\%$ **confidence interval for the population proportion** is given by the expression

$$\hat{p} \pm z_{\alpha/2} \sigma_{\hat{p}},$$

where $z_{\alpha/2}$ is the distance from the point estimate to the end of the interval in standard deviation units, and $\sigma_{\hat{p}}$ is the standard deviation of $\hat{p}$. For this confidence interval $E = z_{\alpha/2} \sigma_{\hat{p}}$ where

$$\sigma_{\hat{p}} \approx \sqrt{\frac{\hat{p}(1-\hat{p})}{n}}.$$

FORMULA

∽ Technology

For instructions on how to calculate a confidence interval for proportions using a TI-83/84 Plus calculator, or using other technologies, please visit stat.hawkeslearning.com and navigate to **Technology Instructions > Confidence Intervals > Proportion.**

```
1-PropZInt
 x:48
 n:410
 C-Level:.95
 Calculate
```

```
1-PropZInt
 (.08595,.14819)
 p=.1170731707
 n=410
```

Example 10.3.2

Suppose a sample of 410 randomly selected radio listeners revealed that 48 listened to WXQI. Find a 95% confidence interval for the proportion of radio listeners that listen to WXQI.

Solution

A point estimate of the proportion that listen to WXQI is calculated by

$$\hat{p} = \frac{48}{410} \approx 0.1171.$$

Note our sample is large enough such that $np = 48 > 10$ and $n(1-p) = 362 > 10$.

To obtain an interval estimate, we first calculate the appropriate z-value and $\sigma_{\hat{p}}$

$$z_{\alpha/2} = z_{0.05/2} = z_{0.025} = 1.96, \text{ and } \sigma_{\hat{p}} \approx \sqrt{\frac{\hat{p}(1-\hat{p})}{n}} = \sqrt{\frac{0.1171(1-0.1171)}{410}} \approx 0.0159.$$

Note that the sample proportion $\hat{p}$ is used in place of p in the computation of $\sigma_{\hat{p}}$. For any realistic problem, this will always be the case. Fortunately, unless $\hat{p}$ and p are far apart, the value of $\sigma_{\hat{p}}$ will not be greatly affected.

Computing the confidence interval $\hat{p} \pm z_{\alpha/2} \sigma_{\hat{p}}$ results in

$$0.1171 \pm 1.96\,(0.0159)$$
$$0.1171 \pm 0.0312$$
$$0.0859 \text{ to } 0.1483.$$

We are 95% confident in the procedure that created this interval. Another interpretation would be that we are 95% confident that the point estimate, 0.1171, has a margin of error of 0.0312. A maximum error of only 0.0312 with 95% confidence suggests a rather high level of accuracy in the estimation of the proportion.

Precision and Sample Size for Estimating the Population Proportion

Just as for the population mean, a specific level of accuracy in estimating a population proportion is desirable. Suppose, for example, that a direct-mail marketer would like to estimate the fraction of a mailing list that will purchase the company's product. To be profitable, a purchase response of at least 0.008 is required. Because the proportion to be estimated is of such a small magnitude, a high degree of precision in estimating the proportion is necessary. How large a sample would be required if the population proportion (the actual proportion of persons on the mailing list that will buy the product) is to be estimated with an accuracy of 0.002? We are saying that we want our maximum error to be less than two one-thousandths. That would seem to be a highly precise estimate. But, the quantity we are trying to estimate (the proportion of people on the list that will buy our product) could easily be near 0.008. The maximum error is about 25% as large as the value we are trying to estimate. When we estimate extremely small quantities, highly precise estimates are necessary. The technique for deriving the sample size parallels the discussion of the sample mean. Setting one-half the entire width of the confidence interval equal to the maximum allowable error yields

$$E = z_{\alpha/2}\sigma_{\hat{p}} = z_{\alpha/2}\sqrt{\frac{p(1-p)}{n}}.$$

Solving for n yields

$$n = \frac{z_{\alpha/2}^2 \, p(1-p)}{E^2}.$$

Generally the population proportion is unknown and is estimated from a **pilot study**. If an estimate of the population proportion is not available, then the population proportion is set equal to 0.5. The value 0.5 maximizes the quantity $p(1-p)$ and thus provides the most conservative estimate of the sample size possible.

> **Note**
>
> When you play the game in the lesson "Direct Mail," you will confront estimation problems of this nature.

Sample Size Determination for Estimating a Population Proportion

The sample size necessary to estimate the population proportion to within a particular error with a certain level of confidence is given by

$$n \approx \frac{z_{\alpha/2}^2 \, \hat{p}(1-\hat{p})}{E^2},$$

where $\hat{p}$ is the estimate of the population proportion obtained from the pilot study.

If an estimate of the population proportion is not available, then the population proportion is set to 0.5. The value 0.5 maximizes the quantity $p(1-p)$ and thus provides the most conservative estimate of the sample size possible. Hence if no estimate of the population proportion is available, the sample size necessary to estimate the population proportion to within a particular error with a certain level of confidence is given by

$$n = \frac{z_{\alpha/2}^2 \, (0.5)(1-0.5)}{E^2} = \frac{z_{\alpha/2}^2 \, 0.25}{E^2}.$$

FORMULA

By selecting a level of confidence and an error, a sample size can be determined that will likely (at the level of confidence) produce an estimate with at least the desired accuracy. Remember to always round the sample size to the next largest integer to assure the desired level of accuracy.

Example 10.3.3

How large a sample would be required to estimate the proportion of buyers on a mailing list with an accuracy of 0.002 and a 95% degree of confidence, if the true proportion is approximately 0.008?

Solution

From the statement of the problem we have

$$p \approx 0.008,$$
$$z_{\alpha/2} = 1.96 \text{ for 95\% confidence, and}$$
$$E = 0.002.$$

Using the sample size determination expression and the values above yields

$$n = \frac{z_{\alpha/2}^2 p(1-p)}{E^2} = \frac{1.96^2 (0.008)(1-0.008)}{0.002^2} = 7621.7344 \approx 7622 \text{ (Always}$$
round up.)

Thus, to be 95% confident that the proportion is estimated with an error of at most 0.002 requires a sample size of 7622.

Example 10.3.4

Using Example 10.3.2, suppose that radio station WXQI desires to estimate the proportion of the market they hold with a maximum error of 0.01 and a confidence of 0.95. How large a sample would be required to estimate the fraction of listeners to within the desired level of accuracy? Since we don't know the true population proportion, let's assume the previous point estimate of 0.1171 is the true proportion.

Solution

So, we have

$$p \approx 0.1171,$$
$$z_{\alpha/2} = 1.96 \text{ for 95\% confidence, and}$$
$$E = 0.01.$$

Using the sample size determination expression and the values above yields

$$n = \frac{z_{\alpha/2}^2 p(1-p)}{E^2} = \frac{1.96^2 (0.1171)(1-0.1171)}{0.01^2} = 3971.7 \approx 3972 \text{ (Always round up.)}$$

Thus, to be 95% confident that the proportion of listeners is estimated with an accuracy of at least 0.01 would require a sample size of 3972.

Suppose in the previous example that we did not have an estimate of the population proportion. In this case we would estimate p with 0.5. The sample size necessary to estimate the true proportion of listeners to within 1% with 95% confidence is given by

$$n = \frac{z_{\alpha/2}^2 \, 0.5(1-0.5)}{E^2} = \frac{1.96^2 \, (0.5)(1-0.5)}{0.01^2} = 9604$$

Notice that the required sample size is significantly larger when an estimate of the population proportion is not available.

The value of drawing random samples resides in the ability to assess the reliability of sample inferences. Reliability is expressed in probability. That is why so much of the text has been devoted to probabilistic ideas.

Predictive Analytics

Direct Mail

One of the illusions magicians try to create is the ability to accurately forecast complex future events. The goal of predictive analytics is similar and rather magical, but it is not an illusion. As the name implies, predictive analytics is a broad set of statistical, machine learning, and data mining techniques used to forecast complex future events with a significant degree of accuracy.

In the appendix of the Hawkes Learning courseware, there is a role playing game called Direct Mail. The purpose of the game is for the player to develop a predictive strategy for direct mail marketing.

The direct mail game is a simulation game in which you will play the role of a junior marketing manager in charge of direct mail marketing for a product you have been given to help manage. You are a new hire and are anxious to impress the marketing manager with some cool predictive analytics.

In your company the marketing department will develop a brochure to send out to members of various mailing lists. The only thing you will know about the mailing lists are that the marketing manager has given you a set of lists which she believes may be potentially profitable using the developed brochure. You have been asked to develop a strategy to evaluate the risks and opportunities associated with each list for any potential profitability. If the marketing manager believes your initial assessments are good, you will be allowed to do the remainder of the lists on your own. Is this just a guessing game, or is there some statistical science that can be applied to aid you? As you likely guessed, the latter is the correct answer.

In direct mail marketing one of the big problems is getting the recipient to open your mail. How personal the mail looks will influence the probability it will be opened. In addition to choosing whether to mail a list or not, you can define your own mailing tactic that may impact whether your mail is opened. There are two mailing choices. First, you must decide whether to use first class or bulk mail. First class costs $0.68 per piece and bulk mail costs $0.49 for each piece mailed. First class looks more personal, but bulk is cheaper; which will be best for your particular list? Another personalizing feature you can invest in is whether you want to use mailing labels or have the envelopes typed with the name and address.

The marketing manager is anxiously awaiting your predictive analytic model.

10.3 **Exercises**

Basic Concepts

1. Describe, in layman's terms, how a confidence interval is constructed for a population proportion.

2. It seems that estimating proportions produces estimates which are much more precise than those for means. Explain why this is the case or is not the case.

3. When determining the sample size required to estimate a population proportion within some specified error level with a specific level of confidence, what is the guideline to follow when there is no estimate available for the population proportion? Why is this done?

Exercises

4. Acid rain accumulations in lakes and streams in the northeastern part of the United States are a major environmental concern. A researcher wants to know what fraction of lakes contain hazardous pollution levels. He randomly selects 200 lakes and determines that 45 of the selected lakes have an unsafe concentration of acid rain pollution.

   a. Calculate the best point estimate of the population proportion of lakes that have unsafe concentrations of acid rain pollution.

   b. Determine a 95% confidence interval for the population proportion.

   c. If a local politician states that only 20% of the lakes are contaminated, does the study provide overwhelming evidence at the 95% level to contradict his views?

5. *The Richland Gazette*, a local newspaper, conducted a poll of 1000 randomly selected readers to determine their views concerning the city's handling of snow removal. The paper found that 650 people in the sample felt the city did a good job.

   a. Compute the best point estimate for the percentage of readers who believe the city is doing a good job of snow removal.

   b. Construct a 90% confidence interval for this percentage.

6. The clinical testing of drugs involves many factors. For example, patients that have been given placebos, which are harmless compounds that have no effect on the patient, often will still report that they feel better. Assume that in a study of 500 random subjects conducted by the Poppins Sucre Drug Company, the percentage of patients reporting improvement when given a placebo was 37%.

   a. What would be a 95% confidence interval for the true proportion of patients who exhibit the placebo effect? Interpret this interval in terms of the problem.

   b. What would the 99% confidence interval be?

   c. To gain the additional 4% of confidence how much wider did the interval become?

7. The Peacock Electric Company thinks that 40% of their customers would be interested in bundling solar power purchasing with their electric bill. A random sample of 400 households reveals that 110 of the households are interested in this.

   a. Construct a 99% confidence interval for the true proportion of households interested in bundling solar with their utilities.

   b. Do you feel the company is accurate in its belief about the proportion of customers who have interest in bundling solar power with their utilities? Justify your answer.

8. Running continues to be a very popular sport in America. At a major race, there may be over 10,000 people entered to run. The race promoters for a road race in the Pacific Northwest took a random sample of 750 runners out of the 5000 runners entered to estimate the number of runners who will need hotel accommodations. Five hundred runners indicated they would need hotel accommodations.

   a. Construct a 90% confidence interval for the true proportion of runners who will need hotel accommodations.

   b. Is the confidence interval obtained sufficiently narrow to be of help in planning the number of hotel rooms which will be necessary to accommodate the runners? Justify your answer.

9. In the fourth quarter of 2010 the home ownership rate was 66.5%.[1] This rate was 2.7 percentage points lower than the 2004 peak of 69.2%, and the lowest rate since 1998. Home ownership fell at an alarming pace in the fourth quarter of the year, despite the fact that home prices fell, affordability was much improved, and inventories of new and existing homes were running quite high. Suppose that a random sample of 120 households was selected from an area in the Midwest that is particularly economically depressed. Suppose that 57 of the households sampled were owned by the residents of the homes.

   a. Construct a 95% confidence interval for the proportion of households in the area sampled that are owned by the residents of the homes.

   b. Is there evidence at the 95% level that the proportion of the households in the area sampled that are owned by residents is less than the national rate?

10. In the *Gallup Poll Monthly*, it was reported that 31% of the people surveyed in a recent poll claimed that vegetables were their least favorite food. Surprisingly, only 14% responded with liver, and 10% of those surveyed did not submit a response because they claimed that they liked everything. The poll was based upon a sample of 1001 people. Assume that a random sample of Americans was chosen, and construct a 90% confidence interval for the percentage of all Americans who say that vegetables are their least favorite food.

11. The Big Green Poster Company wants to estimate the fraction of poster sites controlled by their competition, Bird's Billboard Service. What sample size would be necessary to estimate this fraction to within 3% with 95% confidence? (They think Bird's controls about 33 percent of the boards.)

12. Researchers working in a remote area of Africa feel that 40% of families in the area are without adequate drinking water either through contamination or unavailability. What sample size will be necessary to estimate the percentage without adequate water to within 5% with 99% confidence?

13. Companies that provide environmental cleanup for hazardous waste and toxic chemicals are growing rapidly. W.R. Gross is thinking about entering this field with a subsidiary called Saf-t-Soil. They wish to estimate the true proportion of U.S. corporations that produce hazardous waste as a by-product of their manufacturing process to within 10% with 80% confidence. What sample size will be needed?

14. The public relations manager for a political candidate would like to determine if the registered voters in the candidate's district agree with the politician's view on a particular issue. Find the sample size necessary for the public relations manager to estimate the true proportion to within 5% with 85% confidence.

10.4 Estimating the Population Standard Deviation or Variance

In this section, we will develop a confidence interval for the population variance and population standard deviation. To do this we will need to introduce a new distribution called the chi-square.

Recall that the sample variance is

$$s^2 = \frac{\sum(x_i - \overline{x})^2}{n-1}$$

and it serves as the point estimate of the population variance, σ^2. We need to develop a sampling distribution for

$$\frac{(n-1)s^2}{\sigma^2}$$

Note

The requirement of normality is very strict, regardless of sample size, as large errors may result.

that will allow us to calculate a confidence interval for the population variance.

Note that if we have a random sample of size n, taken from a normal population, then the sampling distribution of $\frac{(n-1)s^2}{\sigma^2}$ follows a chi-square distribution with $n-1$ degrees of freedom.

The chi-square distribution is a positively skewed (or skewed to the right) distribution. Like the t-distribution, the shape of the distribution is a function of its degrees of freedom. See Figure 10.4.1, which illustrates the chi-square distributions with 4 and 10 degrees of freedom.

χ^2 Distributions with 4 and 10 Degrees of Freedom

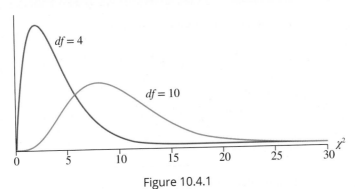

Figure 10.4.1

To use the chi-square distribution, we need a chi-square value, denoted by χ_α^2 (the Greek letter χ, pronounced *Ki*). We'll later call this our critical value for the chi-square distribution. As is shown in Figure 10.4.2, χ_α^2 is the point on the horizontal axis under the curve with an area of α to the right of it. The value of χ_α^2 depends on the right-hand tail area, α, and the number of degrees of freedom of the chi-square distribution. The values are tabulated in Table G in Appendix A. Looking at the chi-square table, the rows correspond to the appropriate number of degrees of freedom (the first column listed down the left side of the table), while the columns represent the right-hand tail area.

χ^2 Distribution

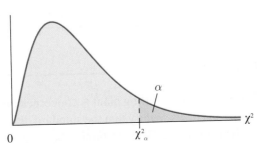

Figure 10.4.2

Using Table G in Appendix A, suppose we want to find the chi-square value that gives us a right-hand tail area of 0.05 with 5 degrees of freedom. To do this, we would look down the left-most column for 5 degrees of freedom and then the column labeled $\chi_{0.05}^2$. Doing so, we find that $\chi_{0.05}^2$ is 11.070.

df	$\chi_{0.100}^2$	$\chi_{0.050}^2$	$\chi_{0.025}^2$	$\chi_{0.010}^2$	$\chi_{0.005}^2$
1	2.706	3.841	5.024	6.635	7.879
2	4.605	5.991	7.378	9.210	10.597
3	6.251	7.815	9.348	11.345	12.838
4	7.779	9.488	11.143	13.277	14.860
5	9.236	11.070	12.833	15.086	16.750
6	10.645	12.592	14.449	16.812	18.548

Now that we've established the sampling distribution associated with the sample variance, we can make inferences about the population variance. Suppose we have a random sample of size n taken from a normal population and that s^2 is the estimate of the population variance, σ^2.

⌘ Technology

The chi-square value can be easily found using technology, such as R. For instructions, please visit stat.hawkeslearning.com and navigate to **Technology Instructions > Chi-Square Distribution > Critical Values**.

```
> qchisq(.95,5)
[1] 11.0705
```

Note

Recall from Chapter 9 that although s^2 is an unbiased point estimate for σ^2, s is a biased estimator for σ.

Note

Since the chi-square distribution is not symmetric, confidence intervals for the population variance and standard deviation do not fit the format of previously studied confidence intervals where you add and subtract the margin of error, E, to a point estimate to get the upper and lower values for the confidence interval. The endpoints of the confidence intervals must be calculated separately.

100(1 − α)% Confidence Interval for σ^2

A $100(1-\alpha)\%$ confidence interval for σ^2 is given by

$$\frac{(n-1)s^2}{\chi^2_{\alpha/2}} < \sigma^2 < \frac{(n-1)s^2}{\chi^2_{1-\alpha/2}}$$

where $\chi^2_{\alpha/2}$ and $\chi^2_{1-\alpha/2}$ are points under the curve of the chi-square distribution with $n-1$ degrees of freedom.

FORMULA

The confidence interval for the population standard deviation is found by taking the square root of the endpoints of the confidence interval for the population variance.

100(1 − α)% Confidence Interval for σ

A $100(1-\alpha)\%$ confidence interval for σ is given by

$$\sqrt{\frac{(n-1)s^2}{\chi^2_{\alpha/2}}} < \sigma < \sqrt{\frac{(n-1)s^2}{\chi^2_{1-\alpha/2}}}$$

where $\chi^2_{\alpha/2}$ and $\chi^2_{1-\alpha/2}$ are points under the curve of the chi-square distribution with $n-1$ degrees of freedom.

FORMULA

Example 10.4.1

The quality control supervisor of a bottling plant is concerned about the variance of fill per bottle. Regulatory agencies specify that the standard deviation of the amount of fill should be less than 0.1 ounce. To determine whether the process is meeting this specification, the supervisor randomly selects ten bottles, weighs the contents of each, and finds that the sample standard deviation of these measurements is 0.04. Compute a 95% confidence interval for the standard deviation of ounces of fill for the bottling plant.

Solution

We want to find a 95% confidence interval for the variance. We are given that

$$n = 10, \ s = 0.04, \text{ and } \alpha = 0.05.$$

To calculate a 95% confidence interval, we use the following formula.

$$\frac{(n-1)s^2}{\chi^2_{\alpha/2}} < \sigma^2 < \frac{(n-1)s^2}{\chi^2_{1-\alpha/2}}$$

Thus, we need to find the values of $\chi^2_{0.025}$ and $\chi^2_{0.975}$ for $n-1 = 10-1 = 9$ degrees of freedom.

Using Table G in Appendix A, at 9 degrees of freedom,

$$\chi^2_{0.025} = 19.023$$
$$\chi^2_{0.975} = 2.700.$$

Substituting the values in the formula above, we have

$$\frac{(10-1)(0.04)^2}{19.023} < \sigma^2 < \frac{(10-1)(0.04)^2}{2.700}$$
$$0.000757 < \sigma^2 < 0.00533$$

So, a 95% confidence interval for the variance of fill of the bottles is between 0.000757 and 0.00533 ounce². However, the problem mentions the tolerance for the standard deviation of fill. So, to ensure that we make our interpretation in terms of the problem, to find a 95% confidence interval for the standard deviation, we take the square root of the endpoints of the confidence interval for the variance, yielding

$$0.0275 \le \sigma \le 0.0730.$$

The 95% confidence interval for the standard deviation of fill for the bottles is between 0.0275 and 0.0730 ounces, indicating that the process is meeting the specifications of being less than 0.1 ounces.

⊗ Technology

The confidence interval for the population variance can be obtained using Minitab. For detailed instructions, visit stat.hawkeslearning.com and navigate to **Technology Instructions > Confidence Intervals > Variance**.

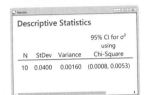

10.4 **Exercises**

Basic Concepts

1. What is the sampling distribution for $\dfrac{(n-1)s^2}{\sigma^2}$?

2. What assumption must hold to use the chi-square distribution to make inferences about the population variance?

3. True or False: The chi-square distribution is skewed to the right.

4. What is the symbol for a critical value for the chi-square distribution? Describe the meaning of this critical value.

5. Give an example where we would want to calculate a confidence interval for σ^2.

Exercises

6. Determine the critical value(s) of the test statistic for each of the following tests for a population variance where the assumption of normality is satisfied.

    a. Right-tailed test, $\alpha = 0.01$, $n = 20$

    b. Right-tailed test, $\alpha = 0.005$, $n = 5$

7. Determine the critical value(s) of the test statistic for each of the following tests for a population variance where the assumption of normality is satisfied.

    a. Right-tailed test, $\alpha = 0.025$, $n = 18$

    b. Right-tailed test, $\alpha = 0.05$, $n = 41$

8. A bolt manufacturer is very concerned about the consistency with which his machines produce bolts that are $\frac{3}{4}$ inches in diameter. When the manufacturing process is working normally the standard deviation of the bolt diameter is 0.05 inches. A random sample of 30 bolts has an average diameter of 0.25 inches with a standard deviation of 0.07 inches.

   a. Construct a 95% confidence interval for the standard deviation of the bolt diameter. Interpret the interval.

   b. What assumption did you make about the diameter of the bolts in constructing the confidence interval in part **a.**?

9. A drug that is used for treating cancer has potentially dangerous side effects if it is taken in doses that are larger than the required dosage for the treatment. The pharmaceutical company that manufactures the drug must be certain that the standard deviation of the drug content in the tablet is not more than 0.1 mg. Twenty-five tablets are randomly selected and the amount of drug in each tablet is measured. The sample has a mean of 20 mg and a variance of 0.015 mg.

   a. Construct a 99% confidence interval for the variance of the amount of drug in each tablet. Interpret the interval.

   b. What assumption did you make about the amount of drug contained in the tablets in constructing the confidence interval in part **a.**?

CR   Chapter Review

Key Terms and Ideas

- Statistical Inference
- Estimator
- Estimate
- Point Estimator
- Point Estimate
- Interval Estimate
- Mean Squared Error
- Unbiasedness
- Unbiased Estimator
- Interval Estimator
- Confidence Interval

- Confidence Level
- Confidence Interval for the Population Mean
- Margin of Error (Maximum Error of Estimation)
- Student's t-Distribution
- Degrees of Freedom
- Pilot Study
- Proportion
- Sample Proportion
- Confidence Interval for the Population Proportion

Key Formulas	
	Section
Mean Squared Error for the Sample Mean $$\mathrm{MSE}\left(\bar{x}\right)=E\left(\bar{x}-\mu\right)^2$$	10.1
$100(1-\alpha)\%$ Confidence Interval for the Population Mean: σ Known $$\bar{x} \pm z_{\alpha/2}\frac{\sigma}{\sqrt{n}}$$ where $\bar{x}$ is the sample mean, $z_{\alpha/2}$ is the critical value for a z-distribution which captures an area of $\alpha/2$ in the right tail of the distribution, σ is the population standard deviation, and n is the sample size.	10.2
Student's t-Distribution $$t = \frac{\bar{x}-\mu}{s/\sqrt{n}}$$ where $\bar{x}$ is the sample mean, s is the sample standard deviation, and n is the sample size.	10.2
Degrees of Freedom $$df = \text{number of sample observations} - 1 = n - 1$$	10.2
$100(1-\alpha)\%$ Confidence Interval for the Population Mean: σ Unknown $$\bar{x} \pm t_{\alpha/2,n-1}\frac{s}{\sqrt{n}}$$ where $t_{\alpha/2,n-1}$ is the critical value for a t-distribution with $n-1$ degrees of freedom which captures an area of $\alpha/2$ in the right tail of the distribution.	10.2
Margin of Error for the Population Mean (Maximum Error of Estimation) $$E = z_{\alpha/2}\frac{\sigma}{\sqrt{n}}$$	10.2
Determining the Sample Size for the Population Mean: σ Known $$n = \left(\frac{z_{\alpha/2}\sigma}{E}\right)^2$$ Round your calculated answer up to the nearest integer.	10.2

Key Formulas	
	Section
Determining the Sample Size for the Population Mean: σ Unknown $$n = \left(\frac{z_{\alpha/2} s}{E} \right)^2$$ Round your calculated answer up to the nearest integer.	10.2
Point Estimate of the Population Proportion $$\hat{p} = \frac{x}{n}$$ where x is the number in the sample that possesses the attribute and n is the sample size.	10.3
100(1 − α)% Confidence Interval for the Population Proportion $$\hat{p} \pm z_{\alpha/2} \sigma_{\hat{p}}$$ where $z_{\alpha/2}$ is the critical value for a z-distribution which captures an area of $\alpha/2$ in the right tail of the distribution, and $\sigma_{\hat{p}}$ is the standard deviation of $\hat{p}$.	10.3
Margin of Error for the Population Proportion (Maximum Error of Estimation) $$E = z_{\alpha/2} \sigma_{\hat{p}} = z_{\alpha/2} \sqrt{\frac{p(1-p)}{n}}$$ where $z_{\alpha/2}$ is the critical value for a z-distribution which captures an area of $\alpha/2$ in the right tail of the distribution, p is the population proportion, and n is the sample size.	10.3
Determining the Sample Size for the Population Proportion $$n = \frac{z_{\alpha/2}^2 p(1-p)}{E^2} \approx \frac{z_{\alpha/2}^2 \hat{p}(1-\hat{p})}{E^2}$$ where $z_{\alpha/2}$ is the critical value for a z-distribution which captures an area of $\alpha/2$ in the right tail of the distribution, p is the population proportion, and $\hat{p}$ is the sample proportion. Round your calculated answer up to the nearest integer.	10.3

Key Formulas	
	Section
Determining the Sample Size for the Population Proportion: No Estimate $\left(\hat{p}\right)$ Available $$n = \frac{z_{\alpha/2}^2 (0.5)(1-0.5)}{E^2} \approx \frac{z_{\alpha/2}^2 (0.25)}{E^2}$$ Round your calculated answer up to the nearest integer.	10.3
$100(1-\alpha)$% Confidence Interval for the Population Variance A $100(1-\alpha)$% confidence interval for σ^2 is given by $$\frac{(n-1)s^2}{\chi_{\alpha/2}^2} < \sigma^2 < \frac{(n-1)s^2}{\chi_{1-\alpha/2}^2}$$ where $\chi_{\alpha/2}^2$ and $\chi_{1-\alpha/2}^2$ are points under the curve of the chi-square distribution with $n-1$ degrees of freedom.	10.4
$100(1-\alpha)$% Confidence Interval for the Population Standard Deviation A $100(1-\alpha)$% confidence interval for σ is given by $$\sqrt{\frac{(n-1)s^2}{\chi_{\alpha/2}^2}} < \sigma < \sqrt{\frac{(n-1)s^2}{\chi_{1-\alpha/2}^2}}$$ where $\chi_{\alpha/2}^2$ and $\chi_{1-\alpha/2}^2$ are points under the curve of the chi-square distribution with $n-1$ degrees of freedom	10.4

Additional Exercises

1. A random sample of fifteen eleven-year-old boys is selected in order to estimate the mean height for boys belonging to that age group. The resulting measurements in inches are given in the table below.

Heights (Inches)				
55	58	52	58	54
57	56	54	58	56
52	59	55	61	57

   a. Calculate the sample mean and the sample standard deviation of the heights.

   b. Construct a 95% confidence interval for the mean height of all eleven-year-old boys.

    c. What assumption did you make about the heights in constructing your interval?

2. R. Cramden, chief development officer for Fontana Area Transport bus company, is concerned about the declining use of the bus system. He wishes to estimate the percentage of Fontana residents who consider safety a significant factor in their decision about whether or not to ride a bus. This will be a preliminary study so he is willing to develop an estimate with an error of 10% at a confidence level of 90%.

    a. What sample size will be needed?

    b. If 150 residents in a random sample of 500 Fontana residents say that they consider safety a significant factor in their decision about whether or not to ride a bus, estimate the true proportion of Fontana residents who think safety is a significant factor in their decision about whether or not to ride a bus with 95% confidence.

3. According to a study conducted by the American Stock Exchange, 87% of 500 young Americans surveyed said that they can't count on Social Security as a source of income when they retire. Construct a 90% confidence interval for the proportion of young Americans who feel they can't count on Social Security as a source of income when they retire. (Assume the sample was randomly selected.)

4. The State Bureau of Standards must inspect gasoline station pumps on a regular basis to be sure they are operating properly. A recent survey of a randomly selected group of 61 pumps produced a sample mean of 9.75 gallons dispensed for a pump reading ten gallons. If the sample had a standard deviation of 1.12 gallons, find the 80% confidence interval for the mean amount of gas dispensed when a gas pump reads ten gallons.

5. In a population of non-unionized employees, 55% are sympathetic toward unionization. The American Federation of Labor has drawn a random sample of 250 persons selected from this population to investigate union interest. Construct a 90% confidence interval for the proportion of the sample that will be sympathetic toward unionization.

6. Suppose a study designed to collect data on smokers and nonsmokers uses a preliminary estimate of the proportion that smoke of 22%. How large a sample should be taken to estimate the proportion of smokers in the population with a margin of error of 0.02 with 80% confidence?

7. As part of an annual review of its accounts, a discount brokerage firm selects a random sample of 15 customers. Their accounts are reviewed for a total account valuation, which showed a mean of $32,000 with a sample standard deviation of $8200.

    a. What is a 99% confidence interval for the mean account valuation of the population of customers? Interpret the interval in terms of the problem.

    b. What assumption about the account distribution is necessary to solve this problem?

8. Direct Shoes has 250 retail outlets throughout the United States. The firm is evaluating a potential location for a new outlet, based in part, on the mean annual income of the individuals in the marketing area of the new location. A random sample of size 36 was taken from the marketing area; the sample mean income is $31,100. The population standard deviation is estimated to be $4500. Construct a confidence interval using a confidence level of 0.95.

9. Suppose we want to determine the sample size required to give us a 95% confidence interval that estimates, to within $500, the average salary of a state employee. Also, suppose that from a previous experiment, we know that $s = \$6300$. What is the minimum sample size required?

10. A reporter for a student newspaper is writing an article on the cost of off-campus housing. A sample of 16 efficiency apartments within a half-mile of campus resulted in a sample mean of $1100 per month and a sample standard deviation of $55. Construct a 95% confidence interval estimate of the mean rent per month for the population of efficiency apartments within a half-mile of campus. We will assume that this population is normally distributed.

11. Voting, Inc. specializes in voter polls and surveys designed to keep political office seekers informed of their position in a race. Using telephone surveys, interviewers ask registered voters who they would vote for if the election were held that day. In a current election campaign, Voting, Inc. has found that 220 registered voters, out of 500 contacted, favor a particular candidate. Find a 95% confidence interval estimate for the proportion of the population of registered voters that favor the candidate.

12. According to the National Funeral Directors Association, the nation's 19,000 funeral homes take in $13 billion a year, with the average cost of a funeral being $7181 in 2014. Suppose that the costs of ten random funerals taking place in an affluent suburb of a Pennsylvania city are given below:

$8206	$5819	$10,225	$6450	$8575
$5450	$7335	$9775	$10,455	$8225

   a. Construct a 90% confidence interval for the average funeral cost in this suburb.

   b. Is the average funeral cost in this suburb higher than in the U.S. as a whole?

   c. What population assumption needs to be made here?

"The great tragedy of science–the slaying of a beautiful hypothesis by an ugly fact."

— Thomas Henry Huxley

11 CHAPTER
Hypothesis Testing: Single Samples

Introduction

People often start the day with hypothesis testing. The alarm rings and a semi-conscious hand reaches up, shutting it off. Lying in bed, there are two rival alternatives fighting for acceptance.

Wake Up Hypotheses

- I can rest for a few more minutes; I need just a little more sleep.
- I better get up; I will probably fall asleep again.

A hypothesis is a claim. In the wake-up example, there are two rival claims, one of which will be chosen. The decision is subjective, relying on personally accumulated data, and the amount of abuse your body was subjected to the previous evening. The process of choosing between these two competing views of the world is called a hypothesis test. In this example, the process is informal, there is no population to define, there are no data gathering guidelines, and there is no specific procedure that is consistently used to help decide which of the two views is more reasonable.

After getting up, you'll probably need a shower. No one gets in the shower unless the water temperature is reasonable. Again, there are two rival alternatives.

Shower Hypotheses

- The shower water temperature is acceptable.
- The shower water is not acceptable (too hot or too cold).

What distinguishes this decision from the previous one is the explicit use of data collection in the decision making process. You collect water temperature data by sticking a hand or foot in the shower before reaching a conclusion.

You continue making everyday hypothesis tests in your choice of what to eat for breakfast, what clothes to wear, and what time to leave for work. What distinguishes statistical hypothesis testing from the everyday variety is the use of statistical measures in the statement of the hypothesis, the collection of sample data, and the use of the sample data in a well-defined decision-making process.

Hypothesis Testing

A **hypothesis** is a statement or claim about a characteristic of one or more populations.

A **hypothesis test** is a procedure, based on sample evidence, that is used to test a statement or claim about a characteristic of one or more populations.

DEFINITION

11.1 Introduction to Hypothesis Testing

It should come as no surprise that the first step in all statistical hypothesis testing is a statement of hypothesis, regardless of the nature of the problem. In a statistical test of a hypothesis, the **null hypothesis**, H_0, is a statement that is presumed to be true unless there is overwhelming evidence in favor of the alternative, H_a. In other words, the null hypothesis is given the benefit of the doubt.

A familiar example of the disparate treatment of H_0 and H_a is found in our judicial system.

H_0: Defendant is not guilty.   (null hypothesis)

H_a: Defendant is guilty.   (alternative hypothesis)

A jury must believe that the evidence (data) demonstrates guilt "beyond a shadow of a doubt" in order to convict a defendant (H_a). However, the defendant only has to demonstrate there is insufficient evidence of guilt in order to be acquitted (H_0). In other words, *the null hypothesis (H_0: Defendant is not guilty.) is presumed to be true unless there is overwhelming evidence to the contrary*. In our judicial systems, the defendant is innocent until proven guilty.

This example is somewhat abstract. In order to conduct a hypothesis test using statistical methods, the hypothesis must be stated in terms of statistical measures such as the population mean, population proportion, or population variance.

Example 11.1.1

A molecular biologist has been investigating several species of wild potato plants and believes she has discovered genetic properties that will increase the yield of the standard species. She has genetically engineered these new properties into the standard variety and produced a new variety. The standard species yields an average of 2.34 pounds per plant. She would like to know if her new plant has superior yield. The answer to this question can be investigated by testing the following rival hypotheses.

- The new variety does not have superior yield.
- The new variety does have superior yield.

To apply statistical methodology to answer this question, the preceding hypotheses must be translated into a problem statement concerning a statistical measure (e.g., mean, proportion, or variance). The statistical measure will be used in the definition of a criterion to decide the issue. There is a great deal of variability in the yields of potato plants. Comparing mean yield per plant of the new variety with the standard variety would provide a reasonable method of evaluating the new variety. The mean yield of the standard variety is known to be 2.34 pounds. However, the mean of the new variety is unknown, and that uncertainty is what makes the problem difficult. If the new variety does possess a superior yield, then the mean yield ought to be higher than the standard variety's mean yield. If μ is defined as

μ = the average yield per plant for the new variety (population parameter),

then the two claims can be written in the following manner.

$H_0: \mu = 2.34$ lb   The yield of the new variety is equal to the standard yield.

$H_a: \mu > 2.34$ lb   The new variety has superior yield.

H_0, called the **null hypothesis**, contends that the mean yield of the new variety is equal to the mean yield of the standard variety. If this is the case, H_0 asserts that the new variety is no better than the standard variety. This would be a disappointing result for the genetic researcher. H_a, called the **alternative hypothesis**, declares that the mean yield for the new plant is superior to the mean yield of the standard variety. Once the problem statement is formulated in terms of a population parameter (in this case, the parameter is μ, the mean yield), sample data can be developed to help decide which hypothesis is more reasonable.

This example illustrates another important component of a hypothesis test, namely, deciding whether H_a should be one-sided or two-sided. In Example 11.1.1, H_a involves a **one-sided alternative**, since the researcher is only interested in learning if there is sufficient evidence that yields are above the standard. If the researcher were interested in yields that were below the standard, then H_a would also have been one-sided, but the inequality would have been in the other direction ($H_a: \mu < 2.34$). A **two-sided alternative** ($H_a: \mu \neq 2.34$) would indicate that the researcher is concerned with yields that are *above or below* the standard.

In Example 11.1.1, why didn't we put $\mu > 2.34$ lb in the null hypothesis? Recall that the hypotheses were formulated as follows.

Correct Formulation		**Incorrect Formulation**
$H_0: \mu = 2.34$ lb	instead of	~~$H_0: \mu > 2.34$ lb~~
$H_a: \mu > 2.34$ lb		~~$H_a: \mu = 2.34$ lb~~

The Incorrect Formulation of the Null Hypothesis, $H_0: \mu > 2.34$

The incorrect formulation states in the null hypothesis, H_0, that the new variety has superior yield. By placing this statement in H_0, the statement is presumed to be true unless there is overwhelming evidence to the contrary. This does not make sense! Why would a researcher who is trying to prove her new variety is superior to the standard variety start out assuming the new variety is superior?

The Correct Formulation of the Null Hypothesis, $H_0: \mu = 2.34$

The researcher must demonstrate overwhelming evidence that the new variety has superior yield for her new plant to be accepted. To achieve this goal, she must place the statement, $\mu > 2.34$ lb, in the alternative hypothesis. In the *correct* version, the null hypothesis, $H_0: \mu = 2.34$ lb, states that we believe the new variety's yield is equal to that of the standard variety. Because the null hypothesis is presumed to be true, this hypothesis is not rejected unless there is overwhelming evidence to the contradict H_0. If $H_0: \mu = 2.34$ lb is rejected in favor of $H_a: \mu > 2.34$ lb, then there is overwhelming evidence that the new variety has superior yield.

To summarize, the researcher wants to know if the yield of the new variety is going to be greater than the standard yield of 2.34 lb. If the researcher's genetic design is successful, the null hypothesis will be rejected in favor of the alternative. Rejecting the null in favor of the alternative means the sample data overwhelmingly supports the idea that the newly developed variety of potato yields more potatoes (in weight) than the standard variety. Failing to reject the null hypothesis would mean that there is insufficient evidence to warrant concluding the new potato has superior yield.

This type of formulation is typical of a test of a hypothesis in a research environment, testing a new theory or idea against an established one. In many research hypothesis tests, the investigator hopes to reject the null hypothesis in order to demonstrate the significance of a new idea. It is often the case that if there is a **standard value** for a population parameter, the null hypothesis states that the population parameter is equal to the standard value.

When formulating hypotheses, remember that the equality statement will always be contained in the null hypothesis. That is, the null hypothesis will contain =, whereas the alternative hypothesis will contain <, >, or ≠.

Properties of H_0 and H_a

The **null hypothesis**, denoted H_0, is a statement about the value of a population parameter. This statement is assumed to be true unless we find sample evidence that indicates it is not. If the sample evidence is strong enough to indicate it is not true, then we reject the null hypothesis. Otherwise, we fail to reject the null hypothesis.

The **alternative hypothesis**, denoted H_a or H_1, is also a statement about the value of a population parameter. It is the statement or claim that we are trying to find evidence to support.

DEFINITION

Example 11.1.2

Suppose a potato chip manufacturer is concerned that the bagging equipment is not functioning properly when filling 10-ounce bags. He wants to test a hypothesis that will help determine if there is a problem with the bagging equipment. What is the correct hypothesis?

$$H_0: \mu = 10 \text{ oz} \qquad \text{or} \qquad H_0: \mu \neq 10 \text{ oz}$$
$$H_a: \mu \neq 10 \text{ oz} \qquad\qquad\qquad H_a: \mu = 10 \text{ oz}$$

Solution

Since the standard value in this problem is 10 ounces, the null hypothesis is $H_0: \mu = 10$ oz. The bagging equipment ordinarily functions properly; thus the manufacturer requires overwhelming evidence that the machine is overfilling or underfilling the bags before shutting down the equipment.

When the alternative hypothesis allows values above and below the standard value, it is called a **two-sided alternative**. In this case, the manufacturer hopes that he *fails to reject* the null hypothesis, since that would suggest that his equipment is putting the right amount in the bags. This type of hypothesis is quite common in quality control and other kinds of system monitoring.

Example 11.1.3

Martha Brandon wants to assess her candidacy in a forthcoming race for the state senate. She is an incumbent and wants to raise sufficient support to retain her seat. How should she formulate an appropriate hypothesis to determine if there is overwhelming evidence she will retain her seat?

Solution

The correct formulation of the hypotheses is

$H_0: p = 0.5$ Martha does not have sufficient support to retain her seat.

$H_a: p > 0.5$ Martha does have sufficient support to retain her seat.

where $p =$ the fraction of voters that will vote for her.

This problem differs significantly from the other two examples. The problem's formulation requires the use of a different statistical measure, p, the population proportion. The crucial value of the proportion is 0.5, since in order to retain the seat she must obtain more than half of the votes cast (assuming there is only one other candidate). The null hypothesis contends that she does not have sufficient support to retain her seat. Why would she want to presume that she will lose the election? If the null hypothesis is rejected in favor of the alternative, $H_a: p > 0.5$, there is overwhelming evidence that she has the blessing of more than half the voters.

The alternative is one-sided, since the intent of the study is to learn if she will win. (A two-sided alternative would imply interest in finding out if she will win or lose the election, a rather meaningless idea.) She hopes the conclusion of the test will be to reject the null hypothesis, since that implies that there is overwhelming sample evidence that she will receive more than half the votes cast.

Formulating Hypothesis Testing Problems

To be successful at formulating hypothesis testing problems you must be able to:

1. Determine the appropriate statistical measure to test the desired hypothesis (population mean, proportion, or variance).

2. Determine the appropriate value to use in the null hypothesis. (This may be stated in the problem as a standard value or may need to be deduced from the information at hand.)

3. Decide whether the alternative should be one-sided or two-sided.

PROCEDURE

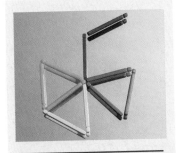

A Proof By Contradiction?

Imagine a circumstance in which there are two conflicting propositions of which only one can be true. If you could prove that one of these is not true, then implicitly, the other is the truthful proposition. This is called a proof by contradiction and there are many famous examples in mathematics. This method of proof dates back to Aristotle.

Some important concepts that have been classically proven by contradiction include:

*   Irrationality of the square root of 2,

*   The length of the hypotenuse of a triangle is less than the sum of the lengths of the two remaining sides,

*   No smallest rational number greater than 0.

Hypothesis testing is similar to a proof by contradiction in that the null is assumed to be true unless there is overwhelming evidence to the contrary. Frequently, the aim of the hypothesis test is to disprove the null hypothesis, hence the connection to the proof by contradiction.

Reaching a Conclusion

The point of a hypothesis test is to select one of the competing hypotheses (H_0 or H_a) as the *correct* decision. Once you have reached a conclusion, there will remain a possibility that the inference (decision) is incorrect. The idea of performing the correct statistical test, exactly following the procedure, and still possibly making an incorrect decision may be bothersome. Uncertainty, however, is a part of every statistical inference.

How Uncertain Are Our Conclusions?

Errors can happen in two ways. In statistical terminology, we call these Type I errors and Type II errors.

Errors in Hypothesis Testing

Rejecting H_0 when in fact H_0 is the correct choice is called a **Type I error**.

Failing to reject H_0 when in fact H_a is the correct choice is called a **Type II error**.

DEFINITION

In a statistical test of hypothesis, we can only control for Type I errors. This fact often influences how we construct hypotheses.

Example 11.1.4

Suppose Jeremy was in a car accident and a doctor in the emergency room believes he is dead. Jeremy's body has been sent to a mortician for preparation. Preparation, in this context, is a euphemism for draining the blood out of his body and replacing it with fluids which retard deterioration. If Jeremy isn't dead when he gets to the mortician, he will be dead after he is *prepared*. How should the mortician frame the hypothesis when he/she begins to work on Jeremy's body?

Solution

Formulation A

H_0: Jeremy is dead.

H_a: Jeremy is alive.

Type I error using Formulation A

To have an error you must make a mistake. Suppose this is what happened.

Truth: **H_0: Jeremy is dead.**

Mortician's Decision: H_a: Jeremy is alive.

In order to have a Type I error, you must reject the null hypothesis when it is true. In this case, the mortician believes Jeremy is alive even though he is actually dead. What's the consequence to the mortician?

Consequence: None, since Jeremy is already dead. From Jeremy's vantage point, or the lack of it in this case, no problem. R.I.P.

Type II error using Formulation A

Mortician's Decision: H_0: Jeremy is dead.

Truth: **H_a: Jeremy is alive.**

A Type II error means failing to reject the null, when it is false. If the null is false, then the alternative is true. Jeremy is alive. Good news! Unfortunately, the mortician thought he was dead.

Consequence: Jeremy will die as soon as *preparations* begin.

For the two errors, which has the worst consequence? Clearly, the Type II error has the worst consequence. Does Formulation A place the most serious error as a Type I? Not if life matters! Let's try another formulation.

> ## Formulation B
>
> H_0: Jeremy is alive.
>
> H_a: Jeremy is dead.

Type I error using Formulation B

Truth: H_0: **Jeremy is alive.**

Mortician's Decision: H_a: Jeremy is dead.

The mortician believes Jeremy is dead when, in fact, he is alive. He is *prepared.*
Consequence: Jeremy will die. R.I.P.

Type II error using Formulation B

Mortician's Decision: H_0: Jeremy is alive.

Truth: H_a: **Jeremy is dead.**

The mortician believes Jeremy is alive, when in fact, he is dead.

Consequence: None, since Jeremy is already dead.

Formulation B is the correct formulation of the problem, since the most serious consequence (death!) is the result of a Type I error. That's good, because the probability of a Type I error can be controlled in the hypothesis testing procedure.

Admittedly, the last example was rather bleak, but it does demonstrate an important consideration when formulating hypotheses that is worth repeating. ***Formulate the hypotheses so that the most serious consequence of a mistaken decision is associated with a Type I error.***

> ### α, Type I Error
>
> The probability of a Type I error is denoted by α (the Greek letter alpha), and is referred to as the **level of the test**, or the **significance level of the test**.
>
> **DEFINITION**

The level of the test, α, is the probability value used as the cutoff to determine if the sample evidence is significant enough to reject the null hypothesis. It is up to the researcher to select α prior to the start of the hypothesis test. Common choices for the value of α are 0.10, 0.05, and 0.01.

> ### β, Type II Error
>
> The probability of a Type II error is denoted by β (the Greek letter beta). Unfortunately, the value of β depends on the actual value of the population parameter and thus cannot be determined unless the actual value of the population parameter is known, which is rarely the case.
>
> **DEFINITION**

The Trial of the Pyx

A very early instance of the hypothesis testing approach occurred in England in the twelfth century and is mysteriously named the Trial of the Pyx. There was a lot of concern over the weight of the gold and silver coins distributed by the London Mint. The king would provide gold and silver to the Mint where the metals were melted down and turned into coins. To ensure the coins were meeting the proper standards, every few months a trial would occur in front of a panel of judges, where recently minted coins selected seemingly at random were weighed—placed inside a box called a Pyx—to make sure they were within a fixed tolerance.

The null hypothesis in this test is that the weight of the coins equals the target weight. The alternative hypothesis would be that the weight of the coins is not equal to the target weight.

Type I and Type II Errors in the Trial of the Pyx

If the coins did in fact weigh less than they were intended to, the currency would become debased, and the Mint would be making a profit because they would be pocketing some of the metals they should be turning into coins. If the coins weighed more than they were supposed to, someone could collect these overweight coins, and sell them back to the Mint for a profit. Either way, the king is not happy that someone besides him is able to profit. And in those days, if the king is not happy, there is a high likelihood of important body parts being involuntarily cut off. So, if the coins are found to be off from the standard value, it could mean serious consequences for the head of the Mint.

The hypotheses are set up such that a Type I error implies that the coins were believed to be off from the standard value, when in fact they were meeting the standard. A Type II error would mean that the panel has believed the coins to be matching the weight standard, when in fact they are overweight or underweight. This is the preferred formulation for the head of the Mint, as the Type I error is the one he would like to control so that he does not lose his extremities for no reason! A Type II error would serve the Mint well, as it means the coins were in error, but it went undetected.

In examining the relationship between α and β, a natural question which might arise is:

Why not make both α and β as small as possible?

Unfortunately, the probability of making a Type I error, α, and the probability of making a Type II error, β, are inversely related. Thus, the smaller we make the probability of making a Type I error, the more likely we are to make a Type II error. In general, choose the largest level of α which is tolerable to avoid unnecessarily increasing the probability of making a Type II error.

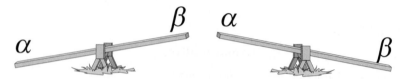

A Procedure for Hypothesis Testing

The hypothesis testing procedure is a method for choosing between two competing hypotheses. Although the procedure will change for different kinds of hypotheses, there are common elements among all tests.

Elements of Hypothesis Testing

- The null hypothesis is presumed to be true unless sample data produces overwhelming evidence to the contrary. That is, the test statistic is calculated under the assumption that the null hypothesis is true.

- Sample data from a random sample are used to calculate a **test statistic**.

- The form of the test statistic will change depending upon the statistical measure used in the hypothesis statement, μ, p, or σ^2 (as well as with the assumptions about knowledge of the population).

- Simple hypothesis testing models related to a single population parameter are explored in this chapter. Each model will have its own set of assumptions depending on the population parameter of interest and the underlying distribution of the population. In later chapters we will look at more complicated hypothesis testing models with multiple parameters which will also have a unique set of assumptions. If the researcher's goal is to attach statistical significance to the conclusions of the hypothesis test, it is critically important to validate the assumptions of the hypothesis testing model.

- The conclusion of the hypothesis test results in a decision to either **reject** or **fail to reject** the null hypothesis. Note that we do not *accept* the null hypothesis; we only conclude that there is insufficient evidence to support the alternative.

- There is no way to be absolutely certain your decision is correct, no matter which hypothesis is selected.

PROPERTIES

An exact procedure for testing a hypothesis is given below. In examining this procedure, you will notice we have already discussed the first two steps. The next two steps define a **decision rule**, which is a criterion used to determine whether the null or the alternative hypothesis will be chosen. As you look over these steps, do not be overly concerned if you do not understand everything. You will learn by following the examples.

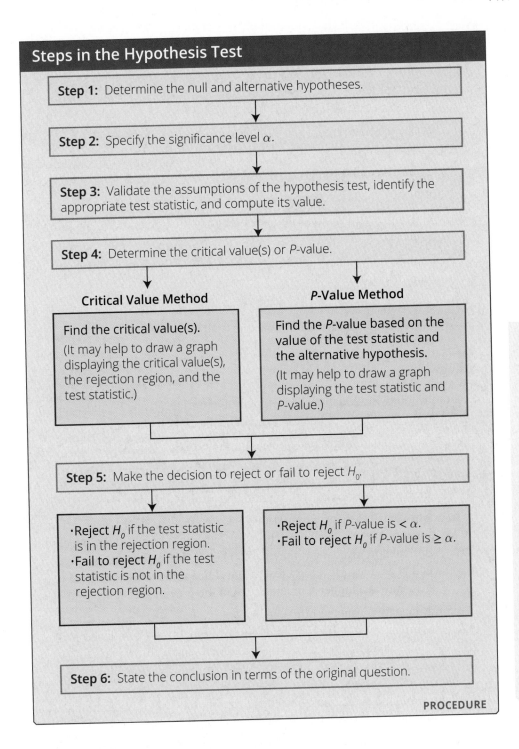

Steps in the Hypothesis Test

Step 1: Determine the null and alternative hypotheses.

Step 2: Specify the significance level α.

Step 3: Validate the assumptions of the hypothesis test, identify the appropriate test statistic, and compute its value.

Step 4: Determine the critical value(s) or P-value.

Critical Value Method

Find the critical value(s).

(It may help to draw a graph displaying the critical value(s), the rejection region, and the test statistic.)

P-Value Method

Find the P-value based on the value of the test statistic and the alternative hypothesis.

(It may help to draw a graph displaying the test statistic and P-value.)

Step 5: Make the decision to reject or fail to reject H_0.

· Reject H_0 if the test statistic is in the rejection region.
· Fail to reject H_0 if the test statistic is not in the rejection region.

· Reject H_0 if P-value is $< \alpha$.
· Fail to reject H_0 if P-value is $\geq \alpha$.

Step 6: State the conclusion in terms of the original question.

PROCEDURE

Note

Note at **Step 4** there are two options; you can find the critical value of the test statistic or the P-value of the test statistic. Both methods will always produce equivalent results; meaning, the decision regarding the hypothesis test will always be the same with both methods. We will often cover both methods in an example to illustrate this. Even though we may show a critical value and a P-value, only one of these is required to make the decision to reject or fail to reject the null hypothesis. You or your instructor may have a preference of one method over another.

11.1 **Exercises**

Basic Concepts

1. What is a hypothesis?

2. What is the first step in the test of a hypothesis?

3. Describe the common elements present in all hypothesis tests.

4. Summarize the difference between the null and alternative hypotheses.

5. Define and give an example of a one-sided alternative. How does this differ from a two-sided alternative?

6. Is there a way to be absolutely certain your decision is correct when performing a hypothesis test? Explain.

7. What are the three important things you must be able to do in order to be successful at formulating hypothesis testing problems?

8. Describe a Type I error.

9. Describe a Type II error.

10. Explain how Type I and Type II errors influence the construction of a hypothesis.

11. Can both Type I and Type II errors be controlled in the hypothesis testing procedure? Explain.

12. What is the level of the test?

13. Why is a Type II error difficult to express numerically?

Exercises

14. For the following situations, develop the appropriate H_0 and H_a and state what the consequences would be for Type I and Type II errors.

    a. The Standard Tire Company has introduced a new tire in Europe that will be guaranteed to last at least 30,000 kilometers. Standard Tire has hired an independent agency to determine if there is overwhelming evidence that their tires will last through the warranty period.

    b. Mrs. Russell, head product tester for Hathaway Tool Corporation, is testing a newly designed series of bar hooks. The hooks have been designed to give way if they get too hot. The previous design gave way at 240 degrees. Develop a test to determine if the newly designed hooks give way at a higher temperature than the previous design.

    c. A manager wants to hire a new network engineer as part of his new IT team and wants to determine with overwhelming confidence if a new candidate is competent for the position. What would we assign H_0 and H_a? Describe the Type I and Type II errors for this hypothesis.

15. For the following situations, develop the appropriate H_0 and H_a and state what the consequences would be for Type I and Type II errors.

    a. A company that manufactures one-half inch bolts selects a random sample of bolts to determine if the diameter of the bolts differs significantly from the required one-half inch.

    b. A company that manufactures safety flares randomly selects 100 flares to determine if the flares last at least three hours on average.

    c. A consumer group believes that a new sports coupe gets significantly fewer miles to the gallon than advertised on the sales sticker. To confirm this belief, they randomly select several of the new coupes and measure the miles per gallon.

11.2 **Testing a Hypothesis about a Population Mean with σ Known and Unknown**

The following example will be used to illustrate the hypothesis-testing procedure for testing a population mean when the population variance is known.

Example 11.2.1

Suppose the average national reading level for high school sophomores is 150 words per minute with a standard deviation of 15. A local school board member wants to know if sophomore students at Lincoln High School read at a level different from the national average for tenth graders. The level of the test is to be set at 0.05. A random sample size of 100 tenth graders from Lincoln High School has been drawn, and the resulting average is 154 words per minute.

Solution

Step 1:   Determine the null and alternative hypotheses.

We will first define the hypotheses in plain English and then using symbols.

The hypotheses are fairly straightforward:

Null Hypothesis: Lincoln High School tenth graders are reading at the national average.

Alternative Hypothesis: They are not.

Since the problem explicitly states that the school board member wishes to compare reading levels to the national **average**, the hypotheses will concern the population mean. Let

μ = the average number of words read per minute by Lincoln High School sophomores.

There is nothing in the problem which suggests that the school board member is just interested in learning if there is evidence of reading levels above average. Nor is there anything which indicates interest only in levels below average. Hence, it is assumed that the board member is interested in discovering any departure from average. Consequently, the problem needs to be formulated with a two-sided alternative. In symbolic form, the hypotheses are as follows.

$$H_0: \mu = 150$$
$$H_a: \mu \neq 150$$

The null hypothesis states that the **average** words read per minute at Lincoln High by a sophomore is equal to the national average (the standard value). The alternative states that it is not. This is an application of testing against a standard value.

For tests of a single mean there are only three possible research questions that can be asked about the population mean and they are all asked in the alternative hypothesis. The correct formulation of the hypotheses for each of these research questions is contained in Table 11.2.1.

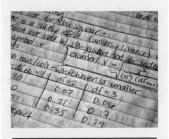

Origins of Hypothesis Testing

Many of the concepts in modern hypothesis testing were first proposed by Jerzy Neyman and Egon Pearson. Egon Pearson was born in 1895 as the son of the well-known statistician Karl Pearson. Jerzy Neyman was a Polish statistician born in 1894 who studied under Karl Pearson in London and Émile Borel in Paris.

A Test of Significance had been previously developed by statisticians including Karl Pearson, William Gosset, and Ronald Fisher. In significance testing the *P*-value would be analyzed by the researcher to informally influence future research or their faith in their null hypothesis. Neyman and Pearson suggested a more objective approach and generalized these ideas developing the notions of Type I and Type II errors, using a preset evidence criterion (set α level), and having a null and alternative hypothesis with a clear-cut rejection region.

Table 11.2.1 - Hypotheses Concerning a Test about a Single Mean			
	Is the population mean different from μ_0?	Is the population mean greater than μ_0?	Is the population mean less than μ_0?
Null Hypothesis, H_0	$\mu = \mu_0$	$\mu = \mu_0$	$\mu = \mu_0$
Alternative Hypothesis, H_a	$\mu \neq \mu_0$	$\mu > \mu_0$	$\mu < \mu_0$
Type of Hypothesis Test	Two-tailed	Right-tailed	Left-tailed

Step 2: Specify the significance level α.

The level of the test has been defined in the problem statement as the $\alpha = 0.05$ level. If it were not specified in the problem statement, then it would be necessary to select the value. Typical values for the level of the test are 0.10, 0.05, and 0.01. It is important to remember that the level of the test specifies the probability of a Type I error.

Step 3: Validate the assumptions of the hypothesis testing model, identify the appropriate test statistic, and compute its value.

Testing a Hypothesis About a Mean, σ Known

Assumptions:

1. The data is quantitative.
2. The data is obtained via a random sample of size n.
3. The population is normally distributed or the sample size n is large, $n > 30$.
4. The population standard deviation σ is known.

Test statistic:

The test statistic is given by

$$z = \frac{\bar{x} - \mu_0}{\sigma / \sqrt{n}}$$

where,

n = the sample size,

$\bar{x}$ = the sample mean,

μ_0 = the population mean (from the null hypothesis), and

σ = the known population standard deviation.

PROCEDURE

Before proceeding with the test, we must check our assumptions.

☑ Quantitative data

☑ Random sample used to obtain data

☑ $n > 30$ or population is normally distributed

☑ σ known   or   ☐ σ unknown

The symbol for the hypothesized mean is μ_0. In this example, $\mu_0 = 150$. The difference between the symbols μ_0 and μ is that μ_0 is a specific claim about the value of μ. The actual value of μ is unknown since it is a population parameter.

In this example, the symbol μ refers to the mean number of words read per minute for the population of Lincoln High sophomores. If μ were known, then it would be easy to decide which of the two claims

$H_0: \mu = 150$ (null hypothesis)

$H_a: \mu \neq 150$ (alternative hypothesis)

is correct. But, since it is not we will rely on hypothesis testing methods to make the decision.

What is the Rationale for the Test Statistic?

Although the true population mean is unknown, the Central Limit Theorem implies that the sample mean, $\bar{x}$, is usually close to the population mean, μ, if the sample data is representative of the population. **If the null hypothesis is true**, the value of the population mean is specified in the null hypothesis, $H_0: \mu = 150$. The sample mean $\bar{x}$ should be close to μ_0, in this case 150, when the null hypothesis is true.

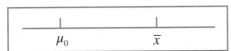

Another way of expressing this idea of closeness is to measure the difference between the sample mean and the hypothesized mean, $\bar{x} - \mu_0$. The difference should be reasonably close to zero, *if the null hypothesis is true*.

Conversely, a large distance between $\bar{x}$ and μ_0

would indicate either an improbable value of $\bar{x}$ has been observed given the null hypothesis is true; or that the null hypothesis is false and μ_0 is not the actual value of the population mean. Although this approach has intuitive appeal, the notion of *close* is too ambiguous to have practical value. Changing the unit of measure from inches to miles may affect one's perception of closeness. What is needed is a metric that will be the same regardless of the scale of measurement the sample data possesses.

Measuring Closeness

Converting the distance, $\bar{x} - \mu_0$, into standard deviation units using the z-transformation eliminates the problems caused by differing measurement scales, since the value of the z-transformation will be the same regardless of the unit of measure.

Recall that the z-transformation is $z = \dfrac{x - \mu}{\sigma}$. The variable x represents the random variable that will be transformed. In this case, the random variable to be transformed is $\bar{x}$. The symbol μ in the z-transformation stands for the mean of the random variable being transformed ($\bar{x}$). In the example above the null hypothesis states that $\mu = 150$. **If the null hypothesis is true**, μ_0 is the mean of the population and thus the mean of the sample means.

Using the data provided in Example 11.2.1 and substituting $\bar{x}$, σ, n, and μ_0 into the formula for the z-transformation yields

$$z = \frac{\bar{x} - \mu_0}{\sigma_{\bar{x}}} = \frac{154 - 150}{1.5} = \frac{4}{1.5} \approx 2.67,$$

$$\text{where } \sigma_{\bar{x}} = \frac{\sigma}{\sqrt{n}} = \frac{15}{\sqrt{100}} = 1.5.$$

The resulting z-value, 2.67, is the number of standard deviations that the sample mean (154) is from the hypothesized value of the mean, $150(\mu_0)$. If $\bar{x}$ is close to the hypothesized value, then the z-value is close to zero. If $\bar{x}$ is far away from the hypothesized value, the z-value becomes large in absolute value. The larger z grows, the more difficult it becomes to believe H_0 is true. In this example, $\bar{x}$ is 2.67 standard deviation units from the hypothesized mean. How far does the hypothesized value of the null hypothesis, μ_0, need to be from $\bar{x}$ before we would be willing to believe that the deviation was not caused by ordinary sampling variability? If $\bar{x}$ is an improbable event given H_0 is true, then we have two choices. We could believe H_0 is true, and we have witnessed a rare event caused by sampling variability, or we say that we doubt that we have witnessed a rare event and believe H_0 is not true.

Is an $\bar{x}$ that is 2.67 standard deviation units from the mean a rare occurrence? When we study P-values later in this chapter we will shed more light on this topic. But to answer that question, an understanding of the sampling variability of the z-value will be essential in judging the likelihood that any difference between $\bar{x}$ and μ_0 is due to ordinary sampling variability.

The original motivation for using the z-transformation was that it provided a reasonable method of measuring how close the sample mean was to the hypothesized mean. While this is true, it suggests concern only with the results of one sample. However, to develop a theory which can be applied to all possible samples, we must broaden the discussion to all potential values of $\bar{x}$ and z. In other words, we must concern ourselves with the sampling distribution of $\bar{x}$.

Fortunately, the Central Limit Theorem provides a great deal of information about the variability of $\bar{x}$. Namely, that it is normally distributed and has the same mean as the population from which the sample is drawn. The standard deviation of $\bar{x}$ is known to be $\dfrac{\sigma}{\sqrt{n}}$, the standard deviation of the population being sampled divided by the square root of the sample size.

The test statistic, z, is a random variable because $\bar{x}$ is a random variable. It will be normally distributed because $\bar{x}$ has a normal distribution.

In addition to measuring the distance between $\bar{x}$ and μ_0, the numerator of the z-transformation $(\bar{x} - \mu_0)$ also centers the distribution of the transformed random variable $\bar{x}$ around 0. If the null hypothesis is true, then the mean of $\bar{x}$ will be correctly specified in the null hypothesis, and the centering will work. If the null hypothesis is false, the mean of z will not be centered at 0. By using the z-transformation, we have shifted the focus of the problem. Instead of focusing our attention directly on $\bar{x}$ and its relation to the hypothesized value of μ, the crux of the hypothesis test will be to decide whether the z-value is near zero, or not. In our case the question is whether 2.67 is *close* to 0 or not?

This question will be addressed when the decision rule is constructed.

Methodology Flaws in the Trial of the Pyx

When the Trial of the Pyx began in the twelfth century, the Central Limit Theorem had not yet been discovered.

Notice in our test statistic, our denominator is the population standard deviation divided by the square root of n. This comes from the Central Limit Theorem as the standard deviation of $\bar{x}$.

When weighing the coins from the Mint, the allowable error was multiplied by the size of the sample. So, if each coin could be off by 1 unit, a batch of 100 coins could be over or under by 100 units. With proper methods known today, the tolerance should have been only 10 units. Thus, for many years, the Trial of the Pyx was overly tolerant of errors in the Mint. If the head of the Mint were aware of this, he could have minted to a target half a unit off from specification, or even a little more, and still very easily passed the trial. In fact, in the first several hundred years of the trials, there are only 2 recorded instances where the coins were not accepted.

> If the null hypothesis is true and all of the assumptions of the test can be validated, the z-test statistic has a normal distribution with a mean of 0 and a standard deviation of 1.

The Standard Normal Distribution

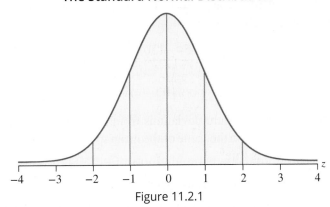

Figure 11.2.1

If the null hypothesis is true and the assumptions of the hypothesis testing model are valid, the distribution of the z-test statistic is known (normal with mean 0 and standard deviation 1), and a plan can be developed for defining ordinary variability of the test statistic. Since the test statistic has a z-distribution, we know that 95% of the time the value of z should be within ± 1.96 standard deviations of the mean.

Standard Normal Random Variable

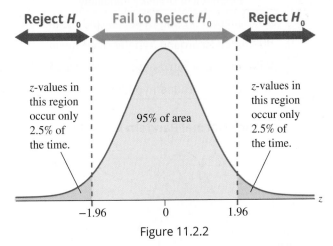

Figure 11.2.2

It is important to recognize that this strategy attempts to define the notion of *close* (for $\alpha = 0.05$) as being within 1.96 standard deviation units. Using this definition of closeness, if $\bar{x}$ is within 1.96 standard deviations of the hypothesized value, it is close enough to the hypothesized value in the null hypothesis to have occurred from ordinary sampling variability; otherwise it is too far to have happened by chance, and we reject the null. In our example, 1.96 is a **critical value** of z.

Note

A Decision Strategy

Suppose we claim that any value of the z-test statistic less than 1.96 in absolute value represents ordinary sampling variability of $\bar{x}$. Any value of z greater than 1.96 in absolute value is attributed to a false null hypothesis.

∞ Technology

The z-test statistic can be found using a TI-83/84 Plus calculator or other technology. For instructions on how to obtain the z-test statistic, please visit stat.hawkeslearning.com and navigate to **Technology Instructions > Hypothesis Testing > z-Test**.

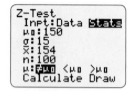

Example 11.2.1 Continued

Step 3 (continued): Validate the assumptions of the hypothesis testing model, identify the appropriate test statistic, and compute its value.

The random sample of 100 tenth graders revealed a mean reading rate of 154 words per minute with a standard deviation of 15 words per minute. As discussed earlier, the z-test statistic is given by

$$z = \frac{\bar{x} - \mu_0}{\sigma_{\bar{x}}} = \frac{154 - 150}{\frac{15}{\sqrt{100}}} = \frac{4}{1.5} \approx 2.67.$$

The sample mean is 2.67 standard deviations from the hypothesized value. Is the sample mean too far away from the value of the mean specified in the null hypothesis for us to believe the null is true?

Step 4: Determine the critical value(s).

In determining the critical value(s) of the test statistic, we must take into account whether the alternative hypothesis is one-sided or two-sided, the level of the test, and the distribution of the test statistic.

Table 11.2.2 – Critical Values of the z-Test Statistic for Two-Sided Alternatives		
Significance Level	**Definition of Ordinary Variability**	$z_{\alpha/2}$
0.20	80% interval around hypothesized mean	1.28
0.10	90% interval around hypothesized mean	1.645
0.05	95% interval around hypothesized mean	1.96
0.01	99% interval around hypothesized mean	2.575

Standard Normal Random Variable

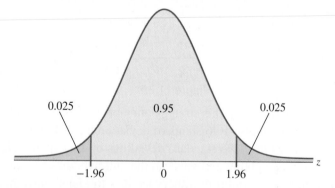

Notice that the **rejection region** is divided into two parts. The right-hand rejection region indicates unexpectedly high reading levels if H_0 is true, and conversely the left-hand rejection region indicates unexpectedly low levels if H_0 is true. Also observe that the probability associated with the level of the test is divided equally between the two rejection regions, each region receiving 0.025. If the probabilities in these two regions are added together, $0.025 + 0.025 = 0.05$, the sum equals the level of the test, α.

The level of the test can be thought of as a tolerance for rareness. The level of the test defines a rejection region which can be thought of as an intolerance zone. If the test statistic falls in this "intolerance" region, then the data has produced a sample mean that has in turn produced a test statistic that is too rare (according to our level of significance α) to have occurred by chance if the null were true and all the assumptions related to the hypothesis test are satisfied.

Essentially, we lose faith in the null hypothesis; the data has cast too much doubt. Consequently, the null hypothesis is rejected. The "fail to reject" zone can be interpreted as the zone of ordinary sampling variation given the null is true. For two-sided tests with the level of the test set to $\alpha = 0.05$, the investigator is stating that any value of the test statistic which falls in a 95% interval around the hypothesized mean represents ordinary sampling variability. For the z-test statistic, this corresponds to a critical value of 1.96 standard deviation units (see Table 11.2.2). If the test statistic falls into the ordinary sampling variation zone, the null hypothesis will not be rejected.

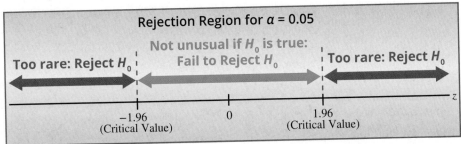

Step 5: Make the decision to reject or fail to reject H_0.

The critical values of the test statistic are ± 1.96. If the null were true, observing a value of z larger in absolute value than 1.96 would occur only 5% of the time.

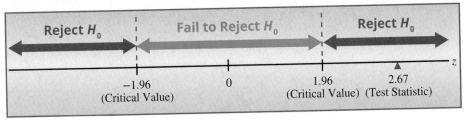

The test statistic $z = 2.67$ implies $\bar{x}$ is 2.67 standard deviation units from the mean which is substantially more than 1.96 standard deviations from the hypothesized value. The decision must be to reject H_0. The sample mean is too far from the hypothesized value for us to believe the difference is caused by ordinary sampling variation. Essentially, $\bar{x}$ exceeds the tolerance for rareness that we have imposed by setting $\alpha = 0.05$.

Step 6: State the conclusion in terms of the original question.

There is not significant evidence at the α level to reject H_0. ⟵ No — Do we reject H_0? — Yes ⟶ There is significant evidence at the α level that we reject H_0 in favor of H_a.

There is significant evidence at the 0.05 level that tenth graders at Lincoln High do not read at the national average. It would be tempting to conclude that they read above national levels, since the sample mean is considerably above the national average. However, we did not test the hypothesis for reading overachievement; we

An English Taste Test

Muriel Bristol was an English woman who, like many English women, often enjoyed an afternoon cup of tea. So developed were her tea taste buds, that she insisted she could tell the difference between a cup of tea which had the tea poured before the milk, from a cup which had the milk poured before the tea. Muriel Bristol, a phycologist, also happened to be a coworker of statistician Ronald Fisher at the Rothamsted Experimental Station. Hearing her rather bold boasts of tasting finesse, Fisher devised an experiment. Eight cups of tea were prepared, four in which the tea was poured first and four in which the milk was first added. The cups were presented to Mrs. Bristol in a random order. She had the opportunity to taste each cup and then identify four which were prepared in the same fashion. The pressure was high. Using a significance level of $\alpha = 0.05$, her ability would only be acknowledged if she did not make a mistake. (The probability of missing none given she randomly guessed is P-value = 1/70 ≈ 0.014, but the probability of missing only one given she randomly guessed is P-value = 17/70 ≈ 0.243.) But Muriel knew her tea. She correctly categorized all eight cups.

tested reading achievement either *over* or *under* the state average, and the conclusions must be consistent with the hypotheses tested.

One temptation might be to reformulate the hypothesis and test for overachievement with the same data. This would be practically unethical. If you already know the z-value for a given set of data, you should not formulate a hypothesis and use the data to "support" that hypothesis.

Part of every hypothesis test is arbitrary. The level of the test, α, is arbitrarily defined by the researcher. As you have seen from Table 11.2.2, the significance level of the test affects the critical value, and hence the decision rule. Since the level of the test is arbitrarily set, the decision rule inherits the arbitrariness.

P-Values

In the previous example we used a "critical value" approach for hypothesis testing. However, most researchers use the P-value method for hypothesis testing. While the decision making of these methods are equivalent, the conclusion phase of the P-value method is simpler.

P-Value

A **P-value** is the probability of observing a value of the test statistic as extreme or more extreme than the observed one, assuming the null hypothesis is true and all the assumptions related to the hypothesis test are satisfied.

DEFINITION

For a left-tailed (or lower-tailed) test, the P-value is given by $P\left(z \le z_0\right)$, where z_0 is the observed value of the test statistic. For a right-tailed (or upper-tailed) test, the P-value is given by $P\left(z \ge z_0\right)$, where z_0 is the observed value of the test statistic. For two-tailed tests, the P-value is given by $2P\left(z \ge \left|z_0\right|\right)$, where z_0 is the observed value of the test statistic. P-values can be determined using the tables in Appendix A or using technology such as a TI-83/84 Plus calculator, Microsoft Excel, or Minitab.

The following graph displays the application of the definition to the test statistic, $z = 2.03$.

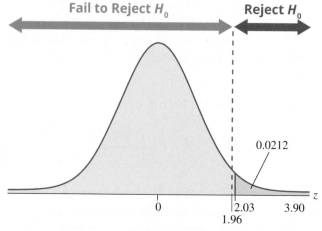

Figure 11.2.3

If the null hypothesis is true and all the assumptions related to the hypothesis test are satisfied, the probability of observing a test statistic greater than or equal to 2.03 is 0.0212, which is the *P*-value. One interpretation of the *P*-value is that if 10,000 researchers were to draw similar size samples, assuming the null hypothesis is true and all assumptions are met, ordinary sampling variation would cause roughly 212 researchers to obtain samples that would produce test statistics as large or larger than 2.03.

Compare this to the test statistic 3.90. If the null hypothesis is true and all assumptions are met, the chance of sampling variation causing a test statistic greater than or equal to 3.90 is 0.0001, which is the *P*-value. If 10,000 researchers drew similar size samples, ordinary sampling variation would cause only about 1 of the researchers to observe test statistics as large or larger than 3.90.

Many statistical computer programs provide *P*-values in their output. It is a fairly easy task to utilize these values to perform a classical hypothesis test.

Performing a Hypothesis Test Using *P*-Values

- If the computed *P*-value is less than α, reject the null hypothesis in favor of the alternative.

- If the computed *P*-value is greater or equal to than α, fail to reject the null hypothesis.

PROCEDURE

The rationale for this approach is that if the *P*-value is less than α, we have observed a test statistic that is more unusual than the level of the test, which defines how rare an event we must observe in order to reject the null hypothesis. Conversely, if the *P*-value is greater than or equal to α, the test statistic is not sufficiently rare (it could have been caused by ordinary sampling variation) to reject the null hypothesis.

Returning to Example 11.2.1

Let's repeat Steps 4 through 6 of the hypothesis testing procedure using the *P*-value approach.

Step 4: Determine the *P*-value.

In the example we have a two-tailed test, a critical value of $z = 2.67$, and $\alpha = 0.05$. For an upper one-tailed test (i.e., $H_a: \mu > 150$), we would calculate the *P*-value as

$$P\text{-value} = P(z \geq 2.67) = P(z \leq -2.67) \approx 0.0038.$$

However, for a two-tailed test, the *P*-value is calculated as

$$P\text{-value} = 2P(z \geq |z_0|), \text{ where } z_0 \text{ is the observed value of the test statistic.}$$

Thus, to compute the *P*-value for a two-tailed hypothesis test, we double the tail area. Hence,

$$P\text{-value} = 0.0038 + 0.0038 = 0.0076.$$

Technology

P-values for a *z*-test can be found using the standard normal tables, but are also found in the output of the Z-Test on the TI-83/84 Plus calculator. Further instruction is available on stat.hawkeslearning.com under **Technology Instructions > Hypothesis Testing > z-Test**. Also recall that a probability given a *z*-score can be obtained using the normalcdf function; see **Technology Instructions > Normal Distribution > Normal Probability (cdf)**.

```
Z-Test
 μ≠150
 z=2.666666667
 p=.0076608502
 x̄=154
 n=100
```

```
2*normalcdf(2.67
,10E6)
     .0075852148
```

More Male Births than Female?

In 1710, John Arbuthnot, a British writer also trained in mathematics and medicine, was one of the first to use something akin to a *P*-value. Beginning with the assumption that male and female births are equally likely, he examined 81 years of christening records. In each year there were more male christenings than female christenings. He reasoned that such a run had only a $\frac{1}{2^{81}} \approx 4.14 \times 10^{-25}$ chance of occurring given the proportion of males and females were equal, and this chance was too small to accept. He therefore argued that this provided evidence of the intervention of a divine being. Arbuthnot's argument was not widely accepted due to flawed logic and technique, but the spirit of the methods carried on.

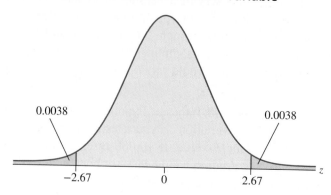

Standard Normal Random Variable

The *P*-value of 0.0038 is the likelihood of observing a value of the test statistic greater than or equal to 2.67 or less than or equal to –2.67 given the null hypothesis is true and all assumptions are met.

Step 5: Make the decision to reject or fail to reject H_0.

The *P*-value of 0.0038 is less than our significance level $\alpha = 0.05$, so we reject the null hypothesis.

Step 6: State the conclusion in terms of the original question.

As expected, our decision is the same one we obtained using the critical value approach, so our conclusion does not change. There is sufficient evidence at the 0.05 level that tenth graders at Lincoln High do not read at the national average.

Example 11.2.2

A microprocessor designer has developed a new fabrication process which he believes will increase the usable life of a chip. Currently the usable life is 16,000 hours with a standard deviation of 2500 hours. Test the hypothesis that the process increases the usable life of a chip, at the 0.01 level. A random sample of 1000 microprocessors will be tested. Assume the standard deviation of the life of the new chips will be equal to the standard deviation of the current chips.

Solution

Step 1: Determine the null and alternative hypotheses.

We first state the hypotheses in plain English.

Null Hypothesis: The new fabrication does not increase the usable life of the chip.

Alternative Hypothesis: The new fabrication increases the usable life of the chip.

Once again, the population mean is a suitable parameter to test this hypothesis. If the mean life of the newly fabricated chip is greater than the mean life of the standard chip, all other things being equal, the newly fabricated chip would be better. Let

$$\mu = \text{the mean life of the newly fabricated chips.}$$

The goal is to determine if there is sufficient evidence that the new fabrication process produces chips with *longer* life. The hypothesis will be one-sided.

In symbolic form the hypotheses are as follows.

$H_0: \mu = 16,000$ The mean life of the newly fabricated chip is equal to the life of the standard chip.

$H_a: \mu > 16,000$ The newly fabricated chip has a longer mean life than the standard chip.

If the purpose is to demonstrate that there is overwhelming evidence in support of a hypothesis, that hypothesis should be placed in the alternative hypothesis. In this example, the aim is to determine if there is sufficient evidence to conclude that the new chip has a longer life.

Step 2: Specify the significance level α.

The level of the test is given in the problem to be $\alpha = 0.01$. If it were not given, the investigator would choose the level.

Step 3: Validate the assumptions of the hypothesis test, identify the appropriate test statistic, and compute its value.

First, we validate the assumptions.

- ☑ Quantitative data (the number of hours of usable life of a chip)

- ☑ Random sample used to obtain data

- ☑ $n > 30$ ($n = 1000$)

- ☑ σ known   or   ☐ σ unknown

All of the assumptions of the z-test statistic are met.

Suppose a random sample of 1000 microprocessors has a mean life of 16,200 hours. The resulting test statistic,

$$z = \frac{16,200 - 16,000}{\dfrac{2500}{\sqrt{1000}}} \approx 2.53,$$

indicates that the sample mean life of new microprocessors is more than 2.5 standard deviations larger than the mean life of current microprocessors. Is it unlikely that ordinary sampling variation could have caused the sample mean to be more than 2.5 standard deviations from the hypothesized value?

Step 4: Determine the critical value(s) or *P*-value.

Since the alternative hypothesis is one-sided, we want to know if there is evidence that μ (the mean life of the newly fabricated chips) is greater than the hypothesized value μ_0 (16,000 hours, the standard life of existing chips). If $\bar{x}$ (the mean life of the 1000 microprocessors samples) is much larger than μ_0, that would suggest that H_a is a more reasonable choice than H_0. Of course, through ordinary sampling variation, $\bar{x}$ could be larger than μ_0. How much greater than μ_0 does $\bar{x}$ have to be in order for us to believe that mean life of the newly fabricated chips is greater than 16,000 hours and select H_a?

Table 11.2.3 – Critical Values of the *z*-Test Statistic for One-Sided (Greater Than) Alternatives		
Significance Level	**Definition of Ordinary Variability**	z_a
0.20	Lower 80% of the distribution	0.84
0.10	Lower 90% of the distribution	1.28
0.05	Lower 95% of the distribution	1.645
0.01	Lower 99% of the distribution	2.33

Standard Normal Random Variable

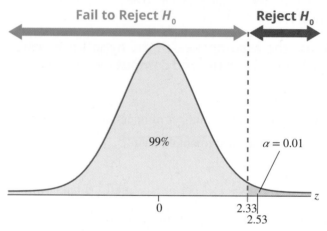

The *z*-test statistic has a standard normal distribution; so critical values are determined from the probability distribution of the standard normal distribution. The alternative hypothesis is one-sided (H_a: $\mu > 16{,}000$) and $\alpha = 0.01$. From Table 11.2.3, we find that the appropriate critical value for the test is 2.33. This critical value means that if $\bar{x}$ is 2.33 standard deviations larger than μ_0, then H_0 should be rejected in favor of H_a. However, if H_0 is true and all assumptions are met, ordinary variation would cause $\bar{x}$ to be greater than 2.33 about 1% of the time. Thus, 1% of the time H_0 will be rejected when it is true, a Type I error. To locate the critical value of z for a one-sided "greater-than" alternative, find the value of z that *cuts off* α worth of probability in the right-hand tail of the distribution. The critical values for "greater than" alternative hypotheses are given in Table 11.2.3 for typical values of α.

To determine the *P*-value for the test we proceed as follows.

$$P\text{-value} = P(\, z \geq 2.53\,) = P(\, z \leq -2.53) \approx 0.0057.$$

Standard Normal Random Variable

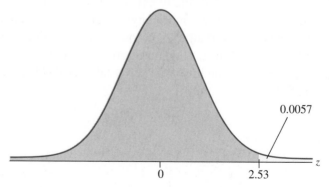

♾ Technology

The *P*-value is found on the output of the Z-Test on the TI-83/84 Plus calculator. For instructions visit stat.hawkeslearning.com and navigate to **Technology Instructions > Hypothesis Testing > z-Test**.

```
Z-Test
 µ>16000
 z=2.529822128
 p=.0057060388
 x̄=16200
 n=1000
```

Step 5: Make the decision to reject or fail to reject H_0.

Since the test statistic value of 2.53 is larger than the critical value, 2.33, the conclusion is to reject H_0 in favor of H_a. Note that the P-value of 0.0057 is less than the significance level, $\alpha = 0.01$, also leading us to the decision to reject H_0.

Step 6: State the conclusion in terms of the original question.

There is sufficient evidence at the $\alpha = 0.01$ level to conclude that the new fabricating technique is superior and leads to longer chip life.

In the previous two examples, we have considered a two-sided alternative and a one-sided "greater than" alternative. When considering a one-sided "less than" alternative, the procedure is very similar to that of a one-sided "greater than" alternative. The null hypothesis will be rejected if the calculated value of the test statistics, z, is less than the critical value, z_α, for the specified level of significance.

One-Sided "Less Than" Alternatives

For tests which are based on a test statistic which has a standard normal distribution and "less than" alternatives, find the value of z that *cuts off α worth* of probability in the left-hand tail of the distribution. The critical values for "less than" alternative hypotheses are given in Table 11.2.4 for typical values of α.

Table 11.2.4 – Critical Values of the z-Test Statistic for One-Sided (Less Than) Alternatives		
Significance Level	**Definition of Ordinary Variability**	**$-z_\alpha$**
0.20	Upper 80% of the distribution	−0.84
0.10	Upper 90% of the distribution	−1.28
0.05	Upper 95% of the distribution	−1.645
0.01	Upper 99% of the distribution	−2.33

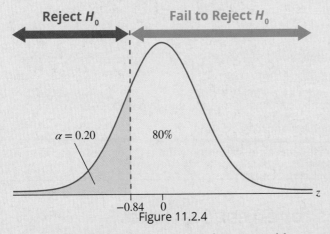

Figure 11.2.4

The figure above shows the rejection region for a test with a one-sided "less than" alternative hypothesis, and a significance level of 0.20. For this test, the null hypothesis will be rejected if the calculated value of the test statistic is less than −0.84.

The P-value is given by $P(z \leq z_0)$, where z_0 is the observed value of the test statistic.

PROCEDURE

Different *P*-Values for Different Folks

In particle physics, the standard for "discovery" is a *P*-value less than 0.0000003. That is the probability which corresponds to observing a value that is at least 5 standard deviations from the mean for a one-tailed test. Particle physicists consider a *P*-value less than 0.003, which is the probability of observing a value at least 2.75 standard deviations from the mean, "evidence of a particle"—an encouraging result, but not "discovery."

The common significance levels we have used in this book are $\alpha = 0.05$ and $\alpha = 0.01$ which correspond to a value at least 1.645 and 2.33 standard deviations from the mean, respectively. This goes to show you that there is not any one significance level that everyone agrees on. Different disciplines have different comfort levels with the idea of significance.

Suppose σ is Unknown?

The previous hypothesis testing strategy assumes the sample data is drawn randomly, the population standard deviation is known, and either the population is normal or the sample size is larger than 30. However, in most instances, the population standard deviation is just as unknown as the population mean. Despite the added uncertainty, the general approach to testing a hypothesis is the same. Some of the technical details concerning the distribution of the test statistic change, since the sample standard deviation, σ, will be used in place of the population standard deviation, σ. This modification will cause a change in the distribution of the test statistic.

If we assume the population we are sampling from is normally distributed or the sample size is greater than 30 ($n > 30$), the test statistic has a *t*-distribution. Consequently, the test statistic will be called a *t*-test statistic. The fundamental notion embodied in the test statistic has not changed. It measures how far the sample mean is from the hypothesized mean in standard deviation units.

In the previous chapter, we discussed the *t*-distribution in conjunction with estimating the population mean using a confidence interval. Steps 3 and 4 in our hypothesis testing procedure must be modified to reflect the change in distribution of the test statistic.

Testing a Hypothesis About a Mean, σ Unknown

Assumptions:

1. The data is quantitative.

2. The data is obtained via a random sample of size n.

3. The population is normally distributed or the sample size n is large, $n > 30$.

4. The population standard deviation σ is unknown.

Test Statistic:

The test statistic is given by where,

$$t = \frac{\bar{x} - \mu_0}{s / \sqrt{n}}$$

n = the sample size,

$\bar{x}$ = the sample mean,

μ_0 = the population mean (from the null hypothesis), and

s = the sample standard deviation.

The test statistic has a *t*-distribution with $n-1$ degrees of freedom.

PROCEDURE

P-Values for *t*-Test Statistics

If technology is not available to calculate *P*-values, we will need to use the *t*-tables. Because there are numerous *t*-distributions, one for each different degree of freedom, the *t*-tables are constructed differently from the *z*-table. The *t*-table only provides *t*-values for frequently used tail probabilities. Because of this limitation, in most instances the exact value of the *t*-test statistic will not be in the table. When this circumstance arises, find the closest *t*-values, with the appropriate degrees of freedom which surround the test statistic. For example, suppose the value of the test statistic was 2.40 with 17 degrees of freedom.

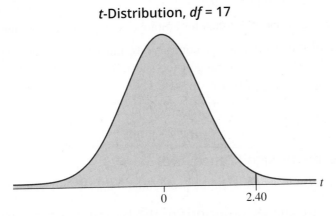

t-Distribution, df = 17

Figure 11.2.5

The value of the test statistic falls between 2.110 (which corresponds to $\alpha = 0.025$) and 2.567, which corresponds to $\alpha = 0.01$.

df	$t_{0.100}$	$t_{0.050}$	$t_{0.025}$	$t_{0.010}$
1	3.078	6.314	12.706	31.821
2	1.886	2.920	4.303	6.965
3	1.638	2.353	3.182	4.541
⋮				
17	1.333	1.740	2.110	2.567
18	1.330	1.734	2.101	2.552
⋮				

Thus, we report a bound for the *P*-value. In this case, $0.01 < P\text{-value} < 0.025$. That is, the *P*-value falls between 0.01 and 0.025. If the level of the test, α, is greater than 0.025, then our test is significant at the 0.025 level. Thus the *P*-value would be reported as being significant at the 0.025 level, but not significant at the 0.01 level. Exact *P*-values for *t*-test statistics can be found using technology such as a TI-83/84 Plus calculator, Microsoft Excel, R, and Minitab. The exact *P*-value for $t = 2.40$ with 17 degrees of freedom can be found to be approximately 0.0141.

⌘ Technology

For instructions on how to find exact *P*-values using different technologies, visit stat.hawkeslearning.com and navigate to **Technology Instructions > Hypothesis Testing > *t*-test** or **Technology Instructions > *t*-Distribution > *t*-Probability (cdf)**.

```
tcdf(2.40,10E6,1
7)
       .0140632427
```

Example 11.2.3

A personnel researcher has designed a questionnaire she believes will take an average time of 35 minutes to complete. Suppose she randomly samples 20 employees and finds that the mean time to take the test is 29 minutes with a standard deviation of $s = 8$ minutes. Determine if there is sufficient evidence to conclude that the completion time of the newly designed test differs from its intended duration. Conduct the test at the 0.05 level. Assume the sample comes from a normally distributed population.

Solution

Step 1: Determine the null and alternative hypotheses.

In plain English the hypotheses are as follows.

Null Hypothesis: The questionnaire takes 35 minutes to complete.

Alternative Hypothesis: It takes more or less than 35 minutes to complete.

The population of interest consists of all employees who could take this test. Since the test is specified as having an **average** duration of 35 minutes, the parameter of interest will be the population mean.

Let μ = the average time in minutes for employees to complete the questionnaire.

From the lack of information to the contrary, we must assume she is interested in detecting whether the test is too long or too short. Thus, the test is two-sided. The resulting hypotheses in symbolic form would be

$$H_0: \mu = 35 \text{ min}$$
$$H_a: \mu \neq 35 \text{ min.}$$

Step 2: Specify the significance level α.

The level of the test is specified in the problem at 0.05.

Step 3: Validate the assumptions of the hypothesis test, identify the appropriate test statistic, and compute its value.

First, we validate the assumptions.

- ☑ Quantitative data (time to complete the questionnaire)
- ☑ Random sample used to obtain data
- ☑ $n < 30$ ($n = 20$), but population assumed to be normally distributed
- ☐ σ known   or   ☑ σ unknown

All of the assumptions are met. Since we do not know σ, we will use the t-test statistic. The computed value of the test statistic is

$$t = \frac{\bar{x} - \mu_0}{s_{\bar{x}}} = \frac{29 - 35}{\dfrac{8}{\sqrt{20}}} \approx -3.35.$$

The observed sample mean is over 3 standard deviations less than the hypothesized mean. The value of the test statistic signifies a noteworthy difference between $\bar{x}$ and the hypothesized value, μ_0. It is unlikely that the cause of such a difference would be ordinary sampling variation.

Step 4: Determine the critical value(s) or P-value.

The t-distribution has a parameter called degrees of freedom, which must be defined in order to utilize the distribution. Since 20 employees were sampled, the degrees of freedom are $df = n - 1 = 20 - 1 = 19$.

Since the alternative hypothesis (H_a) is two-sided, two tails of the distribution must be "cut off" as rejection regions. Each tail will receive half of the allotted significance level of the test. The value of t which begins the right-hand side rejection region is $t_{0.025, 19}$, which corresponds to a value of 2.093. Since the t-distribution is symmetrical, the left-hand side cutoff value for the rejection region is -2.093.

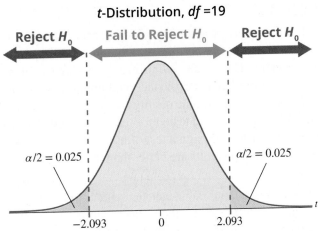

t-Distribution, *df* =19

What the picture says is that it is unlikely (only occurs 5% of the time) that ordinary sampling variability will cause $\bar{x}$ to differ by 2.093 or more standard deviation units from the hypothesized mean of 35.

If you do not have technology, you can refer to Table D in the Appendix. Looking at the row corresponding to 19 degrees of freedom, we see that the absolute value of our test statistic, 3.35, is larger than the largest value, 2.861, displayed. This value has an area of 0.005 in the tail, so we know that the *P*-value corresponding to our test statistic is smaller than $2 \cdot 0.005 = 0.010$.

df	$t_{0.100}$	$t_{0.050}$	$t_{0.025}$	$t_{0.010}$	$t_{0.005}$
19	1.328	1.729	2.093	2.539	2.861

Using technology the exact *P*-value corresponding to $t = -3.35$ with $df = 19$ is found to be approximately 0.0034.

Step 5: Make the decision to reject or fail to reject H_0.

Since the test statistic falls in the rejection region (and *P*-value $< \alpha$), we reject H_0 in favor of H_a.

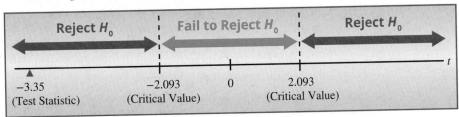

Technology

Once you've found the test statistic, the *P*-value can be easily found using the `tcdf` function on the TI-83/84 Plus calculator. For instructions visit stat.hawkeslearning.com and navigate to **Technology Instructions > t-Distribution > t-Probability (cdf)**.

```
2*tcdf(-10E6,-3.
35,19)
        .0033638466
```

Step 6: State the conclusion in terms of the original question.

There is sufficient evidence at the 0.05 level to conclude that the mean time to take the test is not 35 minutes. Since the sample mean was so much less than 35 minutes, it is tempting to conclude that the test requires less than 35 minutes to complete. However, we did not test the one-sided hypothesis. If the researcher wishes to demonstrate the completion time is significantly less than 35 minutes, we must start the process over: testing a one-sided hypothesis and obtaining new sample data.

Example 11.2.4

The Alexander Bolt Company produces half-inch A-class stainless steel bolts that have a mean tensile strength of more than 4000 pounds per square inch (psi), the specified quality standard. These bolts are primarily used in the manufacturing of farm implements. The company is very concerned about quality and wants to be sure that its A-class product is above the quality standard. A sample of 25 bolts is to be randomly selected from stock and tested for tensile strength. The sample values are recorded in the table below. Design a test of hypothesis to determine if there is overwhelming evidence that the bolts are better than the specified quality standard.

4023	3993	4009	4006	4039	3984	4003	4007
4007	4055	4004	4049	4000	3995	4019	4003	4029
4009	4041	4021	4012	3984	4040	4025	3986

Solution

Step 1: Determine the null and alternative hypotheses.

The hypotheses in plain English are:

Null Hypothesis: The half-inch A-class stainless steel bolts have a mean tensile strength of 4000 psi.

Alternative Hypothesis: The half-inch A-class stainless steel bolts have a mean tensile strength of more than 4000 psi.

Although there is nothing in the problem that specifically defines the population parameter of interest, there is mention of a "standard value." By comparing the mean breaking strength of the population to the **standard value**, 4000 pounds per square inch, a conclusion about quality can be drawn. Let

μ = the mean tensile strength of the half-inch A-class stainless steel bolts.

If μ is significantly above the standard, then there would be evidence that the desired quality is being produced. Thus, the alternative hypothesis will be one-sided.

The resulting hypotheses would be

$H_0: \mu = 4000$ psi   Mean tensile strength is equal to the quality standard of 4000 pounds per square inch. The bolt production system is working at the quality standard.

$H_a: \mu > 4000$ psi   Mean tensile strength is above 4000 pounds per square inch. The bolt production system is working better than the quality standard.

Step 2: Specify the significance level α.

The level of the test is not stated in the problem, and thus the selection is left to the researcher. This is a typical predicament and, unfortunately, leaves us with what appears to be an arbitrary decision regarding the level of the test. What is a reasonable value for the level of the test?

In this problem, making a Type I error (rejecting the null hypothesis when it is true) means that management believes that the bolt production system is not flawed, when it is. If we set α too high, management will too frequently believe the quality level is being met, when it is not and poor quality bolts will not be readily detected. After all is said and done, the decision remains arbitrary. A Type I error could be calamitous and so a small level of α would be desirable. Let's use $\alpha = 0.01$.

Step 3: Validate the assumptions of the hypothesis test, identify the appropriate test statistic, and compute its value.

First, we validate the assumptions.

- ☑   Quantitative data (tensile strength)
- ☑   Random sample used to obtain data

The sample size is less than 30, so we need to confirm that the population is approximately normally distributed. A normal probability plot of the data is given below. The plot does not indicate a significant departure from normality.

🔗 **Technology**

For instructions on creating a Normal Probability Plot, navigate to **Technology Instructions > Graphs > Normal Probability Plot.**

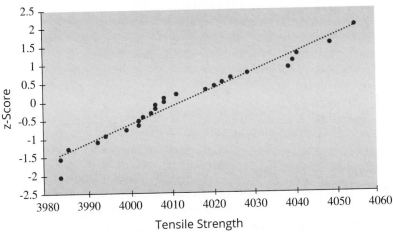

Normal Probability Plot

- ☑   Population is approximately normally distributed
- ☐ σ known   or   ☑ σ unknown

The assumptions are met such that the t-statistic is appropriate.

The average tensile strength is 4014 pounds per square inch, with a standard deviation of 20 pounds. Symbolically this is expressed as

$$\bar{x} = 4014, \quad s = 20, \quad \text{and} \quad n = 25.$$

The resulting test statistic is

$$t = \frac{\bar{x} - \mu_0}{s_{\bar{x}}} = \frac{4014 - 4000}{\dfrac{20}{\sqrt{25}}} = 3.5.$$

The sample mean is 3.5 standard deviations more than the hypothesized value of the mean. Is this difference caused by ordinary sampling variation, or is this evidence of a false null hypothesis? Keep in mind that rejecting the null hypothesis (H_0) will be a desirable outcome since the null states that the bolts are at quality standards.

Step 4: Determine the critical value(s) or P-value.

Since the alternative hypothesis implies that we are interested in discovering if the mean is above the standard value, the rejection region will only be on the right-hand side of the sampling distribution. Because the level of the test has been chosen at

0.01, the interval encompassing 0.01 of the area on the right-hand side of the curve will define the rejection region. The test statistic has a t-distribution.

To obtain the critical value, first determine the degrees of freedom.

$$n - 1 = 25 - 1 = 24.$$

Using Table D in Appendix A, $t_{0.01,24} = 2.492$. If the observed t-value is greater than 2.492 then the observed mean is presumed to be too far from the hypothesized value to have occurred from ordinary sampling variation. If $t > 2.492$, the presumption will be that the mean tensile strength is greater than 4000 pounds per square inch.

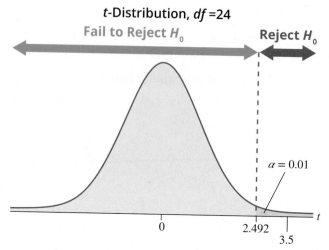

t-Distribution, df =24

∞ Technology

The *P*-value is given by the output of the T-Test on the TI-83/84 Plus calculator. For instructions on how to obtain this output, please visit stat.hawkeslearning.com and navigate to **Technology Instructions > Hypothesis Testing > t-Test**.

```
T-Test
 μ>4000
 t=3.5
 P=9.2118217E-4
 x̄=4014
 Sx=20
 n=25
```

The *P*-value of the test statistic ($t = 3.5$) can be found using technology to be $P(t \geq 3.5) \approx 0.0009$, with degrees of freedom equal to 24. Alternatively, using Table D we observe that the test statistic is greater than the t-value of 2.797, which has a tail area of 0.005. This implies that the *P*-value is less than 0.005.

Step 5: Make the decision to reject or fail to reject H_0.

Since the value of the test statistic (3.5) falls in the rejection region, the sample mean is too far from the hypothesized value to believe it is due to ordinary sampling variation. (In other words, $\bar{x} = 4014$ is a rare observation and has exceeded our tolerance for rareness.) The null hypothesis can be rejected in favor of the alternative hypothesis.

Alternatively, this decision is confirmed by our *P*-value; the *P*-value is 0.0009, which is less than $\alpha = 0.01$.

Step 6: State the conclusion in terms of the original question.

There is sufficient evidence to conclude that bolt tensile strength is above 4000 psi.

This conclusion is stated in a rather absolute manner. However, there is always a degree of subjectivity in any statistical conclusion. In this instance, we arbitrarily selected the value of α, and we assumed a random sample and that all other assumptions were met.

"No scientific worker has a fixed level of significance at which from year to year, and in all circumstances, he rejects hypotheses; he rather gives his mind to each particular case in the light of his evidence and his ideas."

-Ronald Fisher

Scientific Significance, Statistical Significance, and *P*-Values

The famous statistician Karl Pearson wrote "The aim of science is nothing short of the complete interpretation of the universe." If Pearson is correct, then any new piece of knowledge that furthers this aim would be "scientifically significant." How do we know when a researcher is advocating some new piece of "truth" about the universe that it is actually truth? Peer reviewed scientific journals provide quality control for the scientific community and are the gatekeepers for new "truth" candidates to begin to attain the honor of "scientific significance." How is this process connected to statistics?

For anyone using sampling and data in their research, statistical significance of their research results is the first step in the march toward scientific significance. Scientific significance moves forward when other scientists can reproduce the work of another scientist and thus confirm their results. That is why one of the hallmarks of good scientific research is the notion of **reproducibility**. That is, if two or more researchers performed the same experiment, they would likely reach similar conclusions, and with roughly the same level of uncertainty. Yet, in a survey of 1576 scientists in *Nature*, 70% of the researchers had tried and failed to reproduce another scientist's experiments, and amazingly more than half have failed to reproduce their own experiments.

In the opinion of the survey participants the number one reason for the lack of reproducibility was the selective reporting "cherry picking" of data that supports a favorite (or publishable) hypothesis. Data from a complex research experiment can produce many measures of the phenomena under consideration. When a researcher with some overarching research thesis looks at this data there will be many potential choices of hypotheses. Going through data (particularly observational data) looking for summary measures that can produce hypotheses that have "significant *P*-values is called ***P*-hacking** or ***P*-fishing**. In statistical literature this problem is referred to as the **multiple comparisons** problem and leads to data-dependent conclusions.

The reproducibility problem and its relationship to the misinterpretation and abuse of statistical tests, especially *P*-values, has been a concern of statisticians for decades. In 2015 the board of the American Statistical Association (ASA) tasked 20 of its members to produce an ASA statement on *P*-values and significance testing which was published in 2016. The statement provided guidelines with regard to some common errors and misinterpretations that are reported in research publications. You should be aware of these pitfalls and follow the guidelines to avoid such mistakes when interpreting and publishing study results.

No Final Verdict

In their first paper describing their binary approach to statistical testing, Neyman and Pearson wrote that "it is doubtful whether the knowledge that [a P-value] was really 0.03 (or 0.06), rather than 0.05... would in fact ever modify our judgment" and that "The tests themselves give no final verdict, but as tools help the worker who is using them to form his final decision."

ASA Guidelines Regarding P-Values

1. P-values can indicate how incompatible the data are with a specified statistical model.

2. P-values do not measure the probability that the studied hypothesis is true, or the probability that the data were produced by random chance alone.

3. Scientific conclusions and business or policy decisions should not be based only on whether a P-value passes a specific threshold.

4. Proper inference requires full reporting and transparency.

5. A P-value, or statistical significance, does not measure the size of an effect or the importance of a result.

6. By itself, a P-value does not provide a good measure of evidence regarding a model or hypothesis.[1]

There are a complex set of assumptions in any test of hypothesis. In addition to the variability of the underlying data and the test statistic there are other assumptions concerning how the data was collected, analyzed, and reported. Essentially, hypothesis testing requires a disciplined attention to the details of the process. It starts with a definition of the null and alternative hypothesis before we begin examining the data.

You can help eliminate these issues by being a responsible researcher. When making conclusions for important decisions, you should thoroughly consider the results of the hypothesis test. Ask yourself some of the following questions:

- *Is my result practically significant?* With very large samples, it's easy to get a small P-value (large test statistic) even though the sample value may not be practically different than the hypothesized value.

- *Are the assumptions I made to perform the test justifiable?*

- *Can I reproduce my results?*

11.2 **Exercises**

Basic Concepts

1. What is the rationale for the z-statistic?

2. What are the two key questions to be asked in the hypothesis testing procedure in order to determine which test statistic is appropriate?

3. Describe the distribution of the z-test statistic.

4. If the variance for a population is not known, how is the test statistic affected?

5. What are critical values? How do critical values influence the decision rule in the hypothesis testing procedure?

6. Suppose a null hypothesis was rejected at $\alpha = 0.05$. Would it be rejected at 0.10? Explain.

7. Suppose a null hypothesis was rejected at $\alpha = 0.05$. Would it be rejected at 0.01? Explain.

8. What is a P-value?

9. Discuss how P-values are used in the test of a hypothesis.

Exercises

10. Determine the critical value(s) of the test statistic for each of the following tests for the population mean with σ known.

   a.   Left-tailed test, $\alpha = 0.01$

   c.   Two-tailed test, $\alpha = 0.05$

   b.   Right-tailed test, $\alpha = 0.10$

11. For each of the following combinations of the P-value and α, decide whether you would reject or fail to reject the null hypothesis.

   a. P-value = 0.0839, $\alpha = 0.05$

   c. P-value = 0.0444, $\alpha = 0.10$

   b. P-value = 0.0174, $\alpha = 0.02$

   d. P-value = 0.0374, $\alpha = 0.01$

12. Consider the following hypothesis tests for the population mean with σ known. Compute the P-value for each test and decide whether you would reject or fail to reject the null hypothesis at $\alpha = 0.05$.

   a. $H_0: \mu = 15$, $H_a: \mu > 15$, $z = 1.58$

   b. $H_0: \mu = 1.9$, $H_a: \mu < 1.9$, $z = -2.25$

   c. $H_0: \mu = 100$, $H_a: \mu \neq 100$, $z = 1.90$

13. Consider the following hypothesis tests for the population mean with σ known. Compute the P-value for each test and decide whether you would reject or fail to reject the null hypothesis at $\alpha = 0.01$.

   a. $H_0: \mu = 10$, $H_a: \mu > 10$, $z = 2.00$

   b. $H_0: \mu = 82$, $H_a: \mu < 82$, $z = -2.45$

   c. $H_0: \mu = 100$, $H_a: \mu \neq 100$, $z = 2.70$

14. A random sample of 1000 observations produces a sample mean of 53.5. Test the hypothesis that the mean is not equal to 55 at $\alpha = 0.05$. The population standard deviation is known to be 5.3.

15. A random sample of 200 observations indicate a sample mean of 4117. Test the hypothesis that the mean is greater than 4100 at $\alpha = 0.01$. The population standard deviation is known to be 300.

16. Hurricane Andrew swept through southern Florida causing billions of dollars of damage. Because of the severity of the storm and the type of residential construction used in this semitropical area, there was some concern that the average claim size would be greater than the historical average hurricane claim. Historically, the average claim size was $24,000 with standard deviation $2400. Several insurance companies collaborated in a data gathering experiment. They randomly selected 84 homes and sent adjusters to settle the claims. In the sample of 84 homes, the average claim was $27,500.

    a.   What is the population being studied?

    b.   What statistical measure should you use in your hypothesis?

    c.   State your hypotheses.

    d.   Test the hypothesis at the 0.01 level.

    e.   Is there overwhelming evidence (at the 0.01 level) that home damage is greater than the historical average? Write your conclusion in the context of the original problem.

17. In preparation for upcoming wage negotiations with the union, the managers for the Bevel Hardware Company want to establish the time required to assemble a kitchen cabinet. A first line supervisor believes that the job should take 45 minutes on average to complete. A random sample of 125 cabinets has an average assembly time of 47 minutes. The population standard deviation is known to be 10 minutes.

    a.   Is there overwhelming evidence to contradict the first line supervisor's belief at a 0.05 significance level?

    b.   What is the lowest average assembly time that would allow the union to conclude that the supervisor is incorrect?

18. A horticulturist working for a large plant nursery is conducting experiments on the growth rate of a new shrub. Based on previous research, the horticulturist feels the average daily growth rate of the new shrub is 1 cm per day with a standard deviation of 0.30 cm. A random sample of 45 shrubs has an average growth of 0.90 cm per day. Will a test of hypothesis at the 0.05 significance level support the claim that the growth rate is less than 1 cm per day?

19. Government regulations restrict the amount of pollutants that can be released to the atmosphere through industrial smokestacks. To demonstrate that their smokestacks are releasing pollutants below the mandated limit of 5 parts per billion pollutants, REM Industries collects a random sample of 300 readings. The mean pollutant level for the sample is 4.85 parts per billion. The population standard deviation is known to be 0.30 parts per billion. Does the data support the claim that the average pollutants produced by REM Industries are below the mandated level at a 0.01 significance level?

20. The managers of a large department store wish to test reactions of shoppers to a new in-store video screen which will broadcast continuous information about the store and the items currently on sale. The video production company claims that the average shopper will watch for five or more minutes. The managers randomly select 17 shoppers and determine how long they watch the video. The average time spent watching the video screen is 4.5 minutes.

a. Perform a hypothesis test to determine whether there is overwhelming evidence to refute the claim of the video production company. Use $\alpha = 0.01$. Assume the population standard deviation is 2.5 minutes.

b. What assumption did you make in performing the test in part **a.**?

21. Researchers studying the effects of diet on growth would like to know if a vegetarian diet affects the height of a child. The researchers randomly select 12 vegetarian children that are six years old. The average height of the children is 42.5 inches with a standard deviation of 3.8 inches. The average height for all six year old children is 45.75 inches.

a. What is the population being studied?

b. Conduct an hypothesis test to determine whether there is overwhelming evidence at $\alpha = 0.05$ that six year old vegetarian children are not the same height as other six year old children?

c. What assumption did you make in performing the test in part **b.**?

22. Consider the following σ unknown hypothesis tests for the population mean. Compute the P-value for each test and decide whether you would reject or fail to reject the null hypothesis at $\alpha = 0.01$.

a. $H_0: \mu = 25, H_a: \mu > 25, t = 2.7, n = 15$

b. $H_0: \mu = 0.85, H_a: \mu < 0.85, t = -2.5, n = 7$

c. $H_0: \mu = 1000, H_a: \mu \neq 1000, t = 2.0, n = 15$

23. Consider the following σ unknown hypothesis tests for the population mean. Compute the P-value for each test and decide whether you would reject or fail to reject the null hypothesis at $\alpha = 0.05$.

a. $H_0: \mu = 120, H_a: \mu > 120, t = 1.5, n = 20$

b. $H_0: \mu = 0.2, H_a: \mu < 0.2, t = -2.75, n = 18$

c. $H_0: \mu = 50, H_a: \mu \neq 50, t = 2.4, n = 5$

24. The average number of points scored by a team during an NFL football game is known to be 19.55. Use the Super Bowl Stats to test whether the number of points scored by a team during the Super Bowl is different than 19.55 at $\alpha = 0.05$.

⁞ **Data**

stat.hawkeslearning.com
Data Sets > Super Bowl Stats

25. The American IPA style of beer has on average 6.47% alcohol by volume (ABV). Use the Beers and Breweries data set to determine if the American IPAs brewed in California have more ABV than average at $\alpha = 0.05$. Calculate the P-value for this hypothesis test.

⁞ **Data**

stat.hawkeslearning.com
Data Sets > Beers and Breweries

26. According to Trulia[2], the average price per square foot for Mount Pleasant homes sold in 2017 was $210. Using the Mount Pleasant Real Estate data set, perform a hypothesis test to test the claim that the average price per square foot is lower in the Park West neighborhood than the city's average at $\alpha = 0.10$. Calculate the P-value for this hypothesis test.

⁞ **Data**

stat.hawkeslearning.com
Data Sets > Mount Pleasant Real Estate Data

27. Del Valley Foods requires that corn supplied for canning must weigh more than 5 ounces per ear. South Valley Farms claims that the corn they supply meets the required specifications. A sample of 200 ears of corn are selected at random from a delivery. The sample has a mean of 5.01 ounces and a standard deviation of 0.30 ounces. Will a test of hypothesis at $\alpha = 0.10$ support South Valley Farms' claim?

28. The director of the IRS has been flooded with complaints that people must wait more than 45 minutes before seeing an IRS representative. To determine the validity of these complaints, the IRS randomly selects 400 people entering IRS offices across the country and records the times that they must wait before seeing an IRS representative. The average waiting time for the sample is 55 minutes with a standard deviation of 15 minutes.

    a. What is the population being studied?

    b. Are the complaints substantiated by the data at $\alpha = 0.10$?

29. NarStor, a computer disk drive manufacturer, claims that the average time to failure for its hard drives is 14,400 hours. You work for a consumer group that has decided to examine this claim. Technicians ran 16 drives continuously for three years. Recently the last drive failed. The time to failure (in hours) are given below.

Time Until Failure (Hours)							
330	620	1870	2410	4620	6396	7822	8102
8309	12,882	14,419	16,092	18,384	20,916	23,812	25,814

    a. What is the population being studied?

    b. What is the variable being measured?

    c. What level of measurement does the variable possess?

    d. Conduct a hypothesis test to determine whether there is overwhelming evidence that the average time to failure is less than the manufacturer's claim. Use $\alpha = 0.01$.

    e. What assumption did you make in performing the test in part **d.**?

30. Officials in charge of televising an international chess competition in South America want to determine if the average time per move for the top players has remained under five minutes over the last two years. Video tapes of matches which have been played over the two-year period are reviewed and a random sample of 50 moves are timed. The sample mean is 3.5 minutes with a standard deviation of 1.5 minutes.

    a. What is the population under study?

    b. Can the officials conclude at $\alpha = 0.05$ that the time per move is still under five minutes?

31. High power experimental engines are being developed by the Stevens Motor Company for use in their new sports coupe. The engineers have calculated the maximum horsepower for the engine to be 600 HP. Sixteen engines are randomly selected for horsepower testing. The sample has an average maximum HP of 620 with a standard deviation 50 HP.

a.   Perform an hypothesis test to determine whether the data suggests that the average maximum HP for the experimental engine is significantly different than the maximum horsepower calculated by the engineers? Use a significance level of $\alpha = 0.10$.

b.   What assumption did you make in performing the test in part **a.**?

32.   The nutrition label for Oriental Spice Sauce states that one package of the sauce has 1190 milligrams of sodium. To determine if the label is accurate the FDA randomly selects two hundred packages of Oriental Spice Sauce and determines the sodium content. The sample has an average of 1167.34 milligrams of sodium per package with a sample standard deviation of 252.94 milligrams.

a.   Find the P-value for the test of hypothesis that the sodium content is different than the nutrition label states.

b.   Is there sufficient evidence to reject the null hypothesis at a significance level of 0.01?

11.3 The Relationship Between Confidence Interval Estimation and Hypothesis Testing

Previously, we discussed interval estimation for the population mean and the population proportion. We know that when estimating the population mean, a $100(1-\alpha)\%$ confidence interval for μ is given by

$$\bar{x} \pm z_{\alpha/2} \frac{\sigma}{\sqrt{n}}.$$

In this chapter, we have shown that the two-sided hypothesis test about the population mean μ is

$$H_0 : \mu = \mu_0$$
$$H_a : \mu \neq \mu_0.$$

where μ_0 is some specific value of the population mean. From the previous chapter, we know that $100(1-\alpha)\%$ of the confidence intervals will contain μ. Therefore, if we reject the null hypothesis when the confidence interval does not contain the value of μ_0, we will reject the null hypothesis when it is actually true with a probability of α. You may recall that α represents the probability of committing a Type I error (i.e., we reject the null hypothesis when the null hypothesis is true). So, when we construct a $100(1-\alpha)\%$ confidence interval and reject the null hypothesis when the interval does not contain μ_0, this is equivalent to performing a two-tailed hypothesis test using α as the significance level.

Using a Confidence Interval to Test a Two-Sided Hypothesis

Basic Assumptions: The data must be quantitative and obtained via a random sample of size n.

Step 1: If the hypothesis test is of the form

$$H_0 : \mu = \mu_0$$
$$H_a : \mu \neq \mu_0.$$

Step 2: Calculate the $100(1-\alpha)\%$ confidence interval.

If the standard deviation of the population, σ, is known and either the sample is drawn from a normal population or $n > 30$, then the confidence interval is given by

$$\bar{x} \pm z_{\alpha/2} \frac{\sigma}{\sqrt{n}}.$$

If the standard deviation of the population, σ, is unknown and either the sample is drawn from a normal population or $n > 30$, then the confidence interval is given by

$$\bar{x} \pm t_{\alpha/2} \frac{s}{\sqrt{n}}.$$

Step 3: If μ_0 falls within the interval, then we fail to reject the null hypothesis; however, if μ_0 falls outside the calculated interval, then reject the null hypothesis in favor of the alternative.

PROCEDURE

Let's look at Example 11.2.1. Recall that the hypotheses were

$$H_0 : \mu = 150$$
$$H_a : \mu \neq 150.$$

The test statistic for this example was $z = 2.67$ and the null hypothesis was rejected at the 0.05 level.

Note that the value $z_{\alpha/2} = z_{0.025} = 1.96$. Calculating a 95% confidence interval for μ, we get

$$\bar{x} \pm z_{\alpha/2} \frac{\sigma}{\sqrt{n}}$$
$$154 \pm 1.96 \frac{15}{\sqrt{100}}$$
$$151.06 \text{ to } 156.94.$$

Because the hypothesized value ($\mu = 150$) does not fall in this interval, we reject the null hypothesis, which is consistent with the earlier conclusion. Although we presented this demonstration using the confidence interval for the population mean, the same relationship exists for other population parameters.

⌦ **Technology**

Recall that a confidence interval can be constructed on a TI-83/84 Plus calculator. For detailed instructions please visit stat.hawkeslearning.com and navigate to **Technology Instructions > Confidence Intervals > z-Interval**.

```
ZInterval
 (151.06,156.94)
 x̄=154
 n=100
```

11.3 **Exercises**

Basic Concepts

1. How can a confidence interval be used to test a hypothesis?

2. Can a confidence interval be used to test a one-sided hypothesis?

Exercises

Data

stat.hawkeslearning.com
Data Sets > Super Bowl Stats

3. Historically, the average number of points scored by a team during an NFL football game is known to be 19.551. Use the Super Bowl Stats data set and a confidence interval approach to test whether the number of points scored by a team during the Super Bowl is different than 19.551 at $\alpha = 0.05$.

4. AAA Controls makes a switch that is advertised to activate a warning light if the power supplied to a machine reaches 100 volts. A random sample of 250 switches is tested and the mean voltage at which the warning light occurs is 98 volts. The population standard deviation in known to be 3 volts. Using the confidence interval approach, test the hypothesis that the mean voltage activation is different from AAA Controls' claim at the 0.05 level.

5. Researchers studying the effects of diet on growth would like to know if a vegetarian diet affects the height of a child. The researchers randomly selected 12 vegetarian children that were six years old. The average height of the children is 42.5 inches. The average height for all six-year-old children is 45.75 inches with a standard deviation of 3.8 inches.

   a. Using confidence intervals, test to determine whether there is overwhelming evidence at $\alpha = 0.05$ that six-year-old vegetarian children are not the same height as other six-year-old children.

   b. What assumption did you make in performing the test?

6. High-power experimental engines are being developed by the Stevens Motor Company for use in its new sports coupe. The engineers have calculated the maximum horsepower for the engine to be 600 HP. Sixteen engines are randomly selected for horsepower testing. The sample has an average maximum HP of 620 with a standard deviation of 50 HP.

   a. Use the confidence interval approach to determine whether the data suggests that the average maximum HP for the experimental engine is significantly different than the maximum horsepower calculated by the engineers. Use a significance level of $\alpha = 0.01$.

   b. What assumption did you make in performing the test?

7. The nutrition label for Oriental Spice Sauce states that one package of sauce has 1190 milligrams of sodium. To determine if the label is accurate, the FDA randomly selects two hundred packages of Oriental Spice Sauce and determines the sodium content. The sample has an average of 1167.34

milligrams of sodium per package with a sample standard deviation of 252.94 milligrams.

a. Calculate a 99% confidence interval for the mean sodium content in Oriental Spice Sauce.

b. Using the confidence interval approach, is there evidence that the sodium content is different than the nutrition label states?

11.4 Testing a Hypothesis about a Population Proportion

The topic that we will develop in this section will be a hypothesis testing approach for categorical variables (nominal data). The inferences that we will make with this data will concern one population. We will use the information in the sample proportion $(\hat{p})$ to test hypotheses about the population proportion, p.

Testing hypotheses about a population proportion could involve a variety of problems.

- What fraction of a student's grades will be A's?

- What proportion of graduating seniors obtain jobs with starting salaries in excess of $50,000?

- What percent of the products which a company produces are defective?

- What fraction of the voters favor the incumbent in the next election?

- What fraction of the customers who purchase a Honda Civic are extremely satisfied?

- What percent of the time will a baseball player get a hit?

- What proportion of the time will a drug be successful in treating a specific disorder?

Developing the Test

Testing a hypothesis concerning a population proportion is nearly identical to testing a hypothesis about a population mean. The major changes in the procedure include the use of the population proportion (p) in the formulation of the hypothesis, rather than the population mean (μ), and similar changes in the calculation of the test statistic.

Table 11.4.1 contains the correct formulation of the hypotheses for a test about a single proportion.

Table 11.4.1 - Hypotheses for a Test about a Single Proportion			
	Is the population proportion different from p_0?	Is the population proportion greater than p_0?	Is the population proportion less than p_0?
Null hypothesis, H_0	$p = p_0$	$p = p_0$	$p = p_0$
Alternative Hypothesis, H_a	$p \neq p_0$	$p > p_0$	$p < p_0$
Type of Hypothesis Test	Two-tailed	Right-tailed	Left-tailed

Testing a Hypothesis about a Population Proportion, p

Assumptions:

1. The data is obtained via a random sample of size n.

2. The conditions for a binomial random variable are met. That is, there is a fixed number n of independent trials with only two possible outcomes on each trial, referred to as a success or failure. The probability of success on any trial is the same.

3. The conditions $np_0 \geq 10$ and $n(1 - p_0) \geq 10$ are both satisfied.

Test Statistic:

The test statistic is given by

$$z = \frac{\hat{p} - p_0}{\sigma_{\hat{p}}}, \text{ where } \sigma_{\hat{p}} = \sqrt{\frac{p_0(1 - p_0)}{n}},$$

p_0 = the population proportion (the value used in the null hypothesis),

n = the sample size, and

$\hat{p}$ = the sample proportion.

PROCEDURE

Note

Recall from Section 7.4 some examples of binomial random variables were:

- The number of left-handed persons in a sample of 200 unrelated people.

- The number of correct guesses out of 20 True or False questions when you randomly pick the answer.

- The number of winning scratch-off lottery tickets when you purchase 15 of the same type.

Example 11.4.1

A college is trying a new student registration system and would like to know if there is sufficient evidence to conclude that more than 60% of the students favor the new system.

Solution

Step 1: Determine the null and alternative hypotheses.

Let's first state the hypotheses in plain English.

Null Hypothesis: 60% of students favor the new system.

Alternative Hypothesis: More than 60% of the students favor the new system.

Since the problem concerns the percent of students that favor the new system, the appropriate statistical measure will be a **proportion**.

Let p = the proportion of the student population who believe the new system is superior to the old system.

Since the problem is concerned with finding evidence that the percentage is greater than 60%, the formation of the alternative hypothesis will be one-sided.

In symbolic form the hypotheses would then be as follows.

$H_0: p = 0.6$ 60% of the students prefer the new system.

$H_a: p > 0.6$ More than 60% of the students prefer the new system.

Step 2: Specify the significance level α.

Since the level of the test is not specified in the problem, let's use $\alpha = 0.05$.

Step 3: Validate the assumptions of the hypothesis test, identify the appropriate test statistic, and compute its value.

The test statistic measures how far the sample proportion, $\hat{p}$, is from the unknown population proportion, p, measured in standard deviation units. This is exactly the same concept used in testing hypotheses about a population mean. There is one interesting aspect to the calculation of the standard deviation of $\hat{p}$, which is denoted by $\sigma_{\hat{p}}$; it requires knowledge of p. This may seem odd, since the entire purpose of the hypothesis test is to make an inference about the unknown value of p. If p is unknown, how can it be used to compute $\sigma_{\hat{p}}$?

The answer to this riddle lies in the hypothesis testing procedure. The null hypothesis is assumed to be true, unless there is overwhelming evidence to the contrary. *Since the null is presumed to be true, let p equal the value hypothesized in the null hypothesis (p_0).*

In a random sample of 520 students, 352 said that the new registration system is superior.

First, we must check our assumptions.

- ☑ Random sample
- ☑ There are only two outcomes for each of the 520 independent trials—a student prefers the new system or does not—so we have a binomial random variable.
- ☑ $np_0 = 520(0.6) = 312 > 10$ and $n(1 - p_0) = 520(1 - 0.6) = 208 > 10$

We can proceed with the test. The value of $\hat{p}$, is given by

$$\hat{p} = \frac{352}{520} \approx 0.6769, \text{ and}$$

$$z = \frac{\hat{p} - p_0}{\sigma_{\hat{p}}} = \frac{\hat{p} - p_0}{\sqrt{\dfrac{p_0(1 - p_0)}{n}}} = \frac{0.6769 - 0.6}{\sqrt{\dfrac{0.6(1 - 0.6)}{520}}} \approx 3.58.$$

In this case, the difference between p_0 and $\hat{p}$ is 3.58 standard deviation units. If H_0 is true, would we expect a difference between p_0 and $\hat{p}$ to be 3.58 standard deviation units? Or, is this test statistic ($z = 3.58$) overwhelming evidence in favor of the alternative hypothesis?

Step 4: Determine the critical value(s) or *P*-value.

The test statistic, z, has a normal distribution with a mean of zero and a variance of one. So designating the decision rule is exactly like what has been done in previous problems. The test is a one-tailed test, and in **Step 2** we decided to set the level of the test at 0.05.

The decision rule will be to reject H_0: $p = 0.6$ if the value of z is greater than 1.645. In essence, we are saying that ordinary sampling variation might account for a $\hat{p}$ up to 1.645 standard deviations larger than the hypothesized value. But if a z-value is observed that is larger than 1.645, then we will lose faith in the null hypothesis because we have observed something that is too rare by the standards we have set for the level of the test.

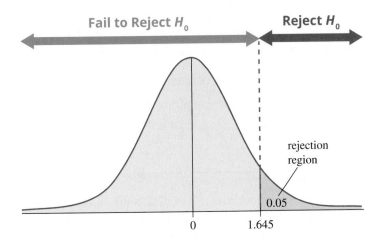

We can use exactly the same idea in determining a *P*-value for a test about a proportion as we did in calculating *P*-values for the test statistic of a hypothesis concerning a population mean.

Calculating *P*-Values for a Hypothesis Test for a Proportion

For an **upper one-tailed test** (i.e., $H_a: p > 0.6$), we calculate the *P*-value as

$$P\text{-value} = P(z \geq z_0) = P(z \leq -z_0),$$ where z_0 is the observed value of the test statistic.

For a **lower one-tailed test** (i.e., $H_a: p < 0.6$), we calculate the *P*-value as

$$P\text{-value} = P(z \leq z_0).$$

For a **two-tailed test** (i.e., $H_a \neq 0.6$), the *P*-value is calculated as

$$P\text{-value} = 2 \cdot P(z \geq |z_0|).$$

If the computed *P*-value is less than α, reject the null hypothesis in favor of the alternative.

If the computed *P*-value is greater than or equal to α, fail to reject the null hypothesis.

PROCEDURE

Since this is an upper one-tailed test, the *P*-value is computed as

$$P\text{-value} = P(z \geq 3.58) = P(z \leq -3.58) \approx 0.0002.$$

Step 5: Make the decision to reject or fail to reject H_0.

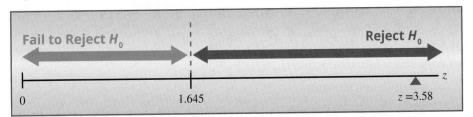

The value of the test statistic, $z = 3.58$, falls into the rejection region. According to the standard of rareness established in **Step 4**, the *z*-value is too rare to believe the null hypothesis ($H_0: p = 0.6$) is true. The sample evidence contradicts the null hypothesis, and it will be rejected in favor of the alternative hypothesis,

⌘ Technology

The *P*-value is found on the output of the 1-Prop Z-Test on the TI-83/84 Plus calculator. For instructions visit stat.hawkeslearning.com and navigate to **Technology Instructions > Hypothesis Testing > One Proportion z-Test**.

```
1-PropZTest
 Prop>.6
 z=3.58057437
 P=1.7145836ε-4
 p̂=.6769230769
 n=520
```

$$H_a: p > 0.6.$$

Comparing the *P*-value to the significance level, we see that $0.0002 < 0.05$, which leads us to the same conclusion to reject the null hypothesis.

Step 6: State the conclusion in terms of the original question.

There is overwhelming evidence that over 60% of the students prefer the new system at a significance level of 0.05.

Example 11.4.2

The city of Savannah wants to know if its citizens are in favor of building a toll bridge across the Savannah River. A research company was hired to survey a sample of local residents to determine their views on the construction of a toll bridge. The mayor would like to know if the majority of the residents are in favor of the bridge before calling a formal referendum on the topic. Test at the $\alpha = 0.01$ level.

Solution

Step 1: Determine the null and alternative hypotheses.

In plain English the hypotheses are

HYPOTHESIZED

■ Do Not Favor ■ Favor

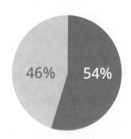

Null Hypothesis: Half of the residents favor the new toll bridge.

Alternative Hypothesis: The majority of the residents favor the new toll bridge.

A majority would be any percentage greater than 50%. Since the problem concerns the percentage of residents, the appropriate statistical measure is a proportion. The mayor wants to take action if there is overwhelming evidence that greater than 50% of the residents favor the new bridge. Therefore, the problem should be formulated with a one-sided alternative.

$H_0: p = 0.5$ 50% of the residents favor the new toll bridge.

$H_a: p > 0.5$ More than 50% of the residents favor the new toll bridge.

SAMPLE RESULTS

■ Do Not Favor ■ Favor

Step 2: Specify the significance level α.

The problem specifies the level of the test is $\alpha = 0.01$.

Step 3: Validate the assumptions of the hypothesis test, identify the appropriate test statistic, and compute its value.

The appropriate test statistic is given by

$$z = \frac{\hat{p} - p_0}{\sigma_{\hat{p}}}, \quad \text{where } \sigma_{\hat{p}} = \sqrt{\frac{p_0(1 - p_0)}{n}}.$$

Of the 420 residents that were randomly selected, 228 favored the new bridge. First, we must check our assumptions.

☑ Random sample

☑ There are only two outcomes for each trial—a resident favors the toll bridge or does not—so we have a binomial random variable.

☑ $np_0 = n(1 - p_0) = 420(0.5) = 210 > 10$

We can proceed with the test. The proportion favoring the new bridge in the sample is

$$\hat{p} = \frac{228}{420} \approx 0.5429,$$

and

$$z = \frac{\hat{p} - p_0}{\sigma_{\hat{p}}} = \frac{0.5429 - 0.5}{0.0244} \approx 1.76, \text{ where } \sigma_{\hat{p}} = \sqrt{\frac{0.5(1 - 0.5)}{420}} \approx 0.0244.$$

The z-value indicates that the sample proportion is 1.76 standard deviation units above the hypothesized proportion. Could this have happened by ordinary sampling variation, or is this overwhelming evidence that the null is not true and the alternative should be selected?

Step 4: Determine the critical value(s) or P-value.

The null hypothesis should only be rejected if there is overwhelming evidence that the population proportion is larger than 0.5. Since the test is one-sided, the entire probability associated with the level of the test ($\alpha = 0.01$) will be placed in the right-hand tail of the distribution.

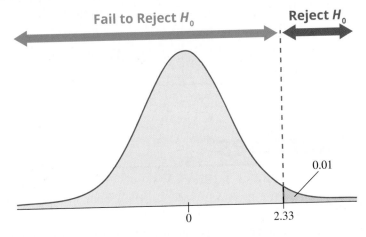

Recall from Table 11.2.3 that the critical value for the test is 2.33. The rejection region is the shaded region in the above graph. The decision will be to reject the null hypothesis if the calculated value of the test statistic is greater than 2.33.

The P-value is computed as

$$P(z \geq 1.76) = P(z \leq -1.76) \approx 0.0392.$$

Step 5: Make the decision to reject or fail to reject H_0.

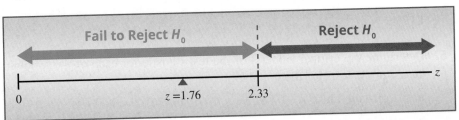

The value of z does not fall in the rejection region. Do not reject H_0: $p = 0.5$. There is not sufficient evidence (at the 0.01 level) to reject the null hypothesis. Another way of thinking about this is that the sample proportion was not sufficiently rare to reject H_0: $p = 0.5$.

The P-value of 0.0392 is greater than $\alpha = 0.01$, so we fail to reject the null hypothesis.

⌫ Technology

The P-value for a z-test statistic can be calculated using the normalcdf function on a TI-83/84 Plus calculator. For instructions, visit stat.hawkeslearning.com and navigate to **Technology Instructions > Normal Distribution > Normal Probability (cdf)**.

```
normalcdf(1.76,1
0E6)
        .0392038577
```

Step 6: State the conclusion in terms of the original question.

There is not **overwhelming evidence** at the $\alpha = 0.01$ level to conclude that the residents favor the new toll bridge.

Setting $\alpha = 0.01$ implies we were only willing to make a Type I error (reject the null hypothesis when it was true) once in every 100 trials of the experiment. Since the P-value of our test statistic 0.0392 is greater than 0.01, the null hypothesis was not rejected.

If the level of the test had been 0.05, then to reject H_0 in favor of H_a would have required a test statistic whose rareness under ordinary sampling variation is less than 0.05. For $\alpha = 0.05$, the null hypothesis is rejected in favor of the alternative, since the test statistic has a P-value (0.0392) less than 0.05.

Table 11.4.2 – If P-Value = 0.0392	
Level of the Test	**Reject or Fail to Reject**
0.10	Reject
0.05	Reject
0.03	Fail to Reject
0.01	Fail to Reject

11.4 Exercises

Basic Concepts

1. How does testing a hypothesis about a proportion differ from testing a hypothesis about a mean?

2. What is the appropriate test statistic to be used in hypothesis testing of a population proportion?

3. What conditions must be met in order to perform a hypothesis test about a population proportion?

4. How are P-values determined for a proportion?

Exercises

5. Determine the critical value(s) of the test statistic for each of the following large sample tests for the population proportion.

   a. Left-tailed test, $\alpha = 0.05$
   b. Right-tailed test, $\alpha = 0.01$
   c. Two-tailed test, $\alpha = 0.10$

6. Determine the critical value(s) of the test statistic for each of the following large sample tests for the population proportion.

   a. Left-tailed test, $\alpha = 0.07$
   b. Right-tailed test, $\alpha = 0.04$
   c. Two-tailed test, $\alpha = 0.09$

7. A commercial airline is concerned about the increase in usage of carry-on luggage. For years, the percentage of passengers with one or more pieces of carry-on luggage has been stable at approximately 68%. The airline recently selected 300 passengers at random and determined that 237 possessed carry-on luggage. Is there overwhelming evidence of an increase in carry-on luggage at a significance level of 0.01?

8. Ordinarily, when a company recruits a technical staff member, about 25% of the applicants are qualified. However, based on the information in 120 recently received resumes, 18 appear to be technically qualified.

   a. Is there overwhelming evidence that the percentage of qualified applicants is less than 25%? Test at the 0.05 level.

   b. What concerns might you have about the data in this problem?

9. The National Center for Drug Abuse is conducting a study to determine if heroin usage among teenagers has changed. Historically, about 1.3 percent of teenagers between the ages of 15 and 19 have used heroin one or more times. In a recent survey of 1824 teenagers, 37 indicated they had used heroin one or more times.

   a. Is there overwhelming evidence of a change in heroin usage among teenagers? Test at the 0.05 level.

   b. What concerns might you have about the data in this problem?

10. Paper International, Inc. has a large staff of salespeople nationwide. Top officials of the company believe that 75% of their salespeople have met their monthly sales goals by the end of the third week of each month. To investigate this, they randomly select 250 salespeople and examine their sales records at the end of the third week of the current month. One-hundred seventy-five of the 250 salespeople surveyed had already met their monthly sales goals.

    a. Does this sample support the belief of the top officials at the company at $\alpha = 0.10$?

    b. What concerns might you have about the manner in which the data were collected?

11. Ships arriving in US ports are inspected by customs officials for contaminated cargo. Assume, for a certain port, that 20% of the ships arriving in the previous year contained cargo that was contaminated. A random selection of 50 ships in the current year included five that had contaminated cargo.

    a. Does the data suggest that the proportion of ships arriving in the port with contaminated cargoes has decreased in the current year at $\alpha = 0.01$?

    b. Do you have any concerns about the sample size? Explain.

12. Electronic circuit boards are randomly selected each day to determine if any of the boards are defective. A random sample of 300 boards from one day's production has twelve boards that are defective.

    a. Based on the data, is there overwhelming evidence that more than 5% of the circuit boards are defective? Test at the $\alpha = 0.10$ level.

    b. Do you have any concerns about the sample size? Explain.

13. Loch Ness Fish Farm breeds fish for commercial sale. The fish are kept in breeder tanks until at least 70% of the fish are five inches long at which time they are transferred to outdoor ponds. To determine if it is the appropriate time to transfer the fish, 50 fish are randomly selected and measured. If 33 of the fish are found to be over five inches long, does the sample data suggest that it is the appropriate time to transfer the fish at $\alpha = 0.05$?

14. Digger and Digger, a precious metals mining company, is considering the development of a new mining area. They have a lease on an area which they believe contains gypsum. The area will be profitable to mine if more than 15% of the rocks contain more than trace amounts of the mineral. Eighty rocks are randomly selected and the amount of gypsum is measured. Thirteen rocks in the sample are observed to have more than trace amounts of the mineral. Based on the sample data, should Digger and Digger conclude that the area will be profitable to mine? Use $\alpha = 0.01$.

15. A socially conscious corporation wants to relocate their headquarters to another part of town. One concern expressed by workers is that their commuting distance will increase. The corporation has decided that if more than 50% of the employees will have to drive farther to the proposed new location, they will cancel the move. In a random sample of 398 employees, 201 indicated that their commuting distance to the new office will be longer. Based on the sample data, should the corporation cancel the move? Use a significance level of 0.01.

16. A production process will normally produce defective parts 0.2% of the time. In a random sample of 1400 parts, three defectives are observed.

   a. Is this overwhelming evidence at the 0.05 level to indicate that the defective rate of the process has increased?

   b. Compute the P-value for the test statistic.

   c. Based on the P-value, would the decision change at $\alpha = 0.01$?

17. Bombay Charlie's, a fast food Indian restaurant, is thinking about adding a certain spice to their chicken curry dish to attract more customers. The restaurant manager has decided to add the spice if more than 80% of his customers prefer the taste of the chicken curry with the spice added. Sixty-five customers are randomly selected to participate in a blind taste test. Fifty-four of these customers prefer the chicken curry with the added spice.

   a. Find the P-value for the hypothesis test that the manager will perform to decide if more than 80% of the customers prefer the taste of the chicken curry with the added spice.

   b. Does the data suggest that more than 80% of the customers prefer the curry with the new spice at $\alpha = 0.05$?

18. The news program for KOPE, the local television station, claims to have 40% of the market. A random sample of 500 viewers conducted by an independent testing agency found 192 who claim to watch the KOPE news program on a regular basis.

   a. Find the P-value for testing the hypothesis that the news program for KOPE does not have at least 40% of the market as it claims.

b. Is there sufficient evidence to reject the hypothesis that KOPE does not have at least 40% of the market at a significance level of 0.05?

19. The length of time that a storm window will last before beginning to leak is of interest to a window manufacturer who wishes to guarantee his windows. He believes that more than 50% of the windows will last at least four years. To research this, 931 windows, which were installed at least four years ago, are randomly selected and checked for leakage. Five hundred of the windows are found to still be leak-free.

   a. Find the *P*-value for testing the hypothesis that more than 50% of the windows will be leak-free in four years.

   b. Does the sample support the hypothesis that more than 50% of the windows will be leak-free in four years at $\alpha = 0.05$?

20. In order to discourage soldiers from smoking, the Pentagon raised the price of cigarettes by $4 a carton. This increased the average price of a carton of brand-name cigarettes to $17.50, an increase of about 30%. Prior to the price increase, about 32% of military personnel smoked, as opposed to 25% of all adult Americans. Suppose that following the price increase, a random sample of military personnel is selected to determine smoking habits. With $\alpha = 0.05$, can we conclude that the price increase was effective in decreasing the percentage of smokers if 50 of the 200 military personnel sampled smoke?

21. Wearing bright or fluorescent orange colored clothing clearly reduces the risk of being shot or killed by hunting. According to an article appearing in *The Augusta Chronicle* (Georgia), about two-thirds of the hunters shot in Georgia and South Carolina during a five year span were not wearing bright clothes. Of the 52 that were killed, only 19 wore orange. Suppose that a random sample of 100 hunters in Georgia are surveyed and it is determined that of the 100, 62 routinely wear fluorescent orange colored clothing while hunting. With $\alpha = 0.10$, can it be concluded that over half the hunters in Georgia routinely wear fluorescent orange colored clothing while hunting?

22. According to the Federal Communications Commission, about 49% of the households in the United States had cable television in 1985. Suppose that a sample of 200 households is selected in 2017 and it is determined that 125 of them have cable television.

   a. With $\alpha = 0.05$, can it be concluded that a higher proportion of households in 2017 have cable television as compared with 1985?

   b. In the sample of 200, what is the fewest number of people who have cable television that would allow the conclusion that a higher proportion of households in 2017 have cable television as compared to 1985?

23. The winner of the coin toss in a football game has their choice of one of three privileges: deciding which team receives the kickoff, deciding which goal his team will defend, deferring and deciding in the second half whether to kick or receive the kickoff. Using the Super Bowl Stats data set, determine if winning the coin toss seemed to impact winning the game by looking at the proportion of game winners who also won the coin toss. Test at the $\alpha = 0.05$ level.

⁘ **Data**

stat.hawkeslearning.com
Data Sets > Super Bowl Stats

11.5 Testing a Hypothesis about a Population Standard Deviation or Variance

In this section we want to adapt the hypothesis testing procedure to test a hypothesis concerning a population variance. Table 11.5.1 contains the correct formulation of the hypotheses for a test of the variance.

	Table 11.5.1 - Hypotheses for a Test about the Variance		
	Is the population variance different from σ_0^2?	Is the population variance greater than σ_0^2?	Is the population variance less than σ_0^2?
Null hypothesis, H_0	$\sigma^2 = \sigma_0^2$	$\sigma^2 = \sigma_0^2$	$\sigma^2 = \sigma_0^2$
Alternative Hypothesis, H_a	$\sigma^2 \neq \sigma_0^2$	$\sigma^2 > \sigma_0^2$	$\sigma^2 < \sigma_0^2$
Type of Hypothesis Test	Two-tailed	Right-tailed	Left-tailed

Let's develop the hypothesis test for the variance with an example.

Example 11.5.1

A pharmaceutical company believes that its manufacturing process is in control when the standard deviation of the dosage in each tablet is 0.10 milligrams. The quality assurance manager is willing to shut down the manufacturing process if there is overwhelming evidence that the process has excessive variation. Use $\alpha = 0.01$ to perform the test.

Solution

Step 1: Determine the null and alternative hypotheses.

Stating the hypotheses in plain English we have:

Null Hypothesis: The manufacturing process does not have excessive variation.

Alternative Hypothesis: The manufacturing process does have excessive variation.

Since the issue in this example is variation, the hypothesis can be stated in terms of the standard deviation or the variance.

Most hypothesis tests concerning a variance will be one-sided since small variation is desirable, while too much variation is undesirable. Because we are interested in determining if there is evidence that the process has excessive variation, the test will be a right-tailed test.

The hypotheses in symbolic form are

$$H_0: \sigma^2 = (0.10)^2 = 0.01 \text{ mg}^2 \quad \text{The variation of the process meets the standard.}$$

$$H_a: \sigma^2 > 0.01 \text{ mg}^2 \quad \text{The variation of the process is excessive.}$$

Step 2: Specify the significance level α.

The level of the test is specified in the problem to be $\alpha = 0.01$.

Step 3: Validate the assumptions of the hypothesis test, identify the appropriate test statistic, and compute its value.

Testing a Hypothesis about a Population Variance

Assumptions:

1. The data is obtained via a random sample of size n.

2. The population is normally distributed with mean μ and standard deviation σ.

Test Statistic:

The test statistic for a hypothesis about a population variance is given by

$$\chi^2 = \frac{(n-1)s^2}{\sigma_0^2} \quad \text{with degrees of freedom} = n-1$$

where,

n = the sample size

σ_0 = the claimed value of the population standard deviation

σ_0^2 = the claimed value of the population variance

s = the sample standard deviation, and

s^2 = the sample variance.

PROCEDURE

Friedrich Robert Helmert

Friedrich Robert Helmert was born in Germany in 1843. His interests were in geodesy, which is a discipline concerned with measuring the earth on a global scale. He studied engineering science at the Polytechnische Schule and while still a student had the opportunity to work on some important geodesy projects with one of his teachers, August Nagel. He later studied mathematics and astronomy to earn his doctorate. Geodesy led him into statistics, first writing a book on least squares. In 1876 he discovered the chi-square as the distribution of the sample variance for a normal distribution. His work was in German and was not translated to English, so later in 1900 English statisticians rediscovered the chi-square distribution (Karl Pearson) and its application to the sample variance (William Gosset, Ronald Fisher).

Note that the test statistic is named χ^2 (chi-square), because that is the type of distribution the statistic has under repeated sampling (repeatedly calculating this statistic using different random samples from the same population). Recall that we used the chi-square distribution in Section 10.4 to construct confidence intervals for the population variance and standard deviation. Let's look at the pieces of this new test statistic. The term σ_0^2 refers to the hypothesized value of the variance. In this sample, $\sigma_0 = 0.10$ which implies that $\sigma_0^2 = 0.01$. The actual variance of the population is unknown, but the sample variance, s^2, should be reasonably close to the unknown population variance, σ^2. If the null hypothesis is true, then $\sigma^2 = 0.01$ and the ratio $\dfrac{s^2}{\sigma_0^2}$ should be near 1, since s^2 should be close to σ_0^2. Assuming the null hypothesis is true, multiplying this ratio by $(n-1)$ should produce a result near $(n-1)$. If the χ^2 expression is a great deal larger than $(n-1)$, then s^2 is a great deal larger than σ_0^2. Such an event would cast doubt on the validity of the null hypothesis.

Suppose the population is verified to be normally distributed. Also suppose a random sample of 30 tablets are evaluated, and the sample standard deviation is found to be 0.14 milligrams. The χ^2 test statistic is

$$\chi^2 = \frac{(n-1)s^2}{\sigma_0^2} = \frac{(30-1)(0.14)^2}{(0.10)^2} = 56.84.$$

Step 4: Determine the critical value(s) or *P*-value.

The role of the critical value in this test is no different from the other hypothesis tests we have discussed. It defines a range of values for the test statistic, called the rejection region, that will be too rare to have occurred from ordinary sampling variability. From a probabilistic standpoint, the significance level of the test defines the size of the rejection region. If the value of the test statistic falls in this region, the null hypothesis will be rejected. Determining the critical value requires knowledge of the sample size. Suppose the pharmaceutical company plans to draw a sample of 30 tablets. Since the level of the test is 0.01 and there are $df = 30 - 1 = 29$ degrees of freedom, the critical value from Table G is 49.588. The test statistic will exceed this value due to ordinary variation only 1% of the time.

df	...	$\chi^2_{0.025}$	$\chi^2_{0.010}$	$\chi^2_{0.005}$
1		5.024	6.635	7.879
2		7.378	9.210	10.597
3		9.348	11.345	12.838
⋮				
29		45.722	49.588	52.336
30		46.979	50.892	53.672
⋮				

Note

For large degrees of freedom, the chi-square distribution looks very similar to a normal. Notice, however, that the right tail is a bit thicker than the left.

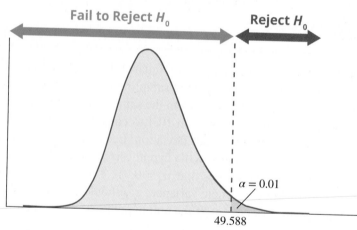

χ^2 Distribution with $df = 29$

Fail to Reject H_0   **Reject H_0**

$\alpha = 0.01$

49.588

∞ Technology

The P-value can be found using the X^2cdf function on the TI-83/84 Plus calculator or using the CHISQ.DIST.RT function in Excel. For instructions visit stat.hawkeslearning.com and navigate to **Technology Instructions > Chi-Square Distribution > Right Tailed Probability (cdf)**.

```
X²cdf(56.84,10ᴇ6
,29)
        .0015015057
```

It is preferable to use technology to find a P-value because it is exact and easy. But if you don't have technology handy, we can use the critical values of the χ^2 table to find the approximate P-value for the test statistic. As shown in the excerpt of Table G, the critical value corresponding to a tail area of 0.005 for 29 degrees of freedom is 52.336. Our calculated test statistic is greater than this value, so the area in the tail to the right of our test statistic is less than 0.005.

The exact P-value can be found using technology; for our example it is calculated as $P(\chi^2 \geq 56.84)$, which is approximately 0.0015 for degrees of freedom equal to 29.

Step 5: Make the decision to reject or fail to reject H_0.

Since the test statistic, $\chi^2 = 56.84$, exceeds the critical value, 49.588, we will conclude that the test statistic is too rare to have been caused by ordinary sampling variation. The null hypothesis is rejected in favor of the alternative hypothesis.

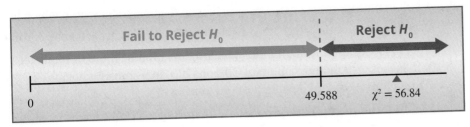

Since the P-value of 0.0015 is less than $\alpha = 0.01$, we reach the same conclusion; reject the null hypothesis.

Step 6: State the conclusion in terms of the original question.

There is overwhelming evidence that the process variation exceeds the desired level.

11.5 Exercises

Basic Concepts

1. How does testing a hypothesis about a variance differ from testing a hypothesis about a mean?

2. What is the sampling distribution for $\dfrac{(n-1)s^2}{\sigma^2}$?

3. What assumption must hold to use the chi-square distribution to make inferences about the population variance?

4. True or False: The chi-square distribution is skewed to the right.

5. What is the symbol for a critical value for the chi-square distribution? Describe the meaning of this critical value.

6. Give an example where we would want to calculate a confidence interval for σ^2.

Exercises

7. Determine the critical value(s) of the test statistic for each of the following tests for a population variance where the assumption of normality is satisfied.

   a. Right-tailed test, $\alpha = 0.01$, $n = 20$

   b. Right-tailed test, $\alpha = 0.05$, $n = 24$

   c. Right-tailed test, $\alpha = 0.005$, $n = 5$

8. Determine the critical value(s) of the test statistic for each of the following tests for a population variance where the assumption of normality is satisfied.

   a. Right-tailed test, $\alpha = 0.025$, $n = 18$

   b. Right-tailed test, $\alpha = 0.10$, $n = 24$

   c. Right-tailed test, $\alpha = 0.05$, $n = 41$

9. A bolt manufacturer is very concerned about the consistency with which his machines produce bolts that are $\frac{3}{4}$ inches in diameter. When the manufacturing process is working normally the standard deviation of the bolt diameter is 0.05 inches. A random sample of 30 bolts has an average diameter of 0.25 inches with a standard deviation of 0.07 inches.

   a. Can the manufacturer conclude that the standard deviation of bolt diameters is greater than 0.05 inches at $\alpha = 0.05$?

   b. What assumption did you make about the diameter of the bolts in performing the test in part **a.**?

10. A drug that is used for treating cancer has potentially dangerous side effects if it is taken in doses that are larger than the required dosage for the treatment. The pharmaceutical company that manufactures the drug must be certain that the standard deviation of the drug content in the tablet is not more than 0.1 mg. Twenty-five tablets are randomly selected and the amount of drug in each tablet is measured. The sample has a mean of 20 mg and a variance of 0.015 mg.

   a. Does the data suggest at $\alpha = 0.01$ that the standard deviation of drug content in the tablets is greater than 0.1 mg?

   b. What assumption did you make about the amount of drug contained in the tablets in performing the test in part **a.**?

11. A conservative investor would like to invest some money in a bond fund. The investor is concerned about the safety of her principal (the original money invested). Colonial Funds claims to have a bond fund which has maintained a consistent share price of $7. They claim that this share price has not varied by more than $0.25 on average since its inception. To test this claim, the investor randomly selects 25 days during the last year and determines the share price for the bond fund. The average share price of the sample is $7 with a standard deviation of $0.35.

   a. Can the investor conclude that the standard deviation of share price of the bond fund is greater than 0.25? Test at the 0.01 level.

   b. What assumption did you make about the share price of the bond fund in your test in part **a.**?

11.6 Practical Significance vs. Statistical Significance

A hypothesis is rarely exactly true. As the sample size becomes larger, the likelihood of rejecting the null hypothesis becomes greater.

Example 11.6.1

Suppose a dog food manufacturer wants to know if the proper amount of dog food is being placed in the 25 pound bags. The hypothesis would be:

$$H_0: \mu = 25 \text{ lb}$$
$$H_a: \mu \neq 25 \text{ lb}$$

A sample of 2000 bags was selected with the following results:

$$\bar{x} = 25.01 \text{ pounds} \quad \text{and} \quad s = 0.1 \text{ pound}.$$

Solution

The resulting test statistic is

$$t = \frac{\bar{x} - \mu_0}{\frac{s}{\sqrt{n}}} = \frac{25.01 - 25.00}{\frac{0.1}{\sqrt{2000}}} \approx 4.47.$$

How often would ordinary sampling variation produce a test statistic with a value of 4.47 or larger? The P-value of the test statistic is approximately 0.0000082 (eight in a million), and suggests that the test statistic is extremely rare, if the null hypothesis is true and all assumptions are met. Considering that a test statistic this large would result from ordinary sampling variation in only about four in a million samples, we should reject the null hypothesis $(H_0: \mu = 25)$ in favor of the alternative. Yet, is the difference between 25 and 25.01 pounds important? It would be hard to imagine that the bag filling equipment would be expected to fill the bags with less than 0.01 pound precision. Certainly one dog food nugget weighs considerably more than 0.01 pound. Despite the "statistical significance" of the result, the practical significance is negligible.

11.6 **Exercises**

Basic Concepts

1. Describe the difference between statistical significance and practical significance.

2. Give an example of a situation in which results could be statistically significant but not practically significant.

Exercises

3. In preparation for upcoming wage negotiations with the union, the managers for the Bevel Hardware Company want to establish the time required to assemble a kitchen cabinet. A first line supervisor believes that the job should take 45 minutes on average to complete. A random sample of 125 cabinets has an average assembly time of 47 minutes with a standard deviation of 10 minutes. Is there overwhelming evidence to contradict the first line supervisor's belief at a 0.05 significance level? Discuss the statistical and practical significance for this problem.

4. A horticulturist working for a large plant nursery is conducting experiments on the growth rate of a new shrub. Based on previous research, the horticulturist feels the average weekly growth rate of the new shrub is 1 cm per week. A random sample of 45 shrubs has an average growth of 0.90 cm per week with a standard deviation of 0.30 cm. Will a test of hypothesis at the 0.05 significance level support the claim that the growth rate is less than 1 cm per week? Discuss the statistical and practical significance for this problem.

5. The director of the IRS has been flooded with complaints that people must wait more than 45 minutes before seeing an IRS representative. To determine the validity of these complaints, the IRS randomly selects 400 people entering IRS offices across the country and records the times which they must wait before seeing an IRS representative. The average waiting time for the sample is 55 minutes with a standard deviation of 15 minutes. Are the complaints substantiated by the data at $\alpha = 0.10$? Discuss the statistical and practical significance for this problem.

6. The managers of a large department store wish to test reactions of shoppers to a new in-store video screen which will broadcast continuous information about the store and the items currently on sale. The video production company claims that the average shopper will watch for five or more minutes. The managers randomly select 17 shoppers and determine how long they watch the video. The average time is 4.5 minutes with a standard deviation of 2.5 minutes. Perform a hypothesis test to determine whether there is overwhelming evidence to refute the claim of the video production company. Use $\alpha = 0.01$. Discuss the statistical and practical significance for this problem.

CR Chapter Review

Key Terms and Ideas

- Hypothesis Testing
- Null Hypothesis (H_0)
- Alternative Hypothesis (H_a)
- One-Sided Alternative
- Two-Sided Alternative
- One-Tailed Test
- Two-Tailed Test
- Test Statistic
- Rejection Region
- Reject H_0
- Fail To Reject H_0
- Standard Value
- Type I Error

- Type II Error
- Level of the Test (Significance Level of the Test)
- Decision Rule
- Left-Tailed (Lower-Tailed) Test
- Right-Tailed (Upper-Tailed) Test
- z-Test Statistic
- Critical Value
- t-Test Statistic
- P-Value
- Practical vs. Statistical Significance

- The Relationship between Confidence Interval Estimation and Hypothesis Testing

- χ^2 Test Statistic

- Using a Confidence Interval to Test a Hypothesis

- Chi-Square Distribution

Key Formulas	
	Section
z-Test Statistic for a Population Mean	**11.2**

$z = \dfrac{\bar{x} - \mu_0}{\sigma_{\bar{x}}}$, where $\sigma_{\bar{x}} = \dfrac{\sigma}{\sqrt{n}}$

Assumptions:
1. The data is quantitative.
2. The data is obtained via a random sample of size n.
3. The population is normally distributed or the sample size n is large, $n > 30$.
4. The population standard deviation σ is known.

t-Test Statistic	**11.2**

$t = \dfrac{\bar{x} - \mu_0}{s_{\bar{x}}}$, where $s_{\bar{x}} = \dfrac{s}{\sqrt{n}}$,
with $n - 1$ degrees of freedom

Assumptions:
1. The data is quantitative.
2. The data is obtained via a random sample of size n.
3. The population is normally distributed or the sample size n is large, $n > 30$.
4. The population standard deviation σ is unknown.

z-Test Statistic for a Population Proportion	**11.4**

If $np_0 \geq 10$ and $n(1 - p_0) \geq 10$, the appropriate test statistic is given by

$z = \dfrac{\hat{p} - p_0}{\sigma_{\hat{p}}}$,

where $\sigma_{\hat{p}} = \sqrt{\dfrac{p_0(1 - p_0)}{n}}$.

Assumptions:
1. The data is obtained via a random sample of size n.
2. The conditions for a binomial random variable are met. That is, there is a fixed number (n) of independent trials with only two possible outcomes on each trial, referred to as a success or failure. The probability of success on any trial is the same.
3. The conditions $np_0 \geq 10$ and $n(1 - p_0) \geq 10$ are both satisfied.

Key Formulas	
	Section
Test Statistic for a Population Variance	**11.5**

$$\chi^2 = \frac{(n-1)s^2}{\sigma_0^2} \text{ with } n-1$$

degrees of freedom

Assumptions:
1. The data is obtained via a random sample of size n.
2. The population is normally distributed with mean μ and standard deviation σ.

Additional Exercises

1. A tire company has found that the mean time required for a mechanic to replace a set of four tires is 62 minutes. After instituting a new installation procedure, the company believes that the expected time required to replace the set of four tires remains unchanged. A test of the company's belief will be performed.

    a. What are the null and alternative hypotheses for the test of the company's belief?

    b. Describe, in terms of the problem, how a Type I error could occur.

    c. Describe, in terms of the problem, how a Type II error could occur.

2. Tech Transit wishes to test whether the mean number of passenger miles on a particular route exceeds 66,000 passenger miles, the number of passenger miles the company needs on that route to cover all allocated costs. A random sample of 25 trips on the route yields a mean of 70,250 miles and a standard deviation of 9000 miles. It is desired to control the significance level at 1%.

    a. State the appropriate hypotheses for this problem.

    b. Describe, in terms of the problem, how a Type I error could occur.

    c. Describe, in terms of the problem, how a Type II error could occur.

3. A pain reliever currently being used in a hospital is known to bring relief to patients in a mean time of 3.5 minutes. To compare a new pain reliever with the one currently being used, the new drug is administered to a random sample of 50 patients. The mean time to relief for the sample of patients is 2.8 minutes and the standard deviation is 1.14 minutes. Does the data provide sufficient evidence to conclude that the new drug was effective in reducing the mean time until a patient receives relief from pain? Test using $\alpha = 0.10$.

4. Tech uses thousands of fluorescent light bulbs each year. The brand of bulb it currently uses has a mean life of 25,000 hours. A manufacturer claims that its new brand of bulbs, which cost the same as the brand the university currently uses, has a mean life of more than 25,000 hours. The university has decided to purchase the new brand if, when tested, the test evidence supports

the manufacturer's claim at the 0.05 significance level. Suppose 64 bulbs were tested and they were found to have an average life of 25,550 hours. The population standard deviation is known to be 2000 hours. Will the university purchase the new brand of fluorescent bulbs?

5. The daily wages in a particular industry are normally distributed with a mean of $13.20 and a standard deviation of $2.50. If a company in this industry employing 40 workers pays these workers, on average, $12.20, can this company be accused of paying inferior wages? Use a significance level of 1%.

6. A coin-operated soft drink machine was designed to discharge, on average, 12 ounces of beverage per cup. In a test of the machine, ten cupfuls of beverage were drawn from the machine and measured. The mean and standard deviation of the ten measurements were 12.1 ounces and 0.12 ounces, respectively. Does these data present sufficient evidence to indicate that the mean discharge differs from 12 ounces? Test using $\alpha = 0.10$.

7. Techside Real Estate, Inc. is a research firm that tracks the cost of apartment rentals in Southwest Virginia. Five years ago, the regional average apartment rental rate was $895 per month. Assume that, based on the historical quarterly surveys, it is reasonable to assume that the population standard deviation is $225. In a current study of apartment rental rates, a sample of 180 apartments in the region provided the apartment rental rates. Does the sample data enable Techside Real Estate, Inc. to conclude that the population mean apartment rental rate now exceeds the level reported five years ago? The sample mean is $915 and the sample standard deviation is $227.50. Make your decision based on $\alpha = 0.10$.

8. Suppose that the national average price for used cars is $10,192. A manager of a local used car dealership reviewed a sample of 25 recent used car sales at the dealership in an attempt to determine whether the population mean price for the used cars at this particular dealership differed from the national mean. The prices for the sample of 25 cars are given in the data with a mean of $9750 and standard deviation of $1400. Test using $\alpha = 0.05$ whether a difference exists in the mean price for used cars at the dealership.

9. Suppose you are responsible for auditing invoices. Historically, about 0.003 of the invoices possessed material errors. During the last audit cycle a number of suggestions were made and implemented, and you hope that the next audit will provide evidence of improvement in the error rate. An audit of 6000 recent invoices reveals 12 material errors.

   a. Does the data suggest an improvement in the invoice error rate at $\alpha = 0.05$?

   b. Compute the P-value of the test statistic.

   c. Based on the P-value, would the decision change at $\alpha = 0.10$?

10. After completing Chemistry 101, Tommy Walker decides to conduct an experiment on his favorite brand of whiskey to determine if the proof rating on the bottle is accurate. He selects eight small eighty-proof bottles from different stores around town and measures the percent of

alcohol in each bottle. (**Note:** 80-proof alcohol contains 40% alcohol.) The resulting measurements are as follows.

Percent of Alcohol per Bottle							
38%	40%	42%	41%	39%	38%	40%	38%

   a. What is the population being studied?

   b. What is the variable being measured?

   c. What level of measurement does the data possess?

   d. Can Tommy conclude that the actual proof of whiskey is not equal to 80 at $\alpha = 0.05$?

   e. What assumption did Tommy make in performing the test in part **d.**?

11. You have decided to become a professional gambler specializing in roulette. If the roulette wheel is fair (each number has a $\frac{1}{38}$ chance) then you will lose in the long run. However, you plan to locate wheels that are not balanced properly. An unbalanced wheel will produce some numbers more often than expected. You believe that you have found such a wheel and have started keeping track of the number 29. After 420 spins of the wheel, the number 29 has been observed 14 times. Is this overwhelming evidence at the $\alpha = 0.05$ level that you should start betting heavily on the number 29?

12. A commercial airline is concerned over the increase in weight of a carry-on luggage. In the past, the airline has estimated that the average piece of carry-on luggage will weigh 12 pounds. A random selection of 148 pieces of carry-on luggage has an average weight of 14.2 pounds with a standard deviation of 3.4 pounds. Do you think that the airline's concern is justified? Use $\alpha = 0.01$.

13. Consider the following hypothesis tests for the population mean with σ known. Compute the P-value for each test and decide whether you would reject or fail to reject the null hypothesis at $\alpha = 0.01$.

   a. $H_0: \mu = 15$, $H_a: \mu > 15$, $z = 2.50$

   b. $H_0: \mu = 80$, $H_a: \mu < 80$, $z = -1.95$

   c. $H_0: \mu = 1200$, $H_a: \mu \neq 1200$, $z = 3.70$

14. Deli Delivery delivers sandwiches to neighboring office buildings during lunch time in New York City. The deli claims that the sandwiches will be delivered within 20 minutes from receiving the order. Given the hectic schedules of their customers, consistent delivery time is a must. The owner has decided that the standard deviation of delivery times should be at most 4 minutes. To determine how consistently the sandwiches are being delivered, the manager randomly selects 27 orders and measures the time from receiving the order to delivery of the sandwich. The average time to delivery of the sample was 20 minutes with a standard deviation of 4.5 minutes.

   a. Will the manager conclude at $\alpha = 0.10$ that the delivery times vary more than the owner desires?

   b. What assumption did you make about the delivery times in performing the test in part **a.**?

15. Consider the following hypothesis tests for the population mean with σ unknown. Compute the P-value for each of the tests and decide whether you would reject or fail to reject the null hypothesis at $\alpha = 0.05$.

   a. $H_0: \mu = 12$, $H_a: \mu > 12$, $t = 1.75$, $n = 25$

   b. $H_0: \mu = 0.12$, $H_a: \mu < 0.12$, $t = -2.95$, $n = 16$

   c. $H_0: \mu = 55$, $H_a: \mu \neq 55$, $t = 2.35$, $n = 8$

16. In each of the following experimental situations, give the appropriate null and alternative hypotheses to be tested. Define all terms that appear in these hypotheses.

   a.   A random sample of 100 customers in a bank are selected and their times to be served are noted. The bank has recently retrained its tellers to be more efficient with the hope of decreasing its average time in servicing its customers, which has been 4 minutes in the past.

   b.   A local driver training school claims that at least 75% of its pupils pass the driving test on their first attempt. A sample of 60 students from the school are selected, and their performances on the driving test are noted. Based upon the data collected, we would like to refute the claim of the school.

   c.   A spokesperson for a popular diet claims that the average weight lost for someone on the diet will be at least 15 pounds over a two-month period. The amount of weight lost for each person in a sample of 10 people on the diet is determined in order to try to refute the claim of the diet spokesperson.

   d.   A tire company tests 68 of its new premium tires to determine if the average lifespan of the tire is more than the average lifespan of its major competitor's best tire. The average lifespan of the competitor's tire is 63,000 miles.

   e.   An elementary statistics student conducts an experiment in order to show that a coin from a magic kit is biased. The student flips the coin 500 times.

17. It is essential in the manufacture of machinery to utilize parts that conform to specifications. In the past, diameters of the ball bearings produced by a certain manufacturer had a variance of 0.00156. To cut costs, the manufacturer instituted a less expensive production method. The variance of the diameters of 101 randomly sampled bearings produced by the new process was 0.0021. Does the data provide sufficient evidence to indicate that the diameters of ball bearings produced by the new process are more variable than those produced by the old process? Test using $\alpha = 0.10$.

18. A national news magazine is interested in the proportion of counties in which the cost of living has decreased in the past 24 months. The news magazine believes that the true proportion is less than 30%. In a random sample of 100 counties, 20 counties had cost of living decreases.

   a.   Test the news magazine's claim at $\alpha = 0.08$.

   b.   Find the P-value for this test.

19. An increasing number of businesses are offering child-care benefits for their workers. However, one union claims that more than 90% of firms in the manufacturing sector still do not offer any child-care benefits to their workers. A random sample of 350 manufacturing firms is selected, and only 28 of them offer child-care benefits.

    a. Does this sample result support the claim of the union? Test using $\alpha = 0.10$.

    b. Calculate the P-value associated with this test.

20. During the holiday season, law enforcement officials estimated that 500 people would be killed and 25,000 injured on the nation's roads. They claimed that more than 50% of the accidents would be caused by drunk driving. A sample of 120 accidents showed that 67 were caused by drunk driving. Use this data to test their claim with $\alpha = 0.05$.

21. The quality control supervisor of a cannery is concerned about the variance of fill per can. Regulatory agencies specify that the standard deviation of the amount of fill should be less than 0.1 ounce. To determine whether the process is meeting this specification, the supervisor randomly selects ten cans, weighs the contents of each, and finds that the sample standard deviation of these measurements is 0.04. Does these data provide sufficient evidence to indicate that the variability is as small as desired? Test using $\alpha = 0.05$.

> "An honorable man will not be bullied by a hypothesis."
>
> — Bergen Evans

12 CHAPTER
Inferences about Two Samples

Introduction

Basic concepts of hypothesis testing were introduced in Chapter 11. We will continue to follow the same basic hypothesis testing procedure developed in the previous chapter. The inferential methods that were previously developed concerned one population and the value of its mean, proportion, or variance. We use the information in the sample statistics $\bar{x}$, $\hat{p}$, and s^2 to test hypotheses about the population parameters.

There are many instances in which we wish to compare two population means or two population proportions. For example, in Chapter 2 we discussed controlled experiments in which we tried to develop data that would be used to efficiently test hypotheses about two or more proportions. In this chapter, we will begin to explore methods for testing differences in means, proportions, and variances.

With respect to comparing two population means, we will develop methods for comparing two population means, and try to answer questions like the following.

- Is $\mu_1 > \mu_2$?
- Is $\mu_1 < \mu_2$?
- Is $\mu_1 = \mu_2$?

Similarly, we will develop methods for comparing two population proportions, and try to answer questions like the following.

- Is $p_1 > p_2$?
- Is $p_1 < p_2$?
- Is $p_1 = p_2$?

12.1 Inference about Two Means: Independent Samples

We developed procedures for testing a hypothesis about a single population mean in Section 11.2. In this section, procedures are developed for comparing two population means. The first procedure is used when the population variances (or standard deviations) are known and the samples are drawn from independent populations that are normally distributed or the sample size of both samples is greater than 30. The second procedure is used when the population variances (or standard deviations) are unknown and the samples are drawn from independent populations that are normally distributed or the sample sizes are greater than 30.

There are many situations where our interest is in comparing two population means or the average response of experimental units to two different treatments. For example, a medical researcher may be interested in comparing the average increase in heart rate for male babies and female babies when a particular drug is used to treat ear infections. A fleet manager may be interested in comparing the average gas mileage for two different makes of cars. A farmer may be interested in comparing the average weight gain for cattle which have been fed two different types of feed.

In each of the above situations, an experiment can be designed for sampling from two separate populations (two different makes of cars, or male babies and female babies), or the experiment can be designed for randomly assigning experimental units to two different treatments (cattle given feed #1 and cattle given feed #2).

When observations are randomly selected from two independent populations or experimental units are randomly assigned to two different treatments where the variation between experimental units is small, the sampling design is called an **independent experimental design** or a **completely randomized design**.

Inferences about the Means of Two Independent Populations, σ_1 and σ_2 Known

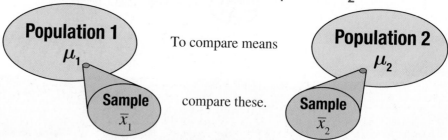

We will use the sample means $\bar{x}_1$ and $\bar{x}_2$ to compare the means of two populations. The sampling distribution for the difference between the sample averages, $\bar{x}_1 - \bar{x}_2$, has an approximately normal distribution (when an independent experimental design is used to make comparisons between two population means and the samples drawn from each population, n_1 and n_2, are "large" or both samples come from populations that are normally distributed). The properties of the sampling distribution for the difference between sample averages are given below.

Properties of the Sampling Distribution of $\bar{x}_1 - \bar{x}_2$

If $n_1 > 30$ and $n_2 > 30$, the sampling distribution of $\bar{x}_1 - \bar{x}_2$ has an approximately normal distribution. As well, the sampling distribution of $\bar{x}_1 - \bar{x}_2$ is normally distributed if both samples come from populations that are normally distributed.

$$\mu_{\bar{x}_1 - \bar{x}_2} = \mu_1 - \mu_2$$

$$\sigma_{\bar{x}_1 - \bar{x}_2} = \sqrt{\frac{\sigma_1^2}{n_1} + \frac{\sigma_2^2}{n_2}} \text{ if the two samples are independent.}$$

σ_1 and σ_2 are known.

PROPERTIES

The sampling distribution of $\bar{x}_1 - \bar{x}_2$ will be used in the development of the confidence interval and test statistic for comparing two population means.

Interval Estimation

Given the sampling distribution of $\bar{x}_1 - \bar{x}_2$, we can develop the confidence interval estimate of the difference between two population means.

$100(1 - \alpha)\%$ Confidence Interval for $\mu_1 - \mu_2$

The $100(1 - \alpha)\%$ confidence interval estimate for the difference in the population means of two independent populations is given by

$$\left(\bar{x}_1 - \bar{x}_2\right) \pm z_{\alpha/2} \sqrt{\frac{\sigma_1^2}{n_1} + \frac{\sigma_2^2}{n_2}}$$

where $z_{\alpha/2}$ is the critical value of the standard normal distribution with an area of $\alpha/2$ in the upper tail. σ_1 and σ_2 are known, and the independent samples are drawn from normally distributed populations or the samples sizes are large; i.e., $n_1 > 30$ and $n_2 > 30$.

FORMULA

Hypothesis Testing

Table 12.1.1 gives a short summary of the possible hypothesis tests that can be conducted when you want to compare two means. These choices are the same regardless of the underlying distribution of the test statistic used.

Table 12.1.1 - Hypotheses Concerning a Test About Two Means			
	Are the population means different?	Is the population mean in group 1 greater than the population mean in group 2?	Is the population mean in group 1 less than the population mean in group 2?
Null hypothesis, H_0	$\mu_1 - \mu_2 = 0$	$\mu_1 - \mu_2 = 0$	$\mu_1 - \mu_2 = 0$
Alternative Hypothesis, H_a	$\mu_1 - \mu_2 \neq 0$	$\mu_1 - \mu_2 > 0$	$\mu_1 - \mu_2 < 0$
Type of Hypothesis Test	Two-tailed	Right-tailed	Left-tailed

When comparing two population means in which the standard deviation (or variance) of both populations are known, the following procedure should be followed, taking care to make sure that the assumptions of the test are satisfied.

Testing a Hypothesis about Two Independent Population Means, σ_1 and σ_2 Known

Assumptions:

1. The samples are independent of one another.

2. Both samples are simple random samples.

3. The populations from which the two samples are drawn are normally distributed or the sample sizes are both large ($n_1 > 30$ and $n_2 > 30$).

4. The population standard deviations, σ_1 and σ_2, are known.

Test Statistic:

The test statistic for a hypothesis test about $\mu_1 - \mu_2$ is given by

$$z = \frac{\left(\overline{x}_1 - \overline{x}_2\right) - \mu_{\overline{x}_1 - \overline{x}_2}}{\sigma_{\overline{x}_1 - \overline{x}_2}} = \frac{\left(\overline{x}_1 - \overline{x}_2\right) - \overbrace{\left(\mu_1 - \mu_2\right)}^{\substack{\text{Hypothesized} \\ \text{Difference} \\ \text{in Means}}}}{\sqrt{\dfrac{\sigma_1^2}{n_1} + \dfrac{\sigma_2^2}{n_2}}}.$$

For Population 1

μ_1 = the population mean,

σ_1 = the population standard deviation,

n_1 = the sample size, and

$\overline{x}_1$ = the sample mean.

For Population 2

μ_2 = the population mean,

σ_2 = the population standard deviation,

n_2 = the sample size, and

$\overline{x}_2$ = the sample mean.

Note that $\mu_1 - \mu_2$ represents the hypothesized difference between the population means and that the z-statistic follows the standard normal distribution.

PROCEDURE

In Example 12.1.1 we will construct a confidence interval and perform a hypothesis test for comparing two population means.

Example 12.1.1

A telecommunications analyst is interested in knowing if there is a significant difference in the average service outage times between cable television subscribers and satellite television subscribers. She randomly selects 50 cable subscribers and 50 satellite subscribers for the study. She gives each subscriber a survey and asks them to record the length of time of each service outage for a month. She summarizes the results of the survey and calculates the mean outage for each television service. The results of the study are shown in the following table.

Service Outage Time (in minutes)			
	n	$\bar{x}$	σ
Cable	50	8.8	3
Satellite	50	9.5	2

a. Calculate a 95% confidence interval for the mean difference in average service outage time between cable and satellite subscribers.

b. Is there persuasive evidence for the analyst to conclude at $\alpha = 0.05$ that there is a difference in mean service outage time between cable and satellite subscribers?

Solution

a. From the information given in the problem, we know the following.

$$n_1 = 50,\ n_2 = 50,\ \sigma_1 = 3,\ \sigma_2 = 2,\ \bar{x}_1 = 8.8,\ \text{and}\ \bar{x}_2 = 9.5$$

Since both sample sizes are greater than 30, we can invoke the Central Limit Theorem and assume that the sample means are approximately normally distributed.

☑ Independent random samples

☑ The samples sizes are large ($n_1 > 30$ and $n_2 > 30$).

☑ σ_1 and σ_2 are known   or   ☐ σ_1 and σ_2 are unknown

Since we want a 95% confidence interval, we need to find the value of $z_{\alpha/2}$. Remember that $z_{\alpha/2}$ represents the z-value required to obtain an area of $(1-\alpha)$ centered under the standard normal curve. For a 95% confidence interval, $\alpha = 0.05$ and therefore, $z_{\alpha/2} = z_{0.025} = 1.96$.

A 95% confidence interval for the difference in the average service outage time between cable and satellite providers is given by

$$\left(\bar{x}_1 - \bar{x}_2\right) \pm z_{\alpha/2}\sqrt{\frac{s_1^2}{n_1} + \frac{s_2^2}{n_2}}.$$

This gives,

$$\left(8.8 - 9.5\right) \pm 1.96\sqrt{\frac{3^2}{50} + \frac{2^2}{50}}$$

$$-0.7 \pm 1.96\sqrt{\frac{13}{50}}$$

$$-1.7 \text{ to } 0.3.$$

Thus, we are 95% confident that the true mean difference in service outage time between cable and satellite subscribers is between -1.7 and 0.3 minutes. Since the confidence interval includes zero, this indicates that the difference in the average service outage time between cable and satellite subscribers is not statistically significant at the 0.05 level.

⌘ Technology

A confidence interval for the difference between two means when the population standard deviations are known can be calculated on the TI-83/84 Plus calculator using the 2-SampZInt function. For instructions please visit stat.hawkeslearning.com and navigate to **Technology Instructions > Confidence Intervals > Two Sample z-Interval.**

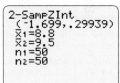

b.   The steps for the hypothesis test are as follows.

Step 1: Determine the null and alternative hypotheses.

Null Hypothesis: There is no difference in average service outage time between cable and satellite subscribers.

Alternative Hypothesis: There is a difference in average service outage time between cable and satellite subscribers.

Since the analyst is interested in comparing the average service outage time between cable and satellite subscribers, the appropriate statistical measures are the following.

μ_1 = the true mean service outage time for cable subscribers

μ_2 = the true mean service outage time for satellite subscribers

The analyst is interested in whether or not there is a difference in the average service outage time between cable and satellite subscribers. Thus, the alternative hypothesis is two-sided and the test is two-tailed.

Since the analyst is interested in comparing the two population means, a natural way to make this comparison is to look at the difference between the two population means. Hence the null and alternative hypotheses are formulated as follows.

$H_0: \mu_1 - \mu_2 = 0$ There is no difference in average service outage time.

$H_a: \mu_1 - \mu_2 \neq 0$ There is a difference in average service outage time.

In this situation, the hypothesized difference in average service outage time is 0. However, it is possible to be interested in nonzero differences. For example, if the analyst had been interested in testing if the difference in average service outage time was one minute, the hypothesized difference would have been one.

Step 2: Specify the significance level α.

The level of the test is specified in the problem as $\alpha = 0.05$.

Step 3: Validate the assumptions of the hypothesis test, identify the appropriate test statistic and compute its value.

The assumptions for the test were validated in part **a.**

The difference in sample means, $\bar{x}_1 - \bar{x}_2$, is an unbiased point estimate of the difference in population means, $\mu_1 - \mu_2$. The sampling distribution for the point estimate, $\bar{x}_1 - \bar{x}_2$, provides essential information for determining the test statistic. If $n_1 > 30$ and $n_2 > 30$ and an independent experimental design is used, the sampling distribution of $\bar{x}_1 - \bar{x}_2$ has an approximately normal distribution with mean, $\mu_{\bar{x}_1 - \bar{x}_2} = \mu_1 - \mu_2$, and standard deviation,

$$\sigma_{\bar{x}_1 - \bar{x}_2} = \sqrt{\frac{\sigma_1^2}{n_1} + \frac{\sigma_2^2}{n_2}}.$$

Thus, the test statistic is a standard normal random variable which is calculated by using the familiar z-transformation. The test statistic is given by

$$z = \frac{(\bar{x}_1 - \bar{x}_2) - \mu_{\bar{x}_1 - \bar{x}_2}}{\sigma_{\bar{x}_1 - \bar{x}_2}} = \frac{(\bar{x}_1 - \bar{x}_2) - \overbrace{(\mu_1 - \mu_2)}^{\substack{\text{Hypothesized}\\\text{Difference}\\\text{in Means}}}}{\sqrt{\dfrac{\sigma_1^2}{n_1} + \dfrac{\sigma_2^2}{n_2}}}.$$

Note

Recall that this is similar to our initial discussion of z-scores in Chapter 4:
$$z = \frac{\bar{x} - \mu}{\sigma}.$$

If the null hypothesis is true, z has an approximately normal distribution. If the observed value of $\bar{x}_1 - \bar{x}_2$ is significantly larger or smaller than $\mu_1 - \mu_2$, the hypothesized value of the difference, this will produce a large or small value of the test statistic, causing us to doubt whether or not the null hypothesis is in fact true. How large is *large*? This is answered by the critical value of the test statistic specified in **Step 4**.

Based on the data in the table, the computed value of the test statistic is given by

$$z = \frac{(8.8 - 9.5) - 0}{\sqrt{\dfrac{3^2}{50} + \dfrac{2^2}{50}}} \approx -1.373.$$

Step 4: Determine the critical value(s) or *P*-value.

The role of the critical value(s) in this test is exactly the same as for all of the hypothesis tests discussed earlier. It defines a range of values for the test statistic, the rejection region, that will be so rare that it is unlikely that the test statistic occurred from ordinary sampling variability, assuming the null is true. The level of the test defines the size of the rejection region. Should the computed value of the test statistic fall within the rejection region, the null hypothesis will be rejected.

If the null hypothesis is true, the test statistic has an approximately normal distribution. Thus the critical value is determined in the same way as for the other tests of hypothesis in which the test statistic had an approximately normal distribution. The rejection region for a two-tailed test with level of significance, $\alpha = 0.05$, is displayed in the figure below.

☁ **Technology**

To do a two-sample hypothesis test between two means when the population standard deviations are known can be calculated on the TI-83/84 Plus calculator using the 2-SampZTest function. For instructions please visit stat.hawkeslearning.com and navigate to **Technology Instructions > Hypothesis Testing > Two-Sample z-Test.**

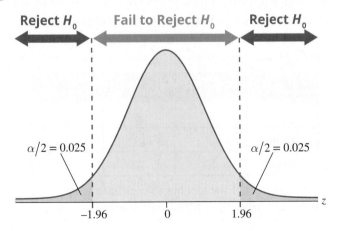

The null hypothesis will be rejected if the computed value of the test statistic is greater than or equal to 1.96 or less than or equal to -1.96. In other words, we will reject the null hypothesis if the observed difference in the average service outage time is at least 1.96 standard deviations above or below the hypothesized value of 0 (no difference in service outage time between cable and satellite).

The P-value for the test statistic of -1.373 can be obtained from the normal table, or more easily using technology, and is approximately 0.1698.

Step 5: Make the decision to reject or fail to reject H_0.

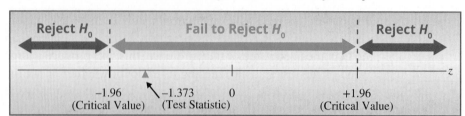

Note

Remember that you can use either P-values or rejection regions to make a decision in a hypothesis test. The examples will show you both methods but you need only use one of them.

As shown above, the calculated value of the test statistic does not fall in the rejection region because -1.373 falls between the critical values -1.96 and 1.96. There is insufficient evidence to conclude that the difference between the observed value and the hypothesized value is due to anything other than ordinary sampling variation. Thus, we fail to reject the null hypothesis at $\alpha = 0.05$.

Since the P-value of 0.1698 is greater than $\alpha = 0.05$, we fail to reject the null hypothesis.

Step 6: State the conclusion in terms of the original problem.

There is not sufficient evidence at the 0.05 level to conclude that the average service outage time is significantly different between cable and satellite television subscribers.

The following is another example of performing a hypothesis test about two population means, but with a one-sided alternative hypothesis.

Example 12.1.2

An elementary school teacher is interested in knowing if fifth-grade girls take longer to read a passage from a book than fifth-grade boys. She randomly selects 40 fifth-grade boys and 40 fifth-grade girls for the study. She gives each student several pages of the same σ book to read. The time it takes each group to complete the reading is recorded in minutes. The results of the study are shown in the following table.

Reading Times (in minutes)			
	n	$\bar{x}$	σ
Girls	40	11	2
Boys	40	10	3

Is there persuasive evidence for the teacher to conclude at $\alpha = 0.05$ that fifth-grade girls have longer reading times than fifth-grade boys?

Solution

Step 1: Determine the null and alternative hypotheses.

State the hypotheses in plain English.

Null Hypothesis: There is no difference in the average reading time of fifth-grade boys and girls.

Alternative Hypothesis: The average reading time of fifth-grade girls is longer than that of fifth-grade boys.

Since the teacher is interested in comparing the *average* reading time of fifth grade boys and fifth grade girls, the appropriate statistical measures are:

μ_1 = the true average reading time of fifth-grade girls;

μ_2 = the true average reading time of fifth-grade boys.

The teacher's interest is in whether the average reading time of fifth-grade girls is longer than that of fifth-grade boys. Thus, this test is one-sided and the null and alternative hypotheses are formulated as follows.

$H_0: \mu_1 - \mu_2 = 0$ There is no difference in average reading times.

$H_a: \mu_1 - \mu_2 > 0$ The average reading time of fifth-grade girls is longer.

Step 2: Specify the significance level α.

The level of the test is specified in the problem as $\alpha = 0.05$.

Step 3: Validate the assumptions of the hypothesis test, identify the appropriate test statistic and compute its value.

- ☑ Independent random samples
- ☑ The samples sizes are large ($n_1 > 30$ and $n_2 > 30$).
- ☑ σ_1 and σ_2 are known   or   ☐ σ_1 and σ_2 are unknown

The test statistic is the standard normal random variable which is calculated by using the familiar z-transformation. The test statistic is as follows.

$$z = \frac{\left(\overline{x}_1 - \overline{x}_2\right) - \mu_{\overline{x}_1 - \overline{x}_2}}{\sigma_{\overline{x}_1 - \overline{x}_2}} = \frac{\left(\overline{x}_1 - \overline{x}_2\right) - \overbrace{\left(\mu_1 - \mu_2\right)}^{\substack{\text{Hypothesized} \\ \text{Difference} \\ \text{in Means}}}}{\sqrt{\dfrac{\sigma_1^2}{n_1} + \dfrac{\sigma_2^2}{n_2}}}.$$

Based on the data in the table, the computed value of the test statistic is given by

$$z = \frac{11 - 10 - 0}{\sqrt{\dfrac{2^2}{40} + \dfrac{3^2}{40}}} \approx 1.754.$$

☁ Technology

A two-sample hypothesis test between two means when the population standard deviations are known can be calculated on the TI-83/84 Plus calculator using the 2-SampZTest function. For instructions please visit stat.hawkeslearning.com and navigate to **Technology Instructions > Hypothesis Testing > Two-Sample z-Test.**

```
2-SampZTest
 μ1>μ2
 z=1.754116039
 p=.0397052687
 x̄1=11
 x̄2=10
↓n1=40
```

Note

Testing $\mu_1 - \mu_2 = 0$ is the same as testing that the two means are equal. Therefore an alternate form of these hypotheses are $H_0: \mu_1 = \mu_2$, $H_a: \mu_1 \neq \mu_2$.

Step 4: Determine the critical value(s) or *P*-value.

Fail to Reject *H*₀   **Reject *H*₀**

$\alpha = 0.05$

0   1.645 z

If the null hypothesis is true, the test statistic has an approximately normal distribution. Thus the critical value is determined in the same way as for the other tests of hypothesis in which the test statistic had an approximately normal distribution.

The rejection region for a one-sided test with level of significance $\alpha = 0.05$ is displayed above.

The null hypothesis will be rejected if the computed value of the test statistic is larger than 1.645. In other words, we will reject the null hypothesis if the observed difference in average reading time is at least 1.645 standard deviations above the hypothesized value of 0 (no difference in reading time).

The *P*-value for the test statistic of 1.754 can be obtained from the normal table or using technology and is approximately 0.0397.

Step 5: Make the decision to reject or fail to reject *H*₀.

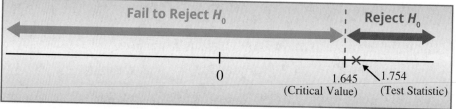

Fail to Reject *H*₀   **Reject *H*₀**

0   1.645   1.754
(Critical Value)   (Test Statistic)

As shown in the figure above, the calculated value of the test statistic falls in the rejection region because 1.754 is greater than 1.645. There is sufficient evidence to conclude that the difference between the observed value and the hypothesized value is due to something other than ordinary sampling variation. Thus, we reject the null hypothesis at $\alpha = 0.05$.

Since the *P*-value of 0.0397 is less than $\alpha = 0.05$, we can also reject the null hypothesis.

Step 6: State the conclusion in terms of the original problem.

There is sufficient evidence at $\alpha = 0.05$ to conclude that the average reading time is significantly higher for fifth-grade girls.

Inferences About the Mean of Two Independent Populations, σ_1 and σ_2 Unknown and Assumed Equal

In actuality, it is rare that the population standard deviations would be known, but the means unknown. It is still possible to make comparisons between two population means if the population standard deviations are unknown and either the populations are (approximately) normally distributed or the samples are large.

Even when the values of σ_1 and σ_2 are not known, it can be assumed that they have the same value and the sample variances can be averaged or *pooled* to better estimate the common population variance. To examine the equal variance assumption, we can compare the variances of the samples drawn from the populations using box plots of the data from each of the distributions and looking at the spread of the box plots. If the spread (difference between Q_1 and Q_3) of the box plots looks approximately the same, it is reasonable to assume that the variances of the two distributions are approximately equal. Figure 12.1.1 displays two box plots of sample data from populations with approximately equal variances, but with slightly different means.

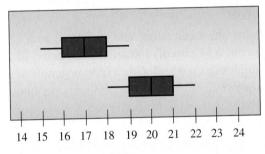

Figure 12.1.1

Interval Estimation

Assumptions

1. The samples are independent of one another.

2. Both samples are simple random samples.

3. The populations from which the two samples are drawn are approximately normally distributed or the sample sizes are both large ($n_1 > 30$ and $n_2 > 30$).

4. The values of σ_1 and σ_2 are unknown but assumed equal.

ASSUMPTIONS

> ### 100(1 − α)% Confidence Interval for $\mu_1 - \mu_2$ Assuming σ_1 and σ_2 are Unknown but Equal
>
> Assuming equal population standard deviations, the $100(1 - \alpha)\%$ interval estimate for the difference between two population means if σ_1 and σ_2 are unknown is given by
>
> $$\left(\bar{x}_1 - \bar{x}_2\right) \pm t_{\alpha/2} \sqrt{s_p^2 \left(\frac{1}{n_1} + \frac{1}{n_2}\right)}$$
>
> where $s_p^2 = \dfrac{(n_1 - 1)s_1^2 + (n_2 - 1)s_2^2}{n_1 + n_2 - 2}$ is the **pooled sample variance** and $t_{\alpha/2}$ is the critical value of the t-distribution with $n_1 + n_2 - 2$ degrees of freedom, capturing an area of $\alpha/2$ in the upper tail.
>
> **FORMULA**

Example 12.1.3

For a consumer product, the mean dollar sales per retail outlet last year in a random sample of 15 stores was $3425 with a standard deviation of $200. For a second product, the mean dollar sales per outlet in a random sample of 16 stores was $3250 with a standard deviation of $175. The sales amounts per outlet are assumed to be approximately normally distributed for both products. Assume that the population variances are equal.

Retail Sales (Dollars)			
	n	**$\bar{x}$**	**s**
Product 1	15	$3425	200
Product 2	16	$3250	175

Calculate a 95% confidence interval for the difference in average dollar sales between the two products.

Solution

From the information given in the problem, we know that

$$n_1 = 15, \; n_2 = 16, \; s_1 = 200, \; s_2 = 175, \; \bar{x}_1 = \$3425, \text{ and } \bar{x}_2 = \$3250.$$

☑ Independent random samples (assumed)

☑ The two samples are drawn from populations that are approximately normally distributed.

☐ σ_1 and σ_2 are known   or   ☑ σ_1 and σ_2 are unknown

☑ The population standard deviations are assumed equal.

Since we have assumed that the samples are drawn from normally distributed populations and that the population variances are equal, we will use the t-distribution and calculate the pooled standard deviation of the two samples. Since we want a 95% confidence interval, we need to find the value of $t_{\alpha/2}$. Note that $df = n_1 + n_2 - 2 = 15 + 16 - 2 = 29$. Thus, $t_{0.025} = 2.045$ is the critical value for a t-distribution with 29 degrees of freedom.

A 95% confidence interval for the difference in average dollar sales between the two products is given by

$$\left(\overline{x}_1 - \overline{x}_2\right) \pm t_{\alpha/2}\sqrt{s_p^2\left(\frac{1}{n_1} + \frac{1}{n_2}\right)} \text{ where } s_p^2 = \frac{\left(n_1 - 1\right)s_1^2 + \left(n_2 - 1\right)s_2^2}{n_1 + n_2 - 2}.$$

First we need to calculate s_p^2.

$$s_p^2 = \frac{(15-1)200^2 + (16-1)175^2}{15 + 16 - 2} \approx 35150.86207$$

The confidence interval is then calculated as follows.

$$(3425 - 3250) \pm 2.045\sqrt{35150.8621\left(\tfrac{1}{15} + \tfrac{1}{16}\right)}$$

$$175 \pm 2.045\sqrt{35150.8621\left(\tfrac{1}{15} + \tfrac{1}{16}\right)}$$

$$37.20 \text{ to } 312.80$$

Thus, we are 95% confident that the true mean difference in dollar sales between Product 1 and Product 2 is between $37.20 and $312.80. That is, on average, Product 1 generates between $37.20 and $312.80 more dollar sales than Product 2.

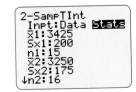

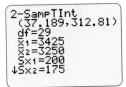

Technology

A confidence interval for the difference between two means when the population standard deviations are unknown and assumed equal can be calculated on the TI-83/84 Plus using the 2-SampTInt function.

For instructions please visit stat.hawkeslearning.com and navigate to **Technology Instructions > Confidence Intervals > Two Sample _t_-Interval.**

Hypothesis Testing

Testing a Hypothesis about Two Independent Population Means, σ_1 and σ_2 Unknown but Equal

Assumptions:

1. The samples are independent of one another.

2. Both samples are simple random samples.

3. The populations from which the two samples are drawn are normally distributed or the sample sizes are both large ($n_1 > 30$ and $n_2 > 30$).

4. Both of the populations have approximately equal, but unknown standard deviations, i.e., $\sigma_1 = \sigma_2 = \sigma$.

Continued…

PROCEDURE

Testing a Hypothesis about Two Independent Population Means, σ_1 and σ_2 Unknown but Equal (Continued)

Test Statistic:

If the assumptions outlined above are satisfied, the sampling distribution of $\bar{x}_1 - \bar{x}_2$ has a t-distribution with $n_1 + n_2 - 2$ degrees of freedom. The t-test statistic is given by

$$t = \frac{(\bar{x}_1 - \bar{x}_2) - (\mu_1 - \mu_2)}{\sqrt{s_p^2\left(\dfrac{1}{n_1} + \dfrac{1}{n_2}\right)}},$$

where $s_p^2 = \dfrac{(n_1 - 1)s_1^2 + (n_2 - 1)s_2^2}{n_1 + n_2 - 2}$ is the **pooled sample variance**.

For Population 1	For Population 2
μ_1 = the population mean,	μ_2 = the population mean,
σ_1 = the population standard deviation,	σ_2 = the population standard deviation,
n_1 = the sample size,	n_2 = the sample size,
$\bar{x}_1$ = the sample mean, and	$\bar{x}_2$ = the sample mean, and
s_1 = the sample standard deviation.	s_2 = the sample standard deviation.

PROCEDURE

Providing the assumptions above have been met, the test procedure developed in Example 12.1.4 may be used for making comparisons between two population means.

Example 12.1.4

A cancer researcher believes that there may be an increase in the life expectancy of women diagnosed with terminal breast cancer if they attend group therapy to discuss their illness. He randomly selects 40 women with breast cancer. Twenty of the women are randomly assigned to a group that attends a group therapy session one day per week. The other 20 women do not attend therapy and are designated as the control group. The life expectancy, in number of years, from diagnosis until death is measured for each of the women. The results of the study are shown in the following tables.

Is there persuasive evidence for the researcher to conclude at $\alpha = 0.05$ that the average life expectancy from diagnosis until death is significantly longer for women diagnosed with terminal breast cancer who attend group therapy once per week than those who do not attend group therapy?

Summary Statistics	
Women in Therapy	**Women Not in Therapy**
$n_1 = 20$	$n_2 = 20$
$\bar{x}_1 = 3.8$	$\bar{x}_2 = 2.0$
$s_1 = 0.6$	$s_2 = 0.5$

Women in Therapy				
4.7	3.8	4	3.5	3.3
2.9	3.5	4.2	2.8	3.1
4.7	4.4	3.4	3.2	4.1
4.2	3.7	3.4	3.6	4.8

Women Not in Therapy				
2.0	2.3	2.7	1.8	1.2
1.6	1.7	2.4	1.5	1.6
1.9	2.5	1.7	1.1	2.9
2.4	2.2	1.4	2.2	2.1

Solution

Step 1: Determine the null and alternative hypotheses.

Null Hypothesis: There is no difference in average life expectancy from diagnosis until death for women with terminal breast cancer whether or not they attend therapy.

Alternative Hypothesis: For women who have been diagnosed with terminal breast cancer the average life expectancy from diagnosis until death is greater for those women who attend weekly group therapy meetings than those who do not.

Since the researcher is interested in comparing the *average* life expectancies from diagnosis until death for each of the groups, the appropriate statistical measures are

μ_1 = the true average life expectancy from diagnosis until death for women diagnosed with terminal breast cancer who attend weekly group therapy;

μ_2 = the true average life expectancy from diagnosis until death for women diagnosed with terminal breast cancer who do not attend weekly group therapy.

Since the researcher's interest is in whether or not the average life expectancy is *higher* for women who attend group therapy than those who don't, this test is a one-sided test.

The researcher is interested in determining if the average life expectancy is higher for the women in the therapy group, μ_1, versus those in the control group, μ_2. A way to state this in terms of the statistical measures in **Step 2** is $\mu_1 > \mu_2$. But in order to perform the hypothesis test, this statement must be rewritten in a form for which we have a point estimate, or $\mu_1 - \mu_2 > 0$. The resulting hypotheses in symbolic notation are as follows.

$H_0: \mu_1 - \mu_2 = 0$ There is no difference in average life expectancy for the two groups.

$H_a: \mu_1 - \mu_2 > 0$ The life expectancy is larger for the group who attend weekly therapy than for those who do not attend therapy.

Step 2: Specify the significance level α.

The level of the test is specified in the problem as $\alpha = 0.05$.

Step 3:   Validate the assumptions of the hypothesis test, identify the appropriate test statistic and compute its value.

To develop the appropriate test statistic, a random variable whose value will be used to make the decision to reject or fail to reject H_0 must be found. The sampling distribution $\bar{x}_1 - \bar{x}_2$ provides essential information in assessing the rareness of the test statistic. Two questions must be answered in order to use the test statistic from the previous example. *Are the samples taken from populations with normal distributions? Are the variances approximately equal?* The normal probability plots of the two data sets do not show any severe departure from normality for either sample. The box plots indicate that the spread of the two samples is similar. Thus we can use a *t*-distribution and pool the variances of the two samples. This combined sample variance is referred to as the pooled variance, s_p^2.

Technology

To create a normal probability plot in Excel for a set of data, please visit stat.hawkeslearning.com and navigate to **Technology Instructions > Graphs > Normal Probability Plot.**

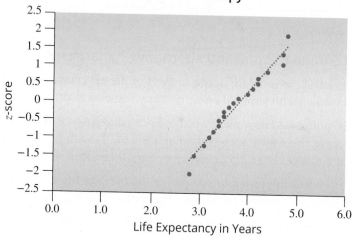

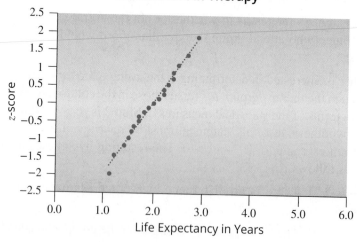

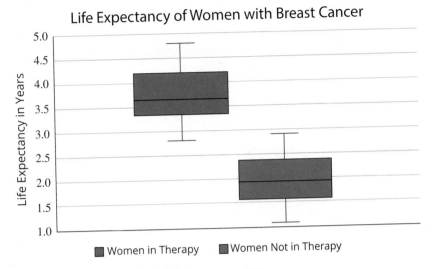

Life Expectancy of Women with Breast Cancer

■ Women in Therapy   ■ Women Not in Therapy

Therefore, the assumptions for the test are as follows:

☑ Independent random samples

☑ The two samples are drawn from populations that are approximately normally distributed.

☐ σ_1 and σ_2 are known   or   ☑ σ_1 and σ_2 are unknown

☑ The population standard deviations are assumed equal.

If the null hypothesis is true, t has a t-distribution with $n_1 + n_2 - 2$ degrees of freedom. If the observed value of $\bar{x}_1 - \bar{x}_2$ is significantly larger than the hypothesized value of the difference (H_0: $\mu_1 - \mu_2 = 0$), this will produce a large value of the test statistic, causing us to doubt whether or not the null hypothesis is in fact true. How large is large? The critical value of the test statistic specified in **Step 4** will implicitly define the notion of "large."

Based on the data given to us in the problem, the computed value of the test statistic is

$$t = \frac{(3.8 - 2.0) - 0}{\sqrt{0.305\left(\frac{1}{20} + \frac{1}{20}\right)}} = 10.307, \text{ where } s_p^2 = \frac{19(0.6)^2 + 19(0.5)^2}{20 + 20 - 2} = 0.305.$$

Step 4: Determine the critical value(s) or *P*-value.

The role of the critical value in this test is exactly the same as for all of the hypothesis tests discussed earlier. It defines a range of values for the test statistic, the rejection region, that will be so rare that it is unlikely that values in this range occurred from ordinary sampling variability if the null hypothesis is true. The level of the test defines the size of the rejection region. Should the computed value of the test statistic fall in the rejection region, we will presume that the value of the test statistic is too large to have occurred from ordinary sampling variation, and the null hypothesis will be rejected.

If the null hypothesis and the assumptions of the hypothesis testing model are true, the test statistic has a t-distribution. Thus, the critical value is determined in the same way as for the other tests of hypothesis where the test statistic had a t-distribution, except that the degrees of freedom are $n_1 + n_2 - 2$, or 38 (20 + 20 − 2). The rejection region corresponding to the alternative hypothesis, H_a: $\mu_1 - \mu_2 > 0$, with $\alpha = 0.05$ for a t-test statistic with 38 degrees of freedom is given in the following figure.

∽ **Technology**

To perform a hypothesis test for the difference between two means when the population standard deviations are unknown and assumed equal on the TI-83/84 Plus use the 2-SampTTest function.

For instructions please visit stat.hawkeslearning.com and navigate to **Technology Instructions > Hypothesis Testing > Two Sample t-Test.**

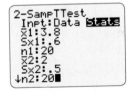

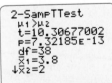

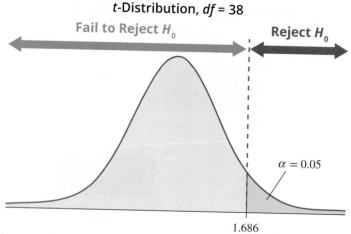

We will reject the null hypothesis if the computed value of the test statistic is larger than 1.686. Also, note that the P-value is extremely small for the test statistic value of 10.307; it is approximately 0.

Step 5: Make the decision to reject or fail to reject H_0.

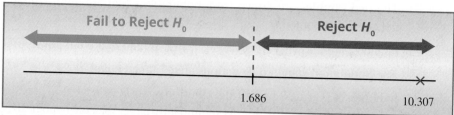

As displayed in the figure above, the value of the test statistic does fall in the rejection region. In fact, a test statistic of 10.307 says that the observed difference between the means is over 10 standard deviations higher than the hypothesized difference of zero. It is highly unlikely that the difference between the observed value and the hypothesized value is due to ordinary sampling variation. The P-value is less than 0.05, thus we reject the null hypothesis using the P-value approach as well.

Step 6: State the conclusion in terms of the original problem.

There is sufficient evidence for the researcher to conclude that the average life expectancy from diagnosis until death for women diagnosed with terminal breast cancer is significantly longer for those women who attend therapy once a week than for those who don't.

Inferences about the Means of Two Independent Populations, σ_1 and σ_2 Unknown and Assumed Unequal

The assumptions for the test where the unknown population standard deviations are assumed to be unequal are outlined here.

Assumptions

1. The samples are independent of one another.

2. Both samples are simple random samples.

3. The populations from which the two samples are drawn are approximately normally distributed or the sample sizes are both large ($n_1 > 30$ and $n_2 > 30$).

4. The values of σ_1 and σ_2 are unknown and we do not assume they are equal.

ASSUMPTIONS

Interval Estimation

We can use an interval estimate to determine the difference in two population means. Previously, we used the following interval estimate for the case when σ_1 and σ_2 were known and either the samples were drawn from normal populations or the sample sizes n_1 and n_2 were greater than 30

$$\left(\overline{x}_1 - \overline{x}_2\right) \pm z_{\alpha/2} \sqrt{\frac{\sigma_1^2}{n_1} + \frac{\sigma_2^2}{n_2}}.$$

Assuming that the population standard deviations, σ_1 and σ_2 are unknown, we will use the sample standard deviations, s_1 and s_2 to estimate the population standard deviations.

$100(1 - \alpha)$% Confidence Interval for $\mu_1 - \mu_2$ Assuming σ_1 and σ_2 are Unknown and Unequal

Assuming unequal population standard deviations, the $100(1 - \alpha)$% interval estimate for the difference between two population means if σ_1 and σ_2 are unknown is given by

$$\left(\overline{x}_1 - \overline{x}_2\right) \pm t_{\alpha/2} \sqrt{\left(\frac{s_1^2}{n_1} + \frac{s_2^2}{n_2}\right)}$$

where $t_{\alpha/2}$ is the critical value of the t-distribution capturing an area of $\alpha/2$ in the upper tail.

Degrees of Freedom

There are two options for determining the degrees of freedom for the t-distribution when the population standard deviations are assumed to be unequal. Although the two methods usually result in different values for the degrees of freedom, the conclusion reached in the hypothesis test is seldom affected by the option selected.

FORMULA

Note

Option 1 is often the easiest method for determining the degrees of freedom and results in a conservative estimate for the critical value(s) or *P*-value.

Note

The calculation of the degrees of freedom as shown in Option 2 is known as Satterthwaite's Approximation.[1]

100(1 − α)% Confidence Interval for $\mu_1 - \mu_2$ Assuming σ_1 and σ_2 are Unknown and Unequal (continued)

Option 1: Use the smaller of $n_1 - 1$ and $n_2 - 1$ for the degrees of freedom.

Option 2: Use the following formula to calculate the degrees of freedom.

$$df = \frac{\left(\dfrac{s_1^2}{n_1} + \dfrac{s_2^2}{n_2}\right)^2}{\dfrac{1}{n_1 - 1}\left(\dfrac{s_1^2}{n_1}\right)^2 + \dfrac{1}{n_2 - 1}\left(\dfrac{s_2^2}{n_2}\right)^2}$$

The calculation for degrees of freedom should be rounded down to the nearest integer.

FORMULA

Example 12.1.5

A statistics instructor wants to know if using the courseware that accompanied her statistics textbook will improve students' test scores. Since she is teaching two sections of a statistics course this term, she decides to use the courseware in one class and not the other. The courseware contained premade homework assignments for each section of the book, so she had the students in one of her classes do the online homework. For the other class she gave them a similar homework assignment from the textbook.

The instructor believes that the immediate feedback from the online courseware on homework assignments will likely improve students' performance on tests. For the first test she gave the students in both classes the same test. She took a simple random sample of 16 students' test scores on the first test from each class. One student subsequently dropped the class, so that student's test score was omitted from the data. The results were as follows.

Test Scores Using Courseware									Test Scores Not Using Courseware							
73	75	76	78	78	80	82	83		60	62	65	67	72	74	74	75
84	85	87	88	88	92	93			77	79	79	80	81	85	88	93

Calculate a 95 % confidence interval for the mean difference between the test scores for the two statistics classes.

Solution

Before calculating the confidence interval we must first check that the assumptions have been satisfied. The samples were simple random samples taken from two statistics classes containing a different set of students, so the samples are independent of one another.

A normal probability plot of each sample is shown below. The plots do not show any significant departures from normality for either sample.

↪ Technology

To create a normal probability plot in Excel for a set of data, please visit stat.hawkeslearning.com and navigate to **Technology Instructions > Graphs > Normal Probability Plot.**

Test Scores Using Courseware

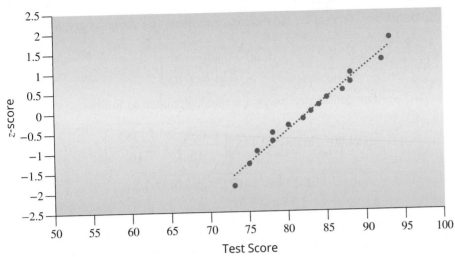

Test Scores Not Using Courseware

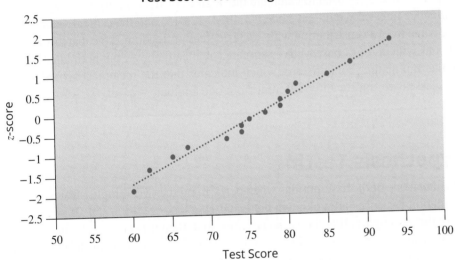

☑ Independent random samples

☑ The two samples are drawn from populations that are approximately normally distributed.

☐ σ_1 and σ_2 are known   or   ☑ σ_1 and σ_2 are unknown

☑ The population standard deviations are assumed to be unequal.

Now we can proceed to calculate the confidence interval estimate for the difference in mean test scores between the two classes. By calculating the summary statistics for each set of data above, we find that

$$n_1 = 15, \ n_2 = 16, \ s_1 = 6.1202, \ s_2 = 9.1340, \ \bar{x}_1 = 82.80, \ \text{and} \ \bar{x}_2 = 75.69.$$

Since the samples are drawn from normally distributed populations we will use the t-distribution to find the critical value for the confidence interval. Since we want a 95% confidence interval, we need to find the value of $t_{\alpha/2}$.

For the degrees of freedom for the t-distribution, we will use Option 1. The degrees of freedom will be the smaller of $n_1 - 1 = 15 - 1 = 14$ or $n_2 - 1 = 16 - 1 = 15$.

⊗ **Technology**

The confidence interval for the difference between two means when the population standard deviations are unknown and unequal, and Option 2 is used for the degrees of freedom, can be calculated on the TI-83/84 Plus using the `2-SampTInt` function. Note we are using `Pooled:` `No` since the variances are not assumed to be equal. The screen shots here were obtained using the summary statistics, so if you input the actual data you may get a slightly different answer. For instructions please visit stat.hawkeslearning.com and navigate to **Technology Instructions > Confidence Intervals > Two Sample t-Interval.**

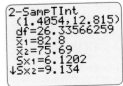

Therefore, the critical value for a t-distribution with 14 degrees of freedom and $\alpha = 1 - 0.95 = 0.05$ is $t_{0.025} = 2.145$.

A 95% confidence interval for the difference in mean test scores is given by

$$\left(\overline{x}_1 - \overline{x}_2 \right) \pm t_{0.025} \sqrt{\left(\frac{s_1^2}{n_1} + \frac{s_2^2}{n_2} \right)}.$$

The confidence interval is then calculated as follows.

$$(82.80 - 75.69) \pm 2.145 \sqrt{\left(\frac{6.1202^2}{15} + \frac{9.1340^2}{16} \right)}$$

$$7.11 \pm 2.145 \sqrt{2.49712 + 5.21437}$$

$$1.15 \text{ to } 13.07$$

Thus, we are 95% confident that the true mean difference in test scores is between 1.15 and 13.07. That is, on average, using the courseware resulted in an increase in the score on the first test between 1.15 and 13.07 points.

If Option 2 had been used to calculate the degrees of freedom for the test, the 95% confidence interval would have been (1.4054, 12.815) and the critical value would have come from a t-distribution with 26.34 degrees of freedom. Note that this interval is not as wide as our conservative estimate calculated above, but both intervals are similar and neither contain zero, which indicates that the mean test scores for the two classes are significantly different from one another.

Hypothesis Testing

Recall that one of the assumptions when performing the two-sample t-test is that the population variances are unknown but equal $\left(\text{that is, } \sigma_1^2 = \sigma_2^2 = \sigma^2 \right)$. If you cannot make the assumption that the variances are equal, then it is not appropriate to pool the two sample variances into one common variance, s_p^2. Instead the test procedure uses the two separate sample variances to calculate the standard error of the test statistic. The computations for the test statistic are shown in the following procedure.

Hypothesis Testing of $\mu_1 - \mu_2$ with σ_1 and σ_2 Unknown and Unequal

Assumptions:

1. The samples are independent of one another.

2. Both samples are simple random samples.

3. The populations from which the two samples are drawn are approximately normally distributed or the sample sizes are both large ($n_1 > 30$ and $n_2 > 30$).

4. The values of σ_1 and σ_2 are unknown and we do not assume they are equal.

Test Statistic:

$$t = \frac{\left(\bar{x}_1 - \bar{x}_2\right) - \left(\mu_1 - \mu_2\right)}{\sqrt{\dfrac{s_1^2}{n_1} + \dfrac{s_2^2}{n_2}}},$$

The test statistic follows a t-distribution and there are two options for calculating the degrees of freedom.

Option 1: Use the smaller of $n_1 - 1$ and $n_2 - 1$ for the degrees of freedom.

Option 2: Use the following formula to calculate the degrees of freedom.

$$df = \frac{\left(\dfrac{s_1^2}{n_1} + \dfrac{s_2^2}{n_2}\right)^2}{\dfrac{1}{n_1-1}\left(\dfrac{s_1^2}{n_1}\right)^2 + \dfrac{1}{n_2-1}\left(\dfrac{s_2^2}{n_2}\right)^2}$$

The calculation for degrees of freedom should be rounded down to the nearest integer.

PROCEDURE

Example 12.1.6

A biologist is interested in comparing the size of blue crabs in two river basins: (1) Cooper and (2) Stono River. Based on the health of the rivers, she believes the crabs in the Stono will have a higher average weight. She samples 32 crabs from the Stono River, and this sample has a mean weight of 800 g with a standard deviation of 225 g. She takes a random sample of 35 crabs from the Cooper River and finds the crabs have a mean weight of 700 g with a standard deviation of 175 g.

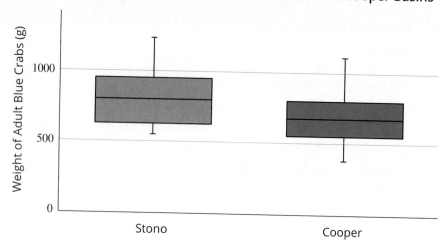

Weight of Adult Blue Crabs in the Stono and Cooper Basins

Is there persuasive evidence at $\alpha = 0.01$ in support of the biologist's belief?

Solution

Step 1: Determine the null and alternative hypotheses.

This is a one-sided test, since the biologist wants to know if the average crab weights are higher in the Stono River than the Cooper. The biologist is interesting in comparing two population means, so we formulate the null and alternative hypotheses to look at the difference between the two population means.

$H_0: \mu_1 - \mu_2 = 0$ There is no difference in average crab weight.

$H_a: \mu_1 - \mu_2 > 0$ The average crab weights in the Stono River are higher.

Step 2: Specify the significance level α.

The significance level is specified to be $\alpha = 0.01$.

Step 3: Validate the assumptions of the hypothesis test, identify the appropriate test statistic and compute its value.

Looking at the box plots, the data for each sample appears to be roughly symmetric and the variances do not appear to be equal (the spreads of the two boxes are different). Also, the samples are from independent random samples.

☑ Independent random samples

☑ The samples sizes are large ($n_1 > 30$ and $n_2 > 30$).

☐ σ_1 and σ_2 are known   or   ☑ σ_1 and σ_2 are unknown

☑ The population standard deviations are assumed unequal.

Since the assumptions are validated we can proceed with the hypothesis test. We use the t-test statistic given by

$$t = \frac{\left(\bar{x}_1 - \bar{x}_2\right) - \left(\mu_1 - \mu_2\right)}{\sqrt{\dfrac{s_1^2}{n_1} + \dfrac{s_2^2}{n_2}}}.$$

Based on the sample statistics, the computed value of the test statistic is

$$t = \frac{800 - 700 - 0}{\sqrt{\dfrac{225^2}{32} + \dfrac{175^2}{35}}} \approx 2.0174.$$

Using Option 1 for the degrees of freedom, our test statistic has $n_1 - 1 = 32 - 1 = 31$ degrees of freedom.

Step 4: Determine the critical value(s) or *P*-value.

The rejection region corresponding to the alternative hypothesis, $H_a\colon \mu_1 - \mu_2 > 0$, with $\alpha = 0.01$ for a *t*-test statistic with 31 degrees of freedom is given in the figure below.

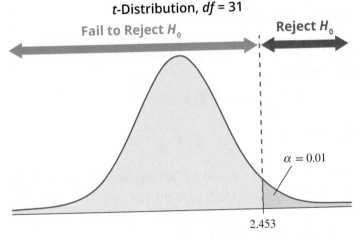

t-Distribution, *df* = 31

We will reject the null hypothesis if the computed value of the test statistic is larger than 2.453.

We find the *P*-value to be $P(t > 2.0174) \approx 0.0262$ for 31 degrees of freedom.

Step 5: Make the decision to reject or fail to reject H_0.

The value of the test statistic does not fall in the rejection region. Also, the *P*-value is greater than 0.01, so we fail to reject the null hypothesis.

Step 6: State the conclusion in terms of the original problem.

There is insufficient evidence for the biologist to conclude that the average weight of blue crabs is higher in the Stono River than in the Cooper River at the 0.01 significance level.

∽ **Technology**

For instruction on finding the *P*-value for a given *t*-statistic using the TI-83/84 Plus calculator, please visit stat.hawkeslearning.com and navigate to **Technology Instructions > *t*-Distribution > *t*-Probability (cdf)**.

```
tcdf(2.0174,10E6
,31)
        .0261914178
```

12.1 **Exercises**

Basic Concepts

1. What questions are we interested in answering when comparing two population means?

2. What is an independent experimental design?

3. Which sampling distribution do we use in the formulation of the test statistic when comparing two population means with large samples? What are the properties of this distribution?

4. Does the determination of the critical value(s) for two-sample hypothesis tests differ from one-sample hypothesis tests?

5. What conditions are necessary to perform a large sample test for the difference between two population means?

6. Why might large samples not be available when attempting to make inferences about two population means?

7. What assumptions are necessary to perform a small sample test for the difference between two population means?

8. What constitutes a "small sample"?

9. What is the test statistic for a small sample hypothesis test about two population means? How does this statistic differ from the test statistic used for large samples?

10. What is a pooled variance? Why is it used?

Exercises

11. Determine the critical value(s) of the test statistic for each of the following tests for the comparison of two population means. Assume the population standard deviations are known and $n_1 = n_2 = 40$.

    a.   Left-tailed test, $\alpha = 0.05$

    b.   Right-tailed test, $\alpha = 0.10$

    c.   Two-tailed test, $\alpha = 0.01$

12. Determine the critical value(s) of the test statistic for each of the following tests for the comparison of two population means. Assume the population standard deviations are unknown but equal, and $n_1 = n_2 = 40$.

    a.   Left-tailed test, $\alpha = 0.04$

    b.   Right-tailed test, $\alpha = 0.08$

    c.   Two-tailed test, $\alpha = 0.02$

13. A luxury car dealer is considering two possible locations for a new auto mall. The rent on the south side of town is cheaper. However, the dealer believes that the average household income is significantly higher on the north side of town. The dealer has decided that he will locate the new auto mall on the north side of town if the results of a study that he commissioned show that the average household income is significantly higher on the north side of town. The results of the study are as follows.

Income (Thousands of Dollars)			
	n	$\bar{x}$	s
North Side	35	50	10
South Side	40	43	5

a. Calculate a 90% confidence interval for the difference in average income between the north and south sides of town, assuming that the population standard deviations are equal. Interpret the interval.

b. Based on the study, will the auto dealer decide to locate the new auto mall on the north side of town? Use $\alpha = 0.05$.

14. An internal auditor for Tiger Enterprises has been asked to determine if there is a difference in the average amount charged for daily expenses by two top salesmen, Mr. Ellis and Mr. Ford. The auditor randomly selects 45 days and determines the daily expenses for each of the salesmen.

Expenses (Dollars)			
	n	$\overline{x}$	s
Mr. Ellis	45	$55	$8
Mr. Ford	45	$60	$3

a. Calculate a 95% confidence interval for the difference in the average amounts charged for daily expenses between Mr. Ellis and Mr. Ford, assuming that the population standard deviations are not equal. Interpret the interval.

b. Based on the survey, can the auditor conclude that there is a difference in the average amounts charged for daily expenses by the two top salesmen? Use $\alpha = 0.05$.

c. Explain how the 95% confidence interval in part **a.** would lead you to make the same decision that was made in part **b.**

15. The military has two different programs for training aircraft personnel. A government regulatory agency has been commissioned to evaluate any differences that may exist between the two programs. The agency administers standardized tests to randomly selected groups of students from the two programs. The results of the tests for the students in each of the programs are as follows.

Military Training Programs			
	n	$\overline{x}$	s
Program A	50	85	10
Program B	55	87	9

a. Calculate a 99% confidence interval for the difference between the average scores of the two military programs, assuming that the population standard deviations are equal. Interpret the interval.

b. Can the agency conclude that there is a difference in the average test scores of students in the two programs? Use $\alpha = 0.01$.

16. Tom Sealack, a supply clerk with the Navy, has been asked to determine if a new battery that has been offered to the Navy (at a reduced price) has a shorter average life than the battery they are currently using. He randomly selects batteries of each type and allows them to run continuously so that he

can measure the time until failure for each battery. The results of the test are as follows. Assume that the population standard deviations are equal.

Battery Life (Hours)			
	n	$\bar{x}$	s
New Battery	35	700	30
Old Battery	35	710	35

a. Does the data suggest at $\alpha = 0.10$ that the time until failure for the new battery is significantly less than the time until failure for the old battery?

b. Calculate the P-value for the test in **a**.

c. Based on the P-value, would the decision change at $\alpha = 0.05$?

17. The City Bank believes that checking account balances are significantly larger for customers who are aged 40 to 49 than those who are aged 30 to 39. To investigate this belief, they randomly select customers from each age group and determine the average daily account balance for each customer for the current month. The results of the study are as follows. Assume that the population standard deviations are not equal.

Checking Account Balances (Dollars)			
Age Group	n	$\bar{x}$	s
30 – 39	200	$2500	$550
40 – 49	150	$3500	$950

a. Does the data suggest at $\alpha = 0.05$ that the average daily account balances are significantly higher for the 40 to 49 age group than the 30 to 39 age group?

b. Calculate the P-value for the test in **a**.

c. Based on the P-value, would the decision change at $\alpha = 0.10$?

18. Determine the critical value(s) of the test statistic for each of the following tests for the comparison of two population means where the assumptions of normality have been satisfied and the population standard deviations are unknown but equal.

a. Left-tailed test, $\alpha = 0.05$, $n_1 = 10$, $n_2 = 15$

b. Right-tailed test, $\alpha = 0.10$, $n_1 = 8$, $n_2 = 12$

c. Two-tailed test, $\alpha = 0.01$, $n_1 = 5$, $n_2 = 7$

19. Determine the critical value(s) of the test statistic for each of the following tests for the comparison of two population means where the assumptions of normality have been satisfied and the population standard deviations are unknown and unequal.

a. Left-tailed test, $\alpha = 0.025$, $n_1 = 13$, $n_2 = 25$

b. Right-tailed test, $\alpha = 0.005$, $n_1 = 7$, $n_2 = 18$

c. Two-tailed test, $\alpha = 0.10$, $n_1 = 15$, $n_2 = 15$

20. *Popular Science* (Vol. 242, No. 3) reported the results of a comparison of several popular minivans. One of the features that they compared was the time required to accelerate from 0 to 60 miles per hour in seconds. The Dodge Grand Caravan ES was able to accelerate from 0 to 60 mph in 11.3 seconds, on average. The Volkswagen Eurovan took 16.5 seconds on average to accelerate from 0 to 60 mph. Suppose that 15 minivans of each type were tested and that the population standard deviation of the times required to accelerate from 0 to 60 for each minivan is expected to be 4 seconds, based on historical data.

    a. Calculate a 95% confidence interval for the difference in average acceleration time between the two types of minivans. Interpret the interval.

    b. Does the data suggest that there is a significant difference in the time required to accelerate from 0 to 60 between the two types of minivans at $\alpha = 0.05$?

    c. What assumptions did you make about the time required to accelerate from 0 to 60 mph in calculating the confidence interval in part **a.** and for performing the test in part **b.**?

21. A cereal manufacturer has advertised that its product, Fiber Oat Flakes, has a lower fat content than its competitor, Bran Flakes Plus. Because of complaints from the manufacturers of Bran Flakes Plus, the FDA has decided to test the claim that Fiber Oat Flakes has a lower average fat content than Bran Flakes Plus. Several boxes of each cereal are selected and the fat content per serving is measured. The results of the study are as follows. Assume that the population variances are approximately equal and that the assumptions of normality have been satisfied.

Fat Content (Grams)			
	n	$\bar{x}$	s
Fiber Oat Flakes	16	5	1
Bran Flakes Plus	15	6	2

    a. Calculate a 90% confidence interval for the difference in average fat content between Fiber Oat Flakes and Bran Flakes Plus. Interpret the interval.

    b. Does the study performed by the FDA substantiate the claim made by the manufacturer of Fiber Oat Flakes at $\alpha = 0.10$?

    c. What assumptions must be made in order to calculate the confidence interval in part **a.** and perform the hypothesis test in part **b.**?

22. A large construction company would like to expand its operations into a new geographic area. The company has narrowed the choice of locations down to two cities. A major consideration in deciding between the two cities will be the average hourly wage they must pay for general laborers. The company randomly selects laborers from each city and determines their hourly wage with the following results. Assume that the population variances are approximately equal and that the assumptions of normality have been satisfied.

Hourly Wages (Dollars)			
	n	$\bar{x}$	s
City A	20	$7	$3
City B	20	$8	$2

a. Calculate a 99% confidence interval for the difference in average hourly wage between City A and City B. Interpret the interval.

b. Does the data indicate that there is a significant difference in hourly wages at $\alpha = 0.05$?

c. Calculate the P-value for the test performed in part **b.**

d. What assumptions must be made in order to calculate the confidence interval in part **a.** and perform the hypothesis test in part **b.**?

23. A Hollywood studio believes that a movie that is considered a drama will draw a larger crowd on average than a movie that is a comedy. To test this theory, the studio randomly selects several movies that are classified as dramas and several movies that are classified as comedies and determines the box office revenue for each movie. The results of the survey are as follows. Assume that the population variances are not equal and that the assumptions of normality have been satisfied.

Box Office Revenues (Millions of Dollars)			
	n	$\bar{x}$	s
Drama	15	180	50
Comedy	13	150	30

a. Calculate a 95% confidence interval for the difference in average revenue at the box office for drama and comedy movies. Interpret the interval.

b. Does the data substantiate the studio's belief that dramas will draw a larger crowd on average than comedies at $\alpha = 0.01$?

c. Calculate the P-value for the test you conducted in part **b.**

d. What assumptions must be made in order to calculate the confidence interval in part **a.** and to perform the hypothesis test in part **b.**?

24. *Consumer Magazine* is reviewing the top of the line amplifiers produced by two major stereo manufacturers. One of the most important qualities of the amplifiers is the maximum power output. Brand A has redone their internal design and claims to have a higher maximum power level than Brand B. To test this claim, *Consumer Magazine* randomly selects amplifiers from each brand and determines the maximum power output. The results of the test are as follows. Assume that the population variances are approximately equal and that the assumptions of normality have been satisfied.

Amplifier Power Output (Watts)			
	n	$\bar{x}$	*s*
Brand A	12	800	25
Brand B	10	780	25

a.   What assumptions must be made in order to perform the hypothesis test?

b.   Does the data substantiate the claim that the Brand A amplifier has a higher average maximum power output than Brand B at $\alpha = 0.05$?

25.   The State Environmental Board wants to compare pollution levels in two of its major cities. Sunshine City thrives on the tourist industry and Service City thrives on the service industry. The environmental board randomly selects several areas within the cities and measures the pollution levels in parts per million with the following results. Assume that the population variances are approximately equal and that the assumptions of normality have been satisfied.

Pollution Levels (ppm)			
	n	$\bar{x}$	*s*
Sunshine City	15	8.5	0.57
Service City	10	7.9	0.50

a.   What assumptions must be made in order to perform a hypothesis test for the difference between these two population means?

b.   Will the State Environmental Board conclude at $\alpha = 0.01$ that Service City has a lower pollution level on average than Sunshine City?

c.   Repeat part **b.**, assuming that the population variances are not equal.

d.   Compare the results of part **b.** and part **c.**

12.2 Inference about Two Means: Dependent Samples (Paired Difference)

We are interested in comparing the durability of the soles of two brands of tennis shoes, Spikes and Kickers. One approach to making this comparison is the independent experimental design discussed in Section 12.1. Using this design one may randomly select 10 people to wear the Spikes brand of shoes for six months and then randomly select 10 other people to wear the Kickers brand of shoes for six months. After the six month period, the average wear for the 10 pairs of Spikes shoes is measured and compared to the average wear for the 10 pairs of Kickers tennis shoes.

While this is a perfectly reasonable approach, it does have shortcomings. For example, what if one of the people selected to wear the Spikes brand of shoes is a cross-country runner? Certainly the wear on the runner's pair of shoes will be much greater than the wear on the shoes for someone who just wears the shoes in the evenings after work. Certainly many factors could have a large effect on the observed wear of the tennis shoes.

What can we do to help reduce the effect of factors that cloud the issue of tennis shoe durability? One approach is to have each person wear a Spikes brand of shoe on one foot and a Kickers brand of shoe on the other foot, where the feet are randomly selected. After six months, the wear on the Spikes shoe would be compared to the wear on the Kickers shoe for each person. By designing the experiment in this fashion, the external effects of weight, amount of usage, and so forth, have been significantly reduced when comparing the two brands of tennis shoes. This type of design is an example of a **paired difference experimental design**. This methodology is extremely useful in reducing the effects of confounding variables.

In a paired design, experimental units are paired such that units within a pair are much more alike than in the population as a whole. If we have been successful at significantly reducing the variation among the sample observations by pairing, we will create very potent data to make decisions.

The paired difference design is frequently used in experiments where we are interested in the average response of an experimental unit before and after some treatment. For example a physician might be interested in comparing a patient's heart rate before and after treatment with some drug. A state legislator may be interested in comparing a person's reaction time before and after drinking one ounce of 100-proof alcohol. An instructor may be interested in comparing a student's math skills before and after being taught a particular course.

Generally, the sample size for a paired difference experimental design is small, and we must make several assumptions for the test to be valid. These assumptions are outlined below.

Assumptions

1. The sample data is dependent, which means that the experimental units can be paired such that they are more alike within the pair than within the population as a whole.

2. The matched pairs are a simple random sample.

3. The number of pairs of sample data is large ($n > 30$) or the differences are from a population that is approximately normally distributed.

ASSUMPTIONS

To test the mean difference between two related population means, we treat the difference scores, denoted by d_i, as values from a single sample. The general data setup is shown in the following table.

General Setup for the Difference between Matched Pairs

Observation	Sample 1	Sample 2	Difference
1	x_{11}	x_{21}	$d_1 = x_{11} - x_{21}$
2	x_{12}	x_{22}	$d_2 = x_{12} - x_{22}$
3	x_{13}	x_{23}	$d_3 = x_{13} - x_{23}$
$\vdots$	$\vdots$	$\vdots$	$\vdots$
n	x_{1n}	x_{2n}	$d_n = x_{1n} - x_{2n}$

Note that d_i is the difference between the ith observations in each sample.

We can use an interval estimate to determine the difference in two related population means. Given the differences, we can use the sample standard deviation of the difference to estimate the population standard deviation of the difference. We can construct a $100(1-\alpha)\%$ confidence interval for the mean difference, μ_d, using the following formula.

$100(1 - \alpha)\%$ Confidence Interval for μ_d

A $100(1 - \alpha)\%$ confidence interval for the mean difference is given by

$$\bar{x}_d \pm t_{\alpha/2} \frac{s_d}{\sqrt{n}}$$

where $\bar{x}_d$ is the sample mean of the differences, n is the number of *pairs* of sample data, $\bar{x}_d = \dfrac{\sum d_i}{n}$, $s_d = \sqrt{\dfrac{\sum(d_i - \bar{x}_d)^2}{n-1}}$, and $t_{\alpha/2,n-1}$ is the critical value of the t-distribution with an area of $\alpha/2$ in the upper tail with $n - 1$ degrees of freedom.

FORMULA

The hypothesis test for testing two dependent population means is summarized as follows.

Testing a Hypothesis about Two Dependent Population Means

Assumptions:

1. The samples are dependent (matched pairs).
2. The matched pairs are a simple random sample.
3. The number of pairs of sample data is large ($n > 30$) or the differences are approximately normally distributed.

Test Statistic:

If the differences are normally distributed and the null hypothesis is assumed to be true, the sampling distribution of $\bar{x}_d$ has a t-distribution with $n - 1$ degrees of freedom. Note that n represents the number of pairs of sample data. The t-test statistic is given by

$$t = \frac{\bar{x}_d - \mu_d}{\frac{s_d}{\sqrt{n}}},$$

where

$\bar{x}_d$ = the mean value of the sample of differences,

μ_d = the mean value of the population of differences,

s_d = the standard deviation of the sample of differences, and

n = the number of pairs of sample data.

PROCEDURE

The methodology for the paired difference test of hypothesis and the calculation of the confidence interval for the paired difference will be presented in Example 12.2.1.

Example 12.2.1

Bull & Bones Brewhaus is a microbrewery that has two restaurants located within 15 miles of each other. The owner of the microbrewery wants to compare the average daily food sales of the two restaurants. To do so, the owner randomly selects 10 days over a five-month period (college football season) and records the daily food sales. The results are given in the table below.

a. Calculate a 95% confidence interval for the mean difference in restaurant sales.
b. The owner wants to know if there is evidence of a difference between the average daily food sales of the two restaurants. Test using $\alpha = 0.01$.

Daily Food Sales for Two Restaurants ($)			
Day	Restaurant 1	Restaurant 2	Difference = Restaurant 1 − Restaurant 2
1	5828	7894	−2066
2	9836	11,573	−1737
3	3984	5319	−1335
4	5845	6389	−544

Daily Food Sales for Two Restaurants ($)			
Day	Restaurant 1	Restaurant 2	Difference = Restaurant 1 − Restaurant 2
5	5210	6055	−845
6	9668	10,631	−963
7	6768	7866	−1098
8	6726	7976	−1250
9	4399	5652	−1253
10	6692	8083	−1391

Solution

a. From the information given, we know that $n = 10$ and $\alpha = 0.05$. The data can be paired by day as shown in the table in order to compare the sales between the two restaurants. Since we only have 10 days' worth of data, we first need to determine if it's reasonable to assume that the differences come from a normal population. Based on the normal probability plot and the histogram below, it appears that the differences are approximately normal and it is safe to calculate the confidence interval using a paired difference approach.

Technology

To create a normal probability plot in Excel for a set of data, please visit stat.hawkeslearning.com and navigate to **Technology Instructions > Graphs > Normal Probability Plot.**

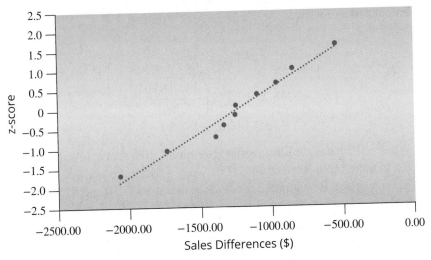

Normal Probability Plot Restaurant Sales

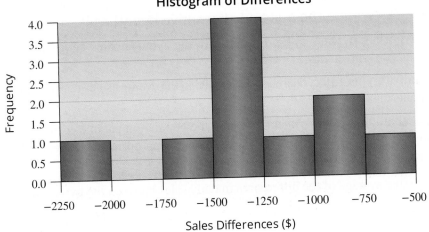

Histogram of Differences

☑ The samples are dependent (matched pairs).

☑ The matched pairs are a simple random sample.

☑ The differences are approximately normally distributed.

Next we calculate the mean and standard deviation of the differences, $\overline{x}_d$ and s_d, respectively.

$$\overline{x}_d = \frac{\sum d_i}{n} = \frac{(-2066)+(-1737)+\cdots+(-1253)+(-1391)}{10} = -1248.20$$

$$s_d = \sqrt{\frac{\sum(d_i - \overline{x}_d)^2}{n-1}}$$

$$= \sqrt{\frac{(-2066-(-1248.20))^2 + (-1737-(-1248.20))^2 + \cdots + (-1253-(-1248.20))^2 + (-1391-(-1248.20))^2}{10-1}}$$

$$\approx 434.3631$$

∽ Technology

A confidence interval for the differences can be calulated using the TInterval function on the TI-83/84 Plus calculator. For instructions please visit stat.hawkeslearning.com and navigate to **Technology Instructions > Confidence Intervals > t-Interval.**

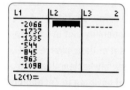

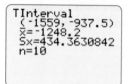

Since we want a 95% confidence interval, we need to find the value of $t_{\alpha/2,n-1}$. Note that $df = n - 1 = 9$. Thus, a 95% confidence interval for the average difference in daily food sales between the two restaurants is calculated as follows.

$$\overline{x}_d \pm t_{\alpha/2,n-1} \frac{s_d}{\sqrt{n}}$$

$$-1248.20 \pm 2.262 \left(\frac{434.3631}{\sqrt{10}} \right)$$

$$-1558.90 \text{ to } -937.50$$

We are 95% confident that the true mean difference in sales between Restaurant 1 and Restaurant 2 is between −$1558.90 and −$937.50. That is, on average, Restaurant 2 averages between $937.50 and $1558.90 more in daily sales.

b. Based on the histogram and normal probability plot in part **a.**, it appears that the differences are approximately normal and it is safe to proceed with the paired difference hypothesis test.

Step 1: Determine the null and alternative hypotheses.

Null Hypothesis: There is no difference in the average sales between the two restaurants on a given day.

Alternative Hypothesis: There is a difference in the average sales between the two restaurants on a given day.

In a paired difference experimental design, the population parameter of interest is the population mean of the differences. Thus, the appropriate statistical measure is given by

μ_d = the average of the differences in daily sales between the two restaurants.

Since the owner is interested in whether or not the average daily sales are different between the two restaurants, the alternative hypothesis will be two-sided and this will be a two-tailed test.

The statistical measure being used is the average difference in daily sales between the two restaurants. Since we have a two-tailed test, the hypotheses will be as follows.

$H_0: \mu_d = 0$ There is no difference in average daily sales between the two restaurants.

$H_a: \mu_d \neq 0$ There is a difference in average daily sales between the two restaurants.

Step 2: Specify the significance level α.

The level of the test is specified in the problem to be $\alpha = 0.01$.

Step 3: Validate the assumptions of the hypothesis test, identify the appropriate test statistic and compute its value.

The assumptions were validated in part **a.**

To develop the appropriate test statistic, a random variable whose value will be used to make the decision to reject or fail to reject H_0 must be developed. It is interesting to notice that by evaluating the differences of the paired data, we have effectively reduced the two-sample problem into a one-sample t-test for a population mean. The point estimate for the population mean of the differences, μ_d, is $\overline{x}_d$, the sample mean of the differences. Hence, the sampling distribution for $\overline{x}_d$ provides essential information for testing the hypothesis. If the differences are normally distributed and the null hypothesis is assumed to be true, the sampling distribution of $\overline{x}_d$ has a t-distribution with $n - 1$ degrees of freedom. Note that n represents the number of differences. The t-test statistic is given by

$$t = \frac{\overline{x}_d - \mu_d}{s_d / \sqrt{n}},$$

where s_d is the sample standard deviation of the differences.

If the observed value of $\overline{x}_d$ is significantly smaller or larger than the hypothesized difference (0), this will produce a large negative (or positive) value of the test statistic, causing us to question whether the null hypothesis is in fact true. How large is *large*? This is answered by the critical value of the test statistic specified in Step 4.

Based on the data in the table on daily food sales, $\overline{x}_d = -1248.20$, and the computed value of the test statistic is as follows.

$$t = \frac{\overline{x}_d - \mu_d}{s_d / \sqrt{n}} = \frac{-1248.20 - 0}{434.3631 / \sqrt{10}} \approx -9.087$$

Step 4: Determine the critical value(s) or *P*-value.

Should the computed value of the test statistic fall in the rejection region, its value will be presumed to be too rare to have occurred because of ordinary sampling variation, and the null hypothesis will be rejected.

If the null hypothesis is true, the test statistic has a t-distribution with $n - 1$ degrees of freedom. Thus, the critical value is determined in the same way as for the other tests of hypothesis where the test statistic had a t-distribution, except that the degrees of freedom are $n - 1 = 10 - 1 = 9$. The rejection region for the alternative

⟠ Technology

The hypothesis test for the differences between dependent samples can be performed on the TI-83/84 Plus calculator using the `T-Test` function. For instructions please visit stat.hawkeslearning.com and navigate to **Technology Instructions > Hypothesis Testing > t-Test**.

```
T-Test
μ≠0
t=-9.087224765
P=7.8897372E-6
x̄=-1248.2
Sx=434.3630842
n=10
```

hypothesis, $H_a: \mu_d \neq 0$, with $\alpha = 0.01$ and 9 degrees of freedom is displayed in the figure below. Because we have a two-sided hypothesis, we reject H_0 if the test statistic is less than -3.250 or if it is greater than 3.250.

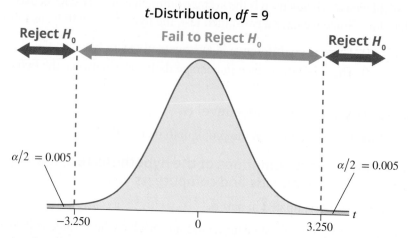

t-Distribution, $df = 9$

Using technology the P-value is approximately 0.000008.

Step 5: Make the decision to reject or fail to reject H_0.

As shown below, the value of the test statistic falls in the rejection region to the left. The test statistic indicates that the observed average daily sales are more than 9 standard deviations below the hypothesized value of 0. It is highly unlikely that the difference between the observed value and the hypothesized value is due to ordinary sampling variation. Thus, the null hypothesis is rejected at $\alpha = 0.01$.

Since the P-value of 0.000008 is less than $\alpha = 0.01$, H_0 is rejected.

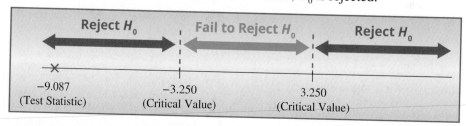

∽ Technology

To find the P-value of the test statistic in this example, be sure to double the probability of being below the test statistic value of -9.087. For instructions on finding the P-value for a given t-statistic using the TI-83/84 Plus calculator, please visit stat.hawkeslearning.com and navigate to **Technology Instructions > t-Distribution > t-Probability (cdf)**.

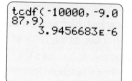

Step 6: State the conclusion in terms of the original problem.

There is sufficient evidence for the owner to conclude at the $\alpha = 0.01$ level that the average daily sales between the two restaurants are significantly different.

Example 12.2.2

A researcher is interested in knowing the effect which one ounce of 100-proof alcohol has on his subjects. To study this effect the researcher randomly selects 10 subjects and records their reaction times (in seconds) both before and after drinking one ounce of 100-proof alcohol. The results of the study are displayed in the following table.

Can the researcher conclude at $\alpha = 0.01$ that the average reaction time is longer after consuming one ounce of 100-proof alcohol?

Reaction Times (in seconds)			
Subject	Before	After	Difference
1	0.4	0.5	−0.1
2	0.5	0.5	0.0
3	0.6	0.7	−0.1
4	0.4	0.6	−0.2
5	0.5	0.6	−0.1
6	0.4	0.4	0.0
7	0.4	0.5	−0.1
8	0.5	0.7	−0.2
9	0.6	0.8	−0.2
10	0.4	0.5	−0.1

Solution

Step 1: Determine the null and alternative hypotheses.

In plain English the hypotheses would be stated as follows.

Null hypothesis: There is no difference in average reaction time before versus after drinking one ounce of 100-proof alcohol.

Alternate hypothesis: The reaction time is significantly longer after drinking one-ounce of 100-proof alcohol.

In a paired difference experimental design, the population parameter of interest is the population mean of the differences. Thus, the appropriate statistical measure is given by

μ_d = the average of the differences in reaction time before and after drinking one ounce of 100-proof alcohol for the population of interest.

Since the researcher is interested in whether or not the average reaction time is longer after drinking one ounce of 100-proof alcohol, this test is one-sided. Note from the table that subtracting the *After* data from the *Before* data would result in a negative difference if the null hypothesis is not true.

The statistical measure being used is the average difference in reaction times before and after consuming the alcohol. If the reaction time is longer after the alcohol has been consumed, then the difference, μ_d, will be negative because the reaction time before drinking the alcohol is shorter than the reaction time after drinking the alcohol. Thus we will use the following hypotheses.

$H_0: \mu_d = 0$ There is no difference in average reaction time before drinking 1 oz. of 100 proof alcohol versus after drinking 1 oz. of 100 proof alcohol.

$H_a: \mu_d < 0$ The average reaction time is higher after drinking 1 oz. of 100 proof alcohol than before drinking the alcohol.

Note that if we had subtracted the *Before* data from the *After* data, the alternative hypothesis would have been $H_a: \mu_d > 0$. The results from the hypothesis test would still be the same.

Step 2: Specify the significance level α.

The level of the test is specified in the problem to be $\alpha = 0.01$.

Histogram of Differences

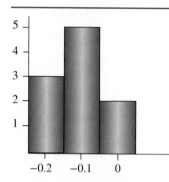

☁ **Technology**

The hypothesis test for the differences between dependent samples can be performed on the TI-83/84 Plus calculator using the T-Test function. For instructions please visit stat.hawkeslearning.com and navigate to **Technology Instructions > Hypothesis Testing > Paired Difference.**

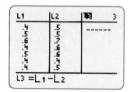

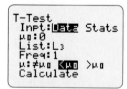

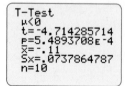

Step 3: Validate the assumptions of the hypothesis test, identify the appropriate test statistic and compute its value.

Before continuing with the test of hypothesis, let's make sure that the assumption that the differences have a normal distribution is reasonable for the reaction time data. A histogram of the differences is shown in the margin. Based on this histogram, it appears that the differences are approximately normal and it is safe to proceed with the paired difference test.

  ☑ The samples are dependent (matched pairs).

  ☑ The matched pairs are a simple random sample.

  ☑ The differences are approximately normally distributed.

Based on the assumptions above being met, the test statistic for the differences is computed as

$$t = \frac{\bar{x}_d - \mu_d}{\frac{s_d}{\sqrt{n}}} = \frac{-0.11 - 0}{\frac{0.074}{\sqrt{10}}} = -4.714.$$

Step 4: Determine the critical value(s) or P-value.

If the null hypothesis is true, the test statistic has a t-distribution with $n - 1$ degrees of freedom. Thus, the critical value is determined in the same way as for the other tests of hypothesis where the test statistic had a t-distribution, except that the degrees of freedom are $n - 1 = 10 - 1 = 9$. The rejection region for the alternative hypothesis, H_a: $\mu_d < 0$, with $\alpha = 0.01$ and 9 degrees of freedom is displayed in the following figure.

t-Distribution, $df = 9$

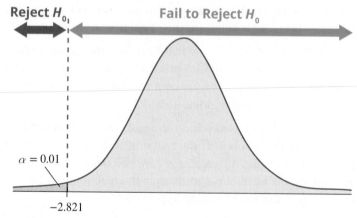

The null hypothesis will be rejected if the computed value of the test statistic is less than -2.821.

Using technology, the P-value of the test statistic, -4.714, for a t-distribution with 9 degrees of freedom is 0.00055.

Step 5: Make the decision to reject or fail to reject H_0.

As shown in the following figure, the value of the test statistic falls in the rejection region. The test statistic indicates that the observed average difference is almost 5 standard deviations below the hypothesized value of 0. It is highly unlikely that the difference between the observed value and the hypothesized value is due to ordinary sampling variation. Thus, the null hypothesis is rejected at $\alpha = 0.01$.

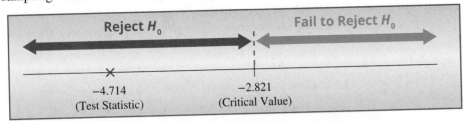

-4.714
(Test Statistic)

-2.821
(Critical Value)

Since the *P*-value of 0.00055 is much smaller than $\alpha = 0.01$, the null hypothesis is rejected.

Technology

To calculate the *P*-value for a *t*-distribution use the tcdf function on the TI-83/84 Plus calculator. The instructions can be found on stat.hawkeslearning.com under **Technology Instructions > *t*-Distribution > *t*-Probability (cdf)**.

Step 6: State the conclusion in terms of the original problem.

There is sufficient evidence for the researcher to conclude at $\alpha = 0.01$ that the average response time is significantly higher for those subjects who have drunk one ounce of 100-proof alcohol than those who have not.

12.2 **Exercises**

Basic Concepts

1. Describe the differences between an independent experimental design and a paired design.

2. What are the assumptions for a paired difference experimental design?

3. What is the appropriate statistical measure to use when performing a hypothesis test about a paired difference experiment?

4. How does the hypothesis testing procedure for a paired difference experiment differ from that of a two-sample *t*-test?

5. What is the test statistic used in a paired difference hypothesis test?

Exercises

6. Determine the critical value(s) of the test statistic for each of the following paired difference tests (assume the differences have an approximately normal distribution).

   a. Left-tailed test, $\alpha = 0.01$, $n = 15$

   b. Right-tailed test, $\alpha = 0.10$, $n = 20$

   c. Two-tailed test, $\alpha = 0.05$, $n = 8$

7. Determine the critical value(s) of the test statistic for each of the following paired difference tests (assume the differences have an approximately normal distribution).

   a. Left-tailed test, $\alpha = 0.005$, $n = 12$

   b. Right-tailed test, $\alpha = 0.025$, $n = 5$

   c. Two-tailed test, $\alpha = 0.10$, $n = 25$

8. Given that most textbooks can now be purchased online, one wonders if students can save money by comparison shopping for textbooks at online retailers and at their local bookstores. To investigate, students at Tech University randomly sampled 25 textbooks on the shelves of their local bookstores. The students then found the "best" available price for the same textbooks via online retailers. The prices for the textbooks are listed in the following table.

Textbook Prices		
	Price ($)	
Textbook	Bookstore	Online Retailer
1	70	60
2	38	36
3	88	89
4	165	149
5	80	136
6	103	95
7	42	50
8	98	111
9	89	65
10	97	86
11	140	130
12	40	30
13	175	150
14	85	75
15	100	85
16	68	62
17	67	69
18	140	142
19	49	40
20	149	127
21	126	130
22	92	93
23	144	129
24	98	84
25	40	52

a.   Is a paired design appropriate for the above study? Explain.

b.   What assumption must be made in order to perform the test of hypothesis?

c.   Does the data appear to satisfy the assumption described in part **b.**? Why or why not?

d.   Based on the data, is it less expensive for the students to purchase textbooks from the online retailers than from local bookstores? Use $\alpha = 0.01$.

e.   Calculate a 99% confidence interval for the mean difference in cost between the bookstores and the online retailers. Interpret the interval.

9. The management for a large grocery store chain would like to determine if a new cash register will enable cashiers to process a larger number of items on average than the cash register they are currently using. Seven cashiers are randomly selected, and the number of grocery items they can process in three minutes is measured for both the old cash register and the new cash register. The results of the test are as follows.

Number of Grocery Items Processed in Three Minutes							
Cashier	1	2	3	4	5	6	7
Old Cash Register	60	70	55	75	62	52	58
New Cash Register	65	71	55	75	65	57	57

   a.   Is a paired design appropriate for the above experiment? Explain.

   b.   What assumption must be made in order to perform the test of hypothesis?

   c.   Does the data appear to satisfy the assumption described in part **b.**? Why or why not?

   d.   Calculate a 95% confidence interval for the mean difference between the number of items processed using the old cash register and the new cash register. Interpret this interval.

   e.   Can the management conclude that the new cash register will allow cashiers to process a significantly larger number of items on average than the old cash register at $\alpha = 0.05$?

10. An auto dealer is marketing two different models of a high-end sedan. Since customers are particularly interested in the safety features of the sedans, the dealer would like to determine if there is a difference in the braking distance (the number of feet required to go from 60 mph to 0 mph) of the two sedans. Six drivers are randomly selected and asked to participate in a test to measure the braking distance for both models. Each driver is asked to drive both models and brake once they have reached exactly 60 mph. The distance required to come to a complete halt is then measured in feet. The results of the test are as follows.

Braking Distance of High-End Sedans (Feet)						
Driver	1	2	3	4	5	6
Model A	150	145	160	155	152	153
Model B	152	146	160	157	154	155

   a.   Is a paired design appropriate for the above experiment? Explain.

   b.   What assumption must be made in order to perform the test of hypothesis?

   c.   Does the data appear to satisfy the assumption described in part **b.**? Why or why not?

   d.   Calculate a 90% confidence interval for the average difference between braking distances for Model A and Model B. Interpret the interval.

   e.   Can the auto dealer conclude that there is a significant difference in the braking distances of the two models of high-end sedans? Use $\alpha = 0.10$.

12.3 Inference about Two Population Proportions

Techniques are developed in this section for comparing two population proportions. A methodology for comparing two population proportions is particularly useful because proportions are among the few measures that can be used for summarizing categorical data. For a more extensive treatment of comparisons for categorical data, see Chapter 16.

There are many situations where comparing two population proportions may be of interest. For example, a sociologist may be interested in comparing the proportion of females who believe that it is okay to cry in public to the proportion of males who think it is okay to cry in public. A marketing manager may be interested in comparing the proportion of customers who favor Product A to the proportion of customers who favor Product B.

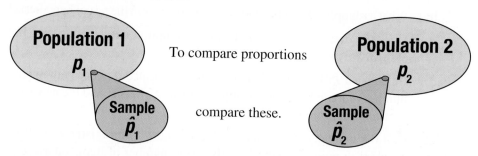

In order to perform a comparison of two population proportions, the assumptions outlined below must be met.

Assumptions for Comparing Two Population Proportions

1. The sample proportions are from two simple random samples.
2. The samples are independent (not paired).
3. The samples are large enough such that there are at least 10 successes and 10 failures for each sample, i.e.,

$$n_1 \hat{p}_1 \geq 10, \; n_1\left(1 - \hat{p}_1\right) \geq 10, \; n_2 \hat{p}_2 \geq 10, \; \text{and } n_2\left(1 - \hat{p}_2\right) \geq 10,$$

where $\hat{p}_1$ and n_1 are the sample proportion and sample size, respectively, from the first population, and $\hat{p}_2$ and n_2 are the sample proportion and sample size, respectively, from the second population.

ASSUMPTIONS

Interval Estimation of $p_1 - p_2$

100(1 − *α*)% Confidence Interval for $p_1 - p_2$

We can construct a $100(1 - \alpha)\%$ confidence interval estimate for the difference between two population proportions using the following.

$$\left(\hat{p}_1 - \hat{p}_2\right) \pm z_{\alpha/2}\sqrt{\frac{\hat{p}_1\left(1 - \hat{p}_1\right)}{n_1} + \frac{\hat{p}_2\left(1 - \hat{p}_2\right)}{n_2}}$$

where $\hat{p}_1$ and n_1 are the sample proportion and sample size, respectively, from the first population, $\hat{p}_2$ and n_2 are the sample proportion and sample size, respectively, from the second population,

$n_1\hat{p}_1 \geq 10$, $n_1\left(1 - \hat{p}_1\right) \geq 10$, $n_2\hat{p}_2 \geq 10$, $n_2\left(1 - \hat{p}_2\right) \geq 10$, and $z_{\alpha/2}$ is the critical value for the *z*-distribution that captures an area of $\alpha/2$ in the upper tail.

FORMULA

Hypothesis Testing about $p_1 - p_2$

Table 12.3.1 gives a short summary of the possible hypothesis tests that can be conducted when you want to compare two proportions.

The hypothesis testing procedure and the confidence interval calculation for comparing two population proportions is developed in Example 12.3.1.

Table 12.3.1 - Hypotheses Concerning a Test About Two Proportions			
	Are the population proportions different?	Is the population proportion in group 1 greater than the population proportion in group 2?	Is the population proportion in group 1 less than the population proportion in group 2?
Null hypothesis, H_0	$p_1 - p_2 = 0$	$p_1 - p_2 = 0$	$p_1 - p_2 = 0$
Alternative Hypothesis, H_a	$p_1 - p_2 \neq 0$	$p_1 - p_2 > 0$	$p_1 - p_2 < 0$
Type of Hypothesis Test	Two-tailed	Right-tailed	Left-tailed

Testing a Hypothesis about Two Population Proportions

Assumptions:

1. The sample proportions are from two simple random samples.

2. The samples are independent (not paired).

3. The samples are large enough such that there are at least 10 successes and 10 failures for each sample, i.e.,
$$n_1 \hat{p}_1 \geq 10, \; n_1\left(1 - \hat{p}_1\right) \geq 10, \; n_2 \hat{p}_2 \geq 10, \text{ and } n_2\left(1 - \hat{p}_2\right) \geq 10.$$
The sample proportion from the first sample is $\hat{p}_1 = \dfrac{x_1}{n_1}$.

The sample proportion from the second sample is $\hat{p}_2 = \dfrac{x_2}{n_2}$.

Test Statistic:

If the null hypothesis is assumed to be true, then $p_1 - p_2 = 0$, which implies that $p_1 = p_2$. Thus $\hat{p}_1$ and $\hat{p}_2$ are estimating the same quantity. Therefore, $\hat{p}_1$ and $\hat{p}_2$ are pooled to derive a better estimate of the population proportion. The test statistic is a standard normal random variable and is given by

$$z = \frac{\left(\hat{p}_1 - \hat{p}_2\right) - \left(p_1 - p_2\right)}{\sqrt{\overline{p}\left(1 - \overline{p}\right)\left(\dfrac{1}{n_1} + \dfrac{1}{n_2}\right)}}$$

where the pooled sample proportion is calculated as

$$\overline{p} = \frac{x_1 + x_2}{n_1 + n_2}.$$

For Population 1

p_1 = the population proportion,

x_1 = the number of successes in the first sample, and

n_1 = the sample size of the first sample.

For Population 2

p_2 = the population proportion,

x_2 = the number of successes in the second sample, and

n_2 = the sample size of the second sample.

PROCEDURE

Example 12.3.1

A cell phone executive has recently been bombarded with complaints from his customers about defective cell phones. He has two plants which produce the cell phones, and he is not sure where the defective phones are coming from. In the past, the plants have had good control over the number of defective phones produced. Because of the recent flurry of complaints, he thinks that one of the plants may have lost control over its production process. To test this theory, he randomly selects 200 phones from each of the plants and counts the number of defective phones. The results of the survey are displayed in the table.

Cell Phone Survey Data		
	Number Sampled	Number of Defectives
Plant A	200	12
Plant B	200	10

a. Are the sample sizes large enough to assume that the sample proportions are approximately normally distributed? Why is this necessary?
b. Calculate a 95% confidence interval for the difference between the proportions of defective phones from Plant A and Plant B.
c. Is there sufficient evidence for the cell phone executive to conclude that there is a difference in the proportion of defective cell phones produced by the two plants at $\alpha = 0.10$?

Solution

a. Let $\hat{p}_1 = $ the sample proportion of defective phones produced in Plant A,

$\hat{p}_2 = $ the sample proportion of defective phones produced in Plant B,

$x_1 = $ the sample number of defective phones produced in Plant A,

$x_2 = $ the sample number of defective phones produced in Plant B,

$n_1 = $ the number of phones sampled from Plant A, and

$n_2 = $ the number of phones sampled from Plant B.

Before we can determine a confidence interval or perform a hypothesis test for the difference between the population proportions, we need to be sure that the sample sizes are large enough. You may recall that when dealing with single samples of proportions, the sample size, n, must be large enough such that the sampling distribution of the sample proportion will be approximately normal. To determine whether the sample sizes are large enough, we need to show that $n_1 \hat{p}_1$, $n_1 \left(1 - \hat{p}_1\right)$, $n_2 \hat{p}_2$, and $n_2 \left(1 - \hat{p}_2\right)$ are all greater than or equal to 10. If both samples are large enough, then we know that the sampling distribution of the difference between the sample proportions is approximately normal, and we can proceed with constructing the confidence interval and performing the hypothesis test. First, we need to calculate the sample proportions for the defective phones produced in Plant A and Plant B.

$$\hat{p}_1 = \frac{x_1}{n_1} = \frac{12}{200} = 0.06$$

$$\hat{p}_2 = \frac{x_2}{n_2} = \frac{10}{200} = 0.05$$

Now, we can use the sample proportions along with the sample sizes to verify that the samples are large enough such that the sampling distribution of the difference between the sample proportions is approximately normal.

$$n_1 \hat{p}_1 = 200(0.06) = 12$$
$$n_1 \left(1 - \hat{p}_1\right) = 200(1 - 0.06) = 188$$
$$n_2 \hat{p}_2 = 200(0.05) = 10$$
$$n_2 \left(1 - \hat{p}_2\right) = 200(1 - 0.05) = 190$$

Since $n_1 \hat{p}_1$, $n_1 \left(1 - \hat{p}_1\right)$, $n_2 \hat{p}_2$, and $n_2 \left(1 - \hat{p}_2\right)$ are all greater than or equal to 10, we can conclude that $\hat{p}_1 - \hat{p}_2$ has an approximately normal distribution.

☑   The sample proportions are from simple random samples.

☑   The samples are independent of one another.

☑   The samples are large enough such that there are at least 10 successes and 10 failures for each sample, i.e., $n_1 \hat{p}_1 \geq 10$, $n_1 \left(1 - \hat{p}_1\right) \geq 10$, $n_2 \hat{p}_2 \geq 10$, and $n_2 \left(1 - \hat{p}_2\right) \geq 10$.

Now that we have verified the conditions required to proceed with the calculation of a confidence interval, we can find the 95% confidence interval for the difference between the population proportions.

b. We know that $n_1 = n_2 = 200$, $x_1 = 12$, and $x_2 = 10$. With the information given, we can calculate the sample proportions.

$$\hat{p}_1 = \frac{x_1}{n_1} = \frac{12}{200} = 0.06$$

$$\hat{p}_2 = \frac{x_2}{n_2} = \frac{10}{200} = 0.05$$

For a 95% confidence interval, $\alpha = 0.05$ and $z_{\alpha/2} = z_{0.025} = 1.96$.

Therefore, the 95% confidence interval is calculated as follows.

$$\left(\hat{p}_1 - \hat{p}_2\right) \pm z_{\alpha/2} \sqrt{\frac{\hat{p}_1\left(1 - \hat{p}_1\right)}{n_1} + \frac{\hat{p}_2\left(1 - \hat{p}_2\right)}{n_2}}$$

$$\left(0.06 - 0.05\right) \pm 1.96 \sqrt{\frac{0.06\left(1 - 0.06\right)}{200} + \frac{0.05\left(1 - 0.05\right)}{200}}$$

$$-0.0347 \text{ to } 0.0547$$

Thus, we are 95% confident that the true difference in the proportion of defectives between Plant A and Plant B is between -0.0347 and 0.0547.

c.   To perform the hypothesis test we proceed as follows.

Step 1: Determine the null and alternative hypotheses.

The hypotheses from the problem can be stated in words as follows.

Null Hypothesis: There is no difference in the proportion of defective cell phones produced at the two plants.

Alternative Hypothesis: There is a difference in the proportion of defective cell phones produced at the two plants.

Since the executive is interested in comparing the proportion of defective phones produced at Plant A to the proportion of defective phones produced at Plant B, the appropriate statistical measures are as follows.

$p_1 =$ the true proportion of defective phones produced at Plant A

$p_2 =$ the true proportion of defective phones produced at Plant B

∞ **Technology**

A confidence interval for the difference in two proportions can be calulated using the 2-PropZInt function on the TI-83/84 Plus calculator. For instructions please visit stat.hawkeslearning.com and navigate to **Technology Instructions > Confidence Intervals > Two Sample Proportions z-Interval**.

```
2-PropZInt
x1:12
n1:200
x2:10
n2:200
C-Level:.95
Calculate
```

```
2-PropZInt
(-.0347,.05467)
p̂1=.06
p̂2=.05
n1=200
n2=200
```

The executive's interest is in whether or not there is a *difference* in the proportion of defective phones produced between the two plants. Thus, the alternative hypothesis is two-sided and this is a two-tailed test.

Since the executive is interested in comparing the two population proportions, a natural way to perform this comparison is to look at the difference between the two population proportions. Hence, the null and alternative hypotheses are as follows:

$$H_0: p_1 - p_2 = 0 \quad \left(\begin{array}{l} \text{There is no difference in the proportion of} \\ \text{defective phones produced at the two plants.} \end{array} \right)$$

$$H_a: p_1 - p_2 \neq 0 \quad \left(\begin{array}{l} \text{There is a difference in the proportion of} \\ \text{defective phones produced at the two plants.} \end{array} \right)$$

Note

In order for the following hypothesis procedure to be valid, the hypothesized difference between the two population proportions in the null hypothesis must be 0.

Step 2: Specify the significance level α.

The level of the test is specified in the problem to be $\alpha = 0.10$.

Step 3: Validate the assumptions of the hypothesis test, identify the appropriate test statistic and compute its value.

The assumptions were validated in part **a.**

To develop the appropriate test statistic, a random variable whose value will be used to help make the decision to reject or fail to reject H_0 must be found. The point estimate of $p_1 - p_2$ is $\hat{p}_1 - \hat{p}_2$. The sampling distribution of $\hat{p}_1 - \hat{p}_2$ will be used in determining the critical values of the test statistic. If the assumptions outlined above are met, and we assume the null hypothesis is true, the sampling distribution of $\hat{p}_1 - \hat{p}_2$ has an approximately normal distribution with mean, 0, and standard deviation,

$$\sigma_{\hat{p}_1 - \hat{p}_2} = \sqrt{\bar{p}(1 - \bar{p})\left(\frac{1}{n_1} + \frac{1}{n_2} \right)},$$

$$\text{where } \bar{p} = \frac{x_1 + x_2}{n_1 + n_2}.$$

Note that $\bar{p}$ is the weighted average of the two sample proportion estimates, $\hat{p}_1$ and $\hat{p}_2$. In hypothesis tests comparing two population proportions, we will always assume that the hypothesized difference between the two proportions is zero.

Therefore, the test statistic will be as follows.

$$z = \frac{\left(\hat{p}_1 - \hat{p}_2 \right) - \left(p_1 - p_2 \right)}{\sqrt{\bar{p}(1 - \bar{p})\left(\frac{1}{n_1} + \frac{1}{n_2} \right)}}$$

If the null hypothesis is true, z has an approximately normal distribution. If the observed value of $\hat{p}_1 - \hat{p}_2$ is significantly different from 0, this will produce a value of the test statistic significantly different from 0, causing us to question whether the null hypothesis is true.

Based on the data given in the problem, the computed value of the test statistic is given by

$$z = \frac{\dfrac{12}{200} - \dfrac{10}{200} - 0}{\sqrt{0.055(1 - 0.055)\left(\dfrac{1}{200} + \dfrac{1}{200}\right)}} \approx 0.4386$$

where $\bar{p} = \dfrac{12 + 10}{200 + 200} = 0.055$.

Step 4: Determine the critical value(s) or P-value.

The role of the critical value in this test is exactly the same as for all of the hypothesis tests discussed earlier. It defines a range of values for the test statistic, the rejection region, that will be so rare that it is unlikely that it occurred from ordinary sampling variability assuming H_0 is true. The level of the test defines the size of the rejection region. Should the computed value of the test statistic fall in the rejection region, the null hypothesis will be rejected.

If the null hypothesis is true, the test statistic has an approximately standard normal distribution. Thus the critical value is determined in the same way as for the other tests of hypotheses where the test statistic had an approximately standard normal distribution. The rejection region for a two-sided test with $\alpha = 0.10$ is displayed in the following figure. We will reject the null hypothesis if the computed value of the test statistic is larger than 1.645 or smaller than -1.645.

If the null hypothesis is true and the assumptions of the test are valid, the probability of obtaining a value of the test statistic above 0.4386 is 0.33047. Since this is a two-sided test, this probability must be doubled to obtain the P-value. Therefore the P-value is 0.6609.

☍ **Technology**

The hypothesis test for the differences between two proportions can be performed on the TI-83/84 Plus calculator using the 2-PropZTest function. For instructions please visit stat.hawkeslearning.com and navigate to **Technology Instructions > Hypothesis Testing > Two Proportion z Test**.

```
2-PropZTest
  x1:12
  n1:200
  x2:10
  n2:200
  p1:≠p2  <p2  >p2
  Calculate Draw
```

```
2-PropZTest
  p1≠p2
  z=.4386344633
  p=.6609264739
  p̂1=.06
  p̂2=.05
  ↓p̂=.055
```

☍ **Technology**

To determine the P-value for a normal random variable use the normalcdf function on the TI-83/84 Plus calculator. See the technology instructions on stat.hawkeslearning.com under **Technology Instructions > Normal Probability (cdf)**.

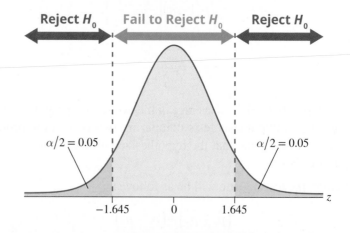

Step 5: Make the decision to reject or fail to reject H_0.

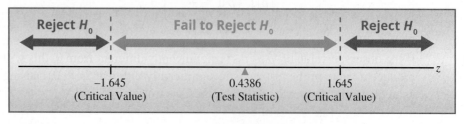

As shown above, the value of the test statistic does not fall in the rejection region because $-1.645 < 0.4386 < 1.645$. Thus, the difference between the observed value and the hypothesized value is likely due to ordinary sampling variation. We fail to reject the null hypothesis at $\alpha = 0.10$.

The P-value of 0.6609 is much greater than $\alpha = 0.10$, so the null hypothesis is not rejected.

Step 6: State the conclusion in terms of the original problem.

There is insufficient evidence at $\alpha = 0.10$ for the cell phone executive to conclude that the proportion of defective phones produced differs between the two plants.

12.3 **Exercises**

Basic Concepts

1. Why is comparing two population proportions particularly useful?

2. Give two examples of situations in which someone would be interested in comparing population proportions.

3. What assumptions are necessary to perform a hypothesis test for the difference between two population proportions?

4. Which sampling distribution is used in a two-sample test of hypothesis about population proportions? What are the characteristics of this sampling distribution?

5. What is the test statistic that is used when comparing two population proportions?

6. True or False: In order to use the specified test statistic, the hypothesized difference in the null hypothesis between the two population proportions must be zero.

Exercises

7. Determine the critical value(s) of the test statistic for each of the following tests for the comparison of two population proportions. Assume that the samples are large enough that the normality assumption is met.

   a. Left-tailed test, $\alpha = 0.01$

   b. Right-tailed test, $\alpha = 0.05$

   c. Two-tailed test, $\alpha = 0.10$

8. Determine the critical value(s) of the test statistic for each of the following tests for the comparison of two population proportions. Assume that the samples are large enough that the normality assumption is met.

   a. Left-tailed test, $\alpha = 0.025$

   b. Right-tailed test, $\alpha = 0.02$

   c. Two-tailed test, $\alpha = 0.04$

9. A fund-raiser believes that women are more likely to say "Yes" when asked to donate to a worthy cause than men. To test this theory, she randomly selects 200 men and 190 women and asks for donations to the same cause. The results of the survey are as follows.

Fund-Raiser Survey		
	Number Surveyed	**# of "Yes" Responses**
Men	200	16
Women	190	21

   a. Are the sample sizes large enough such that a hypothesis test for the difference between two population proportions may be performed? If so, does the data substantiate the fund-raiser's theory at $\alpha = 0.10$?

   b. Calculate the P-value for the test and interpret its meaning.

   c. Calculate a 95% confidence interval for the difference in the proportion of men and women who would most likely donate to a worthy cause. Interpret the interval.

10. A poll is conducted to determine if US citizens think that there should be a national health care system in the U.S. The results of the poll were as follows: 69% of the 300 women surveyed and 63% of the 250 men surveyed think that there should be a national health care system in the U.S. Are the sample sizes large enough such that a hypothesis test for the difference between two population proportions may be performed? If so, is there sufficient evidence to conclude at $\alpha = 0.05$ that men and women feel differently about this issue?

11. A manufacturer is comparing shipments of machine parts from two suppliers. The parts from Supplier A are less expensive; however, the manufacturer is concerned that the parts may be of a lower quality than those from Supplier B. The manufacturer has decided that he will purchase his supplies from Supplier A unless he can show that the proportion of defective parts is significantly higher for Supplier A than for Supplier B. He randomly selects parts from each supplier and inspects them for defects. The results are as follows. Determine whether the sample sizes are large enough such that inferences about the difference between the population proportions can be made. If so, which supplier will the manufacturer choose at $\alpha = 0.05$? Explain.

Number of Defective Parts		
	Number Surveyed	**Number of Defective Parts**
Supplier A	550	11
Supplier B	700	13

12. Suppose you have recently become interested in photography and are shopping on Amazon for a digital single-lens reflex (DSLR) camera. You've narrowed your choice down to two cameras and are leaning towards purchasing the Nikon, unless the Canon has a significantly higher proportion of 5-Star ratings. Given the Amazon rating distributions for the two cameras, which will you choose at $\alpha = 0.05$? Explain.

Amazon Ratings		
Stars	Nikon D3400 Number of Reviews	Canon Rebel T6 Number of Reviews
5-Star	500	207
4-Star	105	30
3-Star	20	10
2-Star	7	6
1-Star	26	7

CR   Chapter Review

Key Terms and Ideas

- Independent Experimental Design
- Completely Randomized Design
- Sampling Distribution of $\bar{x}_1 - \bar{x}_2$
- Interval Estimation of $\mu_1 - \mu_2$
- Hypothesized Difference
- Hypothesis Test about $\mu_1 - \mu_2$
- Assumptions for Inferences about $\mu_1 - \mu_2$
- Interval Estimation of $\mu_1 - \mu_2$ (σ_1 and σ_2 Unknown)
- Hypothesis Test about $\mu_1 - \mu_2$ (σ_1 and σ_2 Unknown)

- Pooled Variance
- t-Test about $\mu_1 - \mu_2$ Assuming Unequal Variances
- t-Test about $\mu_1 - \mu_2$ Assuming Equal Variances
- Paired Difference Experimental Design
- Assumptions for the Paired Difference Experimental Design
- Assumptions for Comparing Two Population Proportions
- Interval Estimation of $p_1 - p_2$
- Hypothesis Test about $p_1 - p_2$

Key Formulas	
	Section
Sampling Distribution of $\bar{x}_1 - \bar{x}_2$	12.1

$$\mu_{\bar{x}_1 - \bar{x}_2} = \mu_1 - \mu_2$$

$$\sigma_{\bar{x}_1 - \bar{x}_2} = \sqrt{\frac{\sigma_1^2}{n_1} + \frac{\sigma_2^2}{n_2}}$$

where n_1 and n_2 are greater than 30 or the samples are drawn from a normal population.

Key Formulas	
	Section
100(1 − α)% Confidence Interval for $\mu_1 - \mu_2$ (σ_1 and σ_2 Known) $$\left(\bar{x}_1 - \bar{x}_2\right) \pm z_{\alpha/2}\sqrt{\frac{\sigma_1^2}{n_1} + \frac{\sigma_2^2}{n_2}}$$ where n_1 and n_2 are greater than 30 or the samples are drawn from a normal population.	**12.1**
Test Statistic for a Hypothesis Test about $\mu_1 - \mu_2$ (σ_1 and σ_2 Known) $$z = \frac{\left(\bar{x}_1 - \bar{x}_2\right) - \mu_{\bar{x}_1 - \bar{x}_2}}{\sigma_{\bar{x}_1 - \bar{x}_2}} = \frac{\left(\bar{x}_1 - \bar{x}_2\right) - \left(\mu_1 - \mu_2\right)}{\sqrt{\dfrac{\sigma_1^2}{n_1} + \dfrac{\sigma_2^2}{n_2}}}$$ where n_1 and n_2 are greater than 30 or the samples are drawn from a normal population.	**12.1**
100(1 − α)% Confidence Interval for $\mu_1 - \mu_2$ (σ_1 and σ_2 Unknown and $\sigma_1 = \sigma_2$) $$\left(\bar{x}_1 - \bar{x}_2\right) \pm t_{\alpha/2}\sqrt{s_p^2\left(\frac{1}{n_1} + \frac{1}{n_2}\right)}$$ where $s_p^2 = \dfrac{\left(n_1 - 1\right)s_1^2 + \left(n_2 - 1\right)s_2^2}{n_1 + n_2 - 2}$, and $t_{\alpha/2}$ is the critical value of the t-distribution with $n_1 + n_2 - 2$ degrees of freedom capturing an area of $\alpha/2$ in the upper tail.	**12.1**
Test Statistic for a Hypothesis Test about $\mu_1 - \mu_2$ (σ_1 and σ_2 Unknown and $\sigma_1 = \sigma_2$) $$t = \frac{\left(\bar{x}_1 - \bar{x}_2\right) - \left(\mu_1 - \mu_2\right)}{\sqrt{s_p^2\left(\frac{1}{n_1} + \frac{1}{n_2}\right)}}$$	**12.1**

Key Formulas

	Section
	12.1

$100(1 - \alpha)$% Confidence Interval for $\mu_1 - \mu_2$ (σ_1 and σ_2 Unknown and $\sigma_1 \neq \sigma_2$)

$$\left(\overline{x}_1 - \overline{x}_2\right) \pm t_{\alpha/2}\sqrt{\frac{s_1^2}{n_1} + \frac{s_2^2}{n_2}},$$

where $t_{\alpha/2}$ is the critical value capturing an area of $\alpha/2$ in the upper tail of the t-distribution and with degrees of freedom equal to:

Option 1: Use the smaller of $n_1 - 1$ and $n_2 - 1$ for the degrees of freedom.

Option 2: Use the following formula to calculate the degrees of freedom.

$$df = \frac{\left(\dfrac{s_1^2}{n_1} + \dfrac{s_2^2}{n_2}\right)^2}{\dfrac{1}{n_1 - 1}\left(\dfrac{s_1^2}{n_1}\right)^2 + \dfrac{1}{n_2 - 1}\left(\dfrac{s_2^2}{n_2}\right)^2}$$

The calculation for degrees of freedom should be rounded down to the nearest integer.

Test Statistic for a Hypothesis Test for $\mu_1 - \mu_2$ (σ_1 and σ_2 Unknown and $\sigma_1 \neq \sigma_2$)

Section 12.1

$$t = \frac{\left(\overline{x}_1 - \overline{x}_2\right) - \left(\mu_1 - \mu_2\right)}{\sqrt{\dfrac{s_1^2}{n_1} + \dfrac{s_2^2}{n_2}}}$$

which follows a t-distribution with degrees of freedom equal to:

Option 1: Use the smaller of $n_1 - 1$ and $n_2 - 1$ for the degrees of freedom.

Option 2: Use the following formula to calculate the degrees of freedom.

$$df = \frac{\left(\dfrac{s_1^2}{n_1} + \dfrac{s_2^2}{n_2}\right)^2}{\dfrac{1}{n_1 - 1}\left(\dfrac{s_1^2}{n_1}\right)^2 + \dfrac{1}{n_2 - 1}\left(\dfrac{s_2^2}{n_2}\right)^2}$$

The calculation for degrees of freedom should be rounded down to the nearest integer.

Key Formulas	
	Section
$100(1 - \alpha)$% Confidence Interval for μ_d	12.2

$$\bar{x}_d \pm t_{\alpha/2} \frac{s_d}{\sqrt{n}},$$

where $\bar{x}_d$ is the sample mean of the differences, s_d is the sample standard deviation of the differences, n is the number of differences, and $t_{\alpha/2}$ is the critical value of the t-distribution with an area of $\alpha/2$ in the upper tail with $n - 1$ degrees of freedom (df).

Test Statistic for a Paired Difference Hypothesis Test	12.2

$$t = \frac{\bar{x}_d - \mu_d}{s_d / \sqrt{n}},$$

where $\bar{x}_d$ is the mean of the sample differences, μ_d is the hypothesized mean of the differences, s_d is the standard deviation of the sample differences, and n is the number of differences.

$100(1 - \alpha)$% Confidence Interval for $p_1 - p_2$	12.3

$$\left(\hat{p}_1 - \hat{p}_2\right) \pm z_{\alpha/2} \sqrt{\frac{\hat{p}_1\left(1 - \hat{p}_1\right)}{n_1} + \frac{\hat{p}_2\left(1 - \hat{p}_2\right)}{n_2}}$$

where $n_1\hat{p}_1 \geq 10$, $n_1\left(1 - \hat{p}_1\right) \geq 10$, $n_2\hat{p}_2 \geq 10$, and $n_2\left(1 - \hat{p}_2\right) \geq 10$ and $z_{\alpha/2}$ is the critical value for the z-distribution that captures an area of $\alpha/2$ in the upper tail.

Sampling Distribution of $\hat{p}_1 - \hat{p}_2$	12.3

$$\mu_{\hat{p}_1 - \hat{p}_2} = p_1 - p_2$$

$$\sigma_{\hat{p}_1 - \hat{p}_2} = \sqrt{\bar{p}\left(1 - \bar{p}\right)\left(\frac{1}{n_1} + \frac{1}{n_2}\right)}$$

where $\bar{p} = \dfrac{x_1 + x_2}{n_1 + n_2}$

Test Statistic for a Hypothesis Test about $p_1 - p_2$	12.3

$$z = \frac{\left(\hat{p}_1 - \hat{p}_2\right) - \left(p_1 - p_2\right)}{\sqrt{\bar{p}\left(1 - \bar{p}\right)\left(\frac{1}{n_1} + \frac{1}{n_2}\right)}}$$

Additional Exercises

1. Black Bark, a Colorado based company, makes wood burning stoves. They are interested in comparing two designs to determine which design will produce a stove with a greater average burning time. Several prototypes of each design are tested and the time required to burn 15 pounds of wood was measured (the burning time is measured in hours). The results of the test are as follows.

Burning Time for Stoves (Hours)			
	n	$\bar{x}$	*s*
Stove A	32	9.35	0.50
Stove B	35	9.75	0.75

Is there sufficient evidence at $\alpha = 0.05$ for Black Bark to conclude that the mean burning time for Stove B is greater than for Stove A? Assume that the population standard deviations are equal.

2. In each of the following experimental situations give the appropriate null and alternative hypotheses to be tested. Define all terms that appear in these hypotheses.

   a. Independent random samples of 50 male nurses and 50 female nurses are selected from the hospitals in a Southern state. Each nurse is asked whether he or she is satisfied with the working conditions in the hospital. It is of interest to see if there is a difference between male nurses and female nurses on satisfaction with working conditions.

   b. A group of 45 high school seniors take the SAT reasoning test both before and after a 3-month training course, which is designed to improve SAT scores. We wish to determine if the training course is effective.

   c. Starting salaries are determined for 40 female and 40 male electrical engineers. It is of interest to determine if female electrical engineers tend to have higher starting salaries than their male counterparts.

   d. Random and independent samples of younger (age ≤ 30) and older (age > 30) automobile drivers are chosen and asked whether they have had a speeding ticket in the past 12 months. It is intended to show that younger drivers are more likely than older drivers to have had a speeding ticket in the past 12 months.

   e. Do women have a shorter reaction time than men when exposed to a certain stimulus? Random and independent samples of 10 men and 10 women are included in an experiment that measures reaction time to the stimulus.

3. A nutritionist is interested in determining the decrease in cholesterol level which a person can achieve by following a particular diet that is low in fat and high in fiber. Seven subjects are randomly selected to try the diet for six months, and their cholesterol levels are measured both before and after the diet. The results of the study are as follows.

Cholesterol Levels							
Subject	1	2	3	4	5	6	7
Before Diet	155	170	145	200	162	180	160
After Diet	152	168	148	195	162	178	157

a.   Is a paired design appropriate for the above experiment? Explain.

b.   What assumption must be made in order to perform the test of hypothesis?

c.   Does the data appear to satisfy the assumption described in part **b.**? Why or why not?

d.   Can the nutritionist conclude that there is a significant decrease in average cholesterol level when the diet is used? Use $\alpha = 0.01$.

4.   The design group for a monofilament cord manufacturer is testing two possible compositions of the cord for tensile strength. Composition A is more difficult to manufacture than Composition B, so the design group has decided that it will recommend Composition A only if the mean tensile strength for Composition A is shown to be significantly greater than the mean tensile strength for Composition B. Several monofilament cords of each sample are tested and the tensile strengths are measured in pounds per square inch. Assume that the population variances are unequal.

Tensile Strength (Pounds per Square Inch)			
	n	$\bar{x}$	s
Composition A	20	52,907	2575
Composition B	20	50,219	1210

a.   What assumptions must be made in order to perform the hypothesis test?

b.   Will the design group recommend Composition A or Composition B for the monofilament cord at $\alpha = 0.10$?

5.   Consider Example 12.2.1. If you were to perform a two-sample t-test, you would find that you would fail to reject the null hypothesis and conclude that there is no difference in average daily sales between the two restaurants. Of course, it would be difficult to believe such a test given that if we examine the data in the table we see that each of the daily sales figures from Restaurant 2 is more than that from Restaurant 1. From this observation, it is clear that the average daily sales between the restaurants are different. Why, then, would the t-test be unable to detect this difference? The answer: **an independent samples t-test is not a valid procedure to use with paired data**. The t-test is inappropriate because the assumption of independent samples is invalid since the dependence between restaurants is a function of the days. Perform the two-sample t-test to verify that the independent samples test would lead the owner to fail to reject the null hypothesis and conclude that there is not a significant difference between average daily sales. Assume the populations are normally distributed and the variances are equal. Use $\alpha = 0.01$.

Daily Food Sales for Two Restaurants ($)			
Day	Restaurant 1	Restaurant 2	Difference = Restaurant 1 – Restaurant 2
1	5828	7894	−2066
2	9836	11,573	−1737
3	3984	5319	−1335
4	5845	6389	−544
5	5210	6055	−845
6	9668	10,631	−963
7	6768	7866	−1098
8	6726	7976	−1250
9	4399	5652	−1253
10	6692	8083	−1391

6. Two independent random samples have been selected, 100 from Population 1 and 150 from Population 2. The sample mean for the first population is 1025 and the sample mean for the second population is 1039. The population standard deviations are 10 and 12 respectively.

   a. Test that there is no difference between the groups using $\alpha = 0.01$.

   b. Construct a 95% confidence interval for the true mean difference between Population 1 and Population 2.

7. The manufacturer of Brand 1 cigarettes claims that his cigarettes are no different with regard to being harmful to one's health than Brand 2 (filtered) cigarettes. Assuming harmfulness is to be associated with nicotine content, the FDA took random samples of 125 cigarettes from Brand 1 and 180 cigarettes from Brand 2. The average nicotine content in the sample of Brand 1 was 24.6 mg with a standard deviation of 1.4 mg; the average nicotine content in the sample of Brand 2 was 24.3 mg with a standard deviation of 1.1 mg. Assume the population standard deviations are equal.

   a. Is there evidence to refute the manufacturer's claim at $\alpha = 0.05$?

   b. Construct an 85% confidence interval for the true mean difference in nicotine content between Brand 1 and Brand 2.

8. A team of organizational behavior managers investigated the effects of an orientation program on "first day of work" anxiety levels of new employees. 72 new employees were randomly assigned to receive or not to receive a two-day company orientation program prior to their first day at work. Two hours after beginning work, each employee was given a test to measure his or her level of anxiety. The mean score was 1002 for the 37 receiving orientation and 1018 for the 35 who did not receive the orientation. Scores of employees who attended similar orientation programs in the past have had a standard deviation of 142. Scores of employees that did not attend the orientation program had this same standard deviation.

a. Test to see if there is evidence of a difference in the mean test scores between those who participate in an orientation program and those who do not. Use a level of significance equal to 0.05.

b. Calculate the observed significance level (*P*-value) of this test.

9. For a consumer product, the mean dollar sales per retail outlet last year in a sample of 25 stores were $3425 with a standard deviation of $400. For a second product, the mean dollar sales per outlet in a sample of 16 stores were $3250 with a standard deviation of $175. The sales amounts per outlet are assumed to be approximately normally distributed for both products. Test to see if the first product has a better mean dollar sales record than the second product. Use the *P*-value approach and base your decision on a significance level of 0.01. Assume that the population variances are not equal.

10. A random sample of 10 filled sports drink bottles is taken in one bottling plant, and the mean weight of the bottles is found to be 22 ounces with a variance of 0.09 ounces squared. At another plant, 10 randomly selected bottles have a mean weight of 21 ounces with a variance of 0.04 ounces squared. Assuming the weights in both populations are normally distributed and the population variances are equal, test whether there is a difference between the average weights of the bottles being filled at the two plants. Use $\alpha = 0.05$.

11. The University of Michigan Transportation Research Institute believes that a teenage rite of passage may be losing its allure among young people. They believe that teens are in no hurry to get their driver's licenses. In a national study conducted in 1983 with a sample of 10,000 16-year-olds in the U.S., 46% had their licenses. In a similar study in 2008, surveying a sample of 10,000 16-year-olds in the U.S., only 31% had their licenses. Using the information provided, test to determine if there is a significant difference between the proportion of 16-year-olds that had their licenses in 1983 and 2008. Use a significance level of 0.05.

12. A new method for temporarily relieving the lung congestion of cystic fibrosis patients has been introduced. The traditional method of relieving the congestion involves a series of manual techniques where the chest and back area are pounded and massaged. The new method is a mechanical vest which has been designed to perform the manual techniques. A study is conducted to measure the effectiveness of the new vest. Five cystic fibrosis patients are randomly selected and the diameter of the blood vessels in their lungs are measured after using the traditional treatment and after using the vest treatment. The larger the diameter of the blood vessels within the lungs the better the treatment. If the study provides conclusive evidence that the vest is at least as effective as the manual method in increasing the diameter of the blood vessels, the hospital will recommend the vest to its patients because the vest allows the patients to be much more independent. The results of the study are as follows:

Diameter of Lung Blood Vessels (in mm)					
Subject	1	2	3	4	5
After Traditional Method	0.5	0.4	0.7	0.6	0.2
After Vest Method	0.6	0.6	0.7	0.7	0.5

a. Is a paired design appropriate for the above experiment? Explain.

b. What assumption must be made in order to perform the test of hypothesis?

c. Does the data appear to satisfy the assumption described in part **b.**? Why or why not?

d. Based on the data will the hospital recommend the Vest method to its cystic fibrosis patients? Use $\alpha = 0.05$.

"Science may be described as the art of systematic over-simplification."

— Karl Popper

13 CHAPTER
Regression, Inference, and Model Building

Introduction

The **regression line** discussed in Chapter 5 was given by the familiar linear equation:

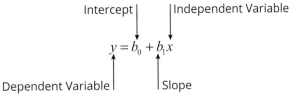

Essentially the line is used as a descriptive tool to summarize the relationship between the two variables. Recall that y is the **dependent variable** since it depends on the value of x, the **independent variable**. By providing estimates of b_0 and b_1, the simple linear relationship between y and x is specified. After data is collected, the method of least squares is the technique used to produce estimates of b_0 and b_1.

Chapter 5 considered only the problem of estimating the linear relationship between two variables from some specific set of measurements. Suppose we want to estimate the relationship between weight and height throughout the world for persons over the age of 18. Assuming the relationship is fundamentally linear, how is the relationship estimated? The number of persons on the earth over age 18 is somewhere in the neighborhood of five billion. Collecting five billion heights and weights would be a formidable task. In its current form, the problem is too large. Suppose the problem is reduced by only considering the population of the United States, where there are roughly 250 million persons over age 18. Even though this reduces the size of the problem from five billion to 250 million, it is still too large.

To make progress on this problem requires the use of sampling and inference. It is quite conceivable that a small random sample of bivariate measurements (height and weight) can be drawn from persons 18 and over in the United States. Since all 250 million measurements will never be available, the best that we will be able to do is to infer that the relationship constructed from the sample will be representative of the 250 million population members.

In Chapter 5 there was no distinction between a regression line estimated from a sample and one estimated from a population. To discuss inference a distinction must be made.

Regression Lines: Population vs. Sample

The **population regression line** is given by

$$y = \beta_0 + \beta_1 x$$

where β_0 is pronounced "beta sub-zero" and β_1 is pronounced "beta sub-one". For the population regression model, β_1 is the slope and β_0 is the y-intercept.

The **sample regression line** is given by

$$y = b_0 + b_1 x$$

where b_0 and b_1 are estimates of their population counterparts. Specifically,

b_0 is an estimate of β_0, and
b_1 is an estimate of β_1.

DEFINITION

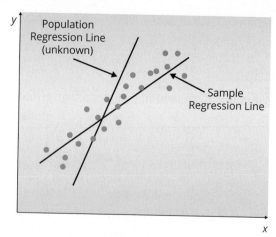

Figure 13.1

If all 250 million bivariate measures were available, then β_0 and β_1 could be determined exactly, and it would be a Big Data problem. Since the entire population will never be at our disposal, we are confronted with a familiar sampling problem. Even if a random sample from the population is drawn, there can be no guarantee the sample will be exactly representative of the population (see Figure 13.1 above). Since there is no guarantee that the sample will be representative, when a linear relationship is estimated from sample data, how accurate will the sample estimates (b_0 and b_1) be? Two familiar inferential techniques, confidence intervals and hypothesis testing, will be used to analyze the model's estimated coefficients and the predicted values. Just as before, being able to make statements about the likely accuracy of an estimated parameter or a predicted value is the value received for using good statistical methodology.

Carl Friedrich Gauss 1777–1855

Carl Friedrich Gauss had a major influence in many fields of mathematics and science, which earned him the title "Prince of Mathematicians." He was a child prodigy, who at the age of 8, was reported to have amazed his teachers by summing the numbers 1 to 100 in just a few seconds. Gauss noted that the sum could be obtained by pairing the numbers together into 50 pairs of numbers summing to 101.

In the field of statistics, Gauss is most noted for his publication of the normal error curve (or Gaussian curve), in relation to the least-squares regression problem. This led Pierre Simon Laplace to see the connection between the Central Limit Theorem and linear estimation.

13.1 **Assumptions of the Simple Linear Model**

A number of assumptions are necessary to make inferences about the linear model. Recall from Chapter 5 that an error term was incorporated in the model because virtually no real set of bivariate data is exactly linear. Incorporating the error term in the population regression line produces the **simple linear regression model**:

$$y_i = \beta_0 + \beta_1 x_i + \varepsilon_i$$

The error term ε_i represents the variation in y_i not accounted for by the linear regression model. In order to perform inference on the model, some assumptions about the nature of the error terms are required.

Assumptions about the Error Term in the Linear Model

1. The ε_i are presumed to be normally distributed with a mean of 0 and a variance of σ_e^2.

2. The ε_i are presumed to be independent of each other.

PROPERTIES

With the addition of the error term, the model's parameters are β_0, β_1, and σ_e^2. The estimation of these quantities was discussed in Chapter 5. The actual verification of these assumptions cannot be made prior to a regression analysis, but they can be validated by doing an analysis of the **residuals**, the difference between the actual values of the independent variable, y_i, and the predicted values, $\hat{y}_i$. A residual analysis is beyond the scope of this book, therefore, we will assume that the error term assumptions are met in order to proceed with the regression analysis.

Sample Estimates of the Regression Model Parameters

Slope:
$$b_1 = \frac{n\left(\sum x_i y_i\right) - \left(\sum x_i\right)\left(\sum y_i\right)}{n\left(\sum x_i^2\right) - \left(\sum x_i\right)^2},$$

y-Intercept:
$$b_0 = \bar{y} - b_1\bar{x} = \frac{1}{n}\left(\sum y_i - b_1 \sum x_i\right),$$

Mean Square Error:
$$s_e^2 = \frac{\sum(y_i - \hat{y}_i)^2}{n-2} = \frac{\text{SSE}}{n-2}.$$

FORMULA

In addition to the formal assumptions stated above, a linear model should be used to fit data that appears to be reasonably linear. Because of the wide availability of computer programs that calculate least squares estimates, you will not need to manually calculate estimates very often.

∞ **Technology**

The instructions for calculating the coefficients for the simple linear regression model using the TI-83/84 Plus calculator, Excel, Minitab, or other technologies can be found on stat.hawkeslearning.com under **Technology Instructions > Regression > Simple Linear Regression.**

13.1 **Exercises**

Basic Concepts

1. Why is an error term incorporated in the simple linear model?

2. What does the error term represent?

3. What assumptions are made about the error term in the simple linear model?

4. What are the parameters of the simple linear regression model? Identify their estimates from the sample.

13.2 **Inference Concerning β_1**

Since β_1 specifies the rate of change between x and y, in most linear models the parameter of interest is β_1. Two inferential techniques are useful in evaluating the estimate of β_1. Confidence intervals, similar in structure to those used for means and proportions, will be developed. In addition, a hypothesis testing procedure will be presented to test whether β_1 is equal to some particular value.

The Confidence Interval for β_1

Developing a confidence interval for β_1 requires thinking about the estimate b_1 as a random variable. Each random sample from the population will produce different data and hence different estimates of b_0 and b_1. The confidence interval will serve two purposes, to place bounds on the location of β_1 as well as to provide information about the quality of the point estimate b_1. The form of the confidence interval is familiar.

$$\begin{pmatrix} \text{Sample} \\ \text{estimate of} \\ \text{parameter} \end{pmatrix} \pm \begin{pmatrix} \text{A certain number of standard} \\ \text{deviations units depending on} \\ \text{the desired confidence} \end{pmatrix} \cdot \begin{pmatrix} \text{The standard} \\ \text{deviation of the} \\ \text{sample estimate} \end{pmatrix}$$

The **sample estimate** of β_1 is b_1. The variance of b_1 is given by

$$\sigma_{b_1}^2 = \frac{\sigma_e^2}{\sum (x_i - \bar{x})^2}$$

but like all population measurements, $\sigma_{b_1}^2$ usually has to be estimated from the data. Notice that the denominator of the expression above is equal to the variance of x, multiplied by the sample size, n. This indicates that the variance of b_1 is reduced if the variance of the error terms decreases, the sample size increases, or the variance of x increases.

The sample estimate of the variance of b_1 is given by

$$s_{b_1}^2 = \frac{s_e^2}{\sum (x_i - \bar{x})^2}.$$

The only difference in the computation of $\sigma_{b_1}^2$ and $s_{b_1}^2$ is the replacement of the population variance of the error terms, σ_e^2, with the corresponding sample statistic, s_e^2. The **standard deviation (standard error) of the sample estimate** b_1 is

$$s_{b_1} = \sqrt{\frac{s_e^2}{\sum (x_i - \bar{x})^2}}.$$

$100(1 - \alpha)\%$ Confidence Interval for β_1

The $100(1 - \alpha)\%$ confidence interval for β_1 is given by

$$b_1 \pm t_{\alpha/2, n-2} \cdot s_{b_1},$$

where $t_{\alpha/2, n-2}$ is the critical value for a t-distribution with $n - 2$ degrees of freedom.

DEFINITION

The expression, $b_1 \pm t_{\alpha/2, n-2} \cdot s_{b_1}$, creates the following interval.

$$\overset{(\quad\quad\quad\quad\quad\mid\quad\quad\quad\quad\quad)}{\underset{\displaystyle b_1 - t_{\alpha/2, n-2} \cdot s_{b_1} \quad\quad\quad b_1 \quad\quad b_1 + t_{\alpha/2, n-2} \cdot s_{b_1}}{}}$$

The expression $t_{\alpha/2, n-2}$ relates the width of the interval to the amount of confidence required. Recall the t-distribution is very similar to the z-distribution. To use the t-distribution requires that its degrees of freedom be specified. In this case the degrees of freedom are

$$\text{degrees of freedom} = n - 2.$$

If a 95% confidence is desired, then $1 - \alpha = 0.95$, which implies $\alpha = 0.05$ and $\frac{\alpha}{2} = \frac{0.05}{2} = 0.025$. Suppose the sample size is $n = 20$. Using the tables for the t-distribution in the appendix, $t_{\%_2,n-2}$ would be

$$t_{0.025,\ 20-2} = t_{0.025,\ 18} = 2.101.$$

df	$t_{0.100}$	$t_{0.050}$	$t_{0.025}$	$t_{0.010}$
1	3.078	6.314	12.706	31.821
2	1.886	2.920	4.303	6.965
⋮				
17	1.333	1.740	2.110	2.567
18	1.330	1.734	2.101	2.552
⋮				

Hence, to be 95% confident of capturing the true value of β_1 in the confidence interval will require placing the interval endpoints 2.101 standard deviation units from the point estimate, b_1.

Example 13.2.1

In Section 5.2, a model relating the age of a Honda Civic LX sedan to the asking price of the automobile was constructed.

$$\text{Asking Price of a Honda Civic} = \beta_0 + \beta_1 \cdot \left(\text{Age of Civic}\right).$$

If the relationship is to be applicable for all Honda Civics, then a substantial amount of data will be required. If the data given below is considered a random sample of Honda Civics, then a relationship can be constructed from the sample data.

Price of a Honda Civic LX Sedan	
Age (Years)	**Asking Price**
1	17,850
1	18,000
2	15,195
2	16,995
2	15,625
3	14,935
3	14,879
4	14,460
4	13,586
5	13,050
5	13,495
6	9,150
6	9,950
6	10,995

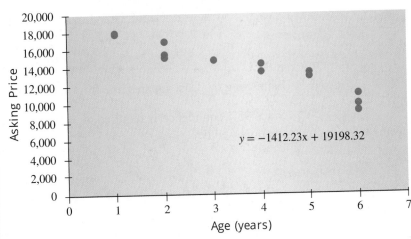

Honda Civic LX Asking Price vs. Age

$y = -1412.23x + 19198.32$

To use the method of least squares to estimate the model parameters from the sample data, we must verify the assumptions. It is evident from the scatterplot, that there is a definite linear relationship between the variables age and asking price.

☑ Random sample of paired data

☑ Error terms are normally distributed and independent (assumed).

☑ If we are fitting a simple linear model, the scatterplot should show a linear relationship between the variables.

The least squares regression line relating age to asking price is

$$\text{Asking Price of Honda Civic} = \$19{,}198.32 - \$1412.23(\text{Age})$$

where

∾ Technology

The regression line can easily be found using the LinReg(ax+b) option on the TI-83/84 Plus calculator. The results are shown here. For instructions please visit stat.hawkeslearning.com and navigate to **Technology Instructions > Regression > Simple Linear Regression.**

```
LinReg
y=ax+b
a=-1412.230263
b=19198.32237
r²=.9053495957
r=-.9514986052
```

$b_0 = \$19{,}198.32$ The sample estimate of β_0, the y-intercept estimate.

$b_1 = -\$1412.23$ The sample estimate of β_1, the slope.

To draw conclusions about the relationship between asking price and age for the entire population of Honda Civics, statistical inference must be applied. We will begin by estimating a 95% confidence interval for β_1.

Solution

Three pieces of information are required to calculate a confidence interval for β_1.

1.   A sample estimate of β_1, which would be b_1;

2.   A t-value corresponding to the level of confidence and the degrees of freedom associated with the data used to estimate the model;

3.   A sample estimate of the standard deviation of b_1, which is denoted by s_{b_1}.

Note

In the calculator output above, a is the sample estimate of the slope (b_1), and b is the sample estimate of the y-intercept (b_0).

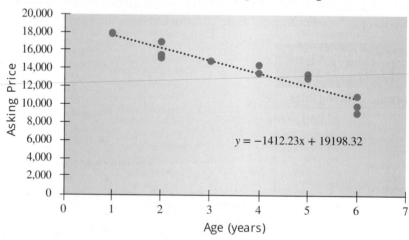

Honda Civic LX Asking Price vs. Age

$$y = -1412.23x + 19198.32$$

Estimating the least squares line from sample data produces $b_1 = -1412.23$.

Since 95% confidence is required, $\alpha = 0.05$ and $\frac{\alpha}{2} = \frac{0.05}{2} = 0.025$. The degrees of freedom will be

$$n - 2 = 14 - 2 = 12.$$

Thus, $t_{0.025,\ 14-2} = t_{0.025,\ 12} = 2.179$.

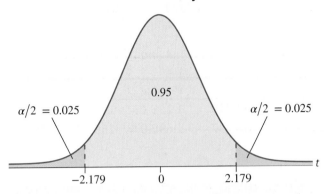

t-Distribution, df = 12

0.95

$\alpha/2 = 0.025$ $\alpha/2 = 0.025$

-2.179 0   2.179 t

The remaining piece of missing information is the standard deviation of b_1,

$$s_{b_1} = \sqrt{\frac{s_e^2}{\sum(x_i - \overline{x})^2}}$$

Determining s_{b_1} will require the knowledge of two quantities: the variance of the error terms (the mean square error), s_e^2, and the sum of the squared deviations of the independent variable, $\sum(x_i - \overline{x})^2$.

Age (Years) x	Sum of Squared Deviations $(x_i - \overline{x})^2$
1	$(1 - 3.57)^2$
1	$(1 - 3.57)^2$
2	$(2 - 3.57)^2$
2	$(2 - 3.57)^2$
2	$(2 - 3.57)^2$
3	$(3 - 3.57)^2$
3	$(3 - 3.57)^2$
4	$(4 - 3.57)^2$
4	$(4 - 3.57)^2$
5	$(5 - 3.57)^2$
5	$(5 - 3.57)^2$
6	$(6 - 3.57)^2$
6	$(6 - 3.57)^2$
6	$(6 - 3.57)^2$
Total	$\sum(x_i - \overline{x})^2 = 43.43$

The mean square error was computed in Section 5.3 as follows,

$$s_e^2 = \frac{\text{SSE}}{n-2} = \frac{9055089.197}{14-2} = 754590.77.$$

The sum of the squared deviations of the independent variable (age), $\sum(x_i - \overline{x})^2$, is given in the bottom row of the table. Thus, the standard deviation of b_1 is calculated as follows.

$$s_{b_1} = \sqrt{\frac{s_e^2}{\sum(x_i - \overline{x})^2}} = \sqrt{\frac{754,590.77}{43.43}} \approx 131.81$$

The manual calculation of s_{b_1} is tedious. Virtually every statistical analysis program that performs regression analysis calculates s_{b_1}. A portion of the summary output from Excel is shown in the following figure. Most software packages will automatically include a confidence interval for β_1 or it will include the pieces required to compute a confidence interval. Microsoft Excel automatically displays the 95% confidence interval for β_1, and is capable of displaying an interval for any level of confidence you choose.

∞ **Technology**

Please visit stat.hawkeslearning.com and navigate to **Technology Instructions > Regression > Simple Linear Regression** for instructions on obtaining regression output using Microsoft Excel or other technologies.

ANOVA

	df	SS	MS	F	Significance F
Regression	1	86613696.0169	86613696.0169	114.7823	1.69218E-07
Residual	12	9055089.1974	754590.77		
Total	13	95668785.2143			

	Coefficients	Standard Error	t Stat	P-value	Lower 95%	Upper 95%
Intercept	19198.3224	524.9047	36.5749	1.12E-13	18054.65333	20341.99141
Age (Years)	-1412.2303	131.8160	-10.7137	1.69E-07	-1699.432551	-1125.027975

$$\underset{b_1}{\uparrow} \qquad \underset{s_{b_1}}{\uparrow}$$

> **Note**
>
> Since the hand calculation of the confidence interval for β_1 used values that were rounded, the interval varies slightly from what is reported by Minitab or Microsoft Excel.

100(1 − α)% Confidence Interval for β_1

$$b_1 \pm t_{\alpha/2,\,n-2} \cdot s_{b_1}$$

FORMULA

$$-1412.23 \pm 2.179 \cdot 131.81$$
$$-1412.23 \pm 287.21$$

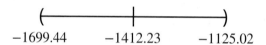

$$-1699.44 \qquad -1412.23 \qquad -1125.02$$

> **Note**
>
> 95% confidence does not imply there is a 95% probability that β_1 is in the interval. We are 95% confident in the procedure, If we create 1000 intervals using this procedure, about 950 would include the true value of β_1.

Putting the pieces together results in an interval which spans from -1699.44 to -1125.02. We are 95% confident that this interval contains the true value of β_1. There are two possible interpretations of this interval.

- We are 95% confident that the true decrease in the price of a Honda Civic for a one-year increase in the age of the car is between $1125.02 and $1699.44.

- We are 95% confident that the maximum error of the point estimate ($b_1 = -1412.23$) in estimating the unknown β_1 (the true decrease in the price of a Honda Civic for a one-year increase in the age of the car) is at most $287.21.

Example 13.2.2

Construct a 99% confidence interval for β_1 using the model described in Example 13.2.1.

Solution

The difference between a 95% confidence interval and a 99% confidence interval is expressed in the value of $t_{\alpha/2,\,n-2}$. For 99% confidence $1 - \alpha = 0.99$, which implies $\alpha = 0.01$; hence, $\frac{\alpha}{2} = \frac{0.01}{2} = 0.005$.

The degrees of freedom will remain $n - 2 = 14 - 2 = 12$.

The appropriate t-value is $t_{0.005,\ 14-2} = t_{0.005,\ 12} = 3.055$.

99% Confidence Interval for β_1

$$b_1 \pm t_{\%_2,\, n-2} \cdot s_{b_1}$$

$$-1412.23 \pm 3.055 \cdot 131.81$$
$$-1412.23 \pm 402.68$$

-1814.91	-1412.23	-1009.55

Requiring more confidence in the interval results in a much wider interval. The trade-off is less precision (interval with wider width) for more confidence.

It is important to remember that the assumptions of the linear model given in Section 13.1 must hold in order to retain the specified degree of confidence in the interval.

⟳ Technology

A 99% confidence interval can be obtained using Microsoft Excel by performing the regression analysis again and changing the confidence level from 95% to 99%. For instructions please visit stat.hawkeslearning.com and navigate to **Technology Instructions > Regression > Simple Linear Regression.**

Example 13.2.3

In Section 5.3 we examined a model relating SAT score to graduating GPA. A portion of the data is repeated here.

SAT Scores and Graduating GPA

Student	SAT Verbal	SAT Math	SAT Total	College GPA
1	680	554	1234	3.42
2	486	562	1048	2.37
3	500	564	1064	2.52
4	501	564	1065	2.25
5	503	583	1086	2.9
...				

⋮⋮ Data

The full data set is available on stat.hawkeslearning. com under **Data Sets > SAT Scores and Graduating GPA.**

Assuming the goal is to estimate a model that could be applied to all students that have graduated from college during the last five years, then the population under consideration would be quite large, too large to obtain all the measurements. If we assume the data in Chapter 5 is a sample, then we can estimate a model using the sample data and make inferences about the population. The population regression model to be estimated is

$$\text{Graduating GPA} = \beta_0 + \beta_1 \cdot (\text{SAT Score}).$$

We will begin by making an inference concerning β_1. Construct a 95% confidence interval for β_1.

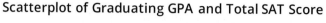

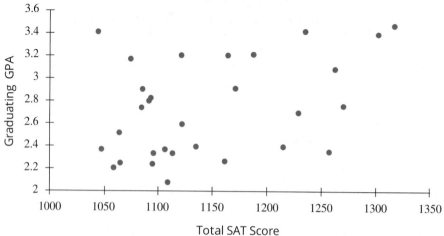

Scatterplot of Graduating GPA and Total SAT Score

Solution

As noted in section 5.3, the paired data on SAT score and graduating GPA are taken from a random sample of students. The scatterplot does not show an overwhelming linear pattern, but a slight linear trend is apparent.

- ☑ Random sample of paired data

- ☑ Error terms are normally distributed and independent (assumed).

- ☑ If we are fitting a simple linear model, the scatterplot should show a linear relationship between the variables.

Using Excel's statistical analysis package to estimate the linear regression model, the output is given below.

ANOVA

	df	SS	MS	F	Significance F
Regression	1	0.854832198	0.854832198	5.321848064	0.028670474
Residual	28	4.497554469	0.160626945		
Total	29	5.352386667			

	Coefficients	Standard Error	t Stat	P-value	Lower 95%	Upper 95%
Intercept	0.273342604	1.067710391	0.256008189	0.799816021	-1.913762987	2.460448195
SAT Score	0.002144823	0.000929737	2.306913103	0.028670474	0.000240343	0.004049304

Note

In the summary output from Excel, the confidence interval is already given (see the highlighted values above), but some technologies may require you to pull the pieces from the output to calculate the confidence interval.

Using the computer output will make the job of calculating a confidence interval easy. Two of the three pieces of information required to calculate a confidence interval are given in the output.

- The sample estimate of β_1 is given in the *Coefficients* column associated with the variable SAT Score. That is, b_1 is 0.0021.

- The standard deviation of b_1 is given in the *Standard Error* column associated with the variable SAT Score. That is, s_{b_1} is 0.00093.

The missing piece of information is the value of $t_{\alpha/2, n-2}$. Determining $t_{\alpha/2, n-2}$ requires the calculation of $\frac{\alpha}{2}$ and the degrees of freedom. Since the level of confidence is specified to be 0.95, then $1 - \alpha = 0.95$, which implies $\alpha = 0.05$ and $\frac{\alpha}{2} = \frac{0.05}{2} = 0.025$. The degrees of freedom are

$$n - 2 = 30 - 2 = 28.$$

Consequently, using technology

$$t_{\%_2, n-2} = t_{0.025, 28} = 2.0484.$$

t-Distribution, df = 28

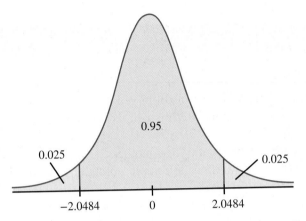

Now, let's assemble all the pieces. The $100(1 - \alpha)\%$ confidence interval for β_1 is

$$b_1 \pm t_{\%_2, n-2} \cdot s_{b_1}$$

$$0.0021 \pm 2.0484 \cdot 0.00093$$

$$0.0021 \pm 0.001905$$

$$\text{(———————+———————)}$$
$$0.0002 \qquad 0.0021 \qquad 0.0040$$

We are 95% confident that the interval contains the true value of β_1. There are two possible interpretations of this interval.

- We are 95% confident that the true increase in GPA for a one-point increase in SAT scores is between 0.0002 and 0.0040.

- We are 95% confident the maximum error of the point estimate ($b_1 = 0.0021$) in estimating the unknown β_1 is at most 0.001905.

⌕ Technology

The *t*-value corresponding to a particular area under the *t*-distribution curve can be found using the invT function on the TI-84 Plus calculator. For instructions please visit stat.hawkeslearning.com and navigate to **Technology Instructions > t-Distribution > Inverse t.**

Testing a Hypothesis Concerning β_1

In constructing a model, we must ask the question, *Does a linear relationship exist between y and x?* In answering this question, remember the linear model connects x to y through the slope parameter β_1.

$$y_i = \beta_0 + \beta_1 x_i + \varepsilon_i, \quad i = 1, 2, \ldots, n$$

If $\beta_1 = 0$, then there is no linear relationship between x and y since the term $\beta_1 x_i = 0$. Regardless of the value of x, the model becomes

$$y_i = \beta_0 + \varepsilon_i.$$

This says that y is equal to a constant β_0 plus a random error. Most of the time when developing a linear model used for predictive purposes, discovering $\beta_1 = 0$ is bad news. Essentially this says that x is not a useful predictor of y. Since β_1 is a model parameter and cannot be known unless all the bivariate population measurements are obtained, the sample estimate, b_1, will be used to make an inference concerning β_1.

If the assumptions of the linear model have been met sufficiently, statistical inference methods can be used to aid in answering the question, *Is b_1 close enough to 0 to believe that $\beta_1 = 0$?* We will follow the hypothesis testing procedure used in Chapter 11.

Testing a Hypothesis about the Slope

Assumptions:

1. The sample is a random sample of paired data, (x,y).
2. The error terms are normally distributed with mean 0 and a constant variance, σ_e^2.
3. The errors are independent of one another.
4. The scatterplot shows that the sample points appear to follow a linear pattern.

Hypotheses:

$$H_0: \beta_1 = 0$$
$$H_a: \beta_1 \neq 0$$

Test Statistic:

The test statistic follows a t-distribution with $n - 2$ degrees of freedom.

$$t = \frac{b_1 - 0}{s_{b_1}} = \frac{b_1}{s_{b_1}}$$

where

b_1 is the estimated value of the slope β_1, s_{b_1} is the standard deviation of b_1, and 0 is the hypothesized value of β_1 in H_0.

PROCEDURE

Example 13.2.4

Using the data in Example 13.2.1, determine if there is overwhelming evidence at the $\alpha = 0.05$ level of a relationship between the price of a Honda Civic and its age.

Solution

Step 1: Determine the null and alternative hypotheses.

Is there a linear relationship between the age of a Honda Civic and its price?

$H_0 : \beta_1 = 0$ Implies there is *no linear relationship* between age and price.

$H_a : \beta_1 \neq 0$ Implies a *linear relationship* exists between age and price.

Step 2: Specify the significance level α.

The level of the test has been defined in the problem statement as the 0.05 level.

Step 3: Validate the assumptions of the hypothesis testing model, identify the appropriate test statistic and compute its value.

The assumptions for conducting a linear regression of the Honda Civic data were verified before constructing a confidence interval for β_1 in Example 13.2.1. Therefore, a test of the slope parameter, b_1, can proceed.

The test statistic is similar in nature to the other test statistics developed in Chapter 11. It measures how far b_1 is from the hypothesized value of β_1, which is 0. This distance is measured in standard deviation units. If t is "close" to 0, then b_1 is "close" to 0 and $H_0 : \beta_1 = 0$ is the more reasonable conclusion. However, if t is far from zero then b_1 is far from its hypothesized value and $H_a : \beta_1 \neq 0$ would seem more reasonable.

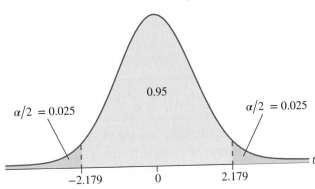

t-Distribution, df = 12

0.95

$\alpha/2 = 0.025$ $\alpha/2 = 0.025$

-2.179 0 2.179 t

SUMMARY OUTPUT

Regression Statistics	
Multiple R	0.951498605
R Square	0.905349596
Adjusted R Square	0.897462062
Standard Error	868.6718405
Observations	14

ANOVA

	df	SS	MS	F	Significance F
Regression	1	86613696.0169	86613696.0169	114.7823	1.69218E-07
Residual	12	9055089.1974	754590.8		
Total	13	95668785.2143			

	Coefficients	Standard Error	t Stat	P-value	Lower 95%	Upper 95%
Intercept	19198.3224	524.9047	36.5749	1.12E-13	18054.65333	20341.99141
Age (Years)	-1412.2303	131.8160	-10.7137	1.69E-07	-1699.432551	-1125.027975

$$t = \frac{b_1 - 0}{s_{b_1}} = \frac{b_1}{s_{b_1}} = \frac{-1412.23}{131.81} \approx -10.71$$

The estimated value of b_1 is nearly eleven standard deviations from zero. This is very persuasive evidence in favor of $\beta_1 \neq 0$.

☁ **Technology**

The output shown in Example 13.2.4 was obtained using Excel. The test can also be done using the TI-83/84 Plus calculator. The results are shown here. For instructions please visit stat.hawkeslearning.com and navigate to **Technology Instructions > Regression > Simple Linear Regression.**

```
LinRegTTest
y=a+bx
B≠0 and ρ≠0
t=-10.71365217
p=1.6921766E-7
df=12
↓a=19198.32237
```

Note

The P-values reported by most forms of technology are already adjusted (doubled) for a two-tailed test.

Step 4: Determine the critical value(s) or P-value.

This criterion is defined by the critical value of the test statistic. The test is two-tailed and the level of the test is specified to be 0.05, which implies

$$\alpha = 0.05 \text{ and } \frac{\alpha}{2} = \frac{0.05}{2} = 0.025 \,.$$

The test statistic has a t-distribution with

$$n - 2 = 14 - 2 = 12.$$

The critical value corresponds to $t_{0.025,12} = 2.179$.

Notice from the output above that the P-value for the age term is approximately 0.

Step 5: Make the decision to reject or fail to reject H_0.

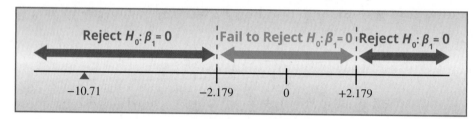

Since the value of the test statistic falls into the rejection region, reject the null hypothesis in favor of the alternative. Similarly, since the P-value is essentially 0, which is less than α, we would also make the decision to reject H_0.

Step 6: State the conclusion in terms of the original problem.

There is overwhelming evidence at the 0.05 level that $H_a : \beta_1 \neq 0$. This implies that it is reasonable to believe (at the 0.05 level) that there is a linear relationship between the age and the price of a Honda Civic. In fact, there appears to be a negative linear relationship between the age and the price of a Honda Civic. However, our hypothesis test did not address the issue of a *negative* relationship, so we cannot make this conclusion.

◆

If a data analyst feels that the assumptions of the simple linear model have been met and decides to make an inference about the model, the P-value of b_1 will be one of the first pieces of computer output that will be examined. The analyst will also look at the value of the coefficient of determination (the value of R Square in the Excel output) to see what proportion of the variation in the data is explained by the regression model (see Section 5.3).

Thus far, the focus in this chapter has been inference on β_1. What about β_0? Since β_0 is merely a constant term, in most problems its value is not of great concern. However, if a confidence interval or test of hypothesis is needed, the methods used would be virtually identical to those presented for analyzing β_1.

13.2 **Exercises**

Basic Concepts

1. Identify two purposes that a confidence interval for β_1 serves.

2. What is the formula for the $100(1-\alpha)\%$ confidence interval for β_1?

3. What are the three pieces of information needed to calculate a confidence interval for β_1?

4. A 99% confidence interval for β_1 is found to be $(5.6, 10.2)$. Give two interpretations of this interval.

5. For the confidence interval given in the previous question, what is b_1, the sample estimate for β_1?

6. If there is no linear relationship between two variables, what is the value of β_1? Explain.

7. What is the test statistic for testing the hypothesis that $\beta_1 \neq 0$? Describe how this test statistic is similar to other test statistics used in hypothesis testing.

8. What are the degrees of freedom for the test statistic in the previous question?

9. Can we make inferences about β_0? Why are we more interested in inferences about β_1?

10. Explain why the P-value corresponding to b_1 is one of the first values examined by data analysts.

Exercises

11. Using the Mount Pleasant Real Estate data set, answer the following questions.
    a. Using statistical software, estimate the simple linear regression model relating List Price (dependent variable) to Square Footage (independent variable).

    b. Interpret the slope coefficient of the model.

    c. Calculate and interpret a 95% confidence interval for β_1.

    d. Is there evidence of a linear relationship between List Price and Square Footage at the 0.05 level?

    e. What proportion of the variation in List Price is explained by Square Footage? (See Section 5.3.)

    f. Using the estimated linear regression model in part **a.**, predict the List Price of a home in Mount Pleasant that has 3000 square feet.

Data

stat.hawkeslearning.com
Data Sets > Mount Pleasant Real Estate Data

12. Using the US County Data data set, answer the following questions.
    a. Using statistical software, estimate the simple linear regression model relating Diabetes.percent to Adult.obesity.percent.

    b. Interpret the slope coefficient of the model.

    c. Calculate and interpret a 95% confidence interval for β_1.

Data

stat.hawkeslearning.com
Data Sets > US County Data

    d.   Is there evidence of a linear relationship between Diabetes.percent and Adult.obesity.percent at the 0.05 level?

    e.   What proportion of the variation in Diabetes.percent is explained by Adult.obesity.percent? (See Section 5.3.)

13. Consider the data in the following table regarding the age of a particular model of car and the asking price for that car.

Car Data			
Age (Years)	Asking Price ($)	Age (Years)	Asking Price ($)
1	11,875	4	6995
1	10,995	5	4450
2	9995	5	5500
2	8500	6	4400
3	8995	6	4800

    a.   Draw a scatterplot of the data. Describe the relationship you observe in the scatterplot.

    b.   Using statistical software, estimate the simple linear model relating age to asking price.

    c.   What is the standard error of b_1?

    d.   Find a 99% confidence interval for β_1.

    e.   Interpret the confidence interval found in part **d.**

14. An economist is studying the relationship between income and IRA contributions. He has randomly selected eight subjects and obtained annual income and IRA contribution data from them. He wishes to predict the amount of money contributed to an IRA based on annual income.

Income and IRA Contributions							
Annual Income (Thousands of Dollars)	28	25	34	43	48	39	74
IRA Contribution (Thousands of Dollars)	0.3	0	1.0	1.3	3.3	2.2	8.5

    a.   Draw a scatterplot of the data. Describe the relationship that you observe between income and IRA contribution.

    b.   Estimate the parameters of the following model using statistical software.

$$\text{IRA Contribution} = \beta_0 + \beta_1(\text{Income}) + \varepsilon_i$$

    c.   Calculate and interpret a 95% confidence interval for β_1.

    d.   What assumptions are being made about the error term in the construction of the confidence interval for β_1?

15. Consider the following summary output, which was generated from a sample of 8 employees relating age to annual salary.

SUMMARY OUTPUT

Regression Statistics	
Multiple R	0.732431223
R Square	0.536455496
Adjusted R Square	0.459198079
Standard Error	15.60374155
Observations	8

ANOVA

	df	SS	MS	F
Regression	1	1690.639497	1690.639	6.943741
Residual	6	1460.860503	243.4768	
Total	7	3151.5		

	Coefficients	Standard Error	t Stat	P-value
Intercept	-2.132440745	20.99597109	-0.10156	0.922412
Age	1.564320608	0.593648001	2.635098	0.038794

   a. What is the estimated regression equation?

   b. Is there evidence of a linear relationship between age and salary at the 0.05 level?

   c. Does the decision in part **b.** change at the 0.01 level? Explain.

   d. What proportion of the variation in annual salary is explained by the model? (See Section 5.3.)

16. The college placement office is developing a model to relate grade point average (GPA) to starting salary for liberal arts majors. Ten recent graduates have been randomly selected, and their graduating GPAs and starting salaries were recorded.

GPA and Starting Salary										
GPA	2.2	3.5	2.1	2.8	3.2	2.5	2.4	2.9	3.1	3.7
Starting Salary (Thousands of Dollars)	35.1	45.2	36.3	39.3	41.4	37.6	34.8	25.7	40.1	39.5

   a. Draw a scatterplot of the data. Describe the relationship you observe between GPA and starting salary.

   b. Using statistical software, estimate the parameters of the model

$$\text{Starting Salary} = \beta_0 + \beta_1 (\text{GPA}) + \varepsilon_i.$$

   c. Is there evidence of a linear relationship between GPA and starting salary? Test at the 0.05 level.

   d. Predict the starting salary for a student with a GPA of 2.5.

   e. Interpret the coefficient of GPA in the model.

   f. What proportion of the variation in starting salaries is explained by GPA? (See Section 5.3.)

   g. To perform statistical inference on the model, what assumptions are being made?

17. A statistics professor would like to build a model relating student scores on the first test to the scores on the second test. The test scores from a random sample of 21 students who have previously taken the course are given in the table.

	Test Scores				
Student	First Test Grade	Second Test Grade	Student	First Test Grade	Second Test Grade
1	69	73	12	54	67
2	66	56	13	57	65
3	69	65	14	85	67
4	75	51	15	75	67
5	57	59	16	79	77
6	75	76	17	44	51
7	75	76	18	82	84
8	82	76	19	57	81
9	91	82	20	75	90
10	66	73	21	69	73
11	88	67			

a. Draw a scatterplot of the two test grades and describe the relationship you observe.

b. Using statistical software, estimate the parameters of the model

$$\text{Second Test Grade} = \beta_0 + \beta_1 \left(\text{First Test Grade}\right) + \varepsilon_i.$$

c. What proportion of the variation in the grades on the second test is explained by the grades on the first test?

d. Is there a linear relationship between the first test grades and the second test grades? Test at the 0.05 level.

e. Suppose you're enrolled in the professor's course this semester. If you scored a 75 on the first test, use the model to predict your second test score. Round your answer to the nearest whole number.

13.3 Inference Concerning the Model's Prediction

Many regression models are developed for predictive purposes. For example, if you built the model relating the price of a Honda Civic to its age, it was probably because you want to use it to predict prices. While it is important to evaluate b_1, the estimate of the slope, the real concern of the model builder is the accuracy of a model's predictions. In the case of the Honda Civic model, how accurate are the prices that the model predicts? If the assumptions of the linear model (detailed in Section 13.1) have been met, then it is possible to make inferences as to the quality of a model's predictions.

The Regression Line as the Mean Value of *y* Given *x*

Examining the Honda Civic data in Example 13.2.1 reveals two cars that are one-year old. For a given value of age (say one year) the prices of the one-year-old cars were $17,850 and $18,000. For anyone who has ever observed the car market, price variation is not unexpected. If you use the model,

$$\text{Asking Price of Honda Civic} = \$19{,}198.32 - \$1412.23(\text{Age})$$

for predictive purposes, then the predicted value of a one-year-old Honda Civic will be

$$\text{Civic Price} = \$19{,}198.32 - \$1412.23(1) = \$17{,}786.09.$$

Using this model, all one-year-old Honda Civics will have a predicted value of $17,786.09. Since the prices of one-year-old Honda Civics vary, how do you interpret the predicted price of $17,786.09? The model's predicted value when Age is set to one is considered to be the average price of a one-year-old Honda Civic. In other words, it is the mean value of y (price) when x (age) equals one. But wait a minute! The prices of the one-year-old Honda Civics were $17,850 and $18,000, and the average of these numbers is not $17,786.09. What kind of average is this? What we are essentially saying is that if we are willing to acknowledge that the relationship between x and y is linear, then all data (not just the data for $x = 1$) will be useful in establishing the estimated relationship. Once the relationship is established, it will be used to estimate the mean value of y for any given x. In fact, if Age = 2, the predicted value would be

$$\text{Civic Price} = \$19{,}198.32 - \$1412.23(2) = \$16{,}373.86,$$

which would be interpreted to be the average price of two-year-old Honda Civics.

The entire regression line can be considered a collection of means of y for different values of x. Unfortunately, the true linear relationship is unknown since all the data in the population will not be available. Since only the estimated model is available, only estimated values of the mean value of y for some given x will be available. How good are these estimates? How good is the estimate of a mean value of $y = \$16{,}373.86$ when $x = 2$? To answer this question, we will once again rely on the notion of a confidence interval.

Confidence Intervals for the Mean Value of *y* Given *x*

> ### 100(1 − α)% Confidence Interval for the Mean Value of *y* Given *x*
>
> If x_p is a value of x for which we wish to know the mean value of y, then the $100(1 - \alpha)\%$ confidence interval is given by
>
> $$\hat{y}_p \pm t_{\alpha/2,\,n-2} \cdot s_e \sqrt{\frac{1}{n} + \frac{\left(x_p - \bar{x}\right)^2}{\sum \left(x_i - \bar{x}\right)^2}} \quad \text{where,}$$
>
> $\hat{y}_p$ is the predicted value of y when $x = x_p$, $\hat{y}_p = b_0 + b_1 x_p$,
>
> $t_{\alpha/2,\,n-2}$ is the t-value associated with $1 - \alpha$ confidence (the same t used in constructing confidence intervals for β_1),
>
> s_e is the standard deviation of the error terms, and
>
> $\dfrac{\left(x_p - \bar{x}\right)^2}{\sum \left(x_i - \bar{x}\right)^2}$ measures how far x_p is from $\bar{x}$ in relation to the total variation
>
> of the x's. The further that x_p is from $\bar{x}$, the larger this ratio will become and consequently the wider the confidence interval.
>
> **FORMULA**

Example 13.3.1

For the Honda Civic model, calculate the 95% confidence interval for the mean value of price when age equals two years.

Solution

Four pieces of information are required to calculate a confidence interval for the mean value of y given $x = x_p$:

1. Use the estimated regression line to calculate $\hat{y}$ for the value given for $x = x_p$,

2. Find a t-value corresponding to the level of confidence and the degrees of freedom associated with the data used to estimate the model,

3. Determine the standard deviation of the error terms,

4. Compute the term $\dfrac{\left(x_p - \bar{x}\right)^2}{\sum \left(x_i - \bar{x}\right)^2}$.

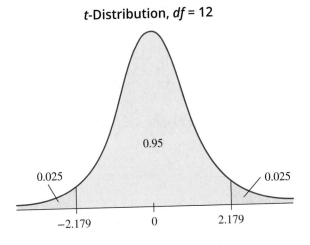

t-Distribution, df = 12

0.95

0.025   0.025

−2.179   0   2.179

In Example 13.2.1, $x_p = 2$ and the predicted value of y for this given x is

$$\hat{y} = b_0 + b_1 x_p = \$19,198.32 - \$1412.23(2) = \$16,373.86.$$

For a 95% confidence interval $\alpha = 0.05$, and the degrees of freedom $= n - 2 = 14 - 2 = 12$. Thus,

$$t_{0.025,14-2} = t_{0.025,12} = 2.179$$

The estimated variance of the error terms, s_e^2, is given in the Excel summary output of Example 13.2.1 under the column labeled MS and the row labeled Residual. The standard deviation of the error terms, s_e, can be computed by taking the square root of the **mean square error**, $s_e^2 = 754,590.77$. Therefore, $s_e = 868.67$.

The last piece of information is the quotient

$$\frac{\left(x_p - \bar{x}\right)^2}{\sum \left(x_i - \bar{x}\right)^2} = \frac{(2-3.57)^2}{43.43} \approx 0.0568.$$

The bottom row of the table contains the calculation for the sum of the squared deviations $\sum \left(x_i - \bar{x}\right)^2$.

Age (Years) x	Sum of Squared Deviations $(x_i - \bar{x})^2$
1	$(1-3.57)^2$
1	$(1-3.57)^2$
2	$(2-3.57)^2$
2	$(2-3.57)^2$
2	$(2-3.57)^2$
3	$(3-3.57)^2$
3	$(3-3.57)^2$
4	$(4-3.57)^2$
4	$(4-3.57)^2$
5	$(5-3.57)^2$
5	$(5-3.57)^2$
6	$(6-3.57)^2$
6	$(6-3.57)^2$
6	$(6-3.57)^2$
Total	$\sum \left(x_i - \bar{x}\right)^2 = 43.43$

Assembling the pieces for the 95% confidence interval, we have

$$\hat{y}_p \pm t_{\frac{\alpha}{2}, n-2} \cdot s_e \sqrt{\frac{1}{n} + \frac{\left(x_p - \bar{x}\right)^2}{\sum\left(x_i - \bar{x}\right)^2}},$$

$$\$16{,}373.86 \pm 2.179 \cdot 868.67 \cdot \sqrt{\frac{1}{14} + 0.0568}$$

$$\$16{,}373.86 \pm 2.179 \cdot 311.06$$

$$\$16{,}373.86 \pm \$677.80$$

$$(\quad\quad\quad\quad | \quad\quad\quad\quad)$$

$\$15{,}696.06$ $\$16{,}373.86$ $\$17{,}051.66$

The confidence interval can be interpreted in two ways.

- We are 95% confident that the mean price of a two-year-old Honda Civic is between $15,696.06 and $17,051.66. (Note, like all confidence intervals, the confidence is in the method not in a particular interval.)

- We are 95% confident that the maximum error of estimation for the mean price of a two-year-old Honda Civic is $677.80.

Virtually all statistical analysis packages compute a confidence interval for the mean value of y for a given value of x. Figure 13.3.1 is an example of the standard output from Minitab. The output in the figure uses the estimated Honda Civic model when Age = 2. The value labeled *Fit* is the predicted value of y when $x = 2$. The value labeled *SE Fit* is the standard deviation of the fitted value when $x = 2$. The 95% *CI* is the 95% confidence interval for the mean value of y when $x = 2$. Note that the confidence interval from Minitab has slightly different endpoints than the one we calculated above due to the rounding of intermediate calculations.

◌ Technology

For instructions on finding the confidence and prediction intervals in Minitab visit stat.hawkeslearning.com and navigate to **Technology Instructions > Regression > Regression Prediction Intervals.**

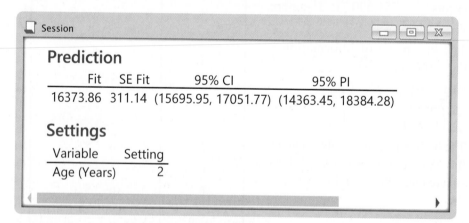

Figure 13.3.1

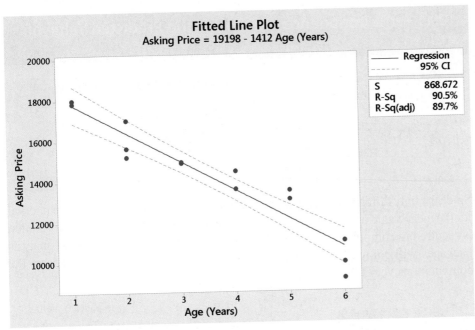

Figure 13.3.2

Figure 13.3.2 is a graph of the regression line and the 95% confidence interval bands around the regression line. Note how the confidence interval widens at the extremes of the data range where the value of x_p is furthest from the average, $\bar{x}$.

The 95% *PI* (prediction interval) will be discussed next.

Confidence Intervals for the Predicted Value of *y* Given *x*

We previously discussed confidence intervals for the mean value of *y* given *x*, rather than individual outcomes. Suppose you have a three-year-old Honda Civic, and you wish to predict the price of the car and compute a 95% confidence interval for the predicted price of your car. Using the model,

$$\text{Civic Price} = \$19{,}198.32 - \$1412.23(3) = \$14{,}961.63,$$

for the average three-year-old car. Your car may be above average or below average, the model has no way of knowing. Consequently, the actual price of your car will likely be different from the average value and that difference will be an error in the model's prediction. That error needs to be accounted for in the confidence interval for the predicted value of *y* given *x*.

The expression for the confidence interval for a predicted value is very similar to the confidence interval for the mean value of *y* given *x*. However, instead of calling this interval a confidence interval (which it is), let's call it a **prediction interval** to distinguish the interval from the confidence interval for the mean value of *y* given *x*.

Technology

In order to graph the regression line, along with the confidence interval bands, using Minitab, please visit stat.hawkeslearning.com and navigate to **Technology Instructions > Regression > Linear Regression Fitted Line Plot with Confidence Interval.**

> ### 100(1 − α)% Confidence Interval for the Predicted Value of y Given x
>
> A 100(1 − α)% confidence interval for the predicted value of y given x, also known as a **prediction interval**, is given by
>
> $$\hat{y}_p \pm t_{\alpha/2,\, n-2} \cdot s_e \sqrt{1 + \frac{1}{n} + \frac{\left(x_p - \bar{x}\right)^2}{\sum\left(x_i - \bar{x}\right)^2}}.$$
>
> **FORMULA**

Since the only difference between the prediction interval and the confidence interval for the mean value of y given x is the "1" inside the square root, the same information is required to compute the interval. However, since virtually all statistical analysis packages will compute the prediction interval, you may not have to perform the computations very often.

Example 13.3.2

Suppose you have a two-year-old Honda Civic you are considering selling. Compute the 95% prediction interval for the price of your Honda Civic.

Solution

The predicted price of your two-year-old Honda Civic is given by

$$\text{Civic Price} = \$19{,}198.32 - \$1412.23(2) = \$16{,}373.86,$$

$$\text{and } t_{0.025,\,14-2} = t_{0.025,\,12} = 2.179, \quad s_e = 868.67,$$

$$\text{and } \frac{\left(x_p - \bar{x}\right)^2}{\sum\left(x_i - \bar{x}\right)^2} = \frac{\left(2 - 3.57\right)^2}{43.43} \approx 0.0568.$$

Computing the interval, we have

$$\$16{,}373.86 \pm 2.179 \cdot 868.67 \cdot \sqrt{1 + \frac{1}{14} + 0.0568}$$

$$\$16{,}373.86 \pm 2.179 \cdot 922.68$$

$$\$16{,}373.86 \pm \$2010.52$$

Note

These values differ slightly from the 95% prediction interval shown in Figure 13.3.1 due to rounding of the values used in the example.

We are 95% confident that the actual price of your two-year-old Honda Civic will be within $2010.52 of the average price for two-year-old Honda Civics, $16,373.86. Specifically, we are 95% confident that the price of your Honda Civic will be between $14,363.34 and $18,384.38.

The diagrams below compare the confidence interval for the mean value of y given $x = 2$ and the predicted value of y given $x = 2$.

Confidence Interval for the Mean Value of y

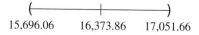

15,696.06   16,373.86   17,051.66

Confidence Interval for the Predicted Value of y

14,363.34   16,373.86   18,384.38

The graph for the prediction interval shown in Figure 13.3.3 has drastically wider confidence bands around the regression line than the graph for the confidence interval for the mean value in Figure 13.3.2. A high price has been paid in order to account for individual variability.

Using the model for prediction outside the range of the *x*-values used to create the model can be dangerous. The nature of the relationship may not be linear outside of the range of the *x*'s used to define the model. In the Honda Civic example, the range of *x*-values spans from 1 to 6 years. Notice in Figure 13.3.3 that as you approach the edges of the data, the confidence interval widens considerably. Using the model to predict the price of a 10-year-old Honda Civic would no doubt have sizable error. Inferential methods are not valid outside the range of the data used to estimate the model.

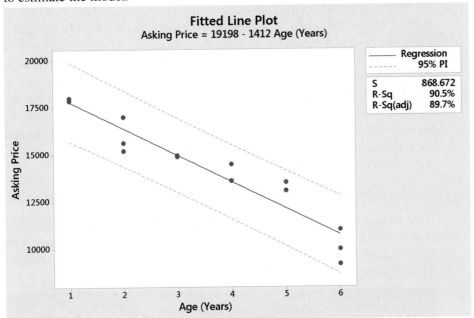

Figure 13.3.3

Technology

In order to graph the regression line, along with the prediction interval bands, using Minitab, please visit stat.hawkeslearning.com and navigate to **Technology Instructions > Regression > Linear Regression Fitted Line Plot with Prediction Interval.**

13.3 **Exercises**

Basic Concepts

1. Describe the difference in the interpretation of confidence intervals for the mean value of *y* given *x* and the predicted value of *y* given *x*.

2. Given a confidence interval and a prediction interval, which interval is wider? Explain why.

3. Why is it dangerous to use a regression model to predict outside the range of the *x*-values used to create the model?

Exercises

4. In Nevada, many forms of gambling are legal and very profitable. Sports betting amounts to billions of dollars annually. In football, a customer will bet on one of the teams to win the contest. However, in an attempt to even the game (from a betting point of view) one of the teams is selected as the favorite. The favorite's score in the game is reduced by an amount called the line. For example, if the Cowboys are favored over the Falcons by four points, then four points are subtracted from the Cowboys' score to determine the outcome of the game for betting purposes. Thus, if the Cowboys defeat the Falcons 32 to 30, in so far as settling any bets, the Cowboys score would be reduced by the spread and the Cowboys would be the loser $32 - 4 = 28$ to 30. Where does the betting line come from? The line is created by a betting market. If too many people are betting on the Cowboys before the game starts, the bookmaker will try to make the game more attractive to potential Falcon bettors by increasing the spread say from four points to five points. On the other hand, if too many people are betting on the Falcons, the spread will diminish from four to perhaps three points. How accurate is the betting spread at predicting the actual spread, which is the actual difference in points between the favorite and the underdog? In the example of the Cowboys and the Falcons, the actual spread was $+2$ $(32 - 30)$. To examine this question, we want to build the following model:

$$\text{Actual Point Spread} = \beta_0 + \beta_1 \left(\text{Betting Spread}\right) + \varepsilon_i.$$

If the betting spread is a good predictor of the actual spread, it should be able to account for a substantial portion of the variation in the actual spreads. The following table contains betting and actual spreads from 15 randomly selected football games.

Betting vs. Actual Spreads															
Betting	4	1	3	2	1	2	5	5	3	4	2	3	5	7	6
Actual	12	−2	6	7	3	1	14	3	−7	5	14	9	2	21	8

a. Draw a scatterplot of the data. Describe the relationship you observe between actual point spread and the betting spread.

b. Estimate the parameters of the model using statistical software.

c. Is there evidence at the 0.05 level of a linear relationship between the betting spread and the actual spread?

d. What proportion of the variation in the actual point spread is explained by the betting spread?

e. Interpret the coefficient of the betting spread in the model $\left(\beta_1\right)$.

f. Construct and interpret a 95% confidence interval for β_1.

g. If the betting spread is five, what is the predicted actual spread?

h. Construct and interpret a 95% prediction interval for a betting spread of five.

i. Construct a 95% confidence interval for the average value of the actual spread when the betting spread is five.

5. Net income is the level of actual profit that a company reports for the year. Net sales is the total sales less adjustment for returns. What is the relationship between net income and net sales for large corporations? Suppose a random sample of 27 large corporations has been selected, and the net income and net sales have been recorded. A regression analysis has been performed to estimate the model, and the output is given.

$$\text{Net Income} = \beta_0 + \beta_1 \left(\text{Net Sales}\right) + \varepsilon_i$$

Regression Analysis: Income versus Sales

The regression equation is
Income = 84 + 18.4 Sales

Predictor	Coef	SE Coef	T	P
Constant	83.6	118.1	0.71	0.486
Sales	18.434	4.446	4.15	0.000

S = 372.478   R-Sq = 40.7%   R-Sq(adj) = 38.4%

Analysis of Variance

Source	DF	SS	MS	F	P
Regression	1	2384660	2384660	17.19	0.000
Residual Error	25	3468497	138740		
Total	26	5853157			

Predicted Values for New Observations

New Obs	Fit	SE Fit	95% CI	95% PI
1	1005.3	147.1	(702.4, 1308.2)	(180.5, 1830.0)

Values of Predictors for New Observations

New Obs	Sales
1	50.0

---

a. Find and interpret the standard deviation of the error terms in the output.

b. Interpret the slope coefficient. (The data used to estimate the model was in millions of dollars.)

c. What proportion of the variation in net income is explained by net sales?

d. Is there evidence of a linear relationship between net income and net sales? Test at the 0.05 level.

e. Construct and interpret a 95% confidence interval for β_1, the slope of the line.

f. The output also contains a predicted value for net income when sales are $50,000,000. Find the predicted value of net income when sales are $50,000,000. (Note that in the original data all observations were measured in millions of dollars. Thus, a predicted value of 10,000,000 would be displayed in the output as 10.)

g. Find and interpret the 95% confidence interval for the average value of net income given that sales are $50,000,000.

h. Suppose your firm generated $50,000,000 in sales. What would be the 95% prediction interval for your firm's net income?

i.   Use the model to predict net income for a company with $60,000,000 in sales. (Note that you must compute this manually.)

6.   The personnel director of a large hospital is interested in determining the relationship (if any) between an employee's age and the number of sick days the employee takes per year. The director randomly selects eight employees and records their age and the number of sick days which they took in the previous year.

Sick Days and Age								
Employee	1	2	3	4	5	6	7	8
Age	30	50	40	55	30	28	60	25
Sick Days	7	4	3	2	9	10	0	8

A regression analysis has been performed to estimate the model and the output is given.

$$\text{Sick Days} = \beta_0 + \beta_1(\text{Age}) + \varepsilon_i$$

Regression Analysis: Sick Days versus Age

The regression equation is
Sick Days = 15.2 - 0.247 Age

Predictor	Coef	SE Coef	T	P
Constant	15.186	1.713	8.86	0.000
Age	-0.24681	0.04105	-6.01	0.001

S = 1.47652   R-Sq = 85.8%   R-Sq(adj) = 83.4%

Analysis of Variance

Source	DF	SS	MS	F	P
Regression	1	78.794	78.794	36.14	0.001
Residual Error	6	13.081	2.180		
Total	7	91.875			

Predicted Values for New Observations

New Obs	Fit	SE Fit	95% CI	95% PI
1	6.547	0.557	(5.184, 7.911)	(2.686, 10.409)

Values of Predictors for New Observations

New Obs	Age
1	35.0

---

a.   Draw a scatterplot of the data. Describe the relationship you observe between the number of sick days and age.

b.   Find and interpret the standard deviation of the error terms in the output.

c.   Interpret the slope coefficient.

d.   What proportion of the variation in the number of sick days an employee takes per year is explained by age?

e.   Is there evidence of a linear relationship between the number of sick days an employee takes per year and age? Test at the 0.05 level.

f.   Construct and interpret a 95% confidence interval for β_1, the slope of the line.

g.   Find the predicted value of the number of sick days an employee will take per year if the employee is 35 years old.

h. Find and interpret the 95% confidence interval for the average number of sick days an employee will take per year, given the employee is 35.

i. Suppose a new employee is 35. Find a 95% prediction interval for the number of sick days this employee will take this year.

j. Use the model to predict the number of sick days per year for an employee who is 45 years old. Round to the nearest whole number.

7. A manufacturing company that produces laminate for countertops is interested in studying the relationship between the number of hours of training that an employee receives and the number of defects per countertop produced. Ten employees are randomly selected. The number of hours of training each employee has received is recorded and the number of defects on the most recent countertop produced is determined. The results are as follows.

Training Hours and Countertop Defects										
Hours of Training	1	4	7	3	2	2	5	5	1	6
Defects per Countertop	1	4	0	3	5	4	3	2	5	1

A regression analysis has been performed to estimate the model, and the following output is produced.

$$\text{Defects per Countertop} = \beta_0 + \beta_1\left(\text{Hours of Training}\right) + \varepsilon_i$$

Regression Analysis: Defects per Countertop versus Hours of Training

The regression equation is
Defects per Countertop = 4.65 - 0.515 Hours of Training

Predictor	Coef	SE Coef	T	P
Constant	4.6535	0.9426	4.94	0.001
Hours of Training	-0.5149	0.2286	-2.25	0.054

S = 1.45306   R-Sq = 38.8%   R-Sq(adj) = 31.2%

Analysis of Variance

Source	DF	SS	MS	F	P
Regression	1	10.709	10.709	5.07	0.054
Residual Error	8	16.891	2.111		
Total	9	27.600			

Predicted Values for New Observations

New Obs	Fit	SE Fit	95% CI	95% PI
1	2.594	0.469	(1.514, 3.674)	(-0.927, 6.115)

Values of Predictors for New Observations

New Obs	Hours of Training
1	4.00

a. Draw a scatterplot of the data. Describe the relationship you observe between the number of defects per countertop and hours of training. Are there any unusual observations?

b. Find and interpret the standard deviation of the error terms in the output.

c. Interpret the slope coefficient.

d. What proportion of the variation in the number of defects per countertop is explained by the hours of training? What other factors might affect the number of defects?

e. Is there evidence of a linear relationship between the number of hours of training and the number of defects per countertop? Test at the 0.05 level and the 0.10 level.

f. Construct and interpret a 95% confidence interval for β_1, the slope coefficient.

g. Find the predicted value of the number of defects per countertop for an employee who has had 4 hours of training.

h. Find and interpret the 95% confidence interval for the average number of defects per countertop for employees who have had 4 hours of training.

i. Suppose a new employee has had 4 hours of training. What would be the 95% prediction interval for the number of defects per countertop?

j. Use the model to predict the number of defects per countertop for an employee who has had 7 hours of training. Round your answer to the nearest whole number.

CR   **Chapter Review**

Key Terms and Ideas

- Simple Linear Regression Model
- Population Regression Line
- Sample Regression Line
- Assumptions about the Error Term
- Residual
- Confidence Interval for β_1

- Testing a Hypothesis Concerning β_1
- Standard Error
- Confidence Interval for the Mean Value of y Given x
- Confidence Interval for the Predicted Value of y Given x
- Population Regression Line
- Sample Regression Line

Key Formulas	
	Section
Simple Linear Regression Model	13.1
$$y_i = \beta_0 + \beta_1 x_i + \varepsilon_i$$	
Estimated Simple Linear Regression Equation	13.1
$$\hat{y}_i = b_0 + b_1 x_i$$	
Sum of Squared Errors	13.1
$$\text{SSE} = \sum \left(y_i - \hat{y}_i\right)^2 = \sum \left(y_i - \left(b_0 + b_1 x_i\right)\right)^2$$	

Key Formulas	
	Section
Slope of the Least Squares Line $$b_1 = \frac{n\sum x_i y_i - \sum x_i \sum y_i}{n\sum x_i^2 - \left(\sum x_i\right)^2}.$$	13.1
y-Intercept of the Least Squares Line $$b_0 = \frac{1}{n}\left(\sum y_i - b_1 \sum x_i\right)$$	13.1
Mean Square Error $$s_e^2 = \frac{\sum\left(y_i - \hat{y}_i\right)^2}{n-2} = \frac{SSE}{n-2}$$	13.1
Standard Error $$s_e = \sqrt{\frac{\sum\left(y_i - \hat{y}_i\right)^2}{n-2}} = \sqrt{\frac{SSE}{n-2}}$$	13.1
Sample Estimate of the Variance of b_1 $$s_{b_1}^2 = \frac{s_e^2}{\sum\left(x_i - \bar{x}\right)^2}$$	13.2
Sample Estimate of the Standard Deviation (Standard Error) of b_1 $$s_{b_1} = \sqrt{\frac{s_e^2}{\sum\left(x_i - \bar{x}\right)^2}}$$	13.2
$100(1-\alpha)$% Confidence Interval for β_1 $$b_1 \pm t_{\alpha/2,n-2} \cdot s_{b_1}$$	13.2
Test Statistic for Testing the Hypothesis $\beta_1 \neq 0$ $$t = \frac{b_1 - 0}{s_{b_1}} = \frac{b_1}{s_{b_1}}$$	13.2
$100(1-\alpha)$% Confidence Interval for the Mean Value of y Given x $$\hat{y}_p \pm t_{\alpha/2,n-2} s_e \sqrt{\frac{1}{n} + \frac{\left(x_p - \bar{x}\right)^2}{\sum\left(x_i - \bar{x}\right)^2}}$$	13.3

Key Formulas	
	Section
100 (1 − α)% Confidence Interval for the Predicted Value of y Given x	13.3

$$\hat{y}_p \pm t_{\alpha/2,n-2} s_e \sqrt{1 + \frac{1}{n} + \frac{\left(x_p - \bar{x}\right)^2}{\sum\left(x_i - \bar{x}\right)^2}}$$

Additional Exercises

1. A pharmacist is interested in studying the relationship between the amount of a particular drug in the bloodstream (in mg) and reaction time (in seconds) of subjects taking the drug. Ten subjects are randomly selected and administered various doses of the drug. The reaction times (in seconds) are measured 15 minutes after the drug is administered with the following results.

Reaction Times			
Amount of Drug (mg)	**Reaction Time (Seconds)**	**Amount of Drug (mg)**	**Reaction Time (Seconds)**
1	0.5	6	0.8
2	0.7	7	0.9
3	0.6	8	0.6
4	0.7	9	0.9
5	0.8	10	1.0

A regression analysis has been performed to estimate the model, and the following output was produced.

$$\text{Reaction Time} = \beta_0 + \beta_1\left(\text{Amount of Drug}\right) + \varepsilon_i$$

Regression Analysis: Reaction Time (Seconds) versus Amount of Drug (mg)

The regression equation is
Reaction Time (Seconds) = 0.533 + 0.0394 Amount of Drug (mg)

Predictor	Coef	SE Coef	T	P
Constant	0.53333	0.07521	7.09	0.000
Amount of Drug (mg)	0.03939	0.01212	3.25	0.012

S = 0.110096   R-Sq = 56.9%   R-Sq(adj) = 51.5%

Analysis of Variance

Source	DF	SS	MS	F	P
Regression	1	0.12803	0.12803	10.56	0.012
Residual Error	8	0.09697	0.01212		
Total	9	0.22500			

```
Predicted Values for New Observations

New Obs    Fit   SE Fit        95% CI              95% PI
   1   0.6909  0.0393   (0.6003, 0.7815)     (0.4214, 0.9605)


Values of Predictors for New Observations

             Amount of
New Obs Drug (mg)
    1        4.00
```

a. Draw a scatterplot of the data. Describe the relationship you observe between the reaction time and the amount of drug in the bloodstream. Are there any unusual observations?

b. Find and interpret the standard deviation of the error terms in the output.

c. Interpret the slope coefficient.

d. What proportion of the variation in reaction time is explained by the amount of drug in the bloodstream? What other factors might affect reaction time?

e. Is there evidence of a linear relationship between the amount of drug in the bloodstream and reaction time? Test at the 0.05 level and the 0.01 level.

f. Construct and interpret a 95% confidence interval for β_1, the slope of the line.

g. Find the predicted value of the reaction time of an individual who has 4 mg of the drug in the bloodstream.

h. Find and interpret a 95% confidence interval for the average reaction time of all individuals who have 4 mg of the drug in their bloodstreams.

i. Suppose a particular individual has 4 mg of the drug in the bloodstream. What would be the 95% prediction interval for the reaction time?

2. A sample of 11 lonely hearts advertisements, all placed by males, was selected from the local newspaper. In each of the selected ads, the males gave their heights, along with other physical characteristics and preferences. Some of the males obviously felt that being taller than average might result in more responses to the ad. Suppose that y, the number of responses to the ad over the next 30 days, was determined for each male. The following table contains the data.

Height and Response										
Height (Inches)	70	62	67	75	78	69	70	64	66	69	75
y	14	7	10	18	17	12	15	9	12	14	17

a. Draw a scatterplot of the data. Does the relationship appear to be linear?

b. Estimate the slope and intercept of the regression equation using statistical software.

c. Is there evidence of a linear relationship between the number of responses and height? Test at the $\alpha = 0.01$ level.

d. Interpret the regression coefficient corresponding to height.

e. Construct a 95% confidence interval for the slope.

f. Compute R^2 and interpret this value.

g. Estimate the number of responses for a male 6 feet tall. Round your answer to the nearest whole number.

h. Construct and interpret a 95% prediction interval for the number of responses for a male who is 6 feet tall.

i. Construct and interpret a 95% confidence interval for the average number of responses for a male who is 6 feet tall.

3. It is believed that when one is in the process of buying a home, the interest rate that is given on the loan is a function of his or her credit score. The Fair Isaac Corporation (FICO) is a major producer of credit scores. They have collected data from major lenders about buyers' history of borrowing and paying back credit. The following table contains 20 randomly selected loan applicants along with their FICO scores and the interest rate that they were given when financing their homes. With the data given, answer the following questions.

Credit Scores and Interest Rates					
Observation	FICO Score	Interest Rate (%)	Observation	FICO Score	Interest Rate (%)
1	756	6.32	11	819	5.86
2	679	7.85	12	630	8.51
3	527	10.20	13	704	6.83
4	839	5.52	14	679	7.72
5	677	7.30	15	663	7.68
6	686	7.37	16	542	9.53
7	512	9.67	17	575	6.86
8	590	8.40	18	508	9.65
9	765	5.82	19	689	7.75
10	502	10.01	20	750	6.89

a. Draw a scatterplot of the data. Does there appear to be a linear relationship between FICO score and interest rate?

b. Estimate the simple linear regression equation using statistical software.

c. What is the estimate of the mean square error? Interpret this value.

d. Test at the 5% level if a linear relationship exists between FICO scores and interest rates.

e. Interpret the regression coefficient corresponding to FICO score.

f. Construct a 95% confidence interval for the slope. Interpret the interval.

g. Compute the coefficient of determination. Interpret this value.

h. Calculate the correlation coefficient. Interpret this value.

i. What is the average interest rate for a credit score of 725?

j. Construct a 90% confidence interval for the average interest rate for people who have FICO scores of 725. Interpret this interval.

k. Construct a 90% prediction interval for the interest rate for a person with a FICO score of 725. Interpret this interval.

4. It appears that many cellular phone service providers are making huge profits from customers using their messaging services such as text and multimedia messaging services (MMS). To that end, the cellular phone companies are using their marketing campaigns to target kids rather than adults. The belief is that kids tend to utilize their messaging services much more than adults. In fact, it is the belief that the younger one is, the more texts and MMS sent via his or her cell phone. Using the data given which reports the number of monthly messages sent by age, formulate a simple linear regression model to answer the following questions.

Age and Message Use			
Age	**Number of Messages**	**Age**	**Number of Messages**
78	7	37	1541
36	1607	69	6
11	3037	69	25
69	26	55	517
56	491	39	1439
74	0	20	2505
22	2373	14	2845
74	5	10	3048
10	3059	80	0
26	2155	59	295
18	2619	40	1374
68	17	67	35
10	3067		

a.   Draw a scatterplot of the data. Does there appear to be a linear relationship between age and the number of messages that one sends?

b.   What is the estimated simple linear regression equation?

c.   What is the estimate of the coefficient of determination? Interpret this value.

d.   Test at the 5% level if a linear relationship exists between age and the number of messages sent via a cellular phone.

e.   Interpret the regression coefficient corresponding to age.

f.   Construct a 95% confidence interval for the slope. Interpret this interval.

g.   Calculate the correlation coefficient. Interpret this value.

h.   What is the average number of messages sent by a 15-year-old? Round your answer to the nearest whole number.

i.   Construct a 95% confidence interval for the average number of messages sent by a 15-year-old. Interpret this interval.

j.   Suppose Jacob's parents are contemplating giving him a cell phone but with a limited messaging plan at 500 per month. Eager to get the cell phone, Jacob, at 15 years old, promises that he won't send more than 500 messages per month and he'll also limit the number of friends that will have his phone number. In spite of Jacob's honesty and loyalty, should his parents believe that he won't send more than 500 messages per month? Explain your answer.

5. For the last 10 years, the Virginia Department of Mines, Minerals, and Energy (VDMME) has been promoting Energy Star, a resource for energy-efficient products and solutions. VDMME wants all energy consumers to take responsibility and exercise leadership by practicing conservation and efficiency on a daily basis. The average annual energy usage for an 1800 square foot home is 18,000 kilowatt hours. VDMME believes that this number can be significantly reduced if consumers started using Energy Star appliances. Answer the following questions based on data of 25 randomly selected homes with Energy Star appliances built within the last five years.

Home Size and Energy Usage			
Home Size (Square Feet)	Annual Energy Usage (kWh)	Home Size (Square Feet)	Annual Energy Usage (kWh)
2895	15,200	2180	13,227
3650	17,333	4492	19,492
2927	15,050	6450	25,353
6289	24,763	1583	11,075
7252	27,098	4170	18,557
4147	18,291	4189	18,636
6505	25,028	3920	18,210
1413	11,099	6833	26,075
2279	13,110	4469	19,232
3251	15,844	6141	24,225
2992	14,904	5084	21,530
6912	26,329	6746	26,333
2503	13,765		

a. Draw a scatterplot of the data. Does there appear to be a linear relationship between home size and the amount of annual kWh used?

b. What is the estimated simple linear regression equation?

c. What is the estimate of the coefficient of determination? Interpret this value.

d. Test at the 5% level if a linear relationship exists between home size and the annual amount of kWh used.

e. Interpret the regression coefficient corresponding to home size.

f. Construct a 99% confidence interval for the slope. Interpret the interval.

g. Calculate the correlation coefficient. Interpret this value.

h. Suppose the James family constructed a 3200 square foot home using all Energy Star appliances. How many kilowatt hours should they expect to use in their first year in the home?

i. Construct a 95% confidence interval for the average number of kWh that will be used by the James family. Interpret this interval.

6. With grade inflation being a major problem in many US high schools, college admissions offices are beginning to look at other performance measures when evaluating student applications. It is believed that many students with high grade point averages in high school will not necessarily score high on the SAT. Using the data of 30 randomly selected students that took the SAT, answer the following questions to determine if there is a linear relationship between high school GPA and SAT score.

High School GPA and SAT Score			
High School GPA	SAT Score	High School GPA	SAT Score
3.21	1448	4.95	1960
2.23	1435	4.69	1717
2.89	1411	2.49	1365
1.84	1291	2.45	1561
3.34	1462	2.57	1474
2.42	1357	1.28	1328
2.75	1396	1.94	1302
2.35	1549	4.75	1622
4.80	1829	1.91	1499
1.98	1508	4.25	1566
2.92	1514	1.15	1413
4.18	1658	2.17	1428
4.50	1694	4.73	1720
4.42	1686	4.39	1783
4.78	1840	2.92	1614

a. Draw a scatterplot of the data. Does there appear to be a linear relationship between high school GPA and SAT score?

b. What is the estimated simple linear regression equation?

c. What is the coefficient of determination? Interpret this value.

d. Test at the 5% level if a linear relationship exists between high school GPA and SAT score.

e. Interpret the regression coefficient corresponding to high school GPA.

f. Construct a 95% confidence interval for the slope. Interpret the interval.

g. Calculate the correlation coefficient. Interpret this value.

h. What SAT score would you expect for students with a GPA of 3.5? Round your answer to the nearest whole number.

"Give me problems, give me work, give me the most abstruse cryptogram or the most intricate analysis, and I am in my proper atmosphere...I crave for mental exaltation."

— Sir Arthur Conan Doyle

14 CHAPTER
Multiple Regression

Introduction

When you need to predict the outcome of some future event, one of the first things that should come to mind is regression analysis. If there are variables that can be measured—and you believe they affect the future value of the outcome you wish to predict—you have even more reason to think about regression analysis. The author's first "real" experience with regression analysis was in trying to predict the outcome of a horse race in the 1970s. Working with a friend, we believed that if we could reasonably predict a horse's speed in a race, then we might be able to profitably pick winners in the race.

To develop our horse-racing model, we started thinking about what variables would likely contain information about a horse's future performance. One of the first variables we thought of was the historical speed of the horse. Another variable we thought would be useful was the number of days since the horse's last race. Since the horse hopefully pays for its boarding and trainer with winnings, if they haven't been racing recently they must be hurt in some way. Also, the quality of the jockey had to be an important factor. In addition to the jockey's skill, jockeys were assigned a weight penalty if their horse had been repeatedly successful in similar recent races. The penalty weight also must factor into the horse's future performance.

Once you have an idea like this, the next step in the process is to carefully define how you intend to measure the variables you have been thinking about. We experimented with many potential ideas on how to measure the "historical speed of the horse." The other variables were fairly self-evident regarding how they should be measured. The next step was getting some data.

We started buying a newspaper called the "Racing Form" which contained a substantial amount of data on the factors we wished to consider in our model. We inputted the data and estimated our first model. This began one of the most fun episodes in the author's life.

14.1 The Multiple Regression Model

Previously, we constructed linear regression models in which one independent variable, x, has been related to one dependent variable, y. For example, in the Honda Civic model only one independent variable (age) is used to explain asking price. But there are many other variables, including mileage and the condition of the car, that may also be useful in explaining price. If a model is to accurately represent real world phenomena, then the model must potentially be able to accommodate many independent variables. **Multiple regression** is an extension of simple regression techniques, allowing more than one independent variable.

The Multiple Regression Model

The **multiple regression model** is given by

$$y = \beta_0 + \beta_1 x_1 + \beta_2 x_2 + \ldots + \beta_k x_k + \varepsilon$$

where

$\beta_0, \beta_1, \beta_2, \ldots, \beta_k$ are the model's parameters. (They are unknown constants which will require estimation.)

$x_1, x_2, \ldots, x_k$ are independent variables which are measured without error.

ε is a random error which is normally distributed with a mean of zero and a standard deviation σ_e. (The errors are independent of each other.)

DEFINITION

The multiple regression model contains additional parameters which must be estimated. Recall from Chapter 13 that the **method of least squares** is used to find the estimated regression line that minimizes the sum of squared errors, $\left(\text{SSE} = \sum \left(y - \hat{y} \right)^2 \right)$. Even though we are now discussing multiple regression, least squares will remain the method of estimation. Because of the complexity of the calculations, formulas for the least squares coefficients will not be presented. Instead, estimates of the model's parameters will be obtained from one of the many statistical analysis programs that perform multiple regression analysis. Although the format of the output varies among the programs, the program outputs all contain the same fundamental information.

Just as with the simple linear regression model, it is not often that an entire population is available. Therefore, we must estimate the parameters of the multiple regression model using sample data. Using data from the sample, we can estimate the coefficients of the **estimated multiple regression equation**.

The Estimated Multiple Regression Equation

The **estimated multiple regression equation** is

$$\hat{y} = b_0 + b_1 x_1 + b_2 x_2 + \cdots + b_k x_k$$

where $b_0, b_1, b_2, \ldots, b_k$ are estimates of their population counterparts. Specifically, b_0 is an estimate of β_0, b_1 is an estimate of β_1, b_2 is an estimate of β_2, etc.

$\hat{y}$ is the predicted value of y for given values of $x_1, x_2, \ldots, x_k$, and is pronounced *y-hat*. The symbol y is reserved for the observed value of y.

DEFINITION

Model building is a process. The greatest challenge in building a multiple regression model is in determining the appropriate variables needed to explain the dependent variable. In practical applications, this usually requires a great deal of experimentation with the model, deleting and adding independent variables, and examining the effects.

There are a number of different professionals who have need of a real estate pricing model for residential property, including tax assessors, appraisers, and investors. There are many variables that potentially affect the price of a home, including square footage, number of baths, number of bedrooms, type of exterior, and size and location of the lot. One possible model might be

$$\text{Price of Home} = \beta_0 + \beta_1 \cdot \begin{pmatrix} \text{Square} \\ \text{Footage} \end{pmatrix} + \beta_2 \cdot \begin{pmatrix} \text{Age of} \\ \text{Home} \end{pmatrix} + \beta_3 \cdot \begin{pmatrix} \text{Number of} \\ \text{Bedrooms} \end{pmatrix}.$$

To have a useful model the parameters β_0, β_1, β_2, and β_3 must be estimated. Estimating these parameters requires the collection of historical data on home prices, square footage, age of home, and number of bedrooms. If inferences concerning the model's predicted values or parameters are desired, then random sampling methods must be employed during data collection. Assume the data in Table 14.1.1 has been collected using random sampling methods.

Table 14.1.1 - Mount Pleasant Real Estate Data

List Price	Square Footage	Age	Bedrooms
$350,000	2592	8	3
119,900	777	17	1
179,900	1137	17	2
124,900	777	17	1
349,999	2151	4	4
...			

⋮ Data

Table 14.1.1 is the first 5 rows of a subset of the data set found on stat.hawkeslearning.com under **Data Sets > Mount Pleasant Real Estate Data**. The full data set has been filtered to rows where the value of the variable *Duplex* is "Yes", and the variables *List Price, Bedrooms, Square Footage,* and *Year Built* have been extracted. The subset contains 34 data points. Note that *Age* is calculated as years before 2017.

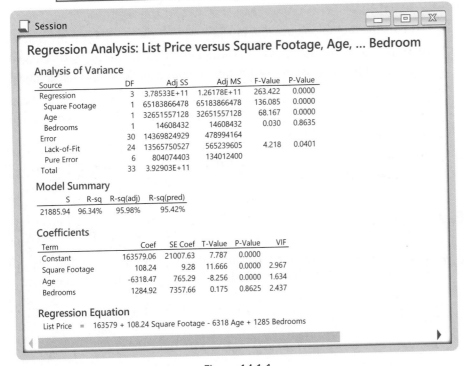

Session

Regression Analysis: List Price versus Square Footage, Age, ... Bedroom

Analysis of Variance

Source	DF	Adj SS	Adj MS	F-Value	P-Value
Regression	3	3.78533E+11	1.26178E+11	263.422	0.0000
Square Footage	1	65183866478	65183866478	136.085	0.0000
Age	1	32651557128	32651557128	68.167	0.0000
Bedrooms	1	14608432	14608432	0.030	0.8635
Error	30	14369824929	478994164		
Lack-of-Fit	24	13565750527	565239605	4.218	0.0401
Pure Error	6	804074403	134012400		
Total	33	3.92903E+11			

Model Summary

S	R-sq	R-sq(adj)	R-sq(pred)
21885.94	96.34%	95.98%	95.42%

Coefficients

Term	Coef	SE Coef	T-Value	P-Value	VIF
Constant	163579.06	21007.63	7.787	0.0000	
Square Footage	108.24	9.28	11.666	0.0000	2.967
Age	-6318.47	765.29	-8.256	0.0000	1.634
Bedrooms	1284.92	7357.66	0.175	0.8625	2.437

Regression Equation

List Price = 163579 + 108.24 Square Footage - 6318 Age + 1285 Bedrooms

⟲ Technology

For instructions to obtain this output using technology please visit stat.hawkeslearning.com and navigate to **Technology Instructions > Regression > Multiple Regression.**

Figure 14.1.1

Output from a statistical analysis package is given in Figure 14.1.1. The estimated model parameters are $b_0 = 163579.06$, $b_1 = 108.24$, $b_2 = -6318.47$, and $b_3 = 1284.92$. The estimated model is:

$$\text{Price of Home} = 163579.06 + 108.24(\text{Square Footage})$$
$$-6318.47(\text{Age}) + 1284.92(\text{Bedrooms}).$$

There are numerous questions about this model.

- Can the model explain a substantial portion of the variation in *home prices*? If not, it will not be very useful.

- Do the signs and magnitudes of the estimated coefficients appear to be reasonable?

- Are the estimates of the coefficients reliable, or do the estimates have substantial sampling variation?

- Are all three independent variables necessary? Do any of the variables not contribute to the explanation of the price of a home?

- Are there other independent variables that could be included that would enhance the model's ability to accurately predict *home prices*?

- Can the model make a useful prediction of the price of a home? How much confidence can be placed in the prediction?

How do we determine whether a model explains a substantial portion of the variation in home prices? We will address this in the next section.

14.1 **Exercises**

Basic Concepts

1. What is the multiple regression model?

2. What are the assumptions about the error term in a multiple regression model? Are these different from the assumptions required for the simple linear model?

3. What method is used to find the estimated multiple regression equation? Is this method different from the one used to find the simple linear regression equation?

4. What is the greatest challenge in building a multiple regression model?

5. What are some questions that should be asked once a multiple regression model is estimated?

Exercises

6. Consider the following computer output of a multiple regression analysis relating annual salary to years of education and years of work experience.

SUMMARY OUTPUT

Regression Statistics	
Multiple R	0.566946595
R Square	0.321428441
Adjusted R Square	0.29192533
Standard Error	10909.996
Observations	49

ANOVA

	df	SS	MS	F	Significance F
Regression	2	2593556200	1296778100	10.89473033	0.000133875
Residual	46	5475288584	119028012.7		
Total	48	8068844784			

	Coefficients	Standard Error	t Stat	P-value	Lower 95%	Upper 95%
Intercept	11214.19915	5625.172956	1.993574106	0.052147881	-108.6867382	22537.08504
Education (Years)	2854.891271	689.6666061	4.139523715	0.000146836	1466.664395	4243.118147
Experience (Years)	839.6360369	261.7094444	3.208275646	0.002433357	312.842248	1366.429826

a. Identify the estimated values of the coefficients b_0, b_1, and b_2.

b. Write the estimated multiple regression equation.

c. Can you think of other independent variables that may be useful in predicting annual salary?

d. Use the model in part **b.** to predict the annual salary of someone with 12 years of education and 2 years of work experience.

7. The manager of a publishing company would like to conduct cost analysis on the most recent books the company has published. He would like to estimate a multiple regression model to relate the cost of printing (per book) to the number of pages in the book and the number of copies printed. A computer output of the multiple regression model for the manager's data is given in the following table.

SUMMARY OUTPUT

Regression Statistics	
Multiple R	0.987606014
R Square	0.975365639
Adjusted R Square	0.972467479
Standard Error	0.445885396
Observations	20

ANOVA

	df	SS	MS	F	Significance F
Regression	2	133.8201656	66.91008281	336.5464936	2.12863E-14
Residual	17	3.379834375	0.198813787		
Total	19	137.2			

	Coefficients	Standard Error	t Stat	P-value	Lower 95%	Upper 95%
Intercept	6.134155476	3.993435752	1.536059638	0.142925974	-2.291257484	14.55956844
Number of Pages	0.010801	0.004147682	2.604105041	0.018522101	0.002050156	0.019551845
Number of Copies	-0.009954478	0.005271436	-1.888380579	0.07616193	-0.021076236	0.00116728

a. Identify the estimated regression coefficients.

b. Write the estimated multiple regression equation.

    c. Do the magnitudes and signs of the coefficients seem reasonable? Explain.

    d. What other variables do you think could be useful in explaining printing cost per book?

8. A nutritionist wishes to study body weight based on height, age, average calories consumed per day, and the average number of minutes spent exercising per day.

    a. Write the multiple regression model the nutritionist is interested in in terms of weight, height, age, calories, and exercise. Assume the coefficients have not yet been estimated.

    b. Identify the independent variables in the multiple regression model.

    c. Predict the sign of the coefficient for each of the independent variables in the model. Explain your answers.

    d. Can you think of any other variables that might be useful for the nutritionist to take into account before performing the regression analysis?

9. Suppose the CEO of an electronics company wants to study the effects of various business practices on annual revenue.

    a. Make a list of independent variables the CEO might be interested in studying.

    b. Suppose the CEO has narrowed his list of factors down, and decided he wants to mainly study the effects of research and development expenditures, advertising expenditures, and the average annual salary paid to employees. Write the multiple regression model in terms of the dependent and independent variables, assuming the coefficients have not yet been estimated.

    c. Make a guess of the sign of the coefficient of research and development expenditures. Explain your prediction.

    d. Why should the CEO be cautious when using this model for revenue estimation and prediction?

Technology

The values for R^2 and adjusted R^2 can be obtained from the multiple regression output produced by Excel and Minitab.

For instructions on how to use these technologies for multiple regression please visit stat.hawkeslearning.com and navigate to **Technology Instructions > Regression > Multiple Regression**.

14.2 The Coefficient of Determination and Adjusted R^2

Just as for simple linear regression, we will discuss methods that can be used to evaluate the overall effectiveness of multiple regression models. For the home price model in the previous section, one of the questions to ask is, how do we determine whether the model explains a substantial portion of the variation in *home prices*? The overall effectiveness and usefulness of multiple regression models can be addressed using the coefficient of determination $\left(R^2\right)$ and the adjusted R^2 $\left(R_a^2\right)$ statistics.

Coefficient of Determination (R^2)

Recall our discussion about the coefficient of determination $\left(R^2\right)$ in Chapter 5. We defined the R^2 statistic as the statistic that directly measures the degree to which the model explains the dependent variable. In multiple regression, the **coefficient of determination** (sometimes called the **multiple coefficient of determination**), still denoted by R^2, represents the proportion of variation in the response variable, y, that is explained by the set of independent variables, x_1, x_2,..., x_k. R^2 is defined in the same way as for the simple linear regression model.

Coefficient of Determination

The **coefficient of determination**, R^2, is given by

$$R^2 = \frac{\text{SSR}}{\text{Total SS}} = 1 - \frac{\text{SSE}}{\text{Total SS}}$$

where

    SSR = the sum of squares of regression,

    SSE = the sum of squared errors, and

    Total SS = the total sum of squares.

R^2 represents the proportion of variation in the dependent variable explained by the set of independent variables in a multiple regression model.

DEFINITION

Just as for simple linear regression,

$$0 \le R^2 \le 1.$$

If all of the slopes are zero $\left(b_i = 0 \text{ for } i = 1, 2,..., k\right)$ then R^2 is also zero, indicating that there is no relationship between the independent variables (x_i's) and the response variable, y. Similarly, if $y = \hat{y}$ for all observations, the value of the coefficient of determination is one $\left(R^2 = 1\right)$. Note that since we are fitting a multiple regression model, we are not fitting a line but a plane or surface.

The output in Figure 14.1.1 reveals that $R^2 = 96.34\%$. Thus, in the *home price* model, the three independent variables (*square footage*, *age*, and number of *bedrooms*) can explain approximately 96.34% of the variation in house prices. Accounting for such a large amount of variation in the dependent variable does demonstrate substantial explanatory power. Unless the data for the model has been collected in some odd way, a model builder would be ecstatic with their initial results.

Adjusted R^2 ($R_a{}^2$)

Adding more independent variables to a regression model will always increase the R^2 value. R^2 will never decrease as variables are added because the SSE can never become smaller with the addition of independent variables and the Total SS is always the same for a given set of responses. Since R^2 can be made larger by including a large number of independent variables, it is sometimes suggested that a modified measure be used that adjusts for the number of independent variables in the model. The **adjusted coefficient of determination** (denoted by R_a^2) adjusts R^2 by dividing each sum of squares by its associated degrees of freedom. Thus, R_a^2 is given by the following formula.

The Proof of the Pudding is in the Eating

How do you know if you have a useful predictive model?

One might think that a useful model would have a high R^2. But, is a high R^2 necessary to have a useful model? In the introduction to Chapter 14, I mentioned a story relating my first experience using regression analysis in predicting the speed of a horse in a race. The R^2 of that model was roughly 0.35. Yet the model predicted well enough to allow us to have a profitable betting experience. Later this same friend and I would start a company that predicted stock prices. The R^2 associated with many of our models was less than 0.1. Yet, we were able to profitably trade substantial volumes of stock with these models.

To judge how effective a model is, you need to use it for its intended purpose. Thus, there are two questions for any predictive model. First, can you predict better with the model than without it? Second, can your model's predictions achieve the goals you have for the model? If the answer is yes to both of these questions, you have a useful model regardless of the value of R^2. Also note, a model with a large value of R^2 may not be a useful model by the two preceding criteria.

Testing a Model's Predictive Ability

If you use all your data to create a model then the "real world" predictive ability of the model is not known since the model was fitted to your data. How would your model perform on data that is was not fitted to? If another set of data is not readily available for this purpose, then researchers often use a hold-out sample for evaluating predictive performance. A sample of observations are withheld from the model estimation process and used for assessing the predictive performance of the model. When multiple models are being considered for the same purpose, the hold-out sample can provide a means of deciding which one is the best predictor.

Adjusted R^2

The adjusted R^2 statistic takes into account the number of independent variables in the model by dividing each sum of squares by its associated degrees of freedom.

$$R_a^2 = 1 - \left(\frac{n-1}{n-k-1} \right) \frac{\text{SSE}}{\text{Total SS}}$$

where n is the number of observations and k is the number of independent variables in the model.

DEFINITION

For example, if one were to fit a simple linear regression model to *home prices* using only *square footage* as the independent variable, we would get $R^2 = 0.8799$ and $R_a^2 = 0.8761$. However, when we add the other two independent variables to the model, we have $R^2 = 0.9634$ and $R_a^2 = 0.9598$. In this case, the value of R^2 increased by 0.0835, indicating that adding the other variables to the model helped explain more variability in *home prices*. On the other hand, the value of R_a^2 increased by slightly more (0.0837). R_a^2 is commonly used as a method of comparison between multiple regression models when one is attempting to find the model that best fits the data. Unlike the R^2 value, the adjusted coefficient of determination may actually become smaller when another independent variable is added to the model. Thus, the adjusted R^2 value is most useful when comparing multiple regression models with different numbers of independent variables.

14.2 **Exercises**

Basic Concepts

1. What does R^2 represent?

2. What range of values can the coefficient of determination take on?

3. Can you think of a way a model might have a large R^2 and not be useful for prediction? Explain.

4. Explain the difference between R^2 and adjusted R^2.

5. Explain why the adjusted R^2 statistic is sometimes a better measure to use to evaluate the fit of a regression model.

6. Will there ever be a situation in which the adjusted R^2 statistic is greater than the R^2 statistic? Explain your answer.

Exercises

⬡ **Data**

stat.hawkeslearning.com
Data Sets > Mount Pleasant Real Estate Data.

7. Using the Mount Pleasant Real Estate data set, construct a multiple regression model relating housing prices (in thousands of dollars) to the number of bedrooms in the house, labeled "Bedrooms", and the size of the lot on which the house was built, labeled "Acreage".

   a. Write the estimated regression equation.

   b. Identify the values of SSR, SSE, and Total SS from the table.

   c. What is the coefficient of determination for this model? Interpret this value in terms of the problem.

   d. What is R_a^2? Interpret this value.

   e. Compare the R^2 and R_a^2 values. Which value should be used to evaluate the fit of the multiple regression model? Explain why.

8. Add an additional variable, Square Footage, to the housing price model from Exercise 7.

   a. Write the estimated regression equation.

   b. What is R_a^2 for this model?

   c. How does the adjusted R^2 value for this model compare to the adjusted R^2 value for the model in Exercise 7?

   d. Do you think adding the additional independent variable, Square Footage, improved the model? Explain your answer.

9. The owner of a new pizzeria in town wants to study the relationship between weekly revenues and advertising expenditures. Both measures were recorded in thousands of dollars. The computer output for the simple linear regression model is given below.

SUMMARY OUTPUT

Regression Statistics	
Multiple R	0.858179902
R Square	0.736472743
Adjusted R Square	0.692551534
Standard Error	1.058296197
Observations	8

ANOVA

	df	SS	MS	F	Significance F
Regression	1	18.78005496	18.78005496	16.76804334	0.006394067
Residual	6	6.719945042	1.11999084		
Total	7	25.5			

	Coefficients	Standard Error	t Stat	P-value	Lower 95%	Upper 95%
Intercept	74.69887795	7.104358625	10.51451396	4.34789E-05	57.31513863	92.08261726
Advertising Expenditures	1.854820243	0.452960815	4.094880138	0.006394067	0.746465058	2.963175428

   a. Write the estimated regression equation.

   b. What is the coefficient of determination for this model? Interpret this value.

   c. What is the value of the adjusted R^2 statistic? Is this statistic useful for the pizzeria owner as he studies this model? Explain.

   d. Do you believe this model is useful in explaining revenues based on advertising expenditures? Explain your answer.

10. How could the restaurant owner improve this model? Are there other independent variables that he should consider including? The owner of the pizzeria discussed in Exercise 9 wishes to build on the model relating revenues to advertising expenditures by breaking the advertising expenditures into three categories: television advertising, newspaper advertising, and direct mail advertising.

a. Write the new regression model in terms of television, newspaper, and mail expenditures. Assume the coefficients have not yet been estimated.

b. Consider the following summary output for the new model. Write the estimated multiple regression equation.

SUMMARY OUTPUT

Regression Statistics	
Multiple R	0.967040091
R Square	0.935166537
Adjusted R Square	0.88654144
Standard Error	0.64289449
Observations	8

ANOVA

	df	SS	MS	F	Significance F
Regression	3	23.8467467	7.948915566	19.23217829	0.007708883
Residual	4	1.653253302	0.413313326		
Total	7	25.5			

	Coefficients	Standard Error	t Stat	P-value	Lower 95%	Upper 95%
Intercept	73.93199827	4.523870838	16.34264127	8.20538E-05	61.3717192	86.49227731
Television	2.383047934	0.318133378	7.490719616	0.001698799	1.499768074	3.266327793
Newspaper	1.454439994	0.355820285	4.087569076	0.015004989	0.466524505	2.442355483
Mail	1.815990841	0.276487962	6.568064755	0.002780349	1.048337191	2.58364449

c. Interpret the coefficient for television advertising expenditures. Remember that revenues and expenditures are in thousands of dollars.

d. What is the adjusted coefficient of determination? Interpret this value.

e. How does the coefficient of determination of this model compare to the coefficient of determination for the simple linear regression model in Exercise 9? Does this appear to be a more useful model? Explain.

f. What is the value of the R^2 statistic for this model? Should we use the R^2 value or the adjusted R^2 value when evaluating the usefulness of this model? Explain why.

14.3 Interpreting the Coefficients of the Multiple Regression Model

In interpreting the coefficients of the model, we ask the question, *Do the signs and magnitudes of the estimated coefficients appear to be reasonable?*

A portion of the output from Figure 14.1.1 is repeated here.

Coefficients

Term	Coef	SE Coef	T-Value	P-Value	VIF
Constant	163579.06	21007.63	7.787	0.0000	
Square Footage	108.24	9.28	11.666	0.0000	2.967
Age	-6318.47	765.29	-8.256	0.0000	1.634
Bedrooms	1284.92	7357.66	0.175	0.8625	2.437

In the simple linear regression, the estimated coefficient, b_1, is the slope of the line. It is interpreted to be the change in the dependent variable associated with a one-unit change in the independent variable. This interpretation remains basically valid for the multiple regression model as well. The coefficient, b_1, is the estimated change in *home price* for a one-unit increase in *square footage* for a given *age* and number of *bedrooms*. Is it reasonable to believe that each additional square foot of living space would cost an additional $108.24? While the cost of construction varies, $108.24 per foot seems sensible given the other variables in the model.

The coefficient, b_2, is the estimated change in *home price* for a one-unit increase in *age* for a given *square footage* and number of *bedrooms*. Houses are like people, they deteriorate with age. Thus, all other conditions being equal, it might be reasonable to expect a negative coefficient for b_2, which would mean as *age* increases *home price* decreases. According to the estimated model, this is the case in this instance. The coefficient for b_2 is −6318.47, which means that for each year of *age* the price of the home decreases by $6318.47, all other things being equal. Intuitively, this coefficient has the correct sign. It is difficult to evaluate whether $6318.47 is a reasonable magnitude, so later, we will rely on statistical inference to evaluate the accuracy of the estimate.

The coefficient, b_3, is the estimated change in *home price* for an additional *bedroom* for a given *square footage* and *age*. Intuitively, we would expect this coefficient to be positive since additional finishing costs are associated with adding a bedroom. The coefficient for b_3 is 1284.92, which means that the price of a home will increase by $1284.92 for each bedroom, all else remaining equal. It is difficult to evaluate whether $1284.92 is a reasonable magnitude, so we will rely on statistical inference to evaluate the coefficients in the next section.

14.3 **Exercises**

Basic Concepts

1. What two aspects of the model coefficients are usually analyzed first when studying a multiple regression model?

2. In the simple linear regression model, what is the interpretation of b_1? Does this interpretation change in the multiple regression model?

3. When interpreting the coefficient of an independent variable in a multiple regression model, what assumption are we making regarding the other independent variables?

Exercises

4. Compare the estimated multiple regression equation from Exercise 7 in 14.2,

$$\hat{y} = -69{,}280.13 + 142{,}935.73(\text{Bedrooms}) + 369{,}879.29(\text{Acreage}),$$

to the multiple regression equation from Exercise 8 in 14.2.

$$\hat{y} = -28{,}520.81 - 34{,}641.71(\text{Bedrooms}) + 194{,}986.08(\text{Acreage}) + 240.21\ (\text{Square Footage})$$

What happened to the coefficient on the Bedrooms term when the additional variable was added? Does this make sense? Explain.

5. Consider the following estimated multiple regression equation relating the number of study hours and GPA to a student's ACT score.

$$\text{Estimated ACT Score} = 8.35 + 1.53(\text{Study Hours}) + 0.30(\text{GPA})$$

   a. Identify the values of b_0, b_1, and b_2.

   b. Interpret the value of b_0 in terms of the problem.

   c. Interpret the value of b_1 in terms of the problem.

   d. Interpret the value of b_2 in terms of the problem.

6. Consider the following estimated regression model relating annual salary to years of education and work experience, which was presented in Section 14.1, Exercise 6.

$$\text{Estimated Salary} = 11214.20 + 2854.89(\text{Education}) + 839.64(\text{Experience})$$

   a. Consider the coefficient for the education variable. Do the sign and magnitude of the coefficient seem to make sense? Explain.

   b. Consider the coefficient for the experience variable. Do the sign and magnitude of the coefficient seem to make sense? Explain.

   c. Interpret the regression coefficient for years of experience.

   d. Suppose an employee with 8 years of education (note that education years are the number of years after 8th grade) has been with the company for 5 years. According to this model, what is her estimated annual salary?

   e. How would you expect her salary to change if she stays at the company for another year?

   f. Suppose two employees at the company have been working there for five years. One has a bachelor's degree (8 years of education) and one has a master's degree (10 years of education). Which employee would you expect to earn a higher salary? How much more money would you expect her to make?

14.4 Inference Concerning the Multiple Regression Model and Its Coefficients

Sometimes we must ask the question, *Is the overall model worthwhile?*

If the model has no redeeming merit, then the independent variables (as a group) will not be related to the dependent variable. Consider the multiple regression model

$$y = \beta_0 + \beta_1 x_1 + \beta_2 x_2 + \ldots + \beta_k x_k + \varepsilon.$$

Suppose $\beta_1 = \beta_2 = \ldots = \beta_k = 0$, then the regression model becomes

$$y = \beta_0 + 0x_1 + 0x_2 + \ldots + 0x_k + \varepsilon.$$

Since multiplying any number by 0 results in 0, all of the independent variables disappear from the model, and we are left with

$$y = \beta_0 + \varepsilon,$$

which says that y is a constant, β_0, plus a random error, ε. So, if $\beta_1 = \beta_2 = \ldots = \beta_k = 0$, then the model is not useful. We will develop a methodology for testing the hypotheses

$$H_0 : \beta_1 = \beta_2 = \ldots = \beta_k = 0$$
$$H_a : \text{At least one } \beta_i \neq 0.$$

To determine the usefulness of a multiple regression model, we must first introduce a new distribution called the F-distribution. The F-distribution, named after the English statistician Sir Ronald A. Fisher, is a continuous distribution. It will be used in this and subsequent chapters to analyze variation in test statistics formed as ratios of two random variables.

The F-distribution is not symmetrical, rather, it is skewed to the right. Like the t-distribution, its parameters are degrees of freedom. F-distributions are associated with test statistics that are quotients. What distinguishes the F-distribution is that it has a pair of values, for its degrees of freedom.

Properties of an *F*-Distribution

1. The F-distribution is skewed to the right.

2. The values of F are always greater than or equal to 0.

3. The shape of the F-distribution is completely determined by its two parameters, the degrees of freedom for the numerator and the degrees of freedom for the denominator.

    PROPERTIES

The shape of the F-distribution is a function of its degrees of freedom. The following figure shows two examples of the F-distribution.

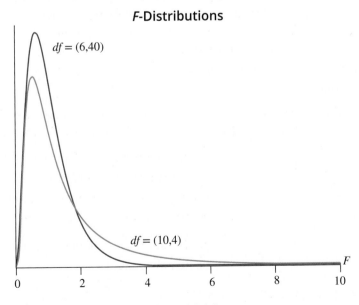

F-Distributions

$df = (6,40)$

$df = (10,4)$

Figure 14.4.1

Like the t-distribution, tables have been compiled (see Appendix A) that show critical values of the F-distribution at common levels of significance. The notation F_α will indicate the value of F such that α of the area under the curve lies to the right of this value.

For example, to find the critical value at $\alpha = 0.05$ for an F-distribution with 3 numerator degrees of freedom and 7 denominator degrees of freedom, consult the table in Appendix A, Table H, with $\alpha = 0.05$. The leftmost column corresponds to the denominator degrees of freedom, and the top row corresponds to the numerator degrees of freedom.

Numerator Degrees of Freedom

Denominator Degrees of Freedom		1	2	3	4
	1	161.4476	199.5000	215.7073	224.5832
	2	18.5128	19.0000	19.1643	19.2468
	3	10.1280	9.5521	9.2766	9.1172
	4	7.7086	6.9443	6.5914	6.3882
	5	6.6079	5.7861	5.4095	5.1922
	6	5.9874	5.1433	4.7571	4.5337
	7	5.5914	4.7374	4.3468	4.1203
	8	5.3177	4.4590	4.0662	3.8379

From the table, we see that $F_{0.05}$ for 3 numerator degrees of freedom and 7 denominator degrees of freedom is 4.3468. Thus, for this F-distribution, an area of 0.05 lies to the right of 4.3468.

In general, the value of F such that an area of α is to the right of F is denoted by F_α, as shown in Figure 14.4.1.

Steps in the Test of Hypothesis

Step 1: Determine the null and alternative hypotheses.

Is the overall model useful in explaining variation in the dependent variable? If some of the model's independent variables are useful predictors of y, then the coefficients, β_i, of these variables will have a nonzero value. The null and alternative hypotheses in plain English would then be as follows.

Null Hypothesis: The overall model is not useful in explaining variation in the dependent variable.

Alternative Hypothesis: The overall model is useful in explaining variation in the dependent variable. That is, at least one of the coefficients is different from zero.

$$H_0: \quad \beta_1 = \beta_2 = \ldots = \beta_k = 0$$

Implies the overall model is not useful. Specifically, that the independent variables (as a group) are not useful predictors of the dependent variable.

$$H_a: \quad \text{At least one } \beta_i \neq 0$$

Implies at least one of the variables is a useful predictor.

Step 2: Specify the significance level α.

The level of the test is specified by the problem or arbitrarily chosen by the analyst.

Step 3: Validate the assumptions of the hypothesis testing model, identify the appropriate test statistic, and compute its value.

The main assumptions in a multiple regression analysis are the same as in simple linear regression. The error terms are presumed to be normally distributed with a mean of 0 and a constant variance. The errors are also presumed to be independent of each other. The validity of these assumptions can be examined after performing a multiple regression by doing a residual analysis, which is beyond the scope of this book.

In all of the previous hypothesis tests, the test statistic involved the sample estimate of the corresponding population measure. This test statistic will be different. If none of the independent variables are useful predictors of y, then the model will not explain much (if any) of the variation in the dependent variable. One way of testing whether the overall model is useful is to examine whether the model explains a sufficient portion of the variation in the dependent variable. We have already studied R^2, which measures the fraction of variation explained by the model. However, the sampling distribution of R^2 for the multiple regression model is too complex.

Testing the Multiple Regression Model

Assumptions:

1. The error terms are normally distributed with mean 0 and a constant variance, σ_e.

2. The errors are independent of one another.

Hypotheses:

H_0: $\beta_1 = \beta_2 = ... = \beta_k = 0$

H_a: At least one $\beta_i \neq 0$

PROCEDURE

Testing the Multiple Regression Model (continued)

Test Statistic:

$$F = \frac{\dfrac{\text{Sum of Squares of Regression}}{k}}{\dfrac{\text{Sum of Squared Errors}}{n-(k+1)}}$$

$$= \frac{\dfrac{SSR}{k}}{\dfrac{SSE}{n-(k+1)}} = \frac{\text{Mean Square Regression}}{\text{Mean Square Error}}$$

The F-statistic has an F-distribution with k and $n - (k + 1)$ degrees of freedom if the null hypothesis, $\beta_1 = \beta_2 = ... = \beta_k = 0$, is true.

The F-statistic is a ratio which compares the variation explained by the model (SSR) to the unexplained variation (SSE). Both of these quantities were discussed in Chapter 13. The number of independent variables in the model is represented by k and the number of observations is n.

PROCEDURE

The F-statistic is a ratio which compares the variation explained by the model (SSR) to unexplained variation (SSE). The sum of squares of regression (SSR) and the sum of squared errors (SSE) were discussed in Section 5.3. The symbol k represents the number of independent variables in the model and n represents the number of observations.

A small value of F means that **mean square regression (MSR)** is small in relation to **mean square error (MSE).** This would mean that the SSR, which is the amount of variation explained by the model, is small in relation to SSE (which represents variation not explained by the model). A small value of F would indicate that the model is of little value in explaining the variation in the dependent variable y. On the other hand, a large F-value indicates that the variation explained by the model is large in relation to the unexplained variation. The fundamental question is how large must the F-value be in order to believe the model has some explanatory power. This question is complicated by sampling variation. Even if there is no relationship between the independent variables and the dependent variable, sampling variation can produce a model that explains some portion of the variation in y.

The F-statistic has an F-distribution with k numerator degrees of freedom and $n-(k+1)$ denominator degrees of freedom. We will reject the null hypothesis if the F-statistic is larger than the F-value corresponding to a one-tailed test for some prescribed α.

Fortunately, the F-statistic is computed by virtually every statistical analysis program. It is found in the analysis of variance (ANOVA) table usually under the heading F or F-Value. (See Section 5.3 for the interpretation of SSR, SSE, and SST.)

Step 4: Determine the critical value(s) or P-value.

Suppose the following decision rule is used.

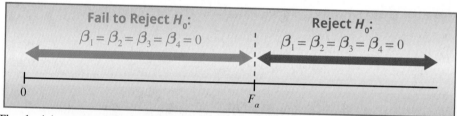

The decision rule defines "rareness" for the F-statistic assuming the null hypothesis is true. Essentially what the rule says is that F-values larger than F_α would be too rare for us to believe that the null hypothesis is reasonable. When such a value occurs, the null hypothesis will be rejected in favor of the alternative.

Analysis of Variance				
Source of Variation	Sum of Squares	Degrees of Freedom	Mean Square	F-Statistic
Regression	SSR	k	SSR/k	MSR/MSE
Residual Error	SSE	$n - (k + 1)$	SSE/$(n - (k + 1))$	
Total	SST	$n - 1$		

Step 5: Make the decision to reject or fail to reject H_0.

If the value of the F-statistic falls in the rejection region or the P-value for the test statistic is less than or equal to α, then reject the null hypothesis. If not, then do not reject the null. Most analysts will use the P-value approach because the P-value of the F-statistic is displayed on the output from statistical software programs.

Step 6: State the conclusion in terms of the original question.

Anyone trying to build a model for predictive purposes hopes the null hypothesis (H_0: $\beta_1 = \beta_2 = ... = \beta_k = 0$) is rejected, since rejecting the null implies the model can explain some of the variation in the dependent variable.

Example 14.4.1

For the Mount Pleasant Real Estate data in Table 14.1.1 determine if there is sufficient evidence at the 0.05 significance level that the overall model is useful in explaining the variation in home prices.

Solution

Step 1: Determine the null and alternative hypotheses.

Is the overall model useful in explaining the variation in home prices? If some of the model's independent variables are useful predictors of y, then the coefficients, β_i, of these variables will have a non-zero value.

H_0: $\beta_1 = \beta_2 = ... = \beta_k = 0$ Implies the overall model is insignificant.

H_a: At least one $\beta_i \neq 0$ Implies at least one of the independent variables is useful in explaining the variation in home prices.

Step 2: Specify the significance level α.

The value of α is given as 0.05.

Step 3: Validate the assumptions of the hypothesis testing model, identify the appropriate test statistic and compute its value.

☑ The errors are presumed to be from a normal distribution with a mean of 0 and a constant variance.

☑ The errors are presumed to be independent of one another.

Tests for these assumptions are beyond the scope of this text. We will use the F-statistic as the test statistic for the hypotheses.

The ANOVA table for the Mount Pleasant Real Estate model from Figure 14.1.1 is repeated below. The value of F is given to be 263.4224.

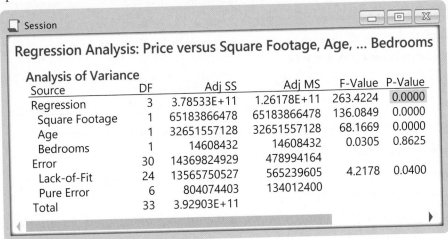

Regression Analysis: Price versus Square Footage, Age, ... Bedrooms

Analysis of Variance

Source	DF	Adj SS	Adj MS	F-Value	P-Value
Regression	3	3.78533E+11	1.26178E+11	263.4224	0.0000
Square Footage	1	65183866478	65183866478	136.0849	0.0000
Age	1	32651557128	32651557128	68.1669	0.0000
Bedrooms	1	14608432	14608432	0.0305	0.8625
Error	30	14369824929	478994164		
Lack-of-Fit	24	13565750527	565239605	4.2178	0.0400
Pure Error	6	804074403	134012400		
Total	33	3.92903E+11			

Technology

For instructions to obtain this output using technology please visit stat.hawkeslearning.com and navigate to **Technology Instructions > Regression > Multiple Regression.**

Step 4: Determine the critical value(s) or *P*-value.

Since there are three independent variables (*square footage*, *age*, and *number of bedrooms*) in the model, the degrees of freedom for the numerator are $k = 3$ and for the denominator $n - (k + 1) = 34 - (3 + 1) = 30$. The critical value for F at the 0.05 level is, therefore, 2.9223.

An *F*-value larger than 2.9223 will indicate a value of F that is too rare to have occurred by chance if the null hypothesis were true.

Note the *P*-value for this test statistic, as shown in the ANOVA table output is approximately 0.

Step 5: Make the decision to reject or fail to reject H_0.

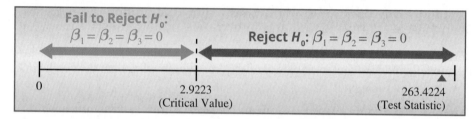

Since the value of the *F*-statistic, 263.4224, falls in the rejection region, the null hypothesis will be rejected in favor of the alternative.

Alternatively, the *P*-value for the *F*-statistic of 263.4224 is 0.0000 to four decimal places. Since 0.0000 is less than 0.05, we reject the null hypothesis.

Step 6: State the conclusion in terms of the original question.

The null hypothesis is rejected in favor of the alternative, which states that at least one of the independent variables is useful in explaining the variation in *home prices*.

Confidence Intervals for Individual Coefficients

Confidence intervals for individual b_i in a multiple regression model are almost identical to the confidence interval for b_1 in the simple regression model found in Section 13.2.

Confidence Interval for Each Coefficient

The **$100(1 - \alpha)\%$ confidence interval for each coefficient**, β_i, in a multiple regression model is given by

$$b_i \pm t_{\alpha/2, n-(k+1)} s_{b_i}, \quad i = 1, ..., k.$$

DEFINITION

To compute the confidence interval requires three pieces of information.

- An estimate of the coefficient β_i, namely b_i.

- The standard deviation of the estimate s_{b_i}. Both b_i and s_{b_i} are reported in the summary output.

- The value of $t_{\alpha/2, n-(k+1)}$, which is the number of standard deviations the endpoint of the interval is from the point estimate. (The degrees of freedom of this t is $n - (k + 1)$, which is the same as the degrees of freedom associated with the error terms in the ANOVA table.)

Example 14.4.2

Compute and interpret the 95% confidence interval for β_1 in the Mount Pleasant Real Estate model.

Solution

The β_1 model coefficient relates to the variable *square footage* in the Mount Pleasant Real Estate model. The output in Figure 14.1.1 provides two parts of the information necessary to develop a confidence interval for β_1. You will find this information under the label Coefficients.

A portion of the output from Figure 14.1.1 is repeated here.

Coefficients

Term	Coef	SE Coef	T-Value	P-Value	VIF
Constant	163579.06	21007.63	7.787	0.0000	
Square Footage	108.24	9.28	11.666	0.0000	2.967
Age	-6318.47	765.29	-8.256	0.0000	1.634
Bedrooms	1284.92	7357.66	0.175	0.8625	2.437

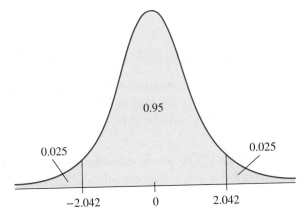

t-Distribution, df = 30

0.95

0.025   0.025

−2.042   0   2.042

b_1 is given in the output to be 108.24.

s_{b_1} is given in the output to be 9.28.

In order to compute the *t*-value, the degrees of freedom must be determined

$$df = n - (k + 1) = 34 - (3 + 1) = 30.$$

For a 95% confidence interval $t_{\%_2, n-(k+1)}$ will be $t_{0.025,\ 30} = 2.042$. The resulting confidence interval will be

$$108.24 \pm 2.042 \cdot 9.28$$

$$108.24 \pm 18.94976 \text{ or } (89.29024, 127.18976).$$

We are 95% confident that the true value of β_1, the increase in the price of a house per square foot given a particular number of bedrooms and age, will be between $89.29 and $127.19.

Testing Hypotheses on Individual β_i

We discussed in Section 13.3 the implications of testing whether the slope coefficient $\beta_1 = 0$. In the case of the simple linear model, if $\beta_1 = 0$, then the independent variable is not related to the dependent variable. However, in multiple regression, there is more than one independent variable. In multiple regression models, deciding whether a particular independent variable is a useful predictor of the dependent variable is an important part of the model building process. For example, is the variable *number of bedrooms* useful in predicting *home price*? The rationale for testing whether an independent variable is useful in predicting the dependent variable is the same as that used in testing whether $\beta_1 = 0$ for the simple linear model. The technique will be illustrated with an example.

Example 14.4.3

For the Mount Pleasant Real Estate model constructed in Figure 14.1.1,

$$\text{Price of Home} = \beta_0 + \beta_1(\text{Square Footage}) + \beta_2(\text{Age of Home}) + \beta_3(\text{Number of Bedrooms}).$$

Is the independent variable *number of bedrooms* a useful predictor of *home price*? Use $\alpha = 0.05$ as the level of significance.

Solution

Step 1: Determine the null and alternative hypotheses.

For the Mount Pleasant Real Estate model, if *number of bedrooms* is **not** a useful predictor of *home price*, then its coefficient in the model, β_3, will equal 0. The sample estimate of β_3, namely b_3, will be used to evaluate the reasonableness of the hypothesis $\beta_3 = 0$.

The alternative hypothesis should be two-sided since the relationship between the *number of bedrooms* and *home price* can be positive or negative. Therefore, our hypotheses are as follows:

$H_0: \beta_3 = 0$ Implies that the *number of bedrooms* is **not** a useful predictor of *home price*.

$H_a: \beta_3 \neq 0$ Implies that the *number of bedrooms* is a useful predictor of *home price*.

Step 2: Specify the significance level α.

The level of the test is specified in the problem as $\alpha = 0.05$.

Step 3: Validate the assumptions of the hypothesis testing model, identify the appropriate test statistic and compute its value.

The assumptions for the Mount Pleasant Real Estate model have been discussed in previous examples.

The test statistic is $t = \dfrac{b_3 - 0}{s_{b_3}} = \dfrac{b_3}{s_{b_3}}$. The test statistic is identical in form to the test statistic used in Section 13.2 for the simple linear model. If the value of the test statistic is near zero, then there is evidence that the *number of bedrooms* variable is not a significant predictor of *home price*.

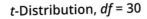

t-Distribution, df = 30

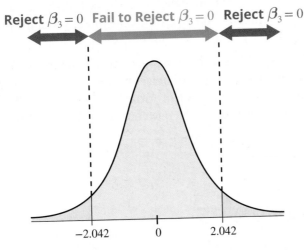

A portion of the output from Figure 14.1.1 is repeated here.

Coefficients

Term	Coef	SE Coef	T-Value	P-Value	VIF
Constant	163579.06	21007.63	7.787	0.0000	
Square Footage	108.24	9.28	11.666	0.0000	2.967
Age	-6318.47	765.29	-8.256	0.0000	1.634
Bedrooms	1284.92	7357.66	0.175	0.8625	2.437

Using the output in Figure 14.1.1 we find that

$$t = \frac{b_3 - 0}{s_{b_3}} = \frac{b_3}{s_{b_3}} = \frac{1284.92}{7357.66} \approx 0.175$$

The estimated value of b_3 is 0.175 standard deviations from zero. Is this persuasive evidence that $\beta_3 \neq 0$?

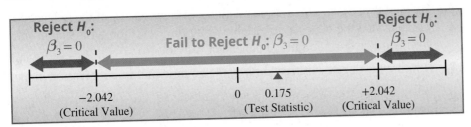

Step 4: Determine the critical value(s) or P-value.

This criteria is defined by the critical value of the test statistic. Since the test is two-tailed and the level of confidence is specified to be 0.95, then $1 - \alpha = 0.95$, which implies $\alpha = 0.05$ and $\frac{\alpha}{2} = \frac{0.05}{2} = 0.025$. The test statistic has a t-distribution with $df = 34 - (3 + 1) = 30$. The critical value corresponds to $t_{0.025, 30} = 2.042$. The P-value for the *number of bedrooms* is given in the output as 0.8625.

Step 5: Make the decision to reject or fail to reject H_0.

Since the value of the test statistic falls into the *Fail to Reject* region, there is insufficient evidence at the 0.05 level to reject the null hypothesis $\beta_3 = 0$. Alternatively, the P-value of 0.8625 is greater than $\alpha = 0.05$, we fail to reject the null hypothesis.

Step 6: State the conclusion in terms of the original question.

Since we did not reject the null hypothesis H_0: $\beta_3 = 0$, then the variable *number of bedrooms* is not a significant predictor of *home price*, given the other variables currently in the model.

We apply the exact same t-test to the other variables in the model. Both b_1 and b_2, the coefficients of the variables *square footage* and *age*, are significant. This suggests that a model with only two independent variables, *square footage* and *age*, may produce a model almost as good as the one containing three variables.

14.4 **Exercises**

Basic Concepts

1. If the overall multiple regression model is not useful, what does this tell us about the coefficients of the independent variables?

2. What is the hypothesis being tested when we test to determine if the overall multiple regression model is useful?

3. When testing the overall model, describe the null and alternative hypotheses in plain English.

4. What is the test statistic used in a hypothesis test to determine if an overall model is significant? What is the distribution of this test statistic?

5. Explain the significance of the ratio of the mean square regression to the mean square error.

6. True or false: Even if there is no relationship between any of the independent variables and the dependent variable, sampling variation will explain some portion of the variation in the dependent variable.

7. How are the degrees of freedom calculated for a multiple regression model?

8. When testing the overall model for significance, do you perform a one or two-tailed test?

9. What is the rejection rule in tests of hypothesis for model significance?

10. What is the expression for a confidence interval for an individual coefficient, β_i?

11. Outline the three pieces of information needed to compute a confidence interval for an individual coefficient.

12. What is the test statistic used to test a hypothesis about an individual coefficient in a multiple regression model? How many degrees of freedom are associated with this test statistic?

13. If we fail to reject the null hypothesis in a hypothesis test about an individual coefficient, should this variable remain in the regression model? Explain.

14. Does a low R^2 imply that a model will not be useful for prediction?

Exercises

⠿ Data

stat.hawkeslearning.com
Data Sets > Moneyball

15. In Lesson 5.3 Exercise 23, we used the Moneyball data set (1962-2001) to look at the individual relationships between runs scored (RS) and on-base percentage (OBP) and runs scored (RS) and slugging percentage (SLG). On-base percentage (OBP) and slugging percentage (SLG) were determined to be two of the most statistically significant variables that contributed to the number of runs scored. Remember that a run differential of 135 runs was identified as necessary to make the MLB playoffs. Use the Moneyball data set, subsetted to only the years 1962-2001, to perform the following.

   a. Build a single model to predict runs scored (RS) using on-base percentage (OBP) and slugging percentage (SLG). Write the estimated regression equation.

   b. Is the overall model significant at the 1% level?

   c. What percent of variation in the runs scored (RS) is explained by on-base percentage (OBP) and slugging percentage (SLG)?

   d. Determine if each independent variable is related to the dependent variable at the 0.01 level of significance.

   e. Should we consider removing any independent variables from this regression model? If yes, identify the variable(s) that should be removed and explain why.

16. Consider the model from Exercise 6 in Section 14.1 relating annual salary to years of work experience and years of education.

SUMMARY OUTPUT

Regression Statistics	
Multiple R	0.566946595
R Square	0.321428441
Adjusted R Square	0.29192533
Standard Error	10909.996
Observations	49

ANOVA

	df	SS	MS	F	Significance F
Regression	2	2593556200	1296778100	10.89473033	0.000133875
Residual	46	5475288584	119028012.7		
Total	48	8068844784			

	Coefficients	Standard Error	t Stat	P-value	Lower 95%	Upper 95%
Intercept	11214.19915	5625.172956	1.993574106	0.052147881	-108.6867382	22537.08504
Education (Years)	2854.891271	689.6666061	4.139523715	0.000146836	1466.664395	4243.118147
Experience (Years)	839.6360369	261.7094444	3.208275646	0.002433357	312.842248	1366.429826

   a. Formulate the hypotheses for testing the multiple regression model for overall significance.

   b. Find the value of the test statistic for a hypothesis test about the overall model.

   c. Is there evidence that the overall model is useful in predicting annual salary?

d. Consider the coefficient for years of education. Find a 95% confidence interval for the value of β_1. Interpret this interval.

e. Formulate the hypotheses for testing the significance of the coefficient β_1.

f. Is there sufficient evidence at the 0.05 level that years of education is useful in predicting annual salary?

17. Consider the printing cost model discussed in Exercise 7 of Section 14.1.

SUMMARY OUTPUT

Regression Statistics	
Multiple R	0.987606014
R Square	0.975365639
Adjusted R Square	0.972467479
Standard Error	0.445885396
Observations	20

ANOVA

	df	SS	MS	F	Significance F
Regression	2	133.8201656	66.91008281	336.5464936	2.12863E-14
Residual	17	3.379834375	0.198813787		
Total	19	137.2			

	Coefficients	Standard Error	t Stat	P-value	Lower 95%	Upper 95%
Intercept	6.134155476	3.993435752	1.536059638	0.142925974	-2.291257484	14.55956844
Number of Pages	0.010801	0.004147682	2.604105041	0.018522101	0.002050156	0.019551845
Number of Copies	-0.009954478	0.005271436	-1.888380579	0.07616193	-0.021076236	0.00116728

a. What percentage of the variation in printing price is explained by the two independent variables number of pages and number of copies?

b. Is the overall model significant at the 1% level?

c. Consider the estimated regression coefficient for the number of pages. Construct a 99% confidence interval for β_1. Interpret this interval.

d. Is the number of pages variable useful in predicting printing cost at the 5% level? Would the decision change at the 1% level?

e. Construct a 95% confidence interval for β_2. Interpret this interval.

f. Is the number of copies useful in explaining the variation in printing cost at the 5% level of significance? Do you think the publisher should consider removing this variable from the model? Explain your answer.

18. The following table contains US Census Bureau data from selected cities regarding rental rates of two-bedroom apartments, city populations, and median incomes. Monthly rent is given in dollars, population is given in thousands of people, and median income is given in thousands of dollars. Suppose we wish to build a multiple regression model to predict the cost of rent based on population and median income.

Monthly Rent, Population, and Median Income in Selected Cities			
City	Monthly Rent ($)	2010 Population (Thousands)	2010 Median Income (Thousands of Dollars)
Denver, CO	868	600.158	45.438
Birmingham, AL	711	212.237	31.704
San Diego, CA	1414	1307.402	61.962
Gainesville, FL	741	124.354	28.653
Winston-Salem, NC	707	229.617	41.979
Memphis, TN	819	646.889	36.535
Austin, TX	966	790.390	50.236
Seattle, WA	1219	608.660	58.990
Richmond, VA	735	204.214	37.735
Charleston, SC	812	120.083	47.799
College Park, MD	1407	30.413	66.900
Savannah, GA	789	136.286	33.778
Minneapolis, MN	988	382.578	45.625
Detroit, MI	805	713.777	29.447
Baton Rouge, LA	827	229.493	35.436

a. Write the multiple regression model using population and median income to predict rent. Assume the regression coefficients have not yet been estimated.

b. Predict the signs of the coefficients β_1 and β_2. Explain your answers.

c. Using statistical software, estimate the multiple regression equation. Identify the values of b_0, b_1, and b_2 and write the estimated multiple regression equation. Interpret the estimated coefficients.

d. At the 1% level of significance, is the overall model useful in predicting monthly rent? Identify the test statistic for this test.

e. Find a 95% confidence interval for β_2. Interpret this interval.

f. Determine if each independent variable is related to the dependent variable at the 0.05 level of significance.

g. Should we consider removing any independent variables from this regression model? If yes, identify the variable(s) that should be removed and explain why.

19. Using the information from Exercise 18, estimate the simple linear regression equation using median income to predict rent.

a. Write the estimated simple regression equation.

b. Is the simple linear regression model significant at $\alpha = 0.01$?

c. Is median income related to the monthly rental rate at $\alpha = 0.01$? Identify the test statistic used in this hypothesis test.

d. What percent of the variation in monthly rent is explained by median income? Compare this to the percent of variation in monthly rent explained by both population and median income in Exercise 19.

e. Which model do you think is a better model to use to predict monthly rental rates? Explain your answer.

14.5 Inference Concerning the Model's Prediction

Many regression models are developed solely to predict the dependent variable. To use the multiple regression model for prediction, insert the values of the independent variables in the model and calculate the predicted value. For a house with 2500 square feet that is ten years old with four bedrooms, the model would predict the price to be

$$\text{Home Price} = 163579.06 + 108.24(2500) - 6318.47(10) + 1284.92(4)$$
$$\approx \$376,134.04$$

This is the point estimate. How good is this estimate? The answer to this question depends on what you are trying to predict. Are you trying to predict the average price for all 2500 square foot homes that are ten years old with four bedrooms, or are you trying to predict the price of a particular home of this type?

Confidence Intervals for the Mean Value of *y* Given *x*

Note

The value of $376,134 for a 2500 square foot home that is 10 years old and has 4 bedrooms that is estimated using the Home Price model, differs slightly from the value calculated in the Minitab output ($376,142) due to rounding.

In Section 13.3 we discussed a confidence interval for the mean (or average) value of y given $x = x_p$ for the simple linear regression model. In our multiple regression model, the point estimate, $376,134, is the mean value of y given $x_1 = 2500$, $x_2 = 10$, and $x_3 = 4$. In other words, the price of $376,134 is the estimated average price for all ten-year-old, 2500 square feet homes with four bedrooms. Since we do not have all homes in the sample, the predicted average price of $376,134 is only an estimate of the true average value. How good is the estimate? For multiple regression, the expression for the confidence interval of the mean value of y given x is beyond the scope of an introductory text.

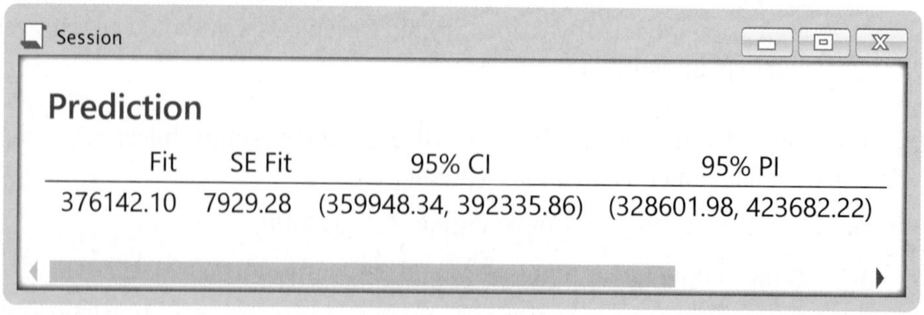

⌾ **Technology**

For instructions to obtain this output using technology please visit stat.hawkeslearning.com and navigate to **Technology Instructions > Regression > Regression Prediction Intervals**.

	Session				

Prediction

Fit	SE Fit	95% CI	95% PI
376142.10	7929.28	(359948.34, 392335.86)	(328601.98, 423682.22)

Figure 14.5.1

Fortunately, almost all statistical analysis programs will compute a confidence interval for the mean value of *y* given *x* for the multiple regression model. According

to the output in Figure 14.5.1, the confidence interval for the average price of a 10
-year-old four-bedroom home with 2500 square feet would be $359,948 to $392,336.

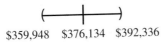

$359,948 $376,134 $392,336

Confidence Intervals for the Predicted Value of *y* Given *x*

Suppose you own a home that has 2500 square feet, is ten years old, and has four
bedrooms. You may not be especially interested in the average price for such a home.
Instead, it would be preferable to create a confidence interval for the price of your
home. Once again, for multiple regression, the expression for the prediction interval
is beyond the scope of the text. Fortunately, most statistical analysis programs
will also compute a prediction interval. Using the output from Figure 14.5.1, the
95% prediction interval for your 2500 square foot, ten-year-old home with four
bedrooms is $328,602 to $423,682. As we observed in Section 13.3, to account for
individual variation, the prediction interval for *y* given *x* is substantially wider than
the confidence interval for the average value of *y* given *x*.

Confidence Interval for Mean Price

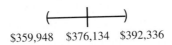

$359,948 $376,134 $392,336

Confidence Interval for Individual Price

$328,602 $376,134 $423,682

Can the model make a useful prediction of the price of a home?

Although the model has an R^2 of 96.34%, surprisingly the 95% prediction interval is
extremely wide. This indicates that not a great deal of confidence can be placed in
the estimated value, $376,134, of the 2500 square foot, ten-year-old, four-bedroom
home we have been pricing.

The prediction interval provides a sense of the degree of confidence you can place
in the model's predictive performance. Wide prediction intervals would suggest
the efficacy of the model is questionable. However, if you are using a model for
predictive purposes you will judge the model by whether it helps you perform a
predictive task, or not.

The author was the cofounder of a firm that performed automated stock trading.
Initially we used multiple regression modeling to predict real time stock prices. The
question for the firm was whether the predictions we were planning on using would
produce profits if trades were made using the model's prediction of future prices of
a given stock. In case you are wondering, the model eventually worked. Before the
company was sold it was trading six percent of all trades on the New York Stock
Exchange and the NASDAQ. Regression modeling is certainly one of the most
powerful tools for modeling real world events. If you are considering model building
as a career, also consider courses in machine learning. What separates machine
learning from statistics (from a modeling perspective) is that machine learning is
mostly focused on how well a model performs a predictive task. In essence, what
is the best model for a predictive task.

14.5 Exercises

Basic Concepts

1. What is a point estimate for a multiple regression model?

2. Explain how a point estimate is interpreted as an "average" value.

3. Distinguish between a confidence interval and a prediction interval for a multiple regression model.

4. What is the price that is paid when making predictions regarding individual values?

5. Suppose an estimated multiple regression model, $\hat{y} = b_0 + b_1 x_1 + b_2 x_2$, produces a 95% confidence interval of (3.292, 7.072) and a 95% prediction interval of (0.364, 10.000) when $x_1 = 6$ and $x_2 = 6$. Interpret both of these intervals.

Exercises

Data

stat.hawkeslearning.com
Data Sets > SAT Scores and Graduating GPA

6. Use the SAT Scores and Graduating GPA data set of 30 students that was discussed in Example 13.2.3. In that example, we estimated a model using only total SAT score to predict graduating GPA. However, with multiple regression, the SAT verbal and SAT math scores can be treated as separate variables in the model. Computer output of the model

$$\text{GPA} = \beta_0 + \beta_1 (\text{SAT Verbal}) + \beta_2 (\text{SAT Math}) + \varepsilon$$

is given.

Regression Analysis: College GPA versus SAT Verbal, SAT Math

Analysis of Variance

Source	DF	Adj SS	Adj Ms	F-Value	P-Value
Regression	2	0.8763	0.4382	2.643	0.0895
Error	27	4.4760	0.1658		
Total	29	5.3524			

Model Summary

S	R-sq	R-sq(adj)
0.407160	16.37%	10.18%

Coefficient

Term	Coef	SE Coef	T-Value	P-Value
Constant	0.13128	1.15417	0.114	0.9103
SAT Verbal	0.00179	0.00137	1.311	0.2009
SAT Math	0.00273	0.00187	1.457	0.1566

Regression Equation

College GPA = 0.13128 + 0.00179 SAT Verbal + 0.00273 SAT Math

```
Prediction for College GPA
    Settings
    Variable              Setting
    SAT Verbal              500
    SAT Math                500

    Prediction

    Fit        SE Fit     95% CI        95% PI
    2.39        0.18    (2.03, 2.75)    (1.48, 3.30)
```

a. Use the output provided to determine the standard deviation of the error terms.

b. Interpret the coefficient of SAT Verbal. What would it mean if the coefficient was negative?

c. Determine if the overall model is useful in explaining graduating GPA. Test at the 0.05 level.

d. What proportion of the variation in GPA is explained by the model?

e. Determine if the SAT Verbal variable is a useful predictor of GPA. Test at the 0.05 level.

f. The output includes a predicted GPA for someone scoring 500 on both the SAT Verbal and SAT Math portions. Find the predicted value in the output.

g. What is the model's estimate of the average GPA for individuals who scored 500 on both the SAT Verbal and SAT Math sections? Find the 95% confidence interval for this average. Interpret this interval.

h. Suppose your nephew scored 500 on both the SAT Verbal and SAT Math sections. What would be the model's prediction for his graduating GPA? Find the 95% prediction interval for your nephew in the output. Interpret this interval.

i. Why is the prediction interval so much wider than the confidence interval in part **g.**?

j. Summarize the strengths and weaknesses of the estimated model.

7. How tall will your child be? A researcher has collected a random sample of heights of parents and their female children (all heights are in inches). The heights of the mother, father, and daughter are recorded in the following table.

Heights of Parents and Daughters (Inches)												
Mother	64	66	62	70	70	58	66	66	64	67	65	66	68
Father	73	70	72	72	72	63	75	75	72	69	77	70	74
Daughter	65	65	61	69	67	59	69	70	68	70	70	65	70

a. Create two scatterplots using the mother with the daughter and the father with the daughter. Does there appear to be a linear relationship in either of the plots?

b. Using statistical software, estimate the parameters of the following regression model.

$$\text{Daughter Height} = \beta_0 + \beta_1\left(\text{Mother Height}\right) + \beta_2\left(\text{Father Height}\right) + \varepsilon$$

c. Is the overall model useful in explaining the variation in daughter height? Test at the 0.05 level.

d. Is the father's height useful in explaining the daughter's height? Test at the 0.05 level.

e. Is the mother's height useful in explaining the daughter's height? Test at the 0.01 level.

f. Interpret each of the regression coefficients.

g. Construct and interpret 95% confidence intervals for β_1 and β_2. Interpret these intervals.

h. Predict the height of a daughter whose father is six feet two inches tall and whose mother is five feet four inches tall.

i. Find a 95% prediction interval for the height of a daughter whose father is six feet two inches tall and whose mother is five feet four inches tall. Interpret this interval.

j. Find a 95% confidence interval for the average height of a daughter whose father is six feet two inches tall and whose mother is five feet four inches tall.

8. On Sunday, January 2, 2011, 16 games were played in the National Football League. The number of rushing yards, passing yards, first downs, and points for the 32 teams participating in these games is given in the table.[1]

Team Data: January 2, 2011									
Team	Rushing Yards	Passing Yards	First Downs	Points	Team	Rushing Yards	Passing Yards	First Downs	Points
Miami	44	240	16	7	Jacksonville	198	140	23	17
New England	181	321	24	38	Houston	244	253	22	34
Buffalo	37	130	6	7	Dallas	159	127	14	14
New York	276	119	17	38	Philadelphia	121	162	14	13
Cincinnati	90	305	20	7	New York	82	243	14	17
Baltimore	98	125	10	13	Washington	67	336	20	14
Pittsburgh	100	325	24	41	San Diego	164	313	20	33
Cleveland	43	210	17	9	Denver	146	205	18	28
Oakland	209	160	21	31	Arizona	78	242	19	7
Kansas City	115	142	17	10	San Francisco	100	276	16	38
Minnesota	74	145	16	13	Chicago	110	168	13	3
Detroit	107	258	22	20	Green Bay	60	229	14	10
Carolina	137	182	12	10	Tennessee	51	300	17	20
Atlanta	99	256	24	31	Indianapolis	101	264	24	23
Tampa Bay	84	255	18	23	Saint Louis	47	155	10	6
New Orleans	106	212	20	13	Seattle	141	192	19	16

a. In order to predict a team's points from rushing yards, passing yards, and first downs, a multiple regression analysis is performed on the data with points as the dependent variable. The associated regression output is given. Write the estimated regression equation for predicting points based on the three predictor variables.

SUMMARY OUTPUT

Regression Statistics	
Multiple R	0.774540403
R Square	0.599912836
Adjusted R Square	0.557046354
Standard Error	7.508433133
Observations	32

ANOVA

	df	SS	MS	F	Significance F
Regression	3	2366.956093	788.9853643	13.99492	9.23535E-06
Residual	28	1578.543907	56.37656811		
Total	31	3945.5			

	Coefficients	Standard Error	t Stat	P-value
Intercept	-15.6150327	5.982932568	-2.609929582	0.014378
Rushing Yards	0.127133936	0.029615758	4.292780033	0.000191
Passing Yards	0.081411959	0.029307161	2.777886231	0.009655
First Downs	0.121492053	0.460140758	0.264032366	0.793689

b. Find the standard deviation of the error terms in the output.

c. Determine if the overall model is useful in predicting points scored. Use $\alpha = 0.05$.

d. What fraction of the total variation in points is explained by the model?

e. Is the rushing yards variable useful in predicting points scored at the 0.01 level?

f. Is the passing yards variable useful in predicting points scored at the 0.01 level?

g. Is the first downs variable useful in predicting points scored at the 0.01 level?

h. The coefficient of rushing yards in the regression equation is 0.1271. Interpret this value.

i. Should any variables be removed from this model? Explain.

9. In the previous exercise, total points was predicted based on rushing yards, passing yards, and first downs. It is noted from the summary output that both rushing yards and passing yards have P-values of less than 0.01. However, first downs does not appear to be significant as an independent variable. Perhaps a simpler model would be better.

a. Using the data from the previous exercise, estimate the regression equation

$$\text{Points} = \beta_0 + \beta_1 (\text{Rushing Yards}) + \beta_2 (\text{Passing Yards}) + \varepsilon.$$

b. Is the overall model significant in predicting total points? Test at $\alpha = 0.01$.

c. What percentage of the variation in total points is explained by rushing yards and passing yards? Compare this to the percentage of the variation in total points that was explained by the three independent variables rushing yards, passing yards, and first downs.

d. Which model do you think would be better to use for estimation and prediction of total points; the model from Exercise 8 or the model in this exercise? Explain your answer.

e. Suppose that in preparation for the upcoming game against Miami, the coach of Buffalo wishes to predict the points that will be scored. He has studied Miami's defense in previous games, and predicts that the Buffalo offense will have approximately 102 rushing yards and 263 passing yards. How many points, according to the model, should Buffalo score in the next game?

f. Construct at 95% confidence interval for the average number of points that will be scored in the game against Miami. Interpret this interval.

g. Construct a 95% prediction interval for the number of points that will be scored in the game against Miami. Interpret this interval.

14.6 Multiple Regression Models with Qualitative Independent Variables

Throughout Chapter 13 and this chapter, we have discussed quantitative variables in the regression models. Quantitative variables take on values on a well-defined scale, such as number of pizzas, miles to destination, income, age, and temperature. Many variables of interest, however, are not quantitative, but qualitative. Examples of qualitative variables are type of college (public or private), season of the year (spring, summer, fall, and winter), and type of investment (stocks, mutual funds, or bonds).

In order to use qualitative variables in regression analysis, we need to identify the classes of the qualitative variable quantitatively. To do this, we will use **indicator** (or **dummy**) **variables** that take on values of 0 and 1. If we have a qualitative variable with c classes, that variable will be represented by $c - 1$ indicator variables in the regression model, with each indicator variable taking on a value of 0 or 1.

Suppose we added a variable to our Home Price model that identified whether the home had a screened porch or not. The variable, let's call it *porch*, has $c = 2$ classes. Thus, the variable *porch* will be represented by $c - 1 = 1$ indicator variable in the model. *Porch* could be modeled as follows.

$$x_4 = \begin{cases} 1 & \text{if the house has a screened porch} \\ 0 & \text{if the house does not have a screened porch} \end{cases}$$

The regression model would then be

$$y = \beta_0 + \beta_1 x_1 + \beta_2 x_2 + \beta_3 x_3 + \beta_4 x_4 + \varepsilon.$$

To understand the meaning of the regression coefficients in this model, consider the difference in the model for no porch $(x_4 = 0)$ and porch $(x_4 = 1)$. For a house without a porch, $x_4 = 0$, and we have

$$y = \beta_0 + \beta_1 x_1 + \beta_2 x_2 + \beta_3 x_3 + \beta_4 (0) + \varepsilon \quad \text{No porch}$$
$$= \beta_0 + \beta_1 x_1 + \beta_2 x_2 + \beta_3 x_3 + \varepsilon.$$

Similarly, for a house with a porch, $x_4 = 1$, and the model becomes

$$y = \beta_0 + \beta_1 x_1 + \beta_2 x_2 + \beta_3 x_3 + \beta_4 (1) + \varepsilon \quad \text{With a porch}$$
$$= (\beta_0 + \beta_4) + \beta_1 x_1 + \beta_2 x_2 + \beta_3 x_3 + \varepsilon.$$

Notice the difference in the two models. The no porch model has an intercept of β_0 and the porch model has an intercept of $(\beta_0 + \beta_4)$. After examining the two models, the difference is clear. The coefficient β_4 indicates how much more (or less) the house price will be for houses with a porch versus houses without a porch, for any given *square footage* (x_1), *age* of house (x_2), and *number of bedrooms* (x_3). Thus, β_4 measures the differential effect of having a porch. In general, β_4 shows how much higher (or lower) the plane of best fit is for the class coded 1 than the class coded 0, for any given level of x_1, x_2, and x_3.

Example 14.6.1

The table below contains the real estate data set from Table 14.1.1, but with the added column of the variable *porch*, indicating whether the house has a screened porch or not.

Mount Pleasant Real Estate Data					
Price	Square Feet	Age	Number of Bedrooms	Porch	Screened Porch?
350000	2592	8	3	1	Yes
119900	777	17	1	1	Yes
179900	1137	17	2	0	No
124900	777	17	1	0	No
349999	2151	4	4	0	No
...					

:·: **Data**

The complete data set can be found on stat.hawkeslearning.com under **Data Sets > Mount Pleasant Real Estate Data**.

You may recall that we are interested in modeling *home price* as a function of the following variables.

$x_1 = square\ footage$

$x_2 = age$

$x_3 = bedrooms$

$$x_4 = \begin{cases} 1 & \text{if the house has a screened porch} \\ 0 & \text{if the house does not have a screened porch} \end{cases}$$

The multiple regression model is given by

$$y = \beta_0 + \beta_1 x_1 + \beta_2 x_2 + \beta_3 x_3 + \beta_4 x_4 + \varepsilon.$$

The fitted regression model is as follows.

$$\text{Price of Home} = 163626.79 + 114.95(square\ footage) - 6152.36(age)$$
$$- 1358.31(bedrooms) - 13506.64(porch)$$

SUMMARY OUTPUT

Regression Statistics	
Multiple R	0.983153945
R Square	0.96659168
Adjusted R Square	0.961983636
Standard Error	21275.07421
Observations	34

ANOVA

	df	SS	MS	F	Significance F
Regression	4	3.79777E+11	94944231937	209.7618082	5.92154E-21
Residual	29	13126234702	452628782.8		
Total	33	3.92903E+11			

	Coefficients	Standard Error	t Stat	P-value	Lower 95%	Upper 95%
Intercept	163626.7916	20421.30079	8.012554798	7.76213E-09	121860.5419	205393.0413
Square Feet	114.9454965	9.88474698	11.62857246	1.93724E-12	94.72891896	135.162074
Age	-6152.363638	750.6484437	-8.196065268	4.89101E-09	-7687.612086	-4617.11519
Number of Bedrooms	-1358.306077	7327.914624	-0.185360522	0.854236625	-16345.57428	13628.96213
Porch	-13506.63879	8148.538447	-1.657553545	0.108188125	-30172.27116	3158.993583

Now that we are fitting the model with *porch* as the indicator variable, we are interested in the effect that having a screened porch or not has on the average home price. The estimate of β_4 is −13506.64. This means that the difference in average home price is approximately $13,506.64. Specifically, the average home price with a porch is about $13,506.64 less. Intuitively, this doesn't make sense.

The important question would be, *is the slope associated with the porch variable significant?* The formal test can be carried out just as we did in Section 14.5. That is, our hypotheses are the following.

$H_0: \beta_4 = 0$ Implies *porch* is **not** a useful predictor of *home price*.
$H_a: \beta_4 \neq 0$ Implies *porch* is a useful predictor of *home price*.

According to the Excel output, we have a *t*-statistic of −1.658 with a *P*-value of 0.1082. Given the large *P*-value associated with this test, we would fail to reject the null hypothesis and conclude that the *porch* variable is not a useful predictor of *home price*.

Example 14.6.2

A real estate investor wants to study the relationship between annual return on his commercial retail shops (measured in thousands of dollars) as it relates to their location and the number of homes near the shops. Specifically, the investor has collected data on the annual return of the shops, the number of households within 15 miles of the shops (measured in thousands), and the location of the shops (whether the shops are in a suburban area, near a shopping mall, or downtown). The annual return data are given in the following table.

Shop Data			
Shop	**Location**	**Annual Return (Thousands of Dollars)**	**Number of Households (Thousands)**
1	Mall	185.69	163
2	Suburban	203.00	215
3	Mall	245.81	232
4	Mall	137.07	108
5	Suburban	207.36	220
		...	

:: **Data**

The complete data set can be found at **Data Sets > Shop Data**.

Solution

Given the data, we can define our variables as follows.

$$x_1 = number\ of\ households$$

Since *location* is a qualitative variable and there are three locations, we will use $c - 1 = 3 - 1 = 2$ variables to represent the locations. The variables representing locations are

$$Mall:\ \ x_2 = \begin{cases} 1 & if\ mall \\ 0 & otherwise \end{cases}$$

$$Downtown:\ \ x_3 = \begin{cases} 1 & if\ downtown \\ 0 & otherwise. \end{cases}$$

The suburban location is known as the **base level variable** since for suburban locations $x_2 = 0$ and $x_3 = 0$. The coefficients estimated for the x_2 and x_3 indicator variables will represent a difference between the mall and downtown locations and the suburban location.

The multiple regression model for *annual return* is given by

$$y = \beta_0 + \beta_1 x_1 + \beta_2 x_2 + \beta_3 x_3 + \varepsilon.$$

The fitted regression model is

$$Estimated\ Annual\ Return = 15.5071 + 0.8704\left(number\ of\ households\right)$$
$$+ 27.8186\left(mall\right) + 6.7185\left(downtown\right).$$

Let's discuss the model and its implications. First of all, we want to know if the *location* and the *number of households* in the area are useful predictors of annual return of the shops. You may recall that the test of the model's significance is conducted using the F-test that tests the following hypothesis.

$$H_0: \beta_1 = \beta_2 = \beta_3 = 0$$
$$H_a: At\ least\ one\ \beta_i \neq 0.$$

SUMMARY OUTPUT

Regression Statistics	
Multiple R	0.999974838
R Square	0.999949677
Adjusted R Square	0.999943871
Standard Error	0.288707033
Observations	30

ANOVA

	df	SS	MS	F	Significance F
Regression	3	43062.89567	14354.29856	172213.5214	5.5533E-56
Residual	26	2.167145526	0.083351751		
Total	29	43065.06282			

	Coefficients	Standard Error	t Stat	P-value	Lower 95%	Upper 95%
Intercept	15.50707387	0.261037514	59.40553771	2.6636E-29	14.97050357	16.04364416
Number of Households	0.870441943	0.001225001	710.5645401	2.77306E-57	0.867923919	0.872959968
Mall	27.81856958	0.138873816	200.3154397	5.45545E-44	27.53311037	28.1040288
Downtown	6.718542409	0.13223228	50.80864057	1.49967E-27	6.446735064	6.990349754

Examining the Excel output, we see that the F-statistic for the test is 172,213.5214 with a P-value near zero. This is an indication that we reject H_0 and conclude that at least one of the slopes in the model is significantly different from zero, and the model can be useful in predicting the variability of *annual returns*.

Having concluded that the model is significant, we focus our attention on the individual regression coefficients. That is, we can test the following hypothesis.

$$H_0: \beta_i = 0$$
$$H_a: \beta_i \neq 0$$

If we examine the P-values in the Excel output for each of the coefficients, it is noted that each of them is near zero, indicating that each coefficient is different from zero, and each independent variable is useful in predicting *annual return*.

Now we can examine the average annual return of the investments as a function of the location of the shops (i.e., whether they are near a mall, downtown, or in a suburban area). The estimated models can be written as follows.

For the mall location $(x_2 = 1, x_3 = 0)$:

Estimated Annual Return $= (b_0 + b_2) + b_1 (number\ of\ households)$
$$= (15.5071 + 27.8186) + 0.8704 (number\ of\ households).$$

For the downtown location $(x_2 = 0, x_3 = 1)$:

Estimated Annual Return $= (b_0 + b_3) + b_1 (number\ of\ households)$
$$= (15.5071 + 6.7185) + 0.8704 (number\ of\ households).$$

For the suburban location $(x_2 = 0, x_3 = 0)$:

Estimated Annual Return $= b_0 + b_1 (number\ of\ households)$
$$= 15.5071 + 0.8704 (number\ of\ households).$$

Notice that the best fit line for each location has a different intercept value, but the same slope. Plotting the three lines illustrates this difference.

Graphical Representation of Regression Models

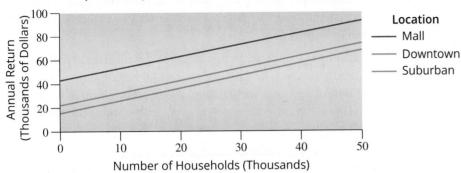

So, modeling with the qualitative variables allows us to compare the average difference in annual return of the shops by location. That is, in order to compare the mall and suburban locations, the difference (as can be seen in the model) is

$$\left(\beta_0 + \beta_1 x_1 + \beta_2\right) - \left(\beta_0 + \beta_1 x_1\right) = \beta_2.$$

Therefore, the estimate of β_2 (which is 27.8186) represents the difference between the average annual return for shops in the mall locations having x_1 households in the area and the average annual return for shops in the suburban locations having x_1 households in the area. Thus, we can say that for any number of households in a given area, the average annual return in a mall location will be approximately $27,818.60 greater than the average annual return in a suburban location.

Similarly, to compare downtown and suburban returns, we get

$$\left(\beta_0 + \beta_1 x_1 + \beta_3\right) - \left(\beta_0 + \beta_1 x_1\right) = \beta_3.$$

Thus, the estimate of β_3 (which is 6.7185) represents the difference between the average annual return for shops in the downtown locations having x_1 households in the area and the average annual return for shops in the suburban locations having x_1 households in the area. So, we can say that for any number of households in a given area, the average annual return in a downtown location will be $6718.50 greater than the average annual return in a suburban location.

Lastly, to compare mall and downtown locations, we look at

$$\left(\beta_0 + \beta_1 x_1 + \beta_2\right) - \left(\beta_0 + \beta_1 x_1 + \beta_3\right) = \beta_2 - \beta_3.$$

The estimated difference between β_2 and β_3 is given by $\beta_2 - \beta_3$ (21.1001) which represents the difference between the average annual return for shops in the mall locations having x_1 households in the area and the average annual return for shops in the downtown locations having x_1 households in the area. In terms of the problem, we can say that for any number of households in a given area, the average annual return in a mall area will be $21,100.10 greater than the average annual return in a downtown location.

There are three potential issues to keep in mind when using these regression results.

1. These results are only meaningful within the relevant range of the data that was used to estimate the regression equation. For example, using the model in Example 14.6.2 to predict annual return for a shop with 1000 households or 1,000,000 households in the surrounding area would likely yield an unreliable point estimate.

2. The regression lines for the three locations in Example 14.6.2 are assumed to have the same slope, but in reality they could have very different slopes. Using a regression model with **interaction terms** allows the slopes for the regression lines to differ.

3. The regression lines estimated in this example are all linear. This implies that annual return increases by the same amount for each additional thousand households within 15 miles of the shops. This assumption is sometimes unrealistic. This issue can be addressed using **polynomial (or nonlinear) regression models**.

Regression models with interaction terms and polynomial regression models are beyond the scope of this text and are not discussed in detail. Multiple regression is a complex topic that involves many methods of estimation. We only present the basics in this text.

14.6 **Exercises**

Basic Concepts

1. Give three examples of qualitative independent variables that may be of interest to someone performing regression analysis to predict annual salary.

2. Explain how qualitative variables are transformed into quantitative variables in order to estimate a regression model.

3. If a qualitative variable has c classes, how many indicator (dummy) variables will there be in the model? Explain why this is the case.

4. When an indicator (dummy) variable is equal to one, does this represent a difference in the slope or the intercept of the model? Explain.

5. What is a base level variable? Interpret the value of an estimated coefficient for an indicator variable in terms of the base level variable.

6. Identify three potential issues to keep in mind when constructing regression models involving indicator variables. Also suggest how these issues can be addressed.

Exercises

7. Consider the following estimated multiple regression model relating GPA to the number of classes attended and the final exam score in a particular class, and if the student is a freshman (= 1 if freshman, = 0 otherwise).

$$\text{Cumulative GPA} = -0.8777 + 0.0672(\text{Attendance})$$
$$+ 0.0678(\text{Exam Score}) - 0.1436(\text{Freshman})$$

   a. Are the signs of the estimated coefficients what you would expect for these three independent variables? Explain.

   b. Interpret the coefficient for the attendance variable.

   c. Interpret the coefficient for the exam score variable.

   d. Interpret the coefficient for the freshman variable.

e. Suppose two students, one a freshman and one a senior, attended the same number of classes and both got a score of 88 on the final exam. What would be the expected difference in GPA for the two students?

8. Consider the following computer output for the multiple regression model discussed in the previous exercise.

SUMMARY OUTPUT

Regression Statistics	
Multiple R	0.714589997
R Square	0.510638864
Adjusted R Square	0.508467143
Standard Error	0.516416069

ANOVA

	df	SS	MS	F	Significance F
Regression	3	188.1180981	62.70603271	235.1309671	1.8485E-104
Residual	676	180.2794359	0.266685556		
Total	679	368.397534			

	Coefficients	Standard Error	t Stat	P-value	Lower 95%
Intercept	-0.877712645	0.138557037	-6.334666683	4.34037E-10	-1.149766538
Attendance	0.067163994	0.003669275	18.3044333	4.30384E-61	0.059959449
Exam Score	0.067820136	0.004265782	15.89864106	1.37161E-48	0.059444361
Freshman	-0.143623671	0.047077779	-3.050774156	0.002371853	-0.236059922

a. Test the usefulness of the overall model in predicting Cumulative GPA using a 5% significance level.

b. What percentage of the variation in Cumulative GPA is explained by the three independent variables?

c. Is the qualitative independent variable, freshman, useful in predicting Cumulative GPA? Use $\alpha = 0.05$.

d. Can you think of other variables that could be added to the model? Name one quantitative variable and one qualitative variable that might be useful.

9. A personnel director is interested in studying the effects which age, experience, and gender have on salary. Eight employees are randomly selected and each employee's salary, age, experience, and gender (= 0 if male, = 1 if female) are recorded.

Employee Data			
Salary ($)	Age	Experience (Years)	Gender
40,500	25	2	1
75,000	55	20	0
72,000	27	5	0
52,500	30	7	1
43,500	22	3	1
87,000	33	8	1
34,500	19	1	0
64,500	45	15	1

a. Create three scatterplots using salary with age, salary with experience, and salary with gender. Does each of the plots have a linear relationship?

b. Using statistical software, estimate the parameters of the following regression model:

$$\text{Salary} = \beta_0 + \beta_1(\text{Age}) + \beta_2(\text{Experience}) + \beta_3(\text{Gender}) + \varepsilon.$$

c. Is the overall model useful in explaining salary? Test at the 0.05 level.

d. Is age useful in explaining salary? Test at the 0.05 level.

e. Is experience useful in explaining salary? Test at the 0.01 level.

f. Is gender useful in explaining salary? Test at the 0.10 level.

g. Interpret each of the regression coefficients.

h. Predict the salary of a female employee who is 35 years old with 10 years of experience.

i. Construct and interpret a 95% prediction interval for a female employee who is 35 years old with 10 years of experience. How useful is this interval?

j. Construct and interpret a 95% confidence interval for the average salary of a female employee who is 35 years old with 10 years of experience. How useful is this interval?

⦂ **Data**

stat.hawkeslearning.com
Data Sets > Campus Crime

10. Consider the following crime data from select college campuses. The table contains the number of crimes committed, the number of campus police employed on campus, the total enrollment of the college, and whether or not the college is private. The full data set is available on the companion site.

Campus Crime Data				
School	Number of Crimes	Number of Police	Total Enrollment	Private School
1	64	12	1131	Yes
2	138	21	12,954	No
3	141	32	16,009	No
4	84	22	1682	Yes
5	86	35	2888	Yes
		...		

a. Create an indicator (dummy) variable for whether or not the college is private. Let Private = 1 if the school is private and Private = 0 if the school is public.

b. Suppose education officials wish to predict the number of crimes on college campuses based on the number of police employed and total enrollment. They would also like to know whether there are fewer crimes committed on private campuses than public ones. Use statistical software to estimate the following regression model.

$$\text{Crimes} = \beta_0 + \beta_1(\text{Police}) + \beta_2(\text{Enrollment}) + \beta_3(\text{Private}) + \varepsilon$$

Write the estimated multiple regression equation.

c. Is the overall model useful in predicting the number of crimes? Use $\alpha = 0.05$.

d. Are the signs of the coefficients of the independent variables what you would expect for these data? Explain.

e. Is there evidence to support the officials' belief that there are fewer crimes committed at private schools than at public schools? Test using $\alpha = 0.05$. Would this decision change if $\alpha = 0.01$?

CR   Chapter Review

Key Terms and Ideas

- Multiple Regression
- Multiple Regression Model
- Method of Least Squares
- Estimated Multiple Regression Equation
- Coefficient of Determination (Multiple Coefficient of Determination)
- Adjusted R^2
- F-Distribution
- Numerator Degrees of Freedom
- Denominator Degrees of Freedom
- F-Statistic
- Sum of Squares of Regression
- Sum of Squared Errors
- Total Sum of Squares
- Mean Square Regression

- Mean Square Error
- Calculating Degrees of Freedom in Multiple Regression Models
- Hypothesis Tests Concerning Individual Coefficients
- Test Statistic for Testing the Hypothesis $\beta_i \neq 0$
- Confidence Intervals for Individual Coefficients
- Confidence Interval for the Mean Value of y Given x
- Confidence Interval for the Predicted Value of y Given x
- Indicator (Dummy) Variable
- Base Level Variable
- Interaction Terms
- Polynomial (Nonlinear) Regression Models

Key Formulas	
	Section
Multiple Regression Model	**14.1**
$$y = \beta_0 + \beta_1 x_1 + \beta_2 x_2 + \ldots + \beta_k x_k + \varepsilon$$	
where β_0, β_1, β_2, ..., β_k are the model's parameters, x_1, x_2, ..., x_k are the independent variables, and ε is a random error.	

Key Formulas	
	Section
Estimated Multiple Regression Equation	14.1

$$\hat{y} = b_0 + b_1 x_1 + b_2 x_2 + \cdots + b_k x_k$$

where b_0, b_1, b_2, ..., b_k are estimates of their population counterparts.

Sum of Squared Errors	14.1

$$SSE = \sum \left(y - \hat{y}\right)^2$$

Coefficient of Determination	14.2

$$R^2 = \frac{SSR}{Total\ SS} = 1 - \frac{SSE}{Total\ SS}$$

Adjusted R^2	14.2

$$R_a^2 = 1 - \left(\frac{n-1}{n-k-1}\right) \frac{SSE}{Total\ SS}$$

where n is the number of observations and k is the number of independent variables in the model.

***F*-Statistic**	14.4

$$F = \frac{\dfrac{Sum\ of\ Squares\ of\ Regression}{k}}{\dfrac{Sum\ of\ Squared\ Errors}{n-(k+1)}}$$

$$= \frac{\dfrac{SSR}{k}}{\dfrac{SSE}{n-(k+1)}} = \frac{Mean\ Square\ Regression}{Mean\ Square\ Error}$$

Test Statistic for Testing the Hypothesis $\beta_i \neq 0$	14.4

$$t = \frac{b_i - 0}{s_{b_i}} = \frac{b_i}{s_{b_i}} \quad i = 1,\ ...,\ k$$

where b_i is the estimated coefficient and s_{b_i} is the standard deviation (standard error) of the estimated coefficient.

100(1 − α)% Confidence Interval for an Individual Coefficient, β_i	14.4

$$b_i \pm t_{\alpha/2,\, n-(k+1)} s_{b_i} \quad i = 1,\ ...,\ k$$

Additional Exercises

1. Drew is undecided about whether to go back to school and get his master's degree. He is trying to perform a cost-benefit analysis to determine whether the cost of attending the school of his choice will be outweighed by the increase in salary he will receive after he attains his degree. He does research and compiles data on annual salaries in the industry he currently works in (he has been working for 10 years), along with the years of experience for each employee and whether or not the employee has a master's degree. Earning his master's degree will require him to take out approximately $30,000 worth of student loans. He has decided that if the multiple regression model shows, with 95% confidence, that earning a master's degree is significant in predicting annual salary, and the estimated increase in salary is at least $20,000, he will enroll in a degree program.

Industry Salaries					
Salary ($)	Years of Experience	Master's Degree	Salary ($)	Years of Experience	Master's Degree
75,240	22	No	73,360	22	No
134,160	27	Yes	58,400	11	Yes
62,560	15	No	66,080	18	No
43,000	2	No	60,120	14	No
150,240	28	Yes	106,600	21	Yes
119,640	25	Yes	45,640	7	No
80,360	15	Yes	145,800	31	Yes
162,720	32	Yes	111,840	22	Yes
70,160	19	No	38,560	0	No
72,160	12	Yes	52,000	7	No

   a. Create an indicator variable, degree, that is equal to 1 if the employee has a master's degree and equal to 0 if the employee does not have a master's degree.

   b. Using statistical software, estimate the following multiple regression model.

   $$\text{Salary} = \beta_0 + \beta_1\left(\text{Experience}\right) + \beta_2\left(\text{Degree}\right) + \varepsilon$$

   Write the estimated multiple regression equation.

   c. According to the model, how much does salary increase on average with each additional year of experience?

   d. According to this model, will Drew decide to enroll in a master's program? Explain your answer.

   e. Why should Drew be cautious when using this model to make his decision?

2. The amount of a certain additive injected into a chemical process has a direct effect on the yield. The following table contains data on the amount of additive and yield.

Amount of Additive and Yield										
Additive	12.0	6.7	5.6	13.2	8.9	7.8	12.9	16.4	4.5	9.6	5.8
Yield	96	50	42	82	76	70	89	94	15	75	32

   a. Assuming that yield is the dependent variable, plot yield against additive. Does the relationship appear to be linear?

   b. Using statistical software, estimate the simple linear regression model. Identify R^2 and s_e^2.

   c. In instances such as this where linearity does not hold, polynomial regression can be used to provide a better fit to the data. Polynomial regression is a special case of multiple regression where new predictor variables are formed by raising other predictor variables to integral powers. In this exercise, a new predictor will be formed by squaring the values of additive (Add_sq). Yield will then be fitted to the predictors Additive and Add_sq. The prediction equation based upon the polynomial regression is Estimated Yield $= -67.53 + 23.04 \left(\text{Additive} \right) - 0.82 \left(\text{Add\_sq} \right)$. R^2 and s_e^2 are 0.95 and 47.53, respectively. Predict the yield when Additive = 16. Make this prediction using both the linear and polynomial fits. Compare your results.

   d. Compare the linear and polynomial fits to the data by the values for R^2 and s_e^2.

   e. Which model do you believe is best to use for estimation and prediction? Explain your answer.

⠿ **Data**

stat.hawkeslearning.com
Data Sets > 2011 Home Sales

3. Suppose that an association of real estate professionals has reported home sales for 2011 in a data set titled Home Sales. The table contains the current sales by region and the inventory for existing-home sales (single-family and condos/co-ops). An excerpt of the full table is given below. The full table can be found on the companion site.

Home Sales							
Sale Price	**Region**	**Home Type**	**Inventory**	**Sale Price**	**Region**	**Home Type**	**Inventory**
$237,000	NE	Condo/Co-op	185,000	$239,600	NE	Single-Family	550,000
$225,400	NE	Condo/Co-op	188,000	$242,400	NE	Single-Family	550,000
$235,200	NE	Condo/Co-op	205,000	$244,600	NE	Single-Family	560,000
$144,900	MW	Condo/Co-op	80,000	$138,800	MW	Single-Family	850,000
$145,000	MW	Condo/Co-op	79,000	$138,900	MW	Single-Family	840,000
$139,200	MW	Condo/Co-op	82,000	$138,600	MW	Single-Family	900,000
$110,400	S	Condo/Co-op	194,000	$153,400	S	Single-Family	1,520,000
$108,100	S	Condo/Co-op	176,000	$153,100	S	Single-Family	1,520,000
$112,100	S	Condo/Co-op	200,000	$150,800	S	Single-Family	1,570,000
...							

a. Suggest a regression model that would allow you to predict sale price as a function of inventory, region, and home type. Use indicator variables for regions (NE, MW, S, and W) and home type (Condo/Co-op or Single-Family)

b. How many indicator variables will you need?

c. Estimate the model that you suggested in part **a.**

d. What is the estimated equation for predicting sale price by region?

e. What is the estimated equation for predicting sale price by type of home?

f. Is your model estimated in part **b.** statistically useful for predicting sale price at a 1% significance level? Explain your answer.

4. The following table contains a list of high-dividend exchange-traded funds (ETFs). Exchange-traded funds are investment funds traded on stock exchanges, much like stocks. ETFs are traditionally index funds, but ETFs can hold assets such as stocks, commodities, or bonds, and trade at approximately the same price as the net asset value of their underlying assets over the course of the trading day. ETFs may be attractive as investments because of their low costs, tax efficiency, and stock-like features. The full data set can be found on the companion site.

⠠⠭ **Data**

stat.hawkeslearning.com
Data Sets > Exchange-Traded Funds

Exchange-Traded Funds							
ETF	Share Price ($)	Dividend Per Share ($)	Dividend Yield (%)	ETF	Share Price ($)	Dividend Per Share ($)	Dividend Yield (%)
1	4.32	0.28	6.49	6	120.55	6.22	5.16
2	15.38	0.92	6.02	7	23.00	1.09	4.74
3	25.25	1.43	5.66	8	13.34	0.62	4.66
4	21.28	1.13	5.31	9	24.82	1.15	4.63
5	698.75	36.88	5.28	10	22.96	1.04	4.53
...							

a. Using the Exchange-Traded Funds data set, can dividend yield be predicted by share price and dividend per share? Is it a useful model? Justify your answers.

b. Which variable explains the greatest amount of variability in dividend yield? Explain your answer.

5. The Supplemental Nutrition Assistance Program (SNAP) provides monthly benefits that help eligible low-income households buy the food they need for good health. For most households, SNAP funds account for only a portion of their food budgets, so they must also use their own funds to buy enough food to last throughout the month. Using the SNAP data set, answer the following questions to help predict monthly benefits to eligible households.

⠠⠭ **Data**

stat.hawkeslearning.com
Data Sets > SNAP

SNAP Benefits					
Monthly Benefit ($)	Family Size	Gross Monthly Income ($)	Monthly Benefit ($)	Family Size	Gross Monthly Income ($)
603.41	5	3753	556.42	1	3098
560.69	3	3778	569.05	8	3707
623.24	6	3609	365.80	8	2071
416.12	5	2262	489.08	5	3166
323.90	1	1966	495.86	4	3126
...					

a. Suggest a regression model that will assist SNAP administrators in providing a monthly benefit to eligible households.

b. Fit the model that you suggested in part **a.** Is this model useful in predicting monthly benefits? Justify your answer.

c. Are all independent variables in the model helpful in explaining the variation in monthly benefits? Explain your answer.

d. Give a 95% confidence interval for average monthly benefits for a four-member household with a gross monthly income of $2500. Interpret this interval.

e. Provide a 99% prediction interval for a four-member household with a gross monthly income of $2500. Interpret this interval.

f. What is the difference between the intervals found in parts **d.** and **e.**?

"Genius is the capacity for seeing relationships where lesser men see none."

— William James

15

CHAPTER

Analysis of Variance (ANOVA)

Introduction

Chapter 12 described methods for comparing two population means. In that chapter, we also began to explore some experimental design issues. For example, if variation among sample observations could be significantly reduced by pairing experimental units, the paired difference test was used. But we paid a price for pairing experimental units by giving up degrees of freedom. If variation could not be significantly reduced by pairing, then experimental units should be randomly selected from each of the populations of interest. Often we will be interested in comparing more than two population means. In the sections that follow, we will extend the concepts presented in Chapter 12 to situations where there are more than two populations of interest.

There are many situations where someone might be interested in comparing several population means. An auto fleet manager may wish to compare the average gas mileage for several different makes of cars. The chairperson of a math department may want to compare the average statistics grades for various statistics professors. A farmer may be interested in the average yield of his tomato plants when various fertilizers are used. A doctor may wish to compare the average decrease in blood pressure for various drugs used to treat hypertension. A nutritionist may want to compare the average weight loss for several different diets. Comparisons of several population means can be made using the **one-way ANOVA** *F*-test, which will be discussed in Section 15.1.

Additionally, there are situations where we are interested in the average response of a variable which depends on two factors. For example, a farmer might be interested in relating the average yield of tomatoes to two factors which he believes have a significant effect on yield: location and fertilizer. This situation can be analyzed using a **two-way ANOVA** *F*-test, which will be discussed in Section 15.3.

15.1 **One-Way ANOVA**

In comparing population means a natural question arises: *is there a significant difference between the means?* A preliminary answer to this question can be obtained by drawing a random sample from each of the populations of interest and computing the sample mean. The larger the differences between the sample means, the more likely it would seem that there is a difference among the population means. How large is large enough to conclude a difference? Since samples have been drawn from each of the populations, we must decide whether or not the observed differences between the sample means are simply due to random variation among the sample observations or to a real difference in the means.

> ### Experimental Units
>
> Individuals or objects on which the experiment is performed are called **experimental units**.
>
> DEFINITION

> ### Treatment
>
> An experimental condition applied to the units is called a **treatment**.
>
> DEFINITION

Note

The tomato plants are called experimental units and the fertilizer is the treatment.

A farmer is interested in knowing whether or not the average yield of his tomato plants is different for three different types of fertilizer: Fertilizer A, which is rich in phosphate, Fertilizer B, which is rich in nitrogen, and Fertilizer C, which is a mixture of A and B. He randomly selects several tomato plants which have been treated with each of the fertilizers and computes the summary measures for yield which result in the box plots in Figure 15.1.1. He finds that the sample average yield for plants treated with Fertilizer A is 17 pounds, the sample average yield for plants treated with Fertilizer B is 20 pounds, and the sample average yield for Fertilizer C is 18 pounds. Is the difference in sample averages large enough to conclude that the average yield for the tomato plants is different between the three fertilizers?

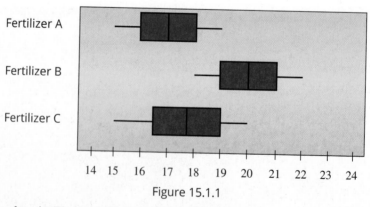

Figure 15.1.1

The box plots in Figure 15.1.1 can give some insight into this question. The box plot for Fertilizer A is centered around 17 pounds, has a range of 4 pounds, and a majority of the yields are between 16 and 18 pounds. The box plot for Fertilizer B is centered around 20 pounds, has a range of 4 pounds, and the majority of the observed yields are between 19 and 21 pounds. The box plot for Fertilizer C is centered around 18 pounds, has a range of 5 pounds, and the majority of the observed yields are between 16.5 and 19 pounds. Although there are a few observed yields that are the same for all the fertilizers, the majority of the observed yields are higher for Fertilizer B than for Fertilizers A and C. Thus, it seems unlikely that the difference we have observed in the sample average yields is due to sample variation. Another way of expressing this concept is that the difference between the sample average yields is large when compared with the variability within the observed yields for each sample. It seems that there is a difference in average yields between the fertilizers. In fact, it appears that Fertilizer B has higher yields than Fertilizer A or C.

Although box plots can provide a sense of whether or not there is a difference among the means, they cannot help us evaluate how likely it is that the observed difference is due to ordinary sampling variation. The following sections will develop measures which will help assess how likely it is that the observed differences among the sample means are due to sampling variation.

In studying regression analysis, we broke apart the total variation in the dependent variable into two parts: SSR (the part explained by the model) and SSE (the part not explained by the model). We will take the same approach in our analysis concerning the differences in means. We will look at the total variation in the data and break it into pieces. One piece will be the sum of squares for treatments, SST (the variation which can be attributed to the treatments) and the sum of squares for error, SSE (the variation not explained by the sum of squares for treatment).

The variation among all the sample observations, without regard to which treatment or population they are from, can be summarized by the sample variance which is given by the following formula.

Sample Variance

$$s^2 = \frac{\displaystyle\sum_{j=1}^{k}\sum_{i=1}^{n_j}\left(x_{ij} - \overline{\overline{x}}\right)^2}{N-1}$$

where

$\overline{\overline{x}}$ is the sample mean of all of the observations, and is called the **grand mean**,

n_j is the number of observations in the jth treatment,

x_{ij} is the ith data value from the jth sample,

k is the number of treatments, and

N is the total number of observations in all samples.

FORMULA

The numerator of s^2 is called the **total sum of squares** since it describes the total variation among all of the sample observations. The denominator of s^2 gives the degrees of freedom associated with the total sum of squares, $N-1$.

Total Sum of Squares

$$\text{Total Sum of Squares} = \text{SST} + \text{SSE} = \sum_{j=1}^{k}\sum_{i=1}^{n_j}\left(x_{ij} - \overline{\overline{x}}\right)^2$$

FORMULA

The total variation in the sample measurements can be partially attributed to the treatments from which they came and partially attributed to random variation inherent in sampling. Thus, the total sum of squares can be divided into two components. The first component measures the variation which can be attributed to the treatments and is called the **sum of squares for treatments** or **SST**.

Sum of Squares for Treatments

The mathematical expression for the **sum of squares for treatments** is given by

$$\text{SST} = \sum_{j=1}^{k} n_j \left(\overline{x}_j - \overline{\overline{x}} \right)^2$$

where

n_j is the number of observations in the jth treatment,

$\overline{x}_j$ is the sample mean of the observations in the jth treatment, and

$\overline{\overline{x}}$ is the **grand mean**.

FORMULA

SST is a summary measure of how far each treatment or population mean differs from the **grand mean**, $\overline{\overline{x}}$, which is the mean of all of the sample observations. The larger the difference between the treatment means $\left(\overline{x}_i \right)$ and the grand mean $\left(\overline{\overline{x}} \right)$, the more likely the variation in sample observations is due to the treatments rather than to ordinary sampling variation. Thus, SST measures the variation between the treatments. If using statistical software to perform ANOVA, the variation between treatments may also be referred to as "Among" variation or "Between" variation. In Microsoft Excel, the source of variation associated with treatments is called "Between Groups" variation. In Minitab, the output yields an ANOVA table that refers to treatment variation as "Factor" variation.

The degrees of freedom associated with SST is $k - 1$, where k is the number of treatments. The **mean square for treatments**, **MST**, is the sum of squares for treatments divided by its degrees of freedom.

$$\text{MST} = \frac{\text{SST}}{k-1}$$

The MST represents the average weighted squared deviation of the sample treatment means from the grand mean. The MST is basically the variance of the weighted sample means.

The second component measures the random variation attributable to sampling and is called the **sum of squares for error**, or **SSE**.

Sum of Squares for Error

The mathematical expression for the sum of squares for error is given by the following formula.

$$\text{SSE} = \underbrace{\sum_{i=1}^{n_1} \left(x_{i1} - \overline{x}_1 \right)^2}_{} + \sum_{i=1}^{n_2} \left(x_{i2} - \overline{x}_2 \right)^2 + \cdots + \sum_{i=1}^{n_k} \left(x_{ik} - \overline{x}_k \right)^2$$

Note: This is the numerator of the sample variance for Sample 1.

FORMULA

The SSE is a summary measure of how much of the total variation in the sample data is not explained by SST. The previous expression is a direct calculation of SSE which shows that the SSE summarizes how much the sample observations within each treatment vary from the treatment mean. In other words, SSE is a measure of the variation within the treatments. In practice, it is much easier to calculate SSE as the total variation in the sample minus the variation explained by the treatments, SST. The variation associated with the error term is often called "Within Groups" variation or simply "Error" variation.

The degrees of freedom associated with SSE are $N - k$. The **mean square for error**, **MSE**, is the SSE divided by its degrees of freedom. The MSE represents the total variance (or common variance) of the model. That is, the estimate of σ^2 is s^2, which is given by the MSE of the ANOVA model.

$$\text{MSE} = \frac{\text{SSE}}{N - k}$$

Thus, we have the following results.

Sums of Squares

Total Sum of Squares = Sum of Squares for Treatments + Sum of Squares for Error

or

Total SS = SST + SSE

$$\sum_{j=1}^{k}\sum_{i=1}^{n_j}\left(x_{ij} - \overline{\overline{x}}\right)^2 = \sum_{j=1}^{k} n_j \left(\overline{x}_j - \overline{\overline{x}}\right)^2 + \left\{\sum_{i=1}^{n_1}\left(x_{i1} - \overline{x}_1\right)^2 + \sum_{i=1}^{n_2}\left(x_{i2} - \overline{x}_2\right)^2 + \cdots + \sum_{i=1}^{n_k}\left(x_{ik} - \overline{x}_k\right)^2\right\}$$

Degrees of Freedom

$$\begin{array}{ccccc} \text{Total} & = & \text{Treatment} & + & \text{Error} \\ N - 1 & = & k - 1 & + & N - k \end{array}$$

As you might expect, these measures of variability are the fundamental pieces which will be used to develop a hypothesis test for determining whether or not there is a significant difference among the population means. This is precisely the reason that the test which we will use to make this decision is often called an **Analysis of Variance**, or **ANOVA**. The expressions are complicated. Fortunately, most statistical analysis programs will compute these quantities.

When the farmer evaluated the sample data to determine if there was a difference in average yield between the three fertilizers, there were two overriding factors which contributed to the analysis. The first factor which he considered was whether or not there was a difference between the sample average yields for the fertilizers, which is summarized by SST. The second factor he considered was whether or not that difference was larger than the differences among the observed yields for the samples from each of the fertilizers, which is summarized by SSE. These sources of variation can be generalized to the situation of comparing many population means, and they will be the basis for answering the question of whether or not we can conclude that there is a difference among the population means.

Sir Ronald Fisher (1890 - 1962)

In 1912 Fisher graduated from Cambridge in mathematics. After leaving Cambridge he had no means of support so he worked on a farm in Canada for a few months. He returned to England and took a job as a statistician. After World War I broke out he tried to enlist but was rejected because of poor eyesight. Fisher then taught mathematics and physics at several English schools until 1919 when he took a position at the Rothamasted Agricultural Experiment Station as chief statistician. As a consequence of taking this position he worked many agricultural experiments. One of his most significant contributions to statistics is the concept of randomization and analysis of variance. Using Fisher's methods, more than one factor could be studied in an experiment.

In addition he introduced the idea of maximum likelihood which has been an important concept for theoretical statisticians.

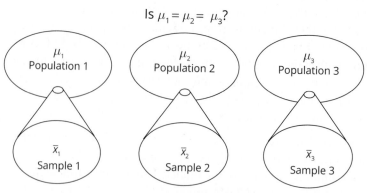

Is $\mu_1 = \mu_2 = \mu_3$?

The null hypothesis will state that the population means are equal.
Figure 15.1.2

Mice, Tigers, and Randomization

In his well-known paper titled "Science and Statistics" that was published in the Journal of the American Statistical Association in 1976, George E. P. Box stated that "It is inappropriate to be concerned about mice when there are tigers abroad." What he was trying to say was that when conducting an experiment, one should worry more about randomization (the tiger), and not worry so much about the type of statistical test (the mouse) being performed. At the time there was a lot of discussion about the use of parametric tests, that required the assumption of normality, and distribution-free tests (nonparametric tests), where no assumptions needed to be made. Box analyzed data taken from three different parent distributions using both the *t*-test and the Mann-Whitney test. He found that the significance level of the *t*-test was only slightly affected when the parent distribution was not normal. This led him to the conclusion that "… it is the act of randomization that is of major importance here not the introduction of the distribution-free test function."

Science and Statistics
George E. P. Box
Journal of the American Statistical Association, Vol. 71, No. 356. (Dec., 1976), pp. 791-799.

ANOVA Formulas

Grand Mean:

$$\bar{\bar{x}} = \frac{\sum_{j=1}^{k} \sum_{i=1}^{n_j} x_{ij}}{N}$$

Sum of Squares for Treatments:

$$\text{SST} = \sum_{j=1}^{k} n_j \left(\bar{x}_j - \bar{\bar{x}} \right)^2$$

Mean Square for Treatments:

$$\text{MST} = \frac{\text{SST}}{k-1}$$

Sum of Squares for Error:

$$\text{SSE} = \sum_{i=1}^{n_1} \left(x_{i1} - \bar{x}_1 \right)^2 + \sum_{i=1}^{n_2} \left(x_{i2} - \bar{x}_2 \right)^2 + \cdots + \sum_{i=1}^{n_k} \left(x_{ik} - \bar{x}_k \right)^2$$

Mean Square for Error:

$$\text{MSE} = \frac{\text{SSE}}{N-k}$$

Total Sum of Squares:

$$\text{Total Sum of Squares} = \text{SST} + \text{SSE} = \sum_{j=1}^{k} \sum_{i=1}^{n_j} \left(x_{ij} - \bar{\bar{x}} \right)^2$$

FORMULA

Having calculated the sum of squares for each element for analysis of variance, the data can be summarized in the following table. This is the table often used when performing the one-way ANOVA *F*-test.

Table 15.1.1 - One-Way ANOVA Table				
Source of Variation	**Sum of Squares**	**Degrees of Freedom**	**Mean Square**	**_F_-Statistic**
Between Groups	SST	$k-1$	$SST / (k-1)$	MST / MSE
Within Groups	SSE	$N-k$	$SSE / (N-k)$	
Total	Total SS	$N-1$	**Note:** Reject H_0 if $F > F_\alpha$	

Assumptions of the Test

Before proceeding with a description of the hypothesis testing procedure for determining whether or not there is a significant difference among several population means, it is important to point out the assumptions upon which the test is based. If the data does not appear to conform to these assumptions, the hypothesis testing procedures described in the subsequent sections will not be valid inferential techniques.

The first assumption is that the distributions of all k populations of interest are approximately normal. The best way to determine whether or not this assumption is satisfied is to construct a histogram or normal probability plot of the sample data for each of the k populations of interest.

If the histograms or normal probability plots suggest that the data comes from a normal distribution, then it is reasonable to proceed. Figure 15.1.3 gives examples of histograms of sample data drawn from normal populations. If one or more of the populations have a distribution that is definitely not normal, then the Kruskal-Wallis test described in Section 17.6 should be used (a nonparametric test). The ANOVA test has been shown to be very robust even with significant departures from normality.

> **Note**
>
> The lesson "Name that Distribution" in Hawkes Learning: Statistics provides practice in recognizing distributions of histograms of sample data drawn from various distributions including the normal distribution.

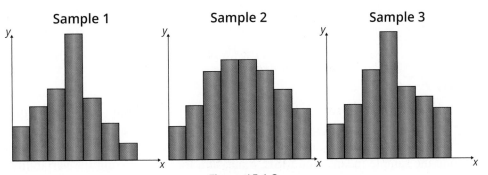

Figure 15.1.3

The second assumption is that the variances of the k populations of interest are equal. We can determine if this assumption is reasonable by drawing box plots of the k samples of data and comparing the spread of the data for each sample. If the spread or variability of the data is approximately the same for each of the k samples, it is reasonable to proceed. For example, consider the box plots for three samples from three populations of interest shown in Figure 15.1.4. Although the spread of the box plots is not exactly the same for each of the samples, they are similar enough that it is likely that the observed difference in spread is due to sample variation, and it is safe to proceed. There is a hypothesis test which can be used to determine if there is a significant difference among the variances, but that testing procedure is beyond the scope of this textbook.

There has to be very large differences in the variances, especially when the sample sizes are equal (or almost equal), before we need to worry about the robustness of the ANOVA test. If the sample sizes for the k populations are very different, then the assumption of equal variances should be verified.

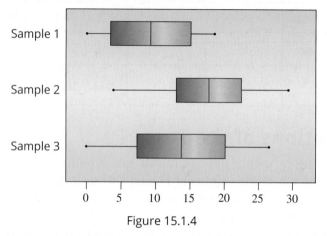

Figure 15.1.4

Note

There is a simple "rule of thumb" that you can use to check the variance assumption. If the largest standard deviation is no more than twice the smallest, then the presumption is that the assumption holds.

The third assumption that must be met is that each of the k samples must be selected independently from each other and in a random fashion from each of the respective populations. According to George E. P. Box, this is the most important assumption of ANOVA and should be met before conducting an analysis of variance test.

ANOVA Assumptions

In order for an analysis of variance to be valid, the following three assumptions must hold.

1. The sample observations are randomly selected and the samples are independent of one another.

2. The distributions of all k populations of interest are approximately normal.

3. The variances of the k populations are equal.

ASSUMPTIONS

The *F*-Test

To this point we have set forth most of the analysis required to determine the appropriate measure for deciding whether or not there is a difference among population means. We developed MST, a measure for summarizing the variability among the sample means, and MSE, a measure for summarizing the variability within the samples themselves. As our farmer discovered, if the variability among the sample means is much larger than the variability within the sample observations, this will cause us to doubt the hypothesis that the population means are the same.

Alternatively, if the variability among the sample means is small when compared to the variability within the sample observations, it is not likely that the population means are significantly different. Again the question arises, *How large is large enough?*

Consider the ratio of the MST, the summary measure of the variability among sample means, to the MSE, the summary measure of the variability within the samples,

$$F = \frac{\text{MST}}{\text{MSE}}.$$

If the assumptions of the test are met and we assume that the population means are equal, this quantity will have an F-distribution with $k-1$ (numerator) degrees of freedom (associated with MST) and $N-k$ (denominator) degrees of freedom (associated with MSE). If the variability among the sample means is close to the variability within the sample observations, F will be close to 1. However, as the variability among the sample means increases relative to the variability within the sample observations, the value of F will become large, causing us to doubt the assumption that the population means are the same.

Thus $F = \dfrac{\text{MST}}{\text{MSE}}$ is a natural test statistic to use in determining whether or not a difference exists among the population means. We will reject the null hypothesis that the population means are equal for large values of the F-test statistic. This is why the test for differences among population means is often referred to as the F-test. A summary of the F-test is given below.

ANOVA *F*-Test

Assumptions

1. The observations from each sample are randomly selected and the samples are independent of one another.

2. The distributions of the k populations of interest are approximately normally distributed.

3. The variances of the k populations are equal.

Hypotheses:

$H_0: \mu_1 = \mu_2 = \ldots = \mu_k$ The k population means are equal.

$H_a:$ At least one μ_i is different.

Test Statistic:

$$F = \frac{\text{MST}}{\text{MSE}} = \frac{\dfrac{\sum\limits_{j=1}^{k} n_j \left(\bar{x}_j - \bar{\bar{x}}\right)^2}{k-1}}{\dfrac{\sum\limits_{i=1}^{n_1}\left(x_{i1} - \bar{x}_1\right)^2 + \sum\limits_{i=1}^{n_2}\left(x_{i2} - \bar{x}_2\right)^2 + \cdots + \sum\limits_{i=1}^{n_k}\left(x_{ik} - \bar{x}_k\right)^2}{N-k}}$$

Rejection Region:

H_0 will be rejected for large values of $F = \dfrac{\text{MST}}{\text{MSE}}$. In particular, we will reject H_0 if $F > F_{\alpha}$ with $\left(k-1\right)$ numerator degrees of freedom and $\left(N-k\right)$ denominator degrees of freedom.

P-value:

The P-value should be available from the output of an ANOVA test performed using technology. The ANOVA test will always be a right-tailed test since large values of the test statistic cause us to reject equality of the population means.

If the computed P-value is less than α, reject the null hypothesis in favor of the alternative.

If the computed P-value is greater than or equal to α, fail to reject the null hypothesis.

PROCEDURE

Unfortunately, the formulas for the MST and the MSE as written are difficult to use for actual calculations. So, we present computational formulas for these summary measures.

Computational Formulas for MST and MSE

Let k be the total number of treatments and $N = n_1 + n_2 + \ldots + n_k$ be the total number of observations, then

$$MST = \frac{\dfrac{\left(\sum\limits_{i=1}^{n_1} x_{i1}\right)^2}{n_1} + \dfrac{\left(\sum\limits_{i=1}^{n_2} x_{i2}\right)^2}{n_2} + \cdots + \dfrac{\left(\sum\limits_{i=1}^{n_k} x_{ik}\right)^2}{n_k} - \dfrac{\left(\sum\limits_{j=1}^{k}\sum\limits_{i=1}^{n_j} x_{ij}\right)^2}{N}}{k-1}$$

$$MSE = \frac{\sum\limits_{j=1}^{k}\sum\limits_{i=1}^{n_j} x_{ij}^2 - \left\{\dfrac{\left(\sum\limits_{i=1}^{n_1} x_{i1}\right)^2}{n_1} + \dfrac{\left(\sum\limits_{i=1}^{n_2} x_{i2}\right)^2}{n_2} + \cdots + \dfrac{\left(\sum\limits_{i=1}^{n_k} x_{ik}\right)^2}{n_k}\right\}}{N-k}$$

FORMULA

Hopefully, you will never have to use these formulas in practice. There are a large number of statistical packages that will calculate the F test statistic and provide its P-value.

Example 15.1.1

You have just been promoted to sales manager of a company manufacturing robots used to assemble automobiles. Although your sales force is given a suggested price at which to sell the robots, they have considerable leeway in negotiating the final price. Past sales records indicate that sometimes there is a large difference in the sales price which different sales reps are able to negotiate. You are interested in knowing if this difference is significant, possibly because of a more effective negotiating strategy or exceptional interpersonal skills, or whether this observed difference in sales price is just due to random variation. You decide to randomly select four sales over the last year for each of your three sales representatives and observe the actual selling price of the robot. The table below shows the amounts at which the robots sold in thousands of dollars.

Selling Prices (Thousands of Dollars)			
	Salesperson 1	**Salesperson 2**	**Salesperson 3**
	10	11	11
	14	16	13
	13	14	12
	12	15	15
Total	49	56	51
Average	12.25	14.00	12.75
Standard Deviation	1.708	2.160	1.708

Based on the results of your survey, can you conclude that there is a significant difference in the average sale price which the three sales reps have been able to negotiate? Use $\alpha = 0.05$.

Solution

Step 1: Determine the null and alternative hypotheses.

In plain English we can write the hypotheses as follows.

Null Hypothesis: There is no difference in average sale price among the three sales reps.

Alternative Hypothesis: There is a difference in average sale price among the three sales reps.

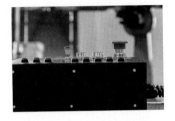

Since the sales manager is interested in comparing the average sale price of the three sales reps, the population parameters of interest are the true average sale price for each salesperson.

μ_1 = the true average sale price for sales rep #1

μ_2 = the true average sale price for sales rep #2

μ_3 = the true average sale price for sales rep #3

Based on the way the test statistic is constructed, we will reject the null hypothesis for large values of the test statistic, meaning that the variability among the sample means is much larger than the variability within the sample observations. Thus, the F-test is always a one-sided test.

Therefore, in symbols the hypotheses can be written as

$H_0: \mu_1 = \mu_2 = \mu_3$ The average sale price is the same for all three sales reps.

H_a: At least one μ_i is different.

Step 2: Specify the significance level α.

The level of the test is specified in the problem as $\alpha = 0.05$.

Step 3: Validate the assumptions of the hypothesis testing model, identify the appropriate test statistic, and compute its value.

There are three key questions which we must ask.

1. Were the sample sale prices for each of the sales reps collected in an independent and random fashion?

2. Are the sale prices for each of the sales reps normally distributed?

3. Do the sale prices for each of the sales reps have essentially the same variance?

Based on prior studies and normal probability plots of each salesperson's sales (only the plot for Salesperson 1 is shown), you have reason to believe that the sale prices of the robots for each of the sales reps has an approximately normal distribution. The standard deviation of the selling prices for each salesperson, shown at the bottom of the table, are reasonably similar. Therefore, we can assume that the variances of the three distributions are approximately equal. Also, you used random sampling to collect your data.

☑ Independent random samples for each salesperson

☑ The distribution of selling prices is approximately normally distributed for each salesperson.

☑ The variances in selling price for each salesperson are approximately equal.

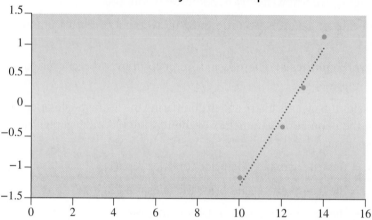

Normal Probability Plot - Salesperson 1

∾ **Technology**

For instructions on how to generate a normal probability plot please visit stat.hawkeslearning.com and navigate to **Technology Instructions > Graphs > Normal Probability Plot**.

∾ **Technology**

The *F*-test can be performed on a TI-83/84 Plus calculator. The results for Example 15.1.1 are shown below. For instructions visit stat.hawkeslearning.com and navigate to **Technology Instructions > ANOVA > One-Way**.

```
One-way ANOVA
 F=.9285714286
 p=.4299038239
 Factor
  df=2
  SS=6.5
↓ MS=3.25
```

```
One-way ANOVA
↑ MS=3.25
 Error
  df=9
  SS=31.5
  MS=3.5
 Sxp=1.87082869
```

Since the assumptions for the ANOVA test have been met, the appropriate test statistic is

$$F = \frac{\text{MST}}{\text{MSE}}.$$

Using the computational formulas presented previously,

$$\text{MST} = \frac{\frac{(49)^2}{4} + \frac{(56)^2}{4} + \frac{(51)^2}{4} - \frac{(156)^2}{12}}{3-1} = 3.25, \text{ and}$$

$$\text{MSE} = \frac{(10)^2 + (14)^2 + \ldots + (15)^2 - \left\{ \frac{(49)^2}{4} + \frac{(56)^2}{4} + \frac{(51)^2}{4} \right\}}{12-3} = 3.5.$$

The resulting calculated value of the test statistic is $F = \dfrac{\text{MST}}{\text{MSE}} = \dfrac{3.25}{3.5} = 0.9286$.

Step 4: Determine the critical value or *P*-value.

The level of the test is $\alpha = 0.05$, and there are $(k - 1) = (3 - 1) = 2$ (numerator) degrees of freedom and $(N - k) = (12 - 3) = 9$ (denominator) degrees of freedom. Thus, the critical value is $F_{0.05} = 4.2565$. We will reject H_0 if the computed value of the test statistic is larger than 4.2565. The following figure displays the rejection region.

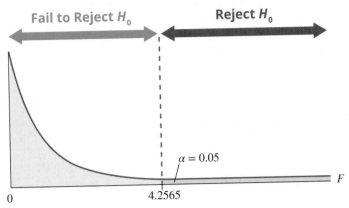

F-Distribution
numerator *df* = 2, denominator *df* = 9

The *P*-value can be obtained through technology,

$$P(F > 0.9286) \approx 0.4299.$$

Step 5: Make the decision to reject or fail to reject H_0.

Since the resulting value of the test statistic, 0.9286, is less than the critical value of 4.2565, we reject the null hypothesis. Likewise, the *P*-value, 0.4299, is greater than $\alpha = 0.05$ so we also fail to reject the null hypothesis using the P-value method.

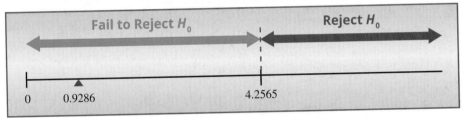

Step 6: State the conclusion in terms of the original problem.

There is not sufficient evidence at $\alpha = 0.05$ to reject the null hypothesis. Thus, we cannot conclude that there i a difference in average sale price among the three sales reps.

It is recommended to use statistical software (rather than computational formulas) to perform an ANOVA. The summary output from Microsoft Excel for this example is as follows.

ANOVA: Single Factor

SUMMARY

Groups	Count	Sum	Average	Variance
Column 1	4	49	12.25	2.916667
Column 2	4	56	12.14	4.666667
Column 3	4	61	12.75	2.916667

ANOVA

Source of Variation	SS	df	MS	F	P-value	F crit
Between Groups	6.5	2	3.25	0.928571	0.429904	4.256495
Within Groups	31.5	9	3.5			
Total		11				

Technology

Notice from the previous technology note that the *P*-value is included in the results of the F-Test on the calculator. It can also be obtained using the Fcdf function after the test statistic has been calculated. For instructions please visit stat.hawkeslearning.com and navigate to **Technology Instructions > F-distribution > F-probability (cdf)**.

Fcdf(.9286,10ᴇ6, 2,9)
          .4298936421

If the null hypothesis that all population means are equal is rejected, the ANOVA procedure does not tell you which means are not equal. There are procedures, called **multiple comparison procedures**, that allow us to determine which means are different. Some of the more popular multiple comparisons procedures are the Bonferroni method, Scheffe's method, and the Tukey method. However, these procedures are beyond the scope of this text.

15.1 **Exercises**

Basic Concepts

1. Give two examples where you might be interested in comparing several population means.

2. What are experimental units?

3. What is a treatment?

4. Explain how box plots can be useful in analyzing data when comparing population means.

5. How is the total variation broken down in an analysis of variance?

6. What does the total sum of squares describe? What are its degrees of freedom?

7. What is the mathematical expression for the sum of squares for treatments?

8. What is the mean square for treatments?

9. What is the relationship between the Total Sum of Squares, SST, and SSE? Explain why this relationship makes sense.

10. Why is it important to validate the assumptions upon which a hypothesis test is based?

11. What are the assumptions for an ANOVA F-test?

12. If you found that MST is much larger than MSE, would you tend to think that the population means were similar or different? Explain how this ratio brings you to this conclusion.

13. If the variability among the sample means is very similar to the variability among the sample observations, what value will F be close to? Explain why.

14. Is the null hypothesis generally rejected for large or small values of the F-statistic? Explain why this is the case.

15. What are the null and alternative hypotheses for the one-way ANOVA F-test?

Exercises

16. Consider the following table containing daily production data from a particular week for three different employee shifts.

Items Produced			
	First Shift (7 AM-3 PM)	**Second Shift** (3 PM-11 PM)	**Third Shift** (11 PM-7 AM)
Monday	140	168	77
Tuesday	181	224	123
Wednesday	127	162	77
Thursday	172	182	101
Friday	161	219	147
Saturday	152	171	145
Sunday	173	217	111

a. Identify the experimental units and the treatment in the context of this problem.

b. Compute the mean and median numbers of items produced for each shift.

c. Compute the values of the minimum, maximum, first, and third quartiles for each shift.

d. Construct side-by-side box plots for the three shifts.

e. Based on the box plots, do you think that there may be a significant difference in the average numbers of items produced during the first and second shifts? Explain.

f. Based on the box plots, do you think that there may be a significant difference in the average numbers of items produced during the second and third shifts? Explain.

g. Based on the box plots, do you think that there may be a significant difference in the average numbers of items produced during the first and third shifts? Explain.

h. Based on your analysis, which shift would you say is the most productive, on average? Explain your answer.

17. Consider the production data given in Exercise 16.

    a. What is the value of the grand mean, $\bar{\bar{x}}$?

    b. What is the value of n_2?

    c. What is the value of k?

    d. What is the value of N?

    e. For this data, identify the degrees of freedom associated with the total sum of squares, the degrees of freedom associated with the sum of squares for treatments, and the degrees of freedom associated with the sum of squares for error. Verify that the relationship between the degrees of freedom (Total = Treatment + Error) holds.

18. For each of the following histograms of sample data, decide whether or not you think it is reasonable to assume that the data was drawn from a population that has an approximately normal distribution.

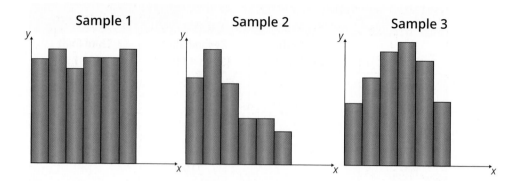

19. For each of the following histograms of sample data, decide whether you think it is reasonable to assume that the data was drawn from a population that has an approximately normal distribution.

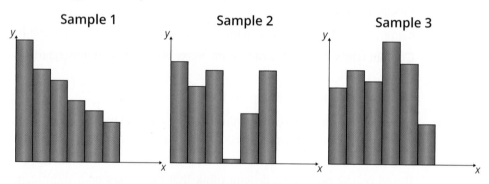

20. Consider the following box plots.

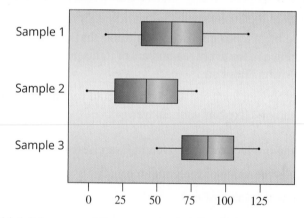

Do you think it is reasonable to assume that the three populations represented by the sample data in these box plots have equal variances? Explain.

21. Consider the following box plots.

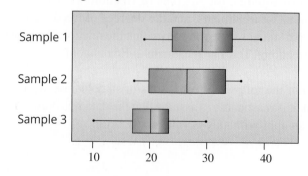

Do you think it is reasonable to assume that the three populations represented by the sample data in these box plots have equal variances? Explain.

22. The results of a comparison of four popular minivans are reported in the following table. One of the features the researchers compared was the distance (in feet) required for the minivan to come to a complete stop when traveling at a speed of 60 miles per hour (braking distance). Suppose the braking distances were measured for five minivans of each type with the following results.

Braking Distances (Feet)			
Minivan A	**Minivan B**	**Minivan C**	**Minivan D**
150	153	155	167
152	150	150	164
151	156	157	169
149	151	158	162
153	155	155	173

a. Can the researchers conclude at $\alpha = 0.10$ that there is a difference among average braking distances for the four minivan models?

b. What assumptions did the researchers make in performing the test procedure in part a.? Does the data appear to satisfy these assumptions? Explain.

23. A steel company is considering the relocation of one of its manufacturing plants. The company's executives have selected four areas that they believe are suitable locations. However, they want to determine if the average wages are significantly different in any of the locations, since this could have a major impact on the cost of production. A survey of hourly wages of similar workers in each of the four areas is performed with the following results.

Hourly Wages ($)			
Area 1	**Area 2**	**Area 3**	**Area 4**
10	15	13	20
12	16	14	16
11	18	15	18
13	17	15	17
10	14	12	16

a. Does the data indicate a significant difference among the average hourly wages in the four areas at $\alpha = 0.05$?

b. What assumptions were made in performing the test in part a.? Does the data appear to satisfy these assumptions? Explain.

24. A director of training at a large temporary services company has learned of three different methods for teaching a person to type. He is interested in determining if there is a difference in the average typing speeds for employees who are taught to type using each of the three methods. He randomly selects 15 new employees and then randomly assigns five employees to learn to type by

each of the training methods. At the end of the course, he measures the number of correct words per minute for each employee. The results are as follows.

Typing Speeds (Correct Words per Minute)		
Method 1	Method 2	Method 3
45	50	60
50	55	63
40	49	55
43	52	52
47	53	58

a. Can the director of training conclude that there is a difference among the average typing speeds of the employees for the three methods at $\alpha = 0.10$?

b. What assumptions did the director of training make in performing the test in part a.? Does the data appear to satisfy these assumptions? Explain.

25. A physical trainer has four workouts that he recommends for his clients. The workouts have been designed so that the average maximum heart rate achieved is the same for each workout. To test this design, he randomly selects 12 people and randomly assigns three of them to use each of the workouts. During each workout, he measures the maximum heart rate in beats per minute with the following results.

Maximum Heart Rates (Beats per Minute)			
Workout #1	Workout #2	Workout #3	Workout #4
180	160	175	185
185	170	180	190
170	175	170	180

a. Can the physical trainer conclude at $\alpha = 0.05$ that there is a difference among the average maximum heart rates which are achieved during the four workouts?

b. What assumptions did the physical trainer make in performing the test procedure in part a.? Does the data appear to satisfy these assumptions? Explain.

26. The results of a survey comparing the costs of staying one night in a full-service hotel (including food, beverages, and telephone calls, but not taxes or gratuities) for several major cities are given in the following table.

Hotel Costs per Night ($)				
New York	Los Angeles	Atlanta	Houston	Phoenix
300	240	190	195	238
320	250	198	190	240
325	230	185	200	236
350	245	195	192	248
275	235	182	198	228

a. Does the data suggest that there is a significant difference among the average costs of one night in a full-service hotel for the five major cities at $\alpha = 0.05$?

b. What assumptions were made in performing the test procedure in part **a.**? Does the data appear to satisfy these assumptions? Explain.

c. Based on the analysis you performed in part **b.**, which cities, if any, do you think have significantly different average costs for a one-night stay in a full-service hotel? Explain.

27. Consider the following information regarding the dividends paid per share by companies in the banking, transportation, and energy industries.

Dividends per Share ($)		
Banking	Transportation	Energy
1.52	1.00	2.08
3.12	1.20	2.68
1.32	0.20	0.70
0.60	0.40	2.00
1.20	1.09	1.91
1.00	0.61	1.60
1.19	0.35	1.28

a. Does the data provide sufficient evidence to conclude that there is a significant difference among the average dividends paid per share for the three different industries? Use $\alpha = 0.10$.

b. What assumptions were made in performing the test procedure in part **a.**? Does the data appear to satisfy these assumptions? Explain.

c. Based on the analysis you performed in part **b.**, which industries, if any, do you think pay significantly different average dividends per share? Explain.

15.2 Two-Way ANOVA: The Randomized Block Design

The purpose of the randomized block design is to control for potentially confounding variables in a research experiment. Suppose a nutritionist is interested in comparing the average weight loss for three different diets: a banana diet, a cabbage diet, and a grapefruit diet. She has been funded to use nine people in studying these diets. One approach in designing this study is to randomly select nine people and then randomly assign three of them to each of the three diets for six months. We could then compare the average weight loss for each of the diets at the end of that period, using the F-test described in Section 15.1. This type of design is called a **completely randomized design**. Although this may be a perfectly reasonable approach, it does have some shortcomings. For example, what if all of the people selected to try the banana diet are at least 100 pounds overweight, whereas all of the people selected to try the grapefruit diet are only 10 pounds overweight? Certainly, how overweight a person currently is will have an effect on how much weight a person is able to lose, regardless of the diet. Controlling for this "nuisance" factor will improve our experimental design.

What can be done to reduce the effect of this factor which affects weight loss, but which is not directly related to how well the diets work? One approach would be to divide our study participants into several weight bands called **blocks:** those people who are more than 100 pounds overweight, those people who are between 51 and 100 pounds overweight, and those people who are between 0 and 50 pounds overweight. Then randomly select people, three from each of the weight bands, to try each of the diets. And finally compare the average weight loss of each of the diets for individuals in each of the three weight bands.

This design is an extension of the paired difference design for comparing two means, which we discussed in Chapter 12. Although the effect that current weight has on the amount of weight loss has not been eliminated, it has probably been greatly reduced by this blocking. As with the paired difference design, we give up degrees of freedom when we block. Thus, we must be sure that the reduction in variation among sample observations is enough to compensate for the loss of degrees of freedom. This type of design is an example of a **randomized block design**.

In a randomized block design, we select experimental units within blocks which categorize experimental units so that they are as much alike as possible. Then we randomly assign the experimental units within each block to the k populations or treatments of interest. Finally, we compare the response of the experimental units to each of the treatments of interest within each of the blocks. In this way we eliminate possible variation due to some of the extraneous factors which are unrelated to the treatments. Table 15.2.1 gives the data collected by the nutritionist for the randomized block design.

Before proceeding with the ANOVA F-test, we need to verify that the assumptions are met. Recall from Section 15.1 that the ANOVA procedure is robust against departures from the normality and equal variance assumptions. For this example, we do not have repeated observations for each combination of treatment and block to be able to verify the normality and equal variance assumptions. The nutritionist should actually collect more data in each cell of the table to verify those assumptions, and to provide additional degrees of freedom for the test. We will demonstrate the ANOVA procedure for this simplified randomized block example nonetheless.

		Blocks		
		>100 lb overweight	51-100 lb overweight	0-50 lb overweight
Treatment	**Banana Diet**	25	15	10
	Cabbage Diet	45	25	15
	Grapefruit Diet	30	20	15

Table 15.2.1 - Completely Randomized Block Design

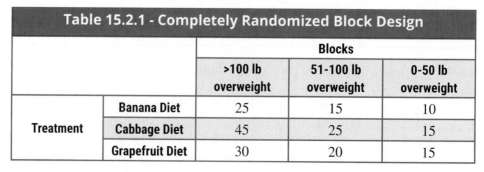

☑ Treatments are assigned at random within blocks and the sample measurements in each cell (treatment and block combination) are random samples that are independent of each other.

☑ The measurements in each cell come from a population that is approximately normally distributed (assumed).

☑ The populations have approximately equal variances (assumed).

☑ All the cells have an equal number of measurements (a **balanced design**).

Don't let the blocking distract from the intent of the experiment. Our interest is still in comparing the treatment means. For the nutritionist, the treatments of interest are the diets. Thus, the null and alternative hypotheses are the same as they were in the one-way ANOVA F-test.

H_0: $\mu_1 = \mu_2 = \mu_3$ The average weight loss on each of the diets is the same.

H_a: At least one of the μ_i is different.

The test statistic appears to be exactly the same as that used for the one-way ANOVA F-test,

$$F = \frac{\text{MST}}{\text{MSE}}.$$

However, the denominator of the F-statistic is calculated differently because it takes into account the fact that we were able to eliminate some of the variation between our sample responses by blocking the experimental units. The total sum of squares and the degrees of freedom which we discussed in Section 15.1 can be broken down further as follows.

Sum of Squares:	Total SS	=	SSTreatment	+	SSBlock	+	SSError
Degrees of Freedom:	$N-1$	=	$k-1$	+	$b-1$		$+(b-1)(k-1)$

where

N is the total number of observations,

k is the number of treatments, and

b is the number of blocks.

If any of the observed variation in the sample observations has been reduced by blocking, then the SSError (SSE) is reduced. But it is important to note that the degrees of freedom which are used by the SSBlock (SSBL) are taken from the SSE, thus the reduction in variation achieved by blocking must offset this loss in degrees of freedom. If we have been successful at significantly reducing variation by blocking and there is a difference among the sample means, we will be more likely to detect it. The test procedure for the randomized block design is outlined here.

Two-Way ANOVA: Randomized Block Design

Assumptions:

1. Treatments are assigned at random within blocks and the sample measurements in each cell are random samples that are independent of each other.

2. The measurements in each cell come from a population that is approximately normally distributed (assumed).

3. The populations have approximately equal variances (assumed).

4. All the cells have an equal number of measurements.

Hypothesis:

H_0: $\mu_1 = \mu_2 = \ldots = \mu_k$ The k treatment means are equal.

H_a: At least one of the μ_i is different.

Test Statistic:

$$F = \frac{\text{MST}}{\text{MSE}} = \frac{\dfrac{\text{SST}}{k-1}}{\dfrac{\text{SSE}}{(k-1)(b-1)}},$$

where SSE = Total Sum of Squares − SST − SSBL.

Rejection Region:

H_0 will be rejected for large values of $F = \dfrac{\text{MST}}{\text{MSE}}$. In particular, we will reject H_0 if $F > F_\alpha$ with $(k-1)$ numerator degrees of freedom and $(k-1)(b-1)$ denominator degrees of freedom.

P-value:

(The P-value should be available from the output of an ANOVA test performed using technology.)

If the computed P-value is less than α, reject the null hypothesis in favor of the alternative.

If the computed P-value is greater than or equal to α, fail to reject the null hypothesis.

PROCEDURE

The calculation formulas for the F-test statistic in the randomized block design are beyond the scope of an elementary statistics text and, therefore, will not be presented in this chapter. We will assume the reader has access to a statistical package which will produce the results of the F-test for the randomized block design. For reference, the general form of the ANOVA table for a randomized block design is given in the following table.

Table 15.2.2 - ANOVA Summary Table for a Randomized Block Design				
Source of Variation	**SS**	**df**	**MS**	**F**
Treatment	SST	$k-1$	MST	$\dfrac{\text{MST}}{\text{MSE}}$
Block	SSBL	$b-1$	MSBL	$\dfrac{\text{MSBL}}{\text{MSE}}$
Error	SSE	$(b-1)(k-1)$	MSE	
Total	Total SS	$N-1$		

The results of the nutritionist's test are given in Figure 15.2.1.

Technology

For instructions on obtaining this output from Minitab visit stat.hawkeslearning.com and navigate to **Technology Instructions > ANOVA > Two-Way.**

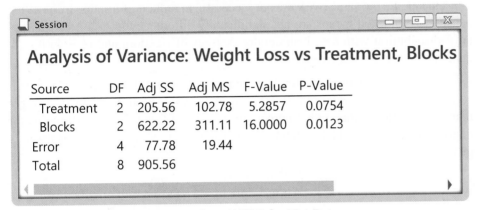

Figure 15.2.1 - ANOVA for Diet Data

The F-test statistic in our diet example has numerator degrees of freedom equal to two and denominator degrees of freedom equal to four. Thus, for $\alpha = 0.05$, the F-critical value is 6.9443. The calculated value of the test statistic is given by

$$F = \frac{\text{MST}}{\text{MSE}} = \frac{102.78}{19.44} = 5.2857.$$

Identify these values in Figure 15.2.1. MST and MSE are given in the Adj MS column. The F-statistic is given in the F-Value column.

Note

When using statistical software programs like Excel and Minitab to perform a two-way ANOVA, it is important to pay attention to how the data is organized so that you can identify treatments and blocks on the summary output and accurately interpret the results.

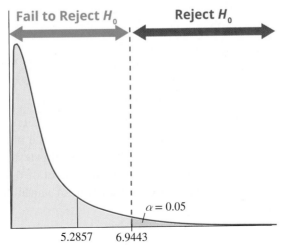

Figure 15.2.2

As shown in Figure 15.2.2, the value of our test statistic, 5.2857, is less than the F critical value of 6.9443. Note also that the P-value from Figure 15.2.1 is 0.0754, which is greater than $\alpha = 0.05$. The nutritionist will fail to reject the null hypothesis.

There is not sufficient evidence to conclude that there is a difference in average weight loss among the three diets. Because the nutritionist did not reject the null hypothesis, she may be concerned that she was not able to significantly reduce the variation by blocking.

Did the Experimental Design Benefit from the Blocking?

To determine if the blocking was successful at reducing variation among the sample observations, we use the test statistic $F = \dfrac{\text{MSBL}}{\text{MSE}}$. Under the null hypothesis that block means are the same (we were not successful in reducing variation by blocking because the blocked means are not significantly different), the F-test statistic has an F-distribution with $b - 1$ numerator degrees of freedom and $(k - 1)(b - 1)$ denominator degrees of freedom.

At $\alpha = 0.05$ the nutritionist will reject the null hypothesis that block means are all equal (blocking was unsuccessful) if the calculated value of the test statistic is larger than the F critical value with 2 numerator degrees of freedom and 4 denominator degrees of freedom, which is 6.9443. The calculated value of the test statistic is given by

$$F = \frac{\text{MSBL}}{\text{MSE}} = \frac{311.11}{19.44} = 16.0000$$

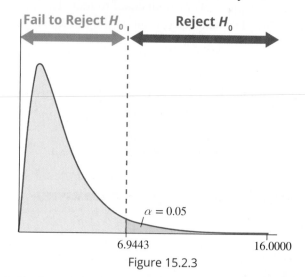

F-Distribution
numerator *df* = 2, denominator *df* = 4

Fail to Reject H_0 Reject H_0

$\alpha = 0.05$

6.9443   16.0000

Figure 15.2.3

Figure 15.2.3 displays the rejection region and the calculated value of the test statistic. Since 16.0000 is larger than 6.9443, we reject the null hypothesis that the block means are all equal. Note that the P-value for this test from the ANOVA output is 0.0123, which is less than the significance level of 0.05. Therefore, the nutritionist was able to reduce a significant amount of variation among sample observations by blocking.

15.2 **Exercises**

Basic Concepts

1. What is a completely randomized design? Give an example.

2. What are blocks? What is their purpose?

3. What is a randomized block design? How is it different from a completely randomized design?

4. What are the null and alternative hypotheses when comparing means using a randomized block design?

5. What is the breakdown of the sum of squares for a randomized block design? Does this breakdown make sense? Explain.

6. If blocking is successful, how does the value of SSE change?

7. What are the assumptions when performing a two-way ANOVA for a randomized block design?

8. What is the rationale for the test statistic used for the randomized block design?

Exercises

9. A car dealer is interested in comparing the average gas mileages of four different car models. The dealer believes that the average gas mileage of a particular car will vary depending on the person who is driving the car due to different driving styles. Because of this, he decides to use a randomized block design. He randomly selects six drivers and asks them to drive each of the cars. He then determines the average gas mileage for each car and each driver. The results of the study are as follows.

Gas Mileage (MPG)				
	Car A	Car B	Car C	Car D
Driver 1	33	29	27	37
Driver 2	36	32	30	40
Driver 3	34	30	28	38
Driver 4	31	27	25	35
Driver 5	33	29	27	37
Driver 6	35	33	31	41

   a. Do you think a randomized block design is appropriate for the car dealer's study? Explain.

   b. The results of the two-way ANOVA for the dealer's survey of the average gas mileages of the different car models are given in the following table. Can the dealer conclude that there is a significant difference in average gas mileages of the four car models? Use $\alpha = 0.05$.

ANOVA

Source of Variation	SS	df	MS
Rows	84.8333	5	16.9667
Columns	348.5000	3	116.1667
Error	2.5000	15	0.1667
Total	435.8333	23	

c.   Was the dealer able to significantly reduce variation among the observed gas mileages by blocking? Use $\alpha = 0.05$.

10. A banana grower has three fertilizers from which to choose. He would like to determine which fertilizer produces banana trees with the largest yield (measured in pounds of bananas produced). The banana grower has noticed that there is a difference in the average yields of the banana trees depending on which side of the farm they are planted (South Side, North Side, West Side, or East Side). Because of the variation in yields among the areas on the farm, the farmer has decided to randomly select three trees within each area and then randomly assign the fertilizers to the trees. After harvesting the bananas, he calculates the yields of the trees within each of the areas. The results are as follows.

Banana Yields (Pounds)			
	Fertilizer A	**Fertilizer B**	**Fertilizer C**
South Side	53	51	58
North Side	48	47	53
West Side	50	48	56
East Side	50	47	54

a.   Do you think a randomized block design is appropriate for the banana grower's study? Explain.

b.   The results of the two-way ANOVA for the banana grower's study are given in the following table. Can the banana grower conclude that there is a significant difference among the average yields of the banana trees for the three fertilizers? Use $\alpha = 0.10$.

ANOVA

Source of Variation	SS	df	MS
Rows	36.2500	3	12.0833
Columns	104.0000	2	52.0000
Error	2.0000	6	0.3333
Total	142.2500	11	

c.   Was the banana grower able to significantly reduce variation among the observed yields by blocking? Use $\alpha = 0.10$.

11. The FAA is interested in knowing if there is a difference in the average numbers of on-time arrivals for four of the major airlines. The FAA believes that the number of on-time arrivals varies by airport. To control for this variation, they randomly select 100 flights for each of the major airlines at

each of four randomly selected airports and record the number of on-time flights. The results of the study are as follows.

On-Time Flights				
	Airline A	**Airline B**	**Airline C**	**Airline D**
Airport A	87	82	79	81
Airport B	88	84	81	82
Airport C	89	84	83	82
Airport D	90	86	85	83

a. Do you think a randomized block design is appropriate for the FAA's study? Explain.

b. The results of the two-way ANOVA for the FAA's study are given in the following table. Can the FAA conclude that there is a significant difference among the average number of on-time arrivals for the four major airlines? Use $\alpha = 0.01$.

ANOVA

Source of Variation	SS	df	MS
Rows	29.2500	3	9.7500
Columns	112.7500	3	37.5833
Error	5.7500	9	0.6389
Total	147.7500	15	

c. Was the FAA able to significantly reduce variation among the observed number of on-time arrivals by blocking? Use $\alpha = 0.01$.

12. A psychologist is interested in determining if there is a difference in the average numbers of suicides for several age groups. The psychologist believes that there may be some variation in the numbers of suicides depending on the region of the country (Northeast, Northwest, Southeast, or Southwest). The psychologist randomly selects 100,000 deaths from each region of the country for each of the age groups of interest and determines the number of suicides. The results of the study are as follows.

Suicides							
	Age 15–24	**Age 25–34**	**Age 35–44**	**Age 45–54**	**Age 55–64**	**Age 65–74**	**Age 75–84**
Northeast	15	17	16	17	55	22	27
Northwest	13	16	16	16	49	19	26
Southeast	12	14	15	15	47	17	24
Southwest	13	15	15	16	53	20	25

a. Do you think a randomized block design is appropriate for the psychologist's study? Explain.

b. The results of the two-way ANOVA for the psychologist's study are given in the following table. Can the psychologist conclude that there is a significant difference among the average number of suicides for the different age groups? Use $\alpha = 0.10$.

ANOVA

Source of Variation	SS	df	MS
Rows	44.9643	3	14.9881
Columns	4223.3571	6	703.8929
Error	25.7857	18	1.4325
Total	4294.1071	27	

c. Was the psychologist able to significantly reduce variation among the observed number of suicides by blocking? Use $\alpha = 0.05$.

13. In an experiment designed to compare automated blood pressure devices with those of the standard cuff method, each man in a sample of six patients has his systolic blood pressure determined by three different automated devices and by the standard cuff method. The data is given in the following table.

Blood Pressure (mmHg)				
	Device 1	Device 2	Device 3	Standard Cuff
Patient 1	126	128	132	131
Patient 2	134	138	137	140
Patient 3	145	144	150	152
Patient 4	129	134	132	136
Patient 5	154	160	162	160
Patient 6	144	144	148	145

a. Why was a randomized block design used in this experiment?

b. From the data, SST and SSE were computed to be 106.4583 and 53.2917, respectively. With $\alpha = 0.05$, can we conclude that the four different methods of determining systolic blood pressure have different mean readings?

c. SSBL was computed to be 2412.8750. With $\alpha = 0.05$, can we conclude that using people as blocks significantly reduced variation in this study?

15.3 Two-Way ANOVA: The Factorial Design

The randomized block test presented in the previous section is one example of a **two-way ANOVA**. There were two independent factors considered in the analysis, namely the block (the different weight classes) and the treatment (diets), and each level of the treatment occurred with each level of the block. However, there was only one factor which was truly of interest to our experimenter, the treatment (diets).

The techniques discussed for the randomized block design can be extended to the situation where there are two factors of interest. A director of personnel might be interested in relating average salary to two factors: age and experience. A supervisor at a manufacturing plant might be interested in relating the average number of defective products to two factors: operator and machine. A doctor might be interested in relating the increase in a patient's blood pressure to two factors: medication and age.

In order for the director of personnel to evaluate the relationship of average salary to age and experience, he chooses the following experimental design. He selects four different age groups and three different experience levels, and observes two salaries for each of the possible combinations of age and experience. The resulting data is displayed in Table 15.3.1.

Table 15.3.1 - Salaries (Thousands of Dollars)				
Years of Experience	**Age**			
	25 – 34	**35 – 44**	**45 – 54**	**55 – 64**
0 – 4	22	25	34	37
	27	35	36	43
5 – 9	34	35	42	49
	36	45	48	51
10 – 14	39	40	53	51
	41	50	57	59

Again, this type of design is called a **two-way analysis of variance** because it involves two classifications. It is also called a **complete factorial experiment** since there is at least one observation for every possible combination of age and salary. Factorial experiments provide valuable information by enabling the interaction between the two variables to be estimated.

Interaction between the two variables means that the average salary is affected by the combination of age and experience. An example of two variables which interact is shown in Figure 15.3.1. This figure is called an **interaction plot**, which is a plot of the means for each level of the factors. An example of two variables which do not interact is shown in Figure 15.3.2.

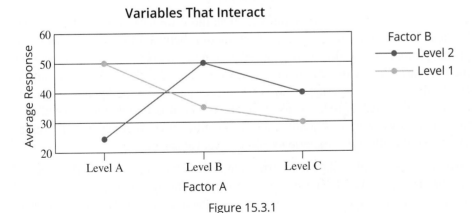

Figure 15.3.1

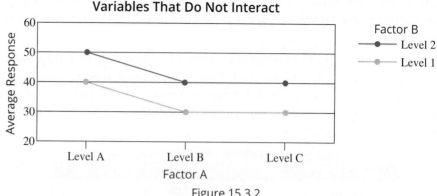

Figure 15.3.2

A similar graph for the salary data is shown in Figure 15.3.3. Based on this graph, there appears to be slight interaction between age and experience when age is between 45 and 54 years and years of experience is between 10-14 years.

There are three effects on average salary that will interest the personnel director. The first is the effect that the interaction between age and experience has on average salary, called the **main effect for interaction**. The second is the effect that experience has on average salary, called the **main effect for experience (Factor A)**. The third is the effect that age has on average salary, called the **main effect for age (Factor B)**.

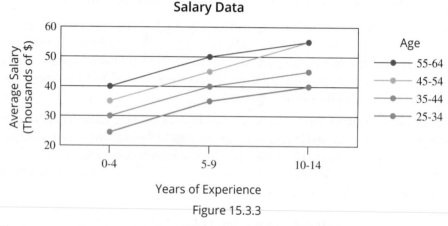

Figure 15.3.3

The test procedure is somewhat different than those we have discussed previously because of the potential presence of interaction between the two variables. Of primary importance is determining whether or not there is any interaction between the two variables. If there is interaction, we will not be able to separate out the effects that age and experience have on average salary, and the hypothesis testing procedure is halted. If there is not interaction, then it is possible to proceed with the hypothesis testing procedure and determine the effect that age has on average salary and the effect that experience has on average salary.

To develop the test procedure for the two-way ANOVA we again rely on the concepts presented in Section 15.1. The variation among the sample observations, represented by the total sum of squares, can be broken down into four pieces: the **sum of squares for Factor A (SSA)**, the **sum of squares for Factor B (SSB)**, the **sum of squares for interaction (SSAB)**, and the sum of squares for error, SSE. Thus,

Sum of Squares	Total Sum of Squares	=	SSA	+	SSB	+	SSAB	+	SSE
Degrees of Freedom	$n-1$	=	$a-1$	+	$b-1$	+	$(a-1)(b-1)$	+	$ab(r-1)$

where

n is the total number of observations,

a is the number of levels of Factor A,

b is the number of levels of Factor B, and

r is the number of observations in the combinations of levels of Factor A and Factor B (i.e., the number of observations in each cell).

The assumptions for the tests in a two-way ANOVA are as follows.

Assumptions

1. The sample measurements in each cell are random samples that are independent of each other.

2. The measurements in each cell come from a population that is approximately normally distributed (assumed).

3. The populations have approximately equal variances (assumed).

4. All the cells have an equal number of measurements (a balanced design).

ASSUMPTIONS

The test statistics for a two-way ANOVA for a factorial design are derived by dividing the sums of squares by the appropriate degrees of freedom to produce mean squares, and then dividing each of the respective mean squares by the mean square for error. The test procedures for interaction and main effects are outlined below.

Test for Interaction between Factors

Hypotheses:

H_0: There is no interaction between Factor A and Factor B.

H_a: There is interaction between Factor A and Factor B.

Test Statistic:

$$F = \frac{\dfrac{\text{SSAB}}{(a-1)(b-1)}}{\dfrac{\text{SSE}}{ab(r-1)}} = \frac{\text{MSAB}}{\text{MSE}}$$

Rejection Region:

Reject the null hypothesis if $F > F_\alpha$ with $(a-1)(b-1)$ numerator degrees of freedom and $ab(r-1)$ denominator degrees of freedom.

P-value:

(The P-value should be available from the output of an ANOVA test performed using technology.)

If the computed P-value is less than α, reject the null hypothesis in favor of the alternative.

If the computed P-value is greater than or equal to α, fail to reject the null hypothesis.

Note: If the null hypothesis is rejected, then interaction exists. If interaction exists, do not proceed with the main effects tests for Factor A and Factor B.

PROCEDURE

Note

To test for interaction between the factors you must have at least 2 observations per cell ($r \geq 2$).

Test for Main Effects for Factor A

Hypotheses:

H_0: Factor A has no effect on average response.

H_a: Factor A has an effect on average response.

Test Statistic:

$$F = \frac{\dfrac{SSA}{(a-1)}}{\dfrac{SSE}{ab(r-1)}} = \frac{MSA}{MSE}$$

Rejection Region:

Reject the null hypothesis if $F > F_\alpha$ with $(a-1)$ numerator degrees of freedom and $ab(r-1)$ denominator degrees of freedom.

P-value:

If the computed P-value is less than α, reject the null hypothesis in favor of the alternative.

If the computed P-value is greater than or equal to α, fail to reject the null hypothesis.

PROCEDURE

Test for Main Effects for Factor B

Hypotheses:

H_0: Factor B has no effect on average response.

H_a: Factor B has an effect on average response.

Test Statistic:

$$F = \frac{\dfrac{SSB}{(b-1)}}{\dfrac{SSE}{ab(r-1)}} = \frac{MSB}{MSE}$$

Rejection Region:

Reject the null hypothesis if $F > F_\alpha$ with $(b-1)$ numerator degrees of freedom and $ab(r-1)$ denominator degrees of freedom.

P-value:

If the computed P-value is less than α, reject the null hypothesis in favor of the alternative.

If the computed P-value is greater than or equal to α, fail to reject the null hypothesis.

PROCEDURE

The calculations of the F-statistics for a two-way analysis of variance are beyond the scope of this text. We will assume that the reader has access to a statistical package that will produce the results of a two-way ANOVA. For reference, the general form of the ANOVA table for a factorial experiment is given in the following table.

Table 15.3.2 - ANOVA Summary Table for a Factorial Experiment

Source of Variation	SS	df	MS	F
Factor A	SSA	$a-1$	MSA	$\dfrac{\text{MSA}}{\text{MSE}}$
Factor B	SSB	$b-1$	MSB	$\dfrac{\text{MSB}}{\text{MSE}}$
Interaction	SSAB	$(a-1)(b-1)$	MSAB	$\dfrac{\text{MSAB}}{\text{MSE}}$
Error	SSE	$ab(r-1)$	MSE	
Total	Total SS	$N-1$		

Before proceeding with the ANOVA test we must verify that the assumptions are met. We know that the ANOVA procedure is robust against departures from the normality and equal variance assumptions. For this example, we do not have sufficient repeated observations for each combination of factors to be able to verify the normality and equal variance assumptions are met. It is highly recommended that as many observations as the budget and time allows be collected for each combination of factors in a factorial experiment. We will demonstrate the ANOVA procedure for this simplified factorial experiment.

- ☑ Cell measurements are independent random samples.
- ☑ Cell measurements come from a population that is approximately normally distributed (assumed).
- ☑ The populations have approximately equal variances (assumed).
- ☑ All the cells have an equal number of measurements.

The results of the two-way ANOVA for the personnel director's salary data are given in Figure 15.3.4.

ANOVA

Source of Variation	SS	df	MS	F	P-value	F crit
Sample	1092.583	2	546.2917	26.59432	3.89E-05	3.885294
Columns	828.4583	3	276.1528	13.44354	0.000382	3.490295
Interaction	24.41667	6	4.069444	0.198107	0.971006	2.99612
Within	246.5	12	20.54167			
Total	2191.958	23				

Figure 15.3.4 - Two-Way ANOVA for Salary Data

In the ANOVA table, the row labeled "Sample" corresponds to Experience (Factor A) since the three experience levels were organized by rows in the original data table. The row of the output labeled "Columns" corresponds to Age (Factor B) since the age groups are organized by column. The row labeled "Interaction" corresponds to the interaction between experience and age, and "Within" corresponds to the variation within the sample observations, or error.

The personnel director must first decide if there is interaction between age and experience. The appropriate test statistic for testing for interaction, which is the mean square of the interaction term divided by the mean square for error, is given by

$$F = \frac{\text{MSAB}}{\text{MSE}}.$$

Note

When using Excel or Minitab to perform a two-way ANOVA, it is important to pay close attention to how the data is organized so that you can identify the factors on the summary output and accurately interpret the results.

Technology

For instructions on performing a two-way ANOVA using Excel, visit stat.hawkeslearning.com and navigate to **Technology Instructions > ANOVA > Two-Way.**

Under the null hypothesis that there is no interaction, the F-test statistic has an F-distribution with six numerator degrees of freedom and 12 denominator degrees of freedom. At $\alpha = 0.05$, the null hypothesis will be rejected if the calculated value of the test statistic is larger than 2.9961.

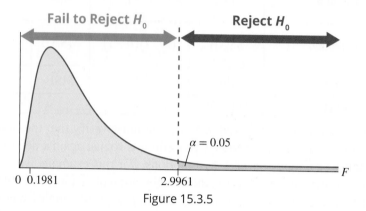

F-Distribution
numerator $df = 6$, denominator $df = 12$

Figure 15.3.5

From Figure 15.3.4, the calculated value of the test statistic is 0.1981 and the P-value is 0.9710. Figure 15.3.5 shows the rejection region and the calculated value of the test statistic. Since 0.1981 is less than the critical value 2.9961, we fail to reject the null hypothesis that there is no interaction between experience and age. Note also that the P-value of 0.9710 is greater than $\alpha = 0.05$. Thus, we fail to reject the null hypothesis using the P-value approach as well. Because there is no evidence of significant interaction between age and experience, it is safe to use the F-test statistic to test whether or not each of the factors, age and experience, has an effect on average salary.

To test whether or not experience has an effect on average salary, we let the null hypothesis be that the average salary is equal for each of the experience levels. The appropriate test statistic, which is the mean square of the experience factor divided by the mean square for error, is given by

$$F = \frac{\text{MSA}}{\text{MSE}}.$$

Under the null hypothesis that the level of experience has no effect on average salary, the F-test statistic has an F-distribution with 2 numerator degrees of freedom and 12 denominator degrees of freedom. At $\alpha = 0.05$, the null hypothesis will be rejected if the calculated value of the test statistic is larger than 3.8853.

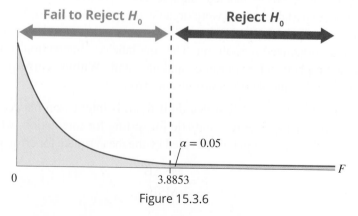

F-Distribution
numerator $df = 2$, denominator $df = 12$

Figure 15.3.6

From Figure 15.3.4, the calculated value of the test statistic is 26.5943 and the P-value is 0.00004. Figure 15.3.6 shows the rejection region. Since 26.5943 is larger than the F critical value of 3.8853, and the P-value of 0.00004 is smaller than $\alpha = 0.05$, we reject the null hypothesis that the level of experience has no effect on average salary. There is persuasive evidence at $\alpha = 0.05$ that the mean salaries are significantly affected by the level of experience.

To test whether or not age has an effect on average salary, we let the null hypothesis be that the average salary is equal for each of the age levels. The appropriate test statistic, which is the mean square of the age factor divided by the mean square for error, is given by

$$F = \frac{MSB}{MSE}.$$

Under the null hypothesis that age has no effect on average salary, the F-test statistic has an F-distribution with 3 numerator degrees of freedom and 12 denominator degrees of freedom. At $\alpha = 0.05$ the null hypothesis will be rejected if the calculated value of the test statistic is larger than 3.4903.

From Figure 15.3.4, the calculated value of the test statistic is 13.4435 and the P-value is 0.00038. Figure 15.3.7 shows the rejection region. Since 13.4435 is larger than 3.4903 and the P-value is less than $\alpha = 0.05$, we reject the null hypothesis that age has no effect on average salary. There is persuasive evidence at $\alpha = 0.05$ that the mean salaries are significantly affected by age.

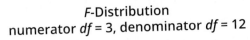

F-Distribution
numerator *df* = 3, denominator *df* = 12

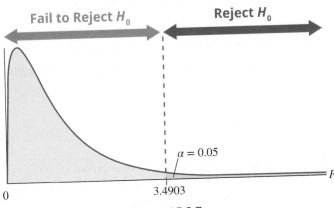

Figure 15.3.7

When using the two-way ANOVA, it is important to remember that the assumptions of normality, equal variances, and independent random samples should be satisfied in order for the test to produce meaningful results. As noted previously, the ANOVA test is robust with regards to the normality and equal variance assumptions.

An important concept in statistics related to ANOVA is the **design of experiments** (DOE). It is much easier to analyze a properly designed experiment as opposed to a poorly designed one. If you are planning on collecting data, you should involve a statistician at the onset, not just employ them to do the analysis once the data has been collected. Experimental design allows you to estimate the effects of several variables simultaneously, thus resulting in a more efficient collection of data that will be much easier to analyze. Design of experiments is a very extensive field of study for which entire books and courses have been developed, but is beyond the scope of this book.

15.3 Exercises

Basic Concepts

1. What is the difference between a randomized block design and a factorial design?

2. What is a complete factorial experiment?

3. What is an interaction plot? What kind of information does this plot give us?

4. Why is it so important to determine if there is interaction between the two variables of interest in a factorial design?

5. Is it possible to perform a two-way analysis of variance if interaction exists between the two variables of interest? Explain why or why not.

6. Identify the four components that make up the total sum of squares in a complete factorial model.

7. Give the degrees of freedom associated with each component of the total sum of squares.

8. What is the test statistic for a test of interaction between factors? What are the degrees of freedom associated with this test statistic?

9. If there is enough evidence to reject the null hypothesis in a test for interaction, may we proceed with the main effects tests? Explain.

10. What is the test statistic for the main effects test for Factor A? What are the degrees of freedom associated with this test statistic?

11. What is the test statistic for the main effects test for Factor B? What are the degrees of freedom associated with this test statistic?

12. What are the rejection rules for the main effects tests? Can P-values be used as rejection criteria?

Exercises

13. The following table contains the results of a survey of daily rental rates of a mid-size car for three major rental car companies at three airport locations on three different days during the year.

Daily Rental Rates of Mid-Size Cars ($)		
	New York	**Chicago**	**Miami**
	93.99	54.99	71.99
	90.99	63.99	87.99
Hertz	96.99	57.99	68.99
	58.86	81.99	61.99
	52.10	85.99	70.99
Avis	68.98	71.99	66.99
	56.00	64.99	66.00
	63.00	67.00	58.99
National	52.00	52.99	71.99

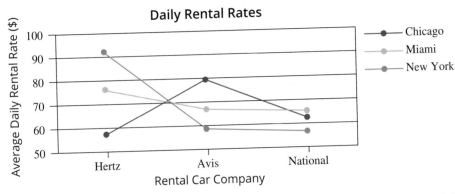

a. Consider the graph of the average daily rental rates for each of the major car rental companies by airport location. Does there appear to be any interaction between the variables airport location and major car rental company?

b. The results of the two-way ANOVA for the study are given in the following table. Perform a hypothesis test to determine if there is any interaction between the variables major rental car company and airport location at $\alpha = 0.05$. Does this agree with your observation in part **a.**?

ANOVA			
Source of Variation	SS	df	MS
Sample	1011.7730	2	505.8865
Columns	58.7126	2	29.3563
Interaction	2514.3099	4	628.5775
Within	819.1289	18	45.5072
Total	4403.9244	26	

c. If there is no interaction found in part **b.**, is there sufficient evidence to conclude that there is a significant difference among the average daily rental rates for mid-size cars for the three rental car companies at the 0.05 level?

14. A doctor is interested in determining the increase in average heart rate caused by a medication used for treating high blood pressure. The doctor believes that the increase in heart rate will be related to two factors: the age of a person and the weight of a person. To test this theory, the doctor randomly selects two patients in each of the age and weight categories listed in the following table and determines the increase in heart rate (in beats per minute) of each patient 15 minutes after administering the drug. The results of the study are as follows.

Increase in Heart Rate (Beats per Minute)			
	25–39 Years	40–54 Years	55–69 Years
100–149 Pounds	2	7	11
	2	6	7
150–199 Pounds	7	11	16
	7	9	12
200–249 Pounds	10	13	18
	8	11	14

a. Consider the following graph of the average increase in heart rate for each of the weight and age categories. Does there appear to be any interaction between the age and weight variables? Explain.

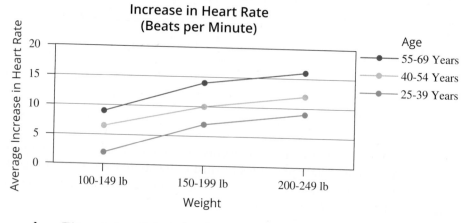

**Increase in Heart Rate
(Beats per Minute)**

Age
— 55-69 Years
— 40-54 Years
— 25-39 Years

b. The results of the two-way ANOVA for the study are given in the following table. Perform a hypothesis test to determine if there is any interaction between the variables age and weight at $\alpha = 0.01$. Does this agree with your observation in part **a.**?

ANOVA

Source of Variation	SS	df	MS
Sample	133.0000	2	66.5000
Columns	147.0000	2	73.5000
Interaction	2.0000	4	0.5000
Within	30.5000	9	3.3889
Total	312.5000	17	

c. Is there sufficient evidence to conclude that there is a significant difference among the average increases in heart rate for the different weight categories? Use $\alpha = 0.01$.

d. Is there sufficient evidence to conclude that there is a significant difference among the average increases in heart rate for the different age groups? Use $\alpha = 0.01$.

15. A supervisor of a manufacturing plant is interested in relating the average number of defects produced per day to two factors: the operator working the machine and the machine itself. The supervisor randomly assigns each operator to use each machine for three days and records the number of defects produced per day. The results of the study are as follows.

Number of Defects Produced per Day			
	Operator A	Operator B	Operator C
	3	7	3
	3	5	2
Machine A	3	3	1

Number of Defects Produced per Day			
	Operator A	**Operator B**	**Operator C**
	2	6	2
	2	4	1
Machine B	2	2	0
	1	5	1
	1	3	0
Machine C	1	2	1

a. Consider the following graph of the average number of defects produced per day for each of the operators by machine. Does there appear to be any interaction between the variables operator and machine?

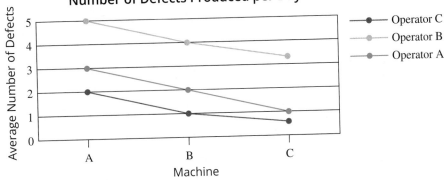

Number of Defects Produced per Day

b. The results of the two-way ANOVA for the supervisor's survey of the number of defects produced per day are given in the following table. Perform a hypothesis test to determine if there is any interaction between the machine and operator variables. Use $\alpha = 0.10$. Does this agree with your observation in part **a.**?

ANOVA			
Source of Variation	*SS*	*df*	*MS*
Sample	12.6667	2	6.3333
Columns	40.2222	2	20.1111
Interaction	0.4444	4	0.1111
Within	25.3333	18	1.4074
Total	78.6667	26	

c. Is there sufficient evidence to conclude that there is a significant difference among the average number of defects produced per day for the different machines? Use $\alpha = 0.10$.

d. Is there sufficient evidence to conclude that there is a significant difference among the average number of defects produced per day for the different operators? Use $\alpha = 0.10$.

16. A dairy farmer thinks that the average weight gain of his cows depends on two factors: the type of grain that they are fed and the type of grass that they are fed. The dairy farmer has four different types of grain from which to choose and three different types of grass from which to choose. He would like to determine if there is a particular combination of grain and grass that would lead to the greatest weight gain on average for his cows. He randomly selects three one-year-old cows and assigns them to each of the possible combinations of grain and grass. After one year he records the weight gain for each cow (in pounds) with the following results.

Cow Weight Gain (Pounds)			
	Grass A	**Grass B**	**Grass C**
	175	225	250
	160	215	240
Grain A	185	230	260
	190	245	275
	185	240	260
Grain B	195	255	285
	210	255	300
	200	245	310
Grain C	220	265	295
	225	275	350
	235	270	360
Grain D	220	280	345

a. Consider the following graph of the average weight gain of the cows for each of the possible combinations of grass and grain. Does there appear to be any interaction between the grass and grain variables?

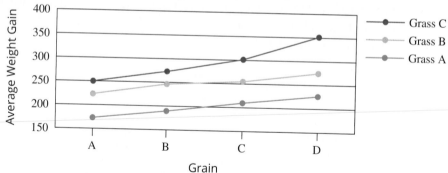

b. The results of the two-way ANOVA for the farmer's study are given in the following table. Perform a hypothesis test to determine if there is any interaction between the variables grass and grain at $\alpha = 0.05$. Does this agree with your observation in part **a.**?

ANOVA

Source of Variation	SS	df	MS
Sample	23097.2222	3	7699.0741
Columns	53272.2222	2	26636.1111
Interaction	3127.7778	6	521.2963
Within	1916.6667	24	79.8611
Total	81413.8889	35	

c. If there is no interaction found in part **b.**, is there sufficient evidence to conclude that there is a significant difference in the average weight gains among the cows for the four different types of grain? Use $\alpha = 0.05$.

d. Is there sufficient evidence to conclude that there is a significant difference in the average weight gains among the cows for the three different types of grass? Use $\alpha = 0.05$.

17. The partially completed analysis of variance table given below is taken from the article, "Power and Status, Exchange, Attribution, and Expectation States (Small Group Research)." The experimenters investigated the effects of power and knowledge on one's emotional reaction in a study involving 52 students selected from a large private university. Each of the factors was run at two levels, with 13 subjects at each of the four different factor combinations.

ANOVA

Source of Variation	SS	df	MS	F
Power	1.2700	1		
Knowledge	0.2500	1		
Interaction		1		
Error	4.1400	48		
Total	5.6700	51		

a. Complete the ANOVA table.

b. Can we conclude, with $\alpha = 0.10$, that there is interaction between power and knowledge?

c. With $\alpha = 0.05$, can we conclude that there is a significant difference in the two levels of power?

d. With $\alpha = 0.05$, can we conclude that there is a significant difference in the two levels of knowledge?

CR   Chapter Review

Key Terms and Ideas

- Experimental Units
- Treatment
- Analysis of Variance (ANOVA)
- Sum of Squares for Treatments (SST)
- Sum of Squares for Error (SSE)
- Sample Variance
- Grand Mean
- Total Sum of Squares (Total SS)
- Mean Square for Treatments (MST)
- Mean Square for Error (MSE)
- F-Statistic
- F-Test
- F-Distribution
- Numerator Degrees of Freedom for F-Statistic

- Denominator Degrees of Freedom for *F*-Statistic
- Multiple Comparison Procedures
- Completely Randomized Design
- Blocks
- Randomized Block Design
- Sum of Squares for Blocks (SSBL)
- Mean Square for Blocks (MSBL)
- Two-Way Analysis of Variance (Two-Way ANOVA)
- Complete Factorial Experiment
- Interaction Plot
- Main Effect for Interaction
- Main Effect for Factor A

- Main Effect for Factor B
- Sum of Squares for Factor A (SSA)
- Sum of Squares for Factor B (SSB)
- Sum of Squares for Interaction (SSAB)
- Test for Interaction between Factors
- Mean Square for Interaction (MSAB)
- Test for Main Effects for Factor A
- Mean Square for Factor A (MSA)
- Test for Main Effects for Factor B
- Mean Square for Factor B (MSB)

Key Formulas		
		Section
Grand Mean $$\bar{\bar{x}} = \frac{\sum\limits_{j=1}^{k}\sum\limits_{i=1}^{n_j} x_{ij}}{N}$$		15.1
Sample Variance $$s^2 = \frac{\sum\limits_{j=1}^{k}\sum\limits_{i=1}^{n_j}\left(x_{ij} - \bar{\bar{x}}\right)^2}{N-1}$$		15.1
Sum of Squares for Treatments (SST) $$SST = \sum\limits_{j=1}^{k} n_j \left(\bar{x}_j - \bar{\bar{x}}\right)^2$$		15.1
Mean Square for Treatments (MST) $$MST = \frac{SST}{k-1}$$		15.1
Sum of Squares for Error (SSE) $$SSE = \sum\limits_{i=1}^{n_1}\left(x_{i1} - \bar{x}_1\right)^2 + \sum\limits_{i=1}^{n_2}\left(x_{i2} - \bar{x}_2\right)^2 + \cdots + \sum\limits_{i=1}^{n_k}\left(x_{ik} - \bar{x}_k\right)^2$$		15.1

Key Formulas

	Section
Total Sum of Squares	15.1

$$\text{Total SS} = \text{SST} + \text{SSE}$$

$$\text{Total SS} = \sum_{j=1}^{k}\sum_{i=1}^{n_j}\left(x_{ij} - \overline{\overline{x}}\right)^2$$

	Section
Mean Square for Error (MSE)	15.1

$$\text{MSE} = \frac{\text{SSE}}{N-k}$$

	Section
***F*-Statistic for One-Way ANOVA**	15.1

$$F = \frac{\text{MST}}{\text{MSE}}$$

$$= \frac{\dfrac{\sum_{j=1}^{k} n_j \left(\overline{x}_j - \overline{\overline{x}}\right)^2}{k-1}}{\dfrac{\sum_{i=1}^{n_1}\left(x_{i1} - \overline{x}_1\right)^2 + \sum_{i=1}^{n_2}\left(x_{i2} - \overline{x}_2\right)^2 + \cdots + \sum_{i=1}^{n_k}\left(x_{ik} - \overline{x}_k\right)^2}{N-k}}$$

	Section
Computational Formula for MST	15.1

$$\text{MST} = \frac{\dfrac{\left(\sum_{i=1}^{n_1} x_{i1}\right)^2}{n_1} + \dfrac{\left(\sum_{i=1}^{n_2} x_{i2}\right)^2}{n_2} + \cdots + \dfrac{\left(\sum_{i=1}^{n_k} x_{ik}\right)^2}{n_k} - \dfrac{\left(\sum_{j=1}^{k}\sum_{i=1}^{n_j} x_{ij}\right)^2}{N}}{k-1}$$

	Section
Computational Formula for MSE	15.1

$$\text{MSE} = \frac{\sum_{j=1}^{k}\sum_{i=1}^{n_j} x_{ij}^2 - \left\{\dfrac{\left(\sum_{i=1}^{n_1} x_{i1}\right)^2}{n_1} + \dfrac{\left(\sum_{i=1}^{n_2} x_{i2}\right)^2}{n_2} + \cdots + \dfrac{\left(\sum_{i=1}^{n_k} x_{ik}\right)^2}{n_k}\right\}}{N-k}$$

	Section
***F*-Statistic for Two-Way ANOVA (Randomized Block Design)**	15.2

$$F = \frac{\text{MST}}{\text{MSE}} = \frac{\dfrac{\text{SST}}{k-1}}{\dfrac{\text{SSE}}{(k-1)(b-1)}}$$

where $\text{SSE} = \text{Total SS} - \text{SST} - \text{SSBL}$

Key Formulas	
	Section
_F_-Statistic for Interaction between Factors	15.3
$$F = \dfrac{\dfrac{SSAB}{(a-1)(b-1)}}{\dfrac{SSE}{ab(r-1)}} = \dfrac{MSAB}{MSE}$$	
_F_-Statistic for Main Effects for Factor A	15.3
$$F = \dfrac{\dfrac{SSA}{(a-1)}}{\dfrac{SSE}{ab(r-1)}} = \dfrac{MSA}{MSE}$$	
_F_-Statistic for Main Effects for Factor B	15.3
$$F = \dfrac{\dfrac{SSB}{(b-1)}}{\dfrac{SSE}{ab(r-1)}} = \dfrac{MSB}{MSE}$$	

Additional Exercises

1. An experimenter often uses a randomized block design to reduce variation by comparing the treatments in homogeneous groups of experimental units called blocks. In many cases, differences in treatments are more likely to be detected with such a design than if the blocking factor were ignored. In each of the following situations, give an example of how one would run a randomized block design to make the comparison in each case. Be aware that there may be more than one correct answer in each example.

    a. Three different methods of teaching science are to be analyzed by comparing final exam scores from classes taught by the different methods. Assume that the same final exam is given to each class.

    b. Five hypertensive treatments are to be compared based on their ability to reduce systolic blood pressure. It is felt that the performance of the drugs is affected by the weight of the participant in the study.

    c. It is desired to compare three different ethnic groups on their knowledge of American history. Each person in the study will be given a 50-question multiple choice test to determine their overall knowledge of the subject.

2. A pharmacist is interested in studying the rate at which three different sinus headache drugs are absorbed into the bloodstream. She randomly selects 12 people, and then randomly assigns four people to try each drug. She administers the drug to each participant and measures the time it takes for the drug to be absorbed into the patient's bloodstream (in minutes). The results of the study are as follows.

Drug Absorption Time (Minutes)		
Drug 1	**Drug 2**	**Drug 3**
5	10	6
4	11	7
6	9	5
3	8	5

   a. Can the pharmacist conclude at $\alpha = 0.01$ that there is a significant difference among the average times required for absorption into the bloodstream for the three drugs?

   b. What assumptions did the pharmacist make in performing the test procedure in part **a.**? Does the data appear to satisfy these assumptions? Explain.

   c. Describe an alternate design that the pharmacist could have used for the above analysis. What are the advantages and disadvantages of this design?

3. An FDA representative is interested in knowing if there is a difference in the average fat contents of three different brands of margarine. The representative randomly selects six samples of each of the brands of margarine and measures the average fat contents per serving. The results of the study are displayed in the following table.

Fat Content per Serving (Grams)		
Margarine #1	**Margarine #2**	**Margarine #3**
6	5	9
7	6	8
6	5	7
8	4	8
6	6	9
8	5	7

   a. Does the data indicate a difference among average fat contents per serving for the three brands of margarine at $\alpha = 0.01$?

   b. What assumptions were made for the test in part **a.**? Does the data appear to satisfy these assumptions? Explain.

   c. Why wouldn't a randomized block design be appropriate for this experiment?

4. Psychological reactance may be viewed as the motivational state resulting when someone's freedom is threatened or eliminated. A study relating psychological reactance to one's age was reported in "Psychological Reactance: Effects of Age and Gender" in the *Journal of Social Psychology*. In order to determine the degree of psychological reactance, participants were asked to fill out a questionnaire which was then scored. The higher the score, the more acute the degree of psychological reactance. The means, standard deviations, and group sizes (for different age groups) are given in the following table.

Psychological Reactance			
Age Group	Mean	Standard Deviation	Group Size
18–24	3.36	0.60	1011
24–29	3.28	0.65	321
30–40	3.16	0.64	385

Although the summary statistics were given in the article, the actual data values upon which the statistics were based were not listed. This is standard procedure in many scientific journals.

a. Compute the sums of squares and their degrees of freedom for treatments and error based upon the statistics given in the table.

b. Compute MST and MSE.

c. With $\alpha = 0.01$, can we conclude that there is a significant difference among the degrees of psychological reactance for the different age groups?

d. What assumptions are necessary for performing the test in part c.? Can they be checked in this instance?

5. Interviews of fans following an Australian Football League game were summarized in the article "On Being a Sore Loser: How Fans React to Their Team's Failure" in the *Australian Journal of Psychology*. The study divided the fans interviewed into losers (those who supported the losing team), winners (those who supported the winning team), and non-partisans (those who were indifferent to the outcome of the game). Each fan was asked several questions, all dealing with the fan's perceptions of the game. The purpose of the study was to see if the groups differed on their responses to any of the questions. One question asked the fans to rate the umpire's performance on a five-point scale from *very bad* (1) to *very good* (5). The mean responses and group sizes associated with this question are given in the following table.

Umpire Performance		
Group	Mean	Group Size
Losers	2.8	49
Winners	3.7	35
Non-Partisans	3.5	57

a. Compute the grand mean and the sum of squares for treatments (SST).

b. Compute the F-statistic for testing for equality of the group means. The sum of squares for error (SSE) was given in the article as 39.3.

c. With $\alpha = 0.01$, can we conclude that there is a significant difference among the groups in the perception of the umpire?

d. What assumptions are necessary for performing the test in part **c.**? Can they be checked in this instance?

6. Consider the following partially completed ANOVA table for a 3×4 factorial experiment with two replications.

ANOVA

Source of Variation	SS	df	MS	F
Factor A	0.800	2		
Factor B	5.300	3		
Interaction	9.600			
Within				
Total	17.000	26		

a. Complete the ANOVA table.

b. At the 0.05 level, is there evidence of significant interaction between A and B? Justify your answer.

c. At the 0.05 level, is there evidence of a significant Factor A effect? Justify your answer.

d. At the 0.05 level, is there evidence of a significant Factor B effect? Justify your answer.

e. Does the result of the test for interaction suggest further investigation? Justify your answer.

7. In an experiment to determine the best method by which to assess college students, a group of students were exposed to one of three types of tests. The three methods were: all multiple choice questions, all free-response questions, and mixed questions (a mixture of multiple choice and free-response questions). The scores were recorded for each test taken. Fifteen students were used in the study and were grouped by class level (freshman, sophomore, junior, senior, and graduate). The following table contains the results of the experiment.

Testing Methods			
Class Level	Multiple Choice	Free-Response	Mixed
Freshman	78	84	90
Sophomore	82	90	95
Junior	90	94	98
Senior	88	96	100
Graduate	95	98	99

a. Graphically plot the test scores by class level and testing method. Discuss the graph.

b. Perform an analysis of the data using the class-level blocks. Are blocking effects significant at the 0.05 level of significance? Explain.

c. Is the experiment useful having been analyzed as a randomized block design? Explain.

8. A randomized block design yielded the following ANOVA table.

ANOVA

Source of Variation	SS	df	MS	F
Treatment	500.000	5	100	7.502
Block	230.000	3	76.67	5.752
Error	120.000	9	13.33	
Total	850.000	17		

a. How many blocks are used in the experiment?

b. How many treatments are used in the experiment?

c. How many observations are used in the experiment?

d. What are the null and alternative hypotheses to test if there is a difference among the treatment means?

e. What test statistic should be used to conduct the test in part **d.**?

f. What is the rejection region for the test in parts **d.** and **e.**?

g. Carry out the test and state your conclusion based on a significance level of 0.05.

9. JAS & Associates, a commercial developer, usually gets three cost estimates for many of the jobs for their building projects. Even though one contractor normally works on each potential job, it is in the best interest of the company to get additional estimates and compare them for consistency, no matter who gets the job. To check the consistency of the estimates, several projects are selected and three contractors are asked to submit estimates. The estimates (in thousands of dollars) for the 10 jobs are given in the following table.

Contractor Cost Estimates (Thousands of Dollars)			
Job	Contractor A	Contractor B	Contractor C
1	27	26	28
2	20	18	22
3	14	13	17
4	18	21	20
5	23	20	22
6	19	17	19
7	12	14	15
8	10	12	13
9	16	20	19
10	40	42	47

a. Perform the appropriate analysis on the data given and generate the ANOVA table for the analysis.

b. Does the data provide sufficient evidence to conclude that there is a difference among the cost estimates supplied by the contractors? Use a significance level of 0.05 to make your decision.

c. What is the P-value for the test performed in part **a.**? Interpret this value.

10. The following table is a 3×3 factorial design with three observations for each factor level.

Factorial Design Data			
	Factor B		
Factor A	**1**	**2**	**3**
1	30	47	36
	30	42	37
	30	42	38
2	12	27	35
	14	24	31
	15	22	33
3	10	34	24
	13	31	20
	12	31	22

a. Make an interaction plot of the treatment means using Factor A along the x-axis and each level of Factor B as a different plotting symbol (see Figure 15.3.1). Do the means appear to be different? Does interaction between factors A and B appear to be present? Justify your answers.

b. Perform the analysis using a software package, generating the ANOVA table.

c. Test for significant interaction using a 0.05 level of significance. Discuss your findings.

d. Test for A and B effects using a 0.05 level of significance. Discuss your findings.

11. Tech SportsPlex (TSP) is conducting a study to determine the effectiveness of three types of marketing/advertising methods: e-coupons, newspaper ads, and price discounts. Three counties (believed to be of equal size and close driving distance to TSP) were selected for the marketing campaign. Each strategy was used for a three-month period. It is known that the sales would be seasonal (i.e. TSP's management expects less activity during the summer months). The revenue data (in thousands of dollars) from the study is given in the following table.

TSP Revenues by Marketing Strategy (Thousands of Dollars)			
Quarter	**e-Coupons**	**Newspaper Ads**	**Price Discounts**
1	48	42	37
2	25	18	21
3	20	15	18
4	40	30	24

a. Specify the null and alternative hypotheses to determine if there is a significant difference among average revenues for the three advertising strategies.

b.   Generate the ANOVA table to test the hypotheses in **a.**

c.   Conduct the test in **a.** using a significance level of 0.05.

d.   Was the variation among the observed revenues significantly reduced by blocking? Explain using $\alpha = 0.05$.

12. In "Death Anxiety in Malaysian and Australian University Students" (The Journal of Social Psychology, 128(1)), the results of an experiment measuring death anxiety was reported. In the study, a total of 153 students were administered the Templer Death Anxiety Scale, a questionnaire which assesses the extent to which the respondent is preoccupied with issues surrounding death. Scores ranged from 0 to 15, with higher scores indicating greater death anxiety. The students were classified into one of three ethnic groups: Chinese, Indian, or Australian. The means, standard deviations (s.d.) and group sizes are given in the following table.

Group	mean	s.d.	size
Chinese	6.0	3.1	62
Indian	4.8	3.1	15
Australian	6.5	2.7	76

Although, the above summary statistics were given in the article, the actual data values upon which the statistics were based were not listed. This is standard procedure in many scientific journals.

a.   Compute the sums of squares and their degrees of freedom for treatments and error based upon the statistics given in the above table. Compute MST and MSE.

b.   With $\alpha = 0.05$, can we conclude that there is a difference in the degree of death anxiety for the 3 groups?

c.   What assumptions are necessary for performing the test in part **c.**? Can they be checked in this instance?

"There are only two ways to live your life. One is as though nothing is a miracle. The other is as though everything is a miracle."

— Albert Einstein

16 CHAPTER

Looking for Relationships in Qualitative Data

Introduction

In Chapter 5 and Chapter 13 we discussed techniques for describing the relationships between quantitative variables. But so far, no means of effectively summarizing relationships between qualitative variables has been presented. This chapter focuses on two methods for summarizing these relationships. The first method compares the actual proportion of observations appearing in a particular category with the proportion of observations which are expected to appear in the category. The second method determines whether or not two categorical variables are related. Both inferential methods rely on the chi-square distribution, which was briefly discussed in Chapter 11.

χ^2 Distribution, *df* = 6

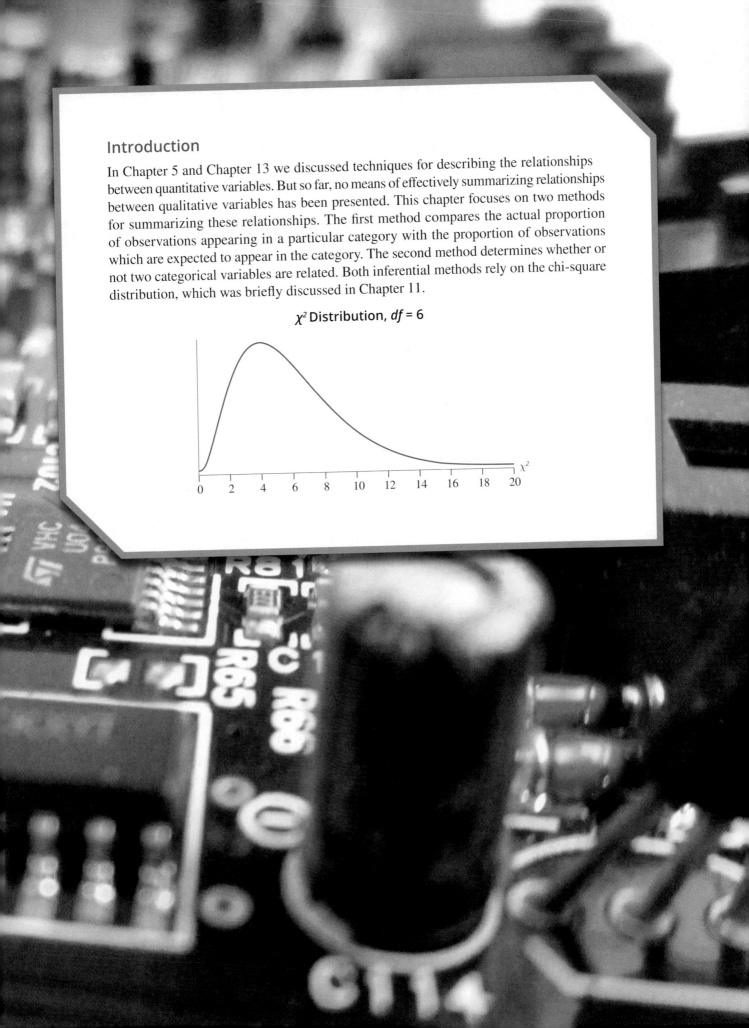

16.1 **The Chi-Square Distribution**

In Section 11.5, we briefly discussed the chi-square distribution in the context of developing a hypothesis testing procedure for testing claims about a population variance. But the chi-square distribution has much broader applications. Before discussing these applications, let's review a few of the basics about the chi-square distribution.

Chi-Square Statistic

If n observations are randomly selected from a normal population with variance σ^2, and s^2 is computed for the sample, then the **chi-square statistic**

$$\chi^2 = \frac{(n-1)s^2}{\sigma^2}$$

has a chi-square distribution with $n-1$ degrees of freedom (df).

FORMULA

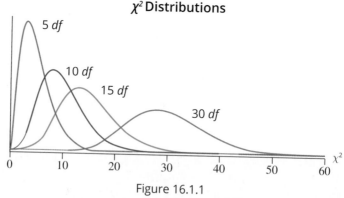

χ^2 **Distributions**

Figure 16.1.1

A chi-square distribution is a continuous distribution. Unlike the normal distribution and the t-distribution, the chi-square distribution is not symmetric. In fact, for small values of n and therefore small values of df, it is very skewed, as you can see from Figure 16.1.1. Another property of the chi-square distribution which is different from the normal and t-distributions is that it only takes on values which are nonnegative. This seems reasonable given that the chi-square distribution is used to represent a ratio which is composed of variances $\left(s^2 \text{ and } \sigma^2\right)$ which must be nonnegative. In fact, σ^2 must be greater than zero for any population in which variation exists.

There are infinitely many chi-square distributions. Each chi-square distribution is uniquely defined by its degrees of freedom. Figure 16.1.1 shows chi-square distributions for various sample sizes. It is interesting to notice that as n becomes large, the chi-square distribution becomes more and more symmetrical, almost normal-looking.

When analyzing the chi-square distribution, we are usually interested in determining critical values rather than particular probabilities. The concept of a critical value was first introduced in the context of constructing a confidence interval and has been used in all of the chapters which have dealt with inference. The critical value for the chi-square distribution is denoted by χ_α^2. It is a value such that the probability that the chi-square random variable is greater than or equal to that value is equal to α. In hypothesis testing, α, our tolerance for making a Type I error, is specified by the researcher. The chi-square tables contain critical values for various levels of

α and many possible degrees of freedom. Tables containing critical values for the chi-square distribution are found in Appendix A. The critical values can also be easily obtained with technology.

Determining Chi-Square Critical Values

Suppose a significance level of $\alpha = 0.05$ has been specified and our sample size is 20. The chi-square distribution has one parameter, degrees of freedom, which is equal to $n - 1$. If the null hypothesis is rejected for large values of the test statistic, we look in the table under the column labeled $\chi^2_{0.050}$ and find the critical value corresponding to $20 - 1$, or 19 degrees of freedom. The corresponding critical value is 30.144, as shown in Figure 16.1.2.

⚭ Technology

A chi-square critical value can be easily found using Excel. For instructions, visit stat.hawkeslearning.com and navigate to **Technology Instructions > Chi-Square Distribution > Critical Value**.

fx	=CHIINV(0.05,19)
	D	E
	30.14353	

df	...	$\chi^2_{0.050}$	$\chi^2_{0.025}$	$\chi^2_{0.010}$
1		3.841	5.024	6.635
2		5.991	7.378	9.210
3		7.815	9.348	11.345
⋮				
19		30.144	32.852	36.191
20		31.410	34.170	37.566
⋮				

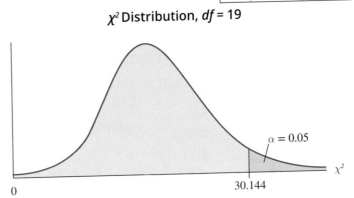

χ^2 Distribution, $df = 19$

$\alpha = 0.05$

30.144

Figure 16.1.2

Suppose a significance level of $\alpha = 0.01$ has been specified and our sample size is 14. If we reject the null hypothesis for large values of the test statistic, we look in the table under the column labeled $\chi^2_{0.010}$ and find the critical value corresponding to $14 - 1$, or 13 degrees of freedom. The corresponding critical value is 27.688, as shown in Figure 16.1.3.

df	...	$\chi^2_{0.050}$	$\chi^2_{0.025}$	$\chi^2_{0.010}$
1		3.841	5.024	6.635
2		5.991	7.378	9.210
3		7.815	9.348	11.345
⋮				
13		22.362	24.736	27.688
14		23.685	26.119	29.141
⋮				

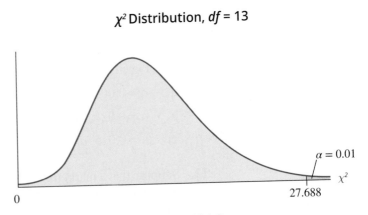

χ^2 Distribution, $df = 13$

$\alpha = 0.01$

27.688

Figure 16.1.3

The analysis in the remainder of the chapter deals with comparing the actual number of observations falling into a particular category with the number of observations that is expected to fall in that category, based on our hypothesis. In certain circumstances this type of formulation can be evaluated with a chi-square distribution.

16.1 Exercises

Basic Concepts

1. Describe the shape of the chi-square distribution.
2. What is the sampling distribution of the sample variance?
3. What are the degrees of freedom associated with the chi-square distribution?
4. Can a chi-square statistic ever be negative? Explain why or why not.
5. Describe how the chi-square distribution changes in shape as n becomes large.
6. Explain the meaning of χ_α^2.
7. Explain the procedure for determining chi-square critical values.

Exercises

8. Find the chi-square critical value for each of the following.

   a. $\alpha = 0.01,\ df = 14$ d. $\alpha = 0.05,\ df = 9$
   b. $\alpha = 0.01,\ df = 26$ e. $\alpha = 0.005,\ df = 12$
   c. $\alpha = 0.05,\ df = 4$

9. Find the chi-square critical value for each of the following.

   a. $\alpha = 0.005,\ df = 21$ d. $\alpha = 0.10,\ df = 90$
   b. $\alpha = 0.025,\ df = 16$ e. $\alpha = 0.10,\ df = 17$
   c. $\alpha = 0.025,\ df = 1$

10. Find the chi-square critical value for each of the following.

    a. $\alpha = 0.01,\ df = 10$ d. $\alpha = 0.05,\ df = 11$
    b. $\alpha = 0.01,\ df = 21$ e. $\alpha = 0.005,\ df = 29$
    c. $\alpha = 0.05,\ df = 6$

11. Find the chi-square critical value for each of the following.

    a. $\alpha = 0.005,\ df = 40$ d. $\alpha = 0.10,\ df = 24$
    b. $\alpha = 0.025,\ df = 15$ e. $\alpha = 0.10,\ df = 50$
    c. $\alpha = 0.025,\ df = 2$

12. Suppose that a marketing manager is studying sales data for products that are not available in stores and only sold on television. She collects the following weekly sales data for 10 products not sold in stores. Assume the population standard deviation for this data is $5000.

Weekly Sales Figures	
Product	**Weekly Sales ($)**
1	26,259
2	18,514
3	21,579
4	18,739
5	27,821
6	22,511
7	29,753
8	20,235
9	16,258
10	15,990

a. Compute the sample standard deviation for this data. Round your answer to the nearest dollar.

b. Compute the value of χ^2. Round your answer to three decimal places.

c. How many degrees of freedom are associated with this chi-square distribution?

d. What is the value of $\chi^2_{0.05}$ for this data?

13. Michael is interested in obtaining a 30-year fixed mortgage rates in Myrtle Beach, SC. He obtained rate quotes from 8 lenders, and the APR rates that were quoted to him are given in the following table.

30-Year Fixed Mortgage Rates	
Lender	**APR (%)**
EverBank	3.918
AimLoan	3.925
Great Western	4.062
Greenlight	4.353
Flagstar	4.350
AuroraBank	4.040
Quicken	4.458
Roundpoint	4.125

a. Calculate the variance of the sample. Round your answer to six decimal places.

b. Assuming the population standard deviation for the rates is 0.1%, calculate the value of χ^2.

c. Determine the value of $\chi^2_{0.025}$ for this data.

**Karl Pearson
1857 - 1936**

Pearson was educated at home until he was nine, then he was sent to University College where he eventually earned a degree in mathematics. After studying in Germany he returned to University College as a teacher and lecturer. Karl Pearson is regarded as one of the founders of modern statistics. In addition to developing the correlation coefficient, he developed the chi-square test (which included the development of the chi-square sampling distribution) as a means of assessing relationships for categorical data.

16.2 The Chi-Square Test for Goodness of Fit

An owner of a grocery market chain suspects that there has been a change in the shopping pattern of his customers. He has always believed that his stores are equally busy regardless of the day of the week, and he has geared his weekly advertised specials accordingly.

If the shopping pattern has changed and some days are in fact busier shopping days than others, he estimates that this could be costing him thousands of dollars in lost sales due to improperly scheduled advertisements. He decides to use statistical inference to test his theory. He randomly samples 105 customers from his customer database and asks them which day of the week they go grocery shopping. The results of the survey are listed in Table 16.2.1. Based on this data, what criteria can the grocer use to decide if some days of the week are preferred for grocery shopping over others?

Table 16.2.1 - Customer Shopping Data						
Monday	**Tuesday**	**Wednesday**	**Thursday**	**Friday**	**Saturday**	**Sunday**
10	15	14	16	11	20	19

In 1900, Karl Pearson developed the **chi-square test for goodness of fit**. The test statistic for the chi-square goodness of fit is a summary measure which compares the actual percentage of observations which fall into a particular category with the expected percentage for that category.

Chi-Square Test for Goodness of Fit

The **chi-square goodness-of-fit** test is a hypothesis test used to determine if an observed frequency distribution follows a specified distribution. It accomplishes this by comparing observed frequencies to expected frequencies based on the specified distribution.

DEFINITION

In order to use the chi-square test for goodness of fit for inference, our experiment must satisfy some basic conditions. First, we must be able to assume that the underlying distribution of the number of shoppers shopping on the various days of the week has a **multinomial probability distribution**.

Multinomial Probability Distribution

The **multinomial probability distribution** is an extension of the binomial probability distribution to more than two possible outcomes on each trial, each with a constant probability of occurring from trial to trial.

DEFINITION

Properties of a Multinomial Experiment

- The experiment consists of n independent, identical trials.
- There are k possible outcomes for each trial.
- The probability of the k outcomes, $p_1, p_2, ..., p_k$ are constant from trial to trial.
- The random variables of interest are the counts for each of the k possible outcomes, $n_1, n_2, ..., n_k$.

PROPERTIES

The grocer's survey of the number of shoppers shopping on the various days of the week seems to satisfy the conditions of a multinomial experiment. Since the customers were randomly selected and each of them was asked the same question, there were 105 independent, identical trials. The true proportions of shoppers shopping on each day of the week are unknown and constant from trial to trial. The proportion of shoppers shopping on each day of the week form a probability distribution whose probabilities sum to one.

Using the procedure outlined in Section 11.1 for testing a hypothesis, we must first define the hypothesis to be tested. Our grocer might formulate his hypothesis as follows.

Null Hypothesis: The proportion of shoppers does not vary by day of the week.

Alternative Hypothesis: The proportion of shoppers does vary by day of the week.

In this situation the proportion is the obvious measure of choice. However, there are several proportions of interest. Namely, the proportion of shoppers shopping on each day of the week. Therefore, let

$p_1 =$ the proportion of shoppers shopping on Monday,
$p_2 =$ the proportion of shoppers shopping on Tuesday,
$\vdots$
$p_7 =$ the proportion of shoppers shopping on Sunday.

Putting everything together, we specify the hypotheses as follows.

$H_0: p_1 = p_2 = p_3 = p_4 = p_5 = p_6 = p_7 = \dfrac{1}{7}$ The proportion of shoppers doesn't vary by day of the week.

$H_a:$ At least one proportion does not equal $\dfrac{1}{7}$.   The proportion of shoppers varies by day of the week.

For **Step 2**, our grocer must choose a significance level. Let's assume that he is willing to live with a 5% chance of making a Type I error. Namely, concluding that the proportion of shoppers varies by day of the week, when in fact it doesn't. Therefore, he chooses a level of $\alpha = 0.05$.

To determine the appropriate test statistic required for **Step 3**, let's consider the statement of the null hypothesis. If the null hypothesis is true

$$p_1 = p_2 = p_3 = p_4 = p_5 = p_6 = p_7 = \frac{1}{7},$$

and 15 customers $\left(\dfrac{1}{7} \text{ of } 105\right)$ of the 105 customers would be expected to shop on each day of the week. If we let $n_1, n_2, \ldots, n_7$ represent the number of customers who shop on the seven days of the week respectively, then this expectation would be formally stated as follows.

$$E\left(n_1\right) = n \cdot p_1 = 105 \cdot \frac{1}{7} = 15.$$

Similarly, $E(n_2) = E(n_3) = \ldots = E(n_7) = 15$.

To test the hypothesis, we need to measure how close reality is (the data given by the shoppers) to what is stated in the null hypothesis. This measure will become a test statistic. The test statistic will be developed as part of a criterion which will be used to make a choice between the null and alternative hypothesis. Intuitively, the test statistic should compare the expected number of shoppers for each day of the week, given that our null hypothesis is true, ($E(n_i)$, $i = 1, \ldots, 7$) to the actual numbers of shoppers reported in the grocer's survey (n_i, $i = 1, \ldots, 7$).

A reasonable test statistic would consist of the differences between the number of shoppers the grocer expected to see each day and the number of shoppers the grocer actually observed each day. In attempting to summarize this information, it is tempting to simply add these differences. However, negative and positive differences will cancel each other out. Further, we have not yet adjusted these differences for any potential differences in scale among the days of the week. (**Note:** In our problem the null hypothesis implies there is no difference in scale. However, the methodology is designed to handle hypothesized differences in scale among the categories.) To compensate for these problems, square the differences, so that positive and negative differences will not cancel each other out, and divide each squared difference by the appropriate $E(n_i)$ to adjust for any differences in scale. This will give us the following test statistic.

$$\chi^2 = \frac{\left[n_1 - E\left(n_1\right)\right]^2}{E\left(n_1\right)} + \frac{\left[n_2 - E\left(n_2\right)\right]^2}{E\left(n_2\right)} + \ldots + \frac{\left[n_7 - E\left(n_7\right)\right]^2}{E\left(n_7\right)}$$

If the null hypothesis is true and the data satisfies the conditions of a multinomial distribution, this test statistic has an approximate chi-square distribution with $n - 1$ degrees of freedom. In our example there are $7 - 1 = 6$ degrees of freedom.

If the differences between what is observed and what is expected are large enough, the chi-square test statistic quantity will become very large, causing us to doubt the reasonableness of the null hypothesis. Thus, for **Step 4** we will reject the null hypothesis for large values of the test statistic (we have a one-tailed test). How large is large?

How large must the value of χ^2 be in order to conclude the null is not reasonable? We must have a criterion. The critical value for a chi-square distribution with a level of significance of 0.05, $\chi^2_{0.05}$, with 6 degrees of freedom is 12.592. Thus, if the null hypothesis is true, a test statistic larger than 12.592 will occur only 5% of the time due to sampling variation. Values larger than 12.592 are relatively rare (occur 5% of the time or less) if the null hypothesis is true. Hence, if we observe a value of the test statistic that is larger than 12.592 we will reject the null hypothesis. This rejection region is drawn in Figure 16.2.1.

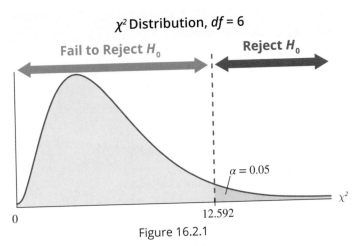

Figure 16.2.1

The resulting value of the test statistic is as follows.

$$\chi^2 = \frac{[10-15]^2}{15} + \frac{[15-15]^2}{15} + \frac{[14-15]^2}{15} + \frac{[16-15]^2}{15}$$
$$+ \frac{[11-15]^2}{15} + \frac{[20-15]^2}{15} + \frac{[19-15]^2}{15} = 5.6$$

Notice that the value of the test statistic does not fall in the rejection region since 5.6 is less than 12.592 as shown in Figure 16.2.2.

The exact P-value for the test statistic of 5.6 can be found using technology. The P-value is 0.4695, which is greater than 0.05. Thus, for **Step 5**, we conclude that the data does not provide enough evidence to reject the null hypothesis.

Technology

The chi-square test statistic and corresponding P-value can be found using the χ^2 GOF-Test function on the TI-84 Plus calculator. For instructions please visit stat.hawkeslearning.com and navigate to **Technology Instructions > Chi-Square Distribution > Test for Goodness of Fit.**

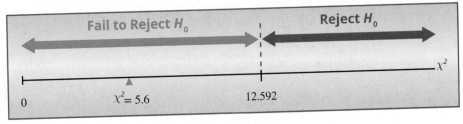

Figure 16.2.2

Our conclusion for **Step 6** is that our grocer's suspicion that some shopping days are busier than others was not substantiated. Based on the evidence gathered in his study he should not change his advertising practice.

The basic steps in performing a chi-square test for goodness of fit are outlined below. It is important to note that in order to use this test we must assume that the sample size, n, is large enough that there will be at least five expected observations per category and that the underlying distribution is a multinomial probability distribution.

Chi-Square Test for Goodness of Fit

Assumptions:

1. The conditions for a multinomial random variable are met.
2. The expected value of n_i is at least 5 for each category.

Hypotheses:

$$H_0: p_1 = p_{1,0}, p_2 = p_{2,0}, \ldots, p_k = p_{k,0}$$
$$H_a: \text{Any possible difference.}$$

Test Statistic:

$$\chi^2 = \sum_{i=1}^{k} \frac{\left[n_i - E\left(n_i\right)\right]^2}{E\left(n_i\right)}$$

where n_i is the actual number of observations in each category, and $E(n_i)$ is the expected number of observations for each category given that the null hypothesis is true.

Given the assumptions are met, the test statistic has a chi-square distribution with $k - 1$ degrees of freedom.

Rejection Region:

Reject H_0 if $\chi^2 > \chi_\alpha^2$ with $k - 1$ degrees of freedom.

P-value:

The P-value is the probability of observing a value as extreme or more extreme than the value of the test statistic, given a chi-square distribution with $k - 1$ degrees of freedom.

If the computed P-value is less than α, reject the null hypothesis in favor of the alternative.

If the computed P-value is greater than or equal to α, fail to reject the null hypothesis.

PROCEDURE

Example 16.2.1

SeQuix has been developed for treating kidney disease. It has been found to have the following side effects in patients when taken over a two-month period.

SeQuix	
Side Effect	**Percent**
At least a 5% increase in systolic blood pressure	50
Less than a 5% change in systolic blood pressure	40
At least a 5% decrease in systolic blood pressure	10

A competitor has developed a new drug for treating kidney disease. The competitor hopes the new drug will not have as severe blood pressure side effects as SeQuix. Two hundred and fifty patients are treated with the new drug and their blood pressures are monitored over a two-month period. The following results are observed.

New Drug	
Side Effect	**Number of Patients**
At least a 5% increase in systolic blood pressure	100
Less than a 5% change in systolic blood pressure	120
At least a 5% decrease in systolic blood pressure	30

Can the researchers conclude that there is a difference in systolic blood pressure side effects between SeQuix and the new drug?

Solution

Step 1: Determine the null and alternative hypotheses.

Null Hypothesis: There is no difference in blood pressure side effects between the two drugs.

Alternative Hypothesis: There is a difference in blood pressure side effects between the two drugs.

The variable to be analyzed is Side Effect, which has three possible values: at least a 5% increase in systolic blood pressure, less than a 5% change in systolic blood pressure, and at least a 5% decrease in systolic blood pressure. Further, our interest is in the proportion (or percent) of the patients who fall into each of the blood pressure side effect categories:

p_1 = the proportion of patients with at least a 5% increase in blood pressure,

p_2 = the proportion of patients with less than a 5% change in blood pressure,

p_3 = the proportion of patients with at least a 5% decrease in blood pressure.

The chi-square test for goodness of fit is always a one-sided test because of the way the test statistic is constructed. We will reject the null hypothesis in favor of the alternative hypothesis for large values of the test statistic.

In symbolic notation the resulting hypotheses would be

H_0: $p_1 = 0.5$, $p_2 = 0.4$, $p_3 = 0.1$ No difference in patient's blood pressure response between the two drugs.

H_a: Any possible difference.

Step 2: Specify the significance level α.

The level of the test is not stated in the problem; therefore, we must choose α ourselves. Let's assume that the researchers are very concerned about making a Type I error (believing that there is a difference in systolic blood pressure side effects between the two drugs when in fact there is not). Although the choice of α is arbitrary, a reasonable choice might be $\alpha = 0.01$.

Step 3: Validate the assumptions of the hypothesis testing model, identify the appropriate test statistic and compute its value.

☑   The number of patients falling into a particular category of blood pressure response satisfies the properties of a multinomial experiment.

☑   The expected number of observations in each category is at least five.

Consequently, the chi-square test for goodness of fit can be used to make inferences concerning the difference in proportions. The chi-square test statistic is

$$\chi^2 = \frac{\left[n_1 - E(n_1)\right]^2}{E(n_1)} + \frac{\left[n_2 - E(n_2)\right]^2}{E(n_2)} + \frac{\left[n_3 - E(n_3)\right]^2}{E(n_3)}.$$

This test statistic has a chi-square distribution with $3 - 1 = 2$ degrees of freedom, assuming the null hypothesis is true.

Since 250 patients were sampled,

$$E(n_1) = 250 \cdot 0.5 = 125,$$
$$E(n_2) = 250 \cdot 0.4 = 100, \text{ and}$$
$$E(n_3) = 250 \cdot 0.1 = 25.$$

Thus,

$$\chi^2 = \frac{\left[100 - 125\right]^2}{125} + \frac{\left[120 - 100\right]^2}{100} + \frac{\left[30 - 25\right]^2}{25} = 10.$$

Step 4: Determine the critical value(s) or *P*-value.

The level of the test is $\alpha = 0.01$, and we will reject the null hypothesis for large values of the test statistic. Large values of the test statistic would indicate that the proportion of patients falling into a category is so different for at least one category that it could not be due to random chance alone.

As shown the following figure, the chi-square critical value is $\chi^2_{0.01}$ with 2 degrees of freedom or 9.210. Any value of the test statistic larger than the critical value will be considered too large to be due to ordinary sampling variation.

☁ **Technology**

The *P*-value can be found in Excel using the CHISQ. DIST.RT function. For instructions, please visit stat.hawkeslearning.com and navigate to **Technology Instructions > Chi-Square Distribution > Right Tailed Probability (cdf).**

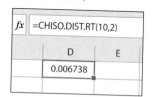

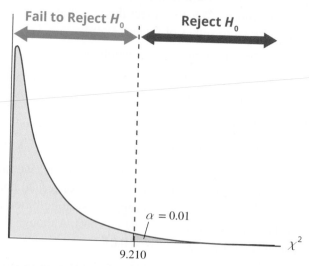

χ^2 **Distribution, *df* = 2**

The *P*-value for a test statistic value of 10 and degrees of freedom equal to 2 is approximately 0.0067.

Step 5: Make the decision to reject or fail to reject H_0.

Since the test statistic falls in the rejection region (10 is greater than 9.210) the null hypothesis should be rejected.

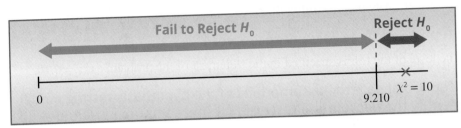

Caution

It may be tempting to conclude that the new drug actually results in less of an increase in blood pressure than SeQuix or that the new drug actually decreases blood pressure. These conclusions would not be valid given that we were testing for any difference in categories. A new test would need to be performed to determine if the new hypothesis is supported by the data.

Likewise, using the *P*-value method the null hypothesis would be rejected since 0.0067 is less than $\alpha = 0.01$.

Step 6: State the conclusion in terms of the original data.

There is sufficient evidence to conclude at $\alpha = 0.01$ that there is a difference in systolic blood pressure side effects between SeQuix and the new drug.

Example 16.2.2

The ABC Distribution company prints sports trading cards. Their 2017 baseball set contains 100 cards and is claimed to contain approximately an equal percentage of four card types: rookies, veterans, All-Stars, and Hall of Famers. A customer recently ordered a set and reported the actual frequency of cards of each type. The chi-square test for goodness of fit can be used to answer the question of whether or not the company's claim is correct. Using $\alpha = 0.10$, determine if the distribution of the four types of cards is approximately the same in the set the customer ordered.

Baseball Cards		
Card Type	Claim Frequency	Actual Frequency
Rookie	25	23
Veteran	25	28
All-Star	25	27
Hall of Famer	25	22

(Since there are 100 cards in the set, the claim of an equal distribution of the four types would result in 25 cards of each type.)

Solution

Step 1: Determine the null and alternative hypotheses.

Null hypothesis: The proportion of the four card types in the set is the same.

Alternative hypothesis: The proportion of the four card types in the set is not the same.

Here we are interested in the proportion of each of the types of cards.

p_1 = the proportion of rookie cards in the set

p_2 = the proportion of veteran cards in the set

p_3 = the proportion of All-Star cards in the set

p_4 = the proportion of Hall of Famer cards in the set

In symbolic notation, the resulting hypotheses would be

$H_0: p_1 = p_2 = p_3 = p_4 = 0.25.$ The proportion of the four card types in the set is the same.

H_a: Any possible difference.

Step 2: Specify the significance level α.

The level of the test is specified in the statement of the problem as $\alpha = 0.10$.

Step 3: Validate the assumptions of the hypothesis testing model, identify the appropriate test statistic and compute its value.

☑ The number of cards of each type of baseball card satisfies the properties of a multinomial probability distribution.

☑ The expected number of observations in each category is at least 5.

Thus, we can use the chi-square test for goodness of fit. The chi-square test statistic is given by,

$$\chi^2 = \frac{\left[n_1 - E\left(n_1\right)\right]^2}{E\left(n_1\right)} + \frac{\left[n_2 - E\left(n_2\right)\right]^2}{E\left(n_2\right)} + \frac{\left[n_3 - E\left(n_3\right)\right]^2}{E\left(n_3\right)} + \frac{\left[n_4 - E\left(n_4\right)\right]^2}{E\left(n_4\right)}.$$

This test statistic has an approximate chi-square distribution with $(4 - 1) = 3$ degrees of freedom, assuming the null hypothesis is true.

Our test statistic would be calculated as

$$\chi^2 = \frac{\left[23 - 25\right]^2}{25} + \frac{\left[28 - 25\right]^2}{25} + \frac{\left[27 - 25\right]^2}{25} + \frac{\left[22 - 25\right]^2}{25} = \frac{26}{25} = 1.04.$$

Step 4: Determine the critical value(s) or P-value.

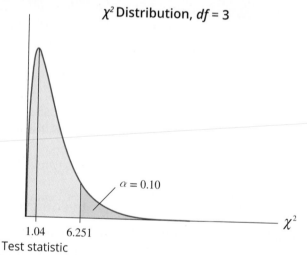

χ^2 Distribution, df = 3

$\alpha = 0.10$

1.04   6.251
Test statistic

χ^2

∽ **Technology**

The P-value can be easily calculated from the test statistic using the χ^2 CDF function on a TI-83/84 Plus calculator. For instructions, please visit stat.hawkeslearning.com and navigate to **Technology Instructions > Chi-Square Distribution > Right Tailed Probability (cdf)**.

χ²cdf(1.04,10ε6,3)
        .7915743931

Since the test level is $\alpha = 0.10$ and we reject the null hypothesis for large values of the test statistic, the chi-square critical value is $\chi^2_{0.10}$ with 3 degrees of freedom or 6.251.

Using technology, the P-value for the test statistic of 1.04 with degrees of freedom equal to 3 is 0.7916.

Step 5: Make the decision to reject or fail to reject H_0.

If the null hypothesis is true, the test statistic will be larger than the critical value 6.251 only 10% of the time. Since $\chi^2 = 1.04$ is not larger than 6.251, we fail to reject H_0.

The P-value is much larger than $\alpha = 0.10$, so we fail to reject the null hypothesis.

Step 6: State the conclusion in terms of the original problem.

At the 0.10 level, there is insufficient evidence to conclude that the distribution of the card types in the set differs from the company claim that the proportion of each card type is approximately equal.

16.2 **Exercises**

Basic Concepts

1. Describe what the test statistic for the chi-square test for goodness of fit measures.

2. What is a multinomial probability distribution? What more familiar probability distribution discussed previously in the text is a multinomial probability distribution related to?

3. List the four requirements for a multinomial experiment.

4. What are the null and alternative hypotheses for a chi-square test for goodness of fit?

5. What is the test statistic for a chi-square test for goodness of fit?

6. How many degrees of freedom does the test statistic for the chi-square test for goodness of fit have?

7. What assumptions are necessary for a chi-square test for goodness of fit?

8. How are the expected values determined in a chi-square test for goodness of fit?

Exercises

9. A telephone company claims that the service calls they receive are equally distributed among the five working days of the week. A survey of 85 randomly selected service calls produced the following results.

Service Calls					
	Monday	**Tuesday**	**Wednesday**	**Thursday**	**Friday**
Number of Calls	15	20	25	15	10

   a. Is the company's claim refuted by the data at $\alpha = 0.05$?

   b. What assumptions were made in the test for part **a.**?

10. Suppose a consumer affairs representative for Mars Incorporated claims that M&M's plain chocolate candies are mixed such that each large production batch has "precisely" the following ratios of colored candies: 30% brown, 20% yellow, 20% red, 10% orange, 10% green, and 10% blue. To test this claim, a professor distributed small sample bags of M&M's to students and had them count the number of candies of each color. The counts of the students were then pooled with the following results.

Candy Colors							
	Brown	**Yellow**	**Red**	**Orange**	**Green**	**Blue**	**Total**
Number of Candies	84	79	75	49	36	47	370

    a.   If the representative's claim is true, what would be the expected number of candies in each of the color categories for 370 candies?

    b.   Is the representative's claim refuted by the data at $\alpha = 0.01$?

    c.   What assumptions were made in performing the test for part **b.**?

11. A highway department executive claims that the number of fatal accidents which occur in her state does not vary from month to month. A survey of 170 fatal accidents produced the following results.

Accidents												
	Jan.	**Feb.**	**Mar.**	**Apr.**	**May**	**Jun.**	**July**	**Aug.**	**Sept.**	**Oct.**	**Nov.**	**Dec.**
Accidents	18	16	7	5	8	12	15	18	15	11	20	25

    a.   Is the executive's claim refuted by the data at $\alpha = 0.01$?

    b.   What assumptions were made in the test for part **a.**?

12. A psychologist conducted an attitude survey of 200 randomly selected individuals several years ago. The individuals were asked to pick the one category which most accurately described their attitudes. The results of the survey were as follows.

1st Attitude Survey	
Attitude	**Percent of Respondents**
Optimistic	15%
Slightly Optimistic	30%
Slightly Pessimistic	30%
Pessimistic	25%

The psychologist believes that these attitudes have changed over time. To test this theory, he randomly selects 200 individuals and asks them the same questions. The results of the second survey are as follows.

2nd Attitude Survey	
Attitude	**Percent of Respondents**
Optimistic	20%
Slightly Optimistic	40%
Slightly Pessimistic	30%
Pessimistic	10%

    a.   Can the psychologist conclude that the attitudes have changed over time at $\alpha = 0.01$?

    b.   What assumptions were made in the test for part **a.**?

16.3 The Chi-Square Test for Association

Our interest sometimes extends beyond one variable to summarizing the relationship between two qualitative variables. For example, a radio executive might be interested in knowing if the gender of an individual affects that person's preference for music. Here the qualitative variables of interest are gender, which could take on the values Male and Female, and preference for music, which could take on the values Classical, Jazz, Easy Listening, Rock, Rap, and Country. Other examples of relationships between two qualitative variables which might be of interest are age and political preference, education level and job performance, income level and occupation, etc. When we are interested in this type of relationship, we often make use of a contingency table.

Contingency Table (or Two-Way Frequency Table)

A **contingency table** organizes data on two characteristics simultaneously. Each cell in a contingency table contains either a count or a proportion which represents the number of observations falling into that cell. It is important to note that contingency tables are composed of two variables which each satisfy the properties of the multinomial distribution.

DEFINITION

Table 16.3.1 below shows the general form of a contingency table.

Table 16.3.1 - General Form of a Contingency Table		Factor A		
		Level A1	Level A2	Total
Factor B	Level B1	n_1	n_2	$n_1 + n_2$
	Level B2	n_3	n_4	$n_3 + n_4$
Total		$n_1 + n_3$	$n_2 + n_4$	$n = n_1 + n_2 + n_3 + n_4$

As an example, consider the following survey on job satisfaction based on income level. For the survey, 14,999 respondents at various income levels were asked if they were satisfied or dissatisfied with their jobs. For those who responded, the contingency table shown in Table 16.3.2 resulted.

Table 16.3.2 - Level of Job Satisfaction			
Income	Satisfied	Dissatisfied	Total
High ($75,000+)	762	475	1237
Medium ($45,000 to $74,999)	3840	2606	6446
Low ($15,000 to $44,999)	4080	3236	7316
Total	8682	6317	14,999

Notice that the column totals and the row totals both sum to the number of respondents in the survey, 14,999. This means that each respondent was allowed to choose only one category. This is necessary if the table is to satisfy the conditions of a multinomial distribution. If the survey is designed such that respondents are allowed to choose more than one category, the following analysis will not apply.

Suppose we are interested in knowing if there is some relationship between income and job satisfaction. Another way of thinking about the same problem is to ask if job satisfaction is dependent on income level. Rephrasing the question in this manner is important because a formal definition of dependence was developed in Chapter 6. We will use this definition in the development of the hypothesis test. Further, stating that two variables are dependent implies that they are related.

Recall the multiplication rule for independent events from Section 6.3. It states that if two events A and B are independent, then $P(A \cap B) = P(A) \cdot P(B)$. If we consider each cell in our contingency table as the intersection of two events, level of income and level of job satisfaction, we can use this multiplication rule to help determine whether or not these two events are dependent. To see this, it is helpful to express our contingency table in terms of relative frequencies or proportions as shown in Table 16.3.3.

Table 16.3.3 - Level of Job Satisfaction (Proportions)			
Income	**Satisfied**	**Dissatisfied**	**Total**
High	0.0508	0.0317	0.0825
Medium	0.2560	0.1737	0.4298
Low	0.2720	0.2157	0.4878
Total	0.5788	0.4212	1.0000

Let the subscript S represent being *Satisfied*, D represent *Dissatisfied*, income level 1 is *High*, income level 2 is *Medium*, and income level 3 is *Low*. The relative frequencies were determined in the following manner.

$\hat{p}_1 = \dfrac{1237}{14999}$ = the proportion of respondents surveyed who had an income of \$75,000+.

$\hat{p}_S = \dfrac{8682}{14999}$ = the proportion of respondents surveyed who were satisfied with their jobs.

$\hat{p}_{1S} = \dfrac{762}{14999}$ = the proportion of respondents surveyed who were satisfied with their jobs *and* had an income of \$75,000+.

If level of income and level of satisfaction are independent, then

$$p_{1S} = p_1 \cdot p_S,$$

$$p_{1D} = p_1 \cdot p_D,$$

$$\vdots$$

$$p_{3D} = p_3 \cdot p_D$$

Given that we are interested in determining whether or not job satisfaction is dependent on level of income and we have developed some relationships which should hold true if the events are independent, it seems reasonable to formulate our hypotheses as follows.

Null Hypothesis: Income level and job satisfaction are independent.

Alternative Hypothesis: Income level and job satisfaction are dependent.

Assuming that the null hypothesis is true (level of income and job satisfaction are independent), then we would expect the number of respondents who were satisfied with their jobs and had incomes of \$75,000 and above, $E(n_{1S})$, to be roughly equal to a theoretical number determined using the data and the definitions of independence and expected value. Using the idea of independence and the notion of expected value we would expect $n \cdot p_1 \cdot p_s$ to be the number of people in the high income and satisfied category.

from expected value of a binomial, np

$$n\,(\underbrace{p_1 \cdot p_s})$$

from independence

Note

The product of the probabilities $p_1 \cdot p_s$ *is the probability* of someone in the population we are surveying having a high income *and* being satisfied with their job (assuming independence of the events).

Since the true probabilities of incomes in the High category and being Satisfied at work are unknown, the results of the survey can be used to estimate these probabilities. This can be written symbolically as

$$E\left(\text{high income and satisfied}\right) = E\left(n_{1s}\right) \approx n \cdot \hat{p}_1 \cdot \hat{p}_s = 14999\left(\frac{1237}{14999} \cdot \frac{8682}{14999}\right) \approx 716.023.$$

Similarly, we can calculate the remaining expected values as shown in Table 16.3.4.

Table 16.3.4 - Calculating Expected Value for Each Category

Expected Value to Calculate	Calculation of Estimated Expected Value	Estimated Expected Value
$E\left(\text{medium income and satisfied}\right)$	$= E\left(n_{2S}\right) \approx n \cdot \hat{p}_2 \cdot \hat{p}_S = 14999\left(\dfrac{6446}{14999} \cdot \dfrac{8682}{14999}\right)$	≈ 3731.194
$E\left(\text{low income and satisfied}\right)$	$= E\left(n_{3S}\right) \approx n \cdot \hat{p}_3 \cdot \hat{p}_S = 14999\left(\dfrac{7316}{14999} \cdot \dfrac{8682}{14999}\right)$	≈ 4234.783
$\vdots$		
$E\left(\text{low income and dissatisfied}\right)$	$= E\left(n_{3D}\right) \approx n \cdot \hat{p}_3 \cdot \hat{p}_D = 14999\left(\dfrac{7316}{14999} \cdot \dfrac{6317}{14999}\right)$	≈ 3081.217

Table 16.3.5 displays observed values and expected values for each cell.

Table 16.3.5 - Actual versus Expected Number of Respondents

Income	Satisfied		Dissatisfied	
	Observed	Expected	Observed	Expected
High	762	716.023	475	520.977
Medium	3840	3731.194	2606	2714.806
Low	4080	4234.783	3236	3081.217

Using the same reasoning employed in the chi-square test for goodness of fit, we can construct a chi-square statistic using the difference between the observed and expected values.

$$\chi^2 = \frac{\left[n_{1S} - E\left(n_{1S}\right)\right]^2}{E\left(n_{1S}\right)} + \frac{\left[n_{2S} - E\left(n_{2S}\right)\right]^2}{E\left(n_{2S}\right)} + \dots + \frac{\left[n_{3D} - E\left(n_{3D}\right)\right]^2}{E\left(n_{3D}\right)}$$

Big differences between the observed values and the expected values will cause the χ^2 statistic to become large. If the statistic is too large to be due to ordinary sampling variation alone, this will cast doubt on the null hypothesis and cause us to reject that income level and level of job satisfaction are independent. If the assumption of independence is true and the expected number of observations in each cell is at least five, then the sampling distribution of the chi-square statistic has an approximate chi-square distribution with $(r-1)(c-1)$ degrees of freedom where r is the number of rows and c is the number of columns.

If we choose $\alpha = 0.01$, we will reject the null hypothesis if the chi-square test statistic is larger than the chi-square critical value of 9.210 which is $\chi^2_{0.01}$ with $(3-1)(2-1) = 2$ degrees of freedom, or if the observed P-value is less than 0.01.

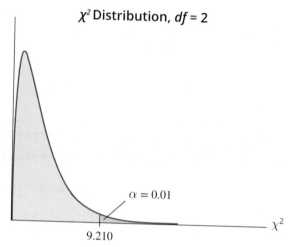

χ^2 Distribution, df = 2

$\alpha = 0.01$

9.210

Figure 16.3.1

Technology

The test for association can be performed on the TI-83/84 Plus calculator. For instructions, visit stat.hawkeslearning.com and navigate to **Technology Instructions > Chi-Square Distribution > Test for Association.**

For our data, the chi-square test statistic is given by

$$\chi^2 = \frac{[762 - 716.023]^2}{716.023} + \frac{[3840 - 3731.194]^2}{3731.194} + \cdots + \frac{[3236 - 3081.217]^2}{3081.217} = 27.976.$$

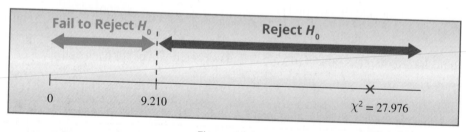

Fail to Reject H_0 Reject H_0

0   9.210 $\chi^2 = 27.976$

Figure 16.3.2

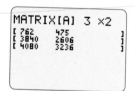

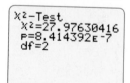

Since the value of the test statistic does fall in the rejection region we will reject the null hypothesis that level of income and job satisfaction are independent. There is sufficient evidence at $\alpha = 0.01$ to conclude that job satisfaction is dependent on level of income. In other words, there is a relationship between level of income and job satisfaction.

Using technology, the P-value for this test is 0.0000008, which is much smaller than $\alpha = 0.01$. Therefore, using the P-value method, the null hypothesis is rejected as well.

A summary of the chi-square test for association follows. It is important to note that n should be large enough so that the expected cell count (number of observations) in each cell will be equal to five or more.

Chi-Square Test for Association

Assumptions:

1. The conditions for a multinomial random variable are met for both variables.

2. The expected value of n_i is at least 5 for each category.

Hypotheses:

H_0: The two qualitative variables are independent (not related).

H_a: The two qualitative variables are dependent (related).

Test Statistic:

$$\chi^2 = \sum_{i=1}^{r} \sum_{j=1}^{c} \frac{\left[n_{ij} - E\left(n_{ij} \right) \right]^2}{E\left(n_{ij} \right)},$$

where r = the number of rows, c = the number of columns. $E\left(n_{ij} \right) = n \hat{p}_i \hat{p}_j$ where n is the total number of observations and $\hat{p}_i$ and $\hat{p}_j$ are estimates of the true population proportions, p_i and p_j, calculated as follows:

$$\hat{p}_i = \frac{\text{number of observations in row } i}{n}$$

$$\hat{p}_j = \frac{\text{number of observations in column } j}{n}.$$

If the null hypothesis is true and n is large enough so that the expected number of observations in each cell is at least 5, then the test statistic has an approximate chi-square distribution with $(r - 1)(c - 1)$ degrees of freedom.

Rejection Region:

Reject H_0 if $\chi^2 > \chi_\alpha^2$ with $(r - 1)(c - 1)$ degrees of freedom.

P-value:

The P-value is the probability of observing a value as extreme or more extreme than the value of the test statistic, given a chi-square distribution with $(r - 1)(c - 1)$ degrees of freedom.

If the computed P-value is less than α, reject the null hypothesis in favor of the alternative.

If the computed P-value is greater than or equal to α, fail to reject the null hypothesis.

PROCEDURE

Note

An alternate way to calculate the expected cell frequencies is given by

$$E\left(n_{ij} \right) = \frac{(\text{row } i \text{ total})(\text{column } j \text{ total})}{n}.$$

Example 16.3.1

Consider a particular question from the Quinnipiac University poll. The Quinnipiac University poll is often used as a barometer of public opinion regarding matters of public concern.

The question: *Would you support or oppose raising the national minimum wage?*

For those who responded to the question, the results of the poll are presented in the table below. Based on the data can we conclude that support for raising the national minimum wage is dependent on political affiliation or is political affiliation independent of support for raising the minimum wage?

Raising the National Minimum Wage			
Political Affiliation	Yes	No	Total
Republican	208	193	401
Democrat	387	30	416
Independent	476	193	669
Total	1071	416	1487

Solution

Step 1: Determine the null and alternative hypotheses.

For this example, we are interested in the proportion of the respondents who fall into each of the *Support for National Minimum Wage* and *Political Affiliation* categories.

The chi-square test for association between two variables is always a one-sided test because of the way we construct the test statistic. We will reject the null hypothesis for large values of the test statistic.

The resulting hypotheses would be

H_0: Support for raising the national minimum wage and political affiliation are independent (not related).

H_a: Support for raising the national minimum wage and political affiliation are dependent (related).

Step 2: Specify the significance level α.

We must specify the level of the test ourselves since we are not given one in the problem. Let's choose $\alpha = 0.10$.

Step 3: Validate the assumptions of the hypothesis testing model, identify the appropriate test statistic and compute its value.

☑ Each respondent was not allowed to respond to more than one category (multinomial random variables).

☑ The expected cell count for each category is greater than 5.

We can use the chi-square test for association. Our test statistic is the chi-square test statistic with $(3 - 1)(2 - 1) = 2$ degrees of freedom. The formula for the test statistic is given as follows.

$$\chi^2 = \frac{\left[n_{rY} - E\left(n_{rY}\right)\right]^2}{E\left(n_{rY}\right)} + \frac{\left[n_{dY} - E\left(n_{dY}\right)\right]^2}{E\left(n_{dY}\right)} + \frac{\left[n_{iY} - E\left(n_{iY}\right)\right]^2}{E\left(n_{iY}\right)}$$
$$+ \frac{\left[n_{rN} - E\left(n_{rN}\right)\right]^2}{E\left(n_{rN}\right)} + \frac{\left[n_{dN} - E\left(n_{dN}\right)\right]^2}{E\left(n_{dN}\right)} + \frac{\left[n_{iN} - E\left(n_{iN}\right)\right]^2}{E\left(n_{iN}\right)}$$

The table below gives the actual responses in each category versus the expected responses in each category.

Raising the National Minimum Wage				
	Yes		No	
Political Affiliation	**Actual**	**Expected**	**Actual**	**Expected**
Republican	208	288.82	193	112.18
Democrat	387	299.62	30	116.38
Independent	476	481.84	193	187.16

Based on these results the test statistic is calculated as follows.

$$\chi^2 = \frac{[208-288.82]^2}{288.82} + \frac{[387-299.62]^2}{299.62} + \frac{[476-481.84]^2}{481.84}$$
$$+ \frac{[193-112.18]^2}{112.18} + \frac{[30-116.38]^2}{116.38} + \frac{[193-187.16]^2}{187.16} = 170.691$$

Step 4: Determine the critical value(s) or *P*-value.

Since the level of the test is $\alpha = 0.10$ and we will reject the null hypothesis for large values of the test statistic, the chi-square critical value is $\chi^2_{0.10}$ with 2 degrees of freedom or 4.605. Values of the test statistic larger than 4.605 would indicate that the apparent dependence of the two classifications could not be due to ordinary sampling variation alone.

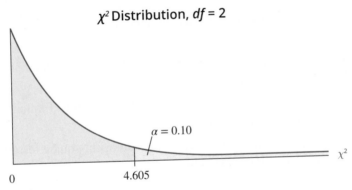

χ^2 Distribution, *df* = 2

Using technology we obtain a test statistic of 170.467 (slightly different from our calculated value due to our intermediate rounding), and find that the *P*-value is essentially zero.

Step 5: Make the decision to reject or fail to reject H_0.

Since the test statistic falls in the rejection region, the null hypothesis should be rejected.

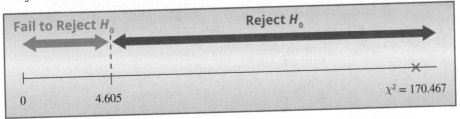

Since the *P*-value, which is approximately 0, is less than $\alpha = 0.10$, we also reject H_0 using the *P*-value method.

Technology

The chi-square test statistic and corresponding *P*-value can be obtained using Minitab. For instructions please visit stat.hawkeslearning.com and navigate to **Technology Instructions > Chi-Square Distribution > Test for Association**.

Step 6: State the conclusion in terms of the original problem.

There is evidence at the 0.10 level to conclude that support for raising the national minimum wage and political affiliation are dependent. The difference in support is too great to believe it to be attributed to ordinary sampling variation alone.

16.3 **Exercises**

Basic Concepts

1. Explain the difference between the chi-square test for goodness of fit and the chi-square test for association.

2. What is a contingency table?

3. Describe the information that each cell in a contingency table gives.

4. What properties must the two categories of the contingency table possess?

5. What level(s) of measurement may the categories of a contingency table have?

6. Consider the variable income. Describe how this variable could be transformed to be included in a contingency table. Is information lost during the transformation?

7. Explain why a test for association is not valid if single data points are allowed to belong to more than one category.

8. Restate the multiplication rule for independent events. Explain how this rule pertains to the chi-square test for association.

9. State the null and alternative hypotheses for a chi-square test for association between two qualitative variables.

Exercises

10. A political analyst is interested in studying the relationship between age and political affiliation. The analyst randomly selects 200 people and determines their age and political affiliation. The number of responses in each of the categories is as follows.

Age and Political Affiliation			
	Political Affiliation		
Age	**Democrat**	**Republican**	**Independent**
18–34	50	10	15
35–51	15	25	15
52–68	25	35	10

a. Can the analyst conclude that age and political affiliation are dependent at $\alpha = 0.05$?

b. What assumptions were made in the test for part **a.**?

11. A sociologist is interested in studying the relationship between education and crime. She randomly selects 450 people and asks their education level and whether or not they have ever been convicted of a felony. The following table displays the number of respondents in each category.

Education and Crime		
Have you ever been convicted of a felony?		
	Response	
Education Level	**Yes**	**No**
Less Than 9 Years	6	105
9 Years to 12 Years	12	93
12 Years to 16 Years	3	93
16+ Years	12	126

   a. Can the sociologist conclude that education level and crime are dependent at $\alpha = 0.10$?

   b. What assumptions were made in the test for part **a.**?

12. A psychologist is preparing his thesis on child abuse. He thinks that there may be a relationship between various types of child abuse and the gender of the child. To study this, he randomly selects the records of 197 abused children and determines both the gender of the child and the documented type of child abuse. The results of the study are as follows.

Child Abuse		
	Gender	
Type of Abuse	**Male**	**Female**
Neglect	50	50
Physical	20	30
Sexual	10	19
Emotional	10	8

   a. Can the psychologist conclude that the type of child abuse and gender of a child are dependent at $\alpha = 0.05$?

   b. What assumptions were made in the test for part **a.**?

13. The National Fire Protection Association is interested in studying the relationship between the causes of fires and the region of the country in which the fires occur. They randomly select 500 fires and determine the region of the country in which the fire occurred and cause of the fire with the following results.

Fires				
	Region			
Cause of Fire	North	South	East	West
Smoking	37	38	40	35
Heating Equipment	25	20	18	19
Arson	17	15	16	15
Electrical	12	13	12	13
Children at Play	10	11	12	11
Other	27	28	29	27

a. Can the association conclude that the cause of the fire and the region of the fire are dependent at $\alpha = 0.01$?

b. What assumptions were made in the test for part **a.**?

CR   Chapter Review

Key Terms and Ideas

- Chi-Square Test for Goodness of Fit
- Chi-Square Test for Association between Two Qualitative Variables
- Chi-Square Distribution
- Chi-Square Critical Values

- Multinomial Probability Distribution
- Multinomial Experiment
- Contingency Table
- Multiplication Rule for Independent Events

Key Formulas	
	Section
Chi-Square Statistic	16.1
$$\chi^2 = \frac{(n-1)s^2}{\sigma^2}$$	
Test Statistic for the Chi-Square Test for Goodness of Fit	16.2
$$\chi^2 = \sum_{i=1}^{k} \frac{\left[n_i - E(n_i)\right]^2}{E(n_i)}$$	
where n_i is the actual number of observations for each category, and $E(n_i)$ is the expected number of observations for each category given that the null hypothesis is true.	

Key Formulas	
	Section
Multiplication Rule for Independent Events $$P(A \cap B) = P(A) \cdot P(B)$$	16.3
Test Statistic for the Chi-Square Test for Association between Two Qualitative Variables $$\chi^2 = \sum_{i=1}^{r} \sum_{j=1}^{c} \frac{\left[n_{ij} - E\left(n_{ij}\right) \right]^2}{E\left(n_{ij}\right)}$$ where r = the number of rows, c = the number of columns, and $$E\left(n_{ij}\right) = n\hat{p}_i\hat{p}_j = \frac{(\text{row } i \text{ total})(\text{column } j \text{ total})}{n}$$ where n is the total number of observations and $\hat{p}_i$ and $\hat{p}_j$ are estimates of the true population proportions.	16.3

Additional Exercises

1. A sales manager for an insurance company believes that customers have the following preferences for life insurance products: 50% prefer Whole Life, 25% prefer Universal Life, and 25% prefer Life Annuities. A survey of 250 customers produced the following results.

Insurance Preferences	
Product	**Number**
Whole Life	60
Universal Life	100
Life Annuities	90

   a. Is the sales manager's claim refuted by the data at $\alpha = 0.05$?

   b. What assumptions were made in the test for part **a.**?

2. Do you think there are people somewhat like ourselves living on other planets in the universe? The responses to this question, which was asked in several different calendar years, were summarized in the *Gallup Poll Monthly*. For the year 1978, 51% answered "Yes," 33% "No," and the remainder had no opinion. Suppose that a sample of 100 people is chosen in 2018 in order to determine if opinions have changed concerning extraterrestrial life. Assume that the same question is asked and that 42 answer "Yes," 30 "No," and that the rest have no opinion. Assuming that the percentages given above accurately represent the attitudes of the people in 1978, can we conclude with $\alpha = 0.05$ that people's attitudes of toward extraterrestrial life have changed since 1978?

3. A traffic engineer feels that on a certain four-lane highway, the probability of being in the innermost lane is twice as great as any of the other lanes. Assume the other lanes have equal probabilities. A random sample of 200 motorists is chosen and the lanes in which they are traveling in are noted. The results (Lane 1 is the innermost lane) are given in the following table.

Traffic Lanes				
Lane	1	2	3	4
Frequency	55	45	62	38

a. Find the probabilities implied by the engineer's claim that a randomly chosen motorist will be in each of the four lanes.

b. With $\alpha = 0.05$, can we refute the claim of the traffic engineer?

4. The National Restaurant Association is interested in determining if there is a relationship between the type of pizza pie Americans prefer and the region of the country in which they live. The association randomly selects 285 Americans and records the category of pizza pie which best describes their preference and the region of the country in which they live with the following results.

Pizza Preference				
	Region			
Type of Pizza Pie Preferred	**North**	**South**	**East**	**West**
Thin Crust	40	30	35	45
Thick Crust	17	15	21	22
Pan Pizza	15	15	15	15

a. Can the association conclude that the type of pizza pie Americans prefer and the region of the country in which they live are dependent at $\alpha = 0.10$?

b. What assumptions were made in the test for part **a.**?

5. Amazon asked consumers to assign stat ratings to different brands of staplers. The results are summarized in the table below.

Amazon Stapler Ratings					
	Rating				
Brand	**5 Star**	**4 Star**	**3 Star**	**2 Star**	**1 Star**
Swingline Optima 40 Compact	589	60	22	15	60
PaperPro inPower	485	60	40	20	60
Rapid Classic K1 Plier Stapler	312	26	11	7	15
EcoElectronix Electric Stapler	361	45	14	5	27
Bostitch Ascend 3 in 1	378	66	44	22	38

a. Can it be concluded that star rating and stapler brand are dependent at $\alpha = 0.10$?

b. What assumptions were made in the test for part **a.**?

"If you can't describe what you are doing as a process, you don't know what you're doing."

— W. Edwards Deming

17 CHAPTER
Nonparametric Tests

Introduction

One of the characteristics of **parametric statistics** is that hypothesis testing procedures rely on assumptions concerning the distribution of the population from which the sample is drawn. For example, when using test statistics which rely on the t-distribution or the F-distribution, we assume that the distribution of the underlying population from which the data is drawn is approximately normal. Figures 17.1 and 17.2 show examples of normal and non-normal distributions, respectively. Inferences made from parametric statistics are valid only to the extent that the assumptions made about the underlying distribution of the population from which the data is sampled are correct.

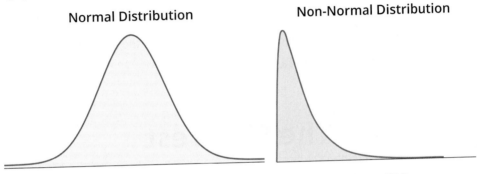

| Normal Distribution | Non-Normal Distribution |
| Figure 17.1 | Figure 17.2 |

In this chapter the focus is on **nonparametric statistical methods**. There are three characteristics of nonparametric statistical methods:

- They do not involve the estimation of specific population parameters.
- These methods are tests of hypotheses using data measured on an ordinal scale (in most instances).
- Assumptions regarding the underlying distribution of the data are not required.

The fact that a distributional assumption about the data is not necessary to make valid inferences is one of the significant advantages of nonparametric techniques.

However, there are some disadvantages of nonparametric statistics. Because nonparametric tests tend to waste information, they are not so powerful as their parametric counterparts. Some nonparametric tests reduce exact ratio level measurements to ordinal level measurements. For example, taking an income measurement of \$48,200 (a ratio measurement) and converting it into an ordinal variable consisting of three ordinal categories (low, medium, high) results in a significant loss of information. A nonparametric test, called the Sign Test, will require us to take ratio measurements and throw everything away except the sign (+ or −) of the measurement.

Several nonparametric techniques are discussed in this chapter. The first two of these, the Sign Test and the Wilcoxon Signed-Rank Test, are used to conduct hypothesis tests involving paired data experiments. Paired data experiments are designed to detect the effect of a treatment on some population measurement. In a paired data experiment, a treatment is applied to a population or sample. There is a comparison of some population characteristic of interest, before and after the treatment is applied. Suppose, for example, database entry personnel are given a course in speed-typing. If the course is successful, there should be a shift in the typing speed of database personnel. A *before* and *after* measurement of typing speed would be desirable to measure the effect of the typing training. Since the population of typists has different typing speeds, the problem becomes, how do you compare the distribution of typing speeds before and after the training? One way is to compare the population medians. If the distribution of typing speed has shifted because of the treatment (training), then the median will also have shifted. The Sign Test is used for testing a hypothesis concerning two population medians or testing the hypothesis that a population median is equal to some hypothesized value.

Other nonparametric tests introduced in this chapter include:

- The Wilcoxon Rank-Sum Test, used for comparing two independent samples.
- The Kruskal-Wallis Test, a test similar to the ANOVA *F*-test.
- The Rank Correlation Test similar to the parametric correlation test.
- The Runs Test for randomness.

17.1 **The Sign Test**

Sign Tests are used in the comparison of paired data when it is not possible to assume that the differences have an approximately normal distribution. The methodology for the Sign Test is based on the assumption that the two populations have the same median. Suppose we were to subtract the paired sample values. If the population medians are identical, the resulting *differences* should be centered around zero. Further, we would expect the number of positive differences to be roughly equal to the number of negative differences. If the number of positive differences significantly outnumbers the number of negative differences or vice-versa, this will cause us to doubt that the two populations have the same median.

Using the Sign Test on Paired Data

We will present the test procedure for the Sign Test by reconsidering the paired data problem from Section 12.2. In that paired data discussion, there is an assumption that the differences of the population of paired values possess an approximately normal distribution. The Sign Test makes no such assumption.

Example 17.1.1

A researcher is interested in knowing the effect one ounce of 100-proof alcohol has on individuals. To study this effect the researcher randomly selects 10 subjects and records their reaction times (in seconds) both before and after drinking one ounce of 100-proof alcohol. The results of the study are displayed in the table below. In addition to the original data from Example 12.2.2, this table contains an extra column of data, the signs of the differences. These signs will be used in the nonparametric test of hypothesis.

Reaction Times (in seconds)			
Subject	Before	After	Difference
1	0.4	0.5	−0.1
2	0.5	0.5	0.0
3	0.6	0.7	−0.1
4	0.4	0.6	−0.2
5	0.5	0.6	−0.1
6	0.4	0.4	0.0
7	0.4	0.5	−0.1
8	0.5	0.7	−0.2
9	0.6	0.8	−0.2
10	0.4	0.5	−0.1

Can the researcher conclude at $\alpha = 0.01$ that the median reaction time is longer after consuming one ounce of 100-proof alcohol?

Solution

This problem was analyzed using parametric statistics in Chapter 12 with the paired difference t-test. In order for this t-test to be valid, we had to make an assumption that the differences had an approximately normal distribution. Suppose we doubt that the differences have a normal distribution. Is it still possible to draw a conclusion about whether or not alcohol increases *median* reaction time? One possible method for making this determination is the Sign Test.

The Sign Test is based on the idea that if two data sets have the same medians, the number of differences with positive signs should approximately equal the number of differences with negative signs. We will conclude that alcohol increases the median reaction time if the number of negative signs is significantly larger than the number of positive signs. How large is large? Let's answer this question by way of example.

Step 1: Determine the null and alternative hypotheses.

Null Hypothesis: There is no difference in median reaction time after drinking one ounce of 100-proof alcohol.

Alternative Hypothesis: The median reaction time is significantly longer after drinking one ounce of 100-proof alcohol.

The procedure we are using is called the Sign Test because it relies on counting the number of positive differences and the number of negative differences. Only the sign of the difference matters, the magnitude is ignored. Differences of zero are also ignored.

Since the researcher is interested in whether or not the median reaction time is *longer* after drinking one ounce of 100-proof alcohol, this is a one-sided test.

The researcher wants to determine if the median reaction time is longer for subjects who have consumed one ounce of 100-proof alcohol. The statistical measures being used are counts of the number of positive signs and negative signs. If the reaction time is prolonged after the alcohol has been consumed, then the reaction time before drinking the alcohol will be less than the reaction time after drinking the alcohol. Consequently, we would expect the number of differences with negative signs to outnumber the differences with positive signs. If the reaction times before and after drinking one ounce of 100-proof alcohol are identical, then we would expect that any difference would be due to random variation, in which case we would have about the same number of positive and negative signs.

Using these ideas, we can translate our plain English hypotheses into the following.

> H_0: The number of positive signs equals the number of negative signs (the median reaction time is the same after drinking one ounce of 100-proof alcohol).
>
> H_a: The number of negative signs significantly outnumbers the number of positive signs (the median reaction time is longer after drinking one ounce of 100-proof alcohol than before drinking the alcohol, i.e., reaction time before minus reaction time after < 0).

Step 2: Specify the significance level α.

The level of the test is specified in the problem to be $\alpha = 0.01$.

Step 3: Validate the assumptions of the hypothesis test, identify the appropriate test statistic and compute its value.

We do need to assume that the sample is random.

> ☑ Pairs of data are selected in a random fashion.

Our discussion has focused on the signs of the differences. Suppose we let

> X = the number of times the less frequent sign is observed.

Assuming that the null hypothesis is true, the number of times the less frequent sign is observed in the paired difference experiment has a binomial distribution with

> $p = 0.5$, and
>
> n = the number of non-zero differences.

If X is too small, then either H_0 is true and a rare phenomenon has been observed, or H_0 is not true. To make the decision whether X is too small, a decision rule must be developed (see **Step 4**).

If $n \le 25$, where n = the number of non-zero differences, the test statistic of the Sign Test is the variable X described above.

If $n > 25$, X can be approximated by a normal distribution and the test statistic is given by

$$z = \frac{X + 0.5 - \left(\dfrac{n}{2}\right)}{\dfrac{\sqrt{n}}{2}}.$$

Assuming the null hypothesis is true, z has an approximately standard normal distribution.

Since $n \le 25$, the value of the test statistic is given by

> X = the number of times the less frequent sign occurs.

The less frequent sign in this case is the positive sign. In fact, the positive sign does not occur at all in this data, meaning that the reaction time never decreased after

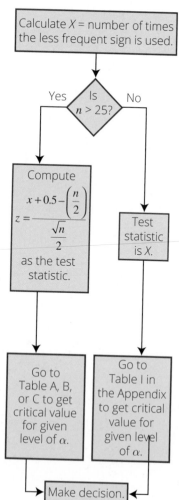

Making the Decision in the Sign Test

Calculate X = number of times the less frequent sign is used.

Is $n > 25$?

Yes → Compute

$$z = \frac{x + 0.5 - \left(\dfrac{n}{2}\right)}{\dfrac{\sqrt{n}}{2}}$$

as the test statistic.

No → Test statistic is X.

Go to Table A, B, or C to get critical value for given level of α.

Go to Table I in the Appendix to get critical value for given level of α.

Make decision.

drinking one ounce of 100-proof alcohol. Since there are eight negative signs $(-)$ and zero positive signs $(+)$, the value of X is

$$X = 0.$$

Note that differences of zero are ignored.

Since the number of positive signs is zero, this tends to support the alternative hypothesis that drinking one ounce of 100-proof alcohol prolongs reaction time. It is safe to proceed with the test. Suppose there were not any negative signs, meaning that all of the reaction times were quicker after drinking the alcohol. This evidence would not support the alternative hypothesis, and the test must be halted at this point with a conclusion that the null hypothesis cannot be rejected. This stage of a one-sided Sign Test will always require thinking to be sure that the sign with the minimum value is the sign that supports the alternative hypothesis.

Step 4: Determine the critical value(s) or *P*-value.

The role of the critical value in this test is exactly the same as for all of the hypothesis tests discussed earlier. It defines a range of values for the test statistic, the rejection region. If the null hypothesis is true, it is unlikely that the test statistic will fall in this range because of ordinary sampling variation.

The level of the test defines the rareness criterion that will be used and implicitly determines the size of the rejection region. Should the computed value of the test statistic fall in the rejection region, its value will be presumed to be too rare to have occurred because of ordinary sampling variation, and the null hypothesis will be rejected.

If $n \leq 25$, the critical values are given in Table I for the Sign Test (in the Appendix). Because the test statistic is defined to be the number of times the less frequent sign occurs, we will always reject the null hypothesis for small values of the test statistic. If the alternative hypothesis is *greater than* or *less than*, use the column in Table I labeled α *for a one-tailed test*. If the alternative is *not equal to*, use the column in Table I labeled α *for a two-tailed test*.

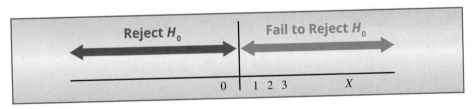

There are $n = 8$ non-zero differences in the alcohol example, $\alpha = 0.01$, and the alternative hypothesis is *greater than*. From Table I in the Appendix, we find that the critical value is 0. We will reject the null hypothesis if the test statistic is less than or equal to 0. The rejection region is drawn above.

If $n > 25$, the critical values are determined in a similar manner to other hypothesis tests whose test statistics have a standard normal distribution. However, because the test statistic is defined to be the number of times the less frequent sign occurs, we will always reject the null hypothesis for small values of the test statistic. Thus, the rejection region will always be established in the left tail, with the critical value defined by α for one-tailed tests, and $\frac{\alpha}{2}$ for two-tailed tests.

Nonparametric Rejection Regions

Most of the rejection regions we will construct for nonparametric tests will look different from those we have previously constructed. Because the test statistics are counts or sums of rank data, the test statistic will not usually be a real number, so the rejection "region" will not be an interval. Most of the test statistics in this chapter will have rejection regions with only a few points in them, sometimes only one point.

Note

Because of the manner in which the test statistic is defined, fail to reject the null hypothesis and do not proceed with the test procedure if the computed value of the test statistic does not tend to support the alternative hypothesis.

Step 5: Make the decision to reject or fail to reject H_0.

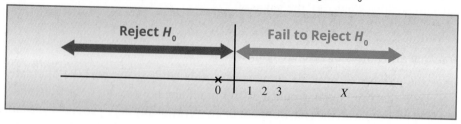

As shown, the value of the test statistic ($X = 0$) falls in the rejection region. Thus, we reject the null hypothesis at $\alpha = 0.01$. It is unlikely that the small number of positive differences could be attributed to ordinary sampling variation.

Step 6: State the conclusion in terms of the original problem.

There is sufficient evidence for the researcher to conclude at $\alpha = 0.01$ that the median response time is higher for those subjects who have drunk one ounce of 100-proof alcohol than for those who have not.

The test procedure for the Sign Test is outlined in the following table.

Test Procedure for the Sign Test

Assumptions:

Pairs of data are selected in a random fashion.

Hypotheses:

H_0: The number of positive (negative) signs equals the number of negative (positive) signs.

H_a: The number of negative (positive) signs is significantly greater than, less than, or not equal to the number of positive (negative) signs (depending on the claim which is being tested.)

Test Statistic:

If $n \leq 25$, then X = the number of times the less frequent sign occurs.
If $n > 25$, then

$$z = \frac{X + 0.5 - \left(\dfrac{n}{2}\right)}{\dfrac{\sqrt{n}}{2}}.$$

Critical Value(s):

If the data tends to support the alternative hypothesis and

- if $n \leq 25$, reject the null hypothesis if the test statistic is less than or equal to the critical value in Table I of the Appendix for the Sign Test.
- if $n > 25$, the critical values are based on the standard normal distribution with the critical values defined such that we reject for small values of the test statistic.

PROCEDURE

> **Note**
>
> No sign is given if the difference is zero and the difference is ignored.

Testing a Population Median with the Sign Test

The median is a more useful measure of the center of the population than is the mean in certain situations such as:

- When there are extreme data values (outliers) which significantly skew the distribution of the data.

- When the mean cannot be used as a measure of the center of the data, as with ordinal level data.

The Sign Test can be used to test claims about the median of the population. The procedure for using the Sign Test to evaluate claims about a single population median is presented in the following example.

Example 17.1.2

In an effort to attract new residents and businesses to the area, the Chamber of Commerce published a report which states that the median home price in Durham, North Carolina, is less than the median price of existing homes in the United States of $312,800. Fifty recent home sales in the Durham area were randomly selected, and of those, 35 had an actual sale price of less than $312,800. Does the data support the claim made by the Chamber of Commerce at $\alpha = 0.10$?

Solution

Step 1 Determine the null and alternative hypotheses.

Null Hypothesis: The median home price in Durham, North Carolina, is at least as large as that of the median home price for the United States.

Alternative Hypothesis: The median home price in Durham, North Carolina, is less than that of the median home price for the United States.

Once again we will look at differences, but in this case the differences will be created by subtracting the median from each data value. The Sign Test will rely on counting the number of positive signs (the number of homes with sale prices larger than the median home price for the United States) and the number of negative signs (the number of homes with sale prices less than the median home price for the United States).

Since the Chamber of Commerce's claim is that the median home price in Durham, North Carolina, is *lower* than the median home price in the United States, this test is a one-sided test.

H_0: The number of positive signs is equal to the number of negative signs (the median home price in Durham, North Carolina, is at least as high as the median home price for the United States).

H_a: The number of negative signs significantly outnumbers the number of positive signs (the median home price in Durham, North Carolina, is *lower* than the median home price for the United States).

Step 2: Specify the significance level α.

The level of the test is specified in the problem to be $\alpha = 0.10$.

Step 3: Validate the assumptions of the hypothesis test, identify the appropriate test statistic and compute its value.

Our assumption is verified in the wording of the question.

☑ Pairs of data are selected in a random fashion.

Since $n > 25$, the test statistic is given by

$$z = \frac{X + 0.5 - \left(\dfrac{n}{2}\right)}{\dfrac{\sqrt{n}}{2}}.$$

Assuming the null hypothesis is true, z has an approximately standard normal distribution.

Negative signs will occur if the median price of a home in Durham, North Carolina is less than the median home for the United States. Thirty-five of the sampled homes had an actual sale price less than the median home price for the United states. Thus, there will be 35 negative signs.

Positive signs will occur if the median price of a home in Durham, North Carolina is greater than the median home for the United States. Fifteen of the sampled homes had an actual sale price greater than the median home price for the United States. Thus, there will be 15 positive signs.

Since X = the number of times the less frequent sign occurs, $X = 15$, and the calculated value of the test statistic is

$$z = \frac{15 + 0.5 - \left(\dfrac{50}{2}\right)}{\dfrac{\sqrt{50}}{2}} = -2.69.$$

Step 4: Determine the critical value(s) or *P*-value.

More than half of the homes surveyed sold for less than the United States median home price, supporting the alternative hypothesis. Thus, it is appropriate to proceed with the test procedure.

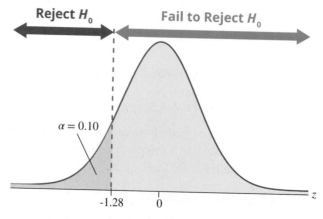

Since $n > 25$, the critical value is determined from the standard normal distribution. Because of the way the test statistic is defined, we will always reject the null hypothesis for small values of the test statistic. If the alternative hypothesis is *greater than* or *less than*, use an area of α in the left tail to determine the critical value. If the alternative is *not equal to*, use an area of $\alpha/2$ in the left tail to determine the critical value. In this example, the alternative is *less than* and $\alpha = 0.10$. The rejection region is shown above. We will reject the null hypothesis if the calculated value of the test statistic is less than -1.28.

Step 5: Make the decision to reject or fail to reject H_0.

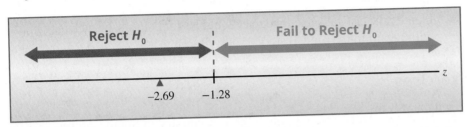

As shown, the value of the test statistic falls in the rejection region (-2.69 is less than -1.28). It is unlikely that the difference between the observed value and the hypothesized value is due to ordinary sampling variation. Thus, we reject the null hypothesis at $\alpha = 0.10$.

Step 6: State the conclusion in terms of the original problem.

There is sufficient evidence for the Chamber of Commerce to conclude at $\alpha = 0.10$ that the median home price in Durham, North Carolina is significantly lower than the median home price in the United States of $312,800.

17.1 **Exercises**

Basic Concepts

1. What are parametric statistics?

2. Identify and explain the main disadvantage of the Sign Test.

3. Under what conditions are parametric statistical methods not appropriate for data analysis?

4. Identify the three characteristics of nonparametric statistical methods.

5. What are the disadvantages of nonparametric statistics?

6. The Sign Test and the Wilcoxon Signed-Rank Test are designed to conduct hypothesis tests involving which kind(s) of experiments? What is the corresponding parametric statistical technique used to analyze these types of experiments?

7. What assumptions are made when conducting the Sign Test?

8. Name the two ways that the Sign Test can be used to perform hypothesis tests.

9. How do the rejection regions for nonparametric tests differ from those for parametric tests? Explain.

10. What is done with measurements that have a difference of zero in a paired difference experiment? Why is this the case?

11. What are the null and alternative hypotheses associated with the Sign Test?

12. What is the test statistic for the Sign Test for small samples? How small is a *small* sample?

13. What is the test statistic for the Sign Test for large samples? How large is a *large* sample?

14. Identify the critical values and rejection rules for both small and large samples with regard to the Sign Test.

Exercises

15. Hurricane Hugo swept through the Lowcountry in South Carolina causing billions of dollars of damage. In the past, the median claim for homes damaged by hurricanes for an insurance company in the Lowcountry had been $25,000. The insurance company believes that the median claim will be significantly larger for homes damaged by Hugo than past hurricanes. In order to investigate this theory, the insurance company randomly selects 55 homes and sends adjusters to settle the claims. In the sample of 55 homes, 40 of the homes had a claim in excess of the historical median. Is there overwhelming evidence at $\alpha = 0.10$ that the median claim for home damage from Hurricane Hugo was greater than the historical median?

16. The manufacturer of Brand X floor polish is developing a new polish that they hope will dry faster than the competition's polish. The competition's polish is advertised to have an average (median) drying time of 10 minutes. In a random sample of 1000 polishes with the new polish, 700 of the polishes dried in less than 10 minutes. Based on the data, can the manufacturer conclude that the median drying time for Brand X is faster than the competition's brand at a 0.05 level of significance?

17. NarStor, a computer disk drive manufacturer, claims that the median time until failure for their hard drives is 14,400 hours. You work for a consumer group that has decided to examine this claim. Technicians ran 16 NarStor hard drives continuously for almost three years. Recently the last drive failed. The times to failure (in hours) are given in the following table.

Time Until Hard Drive Failure (Hours)							
330	620	1870	2410	4620	6396	7822	8102
8309	12,882	14,419	16,092	18,384	20,916	23,812	25,814

a. Is there overwhelming evidence that the median time until failure is less than the manufacturer claims? Use $\alpha = 0.10$

b. What assumption did you make in performing the test in part **a.**?

18. A.C. Bone has developed a duck hunting boot which it claims can remain immersed for more than 12 hours without leaking. 15 of the boots are tested and the time until first leakage is measured. Nine of the boots last more than 12 hours without leaking.

    a. Does the data substantiate A.C. Bone's claim at $\alpha = 0.05$?

    b. What assumption did you make in performing the test in part **a.**?

19. Given that most textbooks can now be purchased online, one wonders if students can save money by comparison shopping for textbooks at online retailers and at their local bookstores. To investigate, students at Tech University randomly sampled 25 textbooks on the shelves of their local bookstores. The students then found the "best" available price for the same textbooks via online retailers. The prices for the textbooks are listed in the following table.

Textbook Prices					
	Price ($)			Price ($)	
Textbook	Bookstore	Online Retailer	Textbook	Bookstore	Online Retailer
1	70	60	14	85	75
2	38	36	15	100	85
3	88	89	16	68	62
4	165	149	17	67	69
5	80	136	18	140	142
6	103	95	19	49	40
7	42	50	20	149	127
8	98	111	21	126	130
9	89	65	22	92	93
10	97	86	23	144	129
11	140	130	24	98	84
12	40	30	25	40	52
13	175	150			

    Using the data in the table, and without making any distributional assumptions, is it less expensive for the students to purchase textbooks from the online retailers than the local bookstores? Use $\alpha = 0.01$.

20. The management for a large grocery store chain would like to determine if a new cash register will enable cashiers to process a larger number of items on average than the cash register which they are currently using. Seven cashiers are randomly selected, and the number of grocery items which they can process in three minutes is measured for both the old cash register and the new cash register. The results of the test are as follows.

Number of Grocery Items Processed in Three Minutes							
Cashier	1	2	3	4	5	6	7
Old Register	60	70	55	75	62	52	58
New Register	65	71	55	75	65	57	57

Without making any assumptions about the distribution, can management conclude that the new cash register will allow cashiers to process a significantly larger number of items on average than the old cash register at $\alpha = 0.05$.

21. An auto dealer is marketing two different models of a high-end sedan. Since customers are particularly interested in the safety features of the sedans, the dealer would like to determine if there is a difference in the braking distance (the number of feet required to go from 60 mph to 0 mph) of the two sedans. Six drivers are randomly selected and asked to participate in a test to measure the braking distance for both models. Each driver is asked to drive both models and brake once they have reached exactly 60 mph. The distance required to come to a complete halt is then measured in feet. The results of the test are as follows.

Braking Distance of High-End Sedans (in Feet)						
Driver	1	2	3	4	5	6
Model A	150	145	160	155	152	153
Model B	152	146	160	157	154	155

Without making assumptions about the distribution of the data, can the auto dealer conclude that there is a significant difference in the braking distance of the two models of high end sedans? Use $\alpha = 0.10$.

22. A nutritionist is interested in determining the decrease in cholesterol level which a person can achieve by following a particular diet which is low in fat and high in fiber. Seven subjects are randomly selected to try the diet for six months, and their cholesterol levels are measured both before and after the diet. The results of the study are as follows.

Cholesterol Levels							
Subject	1	2	3	4	5	6	7
Before Diet	155	170	145	200	162	180	160
After Diet	152	168	148	195	162	178	157

Can the nutritionist conclude that there is a significant decrease in average cholesterol level when the diet is used? We don't have any knowledge about the distribution of the data. Use $\alpha = 0.01$.

17.2 The Wilcoxon Signed-Rank Test

A disadvantage of the Sign Test, discussed in the previous section, is that it wastes information. The Sign Test merely counts the number of positive or negative signs in a paired difference experiment and ignores the magnitude of the differences. The **Wilcoxon Signed-Rank Test** is a nonparametric technique which can be used to evaluate a paired difference experiment. This test is designed to detect populations whose centers are shifted to the right or the left of each other. As with the Sign Test, no distributional assumption is required. However, the pairs of data must have been selected in a random fashion, and it must be possible to rank the differences.

An advantage of the Wilcoxon Signed-Rank Test is that it does not ignore the magnitudes of the differences. But it does not take the magnitude directly into account. Instead, the ranks of the data are analyzed.

Ranking is nothing new. Simply put the data in order from smallest to largest and attach ranks to each data item. In general, the lowest value is assigned a rank of one and the highest value is assigned a rank of n, where n is the number of non-zero differences. How do we handle ties? If there are two or more values with the same magnitude, these values will each be assigned the same rank which is equal to the average of the ranks which would have been assigned to these values if they had slightly different consecutive values. The ranking procedure is explained more fully in the next example.

Example 17.2.1

Rank the following stocks, traded on the New York Stock Exchange, from the smallest price to the largest price.

New York Stock Exchange		
Stock	**Price Per Share**	**Rank**
3M Co.	239.26	9
AT&T Inc.	37.27	2
Citigroup Inc.	77.10	4
Exxon Mobil Corp.	83.57	5
Hewlett-Packard Co.	14.23	1
Merck & Co. Inc.	56.22	3
Procter & Gamble Co.	91.41	6
Wal-Mart Stores Inc.	97.00	7
Walt Disney Co.	110.24	8

The lowest-priced stock is Hewlett-Packard Co. at 14.23. It is assigned a rank of one. The next lowest price stock is AT&T Inc, which is assigned a rank of 2. The highest priced stock is 3M Co., which has a rank of 9. The test procedure for the Wilcoxon Signed-Rank Test will be developed in the following example.

Example 17.2.2

A consulting firm implemented a quality program in an effort to improve the productivity level of its employees. All employees received two and one-half days of intensive training on the concepts of total quality management, with an emphasis on process mapping. In addition to the initial training, each employee participated on a team (a QET-Quality Enhancement Team or CIT-Continuous Improvement Team) which focused on either breakthrough improvements in a process-QET or the continuous improvement of a process-CIT. Each team was given the responsibility and the authority to implement the improvements to the process which it deemed necessary. A year after the initial training, the management of the company conducted a study to see if the productivity level of its employees had improved. The productivity level of employees is measured by *realized billable hours* per week. *Realized billable hours* are the number of hours which an employee works and bills to a client. Nine employees are randomly selected and the *realized billable hours* are calculated before the initial quality training and one year after the initial quality training. The results of the survey are shown in the table below. Based on the data, can the management of the consulting firm conclude that the productivity level of its employees has significantly improved over the past year, at $\alpha = 0.05$?

	"Realized Billable Hours" per week					
Employee	**Realized Billable Hours Before Quality Training**	**Realized Billable Hours After Quality Training**	**Difference (Before – After)**	**Absolute Value of Difference**	**Rank of Absolute Value of Difference**	**Signed Rank**
A	20.5	25.5	−5	5	6	−6
B	33.5	33.5	0	0	Ignore	Ignore
C	29.5	35.5	−6	6	8	−8
D	35.0	32.0	+3	3	3.5	+3.5
E	30.5	35.5	−5	5	6	−6
F	18.5	17.5	+1	1	1	+1
G	27.5	32.5	−5	5	6	−6
H	30.5	33.5	−3	3	3.5	−3.5
I	15.5	17.5	−2	2	2	−2
					$T_+ = 4.5$	
					$T_- = 31.5$	

Step 1: Determine the null and alternative hypotheses.

Null Hypothesis: The productivity level of employees has not improved over the past year.

Alternative Hypothesis: The productivity level of employees has improved over the past year.

Recall that in nonparametric statistics we do not make inferences about population parameters. The Wilcoxon Signed-Rank Test is no exception. It compares the probability distribution of the *realized billable hours* before the quality training to the probability distribution of *realized billable hours* one year after the quality training. How this is accomplished will be discussed in **Step 3**.

Since management is interested in knowing if productivity has improved, they are interested in knowing if realized billable hours have *increased*. Thus, this is a one-sided test.

  H_0: The probability distributions of *realized billable hours* both before and after the quality training are the same.

  H_a: The probability distribution for *realized billable hours* after the training is shifted to the right of *realized billable hours* before the training.

Step 2: Specify the significance level α.

The level of the test is specified in the problem to be $\alpha = 0.05$.

Step 3: Validate the assumptions of the hypothesis test, identify the appropriate test statistic and compute its value.

We must verify that the pairs of data have been selected in a random fashion and are such that the absolute value of their differences can be ranked. The data must be quantitative to assign ranking to differences.

- ☑ Pairs of data have been selected in a random fashion (9 employees randomly selected).

- ☑ Quantitative data (billable hours)

If we let $n =$ the number of non-zero differences, the test statistic for the Wilcoxon Signed-Rank Test is determined in the following manner.

> **Note**
>
> In the following discussion, population X will be the group after training and population Y will be the group before training.

1. Compute the differences for each of the pairs.

2. Rank the absolute value of the differences from lowest to highest (ignoring zero differences).

3. Calculate $T_+ =$ the sum of the ranks associated with positive differences.

4. Calculate $T_- =$ the sum of the ranks associated with negative differences.

The test statistic will vary depending on the sample size, the number of non-zero differences, and the alternative hypothesis.

If $n \leq 25$, and

- The alternative hypothesis is that population X is shifted to the left or to the right of population Y, use $T = \min(T_+, T_-) =$ the sum of the ranks with the smallest value.

> **Note**
>
> This is analogous to the "not equal to" alternative hypothesis.

- The alternative hypothesis is that population X is shifted to the right of population Y, use $T_+ =$ the sum of the ranks associated with positive differences, where differences are defined as observations in population Y minus observations in population X. (The test statistic is defined in this manner because we expect the number of negative differences to outnumber the number of positive differences, and thus expect T_+ to be the rank sum with the smallest value.)

> **Note**
>
> This is analogous to the "greater than" alternative hypothesis.

- The alternative hypothesis is that population X is shifted to the left of population Y, use $T_- =$ the sum of the ranks associated with negative differences, where differences are defined as observations in population Y minus observations in population X. (The test statistic is defined in this manner because we expect the number of positive differences to outnumber the number of negative differences, and thus expect T_- to be the rank sum with the smallest value.)

> **Note**
>
> This is analogous to the "less than" alternative hypothesis.

It is important to note that if the smaller sum of the ranks is not as expected, the test should be halted and the decision should be to fail to reject the null hypothesis since there is no evidence in favor of the alternative hypothesis.

If $n > 25$, the test statistic can be approximated by a standard normal distribution and is specified in the table following this example.

For the example at hand, $n \leq 25$ and the alternative hypothesis is that the probability distribution for *realized billable hours* after the training is shifted to the right of *realized billable hours* before the training. This implies that *realized billable hours* before the training minus *realized billable hours* after the training should generally be negative. If the rank sum with the smallest value is T_-, fail to reject the null hypothesis since there is no evidence that the alternative hypothesis is more reasonable. Otherwise, the test statistic is given by

$$T = T_+ = \text{the sum of the ranks associated with } \textit{positive} \text{ differences.}$$

In order to calculate the test statistic, the signed ranks must be determined. To determine the signed ranks, first compute the difference for each pair of data values. Next, find the absolute value of each difference. Rank the absolute value of the differences using the ranking technique illustrated in Example 17.2.1 (ignore differences of zero). Once the absolute value of the differences has been ranked, reassign the ranks the *sign* which each associated difference had before the absolute value was computed. Finally, add all of the ranks with positive signs to determine $T+$, and add all of the ranks with negative signs to determine T_-. This procedure is illustrated in the table at the beginning of the example.

Using the result from the table, the test statistic is given by

$$T = T_+ = \text{the sum of the ranks associated with positive differences} = 4.5.$$

Step 4: Determine the critical value(s) or *P*-value.

If $n \leq 25$, the critical values are determined from Table J (in the Appendix) for the Wilcoxon Signed-Rank Test. The critical value is specified by the level of α, the number of non-zero differences in the test (n), and the alternative hypothesis. If the alternative hypothesis is *greater than* or *less than*, use the column in Table J labeled α *for a one-tailed test*. If the alternative is *not equal to*, use the column in Table J labeled α *for a two-tailed test*. Because of the way the test statistic is defined, the null hypothesis is always rejected if the test statistic calculated from the data, T, is less than or equal to the critical value in Table J, T_c.

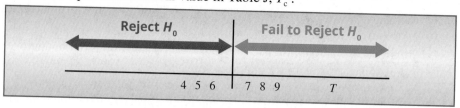

For the quality example, $n = 8$ (recall there was one difference which was zero), $\alpha = 0.05$, and the test is a one-sided test. Based on these specifications, the critical value determined from Table J is $T_c = 6$. The null hypothesis will be rejected if $T \leq 6$. This rejection region is displayed in the figure above.

If $n > 25$, the critical values are determined in a similar manner to test statistics which have an approximate standard normal distribution under the null hypothesis. However, because of the way the test statistic is defined, we will always reject the null hypothesis for small values of the test statistic. Thus, the rejection region will always be established in the left tail, with the critical value defined by α for one-tailed tests, and $\frac{\alpha}{2}$ for two-tailed tests.

Step 5: Make the decision to reject or fail to reject H_0.

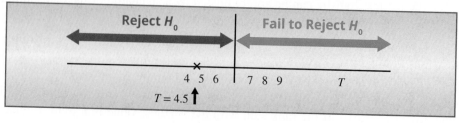

As shown above, the value of the test statistic falls in the rejection region (4.5 is less than 6). Thus, we reject the null hypothesis at $\alpha = 0.05$. It is unlikely that the difference between the observed value and the hypothesized value is due to ordinary sampling variation.

Step 6: State the conclusion in terms of the original problem.

There is sufficient evidence for the management of the consulting firm to conclude at $\alpha = 0.05$ that *realized billable hours* one year after the quality training are significantly higher than the *realized billable hours* before the quality training.

Test Procedure for the Wilcoxon Signed-Rank Test

Assumptions:

1. Pairs of data have been selected in a random fashion.

2. Data are quantitative.

Hypothesis:

H_0: The probability distributions of the two populations of interest are the same.

H_a: > One-Tailed: Population X is to the *right of* Population Y (Diff $= Y - X$).

$\neq$ Two-Tailed: Population X is to the *right of or to the left of* Population Y.

< One-Tailed: Population X is to the *left of* Population Y (Diff $= Y - X$).

Test Statistic:

If $n \leq 25$, and

H_a: >, then $T = T_+ =$ the sum of the ranks of the positive differences.

H_a: $\neq$, then $T = $ Min (T_+, T_-).

H_a: <, then $T = T_- =$ the sum of the ranks of the negative differences.

If $n > 25$, $T = $ Min (T_+, T_-), and the test statistic is given by

$$z = \frac{T - \dfrac{n(n+1)}{4}}{\sqrt{\dfrac{n(n+1)(2n+1)}{24}}}.$$

Critical Value(s):

If $n \leq 25$, reject H_0 if $T \leq T_c$, the critical value in Table J.

If $n > 25$, and

H_a: > or H_a: < , reject H_0 if $z < -z_\alpha$.

H_a: $\neq$, reject H_0 if $z < -z_{\alpha/2}$ or if $z > z_{\alpha/2}$.

PROCEDURE

17.2 Exercises

Basic Concepts

1. What assumptions are required for the Wilcoxon Signed-Rank Test?

2. The Wilcoxon Signed-Rank Test is primarily used to perform hypothesis tests about what type of experiment?

3. What are the advantages and disadvantages of the Wilcoxon Signed-Rank Test?

4. Describe the procedure for assigning ranks to data in order to perform a Wilcoxon Signed-Rank Test. What is to be done when two values are the same?

5. Describe how to calculate the rank sums for a paired difference experiment in order to perform a Wilcoxon Signed-Rank Test.

6. If the sample size is less than or equal to 25, identify the three possible test statistics used for the Wilcoxon Signed-Rank Test. How do you choose which statistic to use?

7. What are the null and alternative hypotheses associated with the Wilcoxon Signed-Rank Test?

8. Explain why the population distributions are important when performing a Wilcoxon Signed-Rank Test.

9. What is the test statistic for the Wilcoxon Signed-Rank Test if the sample size is large? How large is *large* with regard to sample size?

10. Identify the critical values and rejection regions for both large and small samples with regard to the Wilcoxon Signed-Rank Test.

Exercises

11. Rank the following emerging markets mutual funds from lowest to highest price using the methodology presented for the Wilcoxon Signed-Rank Test.

Emerging Markets Mutual Funds	
Mutual Fund	**Price ($)**
American Funds	24.40
Columbia Management	9.41
Morgan Stanley	23.74
Fidelity Investments	24.40
John Hancock	9.41
DWS Investments	15.57
UBS	12.15
Prudential Investments	9.23
Value Line Funds	32.82
The Vanguard Group	34.72

12. Rank the following consumer price indexes (CPI) for selected groups of goods and services in September 2011 using the methodology presented for

the Signed-Rank Test. The data in the table represent the unadjusted percent change in price level from September 2010 to September 2011.[1]

Percent Change in CPI	
Expenditure Category	**CPI (% Change 9/10 to 9/11)**
Food	4.7
Alcoholic Beverages	1.4
Housing	1.8
Apparel	3.5
Public Transportation	7.4
Medical Care	2.8
Education	4.4
Tobacco and Smoking Products	2.4
Gasoline	33.3
New and Used Motor Vehicles	3.6

13. A study conducted by the Orentreich Foundation found that women who practiced transcendental meditation (T.M.) for 20 minutes a day had high levels of DHEA-S, a hormone that may help prevent breast cancer and osteoporosis. Suppose eight women are randomly selected to participate in a study. The DHEA-S levels of the participants are measured prior to practicing transcendental meditation and then measured one year after practicing transcendental meditation for 20 minutes a day. The following table is a summary of the results of the study.

Study Results		
Study Participant	**DHEA-S Level Before T.M. (mg)**	**DHEA-S Level After T.M. (mg)**
A	20	25
B	25	25
C	18	20
D	27	26
E	19	20
F	24	26
G	20	21
H	30	29

a. Using the Sign Test, does the data indicate that the DHEA-S level of women increases after practicing transcendental meditation for 20 minutes per day for one year at $\alpha = 0.05$?

b. What assumptions were necessary to perform the Sign Test?

c. Using the Signed-Rank Test, does the data indicate that the DHEA-S level of women increases after practicing transcendental mediation for 20 minutes per day for one year at $\alpha = 0.05$?

d. What assumptions were necessary to perform the Signed-Rank Test?

e. Which test do you think produces more accurate results? Why?

14. The management for a large grocery store chain would like to determine if a new cash register will enable cashiers to process a larger number of items on average than the cash register which they are currently using. Seven cashiers are randomly selected, and the number of grocery items which they can process in three minutes is measured for both the old cash register and the new cash register. The results of the test are as follows.

Number of Grocery Items Processed in Three Minutes							
Cashier	1	2	3	4	5	6	7
Old Cash Register	60	70	55	75	62	52	58
New Cash Register	65	71	55	75	65	57	57

a. What assumption must be made in order to perform the test of hypothesis using the paired difference t-test?

b. Using the Signed-Rank Test, does the data provide conclusive evidence that the new cash register enables cashiers to process a significantly larger number of items than the old cash register at $\alpha = 0.05$?

c. What assumptions were made in performing the Signed-Rank Test?

d. How do the results of the Signed-Rank Test compare with the paired difference t-test performed in Section 12.2, Exercise 9?

15. An auto dealer is marketing two different models of a high-end sedan. Since customers are particularly interested in the safety features of the sedans, the dealer would like to determine if there is a difference in the braking distance (the number of feet required to go from 60 mph to 0 mph) of the two sedans. Six drivers are randomly selected and asked to participate in a test to measure the braking distance for both models. Each driver is asked to drive both models and brake once they have reached exactly 60 mph. The distance required to come to a complete halt is then measured in feet. The results of the test are as follows.

Braking Distance of High-End Sedans (in Feet)						
Driver	1	2	3	4	5	6
Model A	150	145	160	155	152	153
Model B	152	146	160	157	154	155

a. What assumption must be made in order to perform a test of hypothesis using the paired difference t-test?

b. Using the Signed-Rank Test, does the data provide conclusive evidence that there is a significant difference in the median braking distance of the two sedans at $\alpha = 0.10$?

c. What assumptions were made in performing the Signed-Rank Test?

d. How do the results of the Sign Test performed in Section 17.1, Exercise 21 and the signed-rank test performed in part **b.** compare with the paired difference t-test performed in Section 12.2, Exercise 10?

17.3 The Wilcoxon Rank-Sum Test

We discussed nonparametric procedures for testing claims about a paired difference experiment in the previous two sections. In this section we will discuss a nonparametric procedure for hypothesis tests in which an independent experimental design is used to compare two population medians.

In Chapter 12, we discussed the small sample t-test for comparing two population means when independent random samples are drawn from two separate populations. In order to perform that test we need to make two important assumptions, namely that the distributions of both populations of interest are approximately normal and that they have equal variances.

The **Wilcoxon Rank-Sum Test** is a nonparametric technique which can be used to compare two probability distributions when we are either unwilling or unable to make the assumptions of normality and equal variance. It may also be used in the situation where the level of the data is only ordinal, meaning we can only rank the data. Although the Wilcoxon Rank-Sum Test does not require the assumptions of normality and equal variance for validity, it does require that the two samples are drawn in a random and independent manner and that the data must be such that it can be ranked from largest to smallest.

The test procedure for the Wilcoxon Rank-Sum Test will be illustrated in the following example.

Example 17.3.1

The administrator of a local hospital is attempting to control skyrocketing medical costs. A study has indicated that the longer a patient stays in the hospital the more costly it is for *both* the patient and the hospital. Contrary to popular belief, the hospital suffers in these situations because it is often not able to collect the entire bill for the stay. Generally the insurance company is unwilling to pay for the entire stay, or the individual is unable to pay. Based on the study, it appears that there are two wards with particularly lengthy hospital stays, the pediatric ward and the geriatric ward (excluding long-term care patients). It also appears that of these two areas the length of stay in the hospital is higher in the pediatric ward than in the geriatric ward. If there is overwhelming evidence that this is the case, all initial cost control efforts will be targeted specifically at the pediatric ward. However, it could be that this observed difference is due to ordinary sampling variation as only 10 randomly selected patient stays from each ward were observed for the study. In this case, the hospital will target its initial cost control efforts at both wards equally. Partial results of the study are presented in the table below. Does the data provide sufficient evidence for the administrator to conclude that hospital stays are longer on the pediatric ward than on the geriatric ward at $\alpha = 0.05$?

Length of Hospital Stay in Days			
Pediatric Ward	**Rank**	**Geriatric Ward**	**Rank**
10	9	4	3
2	1	13	10
8	7	7	6
17	12	18	13.5
60	20	32	17
20	15	50	19
30	16	18	13.5
35	18	15	11
5	4	6	5
9	8	3	2
Rank-Sum	**110**		**100**

Histograms of the length of hospital stays for the randomly selected patients are displayed below. The histograms indicate that the length of the hospital stay appears to have a skewed distribution for each ward. Thus, the assumption of normality may not be reasonable for this data. If the assumption of normality is not met, the small sample *t*-test for comparing two population means will not be valid. However, independent random samples were drawn from each ward and the data can be ranked. Thus, the assumptions of the Wilcoxon Rank-Sum Test are satisfied and we can proceed with that test procedure.

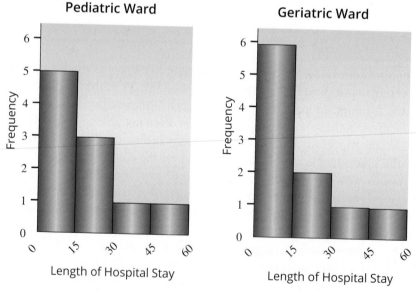

Step 1: Determine the null and alternative hypotheses.

Null Hypothesis: The length of the hospital stay for the two wards is the same.

Alternative Hypothesis: The length of the hospital stay is longer for the pediatric ward than the geriatric ward.

Because we are not making a hypothesis about a specific population parameter, we will delay the discussion of the statistical measures until **Step 3**.

Since the hospital administrator is interested in knowing if the length of stay in the pediatric ward is *longer* than in the geriatric ward, this is a one-sided test.

H_0: The probability distributions of the length of hospital stay for the pediatric ward and the geriatric ward are the same.

H_a: The probability distribution for length of hospital stay in the pediatric ward is shifted to the right of that of the probability distribution of length of stay in the geriatric ward.

Step 2: Specify the significance level α.

The level of the test is specified in the problem to be $\alpha = 0.05$.

Step 3: Validate the assumptions of the hypothesis test, identify the appropriate test statistic and compute its value.

The assumptions have already been verified.

☑ Data can be ranked (length of stay).

☑ The two samples are selected in an independent and random fashion.

The Wilcoxon Rank-Sum Test uses the idea that if the null hypothesis is true, both samples come from the same population and you should be able to combine them. After the samples are combined, rank the data and compute the sum of the ranks for each sample. In our example, the Wilcoxon Rank-Sum Test compares the sum of the ranks, the *Rank-Sum*, for the pediatric ward patients to the sum of the ranks for the geriatric ward patients.

If the null hypothesis is true, we would expect the Rank-Sums to have approximately the same value. If the Rank-Sums are very different, it will cause us to doubt that the observations come from the same population. Thus, the Rank-Sum will be the measure which will be used for our test statistic. How large a difference in the Rank-Sums is necessary before they are considered significantly different? This question is answered by the critical values specified in **Step 4**.

If $n \leq 10$, the test statistic is given by the Rank-Sum associated with the population from which the smallest sample is taken.

$T =$ the Rank-Sum of the population with the smallest sample size.

If the sample sizes are equal, use the Rank-Sum associated with the population in the alternative hypothesis which is specified to be shifted to the right or shifted to the left.

If $n > 10$, the test statistic is given in the procedure following this example. The distribution of the test statistic can be approximated by a standard normal distribution.

For the hospital example, $n_1 = 10$ and $n_2 = 10$. Since the two sample sizes are the same, we will use the Rank-Sum associated with the pediatric ward since it is specified to be shifted to the right of the geriatric ward in the alternative hypothesis.

Since $n_1 = n_2$,

$T =$ the Rank-Sum of the population specified to be shifted to the right.

Step 4: Determine the critical value(s) or *P*-value.

If $n \leq 10$, the critical values are determined from Table K (in the Appendix) for the Wilcoxon Rank-Sum Test. The critical value is specified by the level of α, the size of the first sample (n_1), the size of the second sample (n_2), and whether the test is a one-sided or two-sided test.

- If the alternative hypothesis is one-sided and specifies that population X is to the right of population Y, the null hypothesis is rejected if $T \geq T_U$ from Table K.

- If the alternative hypothesis is two-sided and specifies that population X is either to the left of population Y or population X is to the right of population Y, the null hypothesis is rejected if $T \leq T_L$ or $T \geq T_U$ from Table K.

- If the alternative hypothesis is one-sided, and specifies that population X is to the left of population Y, the null hypothesis is rejected if $T \leq T_L$ from Table K.

Note

The smaller sample size is associated with population X.

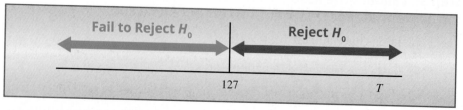

For the hospital example, $n_1 = 10$, $n_2 = 10$, $\alpha = 0.05$, and the alternative hypothesis is that the length of hospital stay in the pediatric ward is longer than in the geriatric ward. Thus, this is a one-sided test with length of stays in the pediatric ward hypothesized to be shifted to the right of length of stays in the geriatric ward. Using Table K we find that the null hypothesis should be rejected if $T > T_U = 127$. The rejection region is displayed in the figure above.

If $n > 10$, the critical values are determined in the usual manner for test statistics which have an approximate standard normal distribution under the null hypothesis. The procedure for determining the rejection region is described in the summary following this example.

Step 5: Make the decision to reject or fail to reject H_0.

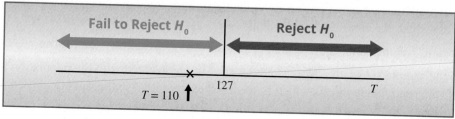

As shown above, the value of the test statistic does not fall in the rejection region (110 is less than 127). Thus, we fail to reject the null hypothesis at $\alpha = 0.05$. The difference between the observed value and the hypothesized value cannot be attributed to anything other than ordinary sampling variation.

Step 6: State the conclusion in terms of the original problem.

There is not enough evidence for the hospital administrator to conclude at $\alpha = 0.05$ that the length of hospital stays in the pediatric ward is longer than the geriatric ward. The hospital should direct the control efforts at both of the wards.

Test Procedure for the Wilcoxon Rank-Sum Test

Assumptions:

1. Data is such that they can be ranked.

2. The two samples are selected in an independent and random fashion.

Hypothesis:

H_0: The probability distributions of the two populations of interest are the same.

H_a: > One-Tailed: Population X is to the *right of* Population Y.

$\neq$ Two-Tailed: Population X is to the *right of or to the left of* Population Y.

< One-Tailed: Population X is to the *left of* Population Y.

Test Statistic:

n_1 = the smaller of the sample sizes

n_2 = the larger of the sample sizes

If $n_1 \leq 10$, and the smaller sample size, n_1, is associated with Population X, and

H_a: >, $T = T_x$ = the rank sum of the sample with the fewest members (if sample sizes are the same, T_x = the rank sum of the population hypothesized to be shifted to the right).

H_a: $\neq$, $T = T_x$ = the rank sum of the sample with the fewest members (if sample sizes are the same, use either rank sum).

H_a: <, $T = T_x$ = the rank sum of the sample with the fewest members (if sample sizes are the same, T_x = the rank sum of the population hypothesized to be shifted to the left).

If $n_1 > 10$, and the smaller sample size, n_1, is associated with Population X, then

$$z = \frac{T_x - \dfrac{n_1(n_1 + n_2 + 1)}{2}}{\sqrt{\dfrac{n_1 n_2(n_1 + n_2 + 1)}{12}}}, \text{ where } T_x \text{ is defined as above.}$$

Critical Value(s):

If $n \leq 10$, and

H_a: <, reject H_0 if $T \leq T_L$, the critical value in Table K.

H_a: $\neq$, reject H_0 if $T \leq T_L$, or $T \geq T_U$ the critical values in Table K.

H_a: >, reject H_0 if $T \geq T_U$, the critical value in Table K.

If $n > 10$, and

H_a: <, reject H_0 if $z < z_\alpha$ or H_a: >, reject H_0 if $z > z_\alpha$.

H_a: $\neq$, reject H_0 if $z < -z_{\alpha/2}$ or if $z > z_{\alpha/2}$.

PROCEDURE

17.3 **Exercises**

Basic Concepts

1. What type of data is the Wilcoxon Rank-Sum Test used to analyze?

2. What is the parametric test used to analyze the type of data that can also be analyzed by the Wilcoxon Rank-Sum Test? What assumptions are associated with this test, and why are they sometimes not reasonable?

3. What assumptions are required for the Wilcoxon Rank-Sum Test?

4. What levels of measurement may data possess in order for the Wilcoxon Rank-Sum Test to be performed?

5. Describe the procedure for ranking data in order to perform a Wilcoxon Rank-Sum Test.

6. What are the null and alternative hypotheses associated with the Wilcoxon Rank-Sum Test?

7. What is the test statistic associated with the Wilcoxon Rank-Sum Test for small samples? What does the test statistic depend on and how small is a *small* sample?

8. What is the test statistic associated with the Wilcoxon Rank-Sum Test for large samples?

9. Identify the critical values associated with the Wilcoxon Rank-Sum Test for both large and small samples.

Exercises

10. A luxury car dealer is considering two possible locations for a new auto mall. The rent on the south side of town is cheaper. However, the dealer believes that the average household income is significantly higher on the north side of town. The dealer has decided that he will locate the new auto mall on the north side of town if the results of a study which he has commissioned show that the median household income is significantly higher on the north side of town. The results of the study are as follows.

Household Incomes	
North Side ($)	South Side ($)
50,000	43,000
45,000	45,000
55,000	42,000
25,000	50,000
75,000	36,000
35,000	48,000
65,000	38,000
55,000	43,000
45,000	43,000

    a.   Use the Wilcoxon Rank-Sum Test to determine if the auto dealer should locate the new auto mall on the north side of town. Use $\alpha = 0.05$.

    b.   What assumptions were made in performing the hypothesis test in part **a.**?

11. An internal auditor for Tiger Enterprises has been asked to determine if there is a difference in the amount charged for daily expenses by two top salesmen, Mr. Ellis and Mr. Ford. The auditor randomly selects seven days and determines the daily expenses for each of the salesmen.

Daily Expenses							
Mr. Ellis ($)	55	53	58	54	56	55	55
Mr. Ford ($)	60	55	65	50	70	55	65

   a. Using the Wilcoxon Rank-Sum Test, can the auditor conclude that there is a difference in the median amount charged for daily expenses by the two top salesmen, Mr. Ellis and Mr. Ford? Use $\alpha = 0.05$.

   b. What assumptions were made in performing the test in part **a.**?

12. The Armed Forces have two different programs for training aircraft personnel. A government regulatory agency has been commissioned to evaluate any differences which may exist between the two programs. The agency administers a standardized test to randomly selected groups of students from the two programs. The results of the test for the students in each of the programs are as follows.

Standardized Test Scores							
Program A	85	95	75	100	70	90	80
Program B	87	96	78	100	74	92	82

   a. Using the Wilcoxon Rank-Sum Test, can the agency conclude that there is a difference in the median test scores of students in the two programs? Use $\alpha = 0.10$.

   b. What assumptions were made in performing the test in part **a.**?

13. A supply clerk with the Navy has been asked to determine if a new battery which has been offered to the Navy (at a reduced price) has a shorter life than the battery which they are currently using. He randomly selects batteries of each type and allows them to run continuously so that he can measure the time until failure for each battery. The results of the test are as follows.

Time Until Failure for Batteries (Hours)						
New Battery	655	730	670	715	685	745
Old Battery	745	675	730	690	760	660

   a. Using the Wilcoxon Rank-Sum Test, does the data suggest at $\alpha = 0.05$ that the median time until failure for the new battery is significantly less than the median time until failure for the old battery?

   b. What assumptions were made in performing the test in part **a.**?

14. A cereal manufacturer has advertised that its product, Fiber Oat Flakes, has a lower fat content than its competitor, Bran Flakes Plus. Because of the complaints from the manufacturer of Bran Flakes Plus, the FDA has decided to test the claim that Fiber Oat Flakes has a lower median fat content than

Bran Flakes Plus. Several boxes of each cereal are selected and the fat content per serving is measured. The results of the study are as follows.

Fat Content of Cereals (Grams)									
Fiber Oat Flakes	5	6	4	7	3	5	5	6	4
Bran Flakes Plus	6	8	4	9	3	7	5	8	4

a. Using the Wilcoxon Rank-Sum Test, does the study performed by the FDA substantiate the claim made by the manufacturer of Fiber Oat Flakes at $\alpha = 0.05$?

b. What assumptions were made in performing the test in part **a.**?

15. A Hollywood studio believes that a movie which is considered a drama will draw a larger crowd on average than a movie which is a comedy. To test this theory, the studio randomly selects several movies which are classified as dramas and several movies which are classified as comedies and determines the box office revenue for each movie. The results of the survey are as follows.

Box Office Revenues (Millions of Dollars)					
Drama	180	240	120	220	140
Comedy	150	190	110	170	130

a. Using the Wilcoxon Rank-Sum Test, does the data substantiate the studio's belief that dramas will draw a larger crowd on average than comedies at $\alpha = 0.05$?

b. What assumptions were made in performing the test in part **a.**?

16. *Consumer Magazine* is reviewing the top selling amplifiers produced by two major stereo manufacturers. One of the most important qualities of the amplifiers is the maximum power output. Brand A has redone their internal design and claims to have a higher maximum power level than Brand B. To test this claim, *Consumer Magazine* randomly selects amplifiers from each brand and determines the maximum power output. The results of the test are as follows.

Maximum Power Output (Watts)							
Brand A	800	828	772	830	770	826	774
Brand B	780	805	755	807	753	803	757

a. Using the Wilcoxon Rank-Sum Test, does the data substantiate the claim that the Brand A amplifier has a higher median maximum power output than Brand B at $\alpha = 0.05$?

b. What assumptions were made in performing the test in part **a.**?

17. A state environmental board wants to compare pollution levels in two of its major cities. Sunshine City thrives on the tourist industry and Service City thrives on the service industry. The environmental board randomly selects several areas within the cities and measures the pollution levels in parts per million with the following results.

Pollution Levels (ppm)								
Sunshine City	8.50	9.00	8.00	9.07	7.93	9.14	7.86	8.50
Service City	7.90	8.35	7.45	8.40	7.40	8.45	7.35	7.90

a. Using the Wilcoxon Rank-Sum Test, can the state environmental board conclude at $\alpha = 0.05$ that Service City has a lower pollution level on average than Sunshine City?

b. What assumptions were made in performing the test in part **a.**?

17.4 **The Rank Correlation Test**

In Section 5.1 we studied the coefficient of correlation as a measure of association between two random variables. In this section instead of directly correlating the variables, we will transform the data into ranks and develop a method for detecting an association between the two variables.

Measure of Correlation

Let us denote the ranks assigned to X_i and Y_i by $R(X_i)$ and $R(Y_i)$ respectively. Then the measure of correlation, also called Spearman's rho, is usually denoted by r_s, and is defined as

$$r_s = 1 - \frac{6T}{n \cdot \left(n^2 - 1\right)},$$

where $T = \sum_{i=1}^{n} \left[R(X_i) - R(Y_i)\right]^2$.

This method is applicable when there are no ties in the rank data. The r_s statistic is called the Spearman rank correlation coefficient. Its values are always between -1 and 1, inclusive. The r_s statistic behaves like the parametric correlation coefficient. If there is a positive relationship r_s will be positive but less than or equal to 1. If there is a negative relationship, r_s will be negative but greater than or equal to -1.

Example 17.4.1

Consider the given data set.

Original Data

X	7	5	8	9
Y	4	7	9	8

Converting the data to ranks, we obtain:

Ranked Data

X	R(X)	Y	R(Y)
7	2	4	1
5	1	7	2
8	3	9	4
9	4	8	3

The value of r_s is then given by

$$r_s = 1 - \frac{6 \cdot 4}{4 \cdot \left(4^2 - 1\right)} = 0.60.$$

Note

The advantage of Spearman's rank correlation coefficient is that it can be used to test for a monotonic, nonlinear relationship, i.e., y increases as x increases or y decreases as x increases, but not necessarily linearly.

We want to test the null hypothesis that there is no correlation between the two variables against the alternative hypothesis that there is a correlation. More specifically, we test

$H_0: \rho = 0$ There is no correlation between the two variables.

$H_a: \rho \neq 0$.   There is a correlation between the two variables.

Rank Correlation Procedure

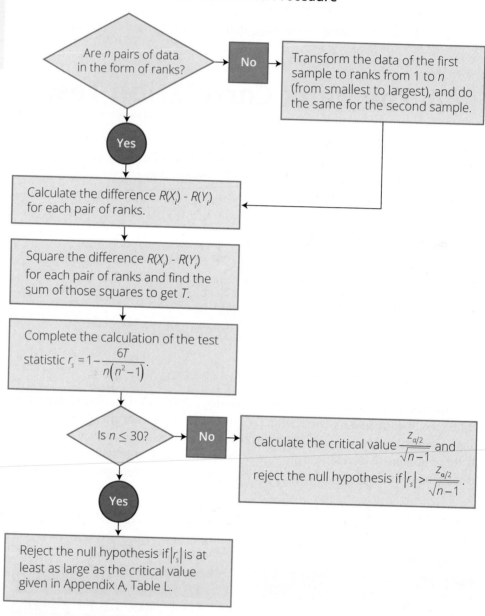

Example 17.4.2

The academic performances of fifteen college graduates are observed to examine the relationship between their SAT scores and their GPAs. The SAT scores and the GPAs are given in the following table.

Student	SAT Total	College GPA	Student	SAT Total	College GPA
1	1064	2.52	9	1122	2.59
2	1085	2.74	10	1163	3.20
3	1270	2.76	11	1187	3.21
4	1093	2.83	12	1302	3.39
5	1170	2.91	13	1044	3.41
6	1135	2.40	14	1234	3.42
7	1262	3.08	15	1316	3.47
8	1074	3.17			

Test the hypothesis that there is no relationship between the variables at the $\alpha = 0.10$ level.

Solution

$H_0: \rho = 0$

$H_a: \rho \neq 0$

In order to test whether an association exists between these two variables at $\alpha = 0.10$, we prepare the following table.

Student	SAT Total (X)	College GPA (Y)	R(X)	R(Y)	$[R(X)-R(Y)]^2$
1	1064	2.52	2	2	0
2	1085	2.74	4	4	0
3	1270	2.76	13	5	64
4	1093	2.83	5	6	1
5	1170	2.91	9	7	4
6	1135	2.40	7	1	36
7	1262	3.08	12	8	16
8	1074	3.17	3	9	36
9	1122	2.59	6	3	9
10	1163	3.20	8	10	4
11	1187	3.21	10	11	1
12	1302	3.39	14	12	4
13	1044	3.41	1	13	144
14	1234	3.42	11	14	9
15	1316	3.47	15	15	0

We then calculate the test statistic $r_s = 1 - \dfrac{6 \cdot 328}{15 \cdot \left(15^2 - 1\right)} = 0.4143$. Since our sample size is 15 ($n \leq 30$), the value of the statistic is compared with the critical value obtained using Appendix A Table L.

n	...	$a = 0.10$	$a = 0.05$	$a = 0.02$
11		0.523	0.623	0.736
12		0.497	0.591	0.703
13		0.475	0.566	0.673
14		0.457	0.545	0.646
15		0.441	0.525	0.623

Note: Table L in Appendix A is constructed for a two-tailed test. So, we want to reject H_0 if $r_s < -0.441$ or $r_s > 0.441$. Since $0.4143 < 0.441$, we fail to reject the null hypothesis at the 10% level of significance. Hence, there does not seem to be an association between SAT scores and GPAs.

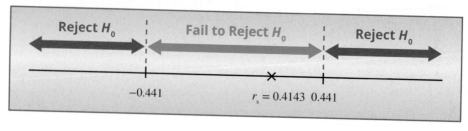

17.4 Exercises

Basic Concepts

1. What is the correlation coefficient? How is this different from the Spearman rank correlation coefficient?

2. What is the formula for calculating Spearman's rho?

3. Can you calculate Spearman's rho if there are ties in the rank data?

4. Identify the difference in notation between Spearman's rho for population and sample data.

5. Explain the similarities in the behavior of the parametric correlation coefficient and Spearman's rho.

6. Identify one main advantage of the Spearman's rank correlation coefficient versus the parametric correlation coefficient.

7. Explain the procedure for ranking data when calculating Spearman's rho.

8. What are the null and alternative hypotheses for the rank correlation test?

9. Consider the value $r_s = 0.12$. Interpret this value in terms of the x and y variables used to calculate Spearman's rho.

Exercises

10. Chris is a new cashier assigned to a cash register in a supermarket. Each day a sample of purchases at that register is examined and a percent of pricing errors is recorded along with the total number of customers who used that register. Does the following data indicate an association between Chris' performance and how busy his register was? Use $\alpha = 0.05$.

% Pricing Errors and Total Customers			
Number of Customers	**Errors (%)**	**Number of Customers**	**Errors (%)**
57	4.2	67	2.5
44	5.5	71	2.9
32	5.7	69	2.6
60	3.9	56	1.0
55	3.2	51	2.0
59	4.1	70	1.7
63	3.3		

11. Twelve new runners were randomly assigned to different training programs, where they were required to run a certain number of miles every week for a year prior to a major race. After the training, the participants ran the race and their finishing times were recorded.

Miles of Training and Race Times			
Miles Logged	**Race Time (Minutes)**	**Miles Logged**	**Race Time (Minutes)**
35	198	30	189
25	165	29	240
45	155	42	224
60	148	24	201
70	135	19	246
21	243	55	166

a. With 95% confidence, is there evidence that the number of miles logged in a week during training affects the runner's race time?

b. Can the linear correlation coefficient, r, be calculated in order to fit a least squares regression line to the data in the table in an effort to predict the finish time of runners based on the number of miles logged during training? Why or why not?

12. The following data consists of college rankings of five universities by two different magazines. Is there a correlation between the rankings of the magazines? Use $\alpha = 0.10$.

College Rankings by Magazines					
College	**A**	**B**	**C**	**D**	**E**
Magazine 1	1	4	2	3	5
Magazine 2	4	3	1	5	2

13. An anthropologist records the heights (in inches) of ten fathers and their sons. Does the following data support (at the 5% level) that taller fathers tend to have taller sons?

Heights of Fathers and Sons (Inches)			
Son's Height	Father's Height	Son's Height	Father's Height
72	70	65	71
68	73	70	78
74	72	69	67
66	68	67	65
71	69	80	66

14. After a mother-daughter golf tournament, mothers and daughters were ranked among themselves. Does the following data show (at the 5% level) a correlation between the daughters' and mothers' golf skills?

Golf Rankings			
Daughter's Ranking	Mother's Ranking	Daughter's Ranking	Mother's Ranking
1	5	5	3
9	4	3	6
10	8	7	7
2	2	6	10
4	1	8	9

17.5 The Runs Test for Randomness

Randomness is an important concept in probability and statistics. In this section, we are going to discuss a method for determining whether a sequence of observations exhibit randomness. To illustrate this concept we will use the familiar coin tossing experiment. One characteristic of the coin-tossing experiment is that in the long run there should be approximately equal numbers of heads and tails. In an ordered sequence, however, randomness implies more than compliance with this frequency criterion. For example, if the outcomes of 20 tosses of a coin were recorded as

$$H H H H H T T T T T T T T T T H H H H H,$$

we would suspect that the process was flawed. We would be equally surprised if the ordered outcomes were

$$H T H T H T H T H T H T H T H T H T H T,$$

but be reasonably happy with the sequence

$$H H T H T T T H T H H H T H T H H H H T T H.$$

A characteristic that reflects our reservations about the first two sequences is the **number of runs**, where a run is a subsequence of one or more heads (or tails). In the first sequence, there are 3 runs: a run of 5 heads, then 10 tails, then 5 heads.

$$H H H H H T T T T T T T T T T H H H H H$$

| Run | Run | Run |

In the second sequence, there are 20 runs, each consisting of a single head or tail.

$$\begin{array}{c} \underline{H}\,\underline{H}\,\underline{T}\,\underline{H}\,\underline{T}\,\underline{T}\,\underline{T}\,\underline{H}\,\underline{T}\,\underline{H}\,\underline{H}\,\underline{H}\,\underline{T}\,\underline{H}\,\underline{T}\,\underline{H}\,\underline{H}\,\underline{H}\,\underline{T}\,\underline{T}\,\underline{H} \\ R\,R\,R\,R\,R\,R\,R\,R\,R\,R\,R\,R\,R\,R\,R\,R\,R\,R\,R\,R \end{array}$$

Intuitively, we feel that these two sequences have respectively too few and too many runs for a truly random sequence. In the last sequence there are 13 runs.

$$\begin{array}{c} \underline{H\,H}\,\underline{T}\,\underline{H}\,\underline{T\,T\,T}\,\underline{H}\,\underline{T}\,\underline{H\,H}\,\underline{H}\,\underline{T}\,\underline{H}\,\underline{T}\,\underline{H\,H\,H}\,\underline{T\,T}\,\underline{H} \\ R\quad R\,R\quad R\quad R\,R\quad R\quad R\,R\,R\quad R\quad R\,R \end{array}$$

Given the number of times the coin was flipped, the number of runs does not seem excessively large or small. This intuitive notion of rejecting "randomness" in the sequence if there are too few or too many runs is the same notion we will use in the test of hypothesis.

In order to test the null hypotheses

H_0: The sequence is random

H_a: The sequence is not random,

we use a test based on the number of runs, R, in a sequence of N ordered observations.

Runs Test for Randomness Procedure

H H T T T H T T H H H

$m = 6$ (number of heads)

$n = 5$ (number of tails)

$R = 5$ (number of runs)

Look at a sequence with two different types.

Let m represent the number of elements in the first type.

Let n represent the number of elements in the second type where $n = N - m$.

Calculate the number of runs (R) in the sequence.

No, $6 < 20$ — Is $m > 20$? — Yes

No, $5 < 20$ — Is $n > 20$? — Yes

Assume $\alpha = 0.05$ — Is $\alpha = 0.05$? — No

Calculate $\mu_R = 1 + \dfrac{2nm}{N}$

Calculate $\sigma_R = \sqrt{\dfrac{2nm(2nm - N)}{[N^2(N-1)]}}$

Calculate $z = \dfrac{(R - \mu_R)}{\sigma_R}$

The test statistic is z. Use Appendix A, Table A, B, or C to get the critical values.

The test statistic is R. Use Appendix A, Table M to get the critical values.

Create two-sided rejection region.

Critical

If the test statistic is in rejection region, reject H_0.

3 and 10

Reject H_0 | Fail to Reject H_0 | Reject H_0

0   3 4   5   9 10   11

Do not reject H_0

Are There Streak Shooters?

Are there streak shooters in basketball? The answer to this question is remarkably consistent from respondents who answer it in the affirmative. Yes, there are streak shooters. But does the data support this strongly held belief?

Psychologists Tversky and Gilovich examined data from several professional NBA teams and especially for free throwing. Free throwing was considered because it removed other dynamics of the game such as defense and various strategies. Examining the data from the Boston Celtics and the Philadelphia 76'ers for an entire season, they failed to observe any streaks. Success and failures in free throws occurred randomly with each player. This study teaches that our concept of randomness and non-randomness are very vague and often wrong.

Tversky, A. and Gilovich, T. (1989). "The cold facts about the 'hot hand' in basketball," Chance, 2, 1, 16-21.

Example 17.5.1

Let us apply the runs test for randomness to each of the sequences of heads and tails seen earlier in this section. In each test the hypotheses are as follows.

H_0: The sequence is random.

H_a: The sequence is not random.

a.   H H H H H T T T T T T T T T T H H H H H

Solution

N (the number of observations) $= 20$

m (the number of heads) $= n$ (the number of tails) $= 10$

R (the number of runs) $= 3$

Using Appendix A Table M we see that $r \leq 6$ or $r \geq 16$ at 0.05 level of significance. Therefore, we conclude that there is strong evidence of nonrandomness.

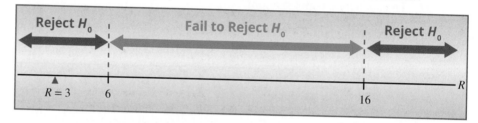

b.   H T H T H T H T H T H T H T H T H T H T

Solution

N (the number of observations) $= 20$

m (the number of heads) $= n$ (the number of tails) $= 10$

R (the number of runs) $= 20$

Using Appendix A Table M we see that $r \leq 6$ or $r \geq 16$ at 0.05 level of significance. Therefore, we conclude that there is strong evidence of nonrandomness.

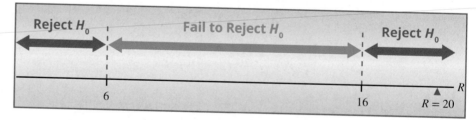

c.   H H T H T T T H T H H H T H T H H H T T H

Solution

N (the number of observations) $= 20$

m (the number of heads) $= 11$

n (the number of tails) $= 9$

R (the number of runs) $= 13$

Using Appendix A Table M we see that $r \leq 6$ or $r \geq 16$ at 0.05 level of significance. Therefore, we conclude that there is no evidence of nonrandomness.

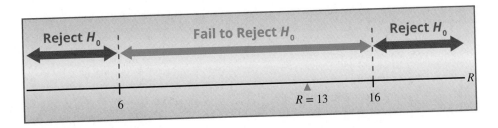

Example 17.5.2

The Admissions Office of a college records the gender of the first 28 applicants in the order their applications arrive. The data set is given as

M F F M M M F F F F M M M M M M M M M M F M M M M M M M.

Is this sequence random? Test at the 0.05 level.

Solution

To test the randomness of this sequence at 5% level of significance, we obtain

N (the number of observations) $= 28$

m (the number of males) $= 21$

n (the number of females) $= 7$

R (the number of runs) $= 7$

Since $m > 20$, we calculate

$$\mu_R = 1 + \frac{2nm}{N}$$
$$= 1 + \frac{2(7 \cdot 21)}{28}$$
$$= 11.5$$

$$\sigma_R = \sqrt{\frac{2nm(2nm - N)}{N^2(N-1)}}$$
$$= \sqrt{\frac{(2 \cdot 7 \cdot 21)\big[(2 \cdot 7 \cdot 21) - 28\big]}{28^2(28-1)}}$$
$$= 1.92$$

Thus,

$$z = \frac{R - \mu_R}{\sigma_R}$$

$$= \frac{7 - 11.5}{1.92}$$

$$= -2.34$$

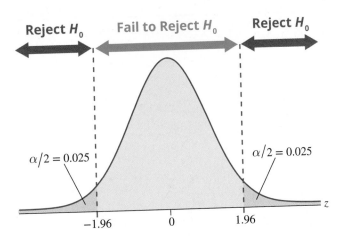

Since the test statistic is in the rejection region, reject the null hypothesis that the gender of arriving students follow a random sequence.

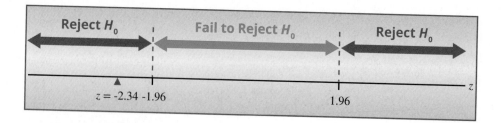

Example 17.5.3

Is the following data random?

$$16, \ 25, \ 52, \ 11, \ 38, \ 47, \ 12, \ 98, \ 4$$

Solution

How do you test randomness with a numerical set? Create a new data set comparing each value to the median value. To do this, substitute each value in the original data set with an A if it is above the median value, a B if it is below the median value, and eliminate any values that equal the median.

H_0: The data is random.

H_a: The data is not random.

$$\text{Median} = 25$$

$$16, \ 25, \ 52, \ 11, \ 38, \ 47, \ 12, \ 98, \ 4$$

$$\text{B}, \ \varnothing, \ \text{A}, \ \text{B}, \ \text{A}, \ \text{A}, \ \text{B}, \ \text{A}, \ \text{B}$$

m (the number of A's) $= 4$

n (the number of B's) $= 4$

R (the number of runs) $= 7$

critical values $= 1,\ldots, 9$

Fail to reject H_0; there is no evidence of nonrandomness.

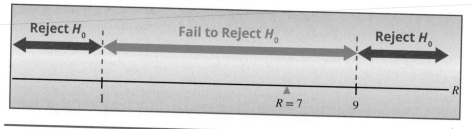

17.5 **Exercises**

Basic Concepts

1. Describe in your own words what is being tested with the runs test.

2. Consider the following sequence of 10 coin tosses.

    H, H, T, T, H, H, H, T, T, H

    Without performing any kind of test, do you believe this sequence is random? Explain why or why not.

3. What are the null and alternative hypotheses associated with the runs test?

4. What parameters need to be calculated in order to perform a runs test?

5. What is the rejection rule for a small sample runs test? How small is a *small* sample?

6. What is the rejection rule for a large sample runs test? How large is a *large* sample?

7. If a numerical set of data is under consideration, which parameter is the data points compared to in order to perform the runs test?

Exercises

8. Suppose that in your city the number of deaths due to traffic accidents involving drunk driving from 1999 to 2011 were 75, 91, 54, 85, 79, 63, 12, 55, 63, 49, 89, 98, and 71. Use the runs test to examine non-randomness at the 0.05 level.

9. A sociologist designs a study that involves a procedure of selecting families randomly from a phone book and then calling them to determine if they own or rent their residence. The results are recorded in the order of phone calls (O = Own, R = Rent).

    O O O R R O R O R R O R R R O R R R O O R R R O R

    Does the sociologist have a random sequence of residential data at the 0.05 level?

10. A car tire manufacturer keeps track of the tires produced by one of the production lines. They observe the following sequence (D for defective items and N for non-defective items).

    D D D N N D N D N D D D

    Test the quality control manager's claim that there is no pattern in producing defective tires at the 0.05 level.

11. A marathon runner tries to run every day except when it is raining during the month of July. He observes the rainy (R) days and sunny (S) days to be able to predict the weather as follows.

    S S S R R S S S R R R S R S R R S S R S R S R R S R S R S S

    Are the rainy days randomly scattered in the month of July at the 0.05 level?

17.6 The Kruskal-Wallis Test

In this section we present a procedure where k random samples are obtained, one from each of k possibly different populations, and we are interested in testing whether all of the populations are identical. Suitable hypotheses for this test would be follows.

H_0: The populations from which the samples were drawn have identical distributions.

H_a: Not all populations have the same distribution.

The **Kruskal-Wallis Test** is a method that can be used to replace the ANOVA F-test. The Kruskal-Wallis Test does not need the assumption of normality of the population. It does require that independent random samples be drawn.

The Kruskal-Wallis Test is similar to the Wilcoxon Rank-Sum Test in that the test statistic will be based on the sums of the ranks of the groups being compared.

The data consists of k random samples (not necessarily the same size) drawn from their respective populations. The data set may be arranged as follows:

Group 1	Group 2		Group k
$X_{1,1}$	$X_{2,1}$		$X_{k,1}$
$X_{1,2}$	$X_{2,2}$		$X_{k,2}$
...	...	....	
$X_{1.n_1}$	$X_{1.n_2}$		$X_{1.n_k}$

Let N be the total number of observations, that is, $N = \sum_{i=1}^{k} n_i$.

To compute the Kruskal-Wallis test statistic we first combine all N observations and order them from the smallest to the largest. Next, we assign rank 1 to the smallest of all observations, rank 2 to the second smallest, and so on, until the largest observation is assigned the rank N. Let us denote the rank of $X_{i,j}$ by r_{ij}, and define

$$R_i = \sum_{j=1}^{n_i} r_{ij} \quad i = 1, 2, ..., k.$$

For example, R_1 is the sum of the ranks received by the group 1 observations. The test statistic for the Kruskal-Wallis Test is then given by

$$H = \frac{12}{N(N+1)} \sum_{i=1}^{k} \frac{R_i^2}{n_i} - 3(N+1).$$

We reject the null hypothesis if $H \geq \chi_\alpha$, where χ_α is obtained from the chi-square table (Appendix A Table G) with $(k-1)$ degrees of freedom and a predetermined value of α.

Example 17.6.1

A real estate agent sells single-family homes in the towns of Mouse Creek, Spring Valley, and Smyrna. Some homes for sale in these towns have the following prices (in thousands of dollars).

Selling Prices (in thousands of dollars)		
Mouse Creek	Spring Valley	Smyrna
89	128	82
114	147	129
142	168	149
164	222	169
219	289	389
	489	

Use the Kruskal-Wallis Test to check whether the house prices in these samples come from identical populations using $\alpha = 0.05$.

Solution

The $N = 16$ house prices are assigned overall ranks. In the following table, the ranks are shown in the column next to each obervation.

Selling Prices Ranked					
Mouse Creek	Rank	Spring Valley	Rank	Smyrna	Rank
89	2	128	4	82	1
114	3	147	7	129	5
142	6	168	10	149	8
164	9	222	13	169	11
219	12	289	14	389	15
		489	16		

The hypotheses for the test can be written as follows.

   H_0: The samples come from populations with the same distribution.

   H_a: The samples come from populations with different distributions.

The sum of the ranks for each city are as follows.

Mouse Creek: $2 + 3 + 6 + 9 + 12 = 32 = R_1$

Spring Valley: $4 + 7 + 10 + 13 + 14 + 16 = 64 = R_2$

Smyrna: $1 + 5 + 8 + 11 + 15 = 40 = R_3$

Hence using $H = \dfrac{12}{N(N+1)} \sum_{i=1}^{k} \dfrac{R_i^2}{n_i} - 3(N+1)$. we get

$$H = \frac{12}{16(16+1)} \left(\frac{32^2}{5} + \frac{64^2}{6} + \frac{40^2}{5} \right) - 3 \cdot 17 = 2.271.$$

There are $k - 1 = 3 - 1 = 2$ degrees of freedom. The critical value can be found in Table G of Appendix A as $\chi^2_{(3-1),.05} = 5.991$. Since $2.271 < 5.991$, we do not reject the null hypothesis and state that the house prices do not differ significantly in these three towns.

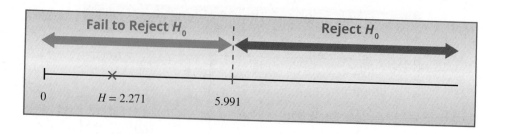

Example 17.6.2

A traffic safety engineer records the braking distances of a test vehicle at a fixed speed using three different brake pads. Braking distances (in feet) and their respective ranks for brake pads of types A, B and C are given in the following table. Is there sufficient evidence at the 0.05 level to conclude that the braking distances for the three pads are not all the same?

Solution

	Braking Distances (in feet) with Ranks					
	Brake Pad A	**Rank**	**Brake Pad B**	**Rank**	**Brake Pad C**	**Rank**
	89	1	97	5	98	6
	99	7	139	15	116	11
	101	8	119	12	104	10
	94	2	103	9	96	4
	95	3	127	14	126	13
Rank Sum	21		55		44	

The hypotheses for this test can be written as follows.

H_0: The braking distances for the three pads are the same.

H_a: At least one of the braking distances is different.

The ranks of the observations are given in the table. The sum of the ranks for each type of brake pad is found in the last row of the table.

$$R_1 = 21 \quad R_2 = 55 \quad R_3 = 44$$

We can now calculate the test statistic,

$$H = \frac{12}{N(N+1)} \sum_{i=1}^{k} \frac{R_i^2}{n_i} - 3(N+1).$$

We find that $H = \dfrac{12}{15(15+1)} \left(\dfrac{21^2}{5} + \dfrac{55^2}{5} + \dfrac{44^2}{5} \right) - 3(15+1) = 6.02$.

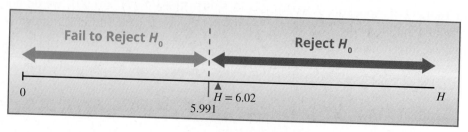

Referring to Appendix A, Table G, we see that $\chi^2_{2,.05} = 5.991$. Because the test statistic exceeds the critical value (6.02 > 5.991) we reject the null hypothesis and conclude that the braking distances are sufficiently different.

17.6 **Exercises**

Basic Concepts

1. Which parametric test corresponds to the nonparametric Kruskal-Wallis Test?

2. What are the null and alternative hypotheses associated with the Kruskal-Wallis Test?

3. What are the assumptions associated with the Kruskal-Wallis Test?

4. How is the Kruskal-Wallis test similar to the Wilcoxon Rank-Sum Test?

5. What is the test statistic for the Kruskal-Wallis Test? How is it calculated?

6. What is the rejection rule for the Kruskal-Wallis Test?

7. How many populations can be compared using the Kruskal-Wallis Test?

Exercises

8. An Internet service provider is considering four different servers for purchase. Potentially, the company would be purchasing hundreds of these servers, so it wants to make sure it is making the best decision. Initially, five of each type of server are borrowed, and each is randomly assigned to one of the 20 technicians (all technicians are similar in skill). Each server is then put through a series of tasks and rated using a standardized test. The higher the score on the test, the better the performance of the server. The data is as follows.

Server Test Scores			
Server 1	Server 2	Server 3	Server 4
48.5	56.4	52.1	64.3
46.5	68.2	56.3	68.3
52.4	68.5	48.3	72.2
54.1	64.2	52.2	70.6
58.9	60.1	54.8	56.5

Perform a Kruskal-Wallis Test on this data using $\alpha = 0.10$. Are there differences between the servers?

9. The following summary is obtained from an experiment where groups of cows were fed according to one of the four different feeding schedules, and their milk productions were recorded. The data given shows the daily milk production in gallons for each cow. Test at $\alpha = 0.10$ to examine whether or not the milk production for all four schedules is the same.

Milk Production by Schedule (Gallons)					
Schedule 1	11.5	12.7	12.9	10.1	10.5
Schedule 2	9.1	10.7	9.5	10.9	10.4
Schedule 3	12.4	11.9	10.0	11.4	12.1
Schedule 4	12.8	12.6	11.7	11.3	10.9

10. The following data set contains the reading speed (in words per minute) of second grade students.

Reading Speeds (wpm)		
Public School	**Private School**	**Home School**
54	66	65
67	55	64
63	62	60
105	69	72
61	71	68

Is there sufficient evidence at the 0.01 level of significance to conclude that the reading speeds vary by school type?

CR   Chapter Review

Key Terms and Ideas

- Parametric Statistics
- Nonparametric Statistical Methods
- Sign Test
- Hypothesis Test about a Population Median
- Wilcoxon Signed-Rank Test
- Rank Sum
- Wilcoxon Rank-Sum Test

- Rank Correlation Test
- Correlation Coefficient
- Spearman Rank Correlation Coefficient (Spearman's Rho)
- Runs Test for Randomness
- Runs
- Randomness
- Non-Randomness
- Kruskal-Wallis Test

Key Formulas	
	Section
Test Statistic for the Sign Test, $n \leq 25$ X = the number of times the less frequent sign occurs	**17.1**

Key Formulas	
	Section

Test Statistic for the Sign Test, $n > 25$ 17.1

$$z = \frac{X + 0.5 - \left(\dfrac{n}{2}\right)}{\dfrac{\sqrt{n}}{2}}$$

Test Statistic for the Wilcoxon Signed-Rank Test, $n \leq 25$ 17.2

If H_a is $>$ One-Tailed:

$\quad T = T_+ =$ the sum of the ranks associated with the positive differences.

If H_a is $<$ One-Tailed:

$\quad T = T_- =$ the sum of the ranks associated with the negative differences.

If H_a is $\neq$ Two-Tailed:

$$T = \text{Min}\left(T_+, T_-\right).$$

Test Statistic for the Wilcoxon Signed-Rank Test, $n > 25$ 17.2

$$z = \frac{T - \dfrac{n(n+1)}{4}}{\sqrt{\dfrac{n(n+1)(2n+1)}{24}}}$$

$$\text{where } T = \text{Min}\left(T_+, T_-\right).$$

Test Statistic for the Wilcoxon Rank-Sum Test, $n_1 \leq 10$ 17.3

If H_a is $>$ One-Tailed:

$T = T_x =$ the rank sum of the sample with the fewest members. (If the sample sizes are the same, $T_x =$ the rank sum of the population hypothesized to be shifted to the right.)

If H_a is $<$ One-Tailed:

$T = T_x =$ the rank sum of the sample with the fewest members. (If the sample sizes are the same, $T_x =$ the rank sum of the population hypothesized to be shifted to the left.)

If H_a is $\neq$ Two-Tailed:

$T = T_x =$ the rank sum of the sample with the fewest members. (If the sample sizes are the same, either rank sum can be used.)

Key Formulas	
	Section
Test Statistic for the Wilcoxon Rank-Sum Test, $n_1 > 10$ $$z = \frac{T - \dfrac{n_1(n_1 + n_2 + 1)}{2}}{\sqrt{\dfrac{n_1 n_2 (n_1 + n_2 + 1)}{12}}}$$	17.3
Spearman Rank Correlation Coefficient (Spearman's Rho) $$r_s = 1 - \frac{6T}{n \cdot (n^2 - 1)},$$ where $T = \sum_{i=1}^{n}\left[R(X_i) - R(Y_i) \right]^2 .$	17.4
Test Statistic for the Runs Test for Randomness, $m > 20$ or $n > 20$ $$z = \frac{R - \mu_R}{\sigma_R}$$ where $\mu_R = 1 + \dfrac{2mn}{N}$ and $\sigma_R = \sqrt{\dfrac{2mn(2mn - N)}{N^2(N-1)}}.$	17.5
Test Statistic for the Kruskal-Wallis Test $$H = \frac{12}{N(N+1)} \sum_{i=1}^{k} \frac{R_i^2}{n_i} - 3(N+1)$$ where $R_i = \sum_{j=1}^{n_i} r_{ij}$ and $N = \sum_{i=1}^{k} n_i .$	17.6

Additional Exercises

1. A new method for temporarily relieving the lung congestion of cystic fibrosis patients has been introduced. The traditional method of relieving the congestion involves a series of manual techniques where the chest and back area are pounded and massaged. The new method is a mechanical vest which has been designed to perform the manual techniques. A study is conducted to measure

the effectiveness of the new vest. Five cystic fibrosis patients are randomly selected and the diameter of the blood vessels in their lungs is measured after using the traditional treatment and after using the vest treatment. The larger the diameter of the blood vessels within the lungs, the better the treatment. If the study provides conclusive evidence that the vest is more effective than the manual method in increasing the diameter of the blood vessels, the hospital will recommend the vest to its patients because the vest allows the patients to be much more independent. The results of the study are as follows.

Diameter of Lung Blood Vessels (in mm)					
Subject	1	2	3	4	5
After Traditional Treatment	0.5	0.4	0.7	0.6	0.2
After Vest Treatment	0.6	0.6	0.7	0.7	0.5

a. What assumption must be made in order to perform the test of hypothesis using the paired difference t-test?

b. Using the Sign Test, does the data provide conclusive evidence that the median diameter of blood vessels in the lungs is significantly larger after using the vest treatment than after using the traditional treatment at $\alpha = 0.01$?

c. What assumptions were made in performing the Sign Test?

d. Using the Signed-Rank Test, does the data provide conclusive evidence that the median diameter of blood vessels in the lungs is significantly larger after using the vest treatment than after using the traditional treatment at $\alpha = 0.01$?

e. What assumptions were made in performing the Signed-Rank Test?

f. Which test do you think produces more accurate results? Why?

g. Perform a paired difference t-test. How do the results of the Sign Test and the Signed-Rank Test compare with the results of the t-test?

2. As private companies prepare to go public, many analysts attempt to predict whether the stock will have a positive or negative return in the first day of trading. One particular analyst believes the return after the first day of trading is positive, on average. Another analyst wishes to test this analyst's claim using 15 recently offered public stocks.[3]

Initial Public Offerings		
Company	Initial Offer Price ($)	Price After 1st Day of Trading ($)
Enduro Royalty Trust (NDRO)	22.00	21.26
ZELTIQ Aesthetics (ZLTQ)	13.00	15.50
Ubiquiti Networks (UBNT)	15.00	17.50
Tudou Holdings Limited (TUDO)	29.00	25.56
Carbonite (CARB)	10.00	12.35
SandRidge Permian Trust (PER)	18.00	18.00
American Capital Mortgage Investment (MTGE)	20.00	18.41

Initial Public Offerings		
Company	Initial Offer Price ($)	Price After 1st Day of Trading ($)
C&J Energy Services (CJES)	29.00	30.50
Chefs Warehouse Holdings (CHEF)	15.00	17.50
Spirit Airlines (SAVE)	12.00	11.55
Pandora Media (P)	16.00	17.42
Wesco Aircraft Holdings (WAIR)	15.00	14.92
American Midstream Partners (AMID)	21.00	20.95
Dunkin Brands Group (DNKN)	19.00	27.85
Skullcandy (SKUL)	20.00	20.00

a. Use the Sign Test to test the hypothesis that the return after the first day of trading is positive. Test at the 0.05 level.

b. Suppose that an analyst claimed that the median return on a stock in the first day of trading is +$1.00. Perform a test of hypothesis to determine if the median return is different than what the analyst claims. Use $\alpha = 0.05$.

c. Use the Wilcoxon Signed-Rank Test to determine if the price after the first day of trading is generally greater than the initial offer price. Test at $\alpha = 0.05$.

d. Analyze the results of the Sign Test performed in part **a.** and the Signed-Rank Test performed in part **c.** in terms of the problem. Which test do you think yields more accurate results?

e. What concerns do you have with the tests performed in this problem?

3. A weight loss center is trying to determine which of its diets results in higher client satisfaction. The center polled 20 clients (10 were on Diet A and 10 on Diet B) and had them rate their satisfaction in the diets from 1 to 100.

Diet Ratings									
Diet A	84	77	89	98	97	100	75	85	96	78
Diet B	94	81	95	93	97	99	82	92	95	89

a. Which nonparametric test do you think is most appropriate to test the claim that Diet B results in higher client satisfaction than Diet A? Explain why.

b. Write the null and alternative hypotheses for a Rank-Sum Test to determine if Diet B results in higher client satisfaction than Diet A.

c. Using the Rank-Sum Test, does the data provide sufficient evidence at $\alpha = 0.05$ that Diet B results in greater client satisfaction than Diet A?

d. What assumptions were made in the test performed in part **c.**?

4. Are students with higher GPAs more likely to get a higher paying job upon graduation? Consider the following data regarding student GPA and starting salary.

GPA and Starting Salary	
GPA	**Starting Salary ($)**
2.37	37,000
3.20	38,000
3.21	42,000
3.39	40,000
3.55	44,000
3.57	48,000
3.76	50,000
3.77	60,000
3.79	59,000
3.90	55,000

a. Determine the ranks for the x-variable, GPA.

b. Determine the ranks for the y-variable, Starting Salary.

c. Calculate the Spearman rank correlation coefficient.

d. Interpret the value of the coefficient. Is the relationship between these two variables positive or negative? Is this relationship what you expected? Explain.

e. Comment on the strength of the relationship between these two variables.

f. Is there evidence at $\alpha = 0.10$ that these two variables are related?

5. *Fortune* magazine releases a list of the world's most admired companies. In the survey they ask business people to vote for companies that they admire most from various industries. The table below lists the top 10 most admired companies of 2011 along with each company's Fortune 500 ranking. Note that the Fortune 500 ranks companies based on revenues.[4]

Top 10 Most Admired Companies and Profits		
Company	**Most Admired Ranking**	**Fortune 500 Ranking**
Apple	1	35
Google	2	92
Berkshire Hathaway	3	7
Southwest Airlines	4	205
Procter & Gamble	5	26
Coca-Cola	6	70
Amazon.com	7	78
FedEx	8	73
Microsoft	9	38
McDonald's	10	111

a. Compute the Spearman rank correlation coefficient. Interpret this value.

b. With 95% confidence, can we conclude that there is an association between company admiration and revenue?

6. The given table shows key dates of the Dow-Jones Industrial Average. Apply the runs test to check for randomness at the 0.05 level. (**Hint:** First find the median of the values, then label each value by A if it is above the median and B if it is below the median.)

Significant Levels on the Dow (December 1974 to February 2009)		
Date	**Dow Jones Industrial Average**	**Significance**
December 6, 1974	577	The last Bear Market bottom
July 12, 1976	1011	Highest point between January, 1973 and October, 1982
August 12, 1982	776	The start of the "Reagan Bull"
August 25, 1987	2722	The 1987 high
October 19, 1987	1738	The (508 point) crash of 1987
February 2, 1994	3975	The top of the post 1987 crash recovery
November 23, 1994	3674	The start of the Clinton "super bull"
March 29, 1999	10,006	The first Dow close above 10,000
January 14, 2000	11,723	The "Clinton bull" high
March 17, 2000	10,630	The biggest one day gain (499 points)
March 20, 2001	9720	Dow closes below previous year low for the first time since 1982
September 11-14, 2001	9605	Terrorist attack closed the Dow for four days
September 17, 2001	8920	The biggest one day fall (685 points)
September 21, 2001	8235	The Dow's second worst week ever (−14.26%)
December 31, 2001	10,021	Dow up 21.7% from September 21 low but down 7.2% on the year
September 30, 2002	7591	New 2002 low – all treasury yields (except 30-year bond) at 2002 lows
October 9, 2002	7286	New 2002 low – Dow down 37.8% from the January, 2000 all-time high
October 31, 2002	8397	Dow up 806 points (10.6%) for October – first positive month since March
November 6, 2002	8771	Federal reserve cuts rates for the first time since December, 2001
December 31, 2002	8341	Dow down 16.8% for 2002 – first three consecutive year loss since 1939-41

Significant Levels on the Dow (December 1974 to February 2009)		
Date	**Dow Jones Industrial Average**	**Significance**
May 23, 2003	8601	Senate passes bill raising the treasury debt limit
June 25, 2003	9011	Federal reserve cuts rates by 0.25%
December 31, 2003	10,453	Dow up 25.32% in 2003
October 3, 2006	11,727	Dow exceeds the previous all-time high in January, 2000
October 9, 2007	14,164	New all-time high on the Dow
July 2, 2008	11,215	Dow closes more than 20% below the October, 2007 high
February 27, 2009	7062	Dow closes more than 50% below the October, 2007 high

7. The irrational number π can be approximated by the rational number $\frac{22}{7}$. Test the randomness of odd and even digits in $\frac{22}{7}$ at the 0.05 level using the first nine digits.

8. A polling agency conducts exit interviews after an election. If R = Republican and D = Democrat, the first 20 voter responses in a random sample are as follows.

    D D D R D R R D D D D R D D R R R D R D

    Test for non-randomness using $\alpha = 0.05$.

9. Consider the following *U.S. News and World Report* college rankings for schools in the Big Ten, the Big 12, and the Atlantic Coast conferences.[5]

College Rankings by Conference		
Atlantic Coast	**Big Ten**	**Big 12**
29	55	101
10	62	45
101	42	58
71	28	143
68	45	90
31	71	94
55	45	101
25	12	75
38	68	101
101	71	132
36	75	160
25		97

With $\alpha = 0.10$, use the Kruskal-Wallis Test to determine if there is a significant difference in *U.S. News and World Report* rankings among the three athletic conferences.

10. Consider the following scores reported by *Condé Nast Traveler* in their annual list of the top cities to visit around the world. The results were determined from more than 8 million votes cast in the Readers' Choice Awards survey.[6]

Readers' Choice City Rankings, 2011					
Asia		**Europe**		**United States**	
Kyoto	82.3	Florence	85.0	Charleston, SC	84.7
Bangkok	81.6	Barcelona	82.8	San Francisco, CA	83.7
Hong Kong	81.1	Rome	82.4	Santa Fe, NM	83.0
Chiang Mai	80.8	Paris	81.9	Chicago, IL	82.2
Ubud	80.0	Bruges	81.7	Honolulu, HI	80.9
Singapore	78.4	Venice	81.7	New York, NY	80.8
Tokyo	76.8	Salzburg	81.4	Savannah, GA	79.1
Luang Prabang	76.4	Vienna	81.0	Carmel, CA	78.5
Thimphu	75.1	Prague	79.7	Seattle, WA	78.4
Shanghai	74.9	Siena	79.7	Boston, MA	78.0

a. Using the Kruskal-Wallis Test and $\alpha = 0.05$, test to determine if there is a difference in rankings between Asia, Europe, and the United States.

b. What assumptions were made for the test performed in part **a.**?

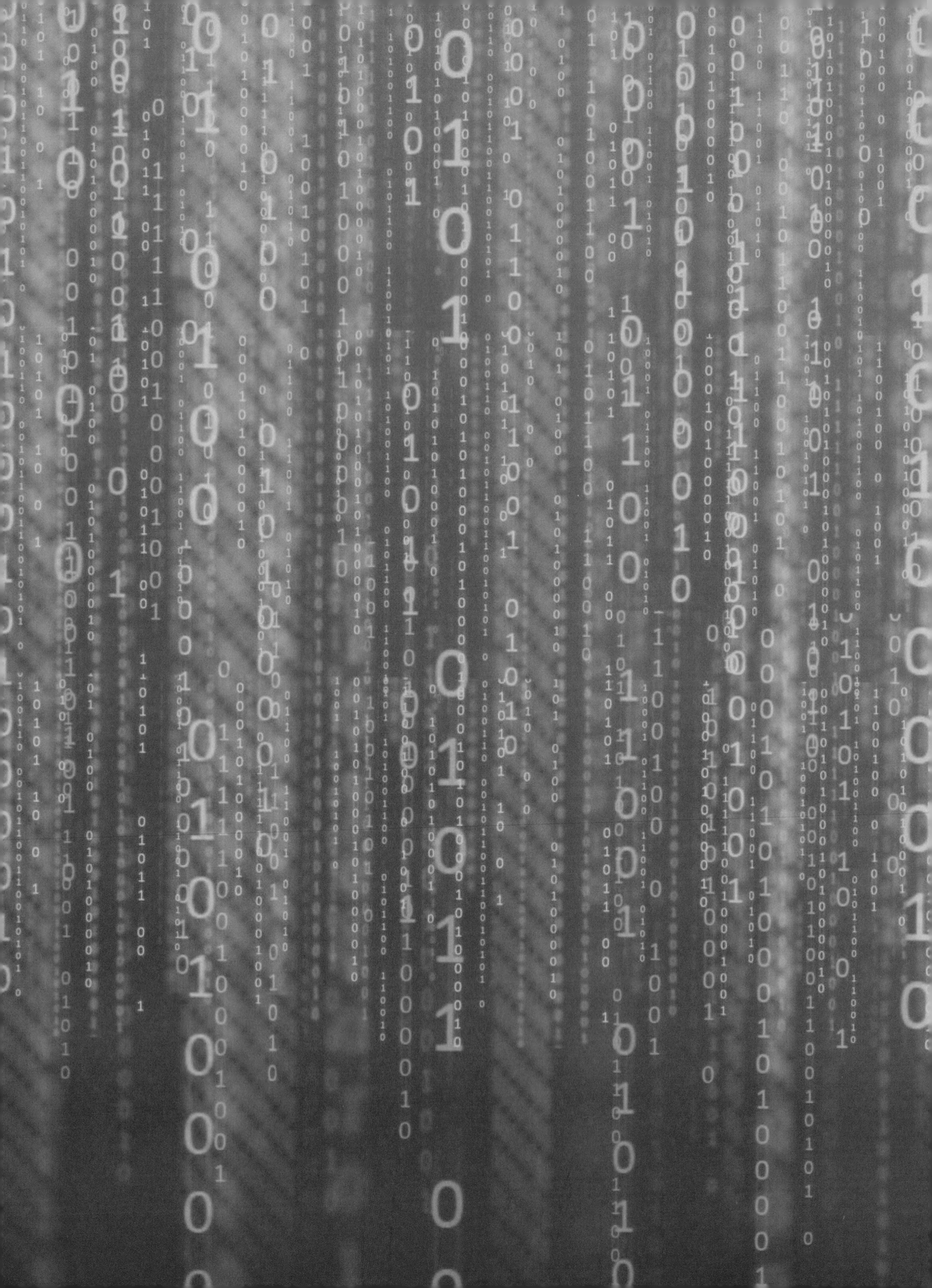

Sources

Appendix A
Statistical Tables

A   Standard Normal Distribution

Numerical entries represent the probability that a standard normal random variable is between $-\infty$ and z where $z = \dfrac{x - \mu}{\sigma}$.

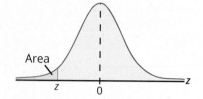

Area

z	0.09	0.08	0.07	0.06	0.05	0.04	0.03	0.02	0.01	0.00
−3.4	0.0002	0.0003	0.0003	0.0003	0.0003	0.0003	0.0003	0.0003	0.0003	0.0003
−3.3	0.0003	0.0004	0.0004	0.0004	0.0004	0.0004	0.0004	0.0005	0.0005	0.0005
−3.2	0.0005	0.0005	0.0005	0.0006	0.0006	0.0006	0.0006	0.0006	0.0007	0.0007
−3.1	0.0007	0.0007	0.0008	0.0008	0.0008	0.0008	0.0009	0.0009	0.0009	0.0010
−3.0	0.0010	0.0010	0.0011	0.0011	0.0011	0.0012	0.0012	0.0013	0.0013	0.0013
−2.9	0.0014	0.0014	0.0015	0.0015	0.0016	0.0016	0.0017	0.0018	0.0018	0.0019
−2.8	0.0019	0.0020	0.0021	0.0021	0.0022	0.0023	0.0023	0.0024	0.0025	0.0026
−2.7	0.0026	0.0027	0.0028	0.0029	0.0030	0.0031	0.0032	0.0033	0.0034	0.0035
−2.6	0.0036	0.0037	0.0038	0.0039	0.0040	0.0041	0.0043	0.0044	0.0045	0.0047
−2.5	0.0048	0.0049	0.0051	0.0052	0.0054	0.0055	0.0057	0.0059	0.0060	0.0062
−2.4	0.0064	0.0066	0.0068	0.0069	0.0071	0.0073	0.0075	0.0078	0.0080	0.0082
−2.3	0.0084	0.0087	0.0089	0.0091	0.0094	0.0096	0.0099	0.0102	0.0104	0.0107
−2.2	0.0110	0.0113	0.0116	0.0119	0.0122	0.0125	0.0129	0.0132	0.0136	0.0139
−2.1	0.0143	0.0146	0.0150	0.0154	0.0158	0.0162	0.0166	0.0170	0.0174	0.0179
−2.0	0.0183	0.0188	0.0192	0.0197	0.0202	0.0207	0.0212	0.0217	0.0222	0.0228
−1.9	0.0233	0.0239	0.0244	0.0250	0.0256	0.0262	0.0268	0.0274	0.0281	0.0287
−1.8	0.0294	0.0301	0.0307	0.0314	0.0322	0.0329	0.0336	0.0344	0.0351	0.0359
−1.7	0.0367	0.0375	0.0384	0.0392	0.0401	0.0409	0.0418	0.0427	0.0436	0.0446
−1.6	0.0455	0.0465	0.0475	0.0485	0.0495	0.0505	0.0516	0.0526	0.0537	0.0548
−1.5	0.0559	0.0571	0.0582	0.0594	0.0606	0.0618	0.0630	0.0643	0.0655	0.0668
−1.4	0.0681	0.0694	0.0708	0.0721	0.0735	0.0749	0.0764	0.0778	0.0793	0.0808
−1.3	0.0823	0.0838	0.0853	0.0869	0.0885	0.0901	0.0918	0.0934	0.0951	0.0968
−1.2	0.0985	0.1003	0.1020	0.1038	0.1056	0.1075	0.1093	0.1112	0.1131	0.1151
−1.1	0.1170	0.1190	0.1210	0.1230	0.1251	0.1271	0.1292	0.1314	0.1335	0.1357
−1.0	0.1379	0.1401	0.1423	0.1446	0.1469	0.1492	0.1515	0.1539	0.1562	0.1587
−0.9	0.1611	0.1635	0.1660	0.1685	0.1711	0.1736	0.1762	0.1788	0.1814	0.1841
−0.8	0.1867	0.1894	0.1922	0.1949	0.1977	0.2005	0.2033	0.2061	0.2090	0.2119
−0.7	0.2148	0.2177	0.2206	0.2236	0.2266	0.2296	0.2327	0.2358	0.2389	0.2420
−0.6	0.2451	0.2483	0.2514	0.2546	0.2578	0.2611	0.2643	0.2676	0.2709	0.2743
−0.5	0.2776	0.2810	0.2843	0.2877	0.2912	0.2946	0.2981	0.3015	0.3050	0.3085
−0.4	0.3121	0.3156	0.3192	0.3228	0.3264	0.3300	0.3336	0.3372	0.3409	0.3446
−0.3	0.3483	0.3520	0.3557	0.3594	0.3632	0.3669	0.3707	0.3745	0.3783	0.3821
−0.2	0.3859	0.3897	0.3936	0.3974	0.4013	0.4052	0.4090	0.4129	0.4168	0.4207
−0.1	0.4247	0.4286	0.4325	0.4364	0.4404	0.4443	0.4483	0.4522	0.4562	0.4602
0.0	0.4641	0.4681	0.4721	0.4761	0.4801	0.4840	0.4880	0.4920	0.4960	0.5000

B   Standard Normal Distribution

Numerical entries represent the probability that a standard normal random variable is between $-\infty$ and z where $z = \dfrac{x - \mu}{\sigma}$.

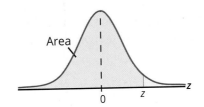

Area

z	0.00	0.01	0.02	0.03	0.04	0.05	0.06	0.07	0.08	0.09
0.0	0.5000	0.5040	0.5080	0.5120	0.5160	0.5199	0.5239	0.5279	0.5319	0.5359
0.1	0.5398	0.5438	0.5478	0.5517	0.5557	0.5596	0.5636	0.5675	0.5714	0.5753
0.2	0.5793	0.5832	0.5871	0.5910	0.5948	0.5987	0.6026	0.6064	0.6103	0.6141
0.3	0.6179	0.6217	0.6255	0.6293	0.6331	0.6368	0.6406	0.6443	0.6480	0.6517
0.4	0.6554	0.6591	0.6628	0.6664	0.6700	0.6736	0.6772	0.6808	0.6844	0.6879
0.5	0.6915	0.6950	0.6985	0.7019	0.7054	0.7088	0.7123	0.7157	0.7190	0.7224
0.6	0.7257	0.7291	0.7324	0.7357	0.7389	0.7422	0.7454	0.7486	0.7517	0.7549
0.7	0.7580	0.7611	0.7642	0.7673	0.7704	0.7734	0.7764	0.7794	0.7823	0.7852
0.8	0.7881	0.7910	0.7939	0.7967	0.7995	0.8023	0.8051	0.8078	0.8106	0.8133
0.9	0.8159	0.8186	0.8212	0.8238	0.8264	0.8289	0.8315	0.8340	0.8365	0.8389
1.0	0.8413	0.8438	0.8461	0.8485	0.8508	0.8531	0.8554	0.8577	0.8599	0.8621
1.1	0.8643	0.8665	0.8686	0.8708	0.8729	0.8749	0.8770	0.8790	0.8810	0.8830
1.2	0.8849	0.8869	0.8888	0.8907	0.8925	0.8944	0.8962	0.8980	0.8997	0.9015
1.3	0.9032	0.9049	0.9066	0.9082	0.9099	0.9115	0.9131	0.9147	0.9162	0.9177
1.4	0.9192	0.9207	0.9222	0.9236	0.9251	0.9265	0.9279	0.9292	0.9306	0.9319
1.5	0.9332	0.9345	0.9357	0.9370	0.9382	0.9394	0.9406	0.9418	0.9429	0.9441
1.6	0.9452	0.9463	0.9474	0.9484	0.9495	0.9505	0.9515	0.9525	0.9535	0.9545
1.7	0.9554	0.9564	0.9573	0.9582	0.9591	0.9599	0.9608	0.9616	0.9625	0.9633
1.8	0.9641	0.9649	0.9656	0.9664	0.9671	0.9678	0.9686	0.9693	0.9699	0.9706
1.9	0.9713	0.9719	0.9726	0.9732	0.9738	0.9744	0.9750	0.9756	0.9761	0.9767
2.0	0.9772	0.9778	0.9783	0.9788	0.9793	0.9798	0.9803	0.9808	0.9812	0.9817
2.1	0.9821	0.9826	0.9830	0.9834	0.9838	0.9842	0.9846	0.9850	0.9854	0.9857
2.2	0.9861	0.9864	0.9868	0.9871	0.9875	0.9878	0.9881	0.9884	0.9887	0.9890
2.3	0.9893	0.9896	0.9898	0.9901	0.9904	0.9906	0.9909	0.9911	0.9913	0.9916
2.4	0.9918	0.9920	0.9922	0.9925	0.9927	0.9929	0.9931	0.9932	0.9934	0.9936
2.5	0.9938	0.9940	0.9941	0.9943	0.9945	0.9946	0.9948	0.9949	0.9951	0.9952
2.6	0.9953	0.9955	0.9956	0.9957	0.9959	0.9960	0.9961	0.9962	0.9963	0.9964
2.7	0.9965	0.9966	0.9967	0.9968	0.9969	0.9970	0.9971	0.9972	0.9973	0.9974
2.8	0.9974	0.9975	0.9976	0.9977	0.9977	0.9978	0.9979	0.9979	0.9980	0.9981
2.9	0.9981	0.9982	0.9982	0.9983	0.9984	0.9984	0.9985	0.9985	0.9986	0.9986
3.0	0.9987	0.9987	0.9987	0.9988	0.9988	0.9989	0.9989	0.9989	0.9990	0.9990
3.1	0.9990	0.9991	0.9991	0.9991	0.9992	0.9992	0.9992	0.9992	0.9993	0.9993
3.2	0.9993	0.9993	0.9994	0.9994	0.9994	0.9994	0.9994	0.9995	0.9995	0.9995
3.3	0.9995	0.9995	0.9995	0.9996	0.9996	0.9996	0.9996	0.9996	0.9996	0.9997
3.4	0.9997	0.9997	0.9997	0.9997	0.9997	0.9997	0.9997	0.9997	0.9997	0.9998

Critical Values

Level of Confidence	$z_{\alpha/2}$
0.80	1.28
0.90	1.645
0.95	1.96
0.98	2.33
0.99	2.575

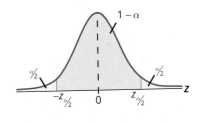

C   Standard Normal Distribution

Numerical entries represent the probability that a
standard normal random variable is between 0 and z
where $z = \dfrac{x - \mu}{\sigma}$.

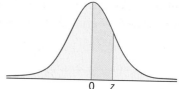

z	0.00	0.01	0.02	0.03	0.04	0.05	0.06	0.07	0.08	0.09
0.0	0.0000	0.0040	0.0080	0.0120	0.0160	0.0199	0.0239	0.0279	0.0319	0.0359
0.1	0.0398	0.0438	0.0478	0.0517	0.0557	0.0596	0.0636	0.0675	0.0714	0.0753
0.2	0.0793	0.0832	0.0871	0.0910	0.0948	0.0987	0.1026	0.1064	0.1103	0.1141
0.3	0.1179	0.1217	0.1255	0.1293	0.1331	0.1368	0.1406	0.1443	0.1480	0.1517
0.4	0.1554	0.1591	0.1628	0.1664	0.1700	0.1736	0.1772	0.1808	0.1844	0.1879
0.5	0.1915	0.1950	0.1985	0.2019	0.2054	0.2088	0.2123	0.2157	0.2190	0.2224
0.6	0.2257	0.2291	0.2324	0.2357	0.2389	0.2422	0.2454	0.2486	0.2517	0.2549
0.7	0.2580	0.2611	0.2642	0.2673	0.2704	0.2734	0.2764	0.2794	0.2823	0.2852
0.8	0.2881	0.2910	0.2939	0.2967	0.2995	0.3023	0.3051	0.3078	0.3106	0.3133
0.9	0.3159	0.3186	0.3212	0.3238	0.3264	0.3289	0.3315	0.3340	0.3365	0.3389
1.0	0.3413	0.3438	0.3461	0.3485	0.3508	0.3531	0.3554	0.3577	0.3599	0.3621
1.1	0.3643	0.3665	0.3686	0.3708	0.3729	0.3749	0.3770	0.3790	0.3810	0.3830
1.2	0.3849	0.3869	0.3888	0.3907	0.3925	0.3944	0.3962	0.3980	0.3997	0.4015
1.3	0.4032	0.4049	0.4066	0.4082	0.4099	0.4115	0.4131	0.4147	0.4162	0.4177
1.4	0.4192	0.4207	0.4222	0.4236	0.4251	0.4265	0.4279	0.4292	0.4306	0.4319
1.5	0.4332	0.4345	0.4357	0.4370	0.4382	0.4394	0.4406	0.4418	0.4429	0.4441
1.6	0.4452	0.4463	0.4474	0.4484	0.4495	0.4505	0.4515	0.4525	0.4535	0.4545
1.7	0.4554	0.4564	0.4573	0.4582	0.4591	0.4599	0.4608	0.4616	0.4625	0.4633
1.8	0.4641	0.4649	0.4656	0.4664	0.4671	0.4678	0.4686	0.4693	0.4699	0.4706
1.9	0.4713	0.4719	0.4726	0.4732	0.4738	0.4744	0.4750	0.4756	0.4761	0.4767
2.0	0.4772	0.4778	0.4783	0.4788	0.4793	0.4798	0.4803	0.4808	0.4812	0.4817
2.1	0.4821	0.4826	0.4830	0.4834	0.4838	0.4842	0.4846	0.4850	0.4854	0.4857
2.2	0.4861	0.4864	0.4868	0.4871	0.4875	0.4878	0.4881	0.4884	0.4887	0.4890
2.3	0.4893	0.4896	0.4898	0.4901	0.4904	0.4906	0.4909	0.4911	0.4913	0.4916
2.4	0.4918	0.4920	0.4922	0.4925	0.4927	0.4929	0.4931	0.4932	0.4934	0.4936
2.5	0.4938	0.4940	0.4941	0.4943	0.4945	0.4946	0.4948	0.4949	0.4951	0.4952
2.6	0.4953	0.4955	0.4956	0.4957	0.4959	0.4960	0.4961	0.4962	0.4963	0.4964
2.7	0.4965	0.4966	0.4967	0.4968	0.4969	0.4970	0.4971	0.4972	0.4973	0.4974
2.8	0.4974	0.4975	0.4976	0.4977	0.4977	0.4978	0.4979	0.4979	0.4980	0.4981
2.9	0.4981	0.4982	0.4982	0.4983	0.4984	0.4984	0.4985	0.4985	0.4986	0.4986
3.0	0.4987	0.4987	0.4987	0.4988	0.4988	0.4989	0.4989	0.4989	0.4990	0.4990
3.1	0.4990	0.4991	0.4991	0.4991	0.4992	0.4992	0.4992	0.4992	0.4993	0.4993
3.2	0.4993	0.4993	0.4994	0.4994	0.4994	0.4994	0.4994	0.4995	0.4995	0.4995
3.3	0.4995	0.4995	0.4995	0.4996	0.4996	0.4996	0.4996	0.4996	0.4996	0.4997
3.4	0.4997	0.4997	0.4997	0.4997	0.4997	0.4997	0.4997	0.4997	0.4997	0.4998

D   Critical Values of *t*

Numerical entries represent the value of *t* such that the area to the right of the *t* is equal to α.

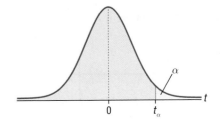

Area to the Right of the Critical Value

Degrees of Freedom	$t_{0.200}$	$t_{0.100}$	$t_{0.050}$	$t_{0.025}$	$t_{0.010}$	$t_{0.005}$
1	1.376	3.078	6.314	12.706	31.821	63.657
2	1.061	1.886	2.920	4.303	6.965	9.925
3	0.978	1.638	2.353	3.182	4.541	5.841
4	0.941	1.533	2.132	2.776	3.747	4.604
5	0.920	1.476	2.015	2.571	3.365	4.032
6	0.906	1.440	1.943	2.447	3.143	3.707
7	0.896	1.415	1.895	2.365	2.998	3.499
8	0.889	1.397	1.860	2.306	2.896	3.355
9	0.883	1.383	1.833	2.262	2.821	3.250
10	0.879	1.372	1.812	2.228	2.764	3.169
11	0.876	1.363	1.796	2.201	2.718	3.106
12	0.873	1.356	1.782	2.179	2.681	3.055
13	0.870	1.350	1.771	2.160	2.650	3.012
14	0.868	1.345	1.761	2.145	2.624	2.977
15	0.866	1.341	1.753	2.131	2.602	2.947
16	0.865	1.337	1.746	2.120	2.583	2.921
17	0.863	1.333	1.740	2.110	2.567	2.898
18	0.862	1.330	1.734	2.101	2.552	2.878
19	0.861	1.328	1.729	2.093	2.539	2.861
20	0.860	1.325	1.725	2.086	2.528	2.845
21	0.859	1.323	1.721	2.080	2.518	2.831
22	0.858	1.321	1.717	2.074	2.508	2.819
23	0.858	1.319	1.714	2.069	2.500	2.807
24	0.857	1.318	1.711	2.064	2.492	2.797
25	0.856	1.316	1.708	2.060	2.485	2.787
26	0.856	1.315	1.706	2.056	2.479	2.779
27	0.855	1.314	1.703	2.052	2.473	2.771
28	0.855	1.313	1.701	2.048	2.467	2.763
29	0.854	1.311	1.699	2.045	2.462	2.756
30	0.854	1.310	1.697	2.042	2.457	2.750
40	0.851	1.303	1.684	2.021	2.423	2.704
50	0.849	1.299	1.676	2.009	2.403	2.678
60	0.848	1.296	1.671	2.000	2.390	2.660
70	0.847	1.294	1.667	1.994	2.381	2.648
80	0.846	1.292	1.664	1.990	2.374	2.639
90	0.846	1.291	1.662	1.987	2.368	2.632
100	0.845	1.290	1.660	1.984	2.364	2.626
120	0.845	1.289	1.658	1.980	2.358	2.617
∞	0.842	1.282	1.645	1.96	2.326	2.576

E   Binomial Probabilities

Numerical entries represent $P(X = x)$.

						p				
n	*x*	0.1	0.2	0.3	0.4	0.5	0.6	0.7	0.8	0.9
1	0	0.9000	0.8000	0.7000	0.6000	0.5000	0.4000	0.3000	0.2000	0.1000
	1	0.1000	0.2000	0.3000	0.4000	0.5000	0.6000	0.7000	0.8000	0.9000
2	0	0.8100	0.6400	0.4900	0.3600	0.2500	0.1600	0.0900	0.0400	0.0100
	1	0.1800	0.3200	0.4200	0.4800	0.5000	0.4800	0.4200	0.3200	0.1800
	2	0.0100	0.0400	0.0900	0.1600	0.2500	0.3600	0.4900	0.6400	0.8100
3	0	0.7290	0.5120	0.3430	0.2160	0.1250	0.0640	0.0270	0.0080	0.0010
	1	0.2430	0.3840	0.4410	0.4320	0.3750	0.2880	0.1890	0.0960	0.0270
	2	0.0270	0.0960	0.1890	0.2880	0.3750	0.4320	0.4410	0.3840	0.2430
	3	0.0010	0.0080	0.0270	0.0640	0.1250	0.2160	0.3430	0.5120	0.7290
4	0	0.6561	0.4096	0.2401	0.1296	0.0625	0.0256	0.0081	0.0016	0.0001
	1	0.2916	0.4096	0.4116	0.3456	0.2500	0.1536	0.0756	0.0256	0.0036
	2	0.0486	0.1536	0.2646	0.3456	0.3750	0.3456	0.2646	0.1536	0.0486
	3	0.0036	0.0256	0.0756	0.1536	0.2500	0.3456	0.4116	0.4096	0.2916
	4	0.0001	0.0016	0.0081	0.0256	0.0625	0.1296	0.2401	0.4096	0.6561
5	0	0.5905	0.3277	0.1681	0.0778	0.0313	0.0102	0.0024	0.0003	0.0000
	1	0.3281	0.4096	0.3602	0.2592	0.1563	0.0768	0.0284	0.0064	0.0005
	2	0.0729	0.2048	0.3087	0.3456	0.3125	0.2304	0.1323	0.0512	0.0081
	3	0.0081	0.0512	0.1323	0.2304	0.3125	0.3456	0.3087	0.2048	0.0729
	4	0.0005	0.0064	0.0284	0.0768	0.1563	0.2592	0.3602	0.4096	0.3281
	5	0.0000	0.0003	0.0024	0.0102	0.0313	0.0778	0.1681	0.3277	0.5905
6	0	0.5314	0.2621	0.1176	0.0467	0.0156	0.0041	0.0007	0.0001	0.0000
	1	0.3543	0.3932	0.3025	0.1866	0.0938	0.0369	0.0102	0.0015	0.0001
	2	0.0984	0.2458	0.3241	0.3110	0.2344	0.1382	0.0595	0.0154	0.0012
	3	0.0146	0.0819	0.1852	0.2765	0.3125	0.2765	0.1852	0.0819	0.0146
	4	0.0012	0.0154	0.0595	0.1382	0.2344	0.3110	0.3241	0.2458	0.0984
	5	0.0001	0.0015	0.0102	0.0369	0.0938	0.1866	0.3025	0.3932	0.3543
	6	0.0000	0.0001	0.0007	0.0041	0.0156	0.0467	0.1176	0.2621	0.5314
7	0	0.4783	0.2097	0.0824	0.0280	0.0078	0.0016	0.0002	0.0000	0.0000
	1	0.3720	0.3670	0.2471	0.1306	0.0547	0.0172	0.0036	0.0004	0.0000
	2	0.1240	0.2753	0.3177	0.2613	0.1641	0.0774	0.0250	0.0043	0.0002
	3	0.0230	0.1147	0.2269	0.2903	0.2734	0.1935	0.0972	0.0287	0.0026
	4	0.0026	0.0287	0.0972	0.1935	0.2734	0.2903	0.2269	0.1147	0.0230
	5	0.0002	0.0043	0.0250	0.0774	0.1641	0.2613	0.3177	0.2753	0.1240
	6	0.0000	0.0004	0.0036	0.0172	0.0547	0.1306	0.2471	0.3670	0.3720
	7	0.0000	0.0000	0.0002	0.0016	0.0078	0.0280	0.0824	0.2097	0.4783
8	0	0.4305	0.1678	0.0576	0.0168	0.0039	0.0007	0.0001	0.0000	0.0000
	1	0.3826	0.3355	0.1977	0.0896	0.0313	0.0079	0.0012	0.0001	0.0000
	2	0.1488	0.2936	0.2965	0.2090	0.1094	0.0413	0.0100	0.0011	0.0000
	3	0.0331	0.1468	0.2541	0.2787	0.2188	0.1239	0.0467	0.0092	0.0004
	4	0.0046	0.0459	0.1361	0.2322	0.2734	0.2322	0.1361	0.0459	0.0046
	5	0.0004	0.0092	0.0467	0.1239	0.2188	0.2787	0.2541	0.1468	0.0331
	6	0.0000	0.0011	0.0100	0.0413	0.1094	0.2090	0.2965	0.2936	0.1488
	7	0.0000	0.0001	0.0012	0.0079	0.0313	0.0896	0.1977	0.3355	0.3826
	8	0.0000	0.0000	0.0001	0.0007	0.0039	0.0168	0.0576	0.1678	0.4305

E   Binomial Probabilities (cont.)

						p				
n	x	0.1	0.2	0.3	0.4	0.5	0.6	0.7	0.8	0.9
9	0	0.3874	0.1342	0.0404	0.0101	0.0020	0.0003	0.0000	0.0000	0.0000
	1	0.3874	0.3020	0.1556	0.0605	0.0176	0.0035	0.0004	0.0000	0.0000
	2	0.1722	0.3020	0.2668	0.1612	0.0703	0.0212	0.0039	0.0003	0.0000
	3	0.0446	0.1762	0.2668	0.2508	0.1641	0.0743	0.0210	0.0028	0.0001
	4	0.0074	0.0661	0.1715	0.2508	0.2461	0.1672	0.0735	0.0165	0.0008
	5	0.0008	0.0165	0.0735	0.1672	0.2461	0.2508	0.1715	0.0661	0.0074
	6	0.0001	0.0028	0.0210	0.0743	0.1641	0.2508	0.2668	0.1762	0.0446
	7	0.0000	0.0003	0.0039	0.0212	0.0703	0.1612	0.2668	0.3020	0.1722
	8	0.0000	0.0000	0.0004	0.0035	0.0176	0.0605	0.1556	0.3020	0.3874
	9	0.0000	0.0000	0.0000	0.0003	0.0020	0.0101	0.0404	0.1342	0.3874
10	0	0.3487	0.1074	0.0282	0.0060	0.0010	0.0001	0.0000	0.0000	0.0000
	1	0.3874	0.2684	0.1211	0.0403	0.0098	0.0016	0.0001	0.0000	0.0000
	2	0.1937	0.3020	0.2335	0.1209	0.0439	0.0106	0.0014	0.0001	0.0000
	3	0.0574	0.2013	0.2668	0.2150	0.1172	0.0425	0.0090	0.0008	0.0000
	4	0.0112	0.0881	0.2001	0.2508	0.2051	0.1115	0.0368	0.0055	0.0001
	5	0.0015	0.0264	0.1029	0.2007	0.2461	0.2007	0.1029	0.0264	0.0015
	6	0.0001	0.0055	0.0368	0.1115	0.2051	0.2508	0.2001	0.0881	0.0112
	7	0.0000	0.0008	0.0090	0.0425	0.1172	0.2150	0.2668	0.2013	0.0574
	8	0.0000	0.0001	0.0014	0.0106	0.0439	0.1209	0.2335	0.3020	0.1937
	9	0.0000	0.0000	0.0001	0.0016	0.0098	0.0403	0.1211	0.2684	0.3874
	10	0.0000	0.0000	0.0000	0.0001	0.0010	0.0060	0.0282	0.1074	0.3487
11	0	0.3138	0.0859	0.0198	0.0036	0.0005	0.0000	0.0000	0.0000	0.0000
	1	0.3835	0.2362	0.0932	0.0266	0.0054	0.0007	0.0000	0.0000	0.0000
	2	0.2131	0.2953	0.1998	0.0887	0.0269	0.0052	0.0005	0.0000	0.0000
	3	0.0710	0.2215	0.2568	0.1774	0.0806	0.0234	0.0037	0.0002	0.0000
	4	0.0158	0.1107	0.2201	0.2365	0.1611	0.0701	0.0173	0.0017	0.0000
	5	0.0025	0.0388	0.1321	0.2207	0.2256	0.1471	0.0566	0.0097	0.0003
	6	0.0003	0.0097	0.0566	0.1471	0.2256	0.2207	0.1321	0.0388	0.0025
	7	0.0000	0.0017	0.0173	0.0701	0.1611	0.2365	0.2201	0.1107	0.0158
	8	0.0000	0.0002	0.0037	0.0234	0.0806	0.1774	0.2568	0.2215	0.0710
	9	0.0000	0.0000	0.0005	0.0052	0.0269	0.0887	0.1998	0.2953	0.2131
	10	0.0000	0.0000	0.0000	0.0007	0.0054	0.0266	0.0932	0.2362	0.3835
	11	0.0000	0.0000	0.0000	0.0000	0.0005	0.0036	0.0198	0.0859	0.3138
12	0	0.2824	0.0687	0.0138	0.0022	0.0002	0.0000	0.0000	0.0000	0.0000
	1	0.3766	0.2062	0.0712	0.0174	0.0029	0.0003	0.0000	0.0000	0.0000
	2	0.2301	0.2835	0.1678	0.0639	0.0161	0.0025	0.0002	0.0000	0.0000
	3	0.0852	0.2362	0.2397	0.1419	0.0537	0.0125	0.0015	0.0001	0.0000
	4	0.0213	0.1329	0.2311	0.2128	0.1208	0.0420	0.0078	0.0005	0.0000
	5	0.0038	0.0532	0.1585	0.2270	0.1934	0.1009	0.0291	0.0033	0.0000
	6	0.0005	0.0155	0.0792	0.1766	0.2256	0.1766	0.0792	0.0155	0.0005
	7	0.0000	0.0033	0.0291	0.1009	0.1934	0.2270	0.1585	0.0532	0.0038
	8	0.0000	0.0005	0.0078	0.0420	0.1208	0.2128	0.2311	0.1329	0.0213
	9	0.0000	0.0001	0.0015	0.0125	0.0537	0.1419	0.2397	0.2362	0.0852
	10	0.0000	0.0000	0.0002	0.0025	0.0161	0.0639	0.1678	0.2835	0.2301
	11	0.0000	0.0000	0.0000	0.0003	0.0029	0.0174	0.0712	0.2062	0.3766
	12	0.0000	0.0000	0.0000	0.0000	0.0002	0.0022	0.0138	0.0687	0.2824

E   Binomial Probabilities (cont.)

n	x	0.1	0.2	0.3	0.4	0.5	0.6	0.7	0.8	0.9
						p				
13	0	0.2542	0.0550	0.0097	0.0013	0.0001	0.0000	0.0000	0.0000	0.0000
	1	0.3672	0.1787	0.0540	0.0113	0.0016	0.0001	0.0000	0.0000	0.0000
	2	0.2448	0.2680	0.1388	0.0453	0.0095	0.0012	0.0001	0.0000	0.0000
	3	0.0997	0.2457	0.2181	0.1107	0.0349	0.0065	0.0006	0.0000	0.0000
	4	0.0277	0.1535	0.2337	0.1845	0.0873	0.0243	0.0034	0.0001	0.0000
	5	0.0055	0.0691	0.1803	0.2214	0.1571	0.0656	0.0142	0.0011	0.0000
	6	0.0008	0.0230	0.1030	0.1968	0.2095	0.1312	0.0442	0.0058	0.0001
	7	0.0001	0.0058	0.0442	0.1312	0.2095	0.1968	0.1030	0.0230	0.0008
	8	0.0000	0.0011	0.0142	0.0656	0.1571	0.2214	0.1803	0.0691	0.0055
	9	0.0000	0.0001	0.0034	0.0243	0.0873	0.1845	0.2337	0.1535	0.0277
	10	0.0000	0.0000	0.0006	0.0065	0.0349	0.1107	0.2181	0.2457	0.0997
	11	0.0000	0.0000	0.0001	0.0012	0.0095	0.0453	0.1388	0.2680	0.2448
	12	0.0000	0.0000	0.0000	0.0001	0.0016	0.0113	0.0540	0.1787	0.3672
	13	0.0000	0.0000	0.0000	0.0000	0.0001	0.0013	0.0097	0.0550	0.2542
14	0	0.2288	0.0440	0.0068	0.0008	0.0001	0.0000	0.0000	0.0000	0.0000
	1	0.3559	0.1539	0.0407	0.0073	0.0009	0.0001	0.0000	0.0000	0.0000
	2	0.2570	0.2501	0.1134	0.0317	0.0056	0.0005	0.0000	0.0000	0.0000
	3	0.1142	0.2501	0.1943	0.0845	0.0222	0.0033	0.0002	0.0000	0.0000
	4	0.0349	0.1720	0.2290	0.1549	0.0611	0.0136	0.0014	0.0000	0.0000
	5	0.0078	0.0860	0.1963	0.2066	0.1222	0.0408	0.0066	0.0003	0.0000
	6	0.0013	0.0322	0.1262	0.2066	0.1833	0.0918	0.0232	0.0020	0.0000
	7	0.0002	0.0092	0.0618	0.1574	0.2095	0.1574	0.0618	0.0092	0.0002
	8	0.0000	0.0020	0.0232	0.0918	0.1833	0.2066	0.1262	0.0322	0.0013
	9	0.0000	0.0003	0.0066	0.0408	0.1222	0.2066	0.1963	0.0860	0.0078
	10	0.0000	0.0000	0.0014	0.0136	0.0611	0.1549	0.2290	0.1720	0.0349
	11	0.0000	0.0000	0.0002	0.0033	0.0222	0.0845	0.1943	0.2501	0.1142
	12	0.0000	0.0000	0.0000	0.0005	0.0056	0.0317	0.1134	0.2501	0.2570
	13	0.0000	0.0000	0.0000	0.0001	0.0009	0.0073	0.0407	0.1539	0.3559
	14	0.0000	0.0000	0.0000	0.0000	0.0001	0.0008	0.0068	0.0440	0.2288
15	0	0.2059	0.0352	0.0047	0.0005	0.0000	0.0000	0.0000	0.0000	0.0000
	1	0.3432	0.1319	0.0305	0.0047	0.0005	0.0000	0.0000	0.0000	0.0000
	2	0.2669	0.2309	0.0916	0.0219	0.0032	0.0003	0.0000	0.0000	0.0000
	3	0.1285	0.2501	0.1700	0.0634	0.0139	0.0016	0.0001	0.0000	0.0000
	4	0.0428	0.1876	0.2186	0.1268	0.0417	0.0074	0.0006	0.0000	0.0000
	5	0.0105	0.1032	0.2061	0.1859	0.0916	0.0245	0.0030	0.0001	0.0000
	6	0.0019	0.0430	0.1472	0.2066	0.1527	0.0612	0.0116	0.0007	0.0000
	7	0.0003	0.0138	0.0811	0.1771	0.1964	0.1181	0.0348	0.0035	0.0000
	8	0.0000	0.0035	0.0348	0.1181	0.1964	0.1771	0.0811	0.0138	0.0003
	9	0.0000	0.0007	0.0116	0.0612	0.1527	0.2066	0.1472	0.0430	0.0019
	10	0.0000	0.0001	0.0030	0.0245	0.0916	0.1859	0.2061	0.1032	0.0105
	11	0.0000	0.0000	0.0006	0.0074	0.0417	0.1268	0.2186	0.1876	0.0428
	12	0.0000	0.0000	0.0001	0.0016	0.0139	0.0634	0.1700	0.2501	0.1285
	13	0.0000	0.0000	0.0000	0.0003	0.0032	0.0219	0.0916	0.2309	0.2669
	14	0.0000	0.0000	0.0000	0.0000	0.0005	0.0047	0.0305	0.1319	0.3432
	15	0.0000	0.0000	0.0000	0.0000	0.0000	0.0005	0.0047	0.0352	0.2059

E   Binomial Probabilities (cont.)

n	x	0.1	0.2	0.3	0.4	0.5	0.6	0.7	0.8	0.9
16	0	0.1853	0.0281	0.0033	0.0003	0.0000	0.0000	0.0000	0.0000	0.0000
	1	0.3294	0.1126	0.0228	0.0030	0.0002	0.0000	0.0000	0.0000	0.0000
	2	0.2745	0.2111	0.0732	0.0150	0.0018	0.0001	0.0000	0.0000	0.0000
	3	0.1423	0.2463	0.1465	0.0468	0.0085	0.0008	0.0000	0.0000	0.0000
	4	0.0514	0.2001	0.2040	0.1014	0.0278	0.0040	0.0002	0.0000	0.0000
	5	0.0137	0.1201	0.2099	0.1623	0.0667	0.0142	0.0013	0.0000	0.0000
	6	0.0028	0.0550	0.1649	0.1983	0.1222	0.0392	0.0056	0.0002	0.0000
	7	0.0004	0.0197	0.1010	0.1889	0.1746	0.0840	0.0185	0.0012	0.0000
	8	0.0001	0.0055	0.0487	0.1417	0.1964	0.1417	0.0487	0.0055	0.0001
	9	0.0000	0.0012	0.0185	0.0840	0.1746	0.1889	0.1010	0.0197	0.0004
	10	0.0000	0.0002	0.0056	0.0392	0.1222	0.1983	0.1649	0.0550	0.0028
	11	0.0000	0.0000	0.0013	0.0142	0.0667	0.1623	0.2099	0.1201	0.0137
	12	0.0000	0.0000	0.0002	0.0040	0.0278	0.1014	0.2040	0.2001	0.0514
	13	0.0000	0.0000	0.0000	0.0008	0.0085	0.0468	0.1465	0.2463	0.1423
	14	0.0000	0.0000	0.0000	0.0001	0.0018	0.0150	0.0732	0.2111	0.2745
	15	0.0000	0.0000	0.0000	0.0000	0.0002	0.0030	0.0228	0.1126	0.3294
	16	0.0000	0.0000	0.0000	0.0000	0.0000	0.0003	0.0033	0.0281	0.1853
17	0	0.1668	0.0225	0.0023	0.0002	0.0000	0.0000	0.0000	0.0000	0.0000
	1	0.3150	0.0957	0.0169	0.0019	0.0001	0.0000	0.0000	0.0000	0.0000
	2	0.2800	0.1914	0.0581	0.0102	0.0010	0.0001	0.0000	0.0000	0.0000
	3	0.1556	0.2393	0.1245	0.0341	0.0052	0.0004	0.0000	0.0000	0.0000
	4	0.0605	0.2093	0.1868	0.0796	0.0182	0.0021	0.0001	0.0000	0.0000
	5	0.0175	0.1361	0.2081	0.1379	0.0472	0.0081	0.0006	0.0000	0.0000
	6	0.0039	0.0680	0.1784	0.1839	0.0944	0.0242	0.0026	0.0001	0.0000
	7	0.0007	0.0267	0.1201	0.1927	0.1484	0.0571	0.0095	0.0004	0.0000
	8	0.0001	0.0084	0.0644	0.1606	0.1855	0.1070	0.0276	0.0021	0.0000
	9	0.0000	0.0021	0.0276	0.1070	0.1855	0.1606	0.0644	0.0084	0.0001
	10	0.0000	0.0004	0.0095	0.0571	0.1484	0.1927	0.1201	0.0267	0.0007
	11	0.0000	0.0001	0.0026	0.0242	0.0944	0.1839	0.1784	0.0680	0.0039
	12	0.0000	0.0000	0.0006	0.0081	0.0472	0.1379	0.2081	0.1361	0.0175
	13	0.0000	0.0000	0.0001	0.0021	0.0182	0.0796	0.1868	0.2093	0.0605
	14	0.0000	0.0000	0.0000	0.0004	0.0052	0.0341	0.1245	0.2393	0.1556
	15	0.0000	0.0000	0.0000	0.0001	0.0010	0.0102	0.0581	0.1914	0.2800
	16	0.0000	0.0000	0.0000	0.0000	0.0001	0.0019	0.0169	0.0957	0.3150
	17	0.0000	0.0000	0.0000	0.0000	0.0000	0.0002	0.0023	0.0225	0.1668
18	0	0.1501	0.0180	0.0016	0.0001	0.0000	0.0000	0.0000	0.0000	0.0000
	1	0.3002	0.0811	0.0126	0.0012	0.0001	0.0000	0.0000	0.0000	0.0000
	2	0.2835	0.1723	0.0458	0.0069	0.0006	0.0000	0.0000	0.0000	0.0000
	3	0.1680	0.2297	0.1046	0.0246	0.0031	0.0002	0.0000	0.0000	0.0000
	4	0.0700	0.2153	0.1681	0.0614	0.0117	0.0011	0.0000	0.0000	0.0000
	5	0.0218	0.1507	0.2017	0.1146	0.0327	0.0045	0.0002	0.0000	0.0000
	6	0.0052	0.0816	0.1873	0.1655	0.0708	0.0145	0.0012	0.0000	0.0000
	7	0.0010	0.0350	0.1376	0.1892	0.1214	0.0374	0.0046	0.0001	0.0000
	8	0.0002	0.0120	0.0811	0.1734	0.1669	0.0771	0.0149	0.0008	0.0000
	9	0.0000	0.0033	0.0386	0.1284	0.1855	0.1284	0.0386	0.0033	0.0000
	10	0.0000	0.0008	0.0149	0.0771	0.1669	0.1734	0.0811	0.0120	0.0002
	11	0.0000	0.0001	0.0046	0.0374	0.1214	0.1892	0.1376	0.0350	0.0010
	12	0.0000	0.0000	0.0012	0.0145	0.0708	0.1655	0.1873	0.0816	0.0052
	13	0.0000	0.0000	0.0002	0.0045	0.0327	0.1146	0.2017	0.1507	0.0218

E Binomial Probabilities (cont.)

n	x	0.1	0.2	0.3	0.4	0.5	0.6	0.7	0.8	0.9
18	14	0.0000	0.0000	0.0000	0.0011	0.0117	0.0614	0.1681	0.2153	0.0700
	15	0.0000	0.0000	0.0000	0.0002	0.0031	0.0246	0.1046	0.2297	0.1680
	16	0.0000	0.0000	0.0000	0.0000	0.0006	0.0069	0.0458	0.1723	0.2835
	17	0.0000	0.0000	0.0000	0.0000	0.0001	0.0012	0.0126	0.0811	0.3002
	18	0.0000	0.0000	0.0000	0.0000	0.0000	0.0001	0.0016	0.0180	0.1501
19	0	0.1351	0.0144	0.0011	0.0001	0.0000	0.0000	0.0000	0.0000	0.0000
	1	0.2852	0.0685	0.0093	0.0008	0.0000	0.0000	0.0000	0.0000	0.0000
	2	0.2852	0.1540	0.0358	0.0046	0.0003	0.0000	0.0000	0.0000	0.0000
	3	0.1796	0.2182	0.0869	0.0175	0.0018	0.0001	0.0000	0.0000	0.0000
	4	0.0798	0.2182	0.1491	0.0467	0.0074	0.0005	0.0000	0.0000	0.0000
	5	0.0266	0.1636	0.1916	0.0933	0.0222	0.0024	0.0001	0.0000	0.0000
	6	0.0069	0.0955	0.1916	0.1451	0.0518	0.0085	0.0005	0.0000	0.0000
	7	0.0014	0.0443	0.1525	0.1797	0.0961	0.0237	0.0022	0.0000	0.0000
	8	0.0002	0.0166	0.0981	0.1797	0.1442	0.0532	0.0077	0.0003	0.0000
	9	0.0000	0.0051	0.0514	0.1464	0.1762	0.0976	0.0220	0.0013	0.0000
	10	0.0000	0.0013	0.0220	0.0976	0.1762	0.1464	0.0514	0.0051	0.0000
	11	0.0000	0.0003	0.0077	0.0532	0.1442	0.1797	0.0981	0.0166	0.0002
	12	0.0000	0.0000	0.0022	0.0237	0.0961	0.1797	0.1525	0.0443	0.0014
	13	0.0000	0.0000	0.0005	0.0085	0.0518	0.1451	0.1916	0.0955	0.0069
	14	0.0000	0.0000	0.0001	0.0024	0.0222	0.0933	0.1916	0.1636	0.0266
	15	0.0000	0.0000	0.0000	0.0005	0.0074	0.0467	0.1491	0.2182	0.0798
	16	0.0000	0.0000	0.0000	0.0001	0.0018	0.0175	0.0869	0.2182	0.1796
	17	0.0000	0.0000	0.0000	0.0000	0.0003	0.0046	0.0358	0.1540	0.2852
	18	0.0000	0.0000	0.0000	0.0000	0.0000	0.0008	0.0093	0.0685	0.2852
	19	0.0000	0.0000	0.0000	0.0000	0.0000	0.0001	0.0011	0.0144	0.1351
20	0	0.1216	0.0115	0.0008	0.0000	0.0000	0.0000	0.0000	0.0000	0.0000
	1	0.2702	0.0576	0.0068	0.0005	0.0000	0.0000	0.0000	0.0000	0.0000
	2	0.2852	0.1369	0.0278	0.0031	0.0002	0.0000	0.0000	0.0000	0.0000
	3	0.1901	0.2054	0.0716	0.0123	0.0011	0.0000	0.0000	0.0000	0.0000
	4	0.0898	0.2182	0.1304	0.0350	0.0046	0.0003	0.0000	0.0000	0.0000
	5	0.0319	0.1746	0.1789	0.0746	0.0148	0.0013	0.0000	0.0000	0.0000
	6	0.0089	0.1091	0.1916	0.1244	0.0370	0.0049	0.0002	0.0000	0.0000
	7	0.0020	0.0545	0.1643	0.1659	0.0739	0.0146	0.0010	0.0000	0.0000
	8	0.0004	0.0222	0.1144	0.1797	0.1201	0.0355	0.0039	0.0001	0.0000
	9	0.0001	0.0074	0.0654	0.1597	0.1602	0.0710	0.0120	0.0005	0.0000
	10	0.0000	0.0020	0.0308	0.1171	0.1762	0.1171	0.0308	0.0020	0.0000
	11	0.0000	0.0005	0.0120	0.0710	0.1602	0.1597	0.0654	0.0074	0.0001
	12	0.0000	0.0001	0.0039	0.0355	0.1201	0.1797	0.1144	0.0222	0.0004
	13	0.0000	0.0000	0.0010	0.0146	0.0739	0.1659	0.1643	0.0545	0.0020
	14	0.0000	0.0000	0.0002	0.0049	0.0370	0.1244	0.1916	0.1091	0.0089
	15	0.0000	0.0000	0.0000	0.0013	0.0148	0.0746	0.1789	0.1746	0.0319
	16	0.0000	0.0000	0.0000	0.0003	0.0046	0.0350	0.1304	0.2182	0.0898
	17	0.0000	0.0000	0.0000	0.0000	0.0011	0.0123	0.0716	0.2054	0.1901
	18	0.0000	0.0000	0.0000	0.0000	0.0002	0.0031	0.0278	0.1369	0.2852
	19	0.0000	0.0000	0.0000	0.0000	0.0000	0.0005	0.0068	0.0576	0.2702
	20	0.0000	0.0000	0.0000	0.0000	0.0000	0.0000	0.0008	0.0115	0.1216

E   Cumulative Binomial Probabilities

Numerical entries represent $P(X \le x)$.

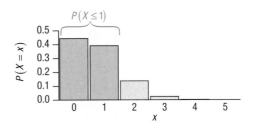

n	x	p 0.1	0.2	0.3	0.4	0.5	0.6	0.7	0.8	0.9
1	0	0.9000	0.8000	0.7000	0.6000	0.5000	0.4000	0.3000	0.2000	0.1000
	1	1.0000	1.0000	1.0000	1.0000	1.0000	1.0000	1.0000	1.0000	1.0000
2	0	0.8100	0.6400	0.4900	0.3600	0.2500	0.1600	0.0900	0.0400	0.0100
	1	0.9900	0.9600	0.9100	0.8400	0.7500	0.6400	0.5100	0.3600	0.1900
	2	1.0000	1.0000	1.0000	1.0000	1.0000	1.0000	1.0000	1.0000	1.0000
3	0	0.7290	0.5120	0.3430	0.2160	0.1250	0.0640	0.0270	0.0080	0.0010
	1	0.9720	0.8960	0.7840	0.6480	0.5000	0.3520	0.2160	0.1040	0.0280
	2	0.9990	0.9920	0.9730	0.9360	0.8750	0.7840	0.6570	0.4880	0.2710
	3	1.0000	1.0000	1.0000	1.0000	1.0000	1.0000	1.0000	1.0000	1.0000
4	0	0.6561	0.4096	0.2401	0.1296	0.0625	0.0256	0.0081	0.0016	0.0001
	1	0.9477	0.8192	0.6517	0.4752	0.3125	0.1792	0.0837	0.0272	0.0037
	2	0.9963	0.9728	0.9163	0.8208	0.6875	0.5248	0.3483	0.1808	0.0523
	3	0.9999	0.9984	0.9919	0.9744	0.9375	0.8704	0.7599	0.5904	0.3439
	4	1.0000	1.0000	1.0000	1.0000	1.0000	1.0000	1.0000	1.0000	1.0000
5	0	0.5905	0.3277	0.1681	0.0778	0.0313	0.0102	0.0024	0.0003	0.0000
	1	0.9185	0.7373	0.5282	0.3370	0.1875	0.0870	0.0308	0.0067	0.0005
	2	0.9914	0.9421	0.8369	0.6826	0.5000	0.3174	0.1631	0.0579	0.0086
	3	0.9995	0.9933	0.9692	0.9130	0.8125	0.6630	0.4718	0.2627	0.0815
	4	1.0000	0.9997	0.9976	0.9898	0.9688	0.9222	0.8319	0.6723	0.4095
	5	1.0000	1.0000	1.0000	1.0000	1.0000	1.0000	1.0000	1.0000	1.0000
6	0	0.5314	0.2621	0.1176	0.0467	0.0156	0.0041	0.0007	0.0001	0.0000
	1	0.8857	0.6554	0.4202	0.2333	0.1094	0.0410	0.0109	0.0016	0.0001
	2	0.9842	0.9011	0.7443	0.5443	0.3438	0.1792	0.0705	0.0170	0.0013
	3	0.9987	0.9830	0.9295	0.8208	0.6563	0.4557	0.2557	0.0989	0.0159
	4	0.9999	0.9984	0.9891	0.9590	0.8906	0.7667	0.5798	0.3446	0.1143
	5	1.0000	0.9999	0.9993	0.9959	0.9844	0.9533	0.8824	0.7379	0.4686
	6	1.0000	1.0000	1.0000	1.0000	1.0000	1.0000	1.0000	1.0000	1.0000
7	0	0.4783	0.2097	0.0824	0.0280	0.0078	0.0016	0.0002	0.0000	0.0000
	1	0.8503	0.5767	0.3294	0.1586	0.0625	0.0188	0.0038	0.0004	0.0000
	2	0.9743	0.8520	0.6471	0.4199	0.2266	0.0963	0.0288	0.0047	0.0002
	3	0.9973	0.9667	0.8740	0.7102	0.5000	0.2898	0.1260	0.0333	0.0027
	4	0.9998	0.9953	0.9712	0.9037	0.7734	0.5801	0.3529	0.1480	0.0257
	5	1.0000	0.9996	0.9962	0.9812	0.9375	0.8414	0.6706	0.4233	0.1497
	6	1.0000	1.0000	0.9998	0.9984	0.9922	0.9720	0.9176	0.7903	0.5217
	7	1.0000	1.0000	1.0000	1.0000	1.0000	1.0000	1.0000	1.0000	1.0000

E Cumulative Binomial Probabilities (cont.)

n	x	0.1	0.2	0.3	0.4	0.5	0.6	0.7	0.8	0.9
8	0	0.4305	0.1678	0.0576	0.0168	0.0039	0.0007	0.0001	0.0000	0.0000
	1	0.8131	0.5033	0.2553	0.1064	0.0352	0.0085	0.0013	0.0001	0.0000
	2	0.9619	0.7969	0.5518	0.3154	0.1445	0.0498	0.0113	0.0012	0.0000
	3	0.9950	0.9437	0.8059	0.5941	0.3633	0.1737	0.0580	0.0104	0.0004
	4	0.9996	0.9896	0.9420	0.8263	0.6367	0.4059	0.1941	0.0563	0.0050
	5	1.0000	0.9988	0.9887	0.9502	0.8555	0.6846	0.4482	0.2031	0.0381
	6	1.0000	0.9999	0.9987	0.9915	0.9648	0.8936	0.7447	0.4967	0.1869
	7	1.0000	1.0000	0.9999	0.9993	0.9961	0.9832	0.9424	0.8322	0.5695
	8	1.0000	1.0000	1.0000	1.0000	1.0000	1.0000	1.0000	1.0000	1.0000
9	0	0.3874	0.1342	0.0404	0.0101	0.0020	0.0003	0.0000	0.0000	0.0000
	1	0.7748	0.4362	0.1960	0.0705	0.0195	0.0038	0.0004	0.0000	0.0000
	2	0.9470	0.7382	0.4628	0.2318	0.0898	0.0250	0.0043	0.0003	0.0000
	3	0.9917	0.9144	0.7297	0.4826	0.2539	0.0994	0.0253	0.0031	0.0001
	4	0.9991	0.9804	0.9012	0.7334	0.5000	0.2666	0.0988	0.0196	0.0009
	5	0.9999	0.9969	0.9747	0.9006	0.7461	0.5174	0.2703	0.0856	0.0083
	6	1.0000	0.9997	0.9957	0.9750	0.9102	0.7682	0.5372	0.2618	0.0530
	7	1.0000	1.0000	0.9996	0.9962	0.9805	0.9295	0.8040	0.5638	0.2252
	8	1.0000	1.0000	1.0000	0.9997	0.9980	0.9899	0.9596	0.8658	0.6126
	9	1.0000	1.0000	1.0000	1.0000	1.0000	1.0000	1.0000	1.0000	1.0000
10	0	0.3487	0.1074	0.0282	0.0060	0.0010	0.0001	0.0000	0.0000	0.0000
	1	0.7361	0.3758	0.1493	0.0464	0.0107	0.0017	0.0001	0.0000	0.0000
	2	0.9298	0.6778	0.3828	0.1673	0.0547	0.0123	0.0016	0.0001	0.0000
	3	0.9872	0.8791	0.6496	0.3823	0.1719	0.0548	0.0106	0.0009	0.0000
	4	0.9984	0.9672	0.8497	0.6331	0.3770	0.1662	0.0473	0.0064	0.0001
	5	0.9999	0.9936	0.9527	0.8338	0.6230	0.3669	0.1503	0.0328	0.0016
	6	1.0000	0.9991	0.9894	0.9452	0.8281	0.6177	0.3504	0.1209	0.0128
	7	1.0000	0.9999	0.9984	0.9877	0.9453	0.8327	0.6172	0.3222	0.0702
	8	1.0000	1.0000	0.9999	0.9983	0.9893	0.9536	0.8507	0.6242	0.2639
	9	1.0000	1.0000	1.0000	0.9999	0.9990	0.9940	0.9718	0.8926	0.6513
	10	1.0000	1.0000	1.0000	1.0000	1.0000	1.0000	1.0000	1.0000	1.0000
11	0	0.3138	0.0859	0.0198	0.0036	0.0005	0.0000	0.0000	0.0000	0.0000
	1	0.6974	0.3221	0.1130	0.0302	0.0059	0.0007	0.0000	0.0000	0.0000
	2	0.9104	0.6174	0.3127	0.1189	0.0327	0.0059	0.0006	0.0000	0.0000
	3	0.9815	0.8389	0.5696	0.2963	0.1133	0.0293	0.0043	0.0002	0.0000
	4	0.9972	0.9496	0.7897	0.5328	0.2744	0.0994	0.0216	0.0020	0.0000
	5	0.9997	0.9883	0.9218	0.7535	0.5000	0.2465	0.0782	0.0117	0.0003
	6	1.0000	0.9980	0.9784	0.9006	0.7256	0.4672	0.2103	0.0504	0.0028
	7	1.0000	0.9998	0.9957	0.9707	0.8867	0.7037	0.4304	0.1611	0.0185
	8	1.0000	1.0000	0.9994	0.9941	0.9673	0.8811	0.6873	0.3826	0.0896
	9	1.0000	1.0000	1.0000	0.9993	0.9941	0.9698	0.8870	0.6779	0.3026
	10	1.0000	1.0000	1.0000	1.0000	0.9995	0.9964	0.9802	0.9141	0.6862
	11	1.0000	1.0000	1.0000	1.0000	1.0000	1.0000	1.0000	1.0000	1.0000

E   Cumulative Binomial Probabilities (cont.)

n	x	0.1	0.2	0.3	0.4	0.5	0.6	0.7	0.8	0.9
12	0	0.2824	0.0687	0.0138	0.0022	0.0002	0.0000	0.0000	0.0000	0.0000
	1	0.6590	0.2749	0.0850	0.0196	0.0032	0.0003	0.0000	0.0000	0.0000
	2	0.8891	0.5583	0.2528	0.0834	0.0193	0.0028	0.0002	0.0000	0.0000
	3	0.9744	0.7946	0.4925	0.2253	0.0730	0.0153	0.0017	0.0001	0.0000
	4	0.9957	0.9274	0.7237	0.4382	0.1938	0.0573	0.0095	0.0006	0.0000
	5	0.9995	0.9806	0.8822	0.6652	0.3872	0.1582	0.0386	0.0039	0.0001
	6	0.9999	0.9961	0.9614	0.8418	0.6128	0.3348	0.1178	0.0194	0.0005
	7	1.0000	0.9994	0.9905	0.9427	0.8062	0.5618	0.2763	0.0726	0.0043
	8	1.0000	0.9999	0.9983	0.9847	0.9270	0.7747	0.5075	0.2054	0.0256
	9	1.0000	1.0000	0.9998	0.9972	0.9807	0.9166	0.7472	0.4417	0.1109
	10	1.0000	1.0000	1.0000	0.9997	0.9968	0.9804	0.9150	0.7251	0.3410
	11	1.0000	1.0000	1.0000	1.0000	0.9998	0.9978	0.9862	0.9313	0.7176
	12	1.0000	1.0000	1.0000	1.0000	1.0000	1.0000	1.0000	1.0000	1.0000
13	0	0.2542	0.0550	0.0097	0.0013	0.0001	0.0000	0.0000	0.0000	0.0000
	1	0.6213	0.2336	0.0637	0.0126	0.0017	0.0001	0.0000	0.0000	0.0000
	2	0.8661	0.5017	0.2025	0.0579	0.0112	0.0013	0.0001	0.0000	0.0000
	3	0.9658	0.7473	0.4206	0.1686	0.0461	0.0078	0.0007	0.0000	0.0000
	4	0.9935	0.9009	0.6543	0.3530	0.1334	0.0321	0.0040	0.0002	0.0000
	5	0.9991	0.9700	0.8346	0.5744	0.2905	0.0977	0.0182	0.0012	0.0000
	6	0.9999	0.9930	0.9376	0.7712	0.5000	0.2288	0.0624	0.0070	0.0001
	7	1.0000	0.9988	0.9818	0.9023	0.7095	0.4256	0.1654	0.0300	0.0009
	8	1.0000	0.9998	0.9960	0.9679	0.8666	0.6470	0.3457	0.0991	0.0065
	9	1.0000	1.0000	0.9993	0.9922	0.9539	0.8314	0.5794	0.2527	0.0342
	10	1.0000	1.0000	0.9999	0.9987	0.9888	0.9421	0.7975	0.4983	0.1339
	11	1.0000	1.0000	1.0000	0.9999	0.9983	0.9874	0.9363	0.7664	0.3787
	12	1.0000	1.0000	1.0000	1.0000	0.9999	0.9987	0.9903	0.9450	0.7458
	13	1.0000	1.0000	1.0000	1.0000	1.0000	1.0000	1.0000	1.0000	1.0000
14	0	0.2288	0.0440	0.0068	0.0008	0.0001	0.0000	0.0000	0.0000	0.0000
	1	0.5846	0.1979	0.0475	0.0081	0.0009	0.0001	0.0000	0.0000	0.0000
	2	0.8416	0.4481	0.1608	0.0398	0.0065	0.0006	0.0000	0.0000	0.0000
	3	0.9559	0.6982	0.3552	0.1243	0.0287	0.0039	0.0002	0.0000	0.0000
	4	0.9908	0.8702	0.5842	0.2793	0.0898	0.0175	0.0017	0.0000	0.0000
	5	0.9985	0.9561	0.7805	0.4859	0.2120	0.0583	0.0083	0.0004	0.0000
	6	0.9998	0.9884	0.9067	0.6925	0.3953	0.1501	0.0315	0.0024	0.0000
	7	1.0000	0.9976	0.9685	0.8499	0.6047	0.3075	0.0933	0.0116	0.0002
	8	1.0000	0.9996	0.9917	0.9417	0.7880	0.5141	0.2195	0.0439	0.0015
	9	1.0000	1.0000	0.9983	0.9825	0.9102	0.7207	0.4158	0.1298	0.0092
	10	1.0000	1.0000	0.9998	0.9961	0.9713	0.8757	0.6448	0.3018	0.0441
	11	1.0000	1.0000	1.0000	0.9994	0.9935	0.9602	0.8392	0.5519	0.1584
	12	1.0000	1.0000	1.0000	0.9999	0.9991	0.9919	0.9525	0.8021	0.4154
	13	1.0000	1.0000	1.0000	1.0000	0.9999	0.9992	0.9932	0.9560	0.7712
	14	1.0000	1.0000	1.0000	1.0000	1.0000	1.0000	1.0000	1.0000	1.0000

E   Cumulative Binomial Probabilities (cont.)

n	x	p 0.1	0.2	0.3	0.4	0.5	0.6	0.7	0.8	0.9
15	0	0.2059	0.0352	0.0047	0.0005	0.0000	0.0000	0.0000	0.0000	0.0000
	1	0.5490	0.1671	0.0353	0.0052	0.0005	0.0000	0.0000	0.0000	0.0000
	2	0.8159	0.3980	0.1268	0.0271	0.0037	0.0003	0.0000	0.0000	0.0000
	3	0.9444	0.6482	0.2969	0.0905	0.0176	0.0019	0.0001	0.0000	0.0000
	4	0.9873	0.8358	0.5155	0.2173	0.0592	0.0093	0.0007	0.0000	0.0000
	5	0.9978	0.9389	0.7216	0.4032	0.1509	0.0338	0.0037	0.0001	0.0000
	6	0.9997	0.9819	0.8689	0.6098	0.3036	0.0950	0.0152	0.0008	0.0000
	7	1.0000	0.9958	0.9500	0.7869	0.5000	0.2131	0.0500	0.0042	0.0000
	8	1.0000	0.9992	0.9848	0.9050	0.6964	0.3902	0.1311	0.0181	0.0003
	9	1.0000	0.9999	0.9963	0.9662	0.8491	0.5968	0.2784	0.0611	0.0022
	10	1.0000	1.0000	0.9993	0.9907	0.9408	0.7827	0.4845	0.1642	0.0127
	11	1.0000	1.0000	0.9999	0.9981	0.9824	0.9095	0.7031	0.3518	0.0556
	12	1.0000	1.0000	1.0000	0.9997	0.9963	0.9729	0.8732	0.6020	0.1841
	13	1.0000	1.0000	1.0000	1.0000	0.9995	0.9948	0.9647	0.8329	0.4510
	14	1.0000	1.0000	1.0000	1.0000	1.0000	0.9995	0.9953	0.9648	0.7941
	15	1.0000	1.0000	1.0000	1.0000	1.0000	1.0000	1.0000	1.0000	1.0000
16	0	0.1853	0.0281	0.0033	0.0003	0.0000	0.0000	0.0000	0.0000	0.0000
	1	0.5147	0.1407	0.0261	0.0033	0.0003	0.0000	0.0000	0.0000	0.0000
	2	0.7892	0.3518	0.0994	0.0183	0.0021	0.0001	0.0000	0.0000	0.0000
	3	0.9316	0.5981	0.2459	0.0651	0.0106	0.0009	0.0000	0.0000	0.0000
	4	0.9830	0.7982	0.4499	0.1666	0.0384	0.0049	0.0003	0.0000	0.0000
	5	0.9967	0.9183	0.6598	0.3288	0.1051	0.0191	0.0016	0.0000	0.0000
	6	0.9995	0.9733	0.8247	0.5272	0.2272	0.0583	0.0071	0.0002	0.0000
	7	0.9999	0.9930	0.9256	0.7161	0.4018	0.1423	0.0257	0.0015	0.0000
	8	1.0000	0.9985	0.9743	0.8577	0.5982	0.2839	0.0744	0.0070	0.0001
	9	1.0000	0.9998	0.9929	0.9417	0.7728	0.4728	0.1753	0.0267	0.0005
	10	1.0000	1.0000	0.9984	0.9809	0.8949	0.6712	0.3402	0.0817	0.0033
	11	1.0000	1.0000	0.9997	0.9951	0.9616	0.8334	0.5501	0.2018	0.0170
	12	1.0000	1.0000	1.0000	0.9991	0.9894	0.9349	0.7541	0.4019	0.0684
	13	1.0000	1.0000	1.0000	0.9999	0.9979	0.9817	0.9006	0.6482	0.2108
	14	1.0000	1.0000	1.0000	1.0000	0.9997	0.9967	0.9739	0.8593	0.4853
	15	1.0000	1.0000	1.0000	1.0000	1.0000	0.9997	0.9967	0.9719	0.8147
	16	1.0000	1.0000	1.0000	1.0000	1.0000	1.0000	1.0000	1.0000	1.0000

E   Cumulative Binomial Probabilities (cont.)

		p								
n	x	0.1	0.2	0.3	0.4	0.5	0.6	0.7	0.8	0.9
17	0	0.1668	0.0225	0.0023	0.0002	0.0000	0.0000	0.0000	0.0000	0.0000
	1	0.4818	0.1182	0.0193	0.0021	0.0001	0.0000	0.0000	0.0000	0.0000
	2	0.7618	0.3096	0.0774	0.0123	0.0012	0.0001	0.0000	0.0000	0.0000
	3	0.9174	0.5489	0.2019	0.0464	0.0064	0.0005	0.0000	0.0000	0.0000
	4	0.9779	0.7582	0.3887	0.1260	0.0245	0.0025	0.0001	0.0000	0.0000
	5	0.9953	0.8943	0.5968	0.2639	0.0717	0.0106	0.0007	0.0000	0.0000
	6	0.9992	0.9623	0.7752	0.4478	0.1662	0.0348	0.0032	0.0001	0.0000
	7	0.9999	0.9891	0.8954	0.6405	0.3145	0.0919	0.0127	0.0005	0.0000
	8	1.0000	0.9974	0.9597	0.8011	0.5000	0.1989	0.0403	0.0026	0.0000
	9	1.0000	0.9995	0.9873	0.9081	0.6855	0.3595	0.1046	0.0109	0.0001
	10	1.0000	0.9999	0.9968	0.9652	0.8338	0.5522	0.2248	0.0377	0.0008
	11	1.0000	1.0000	0.9993	0.9894	0.9283	0.7361	0.4032	0.1057	0.0047
	12	1.0000	1.0000	0.9999	0.9975	0.9755	0.8740	0.6113	0.2418	0.0221
	13	1.0000	1.0000	1.0000	0.9995	0.9936	0.9536	0.7981	0.4511	0.0826
	14	1.0000	1.0000	1.0000	0.9999	0.9988	0.9877	0.9226	0.6904	0.2382
	15	1.0000	1.0000	1.0000	1.0000	0.9999	0.9979	0.9807	0.8818	0.5182
	16	1.0000	1.0000	1.0000	1.0000	1.0000	0.9998	0.9977	0.9775	0.8332
	17	1.0000	1.0000	1.0000	1.0000	1.0000	1.0000	1.0000	1.0000	1.0000
18	0	0.1501	0.0180	0.0016	0.0001	0.0000	0.0000	0.0000	0.0000	0.0000
	1	0.4503	0.0991	0.0142	0.0013	0.0001	0.0000	0.0000	0.0000	0.0000
	2	0.7338	0.2713	0.0600	0.0082	0.0007	0.0000	0.0000	0.0000	0.0000
	3	0.9018	0.5010	0.1646	0.0328	0.0038	0.0002	0.0000	0.0000	0.0000
	4	0.9718	0.7164	0.3327	0.0942	0.0154	0.0013	0.0000	0.0000	0.0000
	5	0.9936	0.8671	0.5344	0.2088	0.0481	0.0058	0.0003	0.0000	0.0000
	6	0.9988	0.9487	0.7217	0.3743	0.1189	0.0203	0.0014	0.0000	0.0000
	7	0.9998	0.9837	0.8593	0.5634	0.2403	0.0576	0.0061	0.0002	0.0000
	8	1.0000	0.9957	0.9404	0.7368	0.4073	0.1347	0.0210	0.0009	0.0000
	9	1.0000	0.9991	0.9790	0.8653	0.5927	0.2632	0.0596	0.0043	0.0000
	10	1.0000	0.9998	0.9939	0.9424	0.7597	0.4366	0.1407	0.0163	0.0002
	12	1.0000	1.0000	0.9997	0.9942	0.9519	0.7912	0.4656	0.1329	0.0064
	13	1.0000	1.0000	1.0000	0.9987	0.9846	0.9058	0.6673	0.2836	0.0282
	14	1.0000	1.0000	1.0000	0.9998	0.9962	0.9672	0.8354	0.4990	0.0982
	15	1.0000	1.0000	1.0000	1.0000	0.9993	0.9918	0.9400	0.7287	0.2662
	16	1.0000	1.0000	1.0000	1.0000	0.9999	0.9987	0.9858	0.9009	0.5497
	17	1.0000	1.0000	1.0000	1.0000	1.0000	0.9999	0.9984	0.9820	0.8499
	18	1.0000	1.0000	1.0000	1.0000	1.0000	1.0000	1.0000	1.0000	1.0000

E   Cumulative Binomial Probabilities (cont.)

						p				
n	*x*	0.1	0.2	0.3	0.4	0.5	0.6	0.7	0.8	0.9
19	0	0.1351	0.0144	0.0011	0.0001	0.0000	0.0000	0.0000	0.0000	0.0000
	1	0.4203	0.0829	0.0104	0.0008	0.0000	0.0000	0.0000	0.0000	0.0000
	2	0.7054	0.2369	0.0462	0.0055	0.0004	0.0000	0.0000	0.0000	0.0000
	3	0.8850	0.4551	0.1332	0.0230	0.0022	0.0001	0.0000	0.0000	0.0000
	4	0.9648	0.6733	0.2822	0.0696	0.0096	0.0006	0.0000	0.0000	0.0000
	5	0.9914	0.8369	0.4739	0.1629	0.0318	0.0031	0.0001	0.0000	0.0000
	6	0.9983	0.9324	0.6655	0.3081	0.0835	0.0116	0.0006	0.0000	0.0000
	7	0.9997	0.9767	0.8180	0.4878	0.1796	0.0352	0.0028	0.0000	0.0000
	8	1.0000	0.9933	0.9161	0.6675	0.3238	0.0885	0.0105	0.0003	0.0000
	9	1.0000	0.9984	0.9674	0.8139	0.5000	0.1861	0.0326	0.0016	0.0000
	10	1.0000	0.9997	0.9895	0.9115	0.6762	0.3325	0.0839	0.0067	0.0000
	11	1.0000	1.0000	0.9972	0.9648	0.8204	0.5122	0.1820	0.0233	0.0003
	12	1.0000	1.0000	0.9994	0.9884	0.9165	0.6919	0.3345	0.0676	0.0017
	13	1.0000	1.0000	0.9999	0.9969	0.9682	0.8371	0.5261	0.1631	0.0086
	14	1.0000	1.0000	1.0000	0.9994	0.9904	0.9304	0.7178	0.3267	0.0352
	15	1.0000	1.0000	1.0000	0.9999	0.9978	0.9770	0.8668	0.5449	0.1150
	16	1.0000	1.0000	1.0000	1.0000	0.9996	0.9945	0.9538	0.7631	0.2946
	17	1.0000	1.0000	1.0000	1.0000	1.0000	0.9992	0.9896	0.9171	0.5797
	18	1.0000	1.0000	1.0000	1.0000	1.0000	0.9999	0.9989	0.9856	0.8649
	19	1.0000	1.0000	1.0000	1.0000	1.0000	1.0000	1.0000	1.0000	1.0000
20	0	0.1216	0.0115	0.0008	0.0000	0.0000	0.0000	0.0000	0.0000	0.0000
	1	0.3917	0.0692	0.0076	0.0005	0.0000	0.0000	0.0000	0.0000	0.0000
	2	0.6769	0.2061	0.0355	0.0036	0.0002	0.0000	0.0000	0.0000	0.0000
	3	0.8670	0.4114	0.1071	0.0160	0.0013	0.0000	0.0000	0.0000	0.0000
	4	0.9568	0.6296	0.2375	0.0510	0.0059	0.0003	0.0000	0.0000	0.0000
	5	0.9887	0.8042	0.4164	0.1256	0.0207	0.0016	0.0000	0.0000	0.0000
	6	0.9976	0.9133	0.6080	0.2500	0.0577	0.0065	0.0003	0.0000	0.0000
	7	0.9996	0.9679	0.7723	0.4159	0.1316	0.0210	0.0013	0.0000	0.0000
	8	0.9999	0.9900	0.8867	0.5956	0.2517	0.0565	0.0051	0.0001	0.0000
	9	1.0000	0.9974	0.9520	0.7553	0.4119	0.1275	0.0171	0.0006	0.0000
	10	1.0000	0.9994	0.9829	0.8725	0.5881	0.2447	0.0480	0.0026	0.0000
	11	1.0000	0.9999	0.9949	0.9435	0.7483	0.4044	0.1133	0.0100	0.0001
	12	1.0000	1.0000	0.9987	0.9790	0.8684	0.5841	0.2277	0.0321	0.0004
	13	1.0000	1.0000	0.9997	0.9935	0.9423	0.7500	0.3920	0.0867	0.0024
	14	1.0000	1.0000	1.0000	0.9984	0.9793	0.8744	0.5836	0.1958	0.0113
	15	1.0000	1.0000	1.0000	0.9997	0.9941	0.9490	0.7625	0.3704	0.0432
	16	1.0000	1.0000	1.0000	1.0000	0.9987	0.9840	0.8929	0.5886	0.1330
	17	1.0000	1.0000	1.0000	1.0000	0.9998	0.9964	0.9645	0.7939	0.3231
	18	1.0000	1.0000	1.0000	1.0000	1.0000	0.9995	0.9924	0.9308	0.6083
	19	1.0000	1.0000	1.0000	1.0000	1.0000	1.0000	0.9992	0.9885	0.8784
	20	1.0000	1.0000	1.0000	1.0000	1.0000	1.0000	1.0000	1.0000	1.0000

F   Poisson Probabilities

Numerical entries represent $P(X = x)$.

λ

x	0.02	0.03	0.04	0.05	0.06	0.07	0.08	0.09	0.10	0.20	0.30
0	0.9802	0.9704	0.9608	0.9512	0.9418	0.9324	0.9231	0.9139	0.9048	0.8187	0.7408
1	0.0196	0.0291	0.0384	0.0476	0.0565	0.0653	0.0738	0.0823	0.0905	0.1637	0.2222
2	0.0002	0.0004	0.0008	0.0012	0.0017	0.0023	0.0030	0.0037	0.0045	0.0164	0.0333
3	0.0000	0.0000	0.0000	0.0000	0.0000	0.0001	0.0001	0.0001	0.0002	0.0011	0.0033
4	0.0000	0.0000	0.0000	0.0000	0.0000	0.0000	0.0000	0.0000	0.0000	0.0001	0.0003

x	0.40	0.50	0.60	0.70	0.80	0.90	1.00	1.10	1.20	1.30	1.40
0	0.6703	0.6065	0.5488	0.4966	0.4493	0.4066	0.3679	0.3329	0.3012	0.2725	0.2466
1	0.2681	0.3033	0.3293	0.3476	0.3595	0.3659	0.3679	0.3662	0.3614	0.3543	0.3452
2	0.0536	0.0758	0.0988	0.1217	0.1438	0.1647	0.1839	0.2014	0.2169	0.2303	0.2417
3	0.0072	0.0126	0.0198	0.0284	0.0383	0.0494	0.0613	0.0738	0.0867	0.0998	0.1128
4	0.0007	0.0016	0.0030	0.0050	0.0077	0.0111	0.0153	0.0203	0.0260	0.0324	0.0395
5	0.0001	0.0002	0.0004	0.0007	0.0012	0.0020	0.0031	0.0045	0.0062	0.0084	0.0111
6	0.0000	0.0000	0.0000	0.0001	0.0002	0.0003	0.0005	0.0008	0.0012	0.0018	0.0026
7	0.0000	0.0000	0.0000	0.0000	0.0000	0.0000	0.0001	0.0001	0.0002	0.0003	0.0005
8	0.0000	0.0000	0.0000	0.0000	0.0000	0.0000	0.0000	0.0000	0.0000	0.0001	0.0001

x	1.50	1.60	1.70	1.80	1.90	2.00	2.10	2.20	2.30	2.40	2.50
0	0.2231	0.2019	0.1827	0.1653	0.1496	0.1353	0.1225	0.1108	0.1003	0.0907	0.0821
1	0.3347	0.3230	0.3106	0.2975	0.2842	0.2707	0.2572	0.2438	0.2306	0.2177	0.2052
2	0.2510	0.2584	0.2640	0.2678	0.2700	0.2707	0.2700	0.2681	0.2652	0.2613	0.2565
3	0.1255	0.1378	0.1496	0.1607	0.1710	0.1804	0.1890	0.1966	0.2033	0.2090	0.2138
4	0.0471	0.0551	0.0636	0.0723	0.0812	0.0902	0.0992	0.1082	0.1169	0.1254	0.1336
5	0.0141	0.0176	0.0216	0.0260	0.0309	0.0361	0.0417	0.0476	0.0538	0.0602	0.0668
6	0.0035	0.0047	0.0061	0.0078	0.0098	0.0120	0.0146	0.0174	0.0206	0.0241	0.0278
7	0.0008	0.0011	0.0015	0.0020	0.0027	0.0034	0.0044	0.0055	0.0068	0.0083	0.0099
8	0.0001	0.0002	0.0003	0.0005	0.0006	0.0009	0.0011	0.0015	0.0019	0.0025	0.0031
9	0.0000	0.0000	0.0001	0.0001	0.0001	0.0002	0.0003	0.0004	0.0005	0.0007	0.0009
10	0.0000	0.0000	0.0000	0.0000	0.0000	0.0000	0.0001	0.0001	0.0001	0.0002	0.0002

x	2.60	2.70	2.80	2.90	3.00	3.10	3.20	3.30	3.40	3.50	3.60
0	0.0743	0.0672	0.0608	0.0550	0.0498	0.0450	0.0408	0.0369	0.0334	0.0302	0.0273
1	0.1931	0.1815	0.1703	0.1596	0.1494	0.1397	0.1304	0.1217	0.1135	0.1057	0.0984
2	0.2510	0.2450	0.2384	0.2314	0.2240	0.2165	0.2087	0.2008	0.1929	0.1850	0.1771
3	0.2176	0.2205	0.2225	0.2237	0.2240	0.2237	0.2226	0.2209	0.2186	0.2158	0.2125
4	0.1414	0.1488	0.1557	0.1622	0.1680	0.1733	0.1781	0.1823	0.1858	0.1888	0.1912
5	0.0735	0.0804	0.0872	0.0940	0.1008	0.1075	0.1140	0.1203	0.1264	0.1322	0.1377
6	0.0319	0.0362	0.0407	0.0455	0.0504	0.0555	0.0608	0.0662	0.0716	0.0771	0.0826
7	0.0118	0.0139	0.0163	0.0188	0.0216	0.0246	0.0278	0.0312	0.0348	0.0385	0.0425
8	0.0038	0.0047	0.0057	0.0068	0.0081	0.0095	0.0111	0.0129	0.0148	0.0169	0.0191
9	0.0011	0.0014	0.0018	0.0022	0.0027	0.0033	0.0040	0.0047	0.0056	0.0066	0.0076
10	0.0003	0.0004	0.0005	0.0006	0.0008	0.0010	0.0013	0.0016	0.0019	0.0023	0.0028
11	0.0001	0.0001	0.0001	0.0002	0.0002	0.0003	0.0004	0.0005	0.0006	0.0007	0.0009
12	0.0000	0.0000	0.0000	0.0000	0.0001	0.0001	0.0001	0.0001	0.0002	0.0002	0.0003
13	0.0000	0.0000	0.0000	0.0000	0.0000	0.0000	0.0000	0.0000	0.0000	0.0001	0.0001

x	3.70	3.80	3.90	4.00	4.10	4.20	4.30	4.40	4.50	4.60	4.70
0	0.0247	0.0224	0.0202	0.0183	0.0166	0.0150	0.0136	0.0123	0.0111	0.0101	0.0091
1	0.0915	0.0850	0.0789	0.0733	0.0679	0.0630	0.0583	0.0540	0.0500	0.0462	0.0427
2	0.1692	0.1615	0.1539	0.1465	0.1393	0.1323	0.1254	0.1188	0.1125	0.1063	0.1005
3	0.2087	0.2046	0.2001	0.1954	0.1904	0.1852	0.1798	0.1743	0.1687	0.1631	0.1574
4	0.1931	0.1944	0.1951	0.1954	0.1951	0.1944	0.1933	0.1917	0.1898	0.1875	0.1849
5	0.1429	0.1477	0.1522	0.1563	0.1600	0.1633	0.1662	0.1687	0.1708	0.1725	0.1738
6	0.0881	0.0936	0.0989	0.1042	0.1093	0.1143	0.1191	0.1237	0.1281	0.1323	0.1362
7	0.0466	0.0508	0.0551	0.0595	0.0640	0.0686	0.0732	0.0778	0.0824	0.0869	0.0914
8	0.0215	0.0241	0.0269	0.0298	0.0328	0.0360	0.0393	0.0428	0.0463	0.0500	0.0537

F   Poisson Probabilities (cont.)

λ

x	3.70	3.80	3.90	4.00	4.10	4.20	4.30	4.40	4.50	4.60	4.70
9	0.0089	0.0102	0.0116	0.0132	0.0150	0.0168	0.0188	0.0209	0.0232	0.0255	0.0281
10	0.0033	0.0039	0.0045	0.0053	0.0061	0.0071	0.0081	0.0092	0.0104	0.0118	0.0132
11	0.0011	0.0013	0.0016	0.0019	0.0023	0.0027	0.0032	0.0037	0.0043	0.0049	0.0056
12	0.0003	0.0004	0.0005	0.0006	0.0008	0.0009	0.0011	0.0013	0.0016	0.0019	0.0022
13	0.0001	0.0001	0.0002	0.0002	0.0002	0.0003	0.0004	0.0005	0.0006	0.0007	0.0008
14	0.0000	0.0000	0.0000	0.0001	0.0001	0.0001	0.0001	0.0001	0.0002	0.0002	0.0003
15	0.0000	0.0000	0.0000	0.0000	0.0000	0.0000	0.0000	0.0000	0.0001	0.0001	0.0001

x	4.80	4.90	5.00	5.10	5.20	5.30	5.40	5.50	5.60	5.70	5.80
0	0.0082	0.0074	0.0067	0.0061	0.0055	0.0050	0.0045	0.0041	0.0037	0.0033	0.0030
1	0.0395	0.0365	0.0337	0.0311	0.0287	0.0265	0.0244	0.0225	0.0207	0.0191	0.0176
2	0.0948	0.0894	0.0842	0.0793	0.0746	0.0701	0.0659	0.0618	0.0580	0.0544	0.0509
3	0.1517	0.1460	0.1404	0.1348	0.1293	0.1239	0.1185	0.1133	0.1082	0.1033	0.0985
4	0.1820	0.1789	0.1755	0.1719	0.1681	0.1641	0.1600	0.1558	0.1515	0.1472	0.1428
5	0.1747	0.1753	0.1755	0.1753	0.1748	0.1740	0.1728	0.1714	0.1697	0.1678	0.1656
6	0.1398	0.1432	0.1462	0.1490	0.1515	0.1537	0.1555	0.1571	0.1584	0.1594	0.1601
7	0.0959	0.1002	0.1044	0.1086	0.1125	0.1163	0.1200	0.1234	0.1267	0.1298	0.1326
8	0.0575	0.0614	0.0653	0.0692	0.0731	0.0771	0.0810	0.0849	0.0887	0.0925	0.0962
9	0.0307	0.0334	0.0363	0.0392	0.0423	0.0454	0.0486	0.0519	0.0552	0.0586	0.0620
10	0.0147	0.0164	0.0181	0.0200	0.0220	0.0241	0.0262	0.0285	0.0309	0.0334	0.0359
11	0.0064	0.0073	0.0082	0.0093	0.0104	0.0116	0.0129	0.0143	0.0157	0.0173	0.0190
12	0.0026	0.0030	0.0034	0.0039	0.0045	0.0051	0.0058	0.0065	0.0073	0.0082	0.0092
13	0.0009	0.0011	0.0013	0.0015	0.0018	0.0021	0.0024	0.0028	0.0032	0.0036	0.0041
14	0.0003	0.0004	0.0005	0.0006	0.0007	0.0008	0.0009	0.0011	0.0013	0.0015	0.0017
15	0.0001	0.0001	0.0002	0.0002	0.0002	0.0003	0.0003	0.0004	0.0005	0.0006	0.0007
16	0.0000	0.0000	0.0000	0.0001	0.0001	0.0001	0.0001	0.0001	0.0002	0.0002	0.0002
17	0.0000	0.0000	0.0000	0.0000	0.0000	0.0000	0.0000	0.0000	0.0001	0.0001	0.0001

x	5.90	6.00	6.10	6.20	6.30	6.40	6.50	6.60	6.70	6.80	6.90
0	0.0027	0.0025	0.0022	0.0020	0.0018	0.0017	0.0015	0.0014	0.0012	0.0011	0.0010
1	0.0162	0.0149	0.0137	0.0126	0.0116	0.0106	0.0098	0.0090	0.0082	0.0076	0.0070
2	0.0477	0.0446	0.0417	0.0390	0.0364	0.0340	0.0318	0.0296	0.0276	0.0258	0.0240
3	0.0938	0.0892	0.0848	0.0806	0.0765	0.0726	0.0688	0.0652	0.0617	0.0584	0.0552
4	0.1383	0.1339	0.1294	0.1249	0.1205	0.1162	0.1118	0.1076	0.1034	0.0992	0.0952
5	0.1632	0.1606	0.1579	0.1549	0.1519	0.1487	0.1454	0.1420	0.1385	0.1349	0.1314
6	0.1605	0.1606	0.1605	0.1601	0.1595	0.1586	0.1575	0.1562	0.1546	0.1529	0.1511
7	0.1353	0.1377	0.1399	0.1418	0.1435	0.1450	0.1462	0.1472	0.1480	0.1486	0.1489
8	0.0998	0.1033	0.1066	0.1099	0.1130	0.1160	0.1188	0.1215	0.1240	0.1263	0.1284
9	0.0654	0.0688	0.0723	0.0757	0.0791	0.0825	0.0858	0.0891	0.0923	0.0954	0.0985
10	0.0386	0.0413	0.0441	0.0469	0.0498	0.0528	0.0558	0.0588	0.0618	0.0649	0.0679
11	0.0207	0.0225	0.0244	0.0265	0.0285	0.0307	0.0330	0.0353	0.0377	0.0401	0.0426
12	0.0102	0.0113	0.0124	0.0137	0.0150	0.0164	0.0179	0.0194	0.0210	0.0227	0.0245
13	0.0046	0.0052	0.0058	0.0065	0.0073	0.0081	0.0089	0.0099	0.0108	0.0119	0.0130
14	0.0019	0.0022	0.0025	0.0029	0.0033	0.0037	0.0041	0.0046	0.0052	0.0058	0.0064
15	0.0008	0.0009	0.0010	0.0012	0.0014	0.0016	0.0018	0.0020	0.0023	0.0026	0.0029
16	0.0003	0.0003	0.0004	0.0005	0.0005	0.0006	0.0007	0.0008	0.0010	0.0011	0.0013
17	0.0001	0.0001	0.0001	0.0002	0.0002	0.0002	0.0003	0.0003	0.0004	0.0004	0.0005
18	0.0000	0.0000	0.0000	0.0001	0.0001	0.0001	0.0001	0.0001	0.0001	0.0002	0.0002
19	0.0000	0.0000	0.0000	0.0000	0.0000	0.0000	0.0000	0.0000	0.0001	0.0001	0.0001

x	7.00	7.10	7.20	7.30	7.40	7.50	7.60	7.70	7.80	7.90	8.00
0	0.0009	0.0008	0.0007	0.0007	0.0006	0.0006	0.0005	0.0005	0.0004	0.0004	0.0003
1	0.0064	0.0059	0.0054	0.0049	0.0045	0.0041	0.0038	0.0035	0.0032	0.0029	0.0027
2	0.0223	0.0208	0.0194	0.0180	0.0167	0.0156	0.0145	0.0134	0.0125	0.0116	0.0107
3	0.0521	0.0492	0.0464	0.0438	0.0413	0.0389	0.0366	0.0345	0.0324	0.0305	0.0286

F   Poisson Probabilities (cont.)

λ

x	7.00	7.10	7.20	7.30	7.40	7.50	7.60	7.70	7.80	7.90	8.00
4	0.0912	0.0874	0.0836	0.0799	0.0764	0.0729	0.0696	0.0663	0.0632	0.0602	0.0573
5	0.1277	0.1241	0.1204	0.1167	0.1130	0.1094	0.1057	0.1021	0.0986	0.0951	0.0916
6	0.1490	0.1468	0.1445	0.1420	0.1394	0.1367	0.1339	0.1311	0.1282	0.1252	0.1221
7	0.1490	0.1489	0.1486	0.1481	0.1474	0.1465	0.1454	0.1442	0.1428	0.1413	0.1396
8	0.1304	0.1321	0.1337	0.1351	0.1363	0.1373	0.1381	0.1388	0.1392	0.1395	0.1396
9	0.1014	0.1042	0.1070	0.1096	0.1121	0.1144	0.1167	0.1187	0.1207	0.1224	0.1241
10	0.0710	0.0740	0.0770	0.0800	0.0829	0.0858	0.0887	0.0914	0.0941	0.0967	0.0993
11	0.0452	0.0478	0.0504	0.0531	0.0558	0.0585	0.0613	0.0640	0.0667	0.0695	0.0722
12	0.0263	0.0283	0.0303	0.0323	0.0344	0.0366	0.0388	0.0411	0.0434	0.0457	0.0481
13	0.0142	0.0154	0.0168	0.0181	0.0196	0.0211	0.0227	0.0243	0.0260	0.0278	0.0296
14	0.0071	0.0078	0.0086	0.0095	0.0104	0.0113	0.0123	0.0134	0.0145	0.0157	0.0169
15	0.0033	0.0037	0.0041	0.0046	0.0051	0.0057	0.0062	0.0069	0.0075	0.0083	0.0090
16	0.0014	0.0016	0.0019	0.0021	0.0024	0.0026	0.0030	0.0033	0.0037	0.0041	0.0045
17	0.0006	0.0007	0.0008	0.0009	0.0010	0.0012	0.0013	0.0015	0.0017	0.0019	0.0021
18	0.0002	0.0003	0.0003	0.0004	0.0004	0.0005	0.0006	0.0006	0.0007	0.0008	0.0009
19	0.0001	0.0001	0.0001	0.0001	0.0002	0.0002	0.0002	0.0003	0.0003	0.0003	0.0004
20	0.0000	0.0000	0.0000	0.0001	0.0001	0.0001	0.0001	0.0001	0.0001	0.0001	0.0002
21	0.0000	0.0000	0.0000	0.0000	0.0000	0.0000	0.0000	0.0000	0.0000	0.0001	0.0001

x	8.10	8.20	8.30	8.40	8.50	8.60	8.70	8.80	8.90	9.00	9.10
0	0.0003	0.0003	0.0002	0.0002	0.0002	0.0002	0.0002	0.0002	0.0001	0.0001	0.0001
1	0.0025	0.0023	0.0021	0.0019	0.0017	0.0016	0.0014	0.0013	0.0012	0.0011	0.0010
2	0.0100	0.0092	0.0086	0.0079	0.0074	0.0068	0.0063	0.0058	0.0054	0.0050	0.0046
3	0.0269	0.0252	0.0237	0.0222	0.0208	0.0195	0.0183	0.0171	0.0160	0.0150	0.0140
4	0.0544	0.0517	0.0491	0.0466	0.0443	0.0420	0.0398	0.0377	0.0357	0.0337	0.0319
5	0.0882	0.0849	0.0816	0.0784	0.0752	0.0722	0.0692	0.0663	0.0635	0.0607	0.0581
6	0.1191	0.1160	0.1128	0.1097	0.1066	0.1034	0.1003	0.0972	0.0941	0.0911	0.0881
7	0.1378	0.1358	0.1338	0.1317	0.1294	0.1271	0.1247	0.1222	0.1197	0.1171	0.1145
8	0.1395	0.1392	0.1388	0.1382	0.1375	0.1366	0.1356	0.1344	0.1332	0.1318	0.1302
9	0.1256	0.1269	0.1280	0.1290	0.1299	0.1306	0.1311	0.1315	0.1317	0.1318	0.1317
10	0.1017	0.1040	0.1063	0.1084	0.1104	0.1123	0.1140	0.1157	0.1172	0.1186	0.1198
11	0.0749	0.0776	0.0802	0.0828	0.0853	0.0878	0.0902	0.0925	0.0948	0.0970	0.0991
12	0.0505	0.0530	0.0555	0.0579	0.0604	0.0629	0.0654	0.0679	0.0703	0.0728	0.0752
13	0.0315	0.0334	0.0354	0.0374	0.0395	0.0416	0.0438	0.0459	0.0481	0.0504	0.0526
14	0.0182	0.0196	0.0210	0.0225	0.0240	0.0256	0.0272	0.0289	0.0306	0.0324	0.0342
15	0.0098	0.0107	0.0116	0.0126	0.0136	0.0147	0.0158	0.0169	0.0182	0.0194	0.0208
16	0.0050	0.0055	0.0060	0.0066	0.0072	0.0079	0.0086	0.0093	0.0101	0.0109	0.0118
17	0.0024	0.0026	0.0029	0.0033	0.0036	0.0040	0.0044	0.0048	0.0053	0.0058	0.0063
18	0.0011	0.0012	0.0014	0.0015	0.0017	0.0019	0.0021	0.0024	0.0026	0.0029	0.0032
19	0.0005	0.0005	0.0006	0.0007	0.0008	0.0009	0.0010	0.0011	0.0012	0.0014	0.0015
20	0.0002	0.0002	0.0002	0.0003	0.0003	0.0004	0.0004	0.0005	0.0005	0.0006	0.0007
21	0.0001	0.0001	0.0001	0.0001	0.0001	0.0002	0.0002	0.0002	0.0002	0.0003	0.0003
22	0.0000	0.0000	0.0000	0.0000	0.0001	0.0001	0.0001	0.0001	0.0001	0.0001	0.0001

x	9.20	9.30	9.40	9.50	9.60	9.70	9.80	9.90	10.00	11.00	12.00
0	0.0001	0.0001	0.0001	0.0001	0.0001	0.0001	0.0001	0.0001	0.0000	0.0000	0.0000
1	0.0009	0.0009	0.0008	0.0007	0.0007	0.0006	0.0005	0.0005	0.0005	0.0002	0.0001
2	0.0043	0.0040	0.0037	0.0034	0.0031	0.0029	0.0027	0.0025	0.0023	0.0010	0.0004
3	0.0131	0.0123	0.0115	0.0107	0.0100	0.0093	0.0087	0.0081	0.0076	0.0037	0.0018
4	0.0302	0.0285	0.0269	0.0254	0.0240	0.0226	0.0213	0.0201	0.0189	0.0102	0.0053
5	0.0555	0.0530	0.0506	0.0483	0.0460	0.0439	0.0418	0.0398	0.0378	0.0224	0.0127
6	0.0851	0.0822	0.0793	0.0764	0.0736	0.0709	0.0682	0.0656	0.0631	0.0411	0.0255
7	0.1118	0.1091	0.1064	0.1037	0.1010	0.0982	0.0955	0.0928	0.0901	0.0646	0.0437
8	0.1286	0.1269	0.1251	0.1232	0.1212	0.1191	0.1170	0.1148	0.1126	0.0888	0.0655

F   Poisson Probabilities (cont.)

λ

x	9.20	9.30	9.40	9.50	9.60	9.70	9.80	9.90	10.00	11.00	12.00
9	0.1315	0.1311	0.1306	0.1300	0.1293	0.1284	0.1274	0.1263	0.1251	0.1085	0.0874
10	0.1210	0.1219	0.1228	0.1235	0.1241	0.1245	0.1249	0.1250	0.1251	0.1194	0.1048
11	0.1012	0.1031	0.1049	0.1067	0.1083	0.1098	0.1112	0.1125	0.1137	0.1194	0.1144
12	0.0776	0.0799	0.0822	0.0844	0.0866	0.0888	0.0908	0.0928	0.0948	0.1094	0.1144
13	0.0549	0.0572	0.0594	0.0617	0.0640	0.0662	0.0685	0.0707	0.0729	0.0926	0.1056
14	0.0361	0.0380	0.0399	0.0419	0.0439	0.0459	0.0479	0.0500	0.0521	0.0728	0.0905
15	0.0221	0.0235	0.0250	0.0265	0.0281	0.0297	0.0313	0.0330	0.0347	0.0534	0.0724
16	0.0127	0.0137	0.0147	0.0157	0.0168	0.0180	0.0192	0.0204	0.0217	0.0367	0.0543
17	0.0069	0.0075	0.0081	0.0088	0.0095	0.0103	0.0111	0.0119	0.0128	0.0237	0.0383
18	0.0035	0.0039	0.0042	0.0046	0.0051	0.0055	0.0060	0.0065	0.0071	0.0145	0.0255
19	0.0017	0.0019	0.0021	0.0023	0.0026	0.0028	0.0031	0.0034	0.0037	0.0084	0.0161
20	0.0008	0.0009	0.0010	0.0011	0.0012	0.0014	0.0015	0.0017	0.0019	0.0046	0.0097
21	0.0003	0.0004	0.0004	0.0005	0.0006	0.0006	0.0007	0.0008	0.0009	0.0024	0.0055
22	0.0001	0.0002	0.0002	0.0002	0.0002	0.0003	0.0003	0.0004	0.0004	0.0012	0.0030
23	0.0001	0.0001	0.0001	0.0001	0.0001	0.0001	0.0001	0.0002	0.0002	0.0006	0.0016
24	0.0000	0.0000	0.0000	0.0000	0.0000	0.0000	0.0001	0.0001	0.0001	0.0003	0.0008

x	13.00	14.00	15.00	16.00	17.00	18.00	19.00	20.00	21.00	22.00	23.00
0	0.0000	0.0000	0.0000	0.0000	0.0000	0.0000	0.0000	0.0000	0.0000	0.0000	0.0000
1	0.0000	0.0000	0.0000	0.0000	0.0000	0.0000	0.0000	0.0000	0.0000	0.0000	0.0000
2	0.0002	0.0001	0.0000	0.0000	0.0000	0.0000	0.0000	0.0000	0.0000	0.0000	0.0000
3	0.0008	0.0004	0.0002	0.0001	0.0000	0.0000	0.0000	0.0000	0.0000	0.0000	0.0000
4	0.0027	0.0013	0.0006	0.0003	0.0001	0.0001	0.0000	0.0000	0.0000	0.0000	0.0000
5	0.0070	0.0037	0.0019	0.0010	0.0005	0.0002	0.0001	0.0001	0.0000	0.0000	0.0000
6	0.0152	0.0087	0.0048	0.0026	0.0014	0.0007	0.0004	0.0002	0.0001	0.0000	0.0000
7	0.0281	0.0174	0.0104	0.0060	0.0034	0.0019	0.0010	0.0005	0.0003	0.0001	0.0001
8	0.0457	0.0304	0.0194	0.0120	0.0072	0.0042	0.0024	0.0013	0.0007	0.0004	0.0002
9	0.0661	0.0473	0.0324	0.0213	0.0135	0.0083	0.0050	0.0029	0.0017	0.0009	0.0005
10	0.0859	0.0663	0.0486	0.0341	0.0230	0.0150	0.0095	0.0058	0.0035	0.0020	0.0012
11	0.1015	0.0844	0.0663	0.0496	0.0355	0.0245	0.0164	0.0106	0.0067	0.0041	0.0024
12	0.1099	0.0984	0.0829	0.0661	0.0504	0.0368	0.0259	0.0176	0.0116	0.0075	0.0047
13	0.1099	0.1060	0.0956	0.0814	0.0658	0.0509	0.0378	0.0271	0.0188	0.0127	0.0083
14	0.1021	0.1060	0.1024	0.0930	0.0800	0.0655	0.0514	0.0387	0.0282	0.0199	0.0136
15	0.0885	0.0989	0.1024	0.0992	0.0906	0.0786	0.0650	0.0516	0.0395	0.0292	0.0209
16	0.0719	0.0866	0.0960	0.0992	0.0963	0.0884	0.0772	0.0646	0.0518	0.0401	0.0301
17	0.0550	0.0713	0.0847	0.0934	0.0963	0.0936	0.0863	0.0760	0.0640	0.0520	0.0407
18	0.0397	0.0554	0.0706	0.0830	0.0909	0.0936	0.0911	0.0844	0.0747	0.0635	0.0520
19	0.0272	0.0409	0.0557	0.0699	0.0814	0.0887	0.0911	0.0888	0.0826	0.0735	0.0629
20	0.0177	0.0286	0.0418	0.0559	0.0692	0.0798	0.0866	0.0888	0.0867	0.0809	0.0724
21	0.0109	0.0191	0.0299	0.0426	0.0560	0.0684	0.0783	0.0846	0.0867	0.0847	0.0793
22	0.0065	0.0121	0.0204	0.0310	0.0433	0.0560	0.0676	0.0769	0.0828	0.0847	0.0829
23	0.0037	0.0074	0.0133	0.0216	0.0320	0.0438	0.0559	0.0669	0.0756	0.0810	0.0829
24	0.0020	0.0043	0.0083	0.0144	0.0226	0.0328	0.0442	0.0557	0.0661	0.0743	0.0794
25	0.0010	0.0024	0.0050	0.0092	0.0154	0.0237	0.0336	0.0446	0.0555	0.0654	0.0731
26	0.0005	0.0013	0.0029	0.0057	0.0101	0.0164	0.0246	0.0343	0.0449	0.0553	0.0646
27	0.0002	0.0007	0.0016	0.0034	0.0063	0.0109	0.0173	0.0254	0.0349	0.0451	0.0551
28	0.0001	0.0003	0.0009	0.0019	0.0038	0.0070	0.0117	0.0181	0.0262	0.0354	0.0452
29	0.0001	0.0002	0.0004	0.0011	0.0023	0.0044	0.0077	0.0125	0.0190	0.0269	0.0359
30	0.0000	0.0001	0.0002	0.0006	0.0013	0.0026	0.0049	0.0083	0.0133	0.0197	0.0275
31	0.0000	0.0000	0.0001	0.0003	0.0007	0.0015	0.0030	0.0054	0.0090	0.0140	0.0204
32	0.0000	0.0000	0.0001	0.0001	0.0004	0.0009	0.0018	0.0034	0.0059	0.0096	0.0147
33	0.0000	0.0000	0.0000	0.0001	0.0002	0.0005	0.0010	0.0020	0.0038	0.0064	0.0102
34	0.0000	0.0000	0.0000	0.0000	0.0001	0.0002	0.0006	0.0012	0.0023	0.0041	0.0069

F   Poisson Probabilities (cont.)

λ

x	13.00	14.00	15.00	16.00	17.00	18.00	19.00	20.00	21.00	22.00	23.00
35	0.0000	0.0000	0.0000	0.0000	0.0000	0.0001	0.0003	0.0007	0.0014	0.0026	0.0045
36	0.0000	0.0000	0.0000	0.0000	0.0000	0.0001	0.0002	0.0004	0.0008	0.0016	0.0029
37	0.0000	0.0000	0.0000	0.0000	0.0000	0.0000	0.0001	0.0002	0.0005	0.0009	0.0018
38	0.0000	0.0000	0.0000	0.0000	0.0000	0.0000	0.0000	0.0001	0.0003	0.0005	0.0011
39	0.0000	0.0000	0.0000	0.0000	0.0000	0.0000	0.0000	0.0001	0.0001	0.0003	0.0006
40	0.0000	0.0000	0.0000	0.0000	0.0000	0.0000	0.0000	0.0000	0.0001	0.0002	0.0004
41	0.0000	0.0000	0.0000	0.0000	0.0000	0.0000	0.0000	0.0000	0.0000	0.0001	0.0002
42	0.0000	0.0000	0.0000	0.0000	0.0000	0.0000	0.0000	0.0000	0.0000	0.0000	0.0001
43	0.0000	0.0000	0.0000	0.0000	0.0000	0.0000	0.0000	0.0000	0.0000	0.0000	0.0001

G   Critical Values of χ^2

Numerical entries represent the value of χ_α^2 such that the area to the right of the critical value is equal to α

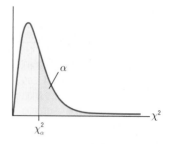

Area to the Right of the Critical Value

df	$\chi_{0.995}^2$	$\chi_{0.990}^2$	$\chi_{0.975}^2$	$\chi_{0.950}^2$	$\chi_{0.900}^2$	$\chi_{0.100}^2$	$\chi_{0.050}^2$	$\chi_{0.025}^2$	$\chi_{0.010}^2$	$\chi_{0.005}^2$
1	0.000	0.000	0.001	0.004	0.016	2.706	3.841	5.024	6.635	7.879
2	0.010	0.020	0.051	0.103	0.211	4.605	5.991	7.378	9.210	10.597
3	0.072	0.115	0.216	0.352	0.584	6.251	7.815	9.348	11.345	12.838
4	0.207	0.297	0.484	0.711	1.064	7.779	9.488	11.143	13.277	14.860
5	0.412	0.554	0.831	1.145	1.610	9.236	11.070	12.833	15.086	16.750
6	0.676	0.872	1.237	1.635	2.204	10.645	12.592	14.449	16.812	18.548
7	0.989	1.239	1.690	2.167	2.833	12.017	14.067	16.013	18.475	20.278
8	1.344	1.646	2.180	2.733	3.490	13.362	15.507	17.535	20.090	21.955
9	1.735	2.088	2.700	3.325	4.168	14.684	16.919	19.023	21.666	23.589
10	2.156	2.558	3.247	3.940	4.865	15.987	18.307	20.483	23.209	25.188
11	2.603	3.053	3.816	4.575	5.578	17.275	19.675	21.920	24.725	26.757
12	3.074	3.571	4.404	5.226	6.304	18.549	21.026	23.337	26.217	28.300
13	3.565	4.107	5.009	5.892	7.042	19.812	22.362	24.736	27.688	29.819
14	4.075	4.660	5.629	6.571	7.790	21.064	23.685	26.119	29.141	31.319
15	4.601	5.229	6.262	7.261	8.547	22.307	24.996	27.488	30.578	32.801
16	5.142	5.812	6.908	7.962	9.312	23.542	26.296	28.845	32.000	34.267
17	5.697	6.408	7.564	8.672	10.085	24.769	27.587	30.191	33.409	35.718
18	6.265	7.015	8.231	9.390	10.865	25.989	28.869	31.526	34.805	37.156
19	6.844	7.633	8.907	10.117	11.651	27.204	30.144	32.852	36.191	38.582
20	7.434	8.260	9.591	10.851	12.443	28.412	31.410	34.170	37.566	39.997
21	8.034	8.897	10.283	11.591	13.240	29.615	32.671	35.479	38.932	41.401
22	8.643	9.542	10.982	12.338	14.041	30.813	33.924	36.781	40.289	42.796
23	9.260	10.196	11.689	13.091	14.848	32.007	35.172	38.076	41.638	44.181
24	9.886	10.856	12.401	13.848	15.659	33.196	36.415	39.364	42.980	45.559
25	10.520	11.524	13.120	14.611	16.473	34.382	37.652	40.646	44.314	46.928
26	11.160	12.198	13.844	15.379	17.292	35.563	38.885	41.923	45.642	48.290
27	11.808	12.879	14.573	16.151	18.114	36.741	40.113	43.195	46.963	49.645
28	12.461	13.565	15.308	16.928	18.939	37.916	41.337	44.461	48.278	50.993
29	13.121	14.256	16.047	17.708	19.768	39.087	42.557	45.722	49.588	52.336
30	13.787	14.953	16.791	18.493	20.599	40.256	43.773	46.979	50.892	53.672
40	20.707	22.164	24.433	26.509	29.051	51.805	55.758	59.342	63.691	66.766
50	27.991	29.707	32.357	34.764	37.689	63.167	67.505	71.420	76.154	79.490
60	35.534	37.485	40.482	43.188	46.459	74.397	79.082	83.298	88.379	91.952
70	43.275	45.442	48.758	51.739	55.329	85.527	90.531	95.023	100.425	104.215
80	51.172	53.540	57.153	60.391	64.278	96.578	101.879	106.629	112.329	116.321
90	59.196	61.754	65.647	69.126	73.291	107.565	113.145	118.136	124.116	128.299
100	67.328	70.065	74.222	77.929	82.358	118.498	124.342	129.561	135.807	140.169

H   Critical Values of the *F*-Distribution
α = 0.005

Numerical entries represent the value of F_α such that
the area to the right of the critical value is α.

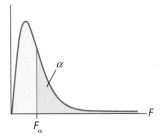

Numerator Degrees of Freedom

	1	2	3	4	5	6	7	8	9
1	16210.7227	19999.5000	21614.7414	22499.5833	23055.7982	23437.1111	23714.5658	23925.4062	24091.0041
2	198.5013	199.0000	199.1664	199.2497	199.2996	199.3330	199.3568	199.3746	199.3885
3	55.5520	49.7993	47.4672	46.1946	45.3916	44.8385	44.4341	44.1256	43.8824
4	31.3328	26.2843	24.2591	23.1545	22.4564	21.9746	21.6217	21.3520	21.1391
5	22.7848	18.3138	16.5298	15.5561	14.9396	14.5133	14.2004	13.9610	13.7716
6	18.6350	14.5441	12.9166	12.0275	11.4637	11.0730	10.7859	10.5658	10.3915
7	16.2356	12.4040	10.8824	10.0505	9.5221	9.1553	8.8854	8.6781	8.5138
8	14.6882	11.0424	9.5965	8.8051	8.3018	7.9520	7.6941	7.4959	7.3386
9	13.6136	10.1067	8.7171	7.9559	7.4712	7.1339	6.8849	6.6933	6.5411
10	12.8265	9.4270	8.0807	7.3428	6.8724	6.5446	6.3025	6.1159	5.9676
11	12.2263	8.9122	7.6004	6.8809	6.4217	6.1016	5.8648	5.6821	5.5368
12	11.7542	8.5096	7.2258	6.5211	6.0711	5.7570	5.5245	5.3451	5.2021
13	11.3735	8.1865	6.9258	6.2335	5.7910	5.4819	5.2529	5.0761	4.9351
14	11.0603	7.9216	6.6804	5.9984	5.5623	5.2574	5.0313	4.8566	4.7173
15	10.7980	7.7008	6.4760	5.8029	5.3721	5.0708	4.8473	4.6744	4.5364
16	10.5755	7.5138	6.3034	5.6378	5.2117	4.9134	4.6920	4.5207	4.3838
17	10.3842	7.3536	6.1556	5.4967	5.0746	4.7789	4.5594	4.3894	4.2535
18	10.2181	7.2148	6.0278	5.3746	4.9560	4.6627	4.4448	4.2759	4.1410
19	10.0725	7.0935	5.9161	5.2681	4.8526	4.5614	4.3448	4.1770	4.0428
20	9.9439	6.9865	5.8177	5.1743	4.7616	4.4721	4.2569	4.0900	3.9564
21	9.8295	6.8914	5.7304	5.0911	4.6809	4.3931	4.1789	4.0128	3.8799
22	9.7271	6.8064	5.6524	5.0168	4.6088	4.3225	4.1094	3.9440	3.8116
23	9.6348	6.7300	5.5823	4.9500	4.5441	4.2591	4.0469	3.8822	3.7502
24	9.5513	6.6609	5.5190	4.8898	4.4857	4.2019	3.9905	3.8264	3.6949
25	9.4753	6.5982	5.4615	4.8351	4.4327	4.1500	3.9394	3.7758	3.6447
26	9.4059	6.5409	5.4091	4.7852	4.3844	4.1027	3.8928	3.7297	3.5989
27	9.3423	6.4885	5.3611	4.7396	4.3402	4.0594	3.8501	3.6875	3.5571
28	9.2838	6.4403	5.3170	4.6977	4.2996	4.0197	3.8110	3.6487	3.5186
29	9.2297	6.3958	5.2764	4.6591	4.2622	3.9831	3.7749	3.6131	3.4832
30	9.1797	6.3547	5.2388	4.6234	4.2276	3.9492	3.7416	3.5801	3.4505
40	8.8279	6.0664	4.9758	4.3738	3.9860	3.7129	3.5088	3.3498	3.2220
60	8.4946	5.7950	4.7290	4.1399	3.7599	3.4918	3.2911	3.1344	3.0083
120	8.1788	5.5393	4.4972	3.9207	3.5482	3.2849	3.0874	2.9330	2.8083
∞	7.8795	5.2983	4.2794	3.7151	3.3499	3.0913	2.8968	2.7444	2.6211

Denominator Degrees of Freedom

H   Critical Values of the *F*-Distribution
α = 0.005 (cont.)

	Numerator Degrees of Freedom								
	10	11	12	13	14	15	16	17	18
1	24224.4868	24334.3581	24426.3662	24504.5356	24571.7673	24630.2051	24681.4673	24726.7982	24767.1704
2	199.3996	199.4087	199.4163	199.4227	199.4282	199.4329	199.4371	199.4408	199.4440
3	43.6858	43.5236	43.3874	43.2715	43.1716	43.0847	43.0083	42.9407	42.8804
4	20.9667	20.8243	20.7047	20.6027	20.5148	20.4383	20.3710	20.3113	20.2581
5	13.6182	13.4912	13.3845	13.2934	13.2148	13.1463	13.0861	13.0327	12.9850
6	10.2500	10.1329	10.0343	9.9501	9.8774	9.8140	9.7582	9.7086	9.6644
7	8.3803	8.2697	8.1764	8.0967	8.0279	7.9678	7.9148	7.8678	7.8258
8	7.2106	7.1045	7.0149	6.9384	6.8721	6.8143	6.7633	6.7180	6.6775
9	6.4172	6.3142	6.2274	6.1530	6.0887	6.0325	5.9829	5.9388	5.8994
10	5.8467	5.7462	5.6613	5.5887	5.5257	5.4707	5.4221	5.3789	5.3403
11	5.4183	5.3197	5.2363	5.1649	5.1031	5.0489	5.0011	4.9586	4.9205
12	5.0855	4.9884	4.9062	4.8358	4.7748	4.7213	4.6741	4.6321	4.5945
13	4.8199	4.7240	4.6429	4.5733	4.5129	4.4600	4.4132	4.3716	4.3344
14	4.6034	4.5085	4.4281	4.3591	4.2993	4.2468	4.2005	4.1592	4.1221
15	4.4235	4.3295	4.2497	4.1813	4.1219	4.0698	4.0237	3.9827	3.9459
16	4.2719	4.1785	4.0994	4.0314	3.9723	3.9205	3.8747	3.8338	3.7972
17	4.1424	4.0496	3.9709	3.9033	3.8445	3.7929	3.7473	3.7066	3.6701
18	4.0305	3.9382	3.8599	3.7926	3.7341	3.6827	3.6373	3.5967	3.5603
19	3.9329	3.8410	3.7631	3.6961	3.6378	3.5866	3.5412	3.5008	3.4645
20	3.8470	3.7555	3.6779	3.6111	3.5530	3.5020	3.4568	3.4164	3.3802
21	3.7709	3.6798	3.6024	3.5358	3.4779	3.4270	3.3818	3.3416	3.3054
22	3.7030	3.6122	3.5350	3.4686	3.4108	3.3600	3.3150	3.2748	3.2387
23	3.6420	3.5515	3.4745	3.4083	3.3506	3.2999	3.2549	3.2148	3.1787
24	3.5870	3.4967	3.4199	3.3538	3.2962	3.2456	3.2007	3.1606	3.1246
25	3.5370	3.4470	3.3704	3.3044	3.2469	3.1963	3.1515	3.1114	3.0754
26	3.4916	3.4017	3.3252	3.2594	3.2020	3.1515	3.1067	3.0666	3.0306
27	3.4499	3.3602	3.2839	3.2182	3.1608	3.1104	3.0656	3.0256	2.9896
28	3.4117	3.3222	3.2460	3.1803	3.1231	3.0727	3.0279	2.9879	2.9520
29	3.3765	3.2871	3.2110	3.1454	3.0882	3.0379	2.9932	2.9532	2.9173
30	3.3440	3.2547	3.1787	3.1132	3.0560	3.0057	2.9611	2.9211	2.8852
40	3.1167	3.0284	2.9531	2.8880	2.8312	2.7811	2.7365	2.6966	2.6607
60	2.9042	2.8166	2.7419	2.6771	2.6205	2.5705	2.5259	2.4859	2.4498
120	2.7052	2.6183	2.5439	2.4794	2.4228	2.3727	2.3280	2.2878	2.2514
∞	2.5188	2.4325	2.3583	2.2938	2.2371	2.1868	2.1417	2.1011	2.0643

Denominator Degrees of Freedom

H   Critical Values of the *F*-Distribution α = 0.005 (cont.)

			Numerator Degrees of Freedom				
	19	**20**	**24**	**30**	**40**	**60**	**120**
1	24803.3549	24835.9709	24939.5653	25043.6277	25148.1532	25253.1369	25358.5735
2	199.4470	199.4496	199.4579	199.4663	199.4746	199.4829	199.4912
3	42.8263	42.7775	42.6222	42.4658	42.3082	42.1494	41.9895
4	20.2104	20.1673	20.0300	19.8915	19.7518	19.6107	19.4684
5	12.9422	12.9035	12.7802	12.6556	12.5297	12.4024	12.2737
6	9.6247	9.5888	9.4742	9.3582	9.2408	9.1219	9.0015
7	7.7881	7.7540	7.6450	7.5345	7.4224	7.3088	7.1933
8	6.6411	6.6082	6.5029	6.3961	6.2875	6.1772	6.0649
9	5.8639	5.8318	5.7292	5.6248	5.5186	5.4104	5.3001
10	5.3055	5.2740	5.1732	5.0706	4.9659	4.8592	4.7501
11	4.8863	4.8552	4.7557	4.6543	4.5508	4.4450	4.3367
12	4.5606	4.5299	4.4314	4.3309	4.2282	4.1229	4.0149
13	4.3008	4.2703	4.1726	4.0727	3.9704	3.8655	3.7577
14	4.0888	4.0585	3.9614	3.8619	3.7600	3.6552	3.5473
15	3.9127	3.8826	3.7859	3.6867	3.5850	3.4803	3.3722
16	3.7641	3.7342	3.6378	3.5389	3.4372	3.3324	3.2240
17	3.6372	3.6073	3.5112	3.4124	3.3108	3.2058	3.0971
18	3.5275	3.4977	3.4017	3.3030	3.2014	3.0962	2.9871
19	3.4318	3.4020	3.3062	3.2075	3.1058	3.0004	2.8908
20	3.3475	3.3178	3.2220	3.1234	3.0215	2.9159	2.8058
21	3.2728	3.2431	3.1474	3.0488	2.9467	2.8408	2.7302
22	3.2060	3.1764	3.0807	2.9821	2.8799	2.7736	2.6625
23	3.1461	3.1165	3.0208	2.9221	2.8197	2.7132	2.6015
24	3.0920	3.0624	2.9667	2.8679	2.7654	2.6585	2.5463
25	3.0429	3.0133	2.9176	2.8187	2.7160	2.6088	2.4961
26	2.9981	2.9685	2.8728	2.7738	2.6709	2.5633	2.4501
27	2.9571	2.9275	2.8318	2.7327	2.6296	2.5217	2.4079
28	2.9194	2.8899	2.7941	2.6949	2.5916	2.4834	2.3690
29	2.8847	2.8551	2.7594	2.6600	2.5565	2.4479	2.3331
30	2.8526	2.8230	2.7272	2.6278	2.5241	2.4151	2.2998
40	2.6281	2.5984	2.5020	2.4015	2.2958	2.1838	2.0636
60	2.4171	2.3872	2.2898	2.1874	2.0789	1.9622	1.8341
120	2.2183	2.1881	2.0890	1.9840	1.8709	1.7469	1.6055
∞	2.0307	1.9999	1.8983	1.7891	1.6692	1.5326	1.3638

Denominator Degrees of Freedom

H   Critical Values of the *F*-Distribution
$\alpha = 0.010$

Numerator Degrees of Freedom

	1	2	3	4	5	6	7	8	9
1	4052.1807	4999.5000	5403.3520	5624.5833	5763.6496	5858.9861	5928.3557	5981.0703	6022.4732
2	98.5025	99.0000	99.1662	99.2494	99.2993	99.3326	99.3564	99.3742	99.3881
3	34.1162	30.8165	29.4567	28.7099	28.2371	27.9107	27.6717	27.4892	27.3452
4	21.1977	18.0000	16.6944	15.9770	15.5219	15.2069	14.9758	14.7989	14.6591
5	16.2582	13.2739	12.0600	11.3919	10.9670	10.6723	10.4555	10.2893	10.1578
6	13.7450	10.9248	9.7795	9.1483	8.7459	8.4661	8.2600	8.1017	7.9761
7	12.2464	9.5466	8.4513	7.8466	7.4604	7.1914	6.9928	6.8400	6.7188
8	11.2586	8.6491	7.5910	7.0061	6.6318	6.3707	6.1776	6.0289	5.9106
9	10.5614	8.0215	6.9919	6.4221	6.0569	5.8018	5.6129	5.4671	5.3511
10	10.0443	7.5594	6.5523	5.9943	5.6363	5.3858	5.2001	5.0567	4.9424
11	9.6460	7.2057	6.2167	5.6683	5.3160	5.0692	4.8861	4.7445	4.6315
12	9.3302	6.9266	5.9525	5.4120	5.0643	4.8206	4.6395	4.4994	4.3875
13	9.0738	6.7010	5.7394	5.2053	4.8616	4.6204	4.4410	4.3021	4.1911
14	8.8616	6.5149	5.5639	5.0354	4.6950	4.4558	4.2779	4.1399	4.0297
15	8.6831	6.3589	5.4170	4.8932	4.5556	4.3183	4.1415	4.0045	3.8948
16	8.5310	6.2262	5.2922	4.7726	4.4374	4.2016	4.0259	3.8896	3.7804
17	8.3997	6.1121	5.1850	4.6690	4.3359	4.1015	3.9267	3.7910	3.6822
18	8.2854	6.0129	5.0919	4.5790	4.2479	4.0146	3.8406	3.7054	3.5971
19	8.1849	5.9259	5.0103	4.5003	4.1708	3.9386	3.7653	3.6305	3.5225
20	8.0960	5.8489	4.9382	4.4307	4.1027	3.8714	3.6987	3.5644	3.4567
21	8.0166	5.7804	4.8740	4.3688	4.0421	3.8117	3.6396	3.5056	3.3981
22	7.9454	5.7190	4.8166	4.3134	3.9880	3.7583	3.5867	3.4530	3.3458
23	7.8811	5.6637	4.7649	4.2636	3.9392	3.7102	3.5390	3.4057	3.2986
24	7.8229	5.6136	4.7181	4.2184	3.8951	3.6667	3.4959	3.3629	3.2560
25	7.7698	5.5680	4.6755	4.1774	3.8550	3.6272	3.4568	3.3239	3.2172
26	7.7213	5.5263	4.6366	4.1400	3.8183	3.5911	3.4210	3.2884	3.1818
27	7.6767	5.4881	4.6009	4.1056	3.7848	3.5580	3.3882	3.2558	3.1494
28	7.6356	5.4529	4.5681	4.0740	3.7539	3.5276	3.3581	3.2259	3.1195
29	7.5977	5.4204	4.5378	4.0449	3.7254	3.4995	3.3303	3.1982	3.0920
30	7.5625	5.3903	4.5097	4.0179	3.6990	3.4735	3.3045	3.1726	3.0665
40	7.3141	5.1785	4.3126	3.8283	3.5138	3.2910	3.1238	2.9930	2.8876
60	7.0771	4.9774	4.1259	3.6490	3.3389	3.1187	2.9530	2.8233	2.7185
120	6.8509	4.7865	3.9491	3.4795	3.1735	2.9559	2.7918	2.6629	2.5586
∞	6.6349	4.6052	3.7816	3.3192	3.0173	2.8020	2.6393	2.5113	2.4074

Denominator Degrees of Freedom

H   Critical Values of the *F*-Distribution α = 0.010 (cont.)

Numerator Degrees of Freedom

	10	11	12	13	14	15	16	17	18
1	6055.8467	6083.3168	6106.3207	6125.8647	6142.6740	6157.2846	6170.1012	6181.4348	6191.5287
2	99.3992	99.4083	99.4159	99.4223	99.4278	99.4325	99.4367	99.4404	99.4436
3	27.2287	27.1326	27.0518	26.9831	26.9238	26.8722	26.8269	26.7867	26.7509
4	14.5459	14.4523	14.3736	14.3065	14.2486	14.1982	14.1539	14.1146	14.0795
5	10.0510	9.9626	9.8883	9.8248	9.7700	9.7222	9.6802	9.6429	9.6096
6	7.8741	7.7896	7.7183	7.6575	7.6049	7.5590	7.5186	7.4827	7.4507
7	6.6201	6.5382	6.4691	6.4100	6.3590	6.3143	6.2750	6.2401	6.2089
8	5.8143	5.7343	5.6667	5.6089	5.5589	5.5151	5.4766	5.4423	5.4116
9	5.2565	5.1779	5.1114	5.0545	5.0052	4.9621	4.9240	4.8902	4.8599
10	4.8491	4.7715	4.7059	4.6496	4.6008	4.5581	4.5204	4.4869	4.4569
11	4.5393	4.4624	4.3974	4.3416	4.2932	4.2509	4.2134	4.1801	4.1503
12	4.2961	4.2198	4.1553	4.0999	4.0518	4.0096	3.9724	3.9392	3.9095
13	4.1003	4.0245	3.9603	3.9052	3.8573	3.8154	3.7783	3.7452	3.7156
14	3.9394	3.8640	3.8001	3.7452	3.6975	3.6557	3.6187	3.5857	3.5561
15	3.8049	3.7299	3.6662	3.6115	3.5639	3.5222	3.4852	3.4523	3.4228
16	3.6909	3.6162	3.5527	3.4981	3.4506	3.4089	3.3720	3.3391	3.3096
17	3.5931	3.5185	3.4552	3.4007	3.3533	3.3117	3.2748	3.2419	3.2124
18	3.5082	3.4338	3.3706	3.3162	3.2689	3.2273	3.1904	3.1575	3.1280
19	3.4338	3.3596	3.2965	3.2422	3.1949	3.1533	3.1165	3.0836	3.0541
20	3.3682	3.2941	3.2311	3.1769	3.1296	3.0880	3.0512	3.0183	2.9887
21	3.3098	3.2359	3.1730	3.1187	3.0715	3.0300	2.9931	2.9602	2.9306
22	3.2576	3.1837	3.1209	3.0667	3.0195	2.9779	2.9411	2.9082	2.8786
23	3.2106	3.1368	3.0740	3.0199	2.9727	2.9311	2.8943	2.8613	2.8317
24	3.1681	3.0944	3.0316	2.9775	2.9303	2.8887	2.8519	2.8189	2.7892
25	3.1294	3.0558	2.9931	2.9389	2.8917	2.8502	2.8133	2.7803	2.7506
26	3.0941	3.0205	2.9578	2.9038	2.8566	2.8150	2.7781	2.7451	2.7153
27	3.0618	2.9882	2.9256	2.8715	2.8243	2.7827	2.7458	2.7127	2.6830
28	3.0320	2.9585	2.8959	2.8418	2.7946	2.7530	2.7160	2.6830	2.6532
29	3.0045	2.9311	2.8685	2.8144	2.7672	2.7256	2.6886	2.6555	2.6257
30	2.9791	2.9057	2.8431	2.7890	2.7418	2.7002	2.6632	2.6301	2.6003
40	2.8005	2.7274	2.6648	2.6107	2.5634	2.5216	2.4844	2.4511	2.4210
60	2.6318	2.5587	2.4961	2.4419	2.3943	2.3523	2.3148	2.2811	2.2507
120	2.4721	2.3990	2.3363	2.2818	2.2339	2.1915	2.1536	2.1194	2.0885
∞	2.3209	2.2477	2.1848	2.1299	2.0815	2.0385	2.0000	1.9652	1.9336

Denominator Degrees of Freedom

H   Critical Values of the *F*-Distribution
α = 0.010 (cont.)

		Numerator Degrees of Freedom					
	19	**20**	**24**	**30**	**40**	**60**	**120**
1	6200.5756	6208.7302	6234.6309	6260.6486	6286.7821	6313.0301	6339.3913
2	99.4465	99.4492	99.4575	99.4658	99.4742	99.4825	99.4908
3	26.7188	26.6898	26.5975	26.5045	26.4108	26.3164	26.2211
4	14.0480	14.0196	13.9291	13.8377	13.7454	13.6522	13.5581
5	9.5797	9.5526	9.4665	9.3793	9.2912	9.2020	9.1118
6	7.4219	7.3958	7.3127	7.2285	7.1432	7.0567	6.9690
7	6.1808	6.1554	6.0743	5.9920	5.9084	5.8236	5.7373
8	5.3840	5.3591	5.2793	5.1981	5.1156	5.0316	4.9461
9	4.8327	4.8080	4.7290	4.6486	4.5666	4.4831	4.3978
10	4.4299	4.4054	4.3269	4.2469	4.1653	4.0819	3.9965
11	4.1234	4.0990	4.0209	3.9411	3.8596	3.7761	3.6904
12	3.8827	3.8584	3.7805	3.7008	3.6192	3.5355	3.4494
13	3.6888	3.6646	3.5868	3.5070	3.4253	3.3413	3.2548
14	3.5294	3.5052	3.4274	3.3476	3.2656	3.1813	3.0942
15	3.3961	3.3719	3.2940	3.2141	3.1319	3.0471	2.9595
16	3.2829	3.2587	3.1808	3.1007	3.0182	2.9330	2.8447
17	3.1857	3.1615	3.0835	3.0032	2.9205	2.8348	2.7459
18	3.1013	3.0771	2.9990	2.9185	2.8354	2.7493	2.6597
19	3.0274	3.0031	2.9249	2.8442	2.7608	2.6742	2.5839
20	2.9620	2.9377	2.8594	2.7785	2.6947	2.6077	2.5168
21	2.9039	2.8796	2.8010	2.7200	2.6359	2.5484	2.4568
22	2.8518	2.8274	2.7488	2.6675	2.5831	2.4951	2.4029
23	2.8049	2.7805	2.7017	2.6202	2.5355	2.4471	2.3542
24	2.7624	2.7380	2.6591	2.5773	2.4923	2.4035	2.3100
25	2.7238	2.6993	2.6203	2.5383	2.4530	2.3637	2.2696
26	2.6885	2.6640	2.5848	2.5026	2.4170	2.3273	2.2325
27	2.6561	2.6316	2.5522	2.4699	2.3840	2.2938	2.1985
28	2.6263	2.6017	2.5223	2.4397	2.3535	2.2629	2.1670
29	2.5987	2.5742	2.4946	2.4118	2.3253	2.2344	2.1379
30	2.5732	2.5487	2.4689	2.3860	2.2992	2.2079	2.1108
40	2.3937	2.3689	2.2880	2.2034	2.1142	2.0194	1.9172
60	2.2230	2.1978	2.1154	2.0285	1.9360	1.8363	1.7263
120	2.0604	2.0346	1.9500	1.8600	1.7628	1.6557	1.5330
∞	1.9048	1.8783	1.7908	1.6964	1.5923	1.4730	1.3246

H   Critical Values of the *F*-Distribution
$\alpha = 0.025$

Numerator Degrees of Freedom

	1	2	3	4	5	6	7	8	9
1	647.7890	799.5000	864.1630	899.5833	921.8479	937.1111	948.2169	956.6562	963.2846
2	38.5063	39.0000	39.1655	39.2484	39.2982	39.3315	39.3552	39.3730	39.3869
3	17.4434	16.0441	15.4392	15.1010	14.8848	14.7347	14.6244	14.5399	14.4731
4	12.2179	10.6491	9.9792	9.6045	9.3645	9.1973	9.0741	8.9796	8.9047
5	10.0070	8.4336	7.7636	7.3879	7.1464	6.9777	6.8531	6.7572	6.6811
6	8.8131	7.2599	6.5988	6.2272	5.9876	5.8198	5.6955	5.5996	5.5234
7	8.0727	6.5415	5.8898	5.5226	5.2852	5.1186	4.9949	4.8993	4.8232
8	7.5709	6.0595	5.4160	5.0526	4.8173	4.6517	4.5286	4.4333	4.3572
9	7.2093	5.7147	5.0781	4.7181	4.4844	4.3197	4.1970	4.1020	4.0260
10	6.9367	5.4564	4.8256	4.4683	4.2361	4.0721	3.9498	3.8549	3.7790
11	6.7241	5.2559	4.6300	4.2751	4.0440	3.8807	3.7586	3.6638	3.5879
12	6.5538	5.0959	4.4742	4.1212	3.8911	3.7283	3.6065	3.5118	3.4358
13	6.4143	4.9653	4.3472	3.9959	3.7667	3.6043	3.4827	3.3880	3.3120
14	6.2979	4.8567	4.2417	3.8919	3.6634	3.5014	3.3799	3.2853	3.2093
15	6.1995	4.7650	4.1528	3.8043	3.5764	3.4147	3.2934	3.1987	3.1227
16	6.1151	4.6867	4.0768	3.7294	3.5021	3.3406	3.2194	3.1248	3.0488
17	6.0420	4.6189	4.0112	3.6648	3.4379	3.2767	3.1556	3.0610	2.9849
18	5.9781	4.5597	3.9539	3.6083	3.3820	3.2209	3.0999	3.0053	2.9291
19	5.9216	4.5075	3.9034	3.5587	3.3327	3.1718	3.0509	2.9563	2.8801
20	5.8715	4.4613	3.8587	3.5147	3.2891	3.1283	3.0074	2.9128	2.8365
21	5.8266	4.4199	3.8188	3.4754	3.2501	3.0895	2.9686	2.8740	2.7977
22	5.7863	4.3828	3.7829	3.4401	3.2151	3.0546	2.9338	2.8392	2.7628
23	5.7498	4.3492	3.7505	3.4083	3.1835	3.0232	2.9023	2.8077	2.7313
24	5.7166	4.3187	3.7211	3.3794	3.1548	2.9946	2.8738	2.7791	2.7027
25	5.6864	4.2909	3.6943	3.3530	3.1287	2.9685	2.8478	2.7531	2.6766
26	5.6586	4.2655	3.6697	3.3289	3.1048	2.9447	2.8240	2.7293	2.6528
27	5.6331	4.2421	3.6472	3.3067	3.0828	2.9228	2.8021	2.7074	2.6309
28	5.6096	4.2205	3.6264	3.2863	3.0626	2.9027	2.7820	2.6872	2.6106
29	5.5878	4.2006	3.6072	3.2674	3.0438	2.8840	2.7633	2.6686	2.5919
30	5.5675	4.1821	3.5894	3.2499	3.0265	2.8667	2.7460	2.6513	2.5746
40	5.4239	4.0510	3.4633	3.1261	2.9037	2.7444	2.6238	2.5289	2.4519
60	5.2856	3.9253	3.3425	3.0077	2.7863	2.6274	2.5068	2.4117	2.3344
120	5.1523	3.8046	3.2269	2.8943	2.6740	2.5154	2.3948	2.2994	2.2217
∞	5.0239	3.6889	3.1161	2.7858	2.5665	2.4082	2.2876	2.1918	2.1137

Denominator Degrees of Freedom

H   Critical Values of the F-Distribution
α = 0.025 (cont.)

Numerator Degrees of Freedom

	10	11	12	13	14	15	16	17	18
1	968.6274	973.0252	976.7079	979.8368	982.5278	984.8668	986.9187	988.7331	990.3490
2	39.3980	39.4071	39.4146	39.4210	39.4265	39.4313	39.4354	39.4391	39.4424
3	14.4189	14.3742	14.3366	14.3045	14.2768	14.2527	14.2315	14.2127	14.1960
4	8.8439	8.7935	8.7512	8.7150	8.6838	8.6565	8.6326	8.6113	8.5924
5	6.6192	6.5678	6.5245	6.4876	6.4556	6.4277	6.4032	6.3814	6.3619
6	5.4613	5.4098	5.3662	5.3290	5.2968	5.2687	5.2439	5.2218	5.2021
7	4.7611	4.7095	4.6658	4.6285	4.5961	4.5678	4.5428	4.5206	4.5008
8	4.2951	4.2434	4.1997	4.1622	4.1297	4.1012	4.0761	4.0538	4.0338
9	3.9639	3.9121	3.8682	3.8306	3.7980	3.7694	3.7441	3.7216	3.7015
10	3.7168	3.6649	3.6209	3.5832	3.5504	3.5217	3.4963	3.4737	3.4534
11	3.5257	3.4737	3.4296	3.3917	3.3588	3.3299	3.3044	3.2816	3.2612
12	3.3736	3.3215	3.2773	3.2393	3.2062	3.1772	3.1515	3.1286	3.1081
13	3.2497	3.1975	3.1532	3.1150	3.0819	3.0527	3.0269	3.0039	2.9832
14	3.1469	3.0946	3.0502	3.0119	2.9786	2.9493	2.9234	2.9003	2.8795
15	3.0602	3.0078	2.9633	2.9249	2.8915	2.8621	2.8360	2.8128	2.7919
16	2.9862	2.9337	2.8890	2.8506	2.8170	2.7875	2.7614	2.7380	2.7170
17	2.9222	2.8696	2.8249	2.7863	2.7526	2.7230	2.6968	2.6733	2.6522
18	2.8664	2.8137	2.7689	2.7302	2.6964	2.6667	2.6404	2.6168	2.5956
19	2.8172	2.7645	2.7196	2.6808	2.6469	2.6171	2.5907	2.5670	2.5457
20	2.7737	2.7209	2.6758	2.6369	2.6030	2.5731	2.5465	2.5228	2.5014
21	2.7348	2.6819	2.6368	2.5978	2.5638	2.5338	2.5071	2.4833	2.4618
22	2.6998	2.6469	2.6017	2.5626	2.5285	2.4984	2.4717	2.4478	2.4262
23	2.6682	2.6152	2.5699	2.5308	2.4966	2.4665	2.4396	2.4157	2.3940
24	2.6396	2.5865	2.5411	2.5019	2.4677	2.4374	2.4105	2.3865	2.3648
25	2.6135	2.5603	2.5149	2.4756	2.4413	2.4110	2.3840	2.3599	2.3381
26	2.5896	2.5363	2.4908	2.4515	2.4171	2.3867	2.3597	2.3355	2.3137
27	2.5676	2.5143	2.4688	2.4293	2.3949	2.3644	2.3373	2.3131	2.2912
28	2.5473	2.4940	2.4484	2.4089	2.3743	2.3438	2.3167	2.2924	2.2704
29	2.5286	2.4752	2.4295	2.3900	2.3554	2.3248	2.2976	2.2732	2.2512
30	2.5112	2.4577	2.4120	2.3724	2.3378	2.3072	2.2799	2.2554	2.2334
40	2.3882	2.3343	2.2882	2.2481	2.2130	2.1819	2.1542	2.1293	2.1068
60	2.2702	2.2159	2.1692	2.1286	2.0929	2.0613	2.0330	2.0076	1.9846
120	2.1570	2.1021	2.0548	2.0136	1.9773	1.9450	1.9161	1.8900	1.8663
∞	2.0483	1.9927	1.9447	1.9028	1.8657	1.8326	1.8028	1.7760	1.7515

Denominator Degrees of Freedom

H   Critical Values of the F-Distribution α = 0.025 (cont.)

		Numerator Degrees of Freedom					
	19	**20**	**24**	**30**	**40**	**60**	**120**
1	991.7973	993.1028	997.2492	1001.4144	1005.5981	1009.8001	1014.0202
2	39.4453	39.4479	39.4562	39.4646	39.4729	39.4812	39.4896
3	14.1810	14.1674	14.1241	14.0805	14.0365	13.9921	13.9473
4	8.5753	8.5599	8.5109	8.4613	8.4111	8.3604	8.3092
5	6.3444	6.3286	6.2780	6.2269	6.1750	6.1225	6.0693
6	5.1844	5.1684	5.1172	5.0652	5.0125	4.9589	4.9044
7	4.4829	4.4667	4.4150	4.3624	4.3089	4.2544	4.1989
8	4.0158	3.9995	3.9472	3.8940	3.8398	3.7844	3.7279
9	3.6833	3.6669	3.6142	3.5604	3.5055	3.4493	3.3918
10	3.4351	3.4185	3.3654	3.3110	3.2554	3.1984	3.1399
11	3.2428	3.2261	3.1725	3.1176	3.0613	3.0035	2.9441
12	3.0896	3.0728	3.0187	2.9633	2.9063	2.8478	2.7874
13	2.9646	2.9477	2.8932	2.8372	2.7797	2.7204	2.6590
14	2.8607	2.8437	2.7888	2.7324	2.6742	2.6142	2.5519
15	2.7730	2.7559	2.7006	2.6437	2.5850	2.5242	2.4611
16	2.6980	2.6808	2.6252	2.5678	2.5085	2.4471	2.3831
17	2.6331	2.6158	2.5598	2.5020	2.4422	2.3801	2.3153
18	2.5764	2.5590	2.5027	2.4445	2.3842	2.3214	2.2558
19	2.5265	2.5089	2.4523	2.3937	2.3329	2.2696	2.2032
20	2.4821	2.4645	2.4076	2.3486	2.2873	2.2234	2.1562
21	2.4424	2.4247	2.3675	2.3082	2.2465	2.1819	2.1141
22	2.4067	2.3890	2.3315	2.2718	2.2097	2.1446	2.0760
23	2.3745	2.3567	2.2989	2.2389	2.1763	2.1107	2.0415
24	2.3452	2.3273	2.2693	2.2090	2.1460	2.0799	2.0099
25	2.3184	2.3005	2.2422	2.1816	2.1183	2.0516	1.9811
26	2.2939	2.2759	2.2174	2.1565	2.0928	2.0257	1.9545
27	2.2713	2.2533	2.1946	2.1334	2.0693	2.0018	1.9299
28	2.2505	2.2324	2.1735	2.1121	2.0477	1.9797	1.9072
29	2.2313	2.2131	2.1540	2.0923	2.0276	1.9591	1.8861
30	2.2134	2.1952	2.1359	2.0739	2.0089	1.9400	1.8664
40	2.0864	2.0677	2.0069	1.9429	1.8752	1.8028	1.7242
60	1.9636	1.9445	1.8817	1.8152	1.7440	1.6668	1.5810
120	1.8447	1.8249	1.7597	1.6899	1.6141	1.5299	1.4327
∞	1.7291	1.7085	1.6402	1.5660	1.4836	1.3883	1.2685

Denominator Degrees of Freedom

H   Critical Values of the F-Distribution
α = 0.050

	Numerator Degrees of Freedom								
	1	2	3	4	5	6	7	8	9
1	161.4476	199.5000	215.7073	224.5832	230.1619	233.9860	236.7684	238.8827	240.5433
2	18.5128	19.0000	19.1643	19.2468	19.2964	19.3295	19.3532	19.3710	19.3848
3	10.1280	9.5521	9.2766	9.1172	9.0135	8.9406	8.8867	8.8452	8.8123
4	7.7086	6.9443	6.5914	6.3882	6.2561	6.1631	6.0942	6.0410	5.9988
5	6.6079	5.7861	5.4095	5.1922	5.0503	4.9503	4.8759	4.8183	4.7725
6	5.9874	5.1433	4.7571	4.5337	4.3874	4.2839	4.2067	4.1468	4.0990
7	5.5914	4.7374	4.3468	4.1203	3.9715	3.8660	3.7870	3.7257	3.6767
8	5.3177	4.4590	4.0662	3.8379	3.6875	3.5806	3.5005	3.4381	3.3881
9	5.1174	4.2565	3.8625	3.6331	3.4817	3.3738	3.2927	3.2296	3.1789
10	4.9646	4.1028	3.7083	3.4780	3.3258	3.2172	3.1355	3.0717	3.0204
11	4.8443	3.9823	3.5874	3.3567	3.2039	3.0946	3.0123	2.9480	2.8962
12	4.7472	3.8853	3.4903	3.2592	3.1059	2.9961	2.9134	2.8486	2.7964
13	4.6672	3.8056	3.4105	3.1791	3.0254	2.9153	2.8321	2.7669	2.7144
14	4.6001	3.7389	3.3439	3.1122	2.9582	2.8477	2.7642	2.6987	2.6458
15	4.5431	3.6823	3.2874	3.0556	2.9013	2.7905	2.7066	2.6408	2.5876
16	4.4940	3.6337	3.2389	3.0069	2.8524	2.7413	2.6572	2.5911	2.5377
17	4.4513	3.5915	3.1968	2.9647	2.8100	2.6987	2.6143	2.5480	2.4943
18	4.4139	3.5546	3.1599	2.9277	2.7729	2.6613	2.5767	2.5102	2.4563
19	4.3807	3.5219	3.1274	2.8951	2.7401	2.6283	2.5435	2.4768	2.4227
20	4.3512	3.4928	3.0984	2.8661	2.7109	2.5990	2.5140	2.4471	2.3928
21	4.3248	3.4668	3.0725	2.8401	2.6848	2.5727	2.4876	2.4205	2.3660
22	4.3009	3.4434	3.0491	2.8167	2.6613	2.5491	2.4638	2.3965	2.3419
23	4.2793	3.4221	3.0280	2.7955	2.6400	2.5277	2.4422	2.3748	2.3201
24	4.2597	3.4028	3.0088	2.7763	2.6207	2.5082	2.4226	2.3551	2.3002
25	4.2417	3.3852	2.9912	2.7587	2.6030	2.4904	2.4047	2.3371	2.2821
26	4.2252	3.3690	2.9752	2.7426	2.5868	2.4741	2.3883	2.3205	2.2655
27	4.2100	3.3541	2.9604	2.7278	2.5719	2.4591	2.3732	2.3053	2.2501
28	4.1960	3.3404	2.9467	2.7141	2.5581	2.4453	2.3593	2.2913	2.2360
29	4.1830	3.3277	2.9340	2.7014	2.5454	2.4324	2.3463	2.2783	2.2229
30	4.1709	3.3158	2.9223	2.6896	2.5336	2.4205	2.3343	2.2662	2.2107
40	4.0847	3.2317	2.8387	2.6060	2.4495	2.3359	2.2490	2.1802	2.1240
60	4.0012	3.1504	2.7581	2.5252	2.3683	2.2541	2.1665	2.0970	2.0401
120	3.9201	3.0718	2.6802	2.4472	2.2899	2.1750	2.0868	2.0164	1.9588
∞	3.8415	2.9957	2.6049	2.3719	2.2141	2.0986	2.0096	1.9384	1.8799

Denominator Degrees of Freedom

H   Critical Values of the *F*-Distribution *α* = 0.050 (cont.)

				Numerator Degrees of Freedom					
	10	11	12	13	14	15	16	17	18
1	241.8817	242.9835	243.9060	244.6898	245.3640	245.9499	246.4639	246.9184	247.3232
2	19.3959	19.4050	19.4125	19.4189	19.4244	19.4291	19.4333	19.4370	19.4402
3	8.7855	8.7633	8.7446	8.7287	8.7149	8.7029	8.6923	8.6829	8.6745
4	5.9644	5.9358	5.9117	5.8911	5.8733	5.8578	5.8441	5.8320	5.8211
5	4.7351	4.7040	4.6777	4.6552	4.6358	4.6188	4.6038	4.5904	4.5785
6	4.0600	4.0274	3.9999	3.9764	3.9559	3.9381	3.9223	3.9083	3.8957
7	3.6365	3.6030	3.5747	3.5503	3.5292	3.5107	3.4944	3.4799	3.4669
8	3.3472	3.3130	3.2839	3.2590	3.2374	3.2184	3.2016	3.1867	3.1733
9	3.1373	3.1025	3.0729	3.0475	3.0255	3.0061	2.9890	2.9737	2.9600
10	2.9782	2.9430	2.9130	2.8872	2.8647	2.8450	2.8276	2.8120	2.7980
11	2.8536	2.8179	2.7876	2.7614	2.7386	2.7186	2.7009	2.6851	2.6709
12	2.7534	2.7173	2.6866	2.6602	2.6371	2.6169	2.5989	2.5828	2.5684
13	2.6710	2.6347	2.6037	2.5769	2.5536	2.5331	2.5149	2.4987	2.4841
14	2.6022	2.5655	2.5342	2.5073	2.4837	2.4630	2.4446	2.4282	2.4134
15	2.5437	2.5068	2.4753	2.4481	2.4244	2.4034	2.3849	2.3683	2.3533
16	2.4935	2.4564	2.4247	2.3973	2.3733	2.3522	2.3335	2.3167	2.3016
17	2.4499	2.4126	2.3807	2.3531	2.3290	2.3077	2.2888	2.2719	2.2567
18	2.4117	2.3742	2.3421	2.3143	2.2900	2.2686	2.2496	2.2325	2.2172
19	2.3779	2.3402	2.3080	2.2800	2.2556	2.2341	2.2149	2.1977	2.1823
20	2.3479	2.3100	2.2776	2.2495	2.2250	2.2033	2.1840	2.1667	2.1511
21	2.3210	2.2829	2.2504	2.2222	2.1975	2.1757	2.1563	2.1389	2.1232
22	2.2967	2.2585	2.2258	2.1975	2.1727	2.1508	2.1313	2.1138	2.0980
23	2.2747	2.2364	2.2036	2.1752	2.1502	2.1282	2.1086	2.0910	2.0751
24	2.2547	2.2163	2.1834	2.1548	2.1298	2.1077	2.0880	2.0703	2.0543
25	2.2365	2.1979	2.1649	2.1362	2.1111	2.0889	2.0691	2.0513	2.0353
26	2.2197	2.1811	2.1479	2.1192	2.0939	2.0716	2.0518	2.0339	2.0178
27	2.2043	2.1655	2.1323	2.1035	2.0781	2.0558	2.0358	2.0179	2.0017
28	2.1900	2.1512	2.1179	2.0889	2.0635	2.0411	2.0210	2.0030	1.9868
29	2.1768	2.1379	2.1045	2.0755	2.0500	2.0275	2.0073	1.9893	1.9730
30	2.1646	2.1256	2.0921	2.0630	2.0374	2.0148	1.9946	1.9765	1.9601
40	2.0772	2.0376	2.0035	1.9738	1.9476	1.9245	1.9037	1.8851	1.8682
60	1.9926	1.9522	1.9174	1.8870	1.8602	1.8364	1.8151	1.7959	1.7784
120	1.9105	1.8693	1.8337	1.8026	1.7750	1.7505	1.7285	1.7085	1.6904
∞	1.8307	1.7887	1.7522	1.7202	1.6918	1.6664	1.6435	1.6228	1.6039

Denominator Degrees of Freedom

H   Critical Values of the F-Distribution α = 0.050 (cont.)

	Numerator Degrees of Freedom						
	19	20	24	30	40	60	120
1	247.6861	248.0131	249.0518	250.0951	251.1432	252.1957	253.2529
2	19.4431	19.4458	19.4541	19.4624	19.4707	19.4791	19.4874
3	8.6670	8.6602	8.6385	8.6166	8.5944	8.5720	8.5494
4	5.8114	5.8025	5.7744	5.7459	5.7170	5.6877	5.6581
5	4.5678	4.5581	4.5272	4.4957	4.4638	4.4314	4.3985
6	3.8844	3.8742	3.8415	3.8082	3.7743	3.7398	3.7047
7	3.4551	3.4445	3.4105	3.3758	3.3404	3.3043	3.2674
8	3.1613	3.1503	3.1152	3.0794	3.0428	3.0053	2.9669
9	2.9477	2.9365	2.9005	2.8637	2.8259	2.7872	2.7475
10	2.7854	2.7740	2.7372	2.6996	2.6609	2.6211	2.5801
11	2.6581	2.6464	2.6090	2.5705	2.5309	2.4901	2.4480
12	2.5554	2.5436	2.5055	2.4663	2.4259	2.3842	2.3410
13	2.4709	2.4589	2.4202	2.3803	2.3392	2.2966	2.2524
14	2.4000	2.3879	2.3487	2.3082	2.2664	2.2229	2.1778
15	2.3398	2.3275	2.2878	2.2468	2.2043	2.1601	2.1141
16	2.2880	2.2756	2.2354	2.1938	2.1507	2.1058	2.0589
17	2.2429	2.2304	2.1898	2.1477	2.1040	2.0584	2.0107
18	2.2033	2.1906	2.1497	2.1071	2.0629	2.0166	1.9681
19	2.1683	2.1555	2.1141	2.0712	2.0264	1.9795	1.9302
20	2.1370	2.1242	2.0825	2.0391	1.9938	1.9464	1.8963
21	2.1090	2.0960	2.0540	2.0102	1.9645	1.9165	1.8657
22	2.0837	2.0707	2.0283	1.9842	1.9380	1.8894	1.8380
23	2.0608	2.0476	2.0050	1.9605	1.9139	1.8648	1.8128
24	2.0399	2.0267	1.9838	1.9390	1.8920	1.8424	1.7896
25	2.0207	2.0075	1.9643	1.9192	1.8718	1.8217	1.7684
26	2.0032	1.9898	1.9464	1.9010	1.8533	1.8027	1.7488
27	1.9870	1.9736	1.9299	1.8842	1.8361	1.7851	1.7306
28	1.9720	1.9586	1.9147	1.8687	1.8203	1.7689	1.7138
29	1.9581	1.9446	1.9005	1.8543	1.8055	1.7537	1.6981
30	1.9452	1.9317	1.8874	1.8409	1.7918	1.7396	1.6835
40	1.8529	1.8389	1.7929	1.7444	1.6928	1.6373	1.5766
60	1.7625	1.7480	1.7001	1.6491	1.5943	1.5343	1.4673
120	1.6739	1.6587	1.6084	1.5543	1.4952	1.4290	1.3519
∞	1.5865	1.5705	1.5173	1.4591	1.3940	1.3180	1.2214

Denominator Degrees of Freedom

H   Critical Values of the *F*-Distribution α = 0.100

	Numerator Degrees of Freedom								
	1	2	3	4	5	6	7	8	9
1	39.8635	49.5000	53.5932	55.8330	57.2401	58.2044	58.9060	59.4390	59.8576
2	8.5263	9.0000	9.1618	9.2434	9.2926	9.3255	9.3491	9.3668	9.3805
3	5.5383	5.4624	5.3908	5.3426	5.3092	5.2847	5.2662	5.2517	5.2400
4	4.5448	4.3246	4.1909	4.1072	4.0506	4.0097	3.9790	3.9549	3.9357
5	4.0604	3.7797	3.6195	3.5202	3.4530	3.4045	3.3679	3.3393	3.3163
6	3.7759	3.4633	3.2888	3.1808	3.1075	3.0546	3.0145	2.9830	2.9577
7	3.5894	3.2574	3.0741	2.9605	2.8833	2.8274	2.7849	2.7516	2.7247
8	3.4579	3.1131	2.9238	2.8064	2.7264	2.6683	2.6241	2.5893	2.5612
9	3.3603	3.0065	2.8129	2.6927	2.6106	2.5509	2.5053	2.4694	2.4403
10	3.2850	2.9245	2.7277	2.6053	2.5216	2.4606	2.4140	2.3772	2.3473
11	3.2252	2.8595	2.6602	2.5362	2.4512	2.3891	2.3416	2.3040	2.2735
12	3.1765	2.8068	2.6055	2.4801	2.3940	2.3310	2.2828	2.2446	2.2135
13	3.1362	2.7632	2.5603	2.4337	2.3467	2.2830	2.2341	2.1953	2.1638
14	3.1022	2.7265	2.5222	2.3947	2.3069	2.2426	2.1931	2.1539	2.1220
15	3.0732	2.6952	2.4898	2.3614	2.2730	2.2081	2.1582	2.1185	2.0862
16	3.0481	2.6682	2.4618	2.3327	2.2438	2.1783	2.1280	2.0880	2.0553
17	3.0262	2.6446	2.4374	2.3077	2.2183	2.1524	2.1017	2.0613	2.0284
18	3.0070	2.6239	2.4160	2.2858	2.1958	2.1296	2.0785	2.0379	2.0047
19	2.9899	2.6056	2.3970	2.2663	2.1760	2.1094	2.0580	2.0171	1.9836
20	2.9747	2.5893	2.3801	2.2489	2.1582	2.0913	2.0397	1.9985	1.9649
21	2.9610	2.5746	2.3649	2.2333	2.1423	2.0751	2.0233	1.9819	1.9480
22	2.9486	2.5613	2.3512	2.2193	2.1279	2.0605	2.0084	1.9668	1.9327
23	2.9374	2.5493	2.3387	2.2065	2.1149	2.0472	1.9949	1.9531	1.9189
24	2.9271	2.5383	2.3274	2.1949	2.1030	2.0351	1.9826	1.9407	1.9063
25	2.9177	2.5283	2.3170	2.1842	2.0922	2.0241	1.9714	1.9292	1.8947
26	2.9091	2.5191	2.3075	2.1745	2.0822	2.0139	1.9610	1.9188	1.8841
27	2.9012	2.5106	2.2987	2.1655	2.0730	2.0045	1.9515	1.9091	1.8743
28	2.8938	2.5028	2.2906	2.1571	2.0645	1.9959	1.9427	1.9001	1.8652
29	2.8870	2.4955	2.2831	2.1494	2.0566	1.9878	1.9345	1.8918	1.8568
30	2.8807	2.4887	2.2761	2.1422	2.0492	1.9803	1.9269	1.8841	1.8490
40	2.8354	2.4404	2.2261	2.0909	1.9968	1.9269	1.8725	1.8289	1.7929
60	2.7911	2.3933	2.1774	2.0410	1.9457	1.8747	1.8194	1.7748	1.7380
120	2.7478	2.3473	2.1300	1.9923	1.8959	1.8238	1.7675	1.7220	1.6842
∞	2.7055	2.3026	2.0838	1.9449	1.8473	1.7741	1.7167	1.6702	1.6315

Denominator Degrees of Freedom

H   Critical Values of the *F*-Distribution
α = 0.100 (cont.)

					Numerator Degrees of Freedom				
	10	11	12	13	14	15	16	17	18
1	60.1950	60.4727	60.7052	60.9028	61.0727	61.2203	61.3499	61.4644	61.5664
2	9.3916	9.4006	9.4081	9.4145	9.4200	9.4247	9.4289	9.4325	9.4358
3	5.2304	5.2224	5.2156	5.2098	5.2047	5.2003	5.1964	5.1929	5.1898
4	3.9199	3.9067	3.8955	3.8859	3.8776	3.8704	3.8639	3.8582	3.8531
5	3.2974	3.2816	3.2682	3.2567	3.2468	3.2380	3.2303	3.2234	3.2172
6	2.9369	2.9195	2.9047	2.8920	2.8809	2.8712	2.8626	2.8550	2.8481
7	2.7025	2.6839	2.6681	2.6545	2.6426	2.6322	2.6230	2.6148	2.6074
8	2.5380	2.5186	2.5020	2.4876	2.4752	2.4642	2.4545	2.4458	2.4380
9	2.4163	2.3961	2.3789	2.3640	2.3510	2.3396	2.3295	2.3205	2.3123
10	2.3226	2.3018	2.2841	2.2687	2.2553	2.2435	2.2330	2.2237	2.2153
11	2.2482	2.2269	2.2087	2.1930	2.1792	2.1671	2.1563	2.1467	2.1380
12	2.1878	2.1660	2.1474	2.1313	2.1173	2.1049	2.0938	2.0839	2.0750
13	2.1376	2.1155	2.0966	2.0802	2.0658	2.0532	2.0419	2.0318	2.0227
14	2.0954	2.0729	2.0537	2.0370	2.0224	2.0095	1.9981	1.9878	1.9785
15	2.0593	2.0366	2.0171	2.0001	1.9853	1.9722	1.9605	1.9501	1.9407
16	2.0281	2.0051	1.9854	1.9682	1.9532	1.9399	1.9281	1.9175	1.9079
17	2.0009	1.9777	1.9577	1.9404	1.9252	1.9117	1.8997	1.8889	1.8792
18	1.9770	1.9535	1.9333	1.9158	1.9004	1.8868	1.8747	1.8638	1.8539
19	1.9557	1.9321	1.9117	1.8940	1.8785	1.8647	1.8524	1.8414	1.8314
20	1.9367	1.9129	1.8924	1.8745	1.8588	1.8449	1.8325	1.8214	1.8113
21	1.9197	1.8956	1.8750	1.8570	1.8412	1.8271	1.8146	1.8034	1.7932
22	1.9043	1.8801	1.8593	1.8411	1.8252	1.8111	1.7984	1.7871	1.7768
23	1.8903	1.8659	1.8450	1.8267	1.8107	1.7964	1.7837	1.7723	1.7619
24	1.8775	1.8530	1.8319	1.8136	1.7974	1.7831	1.7703	1.7587	1.7483
25	1.8658	1.8412	1.8200	1.8015	1.7853	1.7708	1.7579	1.7463	1.7358
26	1.8550	1.8303	1.8090	1.7904	1.7741	1.7596	1.7466	1.7349	1.7243
27	1.8451	1.8203	1.7989	1.7802	1.7638	1.7492	1.7361	1.7243	1.7137
28	1.8359	1.8110	1.7895	1.7708	1.7542	1.7395	1.7264	1.7146	1.7039
29	1.8274	1.8024	1.7808	1.7620	1.7454	1.7306	1.7174	1.7055	1.6947
30	1.8195	1.7944	1.7727	1.7538	1.7371	1.7223	1.7090	1.6970	1.6862
40	1.7627	1.7369	1.7146	1.6950	1.6778	1.6624	1.6486	1.6362	1.6249
60	1.7070	1.6805	1.6574	1.6372	1.6193	1.6034	1.5890	1.5760	1.5642
120	1.6524	1.6250	1.6012	1.5803	1.5617	1.5450	1.5300	1.5164	1.5039
∞	1.5987	1.5705	1.5458	1.5240	1.5046	1.4871	1.4714	1.4570	1.4439

Denominator Degrees of Freedom

H   Critical Values of the *F*-Distribution *α* = 0.100 (cont.)

	Numerator Degrees of Freedom						
	19	20	24	30	40	60	120
1	61.6579	61.7403	62.0020	62.2650	62.5291	62.7943	63.0606
2	9.4387	9.4413	9.4496	9.4579	9.4662	9.4746	9.4829
3	5.1870	5.1845	5.1764	5.1681	5.1597	5.1512	5.1425
4	3.8485	3.8443	3.8310	3.8174	3.8036	3.7896	3.7753
5	3.2117	3.2067	3.1905	3.1741	3.1573	3.1402	3.1228
6	2.8419	2.8363	2.8183	2.8000	2.7812	2.7620	2.7423
7	2.6008	2.5947	2.5753	2.5555	2.5351	2.5142	2.4928
8	2.4310	2.4246	2.4041	2.3830	2.3614	2.3391	2.3162
9	2.3050	2.2983	2.2768	2.2547	2.2320	2.2085	2.1843
10	2.2077	2.2007	2.1784	2.1554	2.1317	2.1072	2.0818
11	2.1302	2.1230	2.1000	2.0762	2.0516	2.0261	1.9997
12	2.0670	2.0597	2.0360	2.0115	1.9861	1.9597	1.9323
13	2.0145	2.0070	1.9827	1.9576	1.9315	1.9043	1.8759
14	1.9701	1.9625	1.9377	1.9119	1.8852	1.8572	1.8280
15	1.9321	1.9243	1.8990	1.8728	1.8454	1.8168	1.7867
16	1.8992	1.8913	1.8656	1.8388	1.8108	1.7816	1.7507
17	1.8704	1.8624	1.8362	1.8090	1.7805	1.7506	1.7191
18	1.8450	1.8368	1.8103	1.7827	1.7537	1.7232	1.6910
19	1.8224	1.8142	1.7873	1.7592	1.7298	1.6988	1.6659
20	1.8022	1.7938	1.7667	1.7382	1.7083	1.6768	1.6433
21	1.7840	1.7756	1.7481	1.7193	1.6890	1.6569	1.6228
22	1.7675	1.7590	1.7312	1.7021	1.6714	1.6389	1.6041
23	1.7525	1.7439	1.7159	1.6864	1.6554	1.6224	1.5871
24	1.7388	1.7302	1.7019	1.6721	1.6407	1.6073	1.5715
25	1.7263	1.7175	1.6890	1.6589	1.6272	1.5934	1.5570
26	1.7147	1.7059	1.6771	1.6468	1.6147	1.5805	1.5437
27	1.7040	1.6951	1.6662	1.6356	1.6032	1.5686	1.5313
28	1.6941	1.6852	1.6560	1.6252	1.5925	1.5575	1.5198
29	1.6849	1.6759	1.6465	1.6155	1.5825	1.5472	1.5090
30	1.6763	1.6673	1.6377	1.6065	1.5732	1.5376	1.4989
40	1.6146	1.6052	1.5741	1.5411	1.5056	1.4672	1.4248
60	1.5534	1.5435	1.5107	1.4755	1.4373	1.3952	1.3476
120	1.4926	1.4821	1.4472	1.4094	1.3676	1.3203	1.2646
∞	1.4318	1.4206	1.3832	1.3419	1.2951	1.2400	1.1686

Denominator Degrees of Freedom

I Critical Values for the Sign Test

α for one-tailed test	0.005	0.01	0.025	0.05
α for two-tailed test	0.01	0.02	0.05	0.10
n				
5	*	*	*	0
6	*	*	0	0
7	*	0	0	0
8	0	0	0	1
9	0	0	1	1
10	0	0	1	1
11	0	1	1	2
12	1	1	2	2
13	1	1	2	3
14	1	2	2	3
15	2	2	3	3
16	2	2	3	4
17	2	3	4	4
18	3	3	4	5
19	3	4	4	5
20	3	4	5	5
21	4	4	5	6
22	4	5	5	6
23	4	5	6	7
24	5	5	6	7
25	5	6	7	7

$$\text{For } n > 25, \ z = \frac{X + 0.5 - \left(\dfrac{n}{2}\right)}{\dfrac{\sqrt{n}}{2}}.$$

Note: * denotes that it is not possible to have values in the critical region.

J   Critical Values for the Wilcoxon Signed - Rank Test

α for one-tailed test	0.005	0.01	0.025	0.05
α for two-tailed test	0.01	0.02	0.05	0.10
n				
5	*	*	*	1
6	*	*	1	2
7	*	0	2	4
8	0	2	4	6
9	2	3	6	8
10	3	5	8	11
11	5	7	11	14
12	7	10	14	17
13	10	13	17	21
14	13	16	21	26
15	16	20	25	30
16	19	24	30	36
17	23	28	35	41
18	28	33	40	47
19	32	38	46	54
20	37	43	52	60
21	43	49	59	68
22	49	56	66	75
23	55	62	73	83
24	61	69	81	92
25	68	77	90	101
26	76	85	98	110
27	84	93	107	120
28	92	102	117	130
29	100	111	127	141
30	109	120	137	152

Note: * denotes that it is not possible to have values in the critical region.

K   Critical Values for the Wilcoxon Rank-Sum Test

For one-tailed tests with $\alpha = 0.025$ or two-tailed tests with $\alpha = 0.05$

n_1	3		4		5		6		7		8		9		10	
n_2	T_L	T_U	T_L	T_U	T_L	T_U	T_L	T_U	T_L	T_U	T_L	T_U	T_L	T_U	T_L	T_U
3	5	16	6	18	6	21	7	23	7	26	8	28	8	31	9	33
4	6	18	11	25	12	28	12	32	13	35	14	38	15	41	16	44
5	6	21	12	28	18	37	19	41	20	45	21	49	22	53	24	56
6	7	23	12	32	19	41	26	52	28	56	29	61	31	65	32	70
7	7	26	13	35	20	45	28	56	37	68	39	73	41	78	43	83
8	8	28	14	38	21	49	29	61	39	73	49	87	51	93	54	98
9	8	31	15	41	22	53	31	65	41	78	51	93	63	108	66	114
10	9	33	16	44	24	56	32	70	43	83	54	98	66	114	79	131

For one-tailed tests with $\alpha = 0.05$ or two-tailed tests with $\alpha = 0.10$

n_1	3		4		5		6		7		8		9		10	
n_2	T_L	T_U	T_L	T_U	T_L	T_U	T_L	T_U	T_L	T_U	T_L	T_U	T_L	T_U	T_L	T_U
3	6	15	7	17	7	20	8	22	9	24	9	27	10	29	11	31
4	7	17	12	24	13	27	14	30	15	33	16	36	17	39	18	42
5	7	20	13	27	19	36	20	40	22	43	24	46	25	50	26	54
6	8	22	14	30	20	40	28	50	30	54	32	58	33	63	35	67
7	9	24	15	33	22	43	30	54	39	66	41	71	43	76	46	80
8	9	27	16	36	24	46	32	58	41	71	52	84	54	90	57	95
9	10	29	17	39	25	50	33	63	43	76	54	90	66	105	69	111
10	11	31	18	42	26	54	35	67	46	80	57	95	69	111	83	127

L   Critical Values of Spearman's Rank Correlation Coefficient r_s

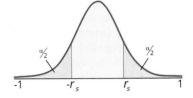

n	$\alpha = 0.10$	$\alpha = 0.05$	$\alpha = 0.02$	$\alpha = 0.01$
5	0.900	*	*	*
6	0.829	0.886	0.943	*
7	0.714	0.786	0.893	*
8	0.643	0.738	0.833	0.881
9	0.600	0.683	0.783	0.833
10	0.564	0.648	0.745	0.794
11	0.523	0.623	0.736	0.818
12	0.497	0.591	0.703	0.780
13	0.475	0.566	0.673	0.745
14	0.457	0.545	0.646	0.716
15	0.441	0.525	0.623	0.689
16	0.425	0.507	0.601	0.666
17	0.412	0.490	0.582	0.645
18	0.399	0.476	0.564	0.625
19	0.388	0.462	0.549	0.608
20	0.377	0.450	0.534	0.591
21	0.368	0.438	0.521	0.576
22	0.359	0.428	0.508	0.562
23	0.351	0.418	0.496	0.549
24	0.343	0.409	0.485	0.537
25	0.336	0.400	0.475	0.526
26	0.329	0.392	0.465	0.515
27	0.323	0.385	0.456	0.505
28	0.317	0.377	0.448	0.496
29	0.311	0.370	0.440	0.487
30	0.305	0.364	0.432	0.478

Note: * denotes that it is not possible to have values in the critical region.

M   Critical Values for the Number of Runs ($\alpha = 0.05$)

									Value of n										
	2	**3**	**4**	**5**	**6**	**7**	**8**	**9**	**10**	**11**	**12**	**13**	**14**	**15**	**16**	**17**	**18**	**19**	**20**
2	1	1	1	1	1	1	1	1	1	1	2	2	2	2	2	2	2	2	2
	6	6	6	6	6	6	6	6	6	6	6	6	6	6	6	6	6	6	6
3	1	1	1	1	2	2	2	2	2	2	2	2	2	3	3	3	3	3	3
	6	8	8	8	8	8	8	8	8	8	8	8	8	8	8	8	8	8	8
4	1	1	1	2	2	2	3	3	3	3	3	3	3	4	4	4	4	4	4
	6	8	9	9	9	10	10	10	10	10	10	10	10	10	10	10	10	10	10
5	1	1	2	2	3	3	3	3	3	4	4	4	4	4	4	4	5	5	5
	6	8	9	10	10	11	11	12	12	12	12	12	12	12	12	12	12	12	12
6	1	2	2	3	3	3	3	4	4	4	4	5	5	5	5	5	5	6	6
	6	8	9	10	11	12	12	13	13	13	13	14	14	14	14	14	14	14	14
7	1	2	2	3	3	3	4	4	5	5	5	5	5	6	6	6	6	6	6
	6	8	10	11	12	13	13	14	14	14	14	15	15	15	16	16	16	16	16
8	1	2	3	3	3	4	4	5	5	5	6	6	6	6	6	7	7	7	7
	6	8	10	11	12	13	14	14	15	15	16	16	16	16	17	17	17	17	17
9	1	2	3	3	4	4	5	5	5	6	6	6	7	7	7	7	8	8	8
	6	8	10	12	13	14	14	15	16	16	16	17	17	18	18	18	18	18	18
10	1	2	3	3	4	5	5	5	6	6	7	7	7	7	8	8	8	8	9
	6	8	10	12	13	14	15	16	16	17	17	18	18	18	19	19	19	20	20
11	1	2	3	4	4	5	5	6	6	7	7	7	8	8	8	9	9	9	9
	6	8	10	12	13	14	15	16	17	17	18	19	19	19	20	20	20	21	21
12	2	2	3	4	4	5	6	6	7	7	7	8	8	8	9	9	9	10	10
	6	8	10	12	13	14	16	16	17	18	19	19	20	20	21	21	21	22	22
13	2	2	3	4	5	5	6	6	7	7	8	8	9	9	9	10	10	10	10
	6	8	10	12	14	15	16	17	18	19	19	20	20	21	21	22	22	23	23
14	2	2	3	4	5	5	6	7	7	8	8	9	9	9	10	10	10	11	11
	6	8	10	12	14	15	16	17	18	19	20	20	21	22	22	23	23	23	24
15	2	3	3	4	5	6	6	7	7	8	8	9	9	10	10	11	11	11	12
	6	8	10	12	14	15	16	18	18	19	20	21	22	22	23	23	24	24	25
16	2	3	4	4	5	6	6	7	8	8	9	9	10	10	11	11	11	12	12
	6	8	10	12	14	16	17	18	19	20	21	21	22	23	23	24	25	25	25
17	2	3	4	4	5	6	7	7	8	9	9	10	10	11	11	11	12	12	13
	6	8	10	12	14	16	17	18	19	20	21	22	23	23	24	25	25	26	26
18	2	3	4	5	5	6	7	8	8	9	9	10	10	11	11	12	12	13	13
	6	8	10	12	14	16	17	18	19	20	21	22	23	24	25	25	26	26	27
19	2	3	4	5	6	6	7	8	8	9	10	10	11	11	12	12	13	13	13
	6	8	10	12	14	16	17	18	20	21	22	23	23	24	25	26	26	27	27
20	2	3	4	5	6	6	7	8	9	9	10	10	11	12	12	13	13	13	14
	6	8	10	12	14	16	17	18	20	21	22	23	24	25	25	26	27	27	28

Value of m

Appendix B
Descriptions of Selected Large Data Sets

There is a massive amount of data associated with this textbook, all available and outlined on the web resource. However, here are additional descriptions of some of the data sets with a large number of variables:

Amazon Stock Price

Beers and Breweries

California DDS Expenditures

CO_2 Emissions

Employee Satisfaction

Moneyball

Mount Pleasant Real Estate

OECD Better Life Index 2016

San Francisco Salaries 2014

Super Bowl Stats

US County Data

US Violent Crime by State

Amazon Stock Price

Data regarding the price per share of Amazon stock from its initial public offering (IPO) in May 1997 to September 2017

Source: http://www.macrotrends.net/stocks/charts/AMZN/prices/amazon-inc-stock-price-history

Date: Date of observation
Open: Price per share when the stock market opened on the specified date
High: The maximum price per share reached on the specified date
Low: The minimum price per share reached on the specified date
Close: Price per share when the stock market closed on the specified date
Log Close: The log transformed value of the close variable
Volume: The number of shares that changed hands on the specified date

Beers and Breweries

Information about several canned beers brewed in the U.S. and the breweries where they were brewed.

Source: https://www.kaggle.com/nickhould/craft-cans
License: https://opendatacommons.org/licenses/odbl/1.0/

id: The ID number of each individual beer
abv: Alcohol by volume
ibu: International Bitterness Units
name: Name of the beer
style: Style of the beer
ounces: Volume of beer in the can, in ounces
brewery id: The ID number of each brewery
brewery name: Name of the brewery that the specified beer was brewed
city: City where the brewery is located
state: State where the brewery is located

California DDS Expenditures

Data regarding the distribution of expenditures for the California Department of Developmental Services (DDS).

Source: http://www.amstat.org/publications/jse/v22n1/mickel/paradox_data.csv

Id: ID number of the consumer
Age Group: The age range the consumer falls into (6 pre-defined Age Groups)

Age: The age of the consumer

Gender: The gender of the consumer

Expenditures: The amount of funding allocated to the consumer from the DDS

Ethnicity: The ethnicity of the consumer

CO$_2$ Emissions

Information regarding the CO$_2$ emissions in thousands of metric tons from nearly every country in the world for the years 1960-2014.

Source: Millennium Development Goals Database, UN Statistics Division

Year: The year the CO$_2$ emissions were recorded

Country Name: The name of the country being measured

Employee Satisfaction

A data set containing data regarding the satisfaction of employees at a company.

Source: https://www.kaggle.com/ludobenistant/hr-analytics
License: https://creativecommons.org/licenses/by-sa/4.0/legalcode

employee_id:	The ID number associated with the individual employee
satisfaction_level:	How satisfied the employee is in their position (scale of 0 to 1)
last_evaluation_score:	How management rated employee performance during the last evaluation (scale of 0 to 1)
number_of_projects:	The number of projects an employee is currently working on
average_monthly_hours:	The average number of hours the employee works in a month
years_spent_at _company:	The number of years the employee has worked at the company
work_accident:	A binary variable that indicates whether the employee experienced an accident at work
left_company:	A binary variable that indicates whether an employee left the company
promotion_in_last _5_years:	A binary variable that indicates whether an employee received a promotion in the last 5 years
department:	The department that the employee works in
salary:	The level of the employee's salary (low, medium, high)
salary_range:	The dollar range for the salary levels

Moneyball

A data set containing selected statistics for Major League Baseball teams for the years 1962-2012.
Source: www.baseball-reference.com

Team: The team name abbreviation

League: The league of the MLB that the team played in

Year: The year associated with the statistics

RS: Runs scored

RA: Runs Allowed

RD: Run Differential

W: Number of wins

OBP: On-base percentage

SLG: Slugging percentage

BA: Batting Average

Playoffs: A binary variable that indicates whether or not a team made the playoffs

RankSeason: Team ranking at the end of the regular season

RankPlayoffs: Team ranking at the end of the post-season

G: Number of games played

OOBP: Opponent on-base percentage

OSLG: Opponent slugging percentage

Mount Pleasant Real Estate

A data set containing information about properties for sale in three subdivisions of Mount Pleasant, South Carolina in the year 2017.

ID: The property ID number

List Price: The price the owner is selling the property for

Duplex: Whether the property is a duplex or not

Bedrooms: The number of bedrooms

Baths – Total: Total number of bathrooms

Baths – Full: Number of full bathrooms

Baths – Half: Number of half bathrooms

Stories: Number of stories

Subdivision: The subdivision the property is in

Square Footage: The estimated floor area inside the house

Year Built: The year the house was constructed

Acreage: The size of the lot

New Owned:	Whether the house has been lived in previously
House Style:	The type of property (traditional, condo, ranch, etc.)
Covered Parking Spots:	The number of covered parking spots included with the property
Misc. Exterior:	Miscellaneous exterior features
Has Pool:	Whether the property has a private pool or not
Has Dock:	Whether the property has a private dock or not
Fenced Yard:	Whether the property has a fenced-in yard or not
Screened Porch:	Whether the property has a screened porch or not
Amenities:	Amenities included with the property
Golf Course:	Whether the property is located on a golf course or not
Fireplace:	Whether the property has a fireplace or not
Number of Fireplaces:	The number of fireplaces

OECD Better Life Index 2016

Data gathered by the Organisation for Economic Co-operation and Development (OECD) regarding the economic strength and well-being of its 35 member countries as well as 3 prominent non-member countries (Brazil, Russia, and South Africa).

Source: stats.oecd.org, Social Protection and Well-being, Better Life Index 2016

country:	Name of the country
percent_of_houses_no_facilities:	Percent of households in the country that lack basic facilities
percent_of_income_spent_on _housing:	Average percent of household income spent on housing
rooms_per_person:	The average number of rooms per person residing in a household
household_net_adj_disposable _income:	The amount a household has to spend after income taxes
household_net_financial_wealth:	The net worth of a household (assets minus liabilities)
percent_labor_market_insecurity:	Expected earnings lost, measured as the percentage of the previous earnings, associated with unemployment.
employment_rate:	Percentage of working age population (15 to 64) that is employed
long_term_unemployment_rate:	Percentage of working age population (15 to 64) that has been unemployed for longer than 27 weeks.
personal_earning_per_year:	The total amount of income earned annually.
quality_of_support:	The quality of the social support network (friends, family, etc.)
percent_of_pop_finish_highschool:	The percentage of the population between the ages of 25 and 64 that holds at least one upper secondary degree

average_PISA_score:	The average score a population receives on the PISA test
average_years_in_education:	Average years of education in which a 5-year-old can expect to enroll during his/her lifetime until the age of 39.
air_pollution:	Micrograms per cubic meter of small particulate matter in the air
water_quality:	Percentage of population that is satisfied with water quality
stakeholder_engagement_score:	The extent of stakeholder engagement that is built in the development of laws and regulations
voter_turnout:	The percentage of people registered to vote that cast a ballot in the most recent parliamentary or presidential election.
life_expectancy_at_birth:	How long on average a person born today could expect to live
self_reported_health:	The percentage of the population 15 years or older who report "good" or better health.
satisfaction_score:	A weighted sum on a scale of 0-10 of how people evaluated their life as a whole.
safety_score:	The percentage of people who responded positively to the question "Do you feel safe walking alone at night in the city or area where you live?"
homicide_rate_per_100000:	The number of homicides per 100,000 residents
percent_employees_working _50+hours_per_week:	percentage of dependent employed whose usual hours of work per week are 50 hours or more.
average_hours_leisure_personal _care:	average hours per day spent on leisure (walking, hiking, sports, entertainment, volunteering, taking nap, etc.) and personal care (sleeping [not napping], eating/drinking, medical or hygienic activities, etc.)

San Francisco Salaries 2014

A data set that provides employment information regarding employees in the San Francisco area for the year 2014.

Source: https://www.kaggle.com/kaggle/sf-salaries
License: https://creativecommons.org/publicdomain/zero/1.0/legalcode

Id:	The ID number assigned to the employee
EmployeeName:	The name of the employee
JobTitle:	The title of the position that the employee holds
BasePay:	The base annual salary (in dollars) that the employee received
OvertimePay:	The amount (in dollars) the employee received in overtime pay
OtherPay:	The amount (in dollars) the employee received in payment from bonuses and other pay

Benefits:	The amount (in dollars) the employee received in the form of company benefits
TotalPay:	The total amount (in dollars) the employee received throughout the year not including benefits
TotalPayBenefits:	The total amount (in dollars) the employee received throughout the year including benefits
LogTotalPay Benefits:	The log transformation of the TotalPayBenefits variable
Year:	The year the data was recorded
Agency:	The location the data was gathered from
Status:	Full-time or part-time

Super Bowl Stats

A data set containing football team statistics for every Super Bowl played from the years 1967 to 2017.

Source: https://www.pro-football-reference.com/

Date:	The date the game was played on
SB:	The roman numeral denoting the name and number of the Super Bowl
Winner:	The team that won the Super Bowl that year
Winner_Pts:	The amount of points the winning team scored in the game
Winner_First Downs:	The number of first downs the winning team earned during the game
Winner_Rush Attempts:	The amount of times the winning team tried to run the football during the game
Winner_Rushing Yards:	The number of yards the winning team gained by running the football during the game
Winner_Rushing TDs:	The number of touchdowns the winning team scored by running the football during the game
Winner_Fumbles:	The amount of times the winning team fumbled the football
Winner_Fumbles Lost:	The amount of times the winning team fumbled the football and turned possession over to their opponent
Winner_Pass Attempts:	The amount of times the winning team tried to pass the football during the game
Winner_Passes Completed:	The amount of times the winning team passed the ball and made a successful catch
Winner_Passing Yards:	The number of yards the winning team gained by passing the football during the game
Winner_Passing TDs:	The number of touchdowns the winning team scored by passing the football during the game
Winner_Interceptions:	The amount of times the winning team intercepted a pass attempt made by their opponent

Winner_Total Yards:	The total number of yards the winning team gained by either rushing or passing the football during the game
Winner_Time of Possession:	The amount of time the game clock ran when the winning team had possession of the football
Loser:	The team that lost the Super Bowl that year
Loser_Pts:	The amount of points the losing team scored in the game
Loser_First Downs:	The number of first downs the losing team earned during the game
Loser_Rush Attempts:	The amount of times the losing team tried to run the football during the game
Loser_Rushing Yards:	The number of yards the losing team gained by running the football during the game
Loser_Rushing TDs:	The number of touchdowns the losing team scored by running the football during the game
Loser_Fumbles:	The amount of times the losing team fumbled the football
Loser_Fumbles Lost:	The amount of times the losing team fumbled the football and turned possession over to their opponent
Loser_Pass Attempts:	The amount of times the losing team tried to pass the football during the game
Loser_Passes Completed:	The amount of times the losing team passed the ball and made a successful catch
Loser_Passing Yards:	The number of yards the losing team gained by passing the football during the game
Loser_Passing TDs:	The number of touchdowns the losing team scored by passing the football during the game
Loser_Interceptions:	The amount of times the losing team intercepted a pass attempt made by their opponent
Loser_Total Yards:	The total number of yards the losing team gained by either rushing or passing the football during the game
Loser_Time of Possession:	The amount of time the game clock ran when the losing team had possession of the football
MVP:	The player that was voted the Super Bowl MVP
Stadium:	The stadium the game was played in
City:	The city the game was played in
State:	The state the game was played in
Coin Toss Result:	Whether the coin toss resulted in heads or tails
Coin Toss Winner:	The team that won the coin toss

US County Data

A data set containing information regarding nearly every county in the United States for the year 2010.

Source: Kirkegaard, E. O. W. (2017, April 7). Inequality across US counties: an S factor analysis. Retrieved from osf.io/cknjr

fips:	The FIPS county code
name_16:	The name of the county
County:	The county name and the state it is in
Less.Than.High.School:	The percentage of the population 18-years old or older with less than a high school education
At.Least.High.School.Diploma:	The percentage of the population 18-years old or older with at least a high school diploma or GED
At.Least.Bachelor.s.Degree:	The percentage of the population 25-years old or older with at least a Bachelor's degree
Graduate.Degree:	The percentage of the population 25-years old or older with at least a Master's degree
School.Enrollment:	School enrollment percentage for the population 3-years old and older
Median.Earnings.2010.dollars:	The median annual income for an individual normalized to the value of a dollar in 2010
White.not.Latino.Population:	The percentage of the county population that identifies as Caucasian with no Latino heritage
African.American.Population:	The percentage of the county population that identifies as African American
Native.American.Population:	The percentage of the county population that identifies as Native American
Asian.American.Population:	The percentage of the county population that identifies as Asian American
Population.some.other.race.or.races:	The percentage of the county population that identifies with another ethnicity or multiples ethnicities
Latino.Population:	The percentage of the county population that identifies as Latino
Children.Under.6.Living.in.Poverty:	The percentage of children under the age of 6 that are living in poverty
Adult.65.and.Older.Living.in.Poverty:	The percentage of adults aged 65 and older that are living in poverty
Total.Population:	The total county population

75+ more variables included on the companion website!

US Violent Crime by State

A data set containing the violent crime rates for every state in the U.S. from 1989 to 2014.

Source: https://www.ucrdatatool.gov/

Year: The year the crime rate is associated with

Alabama: The crime rates in Alabama by year

...

Wyoming: The crime rates in Wyoming by year

Answer Key
Chapter 1

Section 1.6

7. a. Adult females.

   b. Average blood pressure.

   c. 20 females who have high blood pressure.

   d. Inferential statistics.

8. a. All teenagers between 15 and 19.

   b. Percentage of teenagers between the ages of 15 and 19 who have used heroin one or more times.

   c. 1,824 teenagers.

   d. Inferential statistics.

9. a. Students in all colleges and universities in the United States.

   b. The proportion that binge drink.

   c. A total of 17,592 students selected from 140 US 4-year colleges.

   d. The data depends on what the student admits rather than an experimental measurement. The sample covers only students of 4-year colleges within a two week period.

10. a. All boys under 18.

   b. Percentage of boys' heights observed to be at or below a certain height (percentile).

   c. 1,000 boys.

   d. Descriptive statistics.

11. a. All employees of the company.

   b. Average reading comprehension.

   c. 20 employees.

   d. Inferential statistics.

12. a. All women.

   b. Quetelet Index.

   c. Women aged 35-65 years visiting a breast screening clinic in New York City.

   d. Average Quetelet Index of women attending the screening clinic.

   e. 25.2

Additional Exercises

1. Not necessarily. It could be that people who wear seat belts are also more cautious drivers.

2. a. US states with coastlines.

   b. Coastline length.

3. a. All automobile accident claims of the company.

   b. The number of auto accident claims by region.

   c. 50 claims.

   d. Descriptive statistics.

4. a. Nonsmoking US Midwestern university students.

   b. Percent of population that would want a smoker for a roommate/date/spouse.

   c. A sample of 547 nonsmokers was selected from a large Midwestern university. The sample contained 330 women and 217 men.

   d. Answers will vary. Example, 76% of people surveyed strongly agreed they were less likely to want a smoker as a roommate.

   e. We are trying to draw a more general conclusion about all students at the university.

Chapter 2

2.1 Exercises

29. a. Well-defined

b. Well-defined

c. Not well-defined

d. Well-defined

e. Not well-defined

30. Not very reasonable. Answers will vary.

31. There is no well-defined scale to measure cleanliness or aesthetics. Answers will vary.

32. Answers will vary.

33. Answers will vary.

34. Inferential. Data were collected from a sample and the information was used to make a general claim about the population of the company's bulbs.

35. a. By randomly assigning women to two groups and using one of the groups as a "control" group, the experiment should produce data that will reveal the impact of the different diets.

b. Difference in diet (The first group received 1200 calorie per day diet for the entire period whereas the second group received 420 calorie per day diet for 16 weeks and then were shifted to 1200 calorie per day diet for the rest of the experimental period.)

c. Weight loss.

d. Yes, the women receiving the 1200 calorie per day diet represent a control group.

e. Observational studies are subject to self-selection bias. We would not necessarily know the cause of the weight reduction.

36. a. The use of a sibling we tried to control for family environment and genetic factors that might affect academic performance.

b. Effect of the drug Theophylline (for asthma) on academic performance.

c. Academic performance.

d. Yes, the non-asthmatic children constitute the control group.

e. In an observational study the usage of the drug cannot be controlled, the results would have not been conclusive.

37. a. Phase 1: Gather information about the phenomenon being studied.

b. Controlled experiment.

c. Number of major attacks of Multiple Sclerosis.

d. Bovine myelin.

e. Fifteen individuals in the early stages of MS fed bovine myelin.

f. Fifteen individuals in the early stages of MS given a placebo.

38. a. Phase 1: Gather information about the phenomenon being studied.

b. Controlled study.

c. Number of migraine headaches.

d. Chocolate.

e. Twelve migraine-prone subjects given a peppermint-laced chocolate candy.

f. Eight migraine-prone subjects given a peppermint-laced placebo.

39. Jacob's knee could feel better simply because he took a week break from playing basketball. Answers will vary.

40. a. Phase 3: Collect further data to test the hypothesis.

b. Controlled study if the women were randomly selected to participate in the two groups. Otherwise this is an observational study.

c. Number of strokes, number of heart attacks.

d. The amount of beta carotene-rich food consumed per day.

e. Women who ate one cup of beta carotene-rich food a day.

f. Women who ate a quarter cup of beta carotene-rich food a day.

41. There are many factors that affect whether or not someone is happy. Additionally, since both questions require a yes or no reply there is no way to quantify happiness or going to church. Answers will vary.

42. a. Yes

    b. The knowledge of market share statistics allows companies to analyze the effectiveness of marketing campaigns and other business practices. Answers will vary.

43. Generally people that have more money will seek the help of a financial advisor since advisors are paid for their services. Answers will vary.

2.2 Exercises

11. a. Discrete

    b. Continuous

    c. Continuous

    d. Continuous

    e. Discrete

12. a. Discrete

    b. Continuous

    c. Discrete

    d. Continuous

    e. Discrete

13. a. Cadet height, weight, state from which the cadet was appointed, father's occupation, parents' income, type of home residence.

    b. State from which the cadet was appointed, father's occupation, type of home residence are qualitative variables. Cadet height and weight, parents' income, are quantitative variables.

    c. State from which the cadet was appointed – Nominal; Father's occupation – Nominal; Type of home residence –Nominal; Cadet Weight – Ratio; Parent income – Ratio; Cadet Height – Ratio

    d. A lot of information is gathered about the cadets, to be able to derive some conclusions

from the information, a data summary answering the relevant questions is required.

14. a. Gender, Political Affiliation, Opinion on how President Clinton was handling the situation in Bosnia, News media performance.

    b. Gender, Political Affiliation, Opinion, News media performance are qualitative variables. There are no quantitative variables.

    c. Gender – Nominal; Political Affiliation – Nominal; Opinion – Nominal; News media performance – Ordinal

    d. There may be an inordinate number of one party affiliation (Republicans or Democrats) selected for the survey. In general there are no "controls" on the survey.

15. a. Quantitative

    b. Ratio

16. a. Interval

    b. Ratio

    c. Ordinal

    d. Nominal

    e. Ratio

17. a. Ratio

    b. Nominal

    c. Ordinal

    d. Ratio

18. Ratio. Market usage share percentages have a meaningful zero, and the ratio between two market shares is meaningful.

2.3 Exercises

8. a. Time Series

    b. Time Series

    c. Stationary

9. a. Time Series

    b. Non-stationary

10. The table contains time series data. Answers will vary.

11. Cross-sectional data are in the Salary/Bonus column. Answers will vary.

Additional Exercises

1. a. Standardized aptitude test, GPA, etc.

  b. Number of student suspensions, number of student detentions, etc.

  c. Survey students to rate teacher preparedness: Always prepared, Sometimes prepared, Never prepared; or measure the number of times teachers are unprepared on a spot check by the principal.

  d. Number of days missed, number of hours missed (for both teachers and students).

  e. Survey students, survey teachers: e.g. Rate cafeteria food as Excellent, Very Good, Good, Poor, Very Poor.

2. a. Number of checks received after the 10th of the month and number of days after the 10th the checks arrive.

  b. Select a random sample of disabled vets and ask them to report the day which they received the checks. Count the number of days before or after the 10th the check was received.

3. a. Types of investments available, rate of return, amount, etc.

  b. Rates of return on various types of investments: Returns for diversified portfolio of stocks: e.g. S&P 500, Dow Jones Index Returns for diversified portfolio of bonds.

4. Flying Eagle may have more flights daily than the competitor and therefore the number of on-time flights may be larger than the competitor. However, on a percentage basis, the competitor may have a better record of the percentage of flights arriving on time.

5. One example: Make a list of standard grocery items for several randomly selected families. Have families buy groceries from one store and then buy exactly the same groceries from another store and then compare prices.

6. Answers will vary.

7. Survey of customer satisfaction: How would you rate the service you received when purchasing the car: Poor, Average, Good? How would you rate the service after you purchased the car: Poor, Average, Good? How would you rate the car's performance: Poor, Average, Good? How satisfied are you with your purchase: Not Satisfied, Satisfied, Very Satisfied?

8. a. Continuous

  b. Discrete

  c. Continuous

  d. Continuous

9. a. Interval

  b. Interval

  c. Ordinal

  d. Nominal

  e. Ratio

10. a. Daily activity (steps), Age, Body mass index, Height, Weight, Race, Insulin level

  b. Daily activity – Quantitative, Age – Quantitative, Body mass index – Quantitative, Height – Quantitative, Weight – Quantitative, Race – Qualitative, Insulin levels – Quantitative

  c. Daily activity – Discrete, Age – Discrete, Height – Continuous, Weight – Continuous, Insulin level – Continuous

  d. Daily activity – Ratio, Age – Ratio, Body mass index – Interval, Height – Ratio, Weight – Ratio, Race – Nominal, Insulin level – Ratio

  e. Answers will vary.

11. a. The level of measurement for millions of barrels of oil per day is ratio.

4.2 Exercises

9. 24

10. 180

11. a. 94.106

b. 9.701 attempts

c. 44

d. Pass attempts, opponent defensive ability, playbook, etc.

12. a. 44.253

b. 6.652 attempts

c. 27

d. Weather, confidence in running back, number of fumbles, etc.

13. a. .2917

b. .54 or 54 percentage points

c. 1.5%

d. Answers will vary.

14. a. both averages = 76.857

b. male variance = 350.81, female variance = 205.81

c. male std dev = 18.73, female std dev = 14.35

d. Average scores are the same for males and females but the standard deviation of scores of females is lower implying more consistent scores.

e. Answers will vary.

15. a. Ratio

b. Answers will vary

c. Portfolio A:
Average market value = $150, 000,
Standard deviation = $7,906,
Maximum Value = $160,000,
Minimum Value = $140,000,
Portfolio B:
Average market value = $150,000,
Standard deviation = $37,249,
Maximum Value = $195,000,
Minimum Value = $100,000

d. Portfolio B is more risky because it has the larger standard deviation.

16. a. mean of original data = 89.42,
std dev of data = 7.192,
mean of data + 20 = 109.42,
std dev of data + 20 = 7.192

b. mean adjusted data = mean of original data + 20 the standard deviations are the same.

c. These results hold in general. If you add a constant to each data point, the mean of the adjusted data is equal to the mean of the original data + the constant. The standard deviation of the adjusted data is the same as the standard deviation of the original data (i.e. the way in which the data varies does not change if you simply add a constant to each data point.)

17. a. mean of original data = 749.1,
std dev of data = 23.17,
mean of data − 20 = 729.1,
std dev of data − 20 = 23.17

b. mean adjusted data = mean of original data − 20, the standard deviations are the same.

c. Answers will vary.

18. 5 to 47

19. 718 to 1226

20. a. 68.

b. 95

c. Amount of chowder eaten has an approximately normal distribution.

21. a. ($3,750, $5,250).

b. ($3,000, $6,000).

c. ($2,250, $6,750).

d. In order to use the Empirical Rule, we must assume that the daily sales have an approximate normal distribution.

22. a. Job grade 25 ($19,000, $51,000), Job grade 33 ($51,000, $59,000), Job grade 40 ($60,000, $80,000).

b. Answers will vary.

23. a. 2

b. 2.8

c. Since the coefficient of variation is smaller for Brand A than Brand B, the standard deviation of the amounts of Vitamin C in the tablets is smaller relative to the average size of the tablets for Brand A than for Brand B. Thus, Brand A more consistently produces tablets as advertised.

24. a. 12

b. 10

c. The variation in the bolts produced by Machine X is 12% of the mean. The variation in the bolts produced by Machine Y is 10% of the mean. Thus, Machine Y more consistently produces bolts of the same diameter.

4.3 Exercises

10. a. ratio

b. 60.88

c. 86.04

d. 20th percentile: 20% of scores were at or below 60.88, 95th percentile: 95% of scores were at or below 86.04.

11. a. 70th percentile

b. 8th percentile

12. a. ratio

b. 0.161

c. 0.323

d. 20th percentile: 20% of the counties in the USA have less than or equal to 16.1% of their adult population that smoke. 95th percentile: 95% of the counties in the USA have less than or equal to 32.3% of their adult population that smoke

13. a. 99th percentile

b. 6th percentile

14. a. Ratio

b. 40

c. 61

d. 84

e. 25th percentile: 25% of scores were at or below 40. 50th percentile: 50% of scores

were at or below 61. 75th percentile: 75% of scores were at or below 84.

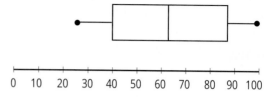

f. 44

g. No outliers

h. 0.826

i. 0.006.

j. Score of 81 is 0.826 standard deviations above the mean. Score of 62 is 0.006 standard deviation above the mean.

15. a. 33rd percentile

b. 93rd percentile

16. a. Ratio

b. 0.312

c. 0.318

d. 0.327

e. 25th percentile: 25% of the on-base percentages are at or below 0.312, 50th percentile: 50% of the on-base percentages are at or below 0.318, 75th percentile 75% of the on-base percentages are at or below 0.327.

f. 0.015

g. Yes, there are a couple outliers both above Q_3 and below Q_1.

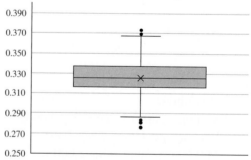

h. −3.086, 0th percentile

i. 1.910, 96th percentile

j. The player with the 0.280 on-base percentage has a batting average 3.086 standard deviations below the average on-base percentage of 0.326, the player with a .355 on-base percentage has a batting average 1.910 standard deviations above the average on-base percentage of 0.326.

17. a. 3rd percentile

   b. 97th percentile

18. a. 0.762, a score of 80 is 0.762 standard deviations above the mean.

   b. 0, a score of 64 is 0 standard deviations above the mean.

   c. −1.143, a score of 40 is 1.143 standard deviations below the mean.

19. First exam: .10, Second exam: −.43. On the first exam, the student's score was .1 standard deviations above the mean; but on the second exam, the student's score was .43 standard deviations below the mean. Thus, although the student achieved a higher absolute score on the second exam, the student performed relatively worse on the second exam than on the first.

20. a. 19.656 in., 49.93 cm.

   b. 1.077 in., 2.735 cm.

   c. −0.377

   d. −0.377

   e. Answers will vary.

4.4 Exercises

4. a. Nominal: Beer ID, Beer Name, Beer Style, Brewery ID, Brewery Name, City, and State; Ratio: ABV, IBU, and Ounces

   b. Style, Ounces, Brewery Name/ID, and State.

   c. 8

   d. Elevation Triple India Pale Ale, Renegade Brewing Company.

   e. 2, American IPA and American Double/Imperial IPA

   f. mean=0.059, st. deviation = 0.013

   g. CVRenegade=28.16%. CVWynkoop=21.30%; The Wynkoop

Brewery has more consistent ABV values since it has a smaller coefficient of variation.

5. a. Nominal: ID, Duplex, Subdivision, New, House Style, Misc. Exterior, Pool, Dock, Fenced Yard, Screened Porch, Golf Course, and Fireplace; Ratio: List Price, No. of bedrooms, No. of bathrooms, Stories, Square Footage, Acreage, Covered Parking Spot, No. of Fireplaces; Interval: Year Built

   b. All but Misc. Exterior and Amenities.

   c. Create intervals that break the variable into a few (2-5) categories such as 'Less than or equal to $500,000' and 'Greater than $500,00' in List Price or 'Acreage less than or equal to 0.5 acres' and 'Acreage greater than 0.5 acres'.

   d. 11; Charleston Single, Colonial, Condo Regime, Condominium, Contemporary, Cottage, Craftsman, Patio, Ranch, Townhouse, and Traditional

   e. 103; Carolina Park with 42 new homes

   f. $552,882

   g. Minimum is in Carolina Park with a List Price of $369,900; Maximum is in Park West with a List Price of $1,800,000.

   h. The minimum priced home is $205.84 per square foot and the maximum priced home is $333.27 per square foot.

   i. Answers may vary. Possible reasons include: 5 beds, 5.5 baths, 5401 sq. ft., has a pool, and has a dock.

4.5 Exercises

3. Mean = 17.5; Variance = 53

4. a. 0.061

   b. 0.0002

   c. 0.014

4.6 Exercises

4. 0.12

5. 0.565

6. 0.2513

7. 0.0833

8. a. 0.111

   b. 0.076

   c. 0.163

9. a. 28%

   b. 22%

   c. Americans are not in the habit of saving money in case of a financial emergency. Around a quarter would not be able to cope at all. Answers will vary.

10. a. 0.231

   b. 0.055

   c. Not necessarily. In this sample the SEC represented the greatest number of players of any single conference, but the SEC only accounts for 23% of the sample whereas the other conferences account for around 77%. Answers will vary.

11. a. Free private jet use

   b. 0.264

   c. 0.240

   d. Many of the clients did not receive a perk and still joined the Wall Street firm. Given that the perks are so expensive, firms might want to reevaluate whether or not offering the perks is worth it. Answers will vary.

Additional Exercises

1. No. Because you did not want any variation in the length of the boards. Answers will vary.

2. a. 361.1111

   b. 19.0029 beats per minute

   c. 60

   d. Age, fitness level, gender, etc. Answers will vary.

e.

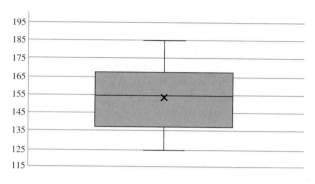

Heart Rate Box Plot

f. 25th percentile

3. a. 0.3438

   b. Mean = 2.4531, Standard Deviation = 2.5754

   c. 0 to 5.0285

   d. 87.5%

   e. The empirical rule predicts that 68.26% of the data falls within one standard deviation of the mean. The percent of the data in this problem falling within one standard deviation is 87.5%, which is not very close to the empirical rule. Answers may vary.

4. a. False

   b. True

   c. True

   d. True

   e. False

5. a. Machine A = 3.1429, Machine B = 3.1429

   b. Machine A = 5.8095, Machine B = 0.8095

   c. Machine A = 2.4103, Machine B = 0.8997

   d. Machine B is probably a better machine because the average number of defects produced by the 2 machines is the same but Machine B is much more consistent in the number of defective circuit boards it produces. Answers may vary.

   e. Answers may vary.

6. a. Ratio

   b. Average points per game and standard deviation of points per game—to get an idea of how well they can shoot and how consistent they are. Answers may vary.

c. Mean (Braudrick) = 30, Standard deviation (Braudrick) = 3.4641,

Mean (Douglas) = 32, Standard deviation (Douglas) = 8.0691

d. Braudrick is a more consistent player because the standard deviation of points scored per game is lower for Braudrick than for Douglas.

e. Coaches relationship with player, attitude of player, high school player plays for.

f. Answers may vary.

7. **a.** 92.0929

b. 9.1383

c. 9

d. 12

e. The literacy rates are normally distributed.

8. **a.** 0.045

b. Yes, 4.5% of the items in the sample were defective. Answers will vary.

9. **a.** Mean = 38.12

b. Median = 21.4

c. Bimodal, Mode 1 = 14.50, Mode 2 = 8.50

d. 25.76

e. The skewness of the distribution will be towards the left.

10. **a.** Yes, the variables measured seem appropriate to study the relationship between reaction time and the amount of drug in the bloodstream.

b. Biases could include differences in reaction time without the drug. Answers will vary.

c. The data are ratio data.

11. **a.** $\sigma = \dfrac{73.24 - 67.8}{3.4} = 1.6$ km/s/Mpc

b. Answers may vary.

Chapter 5

5.1 Exercises

11. **a.** The pattern in Scatterplot A does not follow a linear pattern, but the patter n in Scatterplot B does.

b. There is no discernible pattern in Scatterplot A. The pattern in Scatterplot B is downward sloping.

c. The data values are widely dispersed in Scatterplot A, but they are tightly clustered around a line in Scatterplot B.

d. Scatterplot A does not have a pattern from which to deviate, but there are no significant deviations in Scatterplot B.

12. **a.** The pattern in Scatterplot A does roughly follow a linear pattern. However, Scatterplot B does not follow a linear pattern.

b. The pattern in Scatterplot A is downward sloping, but there is no discernible pattern in Scatterplot B.

c. The data values in Scatterplot A are fairly tightly clustered, but the data values in Scatterplot B are very widely dispersed.

d. Scatterplot A does have a few deviations that are significant enough to require further analysis. Scatterplot B does not have a pattern from which to deviate.

13. **a.**

i. What is the run differential necessary to win 95 games? Answers may vary.

ii. Yes

iii. Possible errors in recording of runs scored and runs allowed. Answers may very.

iv. Run Differential: Ratio; Wins: Ratio

v. Observation

b.

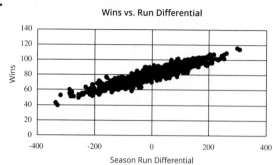

c.

i. Yes, the data follows an obvious linear pattern

ii. Upward sloping

iii. Tightly clustered

iv. Yes, there are a few observations at each end of the plot that are worthy of further analysis

14. **a.** Yes, the pharmacist is interested in studying the relationship between the amount of drug in a person's blood stream and reaction time. It makes sense to collect direct information on those two variables since it is available. Several biases and confounding variables to watch out for: Different people may have different responses to the drug because of tolerance level, weight, condition of heart, other medications person may be taking, etc. The highest level of measurement of both variables is ratio. This is an observational study.

b.

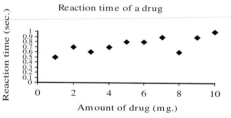

c. Yes, the pattern roughly follows a straight line. The pattern is upward sloping; as the amount of drug increases, the reaction time tends to increase. The data values are tightly clustered. There is one significant deviation from the pattern: the person who was administered 8 mg of the drug had a reaction time of only 0.6 sec.

15.

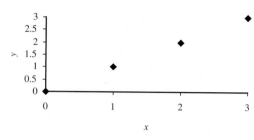

16.

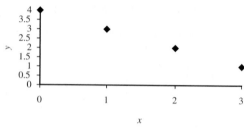

17. **a.** Tightly clustered in a positive linear fashion.

b. Loosely clustered in a positive linear fashion.

c. Tightly clustered in a negative linear fashion.

d. Loosely clustered in a negative linear fashion.

e. No linear relationship.

f. The scatterplots look linear.

18. **a.** Tightly clustered in a positive linear fashion.

b. Loosely clustered in a positive linear fashion.

c. Tightly clustered in a negative linear fashion.

d. Loosely clustered in a negative linear fashion.

e. Loosely clustered in a positive linear fashion.

f. The scatterplots look linear.

19. **a.** Strong positive linear relationship.

b. Moderate positive linear relationship.

c. Strong negative linear relationship.

d. Moderate negative linear relationship.

e. No linear relationship.

f. The scatterplots look linear.

20. **a.** Strong positive linear relationship.

b. Weak positive linear relationship.

c. Strong negative linear relationship.

d. Weak negative linear relationship.

e. Weak positive linear relationship.

f. The scatterplots look linear.

21. a.

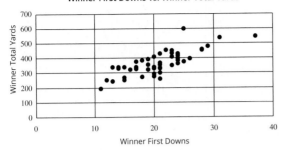

b. There is a positive relationship between the variables.

c. $r = 0.784$

22. a.

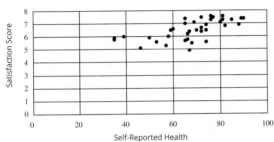

b. $r = 0.647$

c. The correlation coefficient indicates a moderate positive linear relationship. This seems consistent with the scatterplot.

23. a. Age

b. Winter (Flu Season)

c. Christmas

24. a. Summer

b. Valentine's Day, Christmas

c. Winter

5.2 Exercises

16. a. Sales volume, since it is the value we want to predict.

b. Advertising expenditures, since we use it to predict sales volume.

c. $69,650

d. $99,510

e. Random error. This may cause the company to under or over-estimate sales volume, causing budgeting problems. Answers will vary.

17. a. Dependent: Salary. Independent: Years of experience.

b. 25,689.10

c. 2148.35

d. $57,914.35

18. a.

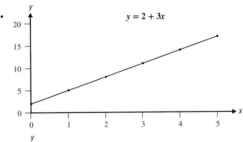

b.

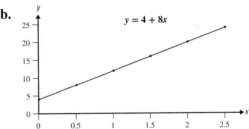

c.

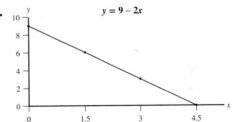

d.

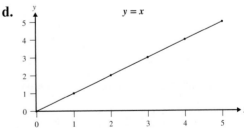

19. a.

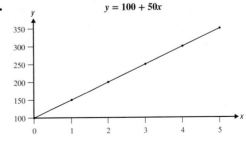

b.

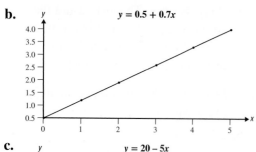

$y = 0.5 + 0.7x$

c.

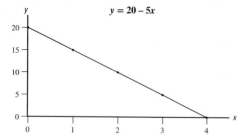

$y = 20 - 5x$

20. a. 15, 45, 65, 85, 95

    b. Positive

    c. We would expect r to be positive, since the variables have a positive relationship.

21. a.

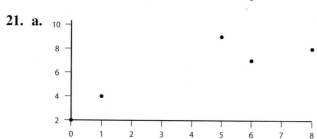

b.

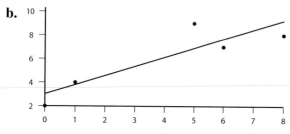

c.

Predicted y	Error	Squared Error
3	−1	1
3.8	0.2	0.04
7	2	4
7.8	−0.8	0.64
9.4	−1.4	1.96

    d. SSE = 7.64

22. a. List Price = $b_0 + b_1$(Square Footage)

b.

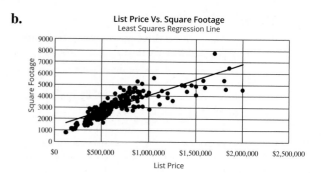

List Price Vs. Square Footage
Least Squares Regression Line

c.

Predicted Selling Price	Error	Squared Error
316,513	58,487	3,420,680,730
403,168	20,432	417,455,775
341,638	106,677	11,379,941,045
477,004	38,246	1,462,729,599
573,658	−17,258	297,833,041
636,470	−35,970	1,293,825,685
654,416	−70,796	5,012,082,041
678,772	4253	18,090,450
661,595	−26,345	694,036,258
555,712	59,588	3,550,781,109
712,101	19,309	372,856,713
758,504	102,246	10,454,156,319
941,813	−106,813	11,408,968,006
840,545	−25,045	627,228,348

    d. SSE = 50,410,665,118

    e. No, Square Footage is the best predictor for List Price in the data set. Any other variable will have a wide dispersion of data values.

23. a. $W = 80.8814 + 0.1058(RD)$

    b. 133

24. a.

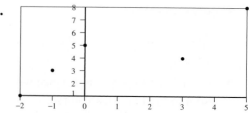

    b. $\hat{y} = 3.4353 + 0.7647x$

c.

$$\hat{y} = 3.4353 + 0.7647x$$

d. −0.9059, 0.3294, 1.5647, −1.7294, 0.7412

25. a. Current value of home

b. Annual salary

c. $152,811

d. $15,700

e. For each additional dollar earned in annual salary, the current value of home is predicted to increase by $3.14.

f. If someone is not earning any annual income, the predicted value of his or her home would be $52,331.

g. It is possible because if you have a greater annual salary you have more money to spend on a home. However, we cannot conclude that there is a causality from the estimated regression equation. Answers will vary.

26. a. Points scored

b. Minutes played

c. 225.3 points

d. 64.5 points

e. 0.645

f. −97.2

g. Possibly because you have to be in the game to score points. However, we cannot conclude that there is a causality from the estimated regression equation. Answers will vary.

27. a. $\hat{y} = 5.7333 + 0.6667x$

b. 16.4

c. No. $\hat{y} = 10.9732 + 0.3065x$

d. 15.8772

e. There is not likely a causal relationship between these two variables. Answers will vary.

28. a. Coefficient is positive as the relationship is positive. Answers may vary.

b. Increased blood pressure leads to increased stroke mortality. The diastolic line have a steeper slope than systolic which means an increase in diastolic blood pressure may have a larger impact on stoke mortality than an increase in systolic blood pressure. Answers may vary.

c. Blood pressure has less relative impact on stroke mortality as age increases, but increased age leads to an increased overall stroke mortality risk. Answers may vary.

5.3 Exercises

21. a. 0.0641

b. 0.2531

22. a. Diabetes.percent = −0.00936 + 0.38128 (Adult.obesity.percent)

b. $b_0 = -0.00936$; $b_1 = 0.38128$

c.

Predicted Diabetes.percent	Error	Squared Error
0.146	0.027	0.000718
0.095	−0.011	0.000132
0.134	−0.019	0.000347
0.124	0.032	0.001043
0.110	−0.040	0.001568
0.136	0.074	0.005433

d. 0.00924

e. 0.00231

f. 0.04807

g. The standard error of the model is relatively small in comparison with the predicted y-values, so yes. Answers will vary.

23. a. Estimated RS = −1079.02442 + 5486.29728(OBP)

b. Estimated RS = −315.51172 + 2610.88272(SLG)

c. Estimated RA = −865.94701 + 4921.06617(OOBP)

d. Estimated RA = −448.44236 + 2908.69139(OSLG)

e.

Predicted RS	Error	Squared Error
671	16	256
841	56	3136
677	47	2209
863	60	3600
693	−51	2601

f. SSE = 11,802.000; Standard Error = 108.637

g.

Predicted RA	Error	Squared Error
709	4	16
831	−25	625
651	−24	576
988	−20	400
823	−57	3249

h. SSE = 4866.000; Standard Error = 69.757

24. a. Ratio

b. Estimated Proportion that Purchased Product = $b_0 + b_1$(Price of Product)

c. Proportion that purchased product

d. Price of product

e.

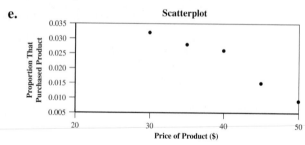

Scatterplot

f. $\hat{y} = 0.0691 - 0.0012x$

g. 0.0271

h. 0

i. 0.000007

j. $R^2 = 0.9408$, This model explains about 94.08% of the variation in the proportion that purchases the product.

25. a. Ratio

b. Savings

c. Income

d.

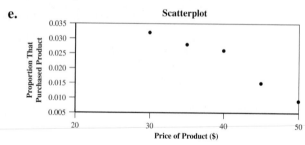

Yes, the data points in the scatterplot appear approximately linear with a positive slope trend.

e. $\hat{y} = -4.8658 + 0.171x$

f. $3684.20

g. Savings is estimated to increase by approximately $171 for each additional $1000 earned in annual income.

h. $R^2 = 0.9495$ Approximately 94.95% of the variation in savings is explained by the variation annual income.

26. a. $b_0 = 2.7845$, $b_1 = 0.0768$

b. If you finance your loan for zero months, the base interest rate is approximately 2.7845%. For each additional month that you extend the term of your car loan, the interest rate you receive is predicted to increase by 0.0768%.

c. 6.4709%

d. No, because it is outside the range of the data used to estimate the model. The data used to estimate the model only range from 1 to 6-year car loans.

e. $R^2 = 0.9675$. Approximately 96.75% of the variation in interest rate is explained by the model

f. $r = 0.9836$. The two variables have a strong positive correlation.

g. 7.3925%

5.4 Exercises

5. a. Upward

b. Independent variable: Year; Dependent variable: CO_2 Emissions per Capita

c. CO_2 Emissions per Capita $= \beta_0 + \beta_1$(Year) $+ \varepsilon_i$

d. CO_2 Emissions per Capita $= -1083.6443 + 0.5537$(Year)

e. CO_2 Emissions per Capita = -1083.6443 $+ 0.5537(2015) = 32.0612$

f. Yes. We can subtract our estimate from the actual observed CO_2 emissions per capita for Trinidad and Tobago for the year 2015 to determine the error. Answers will vary.

6. a. Independent variable: Month; Dependent variable: Sales

b. $\hat{y} = 403.7576 + 40.9091x$

c. MSE = 2622.248, $s_e = 51.2079$

d. $935,575.90

e. Approximately 90.12% of the variation in sales is explained by the time trend model, therefore the model seems to fit the data accurately.

7. a. $\hat{y} = -901.3273 + 0.4527x$

b. $\hat{y} = -1126.7909 + 0.5655x$

c. NC: 9.9578%, SC: 11.5606%

d. $R^2 = 0.4295$

e. $R^2 = 0.6462$

f. The model for South Carolina has a larger coefficient of determination, indicating that it fits the data better than the model for North Carolina. Answers may vary.

5.5 Exercises

4. a. There is a slight upward sloping pattern in the data. As Adjusted GPD per Capita increases, so does Life Expectancy.

b. Between the years 1860 and 1864, the Life Expectancy in the United States decreased from 39.4 in 1860 to 31 in 1864.

c. The Life Expectancy of every country in the world sharply decreases. This was the result of a worldwide influenze pandemic.

d.

   i. GDP per Capita increased from $1050 in 1990 to $40,100 in 2008 for a total increase of $39,049.

ii. Life Expectancy increased from 48.9 in 1990 to 57.5 in 2008 for a total increase of 8.6 years.

iii. In 2008, the life expectancy of Equatorial Guinea is substantially lower than other countries with similar GDP per Capita

Additional Exercises

1. a.

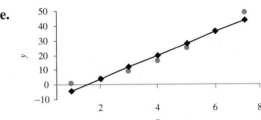

b. $r = 0.977$

c. The correlation coefficient indicates a strong positive linear relationship-but notice that the scatterplot is not linear.

d. $b_1 = 8$ $b_0 = -12$

$y = b_0 + b_1 x = -12 + 8x$

e.

f.

x	y	pred y	error	error^2
1	1	−4	5	25
2	4	4	0	0
3	9	12	−3	9
4	16	20	−4	16
5	25	28	−3	9
6	36	36	0	0
7	49	44	5	25
		Total	0	84

g. Average value of the model's errors = 0/7 = 0

h. variance of the model's errors = $84/(7-2) = 84/5 = 16.8$

2. a.

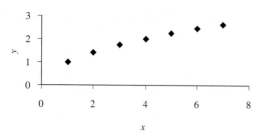

b. $r = 0.992$ (indicating a strong positive linear relationship)

c. There is a strong positive relationship between x and y which can be approximated by a linear relationship over the values of x. But, it is important to notice that there is a nonlinear pattern to the data, that is, y equals the square root of x.

d. $b_1 = .269286$ $b_0 = .849$

$y = b_0 + b_1 x = 0.849 + 0.269x$

e.

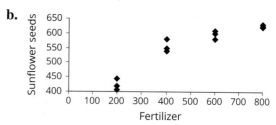

f.

x	y	pred y	error	error²
1	1.0	1.118	−0.1	0.01392
2	1.4	1.387	0.02	0.00053
3	1.7	1.656	0.07	0.00548
4	2.0	1.925	0.08	0.00562
5	2.2	2.194	0.05	0.00212
6	2.5	2.463	0	0.00017
7	2.7	2.732	−0.1	0.00672
	Total		0	0.03456

g. Average value of the model's errors $= 0/7 = 0$

h. Variance of the model's errors $= 0.03456/(7 − 2) = 0.006912$

3. a. ratio

b. Miles per gallon.

c. Haul weight.

d. Data appears to be approximately linear. Thus a linear model is appropriate.

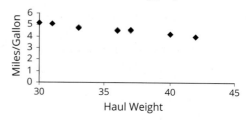

e. Miles per gallon $= b_0 + b_1$ (Haul weight).

f. Miles per gallon $= 7.94 − 0.0935$ (Haul weight).

g. The slope is $−0.0935$. This means that for each additional thousand pounds of haul weight, the miles per gallon decrease by 0.0935 miles per gallon.

h. Miles per gallon $= 7.94 − 0.0935 (38) = 4.387$.

i. It seems reasonable to think that a larger haul weight would contribute to the truck having a lower gas mileage. But, regression analysis does not prove the causality.

j. $r = −0.977$, indicating a strong negative linear relationship between miles/gallon and haul weight.

k. $R^2 = 95.4\%$, indicating that 95.4% of the variation in the observed miles/gallon is explained by the differences in haul weight.

4. a. The level of measurement of both variables (Pounds of fertilizer and Pounds of sunflower seeds) is ratio. The data is developed through a controlled study.

b.

c. There is an apparent linear relationship. The dependent variable is pounds of sunflower seeds.

d. Model: Pounds of sunflower seeds $= 389 + 0.323$ (Pounds of fertilizer used).

e. Slope $= 0.323$. For every additional pound of fertilizer, the yield of the sunflower seeds increases by 0.323 lbs.

f. $R^2 = 84.6\%$, meaning that 84.6% of the variation in the observed yields of the sunflower seeds is explained by the differences in the amounts of fertilizer used.

g. Pounds of sunflower seed = 389 + 0.323 (500) = 550.5

5. a.

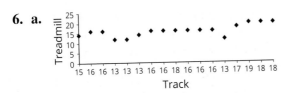

b. −0.66328658

c.

R	P	T	R	P	T
60	320	380	43	328	371
158	124	282	95	192	287
53	183	236	56	237	293
127	164	291	200	132	332
60	115	175	125	310	435
343	50	393	99	184	283
148	242	390	187	189	376
88	190	278	21	366	387
75	183	258	171	87	258
110	182	292	60	337	397

d. 0.230679637

e. Total yards increase as rushing yards increase however passing yards decrease as rushing yards increase.

6. a.

b. A positive relation.

c. 0.927787

d.

Track	Tread	V	W	Track	Tread	V	W
15	14	7.5	2.8	18	16	9	3.2
16	16	8	3.2	16	16	8	3.2
16	16	8	3.2	16	16	8	3.2
13	12	6.5	2.4	16	16	8	3.2
13	12	6.5	2.4	13	12	6.5	2.4
13	14	6.5	2.8	17	18	8.5	3.6
16	16	8	3.2	19	20	9.5	4
16	16	8	3.2	18	20	9	4
				18	20	9	4

e. 0.927787

f. There is no effect on the correlation coefficient by multiplying a constant.

7. a.

b. Negative relationship

c. −0.51883

d.

X	Y	V	W
876	50.1	176	0.1
516	88.2	−184	38.2
598	80.7	−102	30.7
789	39.6	89	−10.4
734	20.5	34	−29.5
667	40.9	−33	−9.1
682	30.6	−18	−19.4
714	22.9	14	−27.1
598	34.8	−102	−15.2

e. −0.51883

f. There is no effect on the correlation coefficient by subtracting a constant.

8. a. Combinatorial $(k, 2)$

b. C(4, 2) = 6

c. Robbery rate and Violent Crime index (0.9289)

d. Murder Rate and Crime Rate (0.073)

e. No pairs are negatively correlated.

Chapter 6

6.1 Exercises

11. a. $S = \{\text{Brand A, Brand B, Brand C, Brand D}\}$

  b. $M = \{\text{Brand B, Brand C, Brand D}\}$

12. a. $S = \{\text{Very Attentive, Somewhat Attentive, Not Attentive}\}$

  b. $A = \{\text{Somewhat Attentive, Not Attentive}\}$

13. a. $P(1) = 0.4242,$

  $P(2) = 0.2121,$

  $P(3) = 0.1515,$

  $P(4) = 0.0606,$

  $P(5) = 0.0909,$

  $P(6) = 0.0606$

  b. 1

14. $P(\text{Yellow}) = 0.3$, $P(\text{Red}) = 0.5$, $P(\text{Blue}) = 0.2$

15. 0.88

16. 0.6667

17. 0.9

18. 0.375

19. a. subjective

  b. relative frequency

  c. subjective

  d. relative frequency

  e. classical

20. a. classical

  b. subjective

  c. subjective

  d. classical

  e. subjective

  f. relative frequency

21. a. $S = \{\text{MM, MF, FM, FF}\}$

  b. $\dfrac{1}{4} = 0.25$

  c. $\dfrac{3}{4} = 0.75$

22. a. $\dfrac{1}{5} = 0.2$

  b. $\dfrac{4}{5} = 0.8$

23. a. $\dfrac{1}{3} \approx 0.3333$

  b. $\dfrac{2}{3} \approx 0.6667$

6.2 Exercises

8. a. Yes

  b. No, probabilities cannot be greater than 1.

  c. Yes

  d. No, probabilities cannot be less than 0.

  e. Yes

9. a. Yes

  b. Yes

  c. No, probabilities cannot be greater than 1.

  d. Yes

  e. No, probabilities cannot be less than 0.

10. a. The event cannot occur.

  b. The event is certain to occur.

  c. Relative Frequency interpretation: If an experiment is performed 100 times, the event will occur, on average, 45 times.

  d. Relative Frequency interpretation: If an experiment is performed 100 times, the event will occur, on average, 65 times.

  e. Not a valid probability because it is negative.

11. a. 1

  b. 0

  c. 1

  d. 0

12. a. 3/8 or 0.375

  b. 5/8 or 0.625

13. a. 0.9696

  b. 0.0523

14. a. 0.3794

   b. 0.6206

   c. 0.2582

   d. 0.2279

   e. 0.4862

   f. 0.3491

   g. 0.6074

   h. Relative frequency

   i. Yes, customers are identified as either suburban or urban, they cannot be both. Answers may vary.

15. a. 0.27

   b. 0.08

   c. 0.165

   d. 0.4

   e. 0.3

   f. 0.51

   g. Relative frequency

   h. No, the wife could have more than $150,000 in insurance and the husband could have between $50,000 and $100,000 of insurance. Answers may vary.

6.3 Exercises

9. a. 0.3194

   b. 0.3472

   c. 0.6327

   d. 0.6032

10. a. 0.3125

   b. 0.9286

   c. 0.0408

   d. 0.125

11. a. 0.8571

   b. 0.1429

12. 0.025

13. a. 0.005

   b. 0.0417

14. No, the events are dependent. If a customer is urban the customer is not suburban, and vice versa.

15. No, the events are dependent. If $A =$ husband has more than $150,000 insurance and $B =$ wife has more than $50,000 insurance, $P(A\mid B) \neq P(A)$.

16. a. $\dfrac{1}{4} = 0.25$

   b. $\dfrac{1}{8} = 0.125$

   c. $\dfrac{1}{16} = 0.0625$

   d. $\dfrac{1}{2^{100}} \approx 0$

17. 0.0001

18. a. 0.855

   b. 0.045

   c. 0.005

   d. The lives of Mandy and Ashley are independent.

19. a. 0.9980

   b. 0.0020

   c. 0.000001

20. a. $\dfrac{2}{16} = \dfrac{1}{8} = 0.125$

   $S = \{$LLLL, LLLW, LLWL, LLWW, LWLL, LWLW, LWWL, LWWW, WLLL, WLLW, WLWL, WLWW, WWLL, WWLW, WWWL, WWWW$\}$

   b. $\dfrac{1}{4} = 0.25$

   c. $\dfrac{5}{16} = 0.3125$

21. a. 0.0004

   b. 0.0004

22. $\dfrac{1}{52} \cdot \dfrac{12}{51} = \dfrac{1}{221} \approx 0.0045$

23. a. $\dfrac{4}{42} \cdot \dfrac{13}{41} = \dfrac{26}{861} \approx 0.0302$

   b. $\dfrac{(9+4+4+2)}{42} \cdot \dfrac{(9+4+4+2-1)}{41}$

   $= \dfrac{57}{287} \approx 0.1986$

24. $\dfrac{16}{(26+19+11+16)} \cdot \dfrac{19}{(26+19+11+16-1)}$

$= \dfrac{38}{639} \approx 0.0595$

6.4 Exercises

5. 120

6. 72

7. a. 1

   b. 6

   c. 120

   d. 5040

8. a. 2

   b. 24

   c. 720

   d. 40,320

9. 665,280

10. 19,958,400

11. 50,400

12. 2520

13. 55

14. 2,598,960

15. $_8C_3 = 56$

16. $_8P_3 = 336$

17. $_{15}C_{10} = 3003$

18. $_{15}P_4 = 32,760$

19. $_{30}C_3 = 4060$

20. $\dfrac{8!}{4!\,2!\,2!} = 420$

21. a. $\dfrac{7!}{3!\,1!\,2!\,1!} = 420$;

   No, he will be 89 codes short.

   b. $\dfrac{10!}{4!\,2!\,1!\,1!\,2!} = 37,800$;

   Yes, there would be plenty.

22. The only word without any repeated letters is the first word, TEARS. Therefore, it will have the most five-letter arrangements possible.

23. $_6C_2 \cdot _5C_2 \cdot _7C_2 = 3150$

24. $_5C_0 + _5C_1 + _5C_2 + _5C_3 + _5C_4 + _5C_5 = 32$

6.5 Exercises

5. $P(\text{Defective} \mid \text{Inspected}) = 0.3947$

6. $P(\text{Dem} \mid \text{Favor}) = 0.7404$

7. $P(\text{Male} \mid \text{Cried}) = 0.2553$

8. $P(\text{Def} \mid \text{Insp}) = 0.2069$

9. $P(\text{Online} \mid \text{Fail}) = 0.1429$

10. $P(\text{Woman's name} \mid \text{Man chosen}) = 0.7347$

Additional Exercises

1. a. $S = \{$MMM, MMF, MFM, MFF, FMM, FMF, FFM, FFF$\}$

   b. $\dfrac{1}{8} = 0.125$

   c. $\dfrac{7}{8} = 0.875$

2. a. 0.4769

   b. 0.5067

   c. 0.5231

   d. 0.2399

   e. 0.4063

   f. 0.1176

   g. No, they are dependent. If A = voter is Democratic and B = voter favors national healthcare policy, then $P(B \mid A) = 0.5941$ and $P(B) = 0.4933$.

3. a. $\dfrac{18}{38} = \dfrac{9}{19} \approx 0.4737$

   b. $\dfrac{12}{38} = \dfrac{6}{19} \approx 0.3158$

   c. $\dfrac{2}{38} = \dfrac{1}{19} \approx 0.0526$

   d. $\dfrac{1}{38} \approx 0.0263$

e. $\dfrac{35}{38} \approx 0.9211$

4. **a.** 0.125

   b. 0.5

5. 0.9989

6. **a.** $\dfrac{9}{15} = \dfrac{3}{5} = 0.6$

   b. $\dfrac{1}{15} \approx 0.0667$

7. **a.** 1 to 5

   b. 1 to 1

   c. 7 to 1

   d. $\dfrac{8}{11} \approx 0.7273$

8. **a.** $\dfrac{1}{4} = 0.25$

   b. $\dfrac{1}{4} = 0.25$

   c. $\dfrac{3}{4} = 0.75$

   d. $\dfrac{1}{3} \approx 0.3333$

   e. $\dfrac{12}{51} = \dfrac{4}{17} \approx 0.2353$

9. $\dfrac{11}{14} \approx 0.7857$

10. 45,697,600

11. **a.** 8%

    b. 16%

    c. 14%

    d. 84%

12. **a.** $7 \cdot 10 \cdot 10 \cdot 5 = 3500$

    b. $6 \cdot 10 \cdot 10 \cdot 5 - 1 = 2999$

    c. $5 \cdot 10 \cdot 10 \cdot 5 = 2500$

13. $_8P_3 = 336$

14. $_{10}C_4 = 210$

15. $\dfrac{\left(_{28}C_2\right)\left(_{41}C_2\right)\left(_{35}C_0\right)\left(_{18}C_0\right)}{_{122}C_4} = \dfrac{4428}{125,477} \approx 0.0353$

Chapter 7

7.1 Exercises

5. **a.** Discrete

   b. Continuous

   c. Discrete

   d. Continuous

   e. Discrete

6. **a.** Continuous

   b. Discrete

   c. Discrete

   d. Discrete

   e. Continuous

7. **a.** Discrete

   b. Continuous

   c. Continuous

   d. Discrete

   e. Continuous

8. **a.** Discrete

   b. Discrete

   c. Continuous

   d. Discrete

   e. Continuous

7.2 Exercises

12. No. The sum of the probabilities is greater than 1.

13. Yes

14. No. Probabilities cannot be negative.

15. No. The sum of the probabilities is less than 1.

16. Yes

17. No. Probabilities cannot be negative.

18. No. The sum of the probabilities is $\dfrac{15}{16}$ which is less than 1.

x	P(X = x)
1	$\dfrac{1}{16}$
2	$\dfrac{2}{16}$
3	$\dfrac{3}{16}$
4	$\dfrac{4}{16}$
5	$\dfrac{5}{16}$

19. Yes

x	P(X = x)
1	$\dfrac{1}{30}$
2	$\dfrac{4}{30}$
3	$\dfrac{9}{30}$
4	$\dfrac{16}{30}$

20.

x	p(x)	xp(x)	$\dfrac{(x-\mu)^2}{p(x)}$
−5	0.06	−0.30	1.446
−2	0.15	−0.30	0.547
0	0.58	0.00	0.005
2	0.18	0.36	0.786
5	0.03	0.15	0.777
Total	1.00	−0.09	3.561

$E(X) = -0.09;\ \sigma^2 = 3.561;\ \sigma = 1.8871$

21.

x	p(x)	xp(x)	$\dfrac{(x-\mu)^2}{p(x)}$
400	0.0	0	0.0
420	0.1	42	291.6
440	0.1	44	115.6
460	0.2	92	39.2
480	0.2	96	7.2
500	0.4	200	270.4
Total	1.0	474	724.0

$E(X) = 474;\ \sigma^2 = 724;\ \sigma = 26.9072$

22.

x	p(x)	xp(x)	$\dfrac{(x-\mu)^2}{p(x)}$
0	0.15	0.00	0.60
1	0.20	0.20	0.20
2	0.34	0.68	0.00
3	0.19	0.57	0.19
4	0.06	0.24	0.24
5	0.05	0.25	0.45
6	0.01	0.06	0.16
Total	1.00	2.00	1.84

a. $E(X) = 2$

b. $\sigma^2 = 1.84$

c. $\sigma = 1.3565$

d. $P(X = 0) = 0.15$

e. $P(X \geq 1) = 0.85$

f. $P(X \leq 2) = 0.69$

g. $P(X > 3) = 0.12$

23.

x	p(x)	xp(x)	$\dfrac{(x-\mu)^2}{p(x)}$
1	0.1	0.1	0.484
2	0.2	0.4	0.288
3	0.3	0.9	0.012
4	0.2	0.8	0.128
5	0.2	1.0	0.648
Total	1.0	3.2	1.560

a. $E(X) = 3.2$

b. $\sigma^2 = 1.56$

c. $\sigma = 1.2490$

d. $P(X = 5) = 0.2$

e. $P(X \geq 2) = 0.9$

f. $P(X \le 3) = 0.6$

g. $P(X < 2) = 0.1$

24.

x	p(x)	xp(x)	$\frac{(x-\mu)^2}{p(x)}$
10	0.10	1	52.9
20	0.20	4	33.8
30	0.30	9	2.7
40	0.20	8	9.8
50	0.10	5	28.9
60	0.10	6	72.9
Total	1.0	33	201.0

a. $E(X) = 33$

b. $\sigma = 14.1774$

c. $\sigma^2 = 201$

d. $P(X > 30) = 0.40$

e. $P(X \le 20) = 0.30$

f. $P(X \ge 40) = 0.40$

g. $P(X = 10) = 0.10$

25. a.

x	p(x)	xp(x)	$\frac{(x-\mu)^2}{p(x)}$
\$50,000	0.4	20,000	518,400,000
−\$10,000	0.6	−6000	345,600,000
Total	1.0	14,000	864,000,000

b. $14,000

c. $29,393.88

26. a. Option 1 = \$10,000; Option 2 = \$0

b. Option 1 = \$82,865.35;
Option 2 = \$14,142.14

c. Option 1 has a greater expected value than option 2, but also a greater standard deviation. If you are willing to take a risk, Option 1 is best because it has a much larger expected value of return. Answers will vary.

27. a. Cereal A = \$260,000; Cereal B = \$284,000.

b. Cereal A = \$88,881.94; Cereal B = \$302,297.87

c. Cereal B has a greater value for expected sales, but also a much greater standard deviation. The difference in the expected sales is much smaller than the difference

in the standard deviation, so Cereal A is probably the best choice. Answers will vary.

7.3 Exercises

3. $\frac{1}{16} = 0.0625$

4. $\frac{2}{10} = 0.2$

5. $\frac{2}{6} \approx 0.3333$

6. a. $\{H1,H2,H3,H4,H5,H6,T1,T2,T3,T4,T5,T6\}$

b. $\frac{1}{12} \approx 0.0833$

c. $\frac{3}{12} = 0.25$

7. $E(X) = 2,\ \sigma^2 = \sqrt{2} \approx 1.4142$

7.4 Exercises

7. a. 5

b. 45

c. 15

d. 1

8. a. 6

b. 495

c. 816

d. 1771

9. a. $E(X) = 0.9$

b. $\sigma = 0.9$

c. $P(X = 2) = 0.1722$

d. $P(X \le 3) = 0.9917$

e. $P(X \ge 2) = 0.2252$

f. $P(X < 5) = 0.9991$

10. a. $E(X) = 9.6$

b. $\sigma = 1.3856$

c. $P(X = 7) = 0.0532$

d. $P(X \le 4) = 0.0006$

e. $P(X \ge 1) = 1$

f. $P(X > 5) = 0.2749$

11. a. Binomial distribution with $n = 10$ and $p = 0.10$

b. $E(X) = 1$

c. $\sigma = 0.9487$

d. $P(X = 1) = 0.3874$

e. $P(X = 5) = 0.0015$

f. $P(X \geq 3) = 0.0702$

12. a. Binomial distribution with $n =$ number of people booked for the flight and $p = 0.8$

b. $P(X > 15) = 0.2713$

c. $P(X > 15) = 0.1182$

d. $P(X > 15) = 0.0281$

e. $P(X < 15) = 0.4990$

f. $P(X < 15) = 0.6904$

g. $P(X < 15) = 0.8593$

h. Answers will vary.

13. a. Binomial distribution with $n = 7$ and $p = 0.1$

b. $P(X = 0) = 0.4783$

There is a 47.83% chance that none of the plants will strike.

$P(X = 4) = 0.0026$ There is a 0.26% chance that exactly 4 of the plants will strike.

$P(X = 7) = 0$

There is a negligible chance that all 7 plants will strike.

c. $E(X) = 0.7$

d. $\sigma = 0.794$. The standard deviation is larger than the expected value. The standard deviation is expressed as the number of plants that strike. Answers may vary.

14. a. $P(X = 0) = 0.8171$

b. $P(X = 0) = 0.5987$

c. i. $P(X \leq 1) = 0.9838$;

ii. $P(X \leq 1) = 0.9139$

15. a. $P(X = 2) = 0.375$

b. $P(X = 4) = 0.0625$

16. a. $P(X \geq 5) = 0.9936$

b. $P(X = 9) = 0.2684$

17. a. $P(X \leq 1) = 0.8290$

b. $E(X) = 0.75$

18. a. $P(X = 12) = 0.2824$

b. $P(X \geq 6) \approx 1$

19. a. $\dfrac{2}{9}$ or 0.2222

b. $P(X = 5) = 0.0389$

c. $P(X = 0) = 0.0810$

d. $E(X) = 2.2222$,
$\sigma^2 = 1.7284$

20. a. $P(X = 7) = 0.1143$

b. $P(X \leq 10) = 0.8594$

c. $P(X \leq 11) = 0.9730$

d. $P(X \geq 3) = 0.9999$

7.5 Exercises

7. $P(X = 2) = 0.0842$

8. a. $P(X = 0) = 0.0183$

b. $P(X = 5) = 0.1563$

c. Expected number of calls is $\mu = \lambda = 4.0$. The variance of the number of calls is $\sigma^2 = \lambda = 4.0$.

d.

Poisson Distribution for $\lambda = 4.0$

9. a. $P(X = 0) = 0.1353$

b. $P(X = 0) = 0.0003$

c. $\mu = \lambda = 2$

d. $\mu = \lambda = 8$

e. $\sigma = 2.8284$

f. $P(X \geq 4) = 0.9576$

10. a. Let $X =$ the number of weaving errors in a 20×10 foot roll of carpet. X has a Poisson distribution with $\lambda = 0.1$.

x	p(x = x)
0	0.9048
1	0.0905
2	0.0045
3	0.0002

b. $P(X < 2) = 0.9953$

c. $P(X > 5) = 0$

11. a. $\lambda = 20$ (If 5 people arrive on average in 15 minutes, then 20 will arrive on average in 60 minutes.)

b. $P(X = 0) = 0$

c. $P(X > 6) = 0.2378$

12. $P(X = 1) = 0.0733$

$P(X > 1) = 0.9084$

13. $P(X = 6) = 0.0771$

7.6 Exercises

5. a. *X* has a hypergeometric distribution with $N = 50$, $A = 3$ and $n = 10$.

b. $E(X) = 0.6$

c. $\sigma = 0.6785$

d. $P(X > 1) = 0.4959$

e. $P(X < 2) = 0.9939$

f. $P(X > 3) = 0$

6. a. *X* has a hypergeometric distribution with $N = 60$, $A = 10$ and $n = 15$.

b. $E(X) = 2.5$

c. $\sigma = 1.2605$

d. $P(X > 2) = 0.7814$

e. $P(X < 2) = 0.2186$

f. $P(X < 4) = 0.9401$

7. a. $E(X) = 5$; $\sigma = 1.5076$

b. $P(X = 10) = 0.0006$

c. $P(X = 0) = 0.0006$

8. a. $E(X) = 12$

b. $\sigma = 2.4801$

c. $P(X = 0) \approx 0$

d. $P(X = 30) \approx 0$

Additional Exercises

1. a. $E(X) = 2.3$

b. $\sigma^2 = 1.41$

c. $\sigma = 1.1874$

d. $P(X = 4.0) = 0.15$

e. $P(X \geq 2.0) = 0.75$

f. $P(X \leq 1.0) = 0.25$

g. $P(X > 3.0) = 0.15$

2. a. $P(X \leq 1) = 0.0691$

b. $P(3 \leq X \leq 5) = 0.5982$

c. $P(X = 10) = 0.0020$

3. a. $P(4 \leq X \leq 6) = 0.6563$

b. $P(X \geq 8) = 0.0547$

c. $P(X = 1) = 0.0098$

4. a. $P(X = 0) = 0.0067$

b. $P(X = 3) = 0.1404$

c. $P(X \geq 1) = 0.9933$

5. a. $E(X) = 1.6667$, $\sigma^2 = 1.3889$

b. $E(X) = 3.25$, $\sigma^2 = 2.4375$

c. $E(X) = 8.8$, $\sigma^2 = 1.056$

d. $E(X) = 0.8333$, $\sigma^2 = 0.4419$

e. $E(X) = 3.5$, $\sigma^2 = 2.9167$

6. a. $P(X \geq 1) = 0.4690$

b. $P(X = 0) = 0.5310$

7. $P(X \geq 1) = 0.9615$

8. a. $E(X) = 12$

b. $P(X = 15) = 0.0352$

c. $P(5 < X < 9) = 0.0179$

9. $0.25

10. $P(X \geq 1) = 0.9648$

11. $P(X \geq 1) = 0.9933$

12. $P(X \geq 3) \approx 1$

13. $P(X \geq 3) = 0.2962$

14. $P(X = 0) = \dfrac{6}{11} \approx 0.5455$

15. a. Binomial distribution with $n =$ the number of buildings inspected and $p = 0.5$. The binomial is used rather than the hypergeometric because it is not known how many buildings in the population of new buildings have violations. Answers may vary.

b. $P(X = 3) = 0.25$

16. a. Possible values of X are $-1, 1$

b. Discrete

c. -1 if ball not in red: $P(-1) = \dfrac{20}{38}$;

   1 if the ball is in red: $P(1) = \dfrac{18}{38}$

d. $\dfrac{-2}{38}$ is the expected loss per dollar bet.

e. A casino is a business operating to earn a profit. Therefore there must be a negative expected gain in order for the casino to profit.

17. a. HH1, HH2, HH3, HH4, HH5, HH6, HT1, HT2, HT3, HT4, HT5, HT6, TH1, TH2, TH3, TH4, TH5, TH6, TT1, TT2, TT3, TT4, TT5, TT6

b. $X =$ Sum of the number of heads on the two coins and number of dots on the die. $X = \{1, 2, 3, 4, 5, 6, 7, 8\}$

c.

x	P(X = x)
1	$\dfrac{1}{24}$

x	P(X = x)
2	$\dfrac{3}{24}$
3	$\dfrac{4}{24}$
4	$\dfrac{4}{24}$
5	$\dfrac{4}{24}$
6	$\dfrac{4}{24}$
7	$\dfrac{3}{24}$
8	$\dfrac{1}{24}$

d. 4.5

18. a. $\lambda = 12$

b. 3.464

c. $P(Y = 0) = 0.0000$

d. $P(Y \geq 1) = 1$

e. $P(Y = 12) = 0.1144$

19. a. 0.3115

b. 0.1094

c. 0.3115

d. 0.1094

Chapter 8

8.1 Exercises

5. a. $\mu = 40$

b. $\sigma = 17.3205$

c. 0.4167

d. 0.3333

e. 0.4167

f. 0

6. a. $\mu = 60$

b. $\sigma = 1.7321$

c. 0.3333

d. 0.5

e. 0.1667

f. 0

7. a.

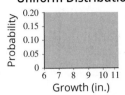

Uniform Distribution

b. $\mu = 8.5$

c. $\sigma = 1.4434$

d. 0.2

e. 0.4

f. 0.4

g. 0

8. a. $\mu = 8\!:\!15$ AM

b. $\sigma = 0.1443$

c. 0.3333

d. 0.1667

e. 0.5

f. 0

8.2 Exercises

8.

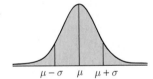

9.

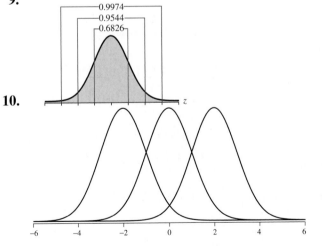

10.

11.

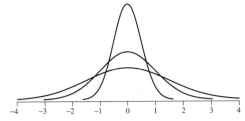

8.3 Exercises

3. a. 0.2486

b. 0.4500

c. 0.4750

d. 0.4950

4. a. 0.2486

b. 0.4500

c. 0.4750

d. 0.4950

5. a. 0.6046

b. 0.4176

c. 0.9167

d. 0.9856

6. a. 0.6680

b. 0.6710

c. 0.9631

d. 0.9422

7. a. $P(z \le 0) = 0.5$

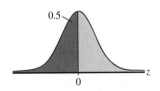

b. $P(z \ge 0) = 0.5$

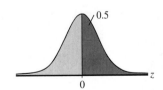

c. $P(z \leq -1) = 0.1587$

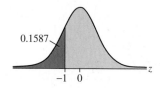

d. $P(z \leq 1) = 0.8413$

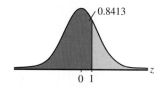

e. $P(z \geq -1) = 0.8413$

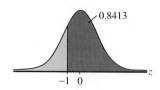

f. $P(z \geq 1) = 0.1587$

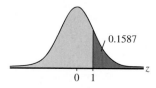

8. a. $P(z \leq -0.44) = 0.3300$

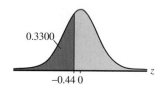

b. $P(z \geq 0.44) = 0.3300$

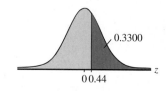

c. $P(-0.44 \leq z \leq 0.44) = 0.3400$

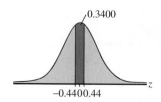

d. $P(z \leq -0.67) = 0.2514$

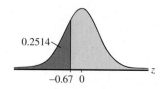

e. $P(z \geq 0.67) = 0.2514$

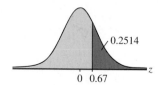

f. $P(-0.67 \leq z \leq 0.67) = 0.4972$

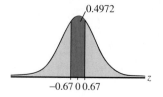

9. a. $P(z \leq -1.28) = 0.1003$

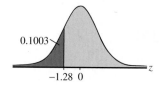

b. $P(z \geq 1.28) = 0.1003$

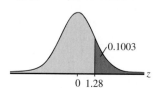

c. $P(-1.28 \leq z \leq 1.28) = 0.7994$

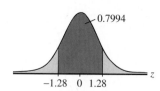

d. $P(z \leq -1.96) = 0.0250$

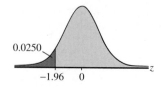

e. $P(z \geq 1.96) = 0.0250$

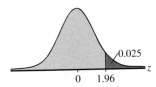

f. $P(-1.96 \leq z \leq 1.96) = 0.9500$

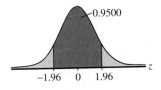

10. a. $P(0 \leq z \leq 0.79) = 0.2852$

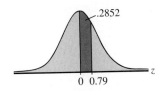

b. $P(-1.57 \leq z \leq 2.33) = 0.9319$

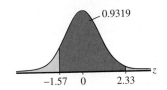

c. $P(z \geq 1.89) = 0.0294$

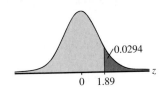

d. $P(z \leq -2.77) = 0.0028$

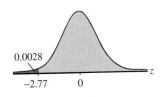

11. a. $P(0 \leq z \leq 1.24) = 0.3925$

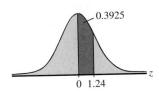

b. $P(-2.64 \leq z \leq 3.32) = 0.9954$

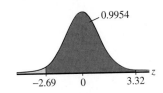

c. $P(z \geq 3.22) = 0.0006$

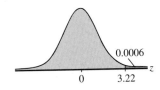

d. $P(z \leq -3.39) = 0.0003$

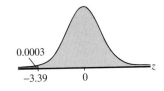

12. 1.645

13. 2.33

14. 1.28

15. −1.645

16. −2.33

17. −1.28

18. 1.14

19. 1.96

20. 1.645

8.4 Exercises

2.

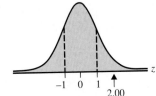

3.

4. a. 0.6826

b. 0.0228

c. 0.0228

5. **a.** 0.7333

   b. 0.0548

   c. 0.0228

6. 0.0548

7. 0.4101

8. 0.0918

9. **a.** $631

   b. 0.2206

   c. 0.1190

   d. 0.4235

   e. Answers will vary.

10. **a.** 9.62

    b. 0.0110

    c. 0.0885

11. **a.** 0.0668

    b. 0.0668

    c. 0.6826

12. **a.** 0.1587

    b. 0.3085

    c. 0.2417

13. **a.** 92.24

    b. No. The score must be at least a 92.24 to be in the top 10% of scores.

    c. 75.28

    d. The student who scored a 65 would receive an F because the score is less than 71.76 and thus is in the lowest 10% of the scores.

14. **a.** At least 131

    b. 0.13%

    c. 6.5%

    d. At least 135

15. **a.** 13.29

    b. Yes, because a weight of more than 13.29 lb is in the top 5%.

    c. No, because a weight of less than 13.29 lb is not in the top 5%.

8.5 Exercises

4. The histogram has a symmetric bell shape. It is reasonable to assume the data comes from a normal distribution.

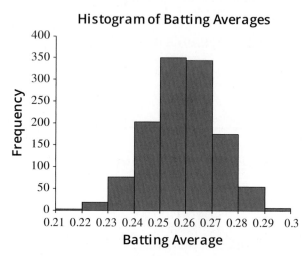

Histogram of Batting Averages

5. The data seem to fit a line very closely. We would also assume from the normal probability plot that the population is normally distributed.

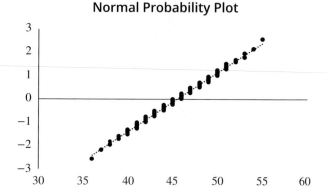

Normal Probability Plot

6. By examining the normal probability plot, we notice a systematic pattern in the data that is not linear. The data do not appear to be normally distributed.

Normal Probability Plot

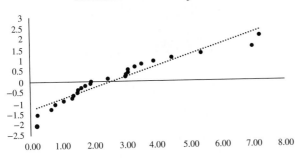

7. By examining the normal probability plot, we notice a substantial deviation from a linear pattern. The data do not appear to be normally distributed.

Normal Probability Plot

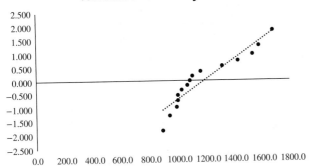

8. The normal probability plot does appear to follow a linear pattern. It is reasonable to assume the data are normally distributed.

Normal Probability Plot

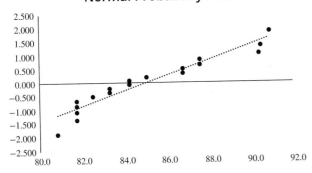

9. By examining the normal probability plot, we notice a substantial deviation from a linear pattern. The data do not appear to be normally distributed.

Normal Probability Plot

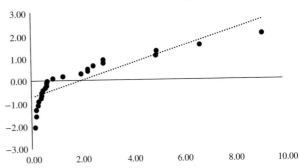

10. The normal probability plot shows that there are two outliers which cause the data to be skewed. Due to the outliers, we must reject normality.

Normal Probability Plot

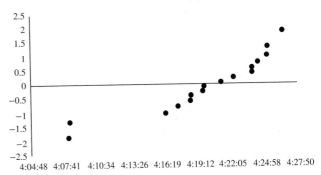

8.6 Exercises

4. Conditions are met.

5. Conditions are not met; $np = 1.5 < 5$.

6. a. 45

   b. 2.1213

   c. 0

   d. 0.9830

   e. 0.0011

7. a. 9

   b. 2.7659

   c. 0.5714

   d. 0

   e. 0.9390

8. a. 120

   b. 6.9282

   c. 0

d. 0.5264

e. 0.0853

9. a. 60

   b. 7.6681

   c. 0

   d. 0.9924

   e. 0.1075

Additional Exercises

1. a. $P(0 \leq z \leq 0.85) = 0.3023$

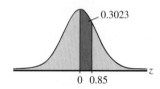

   b. $P(-1.25 \leq z \leq 2.25) = 0.8822$

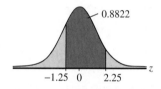

   c. $P(z \geq 1.75) = 0.0401$

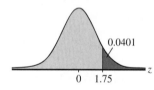

   d. $P(z \leq -2.75) = 0.0030$

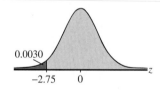

2. a. $P(0 \leq z \leq 1.00) = 0.3413$

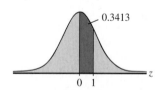

   b. $P(-2.50 \leq z \leq 3.01) = 0.9925$

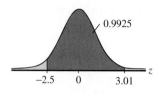

   c. $P(z \geq 3.25) = 0.0006$

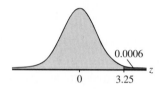

   d. $P(z \leq -2.50) = 0.0062$

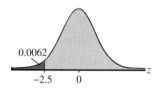

3. 2.575

4. 1.28

5. a. 0.2266

   b. 0.1056

   c. 0.6677

   d. 5.97 lb; Yes, because the lowest 10% of weights are below 5.97 lb and 5 is less than 5.97.

6. a. 5

   b. 2.2349

   c. Using the normal approximation: 0.9778; Using tables: 0.9933

   d. Using the normal approximation: 0.9418; Using tables: 0.9596

   e. Yes, $np = 5$, which is almost too small for the approximation to the binomial to produce accurate results. Answers may vary.

7. $\mu \approx 507$, $\sigma \approx 114$

8. a. 96.08%

   b. 70.88%

   c. 59.48%

   d. 92.65%

   e. Answers will vary.

9. 535 days

10. $\mu \approx 5.71$ ml

11. The time limit should be 100 minutes.

12. The bulbs should be replaced after approximately 397 hours.

13. 0.6915

14. $\mu = \$61,000, \sigma = \$12,000$

15. $\mu \approx 825, \sigma \approx 133.3333$

Chapter 9

9.1 Exercises

10. Answers will vary.

11. Answers will vary.

12. a. Yes, readers voluntarily sent in their responses.

  b. People with strong opinions would be more likely to reply and the categories are not specific so people could have different ideas of what "Frequently" means, for example. Answers will vary.

  c. No. All Americans do not read the magazine, and even if they did, it is likely that only those readers with strong opinions would have responded to the survey.

13. a. Yes, readers voluntarily sent in their responses.

  b. People with strong opinions would be more likely to reply and "Anger" is not well-defined and reader response may be influenced by whether or not they are angry at the moment, for example. Answers will vary.

  c. No. All Americans do not read the magazine, and even if they did, it is likely that only those readers with strong opinions would have responded to the survey. Answers will vary.

14. a. Only students with very strong opinions may have responded, and the response categories are not well-defined. Answers will vary.

  b. No. Only 150 surveys were mailed, and it is possible that only students with strong opinions responded. Answers will vary.

  c. No. Nothing about business majors is mentioned so we don't know how many, if any, business majors responded to this survey. Answers will vary.

  d. Instead of using a voluntary survey they could have surveyed all students in a particular class, for example. Answers will vary.

  e. A question that asked whether or not the participant would enroll in the program if it were created, for example. Answers will vary.

15. No. This is a voluntary survey so only those with strong opinions may reply. People without Twitter accounts are excluded. Answers will vary.

9.3 Exercises

10. a. $\mu_{\bar{x}} = 20, \sigma_{\bar{x}} = 0.8452$

  b. $\mu_{\bar{x}} = 20, \sigma_{\bar{x}} = 0.7071$

  c. $\mu_{\bar{x}} = 20, \sigma_{\bar{x}} = 0.5774$

  d. The standard deviation decreases, reflecting the additional information provided by a larger sample size.

11. a. $\mu_{\bar{x}} = 50, \sigma_{\bar{x}} = 1.5811$

  b. $\mu_{\bar{x}} = 50, \sigma_{\bar{x}} = 1.3484$

  c. $\mu_{\bar{x}} = 50, \sigma_{\bar{x}} = 1$

  d. The standard error decreases, reflecting the additional information provided by a larger sample size.

12. 0.1611

13. 0.0174

14. **a.** 0.1151

 b. 0.2743

 c. 0.5693

 d. 0.2469

15. **a.** 1

 b. 1

 c. 1

 d. 0.0793

16. **a.** 0.4448

 b. 0.9994

17. **a.** 0.2912

 b. 0.0006

18. **a.** 0.0329

 b. 0.0094

 c. 1

19. **a.** 0.0016

 b. 0.0016

 c. 0.9232

20. 0

9.4 Exercises

6. **a.** 0.125

 b. 0.875

7. **a.** 0.3

 b. 0.7

8. **a.** $\mu_{\hat{p}} = 0.45$, $\sigma_{\hat{p}} = 0.0908$

 b. $\mu_{\hat{p}} = 0.45$, $\sigma_{\hat{p}} = 0.0742$

 c. $\mu_{\hat{p}} = 0.45$, $\sigma_{\hat{p}} = 0.0617$

 d. The standard deviation decreases, reflecting the additional information provided by a larger sample size.

9. **a.** $\mu_{\hat{p}} = 0.35$, $\sigma_{\hat{p}} = 0.0774$

 b. $\mu_{\hat{p}} = 0.35$, $\sigma_{\hat{p}} = 0.0661$

 c. $\mu_{\hat{p}} = 0.35$, $\sigma_{\hat{p}} = 0.0551$

 d. The standard deviation decreases, reflecting the additional information provided by a larger sample size.

10. 0.1867

11. 0.4944

12. **a.** 0.0105

 b. 0.0829

 c. 0.7518

 d. 0.2338

13. **a.** 0.8461

 b. 0.0011

 c. 0.4793

 d. 0.4989

14. **a.** 0.0516

 b. 0.5

15. **a.** 0.0023

 b. 0.0384

16. **a.** 0.1894

 b. 0.0384

 c. 0.6212

17. **a.** 0.9767

 b. 0.6536

9.5 Exercises

8. Stratified sampling because the population is split into sub-populations (by gender) and then participants are randomly selected. This could also be a convenience sample or voluntary sample if the employees are not required to respond. The procedure may not be representative because there are 3 times as many females working at the company but they only represent half of the sample. The HR department should also consider the proportion of employees sampled that have children. Answers will vary.

9. A systematic sample is not a random sample because it has potential for bias if there is some inherent data pattern.

10. a. All citizens in the metropolitan area

   b. People without phones or with unlisted phone numbers

   c. People with lower incomes would be under-represented because they do not have a phone. To compensate, you could look at other sources such as the post office or DMV. Answers will vary.

11. a. Families in the state of Florida

   b. The number of children per family

   c. Ratio

   d. Simple random sampling: develop sampling frame, choose participants randomly from sampling frame; Cluster sampling: create clusters, randomly select clusters, survey all members of the chosen clusters; Stratified sampling: create strata, randomly select participants from each stratum such that the population characteristics are adequately represented. Answers will vary.

   e. Cluster sampling, because travel costs would likely be minimized. Answers will vary.

12. a. All stocks traded on the New York Stock Exchange

   b. Simple random sampling: develop sampling frame, choose participants randomly from sampling frame; Cluster sampling: create clusters, randomly select clusters, survey all members of the chosen clusters;

Stratified sampling: create strata, randomly select participants from each stratum such that the population characteristics are adequately represented. Answers will vary.

13. a. Convenience sampling

   b. All of the people surveyed may not be residents of Orlando, Florida because there are a large number of tourists visiting the area.

   c. No, the sample was not representative of the population of interest. Answers will vary.

Additional Exercises

1. a. Voluntary sampling

   b. All Americans do not watch the news program. It is likely that only those with strong opinions responded.

   c. No. Answers will vary.

2. a. All residents of the resort community and tourists who visit the resort community

   b. Phone book or hotel guest lists

   c. Answers will vary.

3. 0

4. a. 0.2643

   b. 0.2643

   c. 0.7924

5. a. Convenience sample

   b. Pre-med majors may be over-represented since there are more pre-med majors in a biology class than in most other classes. Answers will vary.

   c. No, because the sample is biased.

6. a. $\mu_{\bar{x}} = 15\%$, $\sigma_{\bar{x}} = 6.957\%$

   b. 8.043% to 21.957%

7. The sample mean is approximately normally distributed with $\mu_{\bar{x}} = 18$ and $\sigma_{\bar{x}} = 0.6532$.

8. a. 0.0031

   b. Not necessarily. The samples may not have been representative of the population and employees may have not been honest about the amount of time they spend texting at work. Answers will vary.

    c. Survey respondents might not be completely truthful when answering the survey since it is a representation of job performance. Answers will vary.

9. a. 0.0062

    b. The population is infinite.

10. a. 0.0132

    b. 0

    c. No. Noise in excess of 103 decibels only occurs 1.32% of the time.

11. a. $\mu_{\hat{p}} = 0.60,$ $\sigma_{\hat{p}} = 0.0490$

    b. 0.9586

12. a. $\mu_{\hat{p}} = 0.90, \sigma_{\hat{p}} = 0.0134$

b. $\mu_{\hat{p}} = 0.85, \sigma_{\hat{p}} = 0.0179$

    c. 0.8638

    d. 0.9750

13. 0.0045

14. a. 0.9951

    b. 0.8788

    c. 0.1212

15. 0.0571

16. a. $P(\bar{x} > 35) \approx 1,$ indicating that the researchers are likely correct in claiming that the U.S. average is greater than 35 hours (i.e. 50.4 hours).

    b. $\sigma \approx 16.5$

17. a. 0.0618

    b. 0.7324

    c. 0.2676

Chapter 10

10.2 Exercises

20. a. 1.96

    b. 2.575

    c. 1.645

    d. 2.05

    e. 2.33

    f. 1.75

21. a. 2.33

    b. 1.88

    c. 1.75

    d. 2.05

    e. 1.555

    f. 1.44

22. (74, 76)

23. (157, 179)

24. (4964, 5036)

25. 2.160

26. 2.518

27. a. 2.145

    b. 2.861

    c. 1.895

    d. 2.201

    e. 2.898

    f. 1.721

28. (20.4578, 30.0422)

29. (77.3579, 83.3887)

30. a. $\bar{x} = 15\%$ and $s = 2\%$

    b. (13.66, 16.34)

    c. We must assume that the fat contents have an approximately normal distribution.

31. a. (5.6, 7.2)

    b. We are 95% confident that the true average length of stay for the hospital's abdominal surgery patients is between 5.6 days and 7.2 days. We are assuming that the lengths of stay are approximately normally distributed.

32. a. (16.8, 19.8)

b. We are 99% confident that the true average tip (as a percent of the bill) is between 16.8% and 19.8%. We are assuming that the tips are approximately normally distributed.

33. a. (101.36, 128.64)

b. We are 90% confident that the true average price of a regular room with a king size bed in the resort community is between $101.36 and $128.64. We are assuming the prices are normally distributed.

34. $n = 98$

35. $n = 35$

36. $n = 31$

10.3 Exercises

4. a. 0.225

b. (0.1672, 0.2828)

c. No, 0.20 falls inside the confidence interval.

5. a. 65%

b. (62.52, 67.48)

6. a. (0.3277, 0.4123); We are 95% confident that the population proportion of patients who exhibit the placebo effect is between 0.3277 and 0.4123.

b. (0.3144, 0.4256)

c. The interval width increased by 0.0266.

7. a. (0.2176, 0.3324)

b. No, 0.40 falls outside the confidence interval.

8. a. (0.6384, 0.6950)

b. Yes, the organizers of the race know with 90% confidence that between 64% and 70% of the runners will require hotel rooms. This should be good enough to plan the number of rooms necessary to accommodate the runners. Answers will vary.

9. a. (0.3856, 0.5644)

b. Yes, 0.665 falls above the interval.

10. (0.2860, 0.3340)

11. $n = 944$

12. $n = 637$

13. $n = 41$

14. $n = 208$

10.4 Exercises

6. a. $df = 19$, $\chi^2 = 36.191$

b. $df = 4$, $\chi^2 = 14.860$

7. a. $df = 17$, $\chi^2 = 30.191$

b. $df = 40$, $\chi^2 = 55.759$

8. a. (0.0557, 0.0941) We are 95% confident that the standard deviation of the bolt diameters is between 0.0557 inch and 0.0941 inch.

b. The diameters of the bolts have an approximately normal distribution.

9. a. (0.0079, 0.0364) We are 99% confident that the variance of the amount of drug in each tablet is between 0.0079 mg and 0.0364 mg.

b. The amounts of drug in the tablets have an approximately normal distribution.

Additional Exercises

1. a. $\bar{x} = 56.1333$, $s = 2.5317$

b. (54.7311, 57.5355)

c. The heights are normally distributed.

2. a. $n = 68$

b. (0.2598, 0.3402) We are 95% confident that the true proportion of Fontana residents who think safety is a significant factor in their decision about whether or not to ride a bus is between 0.2598 and 0.3402.

3. (0.8453, 0.8947)

4. (9.57, 9.93)

5. (0.4982, 0.6018)

6. $n = 703$

7. a. (25,697, 38,303) We are 99% confident that the true mean valuation of the customer accounts is between \$25,697 and \$38,303.

b. The distribution of the account valuations is approximately normal.

8. (29,630, 32,570)

9. $n = 610$

10. (1071, 1129)

11. (0.3965, 0.4835)

12. a. (7017.67, 9085.33).

b. No, we can't conclude it is higher: The national average funeral cost \$7181 in contained in the confidence interval for this suberb.

c. Funeral costs are normally distributed.

Chapter 11

11.1 Exercises

14. a. $H_0: \mu = 30{,}000$
$H_a: \mu > 30{,}000$

Type I error: They will risk needing to replace tires. Type II error: The company will research ways to make their tires last longer, even though that may be unnecessary.

b. $H_0: \mu = 240$
$H_a: \mu > 240$

Type I error: Mrs. Russell doesn't research ways to improve the bar hooks even though she may need to. Type II error: Mrs. Russell will do research to improve the bar hooks, even though that may be unnecessary.

c. H_0: The network engineer is not competent.
H_a: The network engineer is competent.

Type I error: The manager hires the candidate, but they were not competent for the job. Type II error: The manager doesn't hire the candidate, but they were competent for the job.

15. a. $H_0: \mu = 0.5$
$H_a: \mu \neq 0.5$

Type I error: The company will work on fixing the machines when they are working correctly. Type II error: The company will not fix the machines, even though they are not working correctly.

b. $H_0: \mu = 3$
$H_a: \mu > 3$

Type I error: The company will not do research to make the flares last longer, even though they last less than three hours. Type II error: The company will do research to make the flares last longer, even though it is not necessary.

c. $H_0: \mu =$ advertised mpg,
$H_a: \mu <$ advertised mpg
Type I error: The car manufacturer will do research to improve the mpg, even though that may be unnecessary. Type II error: The car manufacturer will not try to improve the mpg, even though they may need to.

11.2 Exercises

10. a. $z = -2.33$

b. $z = 1.28$

c. $z = 1.96$ and -1.96

11. a. Fail to reject H_0

b. Reject H_0

c. Reject H_0

d. Fail to reject H_0

12. a. P-value $= 0.0571$, Fail to reject H_0.

b. P-value $= 0.0122$, Reject H_0.

c. P-value $= 0.0574$, Fail to reject H_0.

13. a. P-value $= 0.0228$, Fail to reject H_0.

b. P-value $= 0.0071$, Reject H_0.

c. P-value $= 0.0070$, Reject H_0.

14. $H_0: \mu = 55$, $H_a: \mu \neq 55$, Critical values $= -1.96$, 1.96, $z = -8.95$, P-value ≈ 0.000, Reject H_0.

15. $H_0: \mu = 4100$, $H_a: \mu > 4100$, Critical value = 2.33, $z = 0.80$, P-value ≈ 0.2119, Fail to reject H_0.

16. a. The homes that were covered by insurance in the area damaged by hurricane Andrew.

    b. μ = the average size of the claim.

    c. $H_0: \mu = 24{,}000$
        $H_a: \mu > 24{,}000$

    d. Critical value = 2.33, $z = 13.37$, P-value ≈ 0.000, Reject H_0.

    e. Yes, there is overwhelming evidence that the home damage caused by hurricane Andrew is greater than the historical average.

17. a. Yes.
        $H_0: \mu = 45$
        $H_a: \mu \neq 45$
        Critical values = -1.96, 1.96, $z = 2.24$, P-value = 0.025, Reject H_0.

    b. 43.25 minutes

18. Yes. $H_0: \mu = 1$, $H_a: \mu < 1$, Critical value = -1.645, $z = -2.24$, P-value = 0.025, Reject H_0.

19. Yes.
    $H_0: \mu = 5$
    $H_a: \mu < 5$
    Critical value = -2.33, $z = -8.66$, P-value ≈ 0.000, Reject H_0.

20. a. No.
        $H_0: \mu = 5$
        $H_a: \mu < 5$
        Critical value = -2.575, $z = -0.825$, P-value ≈ 0.2048, Fail to reject H_0.

    b. The times customers spend watching the in-store video have an approximately normal distribution.

21. a. 6 year old vegetarian children

    b. Yes. $H_0: \mu = 45.75$, $H_a: \mu \neq 45.75$. Critical values = -1.96, 1.96, $z = -2.963$, P-value ≈ 0.0030, Reject H_0.

    c. We assumed that the heights of 6 year old vegetarian children have an approximately normal distribution.

22. a. P-value = 0.0086, Reject H_0.

    b. P-value = 0.0233, Fail to reject H_0.

    c. P-value = 0.0652, Fail to reject H_0.

23. a. P-value = 0.0750, Fail to reject H_0.

    b. P-value = 0.0068, Reject H_0.

    c. P-value = 0.0744, Fail to reject H_0.

24. $H_0: \mu = 19.55$, $H_a: \mu \neq 19.55$, Critical values = -1.984, 1.984, $t = 3.297$, P-value < 0.10 (tables), P-value ≈ 0.0013, Reject H_0.

25. $H_0: \mu = 0.0647$, $H_a: \mu > 0.0647$, Critical value = 1.680, $t = 1.451$, $0.05 < P$-value < 0.10 (tables), P-value ≈ 0.0769, Fail to reject H_0.

26. $H_0: \mu = 210$, $H_a: \mu < 210$, Critical value = -1.291, $t = -3.158$, P-value < 0.005 (tables), P-value ≈ 0.0011, Reject H_0.

27. No. $H_0: \mu = 5$, $H_a: \mu > 5$, Critical value = 1.29, $t = 0.471$, P-value ≈ 0.3189, Fail to reject H_0.

28. a. IRS customers

    b. Yes.
        $H_0: \mu = 45$
        $H_a: \mu > 45$
        Critical value = 1.28, $z = 13.33$, P-value ≈ 0.0000 Reject H_0.

29. a. NarStor hard drives

    b. Time until failure

    c. Ratio

    d. No. $H_0: \mu = 14400$, $H_a: \mu < 14400$, Critical value = -2.602, $t = -1.727$, P-value ≈ 0.0524, Fail to reject H_0.

    e. We must assume that the time until failure of the NarStor hard drives has an approximately normal distribution.

30. a. Time taken for the moves of top international chess players

    b. Yes. $H_0: \mu = 5$, $H_a: \mu < 5$, Critical value = -1.677, $t = -7.071$, P-value ≈ 0.0000, Reject H_0.

31. a. No. H_0: $\mu = 600$, H_a: $\mu \neq 600$,
Critical value $= 1.753$, $t = 1.6$,
P-value ≈ 0.1304, Fail to reject H_0.

  b. We assumed that the maximum
  horsepower for the engines have an
  approximately normal distribution.

32. a. P-value ≈ 0.2067

  b. No, the FDA cannot conclude that the
  average sodium content is different than
  1190 at $\alpha = 0.01$ since $0.01 < P$-value.

11.3 Exercises

3. $(20.047, 26.228)$; Reject H_0

4. $(97.63, 98.37)$; Reject H_0

5. a. $(40.35, 44.65)$; Reject H_0

  b. Heights of children are approximately
  normally distributed.

6. a. $(583.16, 656.84)$ Fail to reject H_0

  b. Horsepower is approximately
  normally distributed.

7. a. $(1120.82, 1213.86)$

  b. No

11.4 Exercises

5. a. $z = -1.645$

  b. $z = 2.33$

  c. $z = 1.645$ and -1.645

6. a. $z = -1.48$

  b. $z = 1.75$

  c. $z = 1.70$ and -1.70

7. Yes.

  H_0: $p = 0.68$
  H_a: $p > 0.68$
  Critical value $= 2.33$, $z = 4.08$,
  P-value ≈ 0.0000, Reject H_0.

8. a. Yes.

  H_0: $p = 0.25$
  H_a: $p < 0.25$

Critical value $= -1.645$, $z = -2.53$,
P-value ≈ 0.0057, Reject H_0.

  b. We do not know the criteria that
  makes someone "technically
  qualified." Answers will vary.

9. a. Yes.

  H_0: $p = 0.013$
  H_a: $p \neq 0.013$
  Critical values $= -1.96, 1.96$, $z = 2.75$,
  P-value ≈ 0.0030, Reject H_0.

  b. Teenagers may not be honest when answering
  a survey like this. Answers will vary.

10. a. No.

  H_0: $p = 0.75$
  H_a: $p \neq 0.75$
  Critical values $= -1.645, 1.645$,
  $z = -1.83$, P-value ≈ 0.0336, Reject H_0.

  b. We don't know which salespeople were
  chosen, new hires or more experienced
  personnel. Answers will vary.

11. a. No.

  H_0: $p = 0.20$
  H_a: $p < 0.20$
  Critical value $= -2.33$, $z = -1.77$,
  P-value ≈ 0.0384, Fail to reject H_0.

  b. Yes, $np_0 \geq 10$ and $n(1 - p_0) \geq 10$,
  but $np_0 = 10$, which could be a
  concern. Answers may vary.

12. a. No.

  H_0: $p = 0.05$
  H_a: $p > 0.05$

  Critical value $= 1.28$, $z = -0.79$,
  P-value ≈ 0.7866, Fail to reject H_0.

  b. No, $np_0 \geq 10$ and $n(1 - p_0) \geq 10$.

13. No,

  H_0: $p = 0.70$
  H_a: $p > 0.70$

  Critical value $= 1.645$, $z = -0.62$,
  P-value ≈ 0.7315, Fail to reject H_0.

14. No.

  H_0: $p = 0.15$
  H_a: $p > 0.15$

Critical value $= 2.33$, $z = 0.31$,
P-value ≈ 0.3771, Fail to reject H_0.

15. No.

$H_0: p = 0.50$
$H_a: p > 0.50$

Critical value $= 2.33$, $z = 0.20$,
P-value ≈ 0.4205, Fail to reject H_0

16. a. No.

$H_0: p = 0.002$
$H_a: p > 0.002$

Critical value $= 1.645$, $z = 0.12$,
Fail to reject H_0

b. P-value ≈ 0.4524

c. No

17. a. $H_0: p = 0.80$
$H_a: p > 0.80$

$z = 0.62$, P-value $= 0.2676$

b. No

18. a. $H_0: p = 0.40$
$H_a: p < 0.40$

$z = -0.73$, P-value $= 0.2327$

b. No

19. a. $H_0: p = 0.50$
$H_a: p > 0.50$

$z = 2.26$, P-value $= 0.0119$

b. Yes

20. Yes.

$H_0: p = 0.32$
$H_a: p < 0.32$

Critical value $= -1.645$, $z = -2.12$,
P-value ≈ 0.0169, Reject H_0.

21. Yes.

$H_0: p = 0.5$
$H_a: p > 0.5$

Critical value $= 1.28$,
$z = 2.40$, P-value ≈ 0.0082, Reject H_0.

22. a. Yes.

$H_0: p = 0.49$
$H_a: p > 0.49$

Critical value $= 1.645$, $z = 3.82$,
P-value ≈ 0.0000, Reject H_0.

b. ≈ 110 people

23. No.

$H_0: p = 0.50$
$H_a: p \neq 0.50$

Critical values $= -1.96$, 1.96, $z = -0.42$,
P-value ≈ 0.6744, Fail to reject H_0.

11.5 Exercises

7. a. $df = 19$, $\chi^2 = 36.191$

b. $df = 23$, $\chi^2 = 35.172$

c. $df = 4$, $\chi^2 = 14.860$

8. a. $df = 17$, $\chi^2 = 30.191$

b. $df = 23$, $\chi^2 = 32.007$

c. $df = 40$, $\chi^2 = 55.759$

9. a. Yes.

$H_0: \sigma^2 = 0.0025$
$H_a: \sigma^2 > 0.0025$

Critical value $= 42.557$, $\chi^2 = 56.84$,
P-value ≈ 0.0015, Reject H_0.

b. The diameters of the bolts have an approximately normal distribution.

10. a. No.

$H_0: \sigma^2 = 0.01$
$H_a: \sigma^2 > 0.01$

Critical value $= 42.980$, $\chi^2 = 36$,
P-value ≈ 0.0549, Fail to reject H_0.

b. The amounts of drug in the tablets have an approximately normal distribution.

11. a. Yes.

$H_0: \sigma^2 = 0.0625$
$H_a: \sigma^2 > 0.0625$

Critical value $= 42.980$, $\chi^2 = 47.04$,
P-value ≈ 0.0033, Reject H_0.

b. The share prices of the bond fund have an approximately normal distribution.

11.6 Exercises

3. The test is statistically significant since the null hypothesis that the job should take 45 min. to complete was rejected. However, the average of the sample was only 2 min. greater than what the supervisor believed, which might not make a huge difference in the context of the wage negotiations. Answers will vary.

4. The test is statistically significant since the null hypothesis that the average weekly growth of the shrub is greater than or equal to 1 cm per week was rejected. However, it is unlikely that a difference of 0.10 cm growth will be noticeable to the untrained eye. Answers will vary.

5. The test is statistically significant since the null hypothesis that the average waiting time is less than or equal to 45 minutes was rejected. The test is also practically significant since we are dealing with customer complaints, and, based on the sample, customers are having to wait 10 min. longer than they should to talk to an IRS representative. Answers will vary.

6. The test is not statistically significant because the conclusion was to fail to reject the null hypothesis that the average time customers watch the video is greater than or equal to 5 min. The test is practically significant because it lets the store know that customers are spending time watching the new in-store video. Answers will vary.

Additional Exercises

1. **a.** $H_0: \mu = 62$
$H_a: \mu \neq 62$
b. The company believes that the average time to replace a set of 4 tires has changed when in fact the average time is unchanged.

c. The company believes that the average time to replace a set of 4 tires remains unchanged when in fact the average time has changed.

2. **a.** $H_0: \mu = 66{,}000$
$H_a: \mu > 66{,}000$
b. Tech Transit believes that the mean number of passenger miles is more

than 66,000 when in fact the mean number of miles is at most 66,000.

c. Tech Transit believes that the mean number of passenger miles does not exceed 66,000 when in fact the mean number of miles is more than 66,000.

3. Yes.
$H_0: \mu = 3.5$
$H_a: \mu < 3.5$
Critical value $= -1.299$, $t = -4.34$, P-value ≈ 0.0000, Reject H_0.

4. Yes.
$H_0: \mu = 25{,}000$
$H_a: \mu > 25{,}000$
Critical value $= 1.645$, $z = 2.2$, P-value ≈ 0.0139, Reject H_0.

5. Yes.
$H_0: \mu = 13.20$
$H_a: \mu < 13.20$
Critical value $= -2.33$, $z = -2.53$, P-value $= 0.0057$, Reject H_0.

6. Yes.
$H_0: \mu = 12$
$H_a: \mu \neq 12$
Critical values $= -1.833, 1.833$, $t = 2.635$, P-value ≈ 0.0136, Reject H_0.

7. No.
$H_0: \mu = 895$
$H_a: \mu > 895$
Critical value $= 1.28$, $z = 1.19$, P-value ≈ 0.1770, Fail to reject H_0.

8. No.
$H_0: \mu = 10{,}192$
$H_a: \mu \neq 10{,}192$
Critical values $= -2.064, 2.064$, $t = -1.579$, P-value ≈ 0.0637, Fail to reject H_0.

9. **a.** No.
$H_0: p = 0.003$
$H_a: p < 0.003$
Critical value $= -1.645$, $z = -1.42$, Fail to reject H_0.
b. 0.0778

c. Yes, H_0 would be rejected.

10. a. 80-proof bottles of Tommy Walker's favorite brand of whiskey.

  b. The amount of alcohol in the whiskey as a %.

  c. Ratio

  d. $H_0: \mu = 40$
  $H_a: \mu \neq 40$
  Critical values = -2.365, 2.365, $t = -0.935$, P-value ≈ 0.3807, Fail to reject H_0.

  e. Percentage of alcohol is approximately normally distributed.

11. No.
  $H_0: p = 0.2632$
  $H_a: p > 0.2632$
  Critical value = 1.645, $z = 0.90$, P-value ≈ 0.1841, Fail to reject H_0.

12. Yes.
  $H_0: \mu = 12$
  $H_a: \mu > 12$
  Critical value = 2.33, $t = 7.87$, P-value ≈ 0.0000, Reject H_0.

13. a. P-value = 0.0062, Reject H_0.

  b. P-value = 0.0256, Fail to reject H_0.

  c. P-value = 0.0002, Reject H_0.

14. a. No.
  $H_0: \sigma^2 = 16$
  $H_a: \sigma^2 > 16$
  Critical value = 35.563, $\chi^2 = 32.906$, P-value ≈ 0.1648, Fail to reject H_0.

  b. Delivery times are approximately normally distributed.

15. a. P-value = 0.0464, Reject H_0.

  b. P-value = 0.0050, Reject H_0.

  c. P-value = 0.0510, Fail to reject H_0.

16. a. $H_0: \mu = 4$
  $H_a: \mu < 4$

  b. $H_0: p = 0.75$
  $H_a: p < 0.75$

  c. $H_0: \mu = 15$
  $H_a: \mu < 15$

  d. $H_0: \mu = 63,000$
  $H_a: \mu > 63,000$

  e. $H_0: p = 0.5$
  $H_a: p \neq 0.5$

17. Yes.
  $H_0 : \sigma^2 = 0.00156$
  $H_a : \sigma^2 > 0.00156$
  Critical value = 118.498, $\chi^2 = 134.615$, P-value ≈ 0.0120, Reject H_0.

18. a. $H_0: p = 0.30$
  $H_a: p < 0.30$
  Critical value = -1.405, $z = -2.18$, Reject H_0.

  b. 0.0146

19. a. No.
  $H_0: p = 0.90$
  $H_a: p > 0.90$
  Critical value = 1.28, $z = 1.25$, Fail to reject H_0.

  b. 0.1056

20. $H_0: p = 0.50$
  $H_a: p > 0.50$
  Critical value = 1.645, $z = 1.28$, P-value $\approx$ 0.1003, Fail to reject H_0. There is not sufficient evidence to support the claim.

21. No.
  $H_0: \sigma^2 = 0.01$
  $H_a: \sigma^2 < 0.01$
  Critical value = 3.325, $\chi^2 = 1.44$, P-value ≈ 0.0024, Reject H_0.

Chapter 12

12.1 Exercises

11. a. $z = -1.645$

   b. $z = 1.28$

   c. $z = 2.575$ and -2.575

12. a. $t = -1.774$, $df = 78$

   b. $t = 1.28$, $df = 78$

   c. $t = 2.375$ and -2.375, $df = 78$

13. a. (4.0148, 9.9852) We are 90% confident that the average household income on the north side of town is between 4.0148 thousand and 9.9852 thousand dollars higher than on the south side of town.

   b. Yes. H_0: $\mu_1 - \mu_2 = 0$, H_a: $\mu_1 - \mu_2 > 0$, Critical value = 1.666, $t = 3.907$, P-value = 0.0001, Reject H_0.

14. a. (−7.566, −2.436) We are 95% confident that Mr. Ellis' expenses are between $2.44 and $7.57 less than Mr. Ford's.

   b. Yes. H_0: $\mu_1 - \mu_2 = 0$, H_a: $\mu_1 - \mu_2 \neq 0$, Critical values = −2.015, 2.015, $t =$ −3.926, P-value = 0.0002, Reject H_0.

   c. The confidence interval only contains negative values indicating that with 95% confidence the expenses for Mr. Ellis will always be less than those of Mr. Ford.

15. a. (−6.866, 2.866) We are 99% confident that the average score for students in Program A are between 6.866 points lower and 2.866 points higher than the average score for students in Program B.

   b. No. H_0: $\mu_1 - \mu_2 = 0$, H_a: $\mu_1 - \mu_2 \neq 0$, Critical values = −2.624, 2.624, $z = -1.079$, P-value = 0.2833, Fail to reject H_0.

16. a. No. H_0: $\mu_1 - \mu_2 = 0$, H_a: $\mu_1 - \mu_2 < 0$, Critical value = −1.294, $t = -1.2834$, Fail to reject H_0.

   b. P-value = 0.1019

   c. No, we would fail to reject H_0 at $\alpha = 0.05$.

17. a. Yes. H_0: $\mu_1 - \mu_2 = 0$, H_a: $\mu_1 - \mu_2 < 0$, Critical value = −1.655, $t = -11.525$, Reject H_0.

   b. P-value ≈ 0

   c. No, we would also reject H_0 at $\alpha = 0.10$.

18. a. $df = 23$, $t = -1.714$

   b. $df = 18$, $t = 1.330$

   c. $df = 10$, $t = 3.169$ and -3.169

19. a. $df = 12$, $t = -2.179$

   b. $df = 6$, $t = 3.707$

   c. $df = 14$, $t = 1.761$ and -1.761

20. a. (−8.063, −2.337) We are 95% confident that the Dodge Grand Caravan ES takes between 8.063 and 2.337 fewer seconds to accelerate from 0 to 60 mph.

   b. Yes.

   $$H_0: \mu_1 - \mu_2 = 0$$
   $$H_a: \mu_1 - \mu_2 \neq 0$$

   Critical values = −1.96, 1.96, $z = -3.560$, P-value = 0.0004, Reject H_0.

   c. The samples are independent random samples, both populations are approximately normally distributed, and the population standard deviations are known.

21. a. (−1.956, −0.045) We are 90% confident that the fat content in Fiber Oat Flakes is between 1.956 and 0.045 grams less than the fat content in Bran Flakes Plus.

   b. Yes.

   $$H_0: \mu_1 - \mu_2 = 0,$$
   $$H_a: \mu_1 - \mu_2 < 0,$$

   Critical value = −1.311, $t = -1.778$, P-value = 0.0429, Reject H_0.

   c. The samples are independent random samples, both populations are approximately normally distributed, and the variances are unknown but assumed equal.

22. a. (−3.186, 1.186) We are 99% confident that the hourly wage in City A is between $3.19 lower and $1.19 higher than in City B.

　　b. No.

$H_0: \mu_1 - \mu_2 = 0,$
$H_a: \mu_1 - \mu_2 \neq 0,$

Critical values = −2.024, 2.024, $t = -1.240$, Fail to reject H_0.

　　c. P-value = 0.2225

　　d. The samples are independent random samples, both populations are approximately normally distributed, and the variances are unknown but assumed equal.

23. a. (−3.467, 63.467) We are 95% confident that dramas generate between $3.5 million less and $63.5 million more in box office revenues than comedies.

　　b. No.

$H_0: \mu_1 - \mu_2 = 0,$
$H_a: \mu_1 - \mu_2 > 0,$

Critical value = 2.681, $t = 1.953$, Fail to reject H_0.

　　c. P-value = 0.0373

　　d. The samples are independent random samples, both populations are approximately normally distributed, and the variances are unknown and assumed not equal.

24. a. The samples are independent random samples, both populations are approximately normally distributed, and the variances are unknown but assumed equal.

　　b. Yes.

$H_0: \mu_1 - \mu_2 = 0,$
$H_a: \mu_1 - \mu_2 > 0,$

Critical value = 1.725, $t = 1.868$, P-value = 0.0382, Reject H_0.

25. a. The samples are independent random samples, both populations are approximately normally distributed, and the variances are unknown but assumed equal.

　　b. Yes.

$H_0: \mu_1 - \mu_2 = 0,$
$H_a: \mu_1 - \mu_2 > 0,$

Critical value = 2.500, $t = 2.703$, P-value = 0.0063, Reject H_0.

　　c. $H_0: \mu_1 - \mu_2 = 0,$
　　　$H_a: \mu_1 - \mu_2 > 0,$

Critical value = 2.821, $t = 2.778$, P-value = 0.0107, Fail to reject H_0.

　　d. H_0 is rejected in part **b.** but not in part **c.** if the variance assumption changes. Answers will vary.

12.2 Exercises

6. a. $df = 14, t = -2.624$

　　b. $df = 19, t = 1.328$

　　c. $df = 7, t = 2.365$ and -2.365

7. a. $df = 11, t = -3.106$

　　b. $df = 4, t = 2.776$

　　c. $df = 24, t = 1.711$ and -1.711

8. a. Yes. We are considering the same textbook for the price from the bookstore and online retailer, so the samples can be paired. Answers will vary.

　　b. The differences have an approximately normal distribution.

　　c. Answers will vary.

　　d. No.

$H_0: \mu_d = 0,$
$H_a: \mu_d > 0,$

Critical value = 2.492, $t = 1.326$, Fail to reject H_0. P-value = 0.0987, which is greater than $\alpha = 0.01$, Fail to reject H_0.

　　e. (−4.79, 13.43) We are 99% confident that the price of a textbook at a local bookstore is between $4.79 lower and $13.43 higher than the price of the same textbook at an online retailer.

9. a. Yes. The same cashier is using the old register and the new register so the samples can be paired. Answers will vary.

　　b. The differences have an approximately normal distribution.

　　c. Answers will vary.

d. (−4.15, 0.43) With 95% confidence, cashiers using the old cash register process between 4.15 fewer and 0.43 more items than using the new cash register.

e. Yes.

$H_0: \mu_d = 0,$

$H_a: \mu_d < 0,$

Critical value = −1.943, $t = -1.983$, Reject H_0. P-value = 0.0473, which is less than $\alpha = 0.05$, Reject H_0.

10. a. Yes. Drivers are each driving both models so the samples can be paired. Answers will vary.

b. The differences have an approximately normal distribution.

c. Answers will vary.

d. (−2.19, −0.81) With 90% confidence, the braking distance of Model A is between 0.81 and 2.19 feet shorter than the braking distance of Model B.

e. Yes.

$H_0: \mu_d = 0,$

$H_a: \mu_d \neq 0,$

Critical values = −2.015, 2.015, $t = -4.390$, Reject H_0. P-value = 0.0071, which is less than $\alpha = 0.10$, Reject H_0.

12.3 Exercises

7. a. $z = -2.33$

b. $z = 1.645$

c. $z = 1.645$ and -1.645

8. a. $z = -1.96$

b. $z = 2.05$

c. $z = 2.05$ and -2.05

9. a. Yes, the sample sizes are sufficiently large.

$H_0: p_1 - p_2 = 0,$

$H_a: p_1 - p_2 < 0,$

Critical value = −1.28, $z = -1.03$, Fail to reject H_0. There is not sufficient evidence to support the fund-raiser's theory.

b. P-value = 0.1519. This is the probability of making a Type I error. Answers will vary.

c. (−0.0888, 0.0278) We are 95% confident that the proportion of men who answered "Yes" when asked to donate to a worthy cause is between 0.0888 less than and 0.0278 greater than the proportion of women who answered "Yes."

10. Yes, the sample sizes are sufficiently large.

$H_0: p_1 - p_2 = 0,$

$H_a: p_1 - p_2 \neq 0,$

Critical values = −1.96, 1.96, $z = 1.48$, Fail to reject H_0. P-value = 0.1389, which is greater than $\alpha = 0.05$, Fail to reject H_0. There is not sufficient evidence that men and women feel differently.

11. Yes, the sample sizes are sufficiently large.

$H_0: p_1 - p_2 = 0,$

$H_a: p_1 - p_2 > 0,$

Critical value = 1.645, $z = 0.18$, Fail to reject H_0. P-value = 0.4275, which is greater than $\alpha = 0.05$, Fail to reject H_0. The manufacturer will choose Supplier A.

12. $H_0: p_1 - p_2 = 0,$

$H_a: p_1 - p_2 < 0,$

Critical value = −1.645, $z = -1.18$, Fail to reject H_0. P-value = 0.1196, which is greater than 0.05, Fail to reject H_0. You will choose the Nikon camera.

Additional Exercises

1. Yes.

$H_0: \mu_1 - \mu_2 = 0,$

$H_a: \mu_1 - \mu_2 < 0,$

Critical value = −1.669, $t = -2.543$, P-value = 0.0067, Reject H_0.

2. a. $H_0: p_1 - p_2 = 0,$

$H_a: p_1 - p_2 \neq 0$

b. $H_0: \mu_d = 0,$

$H_a: \mu_d < 0$

c. $H_0: \mu_1 - \mu_2 = 0,$

$H_a: \mu_1 - \mu_2 > 0$

d. $H_0: p_1 - p_2 = 0,$

$H_a: p_1 - p_2 > 0$

e. $H_0: \mu_1 - \mu_2 = 0,$
   $H_a: \mu_1 - \mu_2 > 0$

3. a. Yes. The cholesterol levels are measured for the same person before and after the diet so the samples can be paired. Answers will vary.

   b. The differences have an approximately normal distribution.

   c. Answers will vary.

   d. No.

   $H_0: \mu_d = 0,$
   $H_a: \mu_d > 0,$
   Critical value $= 3.143, t = 1.769,$
   P-value $= 0.0637$, Fail to reject H_0.

4. a. The samples are independent random samples, both populations are approximately normally distributed, the population variances are unknown and assumed not equal.

   b. Composition A.

   $H_0: \mu_1 - \mu_2 = 0,$
   $H_a: \mu_1 - \mu_2 > 0,$

   Critical value $= 1.328, t = 4.225,$
   P-value $= 0.0002$, Reject H_0.

5. $H_0: \mu_1 - \mu_2 = 0,$
   $H_a: \mu_1 - \mu_2 \neq 0,$
   Critical values $= -2.878, 2.878, t = -1.388,$
   P-value $= 0.1820$, Fail to reject H_0.

6. a. $H_0: \mu_1 - \mu_2 = 0,$
   $H_a: \mu_1 - \mu_2 \neq 0,$
   Critical values $= -2.575, 2.575, z = -10.00,$
   P-value is approximately 0.0000. Reject H_0.

   b. $(-17.61, -10.39)$

7. a. No.

   $H_0: \mu_1 - \mu_2 = 0,$
   $H_a: \mu_1 - \mu_2 \neq 0,$
   Critical values $= -1.968, 1.968, t = 2.092,$
   P-value $= 0.0373$. Reject H_0.

b. $(0.0931, 0.5070)$

8. a. No.

   $H_0: \mu_1 - \mu_2 = 0,$
   $H_a: \mu_1 - \mu_2 \neq 0,$

   Critical values $= -1.96, 1.96, z = -0.48,$
   Fail to reject H_0.

   b. P-value $= 0.6328$

9. No.

   $H_0: \mu_1 - \mu_2 = 0,$
   $H_a: \mu_1 - \mu_2 > 0,$

   $t = 1.919,$
   P-value $= 0.0371,$
   Fail to reject H_0.

10. $H_0: \mu_1 - \mu_2 = 0,$
   $H_a: \mu_1 - \mu_2 \neq 0,$

   Critical values $= -2.101, 2.101, t = 8.771,$
   P-value is approximately 0.0000, Reject H_0.
   There is sufficient evidence of a difference in the average weights.

11. $H_0: p_1 - p_2 = 0, H_a: p_1 - p_2 \neq 0,$ Critical values $= -1.96, 1.96, z = 21.80, P$-value is approximately 0.0000, Reject H_0. There is sufficient evidence of a difference between the proportion of 16-year-olds that had their licenses in 1983 and 2008.

12. a. Yes. Answers will vary.

   b. We must assume that the differences have an approximately normal distribution.

   c. Answers will vary.

   d. $H_0: \mu_d = 0$
   $H_a: \mu_d < 0$
   Critical value $= -3.747; t = -2.75,$
   P-value $= 0.0258$

   Reject H_0. At the 0.05 level of significance, there is sufficient evidence to conclude that the Vest method is more effective in increasing the diameter of the blood vessels, therefore the hospital will recommend the method to its patients.

Chapter 13

13.2 Exercises

11. a. $\hat{y} = -144193.41 + 256.38x$

   b. For each additional one square-foot increase in house size, the listing price increases by approximately $256.38.

   c. (235.55, 277.20) We are 95% confident that the increase in list price for each additional square foot is between $235.55 and $277.20.

   d. Yes, $H_0: \beta_1 = 0$, $H_a: \beta_1 \neq 0$, $t = 24.250$, P-value is approximately 0, Reject H_0.

   e. Approximately 0.708 or 70.8%

   f. $624,946.59

12. a. $\hat{y} = -0.00936 + 0.38128x$

   b. For each additional 1% increase in Adult.obesity.percent, Diabetes.percent increases by approximately 0.38128%.

   c. (0.36834, 0.39423) We are 95% confident that the increase in Diabetes.percent for each additional Adult.obesity.percent is between 0.36834% and 0.39423%.

   d. Yes, $H_0: \beta_1 = 0$, $H_a: \beta_1 \neq 0$, $t = 57.741$, P-value is approximately 0, Reject H_0.

   e. Approximately 0.515 or 51.5%

13. a. There appears to be a strong negative linear relationship between age and asking price.

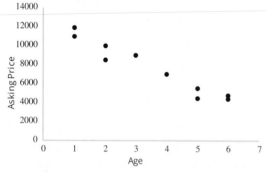

   b. $\hat{y} = 12519.304 - 1391.087x$

   c. 124.6005

   d. (−1809.1701, −973.0039)

   e. We are 99% confident that the true decrease in asking price for a car for each additional year is between $973.00 and $1809.17.

14. a. There appears to be a positive linear relationship between income and IRA contribution.

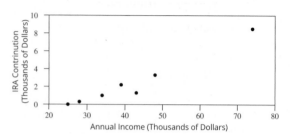

   b. $\hat{y} = -4.8603 + 0.1740x$

   c. (0.1293, 0.2186) We are 95% confident that the true increase in IRA contribution for each additional thousand dollars of income is between $129.30 and $218.60.

   d. The error term is a normally distributed random variable, the expected value of the error term is zero, the variance of the error term is constant, and the errors are independent of each other.

15. a. $\hat{y} = -2.1324 + 1.5643x$

   b. Yes, $H_0: \beta_1 = 0$, $H_a: \beta_1 \neq 0$, $t = 2.635$, P-value = 0.0388, Reject H_0.

   c. Yes, P-value = 0.0388 is greater than α at the 0.01 level, so there is not sufficient evidence of a linear relationship between age and salary.

   d. Approximately 0.5365 or 53.65%

16. a. The two variables appear to have a weak positive linear relationship.

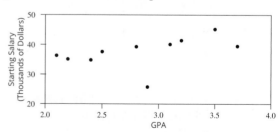

   b. $\hat{y} = 24.9542 + 4.4175x$

   c. No, $H_0: \beta_1 = 0$, $H_a: \beta_1 \neq 0$, $t = 1.471$, P-value = 0.1794, Fail to reject H_0.

   d. $35,997.95

e. For each additional one point increase in GPA, starting salary is expected to increase by approximately $4417.50.

f. Approximately 0.213 or 21.3%

g. The error term is a normally distributed random variable, the expected value of the error term is zero, the variance of the error term is constant, and the errors are independent.

17. a. There appears to be a weak positive linear relationship between the two test grades.

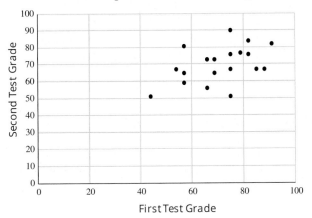

b. $\hat{y} = 42.5154 + 0.3914x$

c. Approximately 0.2076 or 20.76%

d. Yes, $H_0: \beta_1 = 0$, $H_a: \beta_1 \neq 0$, $t = 2.231$, P-value = 0.0379, Reject H_0.

e. 72

13.3 Exercises

4. a. There appears to be a weak linear relationship between actual spreads and betting spreads.

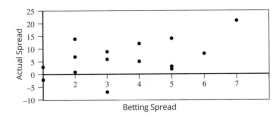

b. $\hat{y} = -0.3834 + 1.9198x$

c. No, $H_0: \beta_1 = 0$, $H_a: \beta_1 \neq 0$, $t = 2.043$, P-value = 0.0619, Fail to reject H_0.

d. Approximately 0.243 or 24.3%

e. The estimated increase in the actual spread for a one point increase in the betting spread is approximately 1.9198 points.

f. (−0.1104, 3.9500) We are 95% confident that the change in actual spread for a one point increase in betting spread is between −0.1104 and 3.9500 points.

g. 9.2156

h. (−5.27, 23.70) We are 95% confident that the actual spread when the betting spread is 5 is between −5.27 and 23.70.

i. (4.59, 13.85)

5. a. $s_e = 372.478$. This is the estimated standard deviation of the errors associated with the model.

b. For each additional one million dollar increase in net sales, net income is expected to increase by approximately 18.4 million dollars.

c. Approximately 0.407 or 40.7%

d. Yes, $H_0: \beta_1 = 0$, $H_a: \beta_1 \neq 0$, $t = 4.15$, P-value = 0.000, Reject H_0.

e. (9.2752, 27.5928) We are 95% confident that the true increase in net income for a one million dollar increase in net sales is between 9.2752 and 27.5928 million dollars.

f. $1005.3 million

g. (702.4, 1308.2) We are 95% confident that the average net income when net sales is equal to $50 million is between $702.4 million and $1308.2 million.

h. (180.5, 1830.0) We are 95% confident that when net sales is equal to $50 million, net income is between $180.5 million and $1308.2 million.

i. $1189.64 million

6. a. There appears to be a moderate negative linear relationship between age and sick days.

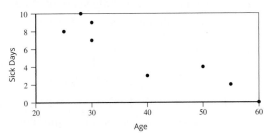

b. $s_e = 1.4765$. This is the estimated standard deviation of the errors associated with the model.

c. With each additional year of age, the number of sick says is expected to decrease by approximately 0.247.

d. Approximately 85.8%

e. Yes, $H_0: \beta_1 = 0$, $H_a: \beta_1 \neq 0$, $t = -6.01$, P-value $= 0.001$, Reject H_0.

f. $(-0.3473, -0.1464)$ We are 95% confident that the true decrease in sick days for a one year increase in age is between 0.3473 and 0.1464 days.

g. Approximately 6.5 days

h. $(5.184, 7.911)$ We are 95% confident that the average number of sick days for a 35-year-old employee is between 5.184 and 7.911.

i. $(2.686, 10.409)$ We are 95% confident that a new 35-year-old employee will take between 2.686 and 10.409 sick days.

j. 4 days

7. a. There appears to be a weak negative linear relationship between hours of training and the number of defects per countertop.

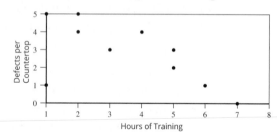

b. $s_e = 1.4531$. This is the estimated standard deviation of the errors associated with the model.

c. With each additional hour of training, the number of defects per countertop is expected to decrease by approximately 0.515.

d. Approximately 0.388 or 38.8%. Other factors could include years of experience, size of countertop, etc. Answers will vary.

e. $H_0: \beta_1 = 0$, $H_a: \beta_1 \neq 0$, $t = -2.25$, P-value $= 0.054$, Fail to reject H_0 at the 0.05 level, Reject H_0 at the 0.10 level.

f. $(-1.0420, 0.0123)$ We are 95% confident that the true change in the number of defects

per countertop for each additional hour of training is between -1.0420 and 0.0123.

g. 2.594 defects per countertop

h. $(1.514, 3.674)$ We are 95% confident that the average number of defects per countertop for an employee with 4 hours of training is between 1.514 and 3.674 defects.

i. $(-0.927, 6.115)$ We are 95% confident that a new employee with 4 hours of training will have between -0.927 and 6.115 defects. Since the number of defects cannot be negative, we can say that we are 95% confident that the number of defects for a new employee with 4 hours of training will be between 0 and 6.

j. 1 defect per countertop

Additional Exercises

1. a. There appears to be a moderate positive linear relationship between amount of drug and reaction time.

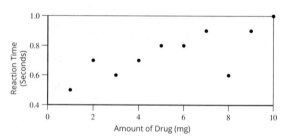

b. $s_e = 0.1101$. This is the estimated standard deviation of the errors associated with the model.

c. Reaction time increases by approximately 0.0394 seconds for each additional milligram of the drug.

d. Approximately 0.569 or 56.9%. Other factors could include age, weight, etc. Answers will vary.

e. $H_0: \beta_1 = 0$, $H_a: \beta_1 \neq 0$, $t = 3.25$, P-value $= 0.012$, Reject H_0 at the 0.05 level, Fail to reject H_0 at the 0.01 level.

f. $(0.011, 0.067)$ We are 95% confident that the true change in reaction time for each additional milligram of the drug is between 0.011 and 0.067 seconds.

g. 0.6909 seconds

h. (0.600, 0.782) We are 95% confident that the average reaction time for an individual with 4 mg of the drug in the bloodstream is between 0.600 and 0.782 seconds.

i. (0.421, 0.961)

2. a. There appears to be a weak positive linear relationship between height and y.

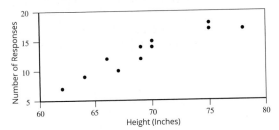

b. $\hat{y} = -34.2765 + 0.6824x$

c. Yes. $H_0: \beta_1 = 0$, $H_a: \beta_1 \neq 0$, $t = 8.316$, P-value = 0.0000, Reject H_0.

d. For each additional inch of height, the number of responses to the ad increases by approximately 0.6824.

e. (0.4968, 0.8680)

f. $R^2 = 0.8849$. Approximately 88.49% of the variation in ad responses is explained by the variation in heights.

g. 15 responses

h. (11.827, 17.887) We are 95% confident that a person that is 6 feet tall will receive between 11.827 and 17.887 responses to the ad.

i. (13.879, 15.834) We are 95% confident that the average number of ad responses for a person that is 6 feet tall is between 13.879 and 15.834.

3. a. There appears to be a strong negative relationship between FICO score and interest rate.

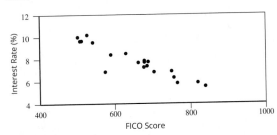

b. $\hat{y} = 16.2146 - 0.0129x$

c. 0.3202

d. Yes. $H_0: \beta_1 = 0$, $H_a: \beta_1 \neq 0$, $t = -10.281$, P-value = 0.0000, Reject H_0.

e. Interest rate decreases by approximately 0.0129 percent for each additional one point increase in FICO score.

f. (−0.0155, −0.0102) We are 95% confident that the true change in interest rate for each additional one point increase in FICO score is between −0.0155 and −0.0102 percentage points.

g. $R^2 = 0.8545$. Approximately 85.45% of the variation in interest rate is explained by the variation in FICO scores.

h. $r = -0.9244$. There is a strong negative linear relationship between FICO score and interest rate.

i. 6.8621%

j. (6.613, 7.148) We are 95% confident that the average interest rate for a FICO score of 725 is between 6.613 and 7.148 percent.

k. (5.864, 7.898) We are 95% confident that a person with a FICO score of 725 will receive an interest rate between 5.864 and 7.898 percent.

4. a. There appears to be a strong negative relationship between age and the number of messages.

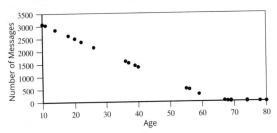

b. $\hat{y} = 344.2472 - 48.6167x$

c. $R^2 = 0.9804$. Approximately 98.04% of the variation in the number of messages is explained by the variation in age.

d. Yes. $H_0: \beta_1 = 0$, $H_a: \beta_1 \neq 0$, $t = -33.959$, P-value = 0.0000, Reject H_0.

e. For each additional year of age, the number of messages you would expect a person to send decreases by approximately 48.6167.

f. (−51.5783, −45.6552) We are 95% confident that the true decrease in the number of messages sent for each additional year of age is between 45.6552 and 51.5783 messages.

g. $r = -0.9902$. There is a strong negative linear relationship between the number of messages sent and age.

h. 2715 messages

i. (2601.0, 2829.0) We are 95% confident that the average number of messages sent by a 15-year-old is between 2601 and 2829 messages.

j. We are 95% confident that a 15-year-old sends an average of over 2000 text messages. That would make them skeptical that Jacob would send less than 500 messages. Answers will vary.

5. a. There appears to be a strong positive linear relationship between home size and annual energy usage.

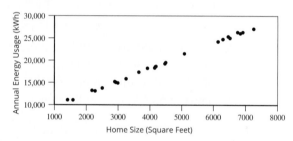

b. $\hat{y} = 6774.4571 + 2.8406x$

c. $R^2 = 0.9982$. Approximately 99.82% of the variation in annual energy usage is explained by the variation in home size.

d. Yes. $H_0: \beta_1 = 0$, $H_a: \beta_1 \neq 0$, $t = 112.114$, P-value = 0.0000, Reject H_0.

e. For each additional square foot of home size, annual energy usage is expected to increase by approximately 2.8406 kWh.

f. (2.7695, 2.9117) We are 99% confident that the true increase in annual energy usage for each additional square foot of home size is between 2.7695 and 2.9117 kWh.

g. $r = 0.9991$. There is a strong positive linear relationship between home size and annual energy usage.

h. 15,864.3771 kWh

i. (15,572.2, 15,976.5) We are 95% confident that the James family will use on average between 15,572.2 and 15,976.5 kWh in their first year in the home.

6. a. There appears to be a positive linear relationship between high school GPA and SAT score.

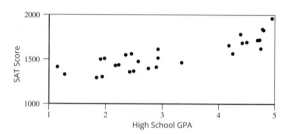

b. $\hat{y} = 1154.6448 + 123.7864x$

c. $R^2 = 0.7301$. Approximately 73.01% of the variation in SAT score is explained by the variation in high school GPA.

d. Yes. $H_0: \beta_1 = 0$, $H_a: \beta_1 \neq 0$, $t = 8.703$, P-value = 0.0000, Reject H_0.

e. SAT score is expected to increase by approximately 123.7864 points for each additional one point increase in high school GPA.

f. (94.6526, 152.9202) We are 95% confident that the true increase in SAT score for each additional one point increase in high school GPA is between 94.6526 and 152.9202 points.

g. $r = 0.8545$. There is a strong positive linear relationship between high school GPA and SAT score.

h. 1588

Chapter 14

14.1 Exercises

6. a. $b_0 = 11214.1992$, $b_1 = 2854.8913$, $b_2 = 839.6360$

b. $\hat{y} = 11214.1992 + 2854.8913x_1 + 839.6360x_2$

c. Age, median income for your location, industry, etc. Answers will vary.

d. $47,152.17

7. a. $b_0 = 6.1342$, $b_1 = 0.0108$, $b_2 = -0.0100$

b. $\hat{y} = 6.1342 + 0.0108x_1 - 0.0100x_2$

c. Yes, the coefficient of the number of pages is positive, indicating that more pages increases printing cost. The coefficient for the number of copies is negative, indicating that if you buy in bulk, the cost is less per book. The magnitudes of $0.01 per page and $0.01 per copy also seem reasonable. Answers may vary.

d. Type of paper, black & white vs. color printing, type of binding, etc. Answers will vary.

8. a. Weight $= \beta_0 + \beta_1(\text{Height}) + \beta_2(\text{Age}) + \beta_3(\text{Calories}) + \beta_4(\text{Exercise}) + \varepsilon_i$

b. Height, Age, Calories, Exercise

c. Positive: Height, Age, Calories; Negative: Exercise

d. Medical history (diabetes, thyroid issues, etc.), Smoker/non-smoker, etc. Answers will vary.

9. a. # of employees, average salary, advertising expenditures, research and development expenditures, charitable gifts to the community, etc. Answers will vary.

b. Revenue $= \beta_0 + \beta_1(\text{R\&D}) + \beta_2(\text{Advertising}) + \beta_3(\text{Salary Paid}) + \varepsilon_i$

c. Answers will vary. The coefficient could be positive because R&D expenditures may result in more and better products, meaning more sales, which would increase revenue. Alternatively, spending on R&D may reduce revenue if the resulting sales do not overcome the amount spent on development.

d. R&D expenditures and advertising expenditures are both costs that should increase revenue in the long run. However, in the short run, spending could decrease revenues, so the model may not be reliable. Answers will vary.

14.2 Exercises

7. a. $\hat{y} = -69,280.13 + 142,935.73(\text{Bedrooms}) + 369,879.29(\text{Acreage})$

b. SSR $= 1.1312\text{E}+13$; SSE $= 1.0668\text{E}+13$; TSS $= 2.3785\text{E}+13$

c. $R^2 = 0.5515$. Approximately 55.15% of the variation in price is explained by the variation in the number of bedrooms and the lot size.

d. $R_a^2 = 0.5478$. Approximately 54.78% of the variation in price is explained by the variation in the number of bedrooms and the lot size, adjusted for the number of independent variables in the model.

e. The value of R^2 is larger than the adjusted R^2 by 0.0037. The adjusted R^2 statistic should be used when comparing with other models. Answers will vary.

8. a. $\hat{y} = -28,520.81 - 34,641.71(\text{Bedrooms}) + 194,986.08(\text{Acreage}) + 240.21 (\text{Square Footage})$

b. $R_a^2 = 0.7738$

c. The adjusted R^2 for this model is larger than the adjusted R^2 from Exercise 7. The adjusted R^2 value indicates that approximately 77.38% of the variation in price is explained by the variation in the independent variables, compared with only 54.78% in the previous model. Answers will vary.

d. Yes, because the adjusted R^2 value is significantly larger for this model. Answers will vary.

9. a. $\hat{y} = 74.6989 + 1.8548x$

b. $R^2 = 0.7365$. Approximately 73.65% of the variation in revenues is explained by the variation in advertising expenditures.

c. $R_a^2 = 0.6926$. No, because there is only one independent variable in the model.

d. Advertising expenditures appear to be significant in explaining weekly revenues. The coefficient for advertising expenditures is statistically significant (P-value $= 0.0064$) and the R^2 value is large. However, there are many additional factors that could also affect revenue. Answers will vary.

10. a. Revenue $= \beta_0 + \beta_1(\text{Television}) + \beta_2(\text{Newspaper}) + \beta_3(\text{Mail}) + \varepsilon_i$

b. $\hat{y} = 73.9320 + 2.3830x_1 + 1.4544x_2 + 1.8160x_3$

c. For each additional $1000 spent on TV advertising, revenue is expected to increase by approximately $2383, assuming newspaper and mail advertising expenditures remain constant.

d. $R_a^2 = 0.8865$. Approximately 88.65% of the variation in revenue is explained by the variation in the three independent variables.

e. The adjusted R^2 value in this model is larger than the R^2 value in the previous model, so this model appears to be more useful. Answers may vary.

f. $R^2 = 0.9352$. The adjusted R^2 value should be used to compare this model to the simple model because additional independent variables have been added.

14.3 Exercises

4. The coefficient became negative. This doesn't make sense as you would expect additional bedrooms to raise the selling price of the house. This variable is likely highly correlated with square footage. Answers will vary.

5. a. $b_0 = 8.35$, $b_1 = 1.53$, $b_2 = 0.30$

b. If a student studies for 0 hours and has a 0.00 GPA, the estimated ACT score would be 8.35.

c. For each additional hour studied, ACT score is expected to increase by 1.53, assuming GPA remains constant.

d. For each additional one point increase in GPA, ACT score is expected to increase by 0.30, assuming the number of study hours remains constant.

6. a. Yes, the coefficient is positive, meaning that as years of education increases, so does estimated salary. The magnitude of $2854.89 for each additional year of education seems reasonable.

b. Yes, the coefficient is positive, meaning that as years of experience increases, so does estimated salary. The magnitude of $839.64 for each additional year of experience seems reasonable.

c. For each additional year of experience, annual salary is expected to increase by $839.64, assuming years of education remains constant.

d. $38,251.52

e. Her annual salary would be expected to increase by $839.64, assuming years of education remains constant.

f. The employee with the master's degree is expected to earn approximately $5709.78 more than the employee with the bachelor's degree.

14.4 Exercises

15. a. $\hat{y} = -811.662 + 2830.705(\text{OBP}) + 1517.578(\text{SLG})$

b. Yes. $H_0: \beta_1 = \beta_2 = 0$, H_a: At least one $\beta_i \neq 0$, $F = 7556.757$, P-value $= 0.0000$, Reject H_0.

c. Approximately 92.48%

d. OBP: Yes; $H_0: \beta_1 = 0$; $H_a: \beta_1 \neq 0$; $t = 36.319$; P-value $= 0.0000$; Reject H_0. SLG: Yes; $\beta_2 = 0$; $H_a: \beta_2 \neq 0$; $t = 43.146$; P-value $= 0.0000$; Reject H_0.

e. No, both variables are significant predictors of runs scored (RS).

16. a. $H_0: \beta_1 = \beta_2 = 0$, H_a: At least one $\beta_i \neq 0$.

b. $F = 10.8947$

c. Yes. P-value $= 0.0001$, Reject H_0.

d. (1466.6644, 4243.1181) We are 95% confident that the true increase in annual salary for each additional year of education is between \$1466.66 and \$4243.12.

e. $H_0: \beta_1 = 0, H_a: \beta_1 \neq 0$

f. Yes. $t = 4.140$, P-value $= 0.0001$, Reject H_0.

17. a. Approximately 97.54%

b. Yes. $H_0: \beta_1 = \beta_2 = 0, H_a:$ At least one $\beta_i \neq 0$, $F = 336.5465$, P-value $= 0.0000$, Reject H_0.

c. (−0.0012, 0.0228) We are 99% confident that the true change in printing cost for a one-page increase in the number of pages is between −\$0.0012 and \$0.0228.

d. $H_0: \beta_1 = 0, H_a: \beta_1 \neq 0$, $t = 2.604$, P-value $= 0.0185$, Reject H_0 at the 5% level (so yes, it is useful), Fail to reject H_0 at the 1% level (so no, it is not useful).

e. (−0.0211, 0.0012) We are 95% confident that for each additional copy, the change in printing cost per book will be between -\$0.0211 and \$0.0012.

f. No. $H_0: \beta_2 = 0, H_a: \beta_2 \neq 0$, $t = -1.888$, P-value $= 0.0762$, Fail to reject H_0. Yes, the publisher should consider removing the variable from the model because there is not sufficient evidence of a linear relationship between the number of copies printed and printing cost.

18. a. Rent $= \beta_0 + \beta_1(\text{Population}) + \beta_2(\text{Income}) + \varepsilon_i$

b. We would expect both coefficients to be positive since larger cities tend to have more expensive rental rates and more expensive rental rates would be expected in areas with greater incomes. Answers will vary.

c. $b_0 = 138.5023$; $b_1 = 0.1199$; $b_2 = 16.8207$; $\hat{y} = 138.5023 + 0.1199x_1 + 16.8207x_2$. A city with 0 population and 0 income would have an expected monthly rent of about \$138.50. For each additional 1000 people in the city, monthly rent is expected to increase by about \$0.12. For each additional \$1000 in average median income, monthly rent is expected to increase by about \$16.82.

d. Yes; $H_0: \beta_1 = \beta_2 = 0$; $H_a:$ At least one $\beta_i \neq 0$; $F = 30.6224$; P-value $= 0.0000$; Reject H_0.

e. (11.4624, 22.1789); We are 95% confident that the true increase in monthly rent for each additional \$1000 increase in median income is between \$11.46 and \$22.18.

f. Population: No; $H_0: \beta_1 = 0$; $H_a: \beta_1 \neq 0$; $t = 1.423$; P-value $= 0.1803$; Fail to reject H_0. Income: Yes; $\beta_2 = 0$; $H_a: \beta_2 \neq 0$; $t = 6.840$; P-value $= 0.0000$; Reject H_0.

g. Yes, the population variable should be removed, as it is not a significant predictor of monthly rent. Answers may vary.

19. a. $\hat{y} = 140.6310 + 17.9366x_1$

b. Yes; $H_0: \beta_1 = 0$; $H_a: \beta_1 \neq 0$; $F = 54.8982$; P-value $= 0.0000$; Reject H_0.

c. Yes; $H_0: \beta_1 = 0$; $H_a: \beta_1 \neq 0$; $t = 7.409$; P-value $= 0.0000$; Reject H_0.

d. Approximately 80.85%. This is slightly lower than the percentage explained by income and population, 83.62%.

e. Though the model including both the income and population variables has a higher R^2 value, the simple linear regression model is probably better because the population variable is not significant in predicting rental rates. The coefficient of determination increases as more independent variables are added to the model, but this does not necessarily mean that the model is better or more useful. Answers will vary.

14.5 Exercises

6. a. 0.4072

b. For each additional point on the SAT Verbal section, graduating GPA is expected to increase by 0.00179 of a point. If the coefficient were negative, that would mean that as the SAT Verbal score increases, graduating GPA is expected to decrease.

c. No; $H_0: \beta_1 = \beta_2 = 0$; $H_a:$ At least one $\beta_i \neq 0$; $F = 2.643$; P-value $= 0.0895$; Fail to reject H_0.

d. Approximately 16.37%

e. No; H_0: $\beta_1 = 0$; H_a: $\beta_1 \neq 0$; $t = 1.311$; P-value = 0.2009; Fail to reject H_0.

f. 2.39

g. 2.39; (2.03, 2.75); We are 95% confident that the average graduating GPA for a person that scored 500 on the SAT Verbal and SAT math portions is between 2.03 and 2.75.

h. 2.39; (1.48, 3.30); We are 95% confident that your nephew's graduating GPA will be between 1.48 and 3.30.

i. The prediction interval allows for individual variation. Answers may vary.

j. The overall model is not significant at the 0.05 level and the R^2 value is not large. Neither one of the estimated coefficients are statistically significant. This does not appear to be a very useful model in predicting graduating GPA. Answers will vary.

7. a. There appears to be a positive relationship between each parent's height and the child height. The mother-daughter plot appears more linear than the father-daughter plot.

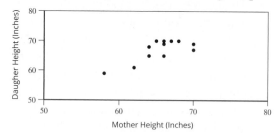

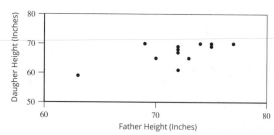

b. $\hat{y} = -4.6456 + 0.5939x_1 + 0.4523x_2$

c. Yes; H_0: $\beta_1 = \beta_2 = 0$; H_a: At least one $\beta_i \neq 0$; $F = 11.2521$; P-value = 0.0028; Reject H_0.

d. No; H_0: $\beta_2 = 0$; H_a: $\beta_2 \neq 0$; $t = 2.176$; P-value = 0.0546; Fail to reject H_0.

e. No; H_0: $\beta_1 = 0$; H_a: $\beta_1 \neq 0$; $t = 2.628$; P-value = 0.0253; Fail to reject H_0.

f. For each additional inch in the mother's height, the daughter's height is expected to increase by approximately 0.5939 inch. For each additional inch in the father's height, the daughter's height is expected to increase by approximately 0.4523 inch.

g. Mother: (0.0903, 1.0974); We are 95% confident that for each additional inch in the mother's height, the daughter will be between 0.0903 and 1.0974 inches taller. Father: (−0.0108, 0.9153); We are 95% confident that for each additional inch in the father's height, the daughter will be between 0.0108 inch shorter and 0.9153 inch taller.

h. 66.8297 inches, or 5 feet 6.8297 inches

i. (61.533, 72.126); We are 95% confident that a particular daughter whose mother is 5 foot 4 and father is 6 foot 2 will be between 61.533 and 72.126 inches tall.

j. (64.785, 68.875)

8. a. $\hat{y} = -15.6150 + 0.1271x_1 + 0.0814x_2 + 0.1215x_3$

b. 7.5084

c. Yes; H_0: $\beta_1 = \beta_2 = \beta_3 = 0$; H_a: At least one $\beta_i \neq 0$; $F = 13.9949$; P-value = 0.0000; Reject H_0.

d. Approximately 59.99%

e. Yes; H_0: $\beta_1 = 0$; H_a: $\beta_1 \neq 0$; $t = 4.293$; P-value = 0.0002; Reject H_0.

f. Yes; H_0: $\beta_2 = 0$; H_a: $\beta_2 \neq 0$; $t = 2.778$; P-value = 0.0097; Reject H_0.

g. No; H_0: $\beta_3 = 0$; H_a: $\beta_3 \neq 0$; $t = 0.264$; P-value = 0.7937; Fail to reject H_0.

h. For each additional rushing yard, the number of points scored is expected to increase by 0.1271.

i. Yes, the first downs variable is not significant in predicting points scored and should be removed from the model.

9. a. $\hat{y} = -15.2395 + 0.1319x_1 + 0.0869x_2$

b. Yes; H_0: $\beta_1 = \beta_2 = 0$; H_a: At least one $\beta_i \neq 0$; $F = 21.6521$; P-value = 0.0000; Reject H_0.

c. Approximately 59.89%. This is slightly lower than the percentage for the model with the 3 independent variables (59.99%). However, the difference is likely due to the additional independent variable in the previous model.

d. The model without the first downs variable is likely the better model. Though the R^2 value is lower, the adjusted R^2 value is larger, indicating that the difference is likely due to the addition of the first downs variable, which is not useful in predicting points scored. Answers will vary.

e. Approximately 21 (21.069)

f. (−2.96, 11.16); We are 95% confident that the average points scored is between 0 and 11 points (since points scored cannot be negative in football) when the offense has 102 rushing yards and 63 passing yards.

g. (−12.70, 20.91); We are 95% confident that in this particular game against Miami, Buffalo will score between 0 and 21 points (since points scored cannot be negative in football).

14.6 Exercises

7. a. The coefficient for attendance is positive, indicating that as the number of classes attended increases, Cumulative GPA increases, which seems reasonable. The coefficient for exam score is positive, indicating that as exam score increases, Cumulative GPA increases, which also makes sense. The coefficient for freshman is negative, indicating that freshmen tend to have lower Cumulative GPAs than other classes. This may not be expected, but it is not unreasonable. Answers will vary.

b. For each additional class attended, one would expect Cumulative GPA to increase by 0.0672 of a point.

c. For each additional point earned on the final exam, one would expect Cumulative GPA to increase by 0.0678 of a point.

d. Freshmen tend to have Cumulative GPAs that are, on average, 0.1436 lower than students in other classes.

e. 0.1436

8. a. Yes, the overall model is significant. $H_0: \beta_1 = \beta_2 = \beta_3 = 0$, H_a: At least one $\beta_i \neq 0$, $F = 235.1310$, P-value = 0.0000, Reject H_0.

b. Approximately 51.06%

c. Yes. $H_0: \beta_3 = 0$, $H_a: \beta_3 \neq 0$, $t = -3.051$, P-value = 0.0024, Reject H_0.

d. Answers will vary. Quantitative: hours of study time, number of credit hours, SAT score, etc. Qualitative: major, gender, extracurricular activities, etc.

9. a. Yes, Salary vs. Age and Salary vs. Experience appear to have a linear relationship. The Salary vs. Gender plot is not very useful since gender is a qualitative variable. Answers will vary.

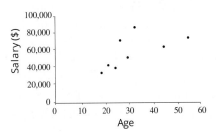

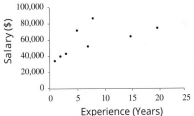

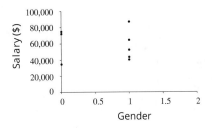

b. $\hat{y} = 38199.3007 + 381.1189x_1 + 1092.6573x_2 - 62.5874x_3$

c. No. $H_0: \beta_1 = \beta_2 = \beta_3 = 0$, H_a: At least one $\beta_i \neq 0$, $F = 0.9068$, P-value = 0.5125, Fail to reject H_0.

d. No. $H_0: \beta_1 = 0$, $H_a: \beta_1 \neq 0$, $t = 0.077$, P-value = 0.9424, Fail to reject H_0.

e. No. $H_0: \beta_2 = 0$, $H_a: \beta_2 \neq 0$, $t = 0.120$, P-value = 0.9102, Fail to reject H_0.

f. No. $H_0: \beta_3 = 0$, $H_a: \beta_3 \neq 0$, $t = -0.004$, P-value = 0.9967, Fail to reject H_0.

g. For each additional year of age, salary is expected to increase by $381.12. For each additional year of experience, salary is expected to increase by \$1092.66. Women are expected to make \$62.59 less than men.

h. \$62,402.45

i. (110, 124695) We are 95% confident that the annual salary for a particular female employee who is 35 years old with 10 years of experience is between \$110 and \$124,695. This interval is not particularly useful because the model is not significant and because the range of salaries contained in the interval is very large.

j. (29927, 94878) We are 95% confident that the average annual salary for a female employee who is 35 years old with 10 years of experience is between \$29,927 and \$94,878. This interval is not very useful because the model is insignificant and the salary range is quite large.

10. a.

School	Private
1	1
2	0
3	0
4	1
5	1
6	0
7	1
8	1
9	0
10	0
11	1
12	0
13	1
14	0
15	1
16	0
17	0
18	1
19	0
20	1

b. $\hat{y} = 105.9195 + 2.5203x_1 - 0.0033x_2 - 65.3808x_3$

c. Yes. H_0: $\beta_1 = \beta_2 = \beta_3 = 0$, H_a: At least one $\beta_i \neq 0$, $F = 35.6335$, P-value $= 0.0000$, Reject H_0.

d. The coefficient for police is positive, indicating that as the number of police increases, so does the number of crimes. This is not what would be expected. The coefficient for enrollment is negative, indicating that as enrollment increases, the number of crimes decreases. This is also surprising, as one would think that a larger student body would result in increased crimes. The coefficient for private is negative, indicating that private schools tend to have less crimes than public schools. This is somewhat expected since private schools are more expensive and generally smaller in size. Answers will vary.

e. H_0: $\beta_3 = 0$, H_a: $\beta_3 \neq 0$, $t = -2.624$, P-value $= 0.0184$, Reject H_0 at the 0.05 level, so it supports the officials' belief, Fail to reject H_0 at the 0.01 level, so yes, the decision would change.

Additional Exercises

1. a.

Observation	Degree
1	0
2	1
3	0
4	0
5	1
6	1
7	1
8	1
9	0
10	1
11	0
12	1
13	0
14	0
15	1
16	0
17	1
18	1
19	0
20	0

b. $\hat{y} = 20839.7273 + 3002.5613x_1$
$+ 26094.8990x_2$

c. $3002.56

d. Yes. H_0: $\beta_2 = 0$, H_a: $\beta_2 \neq 0$, $t = 3.845$, P-value $= 0.0013$, Reject H_0. This indicates that a master's degree is significant in predicting salary, and the estimated increase in annual salary for people with master's degrees is $26,094.90, which is greater than $20,000.

e. There are many other factors that influence annual salary. Answers will vary.

2. a. The relationship appears to be positive, but it does not look linear. Answers will vary.

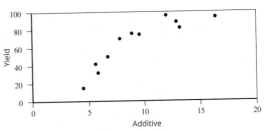

b. $\hat{y} = 5.9860 + 6.3361x_1$, $R^2 = 0.7971$, $s_e^2 = 163.5177$

c. Linear: 107.3638, Polynomial: 91.09. The observed value when the additive was 16.4 was a yield of 94, which is far closer to the polynomial result. Answers will vary.

d. The polynomial model has a higher R^2 value and a lower s_e^2 value, indicating that the polynomial model fits the data better than the linear model. Answers may vary.

e. The polynomial model because it has a higher R^2 value and a lower s_e^2 value. Answers will vary.

3. a. Answers may vary. Price $= \beta_0 + \beta_1$(Inventory) $+ \beta_2$(NE) $+ \beta_3$(MW) $+ \beta_4$(S) $+ \beta_5$(Condo/Co-op) $+ e_i$

b. Answers may vary. 3 indicator variables for region: NE, MW, and S; 1 indicator variable for home type: Condo/Co-op.

c. Answers may vary. $\hat{y} = 161815.0434 + 0.0395$(Inventory) $+ 58499.3038$(NE) $- 41870.1652$(MW) $- 66913.3344$(S) $+ 4646.0503$(Condo/Co-op)

d. Answers may vary. $\hat{y} = 185100 + 52266.6667$(NE) $- 44200$(MW) $- 53783.3333$(S)

e. Answers may vary. $\hat{y} = 188041.6667 - 28741.6667$(Condo/Co-op)

f. Yes. H_0: $\beta_1 = \beta_2 = \beta_3 = \beta_4 = \beta_5 = 0$, H_a: At least one $\beta_i \neq 0$, $F = 47.1165$, P-value $= 0.0000$, Reject H_0. Answers may vary.

4. a. Yes. $\hat{y} = 3.6409 - 0.0144$(Share Price) $+ 0.3333$(Dividend per Share). The model is significant at the 0.01 level ($F = 5.4731$, P-value $= 0.0073$), and both estimated coefficients are statistically significant in predicting dividend yield at the 0.01 level. Answers may vary.

b. Dividends per share is more significant in predicting dividend yield. Answers may vary.

5. a. Benefit $= \beta_0 + \beta_1$(Family Size) $+ \beta_2$(Income) $+ \varepsilon_i$

b. Yes. $\hat{y} = 40.7903 + 3.6594x_1 + 0.1461x_2$, $H_0: \beta_1 = \beta_2 = 0$, H_a: At least one $\beta_i \neq 0$, $F = 397.9462$, P-value $= 0.0000$, Reject H_0.

c. Family size is significant at the 0.10 level ($t = 1.702$, P-value $= 0.0972$), and monthly income is significant at the 0.01 level ($t = 27.955$, P-value $= 0.0000$). Monthly income appears to be a much better predictor for benefits than family size. Answers may vary.

d. (410.70, 430.77), We are 95% confident that the average monthly benefit for a 4-person family with a monthly income of $2500 is between $410.70 and $420.77.

e. (338.93, 502.53), We are 99% confident that the monthly benefit for a particular 4-person family with a monthly income of $2500 is between $338.93 and $502.53.

f. The prediction interval is wider than the confidence interval by 143.53. This is due to the increased confidence level (99% vs. 95%) and the prediction interval accounts for individual variation. Answers may vary.

Chapter 15

15.1 Exercises

16. a. The experimental units are the items produced and the treatment is the shift.

b. First shift:
mean $= 158$, median $= 161$;
Second shift:
mean $= 191.8571$, median $= 182$;
Third shift:
mean $= 111.5714$, median $= 111$

c. First shift:
Min $= 127$, Max $= 181$,
$Q_1 = 140$, $Q_3 = 173$,
Second shift:
Min $= 162$, Max $= 224$,
$Q_1 = 168$, $Q_3 = 219$,
Third shift:
Min $= 77$, Max $= 147$,
$Q_1 = 77$, $Q_3 = 145$,

d.

Box Plots – Items Produced

e. Probably, answers will vary.

f. Yes, answers will vary.

g. Probably, answers will vary.

h. Second shift, answers will vary.

17. a. 153.8095

b. 7

c. 3

d. 21

e. Total $df = 20$, SST $df = 2$, SSE $df = 18$, $20 = 2 + 18$, so the relationship holds.

18. Sample 1: No, the histogram represents data drawn from a population that has a uniform distribution. Sample 2: No, the histogram represents data drawn from a population that has a chi-square distribution. Sample 3: Yes, the histogram represents data drawn from a population that has a normal distribution.

19. Sample 1: No, the histogram represents data drawn from a population that has a negative exponential distribution. Middle histogram Sample 2: No, the histogram represents data drawn from a population that has an unknown distribution. Sample 3: Yes, the histogram represents data drawn from a population that has a normal distribution.

20. Yes, because the boxes are basically the same width, the variation for each population appears to be about the same. Answers may vary.

21. No, because the boxes are not basically the same width. The box plot at the bottom appears to be less than half the size of the box plot in the middle, indicating that the variation for this population is considerably smaller than that of the other two populations. Answers may vary.

22. a. Yes. H_0: $\mu_1 = \mu_2 = \mu_3 = \mu_4$, H_a: at least one μ_i is different, $F = 27.9279$, $F_\alpha = 2.4618$, Reject H_0. P-value is approximately 0.0000, which is less than $\alpha = 0.10$, Reject H_0.

b. Braking distances for each van are approximately normally distributed with equal variances. Observations were collected in an independent and random fashion. Answers will vary.

23. a. Yes. H_0: $\mu_1 = \mu_2 = \mu_3 = \mu_4$, H_a: at least one μ_i is different, $F = 16.8582$, $F_\alpha = 3.2389$, Reject H_0. P-value = 0.00003, which is less than $\alpha = 0.05$, Reject H_0.

b. Hourly wages for employees are approximately normally distributed with equal variances. Observations were collected in an independent and random fashion. Answers will vary.

24. a. Yes. H_0: $\mu_1 = \mu_2 = \mu_3$, H_a: at least one μ_i is different, $F = 15.4961$, $F_\alpha = 2.8068$, Reject H_0. P-value = 0.0005, which is less than $\alpha = 0.10$, Reject H_0.

b. Typing speeds for employees trained by each method are approximately normally distributed with equal variances. Observations were selected in an independent and random fashion. Answers will vary.

25. a. No. H_0: $\mu_1 = \mu_2 = \mu_3 = \mu_4$, H_a: at least one μ_i is different, $F = 3.4667$, $F_\alpha = 4.0662$, Fail to reject H_0. P-value = 0.0709, which is greater than $\alpha = 0.05$, Fail to reject H_0.

b. Maximum heart rates for each workout are approximately normally distributed with equal variances. Observations were selected in an independent and random fashion. Answers will vary.

26. a. Yes. H_0: $\mu_1 = \mu_2 = \mu_3 = \mu_4 = \mu_5$; H_a: at least one μ_i is different, $F = 63.8823$, $F_\alpha = 2.8661$, Reject H_0. P-value is approximately 0.0000, which is less than $\alpha = 0.05$, Reject H_0.

b. Costs of one night in a hotel for each city are approximately normally distributed with equal variances. Observations were selected in an independent and random fashion. Answers will vary.

c. New York appears to be the most expensive city and Atlanta appears to be the least expensive, but the ANOVA test does not tell us which population mean(s) differ significantly. Answers will vary.

27. a. Yes. H_0: $\mu_1 = \mu_2 = \mu_3$; H_a: at least one μ_i is different, $F = 5.1012$, $F_\alpha = 2.5893$, Reject H_0. P-value = 0.0176, which is less than $\alpha = 0.10$, Reject H_0.

b. Dividends per share for each industry are approximately normally distributed with equal variances. Observations were selected in an independent and random fashion. Answers will vary.

c. It appears that the transportation industry pays lower dividends per share than the banking and energy industries, but the ANOVA test does not tell us which population mean(s) differ significantly. Answers will vary.

15.2 Exercises

9. a. Yes, because the dealer believes that the average gas mileage of a particular car will vary depending on the person who is driving the car due to different driving styles. Blocking will reduce the variation in gas mileage which is not due to the type of car.

b. Yes. H_0: $\mu_1 = \mu_2 = \mu_3 = \mu_4$, H_a: at least one μ_i is different, $F = 696.8608$, $F_\alpha = 3.2874$, Reject H_0. P-value is approximately 0.0000, which is less than $\alpha = 0.05$, Reject H_0.

c. Yes. H_0: $\mu_1 = \mu_2 = \mu_3 = \mu_4$, H_a: at least one μ_i is different, $F = 101.7798$, $F_\alpha = 2.9013$, Reject H_0. P-value is approximately 0.0000, which is less than $\alpha = 0.05$, Reject H_0.

10. a. Yes, because the banana grower has noticed that the average yield of banana trees will vary depending on which side of the farm they are planted. Blocking will reduce the variation in yields which is not due to the fertilizer.

b. Yes. $H_0: \mu_1 = \mu_2 = \mu_3$, H_a: at least one μ_i is different, $F = 156.0156$, $F_\alpha = 3.4633$, Reject H_0. P-value $= 0.000007$, which is less than $\alpha = 0.10$, Reject H_0.

c. Yes. $H_0: \mu_1 = \mu_2 = \mu_3 = \mu_4$, H_a: at least one μ_i is different, $F = 36.2535$, $F_\alpha = 3.2888$, Reject H_0. P-value $= 0.00031$, which is less than $\alpha = 0.10$, Reject H_0.

11. a. Yes, because the FAA believes that the number of on-time arrivals varies by airport. Blocking will reduce the variation in on-time arrivals which is not due to airline.

b. Yes. $H_0: \mu_1 = \mu_2 = \mu_3 = \mu_4$, H_a: at least one μ_i is different, $F = 58.8261$, $F_\alpha = 6.9919$, Reject H_0. P-value $= 0.000003$, which is less than $\alpha = 0.01$, Reject H_0.

c. Yes. $H_0: \mu_1 = \mu_2 = \mu_3 = \mu_4$, H_a: at least one μ_i is different, $F = 15.2609$, $F_\alpha = 6.9919$, Reject H_0. P-value $= 0.00071$, which is less than $\alpha = 0.01$, Reject H_0.

12. a. Yes, because the psychologist believes that the number of suicides varies by region of the country. Blocking will reduce the variation in the number of suicides which is not due to age group.

b. Yes. $H_0: \mu_1 = \mu_2 = \mu_3 = \mu_4 = \mu_5 = \mu_6 = \mu_7$, H_a: at least one μ_i is different, $F = 491.3738$, $F_\alpha = 2.1296$, Reject H_0. P-value is approximately 0.0000, which is less than $\alpha = 0.05$, Reject H_0.

c. Yes. $H_0: \mu_1 = \mu_2 = \mu_3 = \mu_4$, H_a: at least one μ_i is different, $F = 10.4629$, $F_\alpha = 3.1599$, Reject H_0. P-value $= 0.00033$, which is less than $\alpha = 0.05$, Reject H_0.

13. a. So that any variation not due to the type of device used to measure systolic blood pressure can be reduced.

b. Yes. $H_0: \mu_1 = \mu_2 = \mu_3 = \mu_4$, H_a: at least one μ_i is different, $F = 9.9883$, $F_\alpha = 3.2874$, Reject H_0. P-value $= 0.00072$, which is less than $\alpha = 0.05$, Reject H_0.

c. Yes. $H_0: \mu_1 = \mu_2 = \mu_3 = \mu_4 = \mu_5 = \mu_6$, H_a: at least one μ_i is different, $F = 135.8303$, $F_\alpha = 2.9013$, Reject H_0. P-value is approximately 0.0000, which is less than $\alpha = 0.05$, Reject H_0.

15.3 Exercises

13. a. Yes, there appears to be interaction between airport location and major rental car company for all three cities.

b. Yes. H_0: There is no interaction, H_a: There is interaction, $F = 13.8127$, $F_\alpha = 2.9277$, Reject H_0. P-value $= 0.000025$, which is less than $\alpha = 0.05$, Reject H_0.

c. We cannot test for effect of company on average daily rental rates because there is interaction.

14. a. There does not appear to be much interaction between age and weight. Answers may vary.

b. No, there is not significant interaction. This agrees with the observation in part **a**. H_0: There is no interaction, H_a: There is interaction, $F = 0.1475$, $F_\alpha = 6.4221$, Fail to reject H_0. P-value $= 0.9595$, which is greater than $\alpha = 0.01$, Fail to reject H_0.

c. Yes. $H_0: \mu_1 = \mu_2 = \mu_3$, H_a: at least one μ_i is different, $F = 19.6229$, $F_\alpha = 8.0215$, Reject H_0. P-value $= 0.00052$, which is less than $\alpha = 0.01$, Reject H_0.

d. Yes. $H_0: \mu_1 = \mu_2 = \mu_3$, H_a: at least one μ_i is different, $F = 21.6885$, $F_\alpha = 8.0215$, Reject H_0. P-value $= 0.00036$, which is less than $\alpha = 0.01$, Reject H_0.

15. a. There appears to be slight interaction between operator and machine. If there was no interaction, the lines would be parallel. Answers may vary.

b. No, there is not significant interaction. This agrees with part **a.**, we only thought the interaction was slight. H_0: There is no interaction, H_a: There is interaction, $F = 0.0789$, $F_\alpha = 2.2858$, Fail to reject H_0. P-value $= 0.9878$, which is greater than $\alpha = 0.10$, Fail to reject H_0.

c. Yes. $H_0: \mu_1 = \mu_2 = \mu_3$, H_a: at least one μ_i is different, $F = 4.5$, $F_\alpha = 2.6240$, Reject H_0. P-value $= 0.0260$, which is less than $\alpha = 0.10$, Reject H_0.

d. Yes. $H_0: \mu_1 = \mu_2 = \mu_3$, H_a: at least one μ_i is different, $F = 14.2895$, $F_\alpha = 2.6240$, Reject H_0. P-value $= 0.00019$, which is less than $\alpha = 0.10$, Reject H_0.

16. a. There appears to be slight interaction between grass and grain. If there was no interaction, the lines would be parallel. Answers may vary.

b. Yes, there is significant interaction. This agrees with our suspicion from part **a.** H_0: There is no interaction, H_a: There is interaction, $F = 6.5275$, $F_\alpha = 2.5082$, Reject H_0. P-value $= 0.00035$, which is less than $\alpha = 0.05$, Reject H_0.

c., d. Since we have significant interaction between the variables, the main effects tests should not be performed.

17. a.

Source	SS	df	MS	F
Power	1.270	1	1.270	14.7246
Knowledge	0.250	1	0.250	2.8986
Interaction	0.010	1	0.010	0.1159
Error	4.140	48	0.0863	
Total	5.670	51		

b. No. H_0: There is no interaction, H_a: There is interaction, $F = 0.1159$, $F_\alpha = 2.8131$, Fail to reject H_0. P-value $= 0.7350$, which is greater than $\alpha = 0.05$, Fail to reject H_0.

c. Yes. $H_0: \mu_1 = \mu_2$, H_a: at least one μ_i is different, $F = 14.7246$, $F_\alpha = 4.0427$, Reject H_0. P-value $= 0.00036$, which is less than $\alpha = 0.05$, Reject H_0.

d. No. $H_0: \mu_1 = \mu_2$, H_a: at least one μ_i is different, $F = 2.8986$, $F_\alpha = 4.0427$, Fail to reject H_0. P-value $= 0.0951$, which is greater than $\alpha = 0.05$, Fail to reject H_0.

Additional Exercises

1. a. Dividing the students of each class into blocks categorized as Below Average, Average, and Above Average. Answers will vary.

b. Dividing participants into blocks, categorized as <100 lb overweight, 50-100 lb overweight, and 0-50 lb overweight. Answers will vary.

c. Dividing the persons into blocks categorized as Low IQ, Average IQ, and High IQ. Answers will vary.

2. a. Yes. $H_0: \mu_1 = \mu_2 = \mu_3$, H_a: at least one μ_i is different, $F = 19.1177$, $F_\alpha = 8.0215$, Reject H_0. P-value $= 0.00058$, which is less than $\alpha = 0.01$, Reject H_0.

b. Absorption times for each drug are approximately normally distributed with equal variances. Observations were collected in an independent and random fashion. Answers will vary.

c. Blocking by participant. Advantages and disadvantages: blocking may reduce variation but degrees of freedom are also sacrificed. Answers will vary.

3. a. Yes. $H_0: \mu_1 = \mu_2 = \mu_3$, H_a: at least one μ_i is different, $F = 15.6429$, $F_\alpha = 6.3589$, Reject H_0. P-value $= 0.00021$, which is less than $\alpha = 0.01$, Reject H_0.

b. Fat contents for each brand of margarine are approximately normally distributed with equal variances. Observations were collected in an independent and random fashion. Answers will vary.

c. The data are obtained from servings. There are no variables associated with the servings that we can block with. Answers will vary.

4. a.

Source	SS	df
Treatments	11.3139	2
Error	1059.76	1714

b. MST $= 5.6570$,
MSE $= 0.6183$

c. Yes. $H_0: \mu_1 = \mu_2 = \mu_3$, H_a: at least one μ_i is different, $F = 9.1493$, $F_\alpha = 4.6176$, Reject H_0. P-value $= 0.00011$, which is less than $\alpha = 0.01$, Reject H_0.

d. The distributions of all populations of interest are approximately normal, the variances of the populations of interest are equal, each of the k samples must be selected independently from each other and in a random fashion. They cannot be checked in this instance because the raw data are not available.

5. a. $\bar{\bar{x}} = 3.3064$,

SST $= 20.1246$

b. $F = 35.3327$

c. Yes. $H_0: \mu_1 = \mu_2 = \mu_3$, H_a: at least one μ_i is different, $F = 35.3327$, $F_\alpha = 4.7623$, Reject H_0. P-value is approximately 0.0000, which is less than $\alpha = 0.01$, Reject H_0.

d. The distributions of all of the populations of interest are approximately normal with equal variances, each of the k samples must be selected independently from each other and in a random fashion. They cannot be checked in this instance because the raw data are not available.

6. a.

Source	SS	df	MS	F
Factor A	0.800	2	0.4000	4.6154
Factor B	5.300	3	1.7677	20.3846
Interaction	9.600	6	1.6000	18.4615
Within	1.300	15	0.0869	
Total	17.000	26		

b. Yes, H_0: there is no interaction, H_a: there is interaction, $F = 18.4615$, $F_\alpha = 2.7905$, Reject H_0. P-value $= 0.000004$, which is less than $\alpha = 0.05$, Reject H_0.

c., d. The main effects tests are not appropriate because there is evidence of interaction.

e. Yes, there is evidence of interaction between factors, so the results of the main effects tests are not reliable.

7. a. The mixed question tests appear to result in the highest average test scores. It also appears that graduate students typically have higher test scores, on average. Answers will vary.

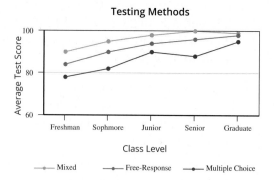

b. Yes. $H_0: \mu_1 = \mu_2 = \mu_3 = \mu_4 = \mu_5$, H_a: at least one μ_i is different, $F = 22.0786$, $F_\alpha = 3.8379$, Reject H_0. P-value $= 0.00055$, which is less than $\alpha = 0.05$, Reject H_0.

c. Yes, because the blocking effects were significant. Answers will vary.

8. a. 4

b. 6

c. 18

d. $H_0: \mu_1 = \mu_2 = \mu_3 = \mu_4 = \mu_5 = \mu_6$, H_a: at least one μ_i is different.

e. $F = \dfrac{\text{MST}}{\text{MSE}}$

f. $F > F_\alpha$

g. There is sufficient evidence that at least one population mean is different. $F = 7.5020$, $F_\alpha = 3.4817$, Reject H_0. P-value $= 0.0049$, which is less than $\alpha = 0.05$, Reject H_0.

9. a.

Source	SS	df	MS	F
Block	2154.1333	9	239.3481	96.8876
Treatment	30.2	2	15.1	6.1124
Error	44.4667	18	2.4704	
Total	2228.8	29		

b. Yes, $H_0: \mu_1 = \mu_2 = \mu_3 = \mu_4$, H_a: at least one μ_i is different, $F = 6.1124$, $F_\alpha = 3.5546$, Reject H_0.

c. $P = 0.0094$. The probability of a Type I error for this hypothesis test is 0.0094.

10. a.

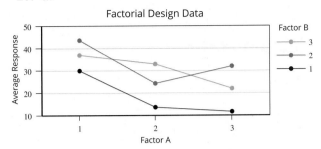

Factorial Design Data

Yes, there appears to be interaction between Factors A and B.

b.

Source	SS	df	MS	F
Rows	1208.9630	2	4.604.4815	173.6277
Columns	1134.5185	2	567.2593	162.9362
Interaction	328.5926	4	82.1481	23.5957
Within	62.6667	18	3.4815	
Total	2734.7407	26		

c. Yes, there is significant interaction. H_0: there is no interaction, H_a: there is interaction, $F = 23.5957$, $F_\alpha = 2.9277$, Reject H_0. P-value = 0.0000006, which is less than $\alpha = 0.05$, Reject H_0.

d. The main effects tests are not appropriate because there is significant interaction between factors A and B.

11. a. H_0: $\mu_1 = \mu_2 = \mu_3$, H_a: at least one μ_i is different.

b.

Source	SS	df	MS	F
Block	1103.0	3	367.6667	31.2908
Treatment	158.1667	2	79.0833	6.7305
Error	70.5	6	11.75	
Total	1331.6667	11		

c. Yes, at least one of the revenues is significantly different. H_0: $\mu_1 = \mu_2 = \mu_3$, H_a: at least one μ_i is different, $F = 6.7305$, $F_\alpha = 5.1433$, Reject H_0. P-value = 0.0293, which is less than $\alpha = 0.05$, Reject H_0.

d. Yes, H_0: $\mu_1 = \mu_2 = \mu_3$, H_a: at least one μ_i is different, $F = 31.2908$, $F_\alpha = 4.7571$, Reject H_0. P-value = 0.00046, which is less than $\alpha = 0.05$, Reject H_0.

12. a.

Source	SS	df
Treatments	37.9856	2
Error	1267.5	150

MST = 18.9928 ; MSE = 8.45

b. H_0: $\mu_1 = \mu_2 = \mu_3$; H_a: At least one μ_i is different; $F = 2.25$; $F_\alpha = 3.04$, No, fail to reject H_0. P-value = 0.1089, which is greater than $\alpha = 0.05$, Fail to reject H_0.

c. The first assumption is that the distributions of all populations of interest are approximately normal. This cannot be verified as the underlying sample data is not provided. The second assumption is that the variances of the populations of interest are equal. This can be verified as the Standard Deviation for each population is provided in the summary statistics. The third assumption which must be met is that each of the k samples must be selected independently from each other and in a random fashion from each of the respective populations. This cannot be verified as the underlying sample data is not provided.

Chapter 16

16.1 Exercises

8. a. 29.141

   b. 45.642

   c. 9.488

   d. 16.919

   e. 28.300

9. a. 41.401

   b. 28.845

   c. 5.024

   d. 107.565

   e. 24.769

10. a. 23.209

   b. 38.932

   c. 12.592

   d. 19.675

   e. 52.336

11. a. 66.766

   b. 27.488

   c. 7.378

   d. 33.196

   e. 63.167

12. a. $4796

   b. 8.281

   c. 9

   d. 16.919

13. a. 0.042982

   b. 30.0874

   c. 16.013

16.2 Exercises

9. a. No.

$$H_0: p_1 = p_2 = \cdots = p_5 = \frac{1}{5}$$

H_a: Any possible difference.

$\chi_\alpha^2 = 9.488; \chi^2 = 7.647; P$-value ≈ 0.154; Fail to reject H_0

   b. The distribution of the number of service calls has a multinomial probability distribution.

10. a. Brown: 111, Yellow: 74, Red: 74, Orange: 37, Green: 37, Blue: 37

   b. No.

$H_0: p_1 = 0.30, p_2 = p_3 = 0.20,$
$p_4 = p_5 = p_6 = 0.10$

H_a: Any possible difference.

$\chi_\alpha^2 = 15.086; \chi^2 = 13.541; P$-value ≈ 0.0015; Fail to reject H_0

   c. The distribution of the number of candies has a multinomial probability distribution.

11. a. Yes.

$$H_0: p_1 = p_2 = \cdots = p_{12} = \frac{1}{12}$$

H_a: Any possible difference.

$\chi_\alpha^2 = 24.725; \chi^2 = 26.376; P$-value ≈ 0.0057; Reject H_0

   b. The distribution of fatal accidents has a multinomial probability distribution.

12. a. Yes.

$H_0: p_1 = 0.15, p_2 = p_3 = 0.30, p_4 = 0.25$

H_a: Any possible difference.

$\chi_\alpha^2 = 11.345; \chi^2 = 28.000;$
P-value ≈ 0.0000; Reject H_0

   b. The distribution of the survey responses has a multinomial probability distribution.

16.3 Exercises

10. a. Yes.

H_0: Age and political affiliation are independent.
H_a: Age and political affiliation are dependent.
$\chi_\alpha^2 = 9.488$; $\chi^2 = 31.881$; P-value ≈ 0.0000
Reject H_0

b. The experiment satisfies the properties of a multinomial experiment, the null hypothesis is true and the expected counts in each cell are all at least 5.

11. a. No.

H_0: Education and crime are independent.
H_a: Education and crime are dependent.
$\chi_\alpha^2 = 6.251$; $\chi^2 = 6.077$; P-value ≈ 0.1080
Fail to reject H_0

b. The experiment satisfies the properties of a multinomial experiment, the null hypothesis is true and the expected counts in each cell are all at least 5.

12. a. No.

H_0: Type of abuse and gender are independent.
H_a: Type of abuse and gender are dependent.
$\chi_\alpha^2 = 7.815$; $\chi^2 = 3.575$; P-value ≈ 0.3112
Fail to reject H_0

b. The experiment satisfies the properties of a multinomial experiment, the null hypothesis is true and the expected counts in each cell are all at least 5.

13. a. No.

H_0: Causes of fires and region are independent.
H_a: Causes of fires and region are dependent.
$\chi_\alpha^2 = 30.578$; $\chi^2 = 1.963$; P-value ≈ 1.0000
Fail to reject H_0

b. The experiment satisfies the properties of a multinomial experiment, the null hypothesis is true and the expected counts in each cell are all at least 5.

Additional Exercises

1. a. Yes.

H_0: $p_1 = 0.50, p_2 = p_3 = 0.25$
H_a: Any possible difference.
$\chi_\alpha^2 = 5.991$; $\chi^2 = 68.400$
P-value ≈ 0.0000; Reject H_0

b. The underlying distribution is a multinomial probability distribution.

2. Yes.

H_0: $p_1 = 0.51, p_2 = 0.33, p_3 = 0.16$
H_a: Any possible difference.
$\chi_\alpha^2 = 5.991$; $\chi^2 = 10.861$
P-value ≈ 0.0044; Reject H_0

3. a. $P(\text{Lane 1}) = 0.4$, $P(\text{Lane 2}) = 0.2$, $P(\text{Lane 3}) = 0.2$, $P(\text{Lane 4}) = 0.2$

b. Yes.

H_0: $p_1 = 0.4, p_2 = p_3 = p_4 = 0.2$
H_a: Any possible difference.
$\chi_\alpha^2 = 7.815$; $\chi^2 = 20.638$
P-value ≈ 0.0001; Reject H_0

4. a. No.

H_0: Preferred pizza and region are independent.
H_a: Preferred pizza and region are dependent.
$\chi_\alpha^2 = 10.645$; $\chi^2 = 1.702$; P-value ≈ 0.9450
Fail to reject H_0

b. The experiment satisfies the properties of a multinomial experiment, the null hypothesis is true and the expected counts in each cell are all at least 5.

5. a. Yes

H_0: Rating and brand are independent.
H_a: Rating and brand are dependent.
$\chi_\alpha^2 = 26.296$; $\chi^2 = 62.895$; P-value ≈ 0.0000
Reject H_0

b. The experiment satisfies the properties of a multinomial experiment, the null hypothesis is true and the expected counts in each cell are all at least 5.

Chapter 17

17.1 Exercises

15. H_0: Median $\leq \$25,000$
H_a: Median $> \$25,000$
Critical value $= -1.28$
$z = -3.25$; Reject H_0

16. H_0: Median ≥ 10 minutes
H_a: Median < 10 minutes
Critical value $= -1.645$
$z = -12.62$; Reject H_0

17. **a.** H_0: Median $\geq 14,400$ hrs
H_a: Median $< 14,400$ hrs
Critical value $= 2$
$X = 6$; Fail to Reject H_0

   b. The data are randomly selected.

18. **a.** H_0: Median ≤ 12 hrs
H_a: Median > 12 hrs
Critical value $= 3$
$X = 6$; Fail to Reject H_0

   b. The data are randomly selected.

19. H_0: # of Positive Signs $\leq$
      # of Negative Signs
H_a: # of Positive Signs $>$
      # of Negative Signs
Critical value $= 6$
$X = 9$; Fail to Reject H_0

20. H_0: # of Negative Signs $\leq$
      # of Positive Signs
H_a: # of Negative Signs $>$
      # of Positive Signs
Critical value $= 0$
$X = 1$; Fail to Reject H_0

21. H_0: # of Negative Signs $=$
      # of Positive Signs
H_a: # of Negative Signs $\neq$
      # of Positive Signs
Critical value $= 0$
$X = 0$; Reject H_0

22. H_0: # of Positive Signs $\leq$
      # of Negative Signs
H_a: # of Positive Signs $>$
      # of Negative Signs
Critical value $= 0$
$X = 1$; Fail to Reject H_0

17.2 Exercises

11.

Mutual Fund	Price	Rank
American Funds	24.4	7.5
Columbia Management	9.41	2.5
Morgan Stanley	23.74	6
Fidelity Investments	24.40	7.5
John Hancock	9.41	2.5
DWS Investments	15.57	5
UBS	12.15	4
Prudential Investments	9.23	1
Value Line Funds	32.82	9
The Vanguard Group	34.72	10

12.

Expenditure Category	CPI	Rank
Food	4.7	8
Alcoholic Beverages	1.4	1
Housing	1.8	2
Apparel	3.5	5
Public Transportation	7.4	9
Medical Care	2.8	4
Education	4.4	7
Tobacco and Smoking Products	2.4	3
Gasoline	33.3	10
New and Used Motor Vehicles	3.6	6

13. **a.** H_0: DHEA-S is not increased
   H_a: DHEA-S is increased
   Critical value $= 0$
   $X = 2$; Fail to Reject H_0

   b. The data are randomly selected.

   c. H_0: DHEA-S is not increased
   H_a: DHEA-S is increased
   Critical value $= 4$
   $T_+ = 5$; Fail to Reject H_0

   d. Pairs of data have been randomly selected
   and are such that the absolute values
   of their differences can be ranked.

e. The signed-rank test because the magnitudes of the differences are not ignored. Answers will vary.

14. a. The paired differences have an approximately normal distribution.

b. H_0: Old Register ≤ New Register
H_a: Old Register > New Register
Critical value = 1
$T_+ = 1.5$; Fail to Reject H_0

c. Pairs of data have been randomly selected and are such that the absolute values of their differences can be ranked.

d. When using a paired difference experiment there was sufficient evidence to reject the null hypothesis and conclude that the new register enables cashiers to process a larger number of items than the old cash register. Using the signed-rank test, no such conclusion can be made. Answers will vary.

15. a. The paired differences have an approximately normal distribution.

b. H_0: Model A = Model B
H_a: Model A ≠ Model B
Critical value = 1
$T_+ = 0$; Reject H_0

c. Pairs of data have been randomly selected and are such that the absolute values of their differences can be ranked.

d. In all three tests the null hypothesis is rejected in favor of the alternative.

17.3 Exercises

10. a. H_0: North Income ≤ South Income
H_a: North Income > South Income
Critical value = 105
$T_x = 102.5$; Fail to Reject H_0

b. The data are such that they can be ranked. The two samples are selected in an independent and random fashion.

11. a. H_0: Mr. Ellis = Mr. Ford
H_a: Mr. Ellis ≠ Mr. Ford
Critical value = 37,68
$T_x = 42,63$; Fail to Reject H_0

b. The data are such that they can be ranked. The two samples are selected in an independent and random fashion.

12. a. H_0: Program A = Program B
H_a: Program A ≠ Program B
Critical value = 39,66
$T_x = 49.5,55.5$; Fail to Reject H_0

b. The data are such that they can be ranked. The two samples are selected in an independent and random fashion.

13. a. H_0: New Battery ≥ Old Battery
H_a: New Battery < Old Battery
Critical value = 28
$T_x = 35$; Fail to Reject H_0

b. The data are such that they can be ranked. The two samples are selected in an independent and random fashion.

14. a. H_0: Fiber Oat Flakes ≥ Bran Flakes Plus
H_a: Fiber Oat Flakes < Bran Flakes Plus
Critical value = 66
$T_x = 74.5$; Fail to Reject H_0

b. The data are such that they can be ranked. The two samples are selected in an independent and random fashion.

15. a. H_0: Dramas ≤ Comedies
H_a: Dramas > Comedies
Critical value = 36
$T_x = 32$; Fail to Reject H_0

b. The data are such that they can be ranked. The two samples are selected in an independent and random fashion.

16. a. H_0: Brand A ≤ Brand B
H_a: Brand A > Brand B
Critical value = 66
$T_x = 62$; Fail to Reject H_0

b. The data are such that they can be ranked. The two samples are selected in an independent and random fashion.

17. a. H_0: Service City ≥ Sunshine City
H_a: Service City < Sunshine City
Critical value = 52
$T_x = 47$; Fail to Reject H_0

b. The data are such that they can be ranked. The two samples are selected in an independent and random fashion.

17.4 Exercises

10. $H_0: \rho_s = 0$
$H_a: \rho_s \neq 0$
$r_s = -0.4451$
Critical values $= -0.566, 0.566$
Fail to Reject H_0

11. a. $H_0: \rho_s = 0$
$H_a: \rho_s \neq 0$
$r_s = -0.8042$
Critical values $= -0.591, 0.591$
Reject H_0

   b. Yes, but the assumption must be made that the relationship between the variables is linear. Answers will vary.

12. $H_0: \rho_s = 0$
$H_a: \rho_s \neq 0$
$r_s = -0.2$
Critical values $= -0.900, 0.900$
Fail to Reject H_0

13. $H_0: \rho_s = 0$
$H_a: \rho_s \neq 0$
$r_s = 0.0182$
Critical values $= -0.648, 0.648$
Fail to Reject H_0

14. $H_0: \rho_s = 0$
$H_a: \rho_s \neq 0$
$r_s = 0.4909$
Critical values $= -0.648, 0.648$
Fail to Reject H_0

17.5 Exercises

8. H_0: The sequence is random.
H_a: The sequence is not random.
Median $= 71$
$N = 12$, $m = 6$, $n = 6$, $R = 4$
Critical values $= 3, 11$
Fail to Reject H_0

9. H_0: The sequence is random.
H_a: The sequence is not random.
$N = 26$, $m = 10$, $n = 16$, $R = 14$
Critical values $= 8, 19$
Fail to Reject H_0

10. H_0: The sequence is random.
H_a: The sequence is not random.
$N = 12$, $m = 8$, $n = 4$, $R = 7$
Critical values $= 3, 10$
Fail to Reject H_0

11. H_0: The sequence is random.
H_a: The sequence is not random.
$N = 31$, $m = 15$, $n = 16$, $R = 19$
Critical values $= 10, 23$
Fail to Reject H_0

17.6 Exercises

8. H_0: The server performances are the same.
H_a: The performance of at least one server is different.
$H = 13.5143$
Critical value $= 6.2514$
Reject H_0

9. H_0: The milk production for all schedules is the same.
H_a: The milk production for at least one of the schedules is different.
$H = 7.0234$
Critical value $= 6.2514$
Reject H_0

10. H_0: The reading speeds are the same for all schools.
H_a: At least one of the readings speeds is different.
$H = 0.26$
Critical value $= 9.2104$
Fail to Reject H_0

Additional Exercises

1. a. The paired differences have an approximately normal distribution.

   b. H_0: Vest Treatment $\leq$ Traditional Treatment
H_a: Vest Treatment $>$ Traditional Treatment
$X = 0$; Fail to Reject H_0

   c. The data are randomly selected.

   d. H_0: Vest Treatment $\leq$ Traditional Treatment
H_a: Vest Treatment $>$ Traditional Treatment
$T_+ = 0$; Fail to Reject H_0

   e. Pairs of data have been randomly selected and are such that the absolute values of their differences can be ranked.

f. The signed-rank test because the magnitudes of the differences are not ignored. Answers will vary.

g. There is not sufficient evidence that the diameter of blood vessels in the lungs is significantly larger after using the vest treatment when performing a paired difference test. There is sufficient evidence using the nonparametric methods. Answers will vary.

H_0: Vest Treatment ≤ Traditional Treatment
H_a: Vest Treatment > Traditional Treatment
$t = -2.75$
Critical value = -3.747
Fail to Reject H_0

2. a. H_0: # of Negative Signs
    ≤ # of Positive Signs
H_a: # of Negative Signs
    > # of Positive Signs
Critical value = 3
$X = 6$; Fail to Reject H_0

b. H_0: Median = $1
H_a: Median ≠ $1
Critical value = 3
$X = 6$; Fail to Reject H_0

c. H_0: Price After First Day ≤ Initial Offer Price
H_a: Price After First Day > Initial Offer Price
Critical value = 30
$T_+ = 29$; Reject H_0

d. The signed-rank test because the magnitudes of the differences are not ignored. Answers will vary.

e. Answers will vary.

3. a. The Wilcoxon rank-sum test because we are not dealing with paired data.

b. H_0: Diet B ≤ Diet A
H_a: Diet B > Diet A

c. H_0: Diet B ≤ Diet A
H_a: Diet B > Diet A
Critical value = 131
$T_x = 113$; Fail to Reject H_0

d. The data are such that they can be ranked. The two samples are selected in an independent and random fashion.

4. Answers for both **a.** and **b.** are in the table below.

GPA	Starting Salary	R(x)	R(y)
2.37	37,000	1	1
3.20	38,000	2	2
3.21	42,000	3	4
3.39	40,000	4	3
3.55	44,000	5	5
3.57	48,000	6	6
3.76	50,000	7	7
3.77	60,000	8	10
3.79	59,000	9	9
3.90	55,000	10	8

c. $r_s = 0.9394$

d. These two variables have a strong positive relationship. Answers will vary.

e. The relationship is strong.

f. H_0: $\rho_s = 0$
H_a: $\rho_s \neq 0$
$r_s = 0.9394$
Critical values = $-0.564, 0.564$
Reject H_0

5. a. $r_s = 0.2727$ these two variables have a weak positive relationship.

b. H_0: $\rho_s = 0$
H_a: $\rho_s \neq 0$
$r_s = 0.2727$
Critical values = $-0.648, 0.648$
Fail to Reject H_0

6. H_0: The sequence is random.
H_a: The sequence is not random.
Median = 8601
$N = 27, m = 14, n = 12, R = 11$
Critical values = 8, 20
Fail to Reject H_0

7. H_0: The sequence is random.
H_a: The sequence is not random.
$N = 9, m = 5, n = 4, R = 4$
Critical values = 2, 9
Fail to Reject H_0

8. H_0: The sequence is random.
H_a: The sequence is not random.
$N = 20$, $m = 8$, $n = 12$, $R = 11$
Critical values $= 6, 16$
Fail to Reject H_0

9. H_0: The rankings are the same for the
three conferences.
H_a: The ranking of at least one conference
is different.
$H = 13.5755$
Critical value $= 4.6052$
Reject H_0

10. a. H_0: The rankings are the same for
each continent.
H_a: The rankings of at least one
continent is different.
$H = 6.2271$
Critical value $= 5.9915$
Reject H_0

b. The samples are independent and random.

Index

Symbols

α (Type I error) 496–497

β (Type II error) 496–497

A

Addition Rule 284

Adjusted coefficient of determination (R_a^2) 661–662

Alternative hypothesis 492–494, 513

Analysis of Variance (ANOVA)

  assumptions 709, 710

  degrees of freedom 707

  formulas 708

  mean square(d) error (MSE) 707, 712

  mean square for treatments (MST) 706, 712

  one-way table 709

  randomized block design 722

  sum of squared errors (SSE) 706

  sum of squares for treatments (SST) 706

  total sum of squares (Total SS) 705

  two-way

    factorial design 730

    randomized block design 724

Analyzing graphs 113–118

Anscombe's Quartet 214

Arithmetic mean 132

Average. *See* Mean

B

Bar charts

  aesthetics of 81

  definition of 81

  Pareto chart 83

  pictograph 118

  stacked 84

Bar graph 115

Bayes' Theorem 307–310

Bias 42

Biased sample 416

Big Data 12

Bimodal 139

Binomial

  distribution 400

  expected value 343

  experiment 337

  probability distribution 338

  random variable 337, 343

  shape of the distribution 342

  variance 343

Bivariate data 200

Box and whisker plot 167

Box plot

  constructing a 167

  five-number summary 166

  modified 168

C

Case 203

Census 18

Central Limit Theorem 428–432, 456

Chart

  bar 81

  Pareto 83

  pie 85

  stacked bar 84

Chebyshev's Theorem 155

Chi-square (χ^2)

  critical value 481

  distribution 480

  statistic 756

  test for association 775

  test for goodness of fit 760, 764

Choropleth map 105

Circle graph 85

Classical probability 272

Cluster sampling 443

Coefficient

  correlation 206, 243

  intercept 230

  of determination (R^2) 239, 242, 661

  slope 230

  Spearman rank correlation 813

  of variation 156

Combinations 303

Common response 210

Comparative experiments 37

Complement of an event 280–281

Complete factorial experiment 731

Completely randomized design 37, 556, 721

Compound event 279

Conditional probability 288–289

Confidence interval

  comparing population means 557, 566, 573–574

  comparing population proportions 599

  for each regression coefficient 672

  for the mean value of y given x 636, 680

  for the population mean

    σ known 459

    σ unknown 463

  for the population proportion 474

  for the population variance 482

  for the predicted value of y given x 640, 681

  for slope (β_1) 620

  for a two-sided hypothesis 528

Confounding 201, 211

Confounding variable 33

Contingency table 771

Continuity correction 402

Continuous data 50

Notes

Notes

Notes

Notes

Notes

Notes

Notes

Notes

Notes

Notes

Symbols

Notation	Description
$\overline{x}$	Sample mean
μ	Population mean (pronounced mu)
$\sum$	Summation (pronounced sigma)
σ^2	Sample variance
σ^2	Population variance
s	Sample standard deviation
σ	Population standard deviation
ℓ	Location of Pth percentile
Q_1	25th percentile
Q_3	75th percentile
z	z-score, z test statistic
$z_{\alpha/2}$	Critical value of z
CV	Coefficient of variation
$\hat{p}$	Sample proportion
p	Population proportion
$\overline{p}$	Pooled sample proportion
SSE	Sum of Squared Errors
f_i	Frequency of group i
M_i	Midpoint of group i
r	Correlation coefficient
b_1	Slope (predicted)
b_0	y-intercept (predicted)
s_e^2	Variance of the error
s_e	Standard deviation of the error
Total SS	Total sum of squares
SSR	Sum of squares of regression
R^2	Coefficient of determination
R_a^2	Adjusted coefficient of determination
$P(A)$	Probability of event A
$P(A^c)$	Probability of a complement
$P(A \cup B)$	Addition rule
$P(A \mid B)$	Conditional probability

Notation	Description
$E(X)$	Expected value
$V(X)$	Variance
$P(X = x)$	Probability distribution
$\sigma_{\overline{x}}^2$	Variance of the sample means
$\mu_{\overline{x}}$	Mean of the sample means
$\mu_{\hat{p}}$	Mean of the sample proportion
$\sigma_{\hat{p}}^2$	Variance of the sample proportion
MSE	Mean squared error
t	t test statistic
df	Degrees of freedom
$t_{\alpha/2}$	Critical value for a t-distribution
n	Sample size
N	Population size
k	Number of samples or groups
H_0	Null hypothesis
H_a	Alternative hypothesis
s_p^2	Pooled sample variance
β_0	y-intercept of linear regression line
β_1	Slope of linear regression line
s_{b_1}	Standard deviation of sample estimate b_1
F	F test statistic
MST	Mean Square for Treatments
SST	Sum of Squares for Treatments
χ^2	Chi-square test statistic
r_s	Spearman Rank Correlation Coefficient
H	Kruskal-Wallis test statistic
$n!$	Factorial
$_nP_k$	Permutation
$_nC_k$	Combination
$P\left(A_1 \cap A_2 \cap ... \cap A_n\right)$	Multiplication rule for Independent events
λ	Poisson parameter (pronounced lambda)